ENCYCLOPEDIA OF

CONTROLLED DRUG DELIVERY

VOLUME 2

ENCYCLOPEDIA OF CONTROLLED DRUG DELIVERY

ENCYCLOPEDIA OF
CONTROLLED DRUG DELIVERY

VOLUME 2

Edith Mathiowitz
Brown University
Providence, Rhode Island

A Wiley-Interscience Publication
John Wiley & Sons, Inc.
New York / Chichester / Weinheim / Brisbane / Singapore / Toronto

Copyright © 1999 by John Wiley & Sons, Inc. All rights reserved.

Published simultaneously in Canada.

For ordering and customer service, call 1-800-CALL-WILEY.

Library of Congress Cataloging-in-Publication Data:

Mathiowitz, Edith, 1952–
    Encyclopedia of controlled drug delivery / Edith Mathiowitz.
       p. cm.
    Includes index.
    ISBN 0-471-14828-8 (set : cloth : alk. paper).—ISBN
0-471-16662-6 (vol 1 : alk. paper).—ISBN 0-471-16663-4 (vol 2 :
alk. paper)
    1. Drugs—Controlled release Encyclopedias.   I. Title.
    [DNLM: 1. Drug Delivery Systems Encyclopedias—English.   2. Drug
Carriers Encyclopedias—English.   QV 13 M431e 1999]
RS201.C64M38 1999
615.7—dc21
DNLM/DLC
for Library of Congress   99-24907
                                                              CIP

Printed in the United States of America.

10 9 8 7 6 5 4 3 2 1

ENCYCLOPEDIA OF

CONTROLLED DRUG DELIVERY

VOLUME 2

M

MICROENCAPSULATION

EDITH MATHIOWITZ
MARK R. KREITZ
Brown University
Providence, Rhode Island
LISA BRANNON-PEPPAS
Biogel Technology
Indianapolis, Indiana

KEY WORDS

Characterization
Coacervation
Emulsion
Formulation
Gelation
Hot melt
Interfacial polymerization
Membrane
Microcapsule
Microencapsulation
Microsphere
Phase separation
Polymer
Solvent evaporation
Solvent removal
Spray-drying

OUTLINE

INTRODUCTION

Microencapsulation is one of the most intriguing fields in the area of drug delivery systems. It is an interdisciplinary field that requires knowledge of the field of pure polymer science, familiarity with emulsion technology (1), and an in-depth understanding of drug and protein stabilization (2). In the early 1970s this area was considered more of an art than a science because most of the research was developed in pharmaceutical companies and very little information was discussed in scientific meetings. Today, the topic of microencapsulation is extensively studied inside major pharmaceutical companies and universities as well as research institutes. Some journals are now solely dedicated to the area of microencapsulation (e.g., *Journal of Microencapsulation*). Although scientists at the beginning of the 1970s were primarily concerned with the encapsulation of dyes to produce carbonless paper, scientists today have mastered the technology to such a level that cells as well as delicate proteins and genes can be encapsulated. Because two entries in this encyclopedia are dedicated to liposomes and nanoparticles, they are not going to be discussed in this article. In addition, traditional methods such as coating are discussed in a separate article related to coatings. This article is divided into three main sections. In the first section we discuss general aspects of polymer topics related to microencapsulation. Then we describe in more detail the main methods of preparing microcapsules and microspheres, and we end with a general summary of the different fields of application of microencapsulation.

BACKGROUND

Classification of Microencapsulation Techniques

Microencapsulation is a technology devoted to entrapping solids, liquids, or gases inside one or more polymeric coatings (3–43). Two major classes of encapsulation methods have evolved, chemical and physical. The first class of encapsulation involves polymerization during the process of preparing the microcapsules. Examples of this class are usually known by the name of interfacial polymerization or in situ polymerization (44–49). The second type involves the controlled precipitation of a polymeric solution wherein physical changes usually occur. Several books examine the different processes of microencapsulation, and readers are strongly recommended to consult them (2,5,19,30,39, 42,49–58). Perhaps one of the best courses on the fabrication of microcapsules is given at the University of Washington by Dr. Thies.

There are a huge and increasing number of encapsulation processes. In addition, many new patents evolve solely on the basis of novel ways to produce microspheres. Thus, many scientists try to develop a systemic nomenclature for encapsulation classification. In Table 1 we classified the different types of methods according to published literature. It is sometimes difficult to classify encapsulation methods because specific techniques can be hybrids of two or more methods or can use different mechanisms simultaneously. Also, many names have changed throughout the years (e.g., solvent evaporation has been called water drying and double emulsion), and this can create confusion.

Interfacial polymerization involves the condensation of two monomers at the interface of the organic and aqueous phases. Polyamide capsules are a great example of this system and are discussed later in this article (44–48).

Complex coacervation was the process used to make the microcapsules in the first successful encapsulated product, carbonless copy paper (11,14,22,27,29,32,59–66). Complex coacervation encapsulation processes use the interaction of two oppositely charged polyelectrolytes in water to form a polymer-rich coating solution called a coacervate (68). This solution (or coacervate) engulfs the liquid or solid being encapsulated, thereby forming an embryo capsule. Cooling the system causes the coacervate (or coating solution) to gel via network formation. Gelatin is a primary component of most complex coacervation systems.

Coacervation uses the common phenomenon of polymer–polymer incompatibility to form microcapsules. The polymer that is to become the capsule wall material is dissolved in a solvent and to this solution a second polymer (called the phase inducer) is introduced. Because the two polymers are incompatible, two polymer-rich phases form.

If drug particles are then introduced, one phase, rich in the desired coating polymer, engulfs the drug being encapsulated thereby forming embryo capsules. In principle, the range of polymers that can be used in this process is essentially infinite. In practice, the number of polymers that have been used successfully is relatively small, for reasons that will be discussed later.

The precipitation and/or gelation processes listed in Table 1 cover many techniques. One example is the precipitation of water-soluble polymers such as gelatin with water-miscible solvents such as isopropanol. Other examples include the precipitation of ethyl cellulose from cyclohexane by cooling, the gelation of sodium alginate with aqueous calcium salt solutions (41,68–74), and the thermally induced precipitation of proteins to form microspheres. In all cases, the objective is to precipitate a preformed polymer around the core (sometimes a multiparticulate core) to cause encapsulation.

Salting-out also listed in Table 1, involves the addition of salt to an aqueous polymer solution ultimately causing the polymer to phase separate from solution. One potential problem with this process is the possibility of incorporating a relatively high concentration of salt in the final capsule wall, as these salts may have an adverse effect on capsule release behavior.

Solvent evaporation (18,36,75–80) is the most popular way to accomplish encapsulation. A core material and capsule wall material are briefly dissolved in a water-immiscible, volatile organic solvent and the resulting solution is emulsified in an aqueous solution. The solvent is allowed to evaporate, thereby producing solid microcapsules or microparticles. Another version involves forming a double emulsion where an aqueous core material solution is emulsified in a polymer–volatile organic solvent solution. The resulting emulsion is emulsified in water giving a double emulsion. Evaporation of the volatile solvent yields a solid microcapsule with an aqueous core. Much of the effort on encapsulation in the pharmaceutical field has concentrated on using biodegradable polymers. A recent review by Brannon-Peppas (43) describes some of these advances with both microparticles and nanoparticles.

Hot melt encapsulation was developed to avoid the use of solvents throughout the process (81). Solvent removal (82,83) was developed as a modification of the solvent evaporation technique, using organic solvents as the extracting medium. In spray-drying, the evaporation of the

Table 1. Classification of Microencapsulation Methods

Process	Coating material	Suspended medium
Interfacial polymerization	Water-soluble and insoluble monomers	Aqueous/organic solvent
Complex coacervation	Water-soluble polyelectrolyte	Water
Coacervation	Hydrophobic polymers	Organic solvent
Thermal denaturation	Proteins	Organic
Salting-out	Water-soluble polymer	Water
Solvent evaporation	Hydrophilic or hydrophobic polymers	Organic or water
Hot melt	Hydrophilic or hydrophobic polymers	Aqueous/organic solvent
Solvent removal	Hydrophilic or hydrophobic polymers	Organic solvents
Spray-drying	Hydrophilic or hydrophobic polymers	Air, nitrogen
Phase separation	Hydrophilic or hydrophobic polymers	Aqueous/organic

solvent is achieved in a special, temperature-controlled cyclone. And finally, phase separation is a new method in which a one-step precipitation of two polymers or more produces double-walled microspheres (84).

When someone is faced with the challenge of encapsulating a substance, the first question should be, "What is the final application of the product?" As examples, if the final target is pesticide encapsulation, one must first choose polymers that are stable and nonerodible, or if one is to encapsulate therapeutic drugs such as proteins, the choice of polymers becomes more restricted to bioerodible ones. Once the polymer system is chosen, the next step is to select an appropriate encapsulation method. This can undertaken by either reviewing the relevant literature or developing new methods of encapsulation. Once the correct method of encapsulation has been determined the next step is to prepare the microcapsules, ensuring reproducibility, high encapsulation efficiency, and preservation of the activity of the encapsulated substance. This is achieved by thorough characterization, both before and after microsphere fabrication. It is an integral component, necessary for replication and optimization, and is discussed later in this article.

Classification of Microspheres and Microcapsules

Two general structures exist: microcapsules and microspheres. A microcapsule is a system that contains a well-defined core and a well-defined envelope: the core can be solid, liquid, or gas; the envelope is made of a continuous, porous or nonporous, polymeric phase. Figure 1a shows the different microcapsule configurations; the drug can be dispersed inside the microcapsule as solid particulates with regular or irregular shapes. Other forms may consist of a pure or dissolved solution, suspension, emulsion, or a combination of suspension and emulsion. Specific applications sometimes require modifications, e.g., when proteins are encapsulated they may contain stabilizers as well as the active ingredient (2). Also, the core can be something other than a chemical meant for release. An interesting application is the encapsulation of gases for the use of ultrasonic imaging (85–87). Alternatively, a microsphere is a structure made of a continuous phase of one or more miscible polymers in which particulate drug is dispersed, at either the macroscopic (particulates) or molecular (dissolution) level (Fig. 1b). However, the difference between the two systems is the nature of the microsphere matrix, in which no well-defined wall or envelope exists. Different methods of encapsulation result, in most cases, in either a microcapsule or a microsphere. For example, interfacial polymerization almost always produces a microcapsule, whereas solvent evaporation may result in a microsphere or a microcapsule, depending on the amount of loading. Yet, one can use solvent evaporation twice to create a sphere within a sphere, or as we discuss later, novel methods have been designed to use solvent evaporation to create in one step a double-walled microsphere, which is essentially a microcapsule (84).

Classification of Polymeric Membranes

Polymeric films and membranes can be classified in various ways. One such classification is based on porosity, with the following categories:

1. Macroporous membranes, which have large pores (0.1–1 μm)
2. Microporous membranes, in which the pores are appreciably smaller (100–500 Å)
3. Nonporous (gel, solution-diffusion) membranes. In the last category the "pores" are of the order of molecular dimensions. They are formed by entanglement and/or cross-linking of the molecular chains and mesh size refers to the space between these chains.

Release Characteristics of Microspheres and Microcapsules

Release of core material from a nonerodible microcapsule can occur in several ways. Figure 2 contains four theoretical curves (A, B, C, and D) that describe four types of release behavior. All curves are plotted as percent drug released versus time. The mathematical descriptions of these release processes have been given (88–90).

Curve A represents the release behavior of a perfect, nonerodible, spherical microcapsule which releases the encapsulated material by steady-state diffusion through a coating of uniform thickness. The rate of release remains constant as long as the internal and external concentrations of core material and the concentration gradient through the membrane are constant. If a finite time is needed to establish the initial, constant concentration gradient in the capsule wall membrane then there is a time lag in core material release. Curve A in Figure 2 displays a system with no time lag. If some of the encapsulated material migrates through the microcapsule membrane during storage, a burst effect occurs, as represented by Curve B. If the microcapsule acts as an inert matrix particle in which core material is dispersed (a microsphere), the Higuchi model is valid up to 60% release (91). In this case, a plot of percent drug released versus square-root time is linear, as shown by Curve C in Figure 2. First-order release is represented by Curve D. The curve is linear if log percent core material left in the capsule is plotted versus time.

Actual capsule release data have been plotted for all of the described ways and analyzed in terms of the appropriate model. Good agreement between actual results and assorted model release curves may exist for some portion of the release curve, but significant deviations occur often, either during initial states of release or after most of the core material carried by a capsule sample has been released. Many capsule samples experience an unusually rapid rate of release when first immersed in an in vitro release medium, i.e., they have a large burst effect. First-order release plots tend to fit a broader range of capsule release data than other plots. It is relevant to note that proper adjustment of the release constant in the first-order release equation can make a first-order release curve approximate, within a few percent, the release curve calculated from the Higuchi equation up to 60% release. If microcapsule release data are linear with square root of time and also fit a first-order release plot, the expression most accurately describing the release behavior can be determined by plotting the total amount of drug released (Q')

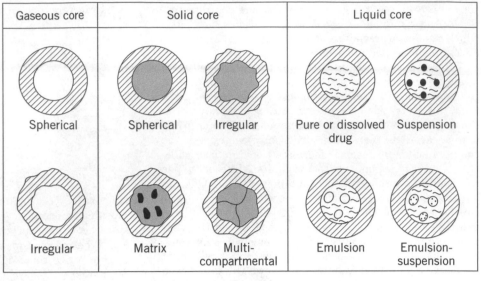

(a)

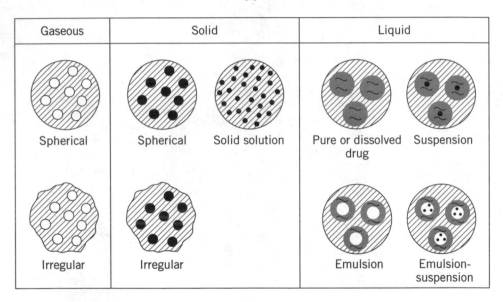

(b)

Figure 1. Various configurations of (a) microcapsules and (b) microspheres.

and $1/Q'$ versus release rate. For the first-order release, Q' is directly proportional to release rate whereas for square root of time release, $1/Q'$ is directly proportional to release rate.

The desire to fit capsule release data to various models is worthwhile. However, it must be recognized that the actual release kinetics of microcapsules and microspheres can vary greatly from those developed to describe release from macroscopic controlled release delivery devices. Microcapsules are small particles and even small doses contain many microcapsules. The release behavior of a microcapsule formulation is the sum of the release of a population of microcapsules (38,39). This population consists of individual microcapsules that differ from each other in the quality of their walls. Some capsule walls are more permeable than others because of irregularities, which may appear as pits or craters under a scanning elec-

tron microscope. Dappert and Thies (38,39,47) discussed the release behavior of microcapsule populations. One capsule population considered contained microcapsules that individually released their contents at a constant rate, but the individual release rate constants fit a log-normal distribution. For such a capsule population, the predicted release curve will approximate first-order release kinetics.

All microcapsule release behaviors reported in the literature represent microcapsule populations and not individual microcapsules. Therefore, the successful replication of microcapsule preparations and confirmation of reproducible release rates is an optimal result. The Lupron Depo™, a product already in the marketplace, demonstrates that these milestones can be achieved. In the following section, we discuss the specific releases as relevant to the specific encapsulation methods.

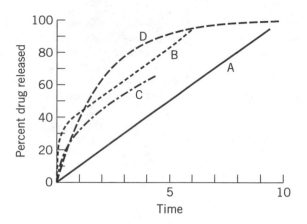

Figure 2. Theoretical release curves expected for different types of nonerodible delivery systems. A, Membrane reservoir-type free of lag time and burst effects; B, same as A, with burst effects; C, matrix or monolithic sphere with square root time-release; D, system with first-order release.

Emulsion Formation

The first step in almost any encapsulation technique (described in Table 1) involves the formation of an emulsion, usually of a polymeric solution inside a continuous phase (1). Similarly, in order to disperse the drug inside this polymeric solution (assuming a nonsoluble drug), emulsions must be created. Thus, an understanding of the properties of emulsions is extremely important. The emulsion formation determines the resulting particle size in the final process of encapsulation. An emulsion is achieved by applying mechanical energy which deforms the interface between the two phases to such an extent that droplets form. These droplets are typically large and are subsequently disrupted or broken up into smaller ones. The ability to disrupt the larger droplets is a critical step in emulsification and in encapsulation where an emulsion is prepared. When considering dyes as the main encapsulate, the problems involved at this stage can be minor because most dyes are quite stable. However, drugs (e.g., labile proteins) or cells may be destroyed by the application of mechanical shear and, if necessary, preventive measures should be taken to stabilize these, even at this stage of the process.

A suitable surfactant is needed to produce a stable emulsion, a result achieved by lowering the surface tension (γ, usually from 40 to 5 mN/m^{-1}). For pharmaceutical applications surfactants must acceptable for therapeutic use (92).

Many devices have been designed to produce emulsions. Depending on the desired particle size, a range of devices from simple overhead stirrers or impellers to more sophisticated devices such as homogenizers, ultrasonic power generators, or ball and roller mills are available. The following is a list of techniques and equipment used to form emulsions. Also, an excellent reference is Chapter 2 in Becher (1).

1. *Shaking.* Shaking is self-evident but in many encapsulation techniques countertop shakers or agitators are used.

2. *Pipe flow: laminar and turbulent.* Pipe flow may include constriction on the flow baffles on which the liquid can infringe to increase the velocity gradient or turbulence.

3. *Injection.* The dispersed phase is injected into a continuous phase as a cylindrical jet, where it is broken up into fairly large droplets.

4. *Stirring: simple stirrer, rotor-stator, scraper, and vibrator.* Many types of stirring exist, e.g., for pumps revolution rates up to 300/s. Rotor-stator machines exist in great variety and are described under the name of homogenizers. In the laboratory the name "Ultra Turrax" is often used.

5. *Colloid mill.* This is a rotor-stator device as well, with the exception of having a very narrow slit (e.g., 0.1 mm) and is designed to achieve very high (simple) shear up to $10^7 s^{-1}$.

6. *Ball and roller mills.* These are more suited for disruption of solid particles or very viscous emulsion droplets.

7. *High-pressure homogenizer.* In the homogenizer the liquid is brought under a high pressure p_h (e.g., 10 to 40 MPa) by a positive pump and is forced through a narrow (e.g., 0.1 mm) valve slit; owing to the pressure, the valve opens against a spring. The potential energy is converted into kinetic energy as the liquid obtains a high velocity u ($p_h = \_u^2/2$; u is, e.g., 200 m s^{-1}). The kinetic energy is dissipated into heat during passage through the valve. This takes a very short time (0.1 ms); so energy density is very high (up to 10^{12} Wm^{-3}).

8. *Ultrasonic: vibrating knife and magneto-striction.* Ultrasonic waves can be generated in many ways. A common one is the "liquid whistle" or Pohlmann generator. The liquid stream impinges on a knife or blade, which is then brought to vibrate at high frequency (6–40 kHz); the liquid is forced through a narrow slit at speeds over 50 m s^{-1}, which requires a pressure of some 1 MPa or more. Magneto-striction devices often work at a frequency of 20 kHz.

9. *Aerosol to liquid: mechanical and electrical.* One may atomize the dispersed phase in air and let the droplets be taken up by the continuous phase.

10. *Foaming or boiling.* Some oils spread over a water–gas interface. If air is beaten in or the water boiled, the thinly spread oil layer is disrupted, and very small droplets may result. This may happen as an additional mechanism during various stirring operations. Also by steam injection, droplets can be disrupted to very small ones, though at high cost of steam.

Some of the methods are exclusively used in laboratories such as shaking, vibrator stirring, magneto-striction ultrasonic systems, and aerosol to liquid systems. For large-scale production of emulsions, rotor-stator stirring, colloidal mills, and high-pressure homogenizers are most often used, with some newer processes also using ultrasonic techniques.

Evaluation of Emulsions

Three types of characteristics are critical in evaluating an emulsion procedure, each with its own methods of evaluation (1). They can easily be adapted to encapsulation techniques such as solvent evaporation or interfacial polymerization. The parameters that should be studied are:

1. *Emulsion capacity.* The maximum amount of dispersed phase that can be emulsified under specific conditions without causing aggregation.
2. *Emulsion stability.* The amount of phase separation taking place, mostly by the sedimentation rate, which is estimated either under by gravity or by centrifugation. The governing theory is that sedimentation rate depends on droplet size. This relation, however, may not be so simple because sedimentation rate depends on fluctuation of the droplets and their apparent viscosity at very low velocity gradients of the continuous phase. This condition may also be affected by the variables studied, leading to misinterpretation. In microcapsules this first step is important because once the emulsion is stabilized the next step of hardening the capsules follows.
3. *Droplet size.* This may be some kind of average or full distribution. Sometimes the number of drops is determined, or some characteristic, depending on the drop size, such as turbidity under specific conditions. Droplet size distribution may change after emulsification. This can be due to coalescence but it also may be due to isothermal distillation, unless the dispersed phase is completely insoluble in the continuous one. Again, the initial size of the emulsion may differ from the final size of the microspheres or microcapsules.

Determination of droplet size distribution as function of the process and product variables is by far the best method to study emulsification, particularly in microencapsulation where the process does not stop at the point of making the emulsion, but continues to the further steps of formation of hard particles. Particle comparison between the original size of the emulsion and the final size of the microsphere is beneficial.

Phase Properties of Emulsion: Hydrophilic-Lipophile Balance

One of the important parameters in studying emulsions is the selection of a surfactant which satisfactorily emulsifies the different phases. For this, the hydrophilic-liphophile balance (HLB) is a useful index. The concept of HLB in its early stage was qualitative; however, schemes designed to put this concept on a quantitative basis have been advanced and a new method, which takes into consideration the temperature and the kind of oil used, has been introduced. Around 1950 Griffin [see also Schick (93)] found that it was possible to define the polarity for nonionic agents in terms of an empirical quantity which he called the HLB. This is represented by an arbitrary scale, in which the least hydrophilic materials have low HLB num-

bers and increasing HLB corresponds to increasingly hydrophilic character. Broadly, these HLB numbers can be used to characterize the applicability of particular surfactant. In a given homologous series of surfactants there is a range in which the HLB is optimal for a particular application. Table 2 lists the HLB ranges suitable for various applications.

In many cases the HLB number may be calculated from composition data. For example, for fatty acid esters of many polyhydric alcohols,

$$HLB = 20\left(1 - \frac{S}{A}\right) \quad (1)$$

where S is the saponification number of the ester and A is the acid number of the fatty acid. In another example, for glyceryl monostearate, $S = 161$ and $A = 198$; hence, its HLB is 3.8.

For some fatty acid esters it is not practical to obtain good saponification-number data, e.g., esters of tall oil and rosin, beeswax, and lanolin fatty acids. However, for these, the HLB may be calculated from the relation

$$HLB = \frac{E + P}{5} \quad (2)$$

where E is the weight percent of oxyethylene content and P is the weight percent of polyol content.

For materials where only ethylene oxide is used to produce the hydrophilic moiety, e.g., fatty-alcohol ethylene oxide adducts, this equation reduces to

$$HLB = E/5 \quad (3)$$

where E has the same meaning as above.

The use of weight percent in these equations is quite significant, because a better dependence of micellar properties on chain length is found when this quantity is used rather than the ethylene oxide mole ratio.

Davies devised a method for calculating HLB numbers for surfactants directly from their formulae using empirically derived group numbers. Thus, a group number is assigned to various component groups in emulsifiers, e.g., CH_3-CH_2-COO-, -CH_2CH_2O, etc., and the HLB is then calculated from the following relation (94):

$$HLB = 7 + \Sigma(\text{hydrophilic group numbers}) - \Sigma(\text{lipophilic group numbers}) \quad (4)$$

For a number of cases, Davies (94) has shown that the HLB numbers calculated from the previous equation and

Table 2. HLB Ranges and Applications

Range	Application
3–6	W/O emulsifier
7–9	Wetting agent
8–15	O/W emulsifier
13–15	Detergent
15–18	Solubilizer

Source: From Ref. 93.

those experimentally determined are in satisfactory agreement. However, this equation contains the implicit assumption that all ethylene oxide groups make the same hydrophilic contribution, which is manifestly incorrect (94), and the equation fails with increasing poly-(oxyethylene) content.

Additional techniques can be used to determine HLB. These include water titration, algebraic addition of contribution from various groups making up the chemical structure from spreading, and by measurements of such properties as dielectric constant, and behavior as a substrate in gas-liquid chromatography [see Schick (95), pp. 607–613].

A rough estimate of HLB can frequently be made on the basis of water solubility or dispersibility. Table 3 shows the ranges of HLB numbers indicated by various types of dispersibility. An up-to-date listing of HLB numbers for a large range of emulsifying agents (including a few ionic species) is given in Schick (95).

A valuable attribute of the HLB scale is that the HLB of mixtures of surfactants can be calculated (to a good first approximation, at least) by algebraic addition. For example, a blend containing 4 parts of Span® 20 and 6 parts of Tween® 60 would have an effective HLB of:

$$0.4 \times 8.6 + 0.6 \times 14.9 = 12.3 \qquad (5)$$

It has recently been shown that this algebraic additivity is not strictly obeyed, but the deviation is usually sufficiently small so that the system is insensitive to the discrepancy. In a few cases, the requirements may be more stringent, but this merely requires final adjustment of the composition of the emulsifier.

As a corollary to the previous discussion, each nonaqueous phase to be emulsified has a *required* HLB, which is of course different depending on whether water or oil is to be the continuous phase. The required HLB for a particular oil is usually determined by preparing emulsions over a range of HLB values (obtained, for example, by blending Span® and Tween® emulsifiers in various proportions) and observing the HLB at which maximum stability occurs. A list of required HLB values for a variety of oil phases is given in Table 4.

Using a particular emulsifier pair, the HLB corresponding to maximum stability may result, however, in an emulsion insufficiently stable for the purpose desired. In this case, it may be necessary to examine the effect of the *chemical type* of the emulsifying agent, i.e., substituting an oleate for a stearate, or an ether-type nonionic for an ester.

Table 3. HLB by Dispersibility

	HLB range
No dispersibility in water	1–4
Poor dispersion	3–6
Milky dispersion after vigorous agitation	6–8
Stable milky dispersion	8–10
Translucent to clear dispersion	10–13
Clear solution	13+

Source: From Ref. 94.

Table 4. HLB Values Required to Emulsify Various 0:1 Phases

Oil phase	W/O emulsion	O/W emulsion
Acetophenone		14
Acid, dimer		14
Acid, lauric		16
Acid, linoleic		16
Acid, oleic		17
Acid, ricinoleic		16
Acid, stearic		17
Alcohol, cetyl		15
Alcohol, decyl		14
Alcohol, lauryl		14
Alcohol, tridecyl		14
Benzene		15
Carbon tetrachloride		16
Castor oil		14
Chlorinated paraffin		8
Kerosene		14
Lanolin, anhydrous	8	12
Oils		
Mineral, aromatic	4	12
Mineral, paraffinic	4	10
Mineral spirits		14
Petrolatum	4	7–8
Pine oil		16
Waxes		
Beeswax	5	9
Candelilla		14–15
Carnuba		12
Microcrystalline		10
Paraffin	4	10

Source: From Ref. 93.

In each case, however, the required HLB is equal to (or nearly equal to) the required HLB determined in the initial experiment.

Geiger et al. (96) studied the behavior of a W/O/W multiple emulsion formulation as potential controlled delivery system. The authors were interested in understanding the release due to a swelling-breakdown phenomenon. The breakdown was caused by the water flow from the external aqueous phase to the internal aqueous phase. Various experimental analyses, such as granulometry, rheology, and conductimetry, as well as a micropipette aspiration method, were used to study the stability of W/O/W emulsions. The predominant role of the lipophilic surfactant during the swelling phase was confirmed. Two different mechanisms were proposed and both imply that the migration of the lipophilic surfactant from one interface to another takes place successively. The lipophilic surfactant could diffuse from the first to the second interface, thus rigidifying the membrane, or from the oily phase to the first interface, resulting in delayed coalescence of the aqueous droplets during swelling. Thus, the more lipophilic the surfactant, the more the oil globule capacity increases and the more the release is delayed.

Polymer Characterization

A broad range of polymers can be used to form microcapsules. However the list of polymers approved for used in oral and/or parenteral drug formulations is limited. This list includes proteins, polysaccharides, cellulose derivatives, synthetic polyesters developed as synthetic suture materials, polyanhydrides, and polyphosphazene. Characterization data for candidate polymer wall materials can play an important role in the development of a successful and reproducible encapsulation procedure. Thus, considerable attention should be paid to obtaining meaningful characterization data for polymer samples being used to form microcapsules. All the physical properties allow better fit of individual polymers to the correct encapsulation techniques. For example, it is not recommended to use polyanhydrides in solvent evaporation because the polymer may degrade during the process of encapsulation. Once the microcapsules are made, a new series of characterizations are required because morphological changes occur during encapsulation.

Phase Separation of Polymers

A wide range of polymer phase separation can be used to encapsulate materials: interfacial coacervation, binary polymer/solvent systems, polymer/solvent/nonsolvent systems, polymer/polymer/solvent systems, complex coacervation, and salting-out.

All these processes provide a way to surround each discrete internal phase droplet or particle of drug with homogeneous and reliably concentrated polymeric layers which can be later solidified in some manner to form a stable capsule. Thus, the next section addresses the general concepts of phase separation relevant to microencapsulation.

Interfacial Coacervation.   The first example of a suitable phase separation process is the case of polymer adsorption, which Chang (49) has used to prepare small capsules. In this process, polymer dissolved in an organic phase migrates to the water–organic liquid interface where it precipitates spontaneously from solution to form a membrane. Chang calls this interfacial coacervation. Phase separation occurs spontaneously. An example of this process is the emulsification of an aqueous protein solution in diethyl ether using an oil-soluble nonionic surfactant. Span® 85, sorbitan trioleate, is preferred because it does not denature the protein. Chang used collodian nitrocellulose as the wall structure.

The emulsification process gives microcapsules that can be separated from much of the ether suspending medium and resuspended in n-butyl benzoate. n-Butybenzoate was selected because it is a poor solvent for collodian, a water-immiscible solvent, and a solvent with a density of 1.0. The suspension is left uncovered in order to allow evaporation of ether.

Chang often uses collodian (i.e., nitrocellulose) as the wall material, but stresses that microcapsules (or membranes) also can be formed in interfacial coacervation or precipitation of other polymers using different solvents (e.g., polystyrene in benzene). The success of this procedure depends on having a sufficiently high initial protein concentration in the aqueous phase. Microencapsulation usually is not possible with a very dilute solution of protein. Nothing more was noted about the mechanism whereby the protein (and probably the emulsifying agent in the system) influences the oil/water interfacial tension ($\gamma_{o/w}$) or how changes in $\gamma_{o/w}$ influences precipitation of the oil phases' polymer.

Phase Separation in Binary Polymer/Solvent Systems.   The most conventional phase equilibria involving nonionic polymers dissolved in organic solvents have been discussed extensively by Flory (97). Flory's book focused on systems where all phases formed are completely liquid in nature and several systems of this nature play a key role in microencapsulation. The simplest case is of a binary system containing polymer and solvent. Figure 3 is a phase diagram of this system. Temperature changes alone are used to induce phase separation. Assuming a monodisperse polymer, phase separation is characterized by formation of two distinct phases, one rich in polymer and the other containing little polymer. Under equilibrium conditions, chemical potentials of the solvent (μ_1) and polymer (μ_2) in Phase I equals that in Phase II (i.e., $\mu_1^I = \mu_1^{II}; \mu_2^I = \mu_2^{II}$). Furthermore, at some critical temperature (T_c), incipient phase separation will take place:

$$\left(\frac{\partial^2 \mu_1}{\partial v_2^2}\right)_{T,P} = 0; \left(\frac{\partial \mu_1}{\partial v_2}\right)_{T,P} = 0 \qquad (6)$$

and from these relations it can be shown that:

$$v_{2C} = \frac{1}{1 + \sqrt{X}}; X_{1C} = \frac{1}{2} + \frac{1}{\sqrt{X}} \qquad (7)$$

where v_2 = volume fraction of polymer, v_{2C} = critical volume fraction of polymer, X = number of segments in a given polymer molecule, and X_{1C} = critical value of polymer–solvent interaction free energy. For this simplest case, theoretical binodials can be calculated and compared with experimental values. Such binodials have some important features. First, v_{2C} is predicted to be small, and this is confirmed by experimentation. In addition, at temperatures well below T_c, the dilute phase may retain an unappreciable amount of solute (especially true at higher

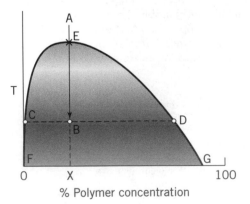

Figure 3. Phase separation in a two-phase system (polymer/solvent) induced by temperature.

M_w values). However, even the so-called concentrated phase contains a large amount of solvent which means that the system is still liquid in nature and thus could flow and engulf the core.

Thus, lowering the temperature (T) of a polymer–solvent mixture at constant v_2 and M_w often is a simple method of inducing phase separation and thereby obtaining a "polymer-rich" phase which can form a capsule wall. This could, in principle, be accomplished at constant T and v_2 by increasing M_w (i.e., continuing polymerization of the polymer). Alternately, at constant T and M_w, v_2 could be varied. Of course, if encapsulation is to occur, the polymer-rich phase must engulf at the internal phase. That is, formation of a concentrated polymer-rich phase having a low total volume does not necessarily mean adsorption and encapsulation occurs. Adsorption of this polymer-rich phase is a prerequisite for wall deposition (see next section) and may not be achieved in many cases.

Phase Separation in Polymer/Solvent/Nonsolvent Systems. A second method to produce phase separation involves addition of nonsolvent to a polymer–solvent system (Fig. 4). In such a case one moves from a two- to a three-component system (polymer/solvent/nonsolvent), thereby grossly complicating theoretical calculations. Nevertheless, it still is true that at equilibrium, chemical potentials of each component must be equal in the two phases:

$$\mu_1^I = \mu_1^{II}; \mu_2^I = \mu_2^{II}; = \mu_3^{II} \qquad (8)$$

where subscripts 1, 2, and 3 refer to nonsolvent, solvent, and polymer, respectively. If it is assumed:

$$V_1 = V_2; X_{23} = 0; X_{12} = X_{13} = 1.5 \qquad (9)$$

(V_1 = molar volume solvent; V_2 = molar volume nonsolvent; X_{23} = polymer–solvent interaction free energy; X_{12} = solvent–nonsolvent interaction free energy; and X_{13} = polymer–nonsolvent interaction free energy), a special case which can be solved is obtained and theoretical bino-

dials can be calculated. Binodials calculated in this manner have critical points which occur at low polymer concentrations. This concentration decreases as M_w increases. As the binodial merges with the solvent–nonsolvent axis, at point D in Figure 4, the polymer concentration in the dilute phase becomes negligible (i.e., approaches zero) if the nonsolvent just slightly exceeds that required at the critical point. Thus, a two-phase system is formed with one phase relatively rich in polymer and the other containing relatively little polymer and mostly solvent. Provided the polymer molecules in the polymer-rich phase adsorb at the internal phase–solution interface, encapsulation occurs. A possible problem with systems of this type is that the nonsolvent could be of such a nature that it is preferentially absorbed by the internal phase and thereby prevents encapsulation even though phase separation occurs. An additional important point is that a mixed solvent system usually cannot be treated like a single solvent system. Generally speaking, the nonsolvent–solvent ratios differ markedly for the two phases in equilibrium whose compositions are indicated by the ends of the tie line. Only if $\mu_{12} \cong \mu_{23}$ will the solvent compositions in each phase be similar (they are equal if $\mu_{13} = \mu_{23}$). A large difference between μ_{13} and μ_{23} favors absorption of the better solvent in the polymer-rich phase and this undoubtedly contributes to serious aggregation problems when efforts are made to prepare microcapsules by encapsulation processes involving polymer solvent–nonsolvent mixtures.

Phase Separation in Polymer/Polymer/Solvent System. A third type of phase separation occurs in systems containing mixtures of two chemically different polymers, as seen in Figure 5. In such cases, formation of true polymer-in-polymer solutions is rarely observed. This is particularly true for polymer mixtures free of solvent. In the presence of solvent, two phases are generally formed under all but dilute solution conditions. The inability of two polymers to mix has led to the general rule of polymer–polymer incompatibility. This incompatibility has proved to be a problem in many cases where homogeneous mixtures of two poly-

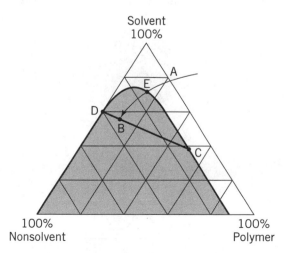

Figure 4. Phase separation diagram for a polymer/solvent/nonsolvent system.

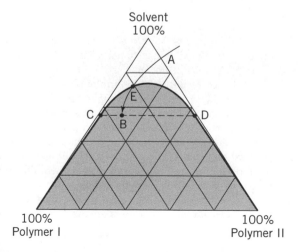

Figure 5. Phase separation diagram for a polymer/polymer/solvent system.

mers are desired (e.g., polymer blends, cases of plasticization), but it is a very important phenomena for use as an encapsulation technique; particularly, our group has used it to make double-walled microspheres in one step (84).

Polymer–polymer incompatibility is a widely encountered phenomenon because the free energy change occurring when the two polymers are mixed is generally >0. The free energy of mixing (ΔG_m) can be described by:

$$\Delta G_m = \Delta H_m - T\Delta S_m \qquad (10)$$
$$\text{For two polymers: } \Delta S_m \text{ is small.}$$

ΔH_m generally is >0 (i.e., endothermic mixing). ΔS_m is so small that even if the heat of mixing (per segment) is just greater than zero, polymer–polymer incompatibility would occur. Thus, the widespread nature of incompatibility is attributable to the small contribution of the ΔS_m term and the tendency for polymer–polymer mixing processes to be endothermic in nature (i.e., $\Delta H_m > 0$).

It was originally predicted that polymer–polymer incompatibility is not influenced by the solvent used. That is, polymer pairs incompatible in one solvent are incompatible in all solvents. This often has been found to be the case, provided that the same molecular weight of polymer is used, but exceptions do exist. Theoretical phase diagrams developed for specific monodisperse model systems also revealed that polymer/polymer/solvent phase separations are characterized by formation of two phases, each of which contains essentially only one of the two polymers involved. Figure 5 is a phase diagram of such a system. The higher the M_w, the sharper the separation of the two polymers. These features have been confirmed experimentally by numerous workers and by our group. The actual phase separation process is influenced by such factors as solvent, temperature, nature of the two polymers involved, and their initial concentrations and the molecular weights. Complete separation of two polymers is not always achieved by polymer–polymer incompatibility. In most cases of encapsulation by phase separation, the low molecular weight polymers commonly used to induce phase separation become entrapped in the microcapsule wall, thereby affecting properties of the wall. Our experience with polymers such as polylactide and polystyrene with M_w in the range of 20,000 to 50,000 always showed complete solubility of 15% W/W, where used with polymer ratios of 1:1.

The importance of polymer–polymer phase separation in encapsulation is its capability to consistently form a distinct, relatively concentrated polymer phase which, if the polymer is adsorbed by the internal drug phase, readily wraps it completely thereby forming a capsule.

These methods are theoretically applicable to encapsulation of both water-soluble and water-insoluble substances. However, when water-insoluble solids or liquids must be encapsulated, an additional useful form of polymer phase separation phenomena is encountered, complex coacervation.

Complex Coacervation. Complex coacervation is the spontaneous liquid–liquid phase separation that fre-

quently occurs when solutions of oppositely charged polyelectrolytes are mixed in the same solvent (usually water). It is encountered in biological systems and differs fundamentally from the polymer–polymer incompatibility mentioned earlier in that one phase contains most of the two polymers whereas the second phase is a dilute polymer solution. Figure 6, a phase diagram for the gelatin–gum arabic–water complex coacervation system, illustrates this point. Polymer–polymer incompatibility yields two phases with each containing predominately one of the two polymers.

Significantly, complex coacervation is truly a complex phenomenon. Polyelectrolytes useful for coacervation come in all shapes and forms with varying numbers and types of charged sites distributed along the polymer chains. The polyelectrolytes may have charged sites that are fully ionized at all pH values (e.g., SO_3) or sites where the group is weakly ionized (e.g., COOH), and the degree of ionization varies strongly with pH. Both positively and negatively charged sites can be on the same molecule (polyampholytes). Furthermore, many useful polyelectrolytes are natural gums, biopolymers, etc., and they often (usually) have complex structures which are not fully resolved. These factors grossly complicate matters, especially when rigorous analyses of such processes are desired.

The best known example of complex coacervation is the gelatin-gum arabic (GGA) system studied by Bungenberg de Jong and co-workers (57). Additional studies by Veis (98) have shown that the interaction of two gelatins of differing ionic points (pI = 5.0 and pI = 9.0) also provides an example of complex coacervation. Each polymer pair (under proper pH conditions) interacts to form a complex which appears as a concentrated, separated phase (i.e., coacervate). Temperatures of 40°C are used in order to obtain the so-called coacervate in a liquid state. These complexes are not the precipitated complexes formed by interacting oppositely charged polyelectrolytes of high charge density. For proper encapsulation, it is preferred to have liquid coacervates which can flow around or completely wrap the internal phase particles or droplets. Of course, the coacervate must wet the internal phase (i.e., be adsorbed by it) if it is to form the capsule wall. As mentioned before, a key

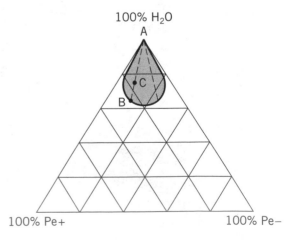

Figure 6. Phase separation diagram for a polyelectrolyte system.

feature of complex coacervation is that the supernatant or equilibrium liquid formed is a dilute polymer solution, whereas the coacervate is a polymer-rich phase (11–15% solids) containing both polymers.

Two factors which affect complex coacervation are pH and neutral salt ions. Because the ionic charge on gelatin and gum arabic varies with pH, coacervation of these species is sensitive to pH. Bungenberg de Jong (67) found that coacervation of alkali-precursor gelatin (pI = 4.8) and gum arabic occurred only between pH 2.0 and 4.8. At pHs outside this range no coacervate formed due to an imbalance in electrostatic charges. Neutral salt ions decrease the coacervation tendency of two polymers. This is attributed to the ability of such ions to screen the charged sites on the polyions involved and thereby reduce their mutual attraction. For example, Bungenberg de Jong (67) reported that 0.02M $CaCl_2$ or 0.035M KCl completely reverses coacervation of gelatin and gum arabic at 40°C. Suppression by salts is stronger the higher the valence of the added ion. Coacervation tendencies of gelatin and gum arabic also decrease with increasing initial concentrations of these polyions. Such self-suppression of coacervation has been attributed to an increase in ionic strength of the system due to increased diffusible microion concentration. Veis (98) reports that the volume of coacervate and fraction of gelatin in the coacervate decreases uniformly with increasing concentration of gelatin for coacervate systems consisting of two isoionic gelatins. The process of coacervation was first treated theoretically by Overbeek and Voorn (99) and later by Veis (98).

Interfacial Phenomenon

Adsorption of polymers on the core phase is a key step in encapsulation processes based on polymer phase separation phenomena. Thus we discuss were the surface free energy (γ, dynes/cm or ergs/cm^2) effects that occur in such processes.

Consider a case in which a droplet of liquid core material (representing the active drug) is engulfed by a liquid phase rich in polymer (i.e., the coacervate phase). Figure 7 is a schematic diagram of the process. Phase 1 is the drop of core material being engulfed, Phase 3 is the coacervate phase that is engulfing the core material, and Phase 2 is the continuous (or supernatant) phase in which Phases 1 and 3 are dispersed. If Phase 1 is designated such that $\gamma_{12} > \gamma_{23}$, the free energy change (ΔG_3) that occurs when Phase 3 spreads over Phase 1 is:

$$\Delta G_3 = G_{after} - G_{before}$$
$$\Delta G3 = \gamma_{13} + \gamma_{32} - \gamma_{12} \tag{11}$$

Because the spreading coefficient S_3 is defined as $-\Delta G_3$:

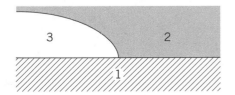

Figure 7. Schematic presentation of a three-phase system.

$$S_3 = -\Delta G_3 = \gamma_{12} - (\gamma_{12} + \gamma_{32}) \tag{12}$$

Because the core material, coacervate, and supernatant form a three-phase system, the spreading of Phase 1 over Phase 2 and the spreading of Phase 2 over Phase 1 must also be considered. The surface free energy change that occurs on spreading of Phase 1 over Phase 2 is given by:

$$\Delta G_1 = G_{after} - G_{before} = \gamma_{12} + \gamma_{13} - \gamma_{23}$$
$$S_1 = -\Delta_1 = \gamma_{23} - (\gamma_{12} + \gamma_{13}) \tag{13}$$

The surface free energy change that occurs on spreading, of Phase 2 over Phase 1 is given by:

$$\Delta G_2 = G_{after} - G_{before} = \gamma_{12} + \gamma_{23} - \gamma_{13}$$
$$S_2 = -\Delta G_2 = \gamma_{13} - (\gamma_{12} + \gamma_{23}) \tag{14}$$

Therefore, three spreading coefficients (S_1, S_2, and S_3) describe the equilibrium state of a three-phase system. The three S values can have three sets of values (100):

$$S_1 < 0, S_2 < 0, S_3 > 0; S_1 < 0, S_2 < 0, S_3$$
$$< 0; S_1 < 0, S_2 > 0, S_3 < 0 \tag{15}$$

Figure 8 shows the equilibrium configurations that results for each of the above three sets of S values. Of greatest significance to capsule-makers is that complete engulfing of core material by the coacervate occurs only when $S_1 < 0$, $S_2 < 0$, $S_3 > 0$, that is, one must have:

$$S_1 < 0 = \gamma_{23} - (\gamma_{12} - \gamma_{13})$$
$$S_2 < 0 = \gamma_{13} - (\gamma_{12} + \gamma_{23}) \tag{16}$$
$$S_3 > 0 = \gamma_{12} - (\gamma_{13} + \gamma_{32})$$

In encapsulation systems involving polymer phase separation (coacervation), γ_{23} usually is >0.2 dyne/cm. Because γ_{23} is so small, it is reasonable to assume that $\gamma_{23} \approx 0$. If this is done, and $\gamma_{12} > \gamma_{13}$, S_3 is > 0, S_1 is <0, and S_2 is <0. Thus, microcapsules form spontaneously. This is an assumption, and this may be part of the reason why methods such as coacervation may fail to produce microspheres.

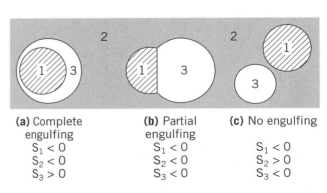

Figure 8. Schematic diagram showing the spreading coefficient, S, necessary for (**a**) complete engulfing of an internal phase (1) by a coacervate phase (3) in a continuous phase (2); (**b**) partial engulfing; (**c**) no engulfing.

But the new method to make double-walled microspheres are more useful.

SOLVENT EVAPORATION

One of the oldest and most widely used methods of microsphere preparation is the solvent evaporation technique (18,36,75–80,101). This method yields drug-loaded polymer particles that could be called microspheres when drug loading is low or microcapsules when the drug loading is high.

The solvent evaporation encapsulation process, depicted in Figure 9, is a way of precipitating small polymer particles from an oil-in-water emulsion. The polymer is dissolved in a volatile organic solvent that is immiscible with water. Methylene chloride is a preferred solvent because of its high volatility (boiling point [bp] 41°C) and its capacity for dissolving a broad range of polymers. Table 5 lists a number of solvents that can be used and, it should be noted that, many solvents suitable for this process have a finite degree of water solubility, even though they are normally classified as water-insoluble solvents. Mixed solvents can also be used. The mixtures used so far tend to contain a water-immiscible solvent (e.g., CH_2Cl_2) and a water-miscible solvent (e.g., acetone). The water-immiscible solvent is the predominant component of the mixture.

Once the desired coating polymer is dissolved in the organic solvent, the drug to be encapsulated is added to this solution. The drug agent may be a solid (crystalline or amorphous) or a nonvolatile liquid. The added drug may completely dissolve in the polymer solution or it may be completely insoluble and simply form a dispersion, suspension, or suspension-emulsion. In the latter case, the solid particles must be micronized so that their mean diameter is much less than the desired mean microsphere size. This is true for any encapsulation technique, and generally, a particle size/microsphere size ratio of 1:10 or less is preferred. The solubility of the drug in the organic solvent is also a major factor in determining the morphology of microspheres produced by the solvent evaporation process and the final state of the polymer itself (crystalline or amorphous).

The drug/polymer/solvent mixture (i.e., the oil phase) is emulsified in water to form an oil-in-water emulsion. The size of the oil phase droplets obtained is determined by how rapidly the system is agitated when the oil phase is added to the aqueous phase, and determines the size of the microspheres produced. Emulsification is carried out in a blender if small microspheres are desired (<20 µm) or with a suspended agitator for larger microspheres. In order to aid emulsification, a surfactant is normally dissolved in the water phase before the oil-in-water emulsion is formed. A good example is partially hydrolyzed (88%) poly(vinyl alcohol) (PVA).

Once the desired oil phase droplet size and emulsion stability have been obtained the system is stirred at a constant rate and the solvent evaporates. This is the basis of the name, because most of the solvent disappears by evaporation. Evaporation can occur in an open system at reduced pressure and range of evaporation temperatures can be used. Once solvent evaporation appears to be complete, the capsules are separated from the suspending medium by filtration, washed, and dried. The maximum drying temperature must remain below the glass-transition temperature of the polymer encapsulant or the microspheres fuse together. Although most of the process depends on evaporation, some of the solvent may diffuse into the aqueous solution and then evaporate. The amount that diffuses into the aqueous solution directly depends on the solubility of the organic solvent in water.

The solvent evaporation process is conceptually simple, but a large number of process variables exist which can profoundly affect the nature of the product obtained. Table 6 lists a number of such variables. How each of these variables influences a given system must be determined experimentally, although some general trends are known. For example, semicrystalline polymers often give porous structures with spherulites on the surface of the microspheres. Uniform, pore-free spheres are most readily obtained with amorphous polymers. If a polymer is not soluble in a single solvent, mixed solvents can be used (e.g., CH_2Cl_2/ethanol or CH_2Cl_2/acetone mixtures).

One requirement of the solvent evaporation process is that the active agent (i.e., drug) partition favorably into the oil phase. This partitioning is favored by using active

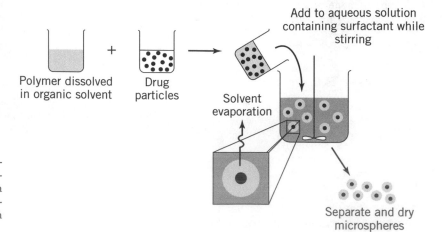

Figure 9. Microencapsulation by solvent evaporation. Note that the dark dots represent drug particles; however when the drug is water-soluble, an additional step is required to prepare a water-in-oil emulsion, which is later encapsulated as shown here.

Table 5. Properties of Some Organic Solvents

Solvent	bp (°C)	fp (°C)	solubility in H$_2$O g/100 g solvent
Methylene chloride	41	−96.7	2
Chloroform	61.2	−63.5	0.82
Ethyl acetate	77.1	−82.4	8.5 (15°C)

Table 6. Parameters Affecting Solvent Evaporation

1. Polymer molecular weight and concentration
2. Polymer crystallization
3. Type of drug and method of incorporation (solid, liquid, suspension).
4. Organic solvent used
5. Type of surfactant in aqueous phase
6. Organic solvent/aqueous phase cation
7. Evaporation temperature
8. Rating of stirring

agents that are insoluble or sparsely soluble in water. Such agents may be insoluble in the organic solvent. In the latter case, the microspheres contain a dispersion of crystals embedded in a polymer matrix. The crystals should be the same ones dispersed initially in the polymer–solvent solution, assuming that there is no partial solubilization and/or recrystallization. If the active agent dissolves completely in the organic solvent phase, it may or may not form crystalline domains in the polymer matrix that makes up the microsphere. For example, microspheres with low active agent payloads (e.g., <20 wt %) have no crystalline domains as determined by differential thermal analysis. At higher payloads, crystallinity appears.

Preventing migration of active agent into the aqueous phase from the solvent phase is often a problem. Crystalline active agents completely soluble in the solvent phase tend to form free crystals in the aqueous phase or on the surface of the microspheres. This effect can be minimized by removing from the system the emulsifier located in the aqueous phase before solvent evaporation is complete. When the emulsifier is left in the system until evaporation is complete, it favors free crystal formation. Thus, by stopping agitation midway through the evaporation process, one can remove the emulsifier by a series of washing and decantation steps. Agitation (and evaporation) is then continued in the presence of emulsifier-free water until solvent loss is complete. This either eliminates or drastically reduces the amount of free crystals formed.

Mathiowitz et al. (55) used this method, with the following modifications, to prepare polyanhydride microspheres. (Please note that this is not a preferred method for polyanhydrides.) Poly(carboxyphenoxypropane-co-sebacic-acid) (poly(CPP-SA) 50:50) was dissolved in methylene chloride. Two different polymer concentrations were used (0.05 and 0.20 g/mL). The solution was loaded with drug and suspended in 200 mL of vigorously stirred distilled water containing 1% (w/v) PVA. After 4 hours of mixing, the microspheres were washed with water and dried overnight in a lyophilizer.

Figure 10a is a scanning electron micrograph (SEM) of the external surface of a poly(CPP-SA) 50:50 polymer microsphere containing 5% (W/W) insulin. For this particular formulation the initial polymer concentration was 0.05 g/mL of methylene chloride. The microspheres are spherical in shape and contain some pores on the surface; a cross-sectional view of the microsphere reveals a very porous internal structure (Fig. 10b), which is typical of this particular process. Porosity can be varied by changing the rate of solvent evaporation (via the temperature or stirring rate) as well as the concentration of the initial polymer solution. When the previously described fabrication was repeated with an initial polymer concentration of 0.20 g/mL, polymer in methylene chloride, the resulting microspheres showed a marked drop in porosity (Fig. 10c).

Besides resulting in high microsphere porosity, solvent evaporation also accelerates polymer degradation during the first stages of preparation due to the presence of the water phase. For these reasons, polyanhydride solvent evaporation is not recommended. Other fabrication methods were developed to make slower releasing and longer acting polyanhydride microspheres (see "Hot Melt Microencapsulation" and "Solvent Removal").

The biological activity of insulin released from microspheres was determined in vivo by monitoring daily blood and urine glucose levels in polymer-implanted diabetic female Sprague-Dawley rats. Diabetes was previously induced with a tail vein injection of 65 mg/kg of streptozotocin in pH 4.5, 0.1 M citrate buffer, the optimal dose for inducing diabetes in these rats. When serum glucose levels reached a minimum of 400 mg/dL the rats were considered diabetic and were treated with the insulin-loaded polyanhydride microspheres. Daily urine glucose outputs were estimated with Chemstrips UG. Blood was drawn daily from the tail vein and serum glucose levels were read on a Glucose Analyzer.

Dry microspheres were implanted subcutaneously through a small (1 cm) surgical incision in the skin of the dorsum of the rat and the skin was closed with monofilament nylon sutures. Where indicated, certain microspheres were injected in an aqueous suspension in 0.1 M pH 7.4 phosphate buffer through a 22-gauge needle. Three groups were studied; healthy rats, diabetic control rats, and diabetic rats that were implanted with the drug-loaded spheres. When insulin-loaded (10%), solvent evaporation microspheres were implanted in diabetic rats, the blood glucose level was lowered precipitously for one day, with the majority of the rats dying due to insulin overdose. The porous structure of the spheres presumably allowed water to enter the sphere quickly and led to complete insulin release in a short period of time, which may explain the extremely fast and generally fatal hypoglycemia that was observed. Figure 10d depicts insulin-loaded microspheres that were found in the rat tissue after one day of implantation (note the porous structure of the microsphere). Better results were obtained with microspheres made by hot-melt and solvent removal (see "Hot Melt Microencapsulation" and "Solvent Removal").

Polyester microspheres made by solvent evaporation were reported on extensively in the last 10 years, and the most successful microsphere product that is being used in

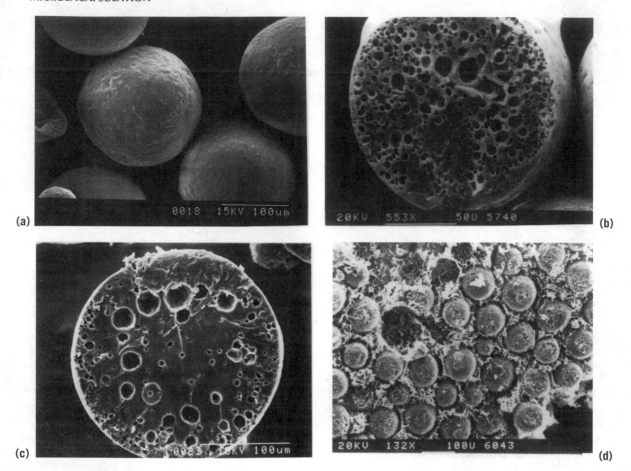

Figure 10. SEM of (**a**) external surface of polyanhydride microsphere made by solvent evaporation; (**b**) cross section of a polyanhydride microsphere made with low polymer concentration; (**c**) cross section of a polyanhydride microsphere made with high concentration; (**d**) insulin-loaded polyanhydride microspheres after two days of subcutaneous implantation in rats.

humans today is the Lupron Depo®. To understand the development of the Lupron Depo® it may be interesting to follow some of the procedures described by Okada (102). In the double emulsion technique used, first the drug is dissolved in an aqueous solution. The patent describes how the pH can be adjusted by adding materials such as carbonic acid, acetic acid, oxalic acid, citric acid, tartaric acid, succinic acid, phosphoric acid, sodium or potassium salts, hydrochloric acid, or sodium hydroxide. In addition, agents such as albumin, gelatin, citric acid, ethylenediamine sodium tetraacetate, dextrin, and sodium hydrosulfite could be added as a stabilizer for the water soluble drug. The inner aqueous layer may also contain a preservative such as *p*-oxybenzoic acid esters (e.g., methylparaben, propylparaben, etc.), benzyl alcohol, chlorobutanol, or thimerosal (102).

Once the inner aqueous layer is prepared it is poured into a polymer solution (oil layer) and the mixture is emulsified to give a water-in-oil emulsion (102). The emulsification can be effected by the conventional dispersion techniques, e.g., intermittent shaking, mixing via an impeller, turbine mixer or the like, colloid mill operation, mechanical homogenization, ultrasonication, etc. (102).

When the viscosity of the inner aqueous layer in such a water-in-oil emulsion is greater than about 5,000 centipoises, or preferably greater than 10,000 centipoises from the beginning, the emulsion is immediately subjected to conditions that change the viscosity (102). Increasing the viscosity can be achieved by either heating or cooling. If gum acacia is used, adding metal ions such as iron or copper ion for carboxymethylcellulose, or calcium or magnesium ion for sodium pectinate, are useful (102).

If heating is used, then the procedure must be carried out in a closed vessel to avoid evaporation of the solvent contained in the oil layer. When proteins are used, the temperature used can be from 40 to 120°C for as little as 5 minutes to about 8 hours. This treatment thickens or solidifies the inner aqueous layer (102).

Cooling the emulsion to a low temperature is accomplished at temperatures of −5 to 35°C which are maintained with stirring for 1 minute to 6 hours. In the case of agar whose gelation point is about 40°C, the emulsification is conducted under heating, at about 50 to 80°C, and then caused to gel at the aforementioned temperature. For all types of inner aqueous layers, freezing may be effected by cooling to about −60 to 0°C, but the temperature should not be below the solidification point of the oil layer (102).

This step seems to reduce the amount of drug lost to the aqueous solution. Using gelatin as an example of a drug-retaining substance: a water-in-oil emulsion of predetermined particle size is first prepared and then cooled to about 0–10°C for 5 to 30 minutes with constant stirring, whereby the inner aqueous layer is caused to gel into a semisolid consistency. When agar is used as the drug-retaining substance, the desired semisolid consistency can be obtained by using a lower concentration than in the case of gelatin and the same procedure as that for gelatin. When albumin is employed, solidification is effected with a condensing agent such as glutaraldehyde (102). For large proteins this step is not recommended.

An attempt at developing leuprolide acetate-loaded, injectable microcapsules capable of one-month, zero-order rate delivery was reported by Ogawa et al. (103). A large amount of leuprolide acetate, a hydrophilic drug, was entrapped in poly(lactic acid) (PLA) and poly(lactide-co-glycolide) (PLGA) microcapsules prepared by an in-water drying method using a (W/O/W) emulsion. Under the conditions used, it was possible for the drug to be completely entrapped by the microcapsules at a loading of 10 to 20% (W/W). However, the release profiles of the drug in vitro fell short of controlled release for one month.

Leuprolide acetate is a highly potent analog of luteinizing hormone-releasing hormone (LHRH). Okada et al. (105) succeeded in preparing one-month release, injectable microcapsules of leuprolide acetate using poly(DL-lactide-co-glycolide) to treat an endocrine-dependent prostate cancer. A single injection of the microcapsules (100 μg/kg/day as leuprolide acetate) suppressed luteinizing hormone (LH), follicle-stimulating hormone (FSH), and estradiol for more than 4 weeks and caused a dramatic regression of growth in the Jones experimental endometriosis model in female rats. These results encouraged scientists to develop a one-month release, parenteral preparation of leuprolide acetate, subsequently used in the therapy of endometriosis in human beings (104).

The drug release profiles of the microcapsules after subcutaneous (s.c.) and intramuscular (i.m.) injection into rats was determined by following the amount of the analog remaining at the incised injection site. The release profiles after s.c. and i.m. injection were almost identical; they provided a pseudo zero-order release for 4 weeks, after a small initial burst. The regression line of the amount remaining, calculated by a least-squares regression analysis, revealed that the rate of release of leuprolide acetate was 2.8% of the dose/day, the initial burst was 17.8%. The correlation coefficient was 0.99. The serum levels of leuprolide acetate in rats after the PLGA microcapsules were injected s.c. showed that the initial burst of the analog was followed by a plateau level for 4 weeks. Administration of the microcapsules to normal female rats resulted in a transient rise and subsequent drastic decrease of serum LH and FSH levels. The decreased serum levels reached minima 2 to 3 weeks after the injection, and were maintained for another 1 to 2 weeks. The estradiol levels reached a minimum 3 weeks after the injection and remained there for another week. Thereafter, the levels of FSH and estradiol recovered gradually and rebounded slightly by 6 or 8 weeks of treatment. In contrast, the suppressed serum levels of LH per-

sisted for 6 weeks. Daily cytological examination of vaginal smears indicated that the estrous cycle had stopped at diestrus in all rats 3 days after the microcapsules were injected, and remained at this stage for 6 weeks. The normal estrous cycle was recovered 8 weeks after the treatment began.

Expected depression in LH, FSH, and estradiol serum levels occurred at doses of more than 100 μg/kg/day. Serum LH levels were decreased already by a dose of 1 to 10 μg/kg/day; the levels were equivalent to those in diestrus rats. At a dose of 100 mg/kg/day, the serum FSH levels were also depressed, and significantly reduced serum levels of estradiol were produced by all doses between 1 to 250 μg/kg/day; the levels at a dose of over 100 μg/kg/day were close to that produced by ovarioectomy.

The infinite area under serum level-time curve in female rats after leuprolide acetate was injected s.c. as a saline solution (100 μg/kg) was 118.8 ng · h/mL, as described previously. The total body clearance (Cl_{tot}) is calculated by:

$$Cl_{tot} = \text{Dose/AUC} = 100 \times 10^3/118.8 = 841.8 \text{ mL/h/kg} \tag{17}$$

The release rate (k) of leuprolide from the microcapsules (TAP-6M), calculated in a similar manner in TAP-3M, was 3.1% of the dose/day, which is equal to:

$$k = 900 \times 10^3\ 0.031/0.305 \times 24 = 3811 \text{ ng/h/kg} \tag{18}$$

where the average body weight during 4 weeks of treatment was 305 g. If the analog is infused at a constant rate (k), the serum drug levels at a steady state (C_{ss}) is given by equation 19.

$$C_{ss} = k/Cl_{tot} = 4.53 \text{ ng/mL} \tag{19}$$

The serum levels estimated using body weight during 4 weeks of treatment as described before are 5.55 ng/mL (body weight, 249 g) to 3.98 ng/mL (body weight, 347 g). The experimental values agreed well with these calculated serum levels at a steady state. The microcapsules eliminated the time lag of the initial drug release and produced a more constant and lasting serum level of the analog throughout the 4 weeks of treatment than did an implantable depot formulation of D-Ser(tBu)-AzaGly LHRH and microcapsules of nafarelin or decapeptyl (104).

Okada et al. (105) worked on developing a more interesting system of Leuprorelin for 3-month delivery. The pharmacological effects of Leuprorelin 3-month depot microspheres were investigated in rats and dogs. After s.c. and i.m. injection, the microspheres provided similar linear drug release and sustained serum drug levels for 3 months. Persistent suppression of serum LH, FSH (in rats) and testosterone (in rats and dogs) for over 16 weeks was achieved when the microspheres were given at a dose of 100 (rat) and 25.6 (dog) μg/kg/day. These hormone release responses, upon periodic challenge tests, revealed that for a single injection of the microspheres over 3 months the strongest suppression was achieved at a dose of 100 μg/kg/

day. This 3-month depot formulation is expected to be more convenient than the 1-month depot with improved patient compliance and therapeutic effects. To obtain a 3-month release injection of leuprolide acetate, microspheres, were prepared with poly(DL-lactide-*co*-/glycolide) (DL-PLGA) or PLA using an in-water drying method, after which drug release was evaluated. The content of water-soluble oligomers in the polymers was found to strongly affect the initial burst, and reducing the content to less than 0.1% was necessary to keep the first-day release below 10%. Drug loading of more than 15% also increased the initial drug release; the acceptable maximum loading was 12%. Elevation of the glass-transition temperature of the microspheres was observed with an increase in drug loading. This suggests formation of a rigid structure, possibly with arrangement of the polymer around the drug cores such as in a micelle. This structure provides a hydrophobic barrier against diffusion of the hydrophilic peptide, resulting in high trapping efficiency and long-term sustained release dependent on polymer erosion. The microspheres prepared with PLA of 12,000 to 18,000 M_w provided linear sustained release and persistent serum levels of the drug in rats for over 3 months (106).

In order to prepare the long-release systems, the microspheres of Leuprorelin were made without the gelatin in the inner drug solution. Briefly, in the case of 12% drug-loaded PLA microspheres, 550 mg of drug dissolved in 1 mL of distilled water (W_1) and 4 g of PLA dissolved in 7.5 mL of CH_2Cl_2 were combined and agitated vigorously with a homogenizer to form a W/O emulsion. This emulsion was poured into 1 L of a 0.25% PVA solution (w_2) under stirring. This $W_1/O/W_2$ emulsion was stirred gently for 3 hours to evaporate the organic solvent, producing microspheres. The microspheres were sieved with a 74-μm screen to remove large particles and then centrifuged at 1,000 rpm for 5 minutes. The resulting microspheres were washed with water and lyophilized. PLGA 75:25 (M_w 9,000–23,000), PLGA 90:10 (M_w 9,200–22,900) and PLA (M_w 4,700–162,100) were used. To determine the effects of drug loading on drug release, microspheres containing 9, 12, 15, and 18% drug were prepared using PLA (M_w 18,200). The volume of the inner water phase and organic solvent and temperature of the W/O emulsion and outer water layer were varied with the kind of polymer and percent drug loading to maintain appropriate viscosity and obtain spherical and similar size microspheres (107).

The results of screening biodegradable polymers, PLA and PLGA, for the 3-month depot formulation indicated that microspheres prepared using PLA with a molecular weight of 12,000 to 18,000 gave linear sustained drug release for over 13 weeks. A similar sustained release pattern was confirmed by serum drug level assays following s.c. injection of these microspheres. The microspheres prepared using PLA (M_w 15,000), containing less than 0.1% water-soluble oligomers and loaded with 12% drug, may be the most desirable formulation for the 3-month depot injection (106).

Analyses of microparticle size and morphology during degradation by Brannon-Peppas et al. (107,108) have shown that the method of incorporating β-estradiol into PLGA microparticles has an effect on drug delivery that

may be followed by changes of the microstructure of the particles over time. Nondestructive observation of microparticles during their full degradation has verified the coupling of drug release during early periods of degradation where small changes in the particle structure may be observed. However, it has also been shown that these particles retain their structural integrity and shape for many months in vitro after all drug delivery has been completed.

Schugens et al. (109) studied two semicrystalline poly(L-lactides) with different molecular weights as coating polymers in microencapsulation by the W/O/W double emulsion-evaporation technique. The scientists have shown that crystallizable chains have clearly a deleterious effect on the encapsulation efficiency of indigocarmine and on the internal morphology of microparticles. Moreover, a substantial increase in the molecular weight of poly(L-lactide) (from 60 to 840 kDa) requires dilution of the polymer solution to prevent exceedingly high viscosity and leads to less stable primary emulsions and more porous solid microspheres. Microparticles of semicrystalline poly(L-lactide) have proved unsuitable for the sustained drug release. When poly(DL-lactide) (M_n 50 kDa), was used, more efficient microencapsulation was obtained. This was true particularly when the primary emulsion was stabilized with gelation.

Using a predictive mathematical model from Li et al. (110) several important extrinsic process variables were developed to simulate process dynamics of microsphere formation. These included the composition profile in the dispersed phase, the solvent concentration profile in the continuous phase, and the solvent removal profile in the dispersed phase. This was one of the attempts to move closer to understanding microencapsulation in detail. By superimposing the composition profile in the dispersed phase with the phase transition boundary, the progression of phase transition in microsphere formation was evaluated. The authors found that a low dispersed phase/continuous phase ratio, high continuous phase-addition rate, high temperature, high heating rate, and high initial polymer concentration in the dispersed phase contributed to enhanced solvent removal. The higher solvent removal led to a heterogeneous composition distribution in the dispersed phase and the early crossover of the gelation point (viscous boundary) of the peripheral region which initiates the onset of solidification in this region. These phenomena resulted in an increasing pore size, lower surface area, denser periphery, higher residual solvent, and slower drug release. In addition, the progress toward the glassy boundary may also play a major role in the ultimate solvent residual. Slow solvent removal gave rise to a homogenous distribution of the components in the dispersed phase due to the delay of hardening. The extrinsic manageable parameters could be varied during microsphere formation to obtain the desired rate of solvent removal as well as the desired microsphere properties. The mathematical model was used to simulate such conditions to facilitate the experimental design for the desired microsphere properties.

Poly(L-lactic acid-*co*-L-lysine(Z)) (PLLA) with different Lys(Z) contents was synthesized by Sn(II) salt-catalyzed ring-opening copolymerization of 3(*s*)-benzyloxycarbonylaminobutyl-6(*S*)-methylmorpholine-2,5-dione with lactide. Microcapsules of the copolymers were prepared by solvent evaporation from W/O/W emulsion, and fluorescein isothiocyanate (FITC) dextran release from the microcapsules was investigated. The FITC-dextran release was dependent on the composition and molecular weight of the copolymers. The release from the microcapsules containing Lys(Z) of 6.5 mol% was slowest among the present microcapsules, which is due to smooth surface and very small microcapsules included in a large microcapsule. On the other hand, the release from microcapsules containing Lys(Z) of 31 or 50 mol% became faster after several days of incubation. Gel permeation chromatography measurement of the microcapsules revealed that the copolymers were degraded during the incubation. Cracks and pores were formed on the microcapsule wall. PLLA microcapsules having comparable molecular weight to the copolymers showed neither release acceleration nor degradation in short-time incubation. Therefore, the introduction of Lys(Z) units made PLLA susceptible to degradation to result in delayed acceleration of release (111).

PLA microspheres containing soluble dyes as water-soluble model compounds were prepared using the W/O/W solvent evaporation method. The authors reported that addition of electrolytes such as NaCl or CaCl₂ into the external aqueous phase significantly improved brilliant blue (BB) entrapment efficiency compared to the case of no additives (75). NaCl was the most effective for obtaining high entrapment efficiency (80–90% of theoretical BB content). The average diameter of the obtained microspheres was in the region of 10–20 μm in all cases. PLA microspheres containing 5 and 10% (W/W) BB exhibited the so-called burst release. The release rate decreased with decrease in the internal aqueous droplet volume in the preparation process. In particular, with PLA microspheres containing 5% (W/W) BB, those prepared with the smallest internal droplet volume (63 μL), the initial burst release was reduced significantly and 50% (W/W) of the loaded BB remained in the microspheres for 7 days.

Reza and Whateley (112) developed sustained local release systems for iodinated iodo-2'-deoxyuridine (IudR) from biodegradable polymeric microspheres to facilitate the controlled delivery of IudR to brain tumors. The selective uptake of IUdR into the cell nucleus results in cell disruption over the short range of the low energy Auger electrons. The biodegradable microspheres can be precisely implanted in the brain by stereotactic techniques and the IUdR within the microspheres is protected from degradation and thus a sustained source of radiolabeled IUdR is available in the vicinity of the residual tumor cells. PLGA 85:15 microspheres containing cold IUdR and the Auger-electron emitter ¹²⁵I, as ¹²⁵IudR were prepared using the O/W, O/O, and W/O/W emulsion-solvent evaporation methods. The W/O/W emulsion method was most effective in achieving good drug loading with the use of bovine plasma in the internal water phase. The use of 20% acetone in the methylene chloride and the presence of Span® 40 in the organic phase improved the drug encapsulation efficiency. Electrolytes (NaCl and IudR) in the external aqueous phase also improved drug loading.

Okumo et al. examined the effects of size, charge, and conformation on the release of peptides from microspheres

of DL-PLGA 50:50. These microspheres were prepared using a double emulsion technique and were characterized for size, morphology, and peptide release kinetics. The volume of water used as the internal phase has a significant effect on the release of the linear hexapeptide Ac-Trp-Ala-Gly-Gly-Asp-Ala-NH₂. For example, when no water was added, the release appears to be erosion-controlled. In contrast, when 150, 500, or 1000 μL of water are added, the release shifts to a diffusion-controlled mechanism. Changing the size, charge, and conformational flexibility of the model peptides had no significant effect on their release kinetics. The authors suggest that release kinetics that were observed for the neutral capped amino acid and the positively charged cyclic hexapeptide are due to unique specific interactions between these compounds and DL-PLGA (113).

A new preparation method for multireservoir-type microspheres was investigated on the basis of the phase separation of PLA and PLGA. Matsumoto et al. (114) have found that distinctive phase separation occurred when the total polymer concentration exceeded a critical level. The critical polymer concentration inducing this phase separation was independent of the PLA/PLGA ratio but highly dependent on the lactide/glycolide ratio, solvent, and molecular weight of PLGA. When various amino acid powders were added to the resultant two-phase polymeric solution, each powder seemed to be distributed either to the PLGA-rich phase or to the PLA-rich phase depending on its solubility parameter. When used, cisplatin powder also was completely distributed in the PLGA-rich phase. Using these findings, the preparation of the multireservoir-type microspheres of cisplatin was tried. The PLGA-PLA biphasic polymeric solution dispersing the drug powder was emulsified, and then solidified by the solvent evaporation method. Microscopic observation proved that the obtained microspheres have the unique "polymer alloys" structure, and the drug was distributed in the internal phase (PLGA-rich phase). The encapsulation efficiency was almost 100% at 10% loading. The in vitro dissolution study revealed that the release of cisplatin lasted 45 days without initial burst.

The distribution of a drug substance between two phases is represented as follows:

$$\frac{[X_a]}{[X_b]} = V_s \frac{(\delta_s - \delta_b)^2 - (\delta_a - \delta_s)^2}{2.3RT} \qquad (20)$$

where $[X_a]$ and $[X_b]$ are concentrations of drug substance s in a phase and b phase, respectively; δ_a, δ_b, and δ_s are solubility parameters of a phase, b phase, and substance s, respectively; V_s is the molecular volume of substance s; R is the gas constant; and T is absolute temperature. This equation means that the distribution of substance s varies depending on the solubility parameters of a phase and b phase. In the present situation, however, because substance s always exists as a solid state, V_s is considerably large so that the distribution of substance s favors one side (114).

To examine the applicability of equation 20 to predict the distribution of drug substance in the PLA-PLGA biphasic polymeric solution, 5 amino acids with different solubility parameters were selected as model compounds. If

PLGA and PLA separated completely, solubility parameters of the PLGA phase ($\delta_{PLGA/p}$) and PLA phase ($\delta_{PLA/p}$) were calculated by the following equations:

$$\delta_{PLGA/p} = \delta_{PLGA} + (1 - a)\delta_{solv}$$
$$\delta_{PLA/p} = b\delta_{PLA} + (1 - b)\delta_{solv} \qquad (21)$$

where a and b are volume fractions of PLGA and PLA, respectively, δ_{PLGA}, δ_{PLA}, δ_{solv} are solubility parameters of PLGA (11.00), PLA (10.69), and solvent (114).

The authors showed that the distribution of drugs was dependent on the solubility parameter difference; that is, in the case of a positive value, drugs had a tendency to be distributed on the PLGA phase; in the case of a negative value, drugs had a tendency to be distributed on the PLA phase; and when the value was close to zero, drugs had a tendency to be distributed on the interface between PLGA and PLA phase.

An additional drug that was evaluated by Matsumoto et al. was cisplatin, known to be one of the most effective anticancer drugs in chemotherapy. However, due to various side effects (e.g., renal disturbances, nausea, vomiting), a lot of care has been taken in its clinical use. To minimize the side effects and to increase the therapeutic effects, it must be possible to restrict the blood level of the drug to the therapeutic level for a long period of time (114).

Cisplatin was predicted to be distributed in the PLGA phase from its solubility parameter (~12.2). This was proven by the fact that the drug was incorporated in the PLGA-rich phase when cisplatin powder was added to the PLGA-PLA biphasic polymeric solution. The distribution of the drug was highly dependent on the mixing ratio of polymers. When the PLGA/PLA ratio was given as 20:80 or 33:67, cisplatin was partitioned to the inner phase (PLGA-rich phase). On the other hand, when the PLGA ratio increased up to 67 or 80%, due to accompanying the phase inversion, the drug powder was distributed in the continuous phase (114).

Cleland et al. described how the administration of a subunit vaccine (e.g., gp120) for acquired immunodeficiency syndrome (AIDS) can be facilitated by a single shot vaccine that mimics repeated immunizations. To achieve this type of vaccine, they developed PLGA microspheres that provide a pulsatile release of gp120. Studies of a water-in-oil-in-water microencapsulation process with either methylene chloride or ethyl acetate as the polymer solvent revealed that the encapsulation efficiency was greatly enhanced by increasing the kinematic viscosity of the polymer phase via a reduction in temperature (~0°C) and an increase in polymer concentration. Excess methylene chloride (1.5% v/v) in the second emulsion reduced the encapsulation efficiency, whereas excess ethyl acetate (9% v/v) in the second emulsion was necessary for microsphere formation. The optimization of process variables allowed for complete encapsulation of the gp120 (100% efficiency). Drying of the microspheres had a significant impact on the initial emulsion, the density of the inner emulsion water droplets in the microspheres was reduced requiring significant polymer erosion to occur prior to protein release. The protein was released under physiological conditions in two discrete phases: an initial burst released over the first day and after several weeks or months a second burst of protein was released. The second burst of protein was dependent upon the PLGA inherent viscosity and lactide:glycolide ratio (bulk erosion). The initial gp120 released under physiological conditions as well as the gp120 extracted from the microspheres maintained their native conformation, as measured by a variety of physicochemical methods. Thus, PLGA or PLA microsphere formulations were developed to provide a second burst of gp120 to mimic immunizations at 1, 2, 3, or 6 months. A single administration vaccine for gp120 may then include two or more microsphere formulations resuspended with soluble gp120 (primary immunization) to provide three immunizations or more over the course of one year (115).

Sah (117) developed a process in which ethyl acetate was used to prepare DL-PLGA microspheres. They first emulsified a polymer/ethyl acetate solution with a 1% aqueous PVA solution (W_1) to make an oil-in-water (O/W_1) emulsion. The $O:W_1$ phase ratio was carefully chosen so as to saturate the W_1 by a small proportion of the dispersed solvent and to form successfully embryonic microspheres without generating polymer precipitates. The effects of the $O:W_1$ phase ratio on the morphology and size of microspheres were interpreted in terms of the solvent miscibility with water, as well as the influence of the W_1 volume on breakup of the dispersed phase. The extraction rate of ethyl acetate from the nascent microspheres was then adjusted by making use of both its miscibility with water and its volatility at atmospheric pressure. Variation of these parameters made it possible to fabricate hollow or matrix-type microspheres with different size distributions. It was also found that the tendency of microspheres to aggregate on drying was related to the extent of microsphere hydration and the residual ethyl acetate in wet microspheres, which probably decreased the glass transition of the polymer.

The use of methylene chloride may impose a problem in obtaining product approval by regulatory agencies. As evidenced by Lupron Depot, a small amount of methylene chloride remaining in a microsphere product is acceptable by the U.S. FDA, but only if the product's therapeutic benefits clearly outweigh a safety concern over the residual solvent. However, when faced with a microsphere product to be marketed as preventive medicament, such as a vaccine, the regulatory agency may raise a concern over the possible risk that the residual solvent triggers: methylene chloride is a suspected carcinogen and mutagen. In recognition of this issue, a number of investigations have sought safer solvents (Table 7). Among those found, ethyl acetate is considered one of the most preferable solvents (116).

Thompson et al. (117) developed biodegradable controlled release microspheres containing rismorelin porcine, a potent analog of growth hormone-releasing hormone (GHRH), using DL-PLGA in a modified solvent evaporation technique. Rismorelin porcine microspheres were prepared with a modified solvent evaporation technique to reduce water leeching of the peptide. A typical batch of microspheres is 2 g, consisting of polymer and drug. Ten percent weight/weight rismorelin porcine-containing microspheres were fabricated by dissolving 1.8 g of PLGA in 50 mL of methylene chloride. To this polymer

Table 7. News Solvent for Solvent Evaporation Process

Solvent	Preparation method
Acetone	A salting-out procedure using an electrolyte-saturated continuous phase
Ethyl acetate	Rapid freezing of a polymeric phase in a liquefied gas, followed by solvent extraction
Ethyl formate	In situ solidification of polymeric materials due
N-methyl-2-pyrrolidone dimethyl sulfoxide	To dissipation of solvents to external aqueous media
Methylethyl ketone	A solvent extraction technique making use of partial water-miscibility of the solvent
Phthalic acid diethyl ether	Freeze-drying of the polymeric solution by ball milling to produce randomly shaped particles

solution, 200 mg of micronized rismorelin porcine was added, forming a suspension of drug in the polymer solution. The viscosity of this polymer solution/drug suspension was intentionally kept low to aid in the formation of small, spherical microspheres. The suspension was sonicated at room temperature for approximately 1 minute to disperse the micronized rismorelin porcine particles. The polymer solution/drug suspension was emulsified with stirring into 250 mL phosphate-buffered saline (PBS) containing 0.4 w/v % AIRVOL™ PVA as an emulsifier to form an oil-in-water emulsion. Rismorelin porcine is insoluble in PBS and other salt-containing solutions. The partitioning of drug into the aqueous phase did not occur under these conditions. Stirring at 300 rev/min was continued at room temperature for approximately 16 hours to allow complete solubilization and evaporation of methylene chloride. The resulting rismorelin porcine microspheres were recovered using vacuum filtration, washed with PBS, dried under vacuum in a desiccator, and sieved to size using 60 mesh and 120 mesh U.S. Standard sieves (250 μm and 125 μm, respectively). Rismorelin porcine PLA/PGA microspheres with different loading values (5%, 10%, and 25%) were prepared by varying the ratio of drug to polymer in the suspension solution (117). Release rates of rismorelin porcine were characterized in vitro by use of a cell perfusion system and evaluated in vivo in pigs. Rismorelin porcine is 4-methylhippuroyl (1) porcine GHRH (2-76)-OH, which is a potent analog of a natural porcine GHRH. The biological efficacy of the rismorelin porcine microspheres was determined in swine by urinary urea nitrogen depression as well as by serum blood urea nitrogen. The physical site of injection of microspheres did not influence release profile in swine. In vivo release of rismorelin porcine from microspheres ceased after 9 to 12 days in all studies.

Diaz et al. (118) studied DL-PLGA microspheres of ^{125}I-bovine calcitonin prepared by the double emulsion technique (including Tween® 80 in the water phase and Span® 60 in the oil phase of the first emulsion) in vitro and in vivo. The release of ^{125}I-bovine calcitonin was determined in vitro at 37°C in isotonic phosphate buffer (pH 7.4). ^{125}I-bovine calcitonin microspheres (5 mg) were administered under the skin on the back of Wistar rats and the radioactivity at the injection site was subsequently measured over a 6-week period. The in vivo and in vitro ^{125}I-bovine calcitonin profiles were affected by the surfactant agents, but in vivo release was much faster than in vitro. Following injection in rats, microspheres made with Tween® 80 and Span® 60 to give a HLB value of 6 and 8 in the first emulsion, released 20 and 14% of the radioactivity within the first 24 hours, but only 1.3 and 1.2%/day at later times (up to 6 weeks), respectively. Under these conditions, they take 8 and 10 weeks, respectively, to release the total amount of calcitonin.

FITC-labeled bovine serum albumin has been entrapped in sub-5 μm particles of DL-PLGA using a W/O/W solvent evaporation technique. The concentration of PVA stabilizer in the external continuous phase was found to affect not only the particle size, size distribution, and protein content, but also the release characteristic and internal structure of the microparticles. The importance of primary emulsification was underlined by the finding that the protein content of microparticles with a mean size of 1 mm could be increased from about 1% W/W to around 12% W/W by increasing the amount of protein added to the primary emulsion and the homogenization time in this stage. Under conditions of low stabilizer concentration, multinucleate particles were formed by polymer precipitation and envelopment of the droplets of the primary W/O emulsion. In this case surface protein loading was on the order of 30% W/W. Under conditions of high PVA stabilizer concentration, disruption of the primary emulsion occurred, resulting in submicrometer particles which were characterized by a high surface protein loading on the order of 70% W/W. A mechanism for protein microencapsulation was presented which is heavily influenced by the shear stresses induced during the process of secondary emulsification (119).

Effects of additives on the drug release kinetics from biodegradable matrices is an important determinant in designing a drug delivery system. Song et al. (120) studied the influence of an array of additives on the drug release from double-layered PLGA matrices. Various additives such as L-tartaric acid dimethyl ester, Pluronic® F127 (F127); 2-hydroxypropyl derivative of β-cyclodextrin (HPB), methyl derivative of β-cyclodextrin and Beeswax (Wax), differing in molecular size, hydrophilicity, and steric configuration were selected for this study. An antiproliferative 2-aminochrome, U-86983 (U-86, Pharmacia and Upjohn), was used as a model agent for local delivery for the inhibition of restenosis. The in vitro release of U-86 from PLGA matrices without additive showed typical biphasic release kinetics, i.e., a slow diffusion release (Phase I) followed by a fast erosion-mediated release (Phase II). Water-soluble additives in the PLGA matrices changed the biphasic release pattern to a near monophasic profile by increasing the release rate of the Phase I. Increasing the ratio of additives to PLGA in matrices causes a significant increase in the U-86 release rates. The high molecular weight, water-soluble additive, F127, resulted in a matrix showing perfect zero-order release kinetics. The water-soluble cyclodextrin derivative, HPB, gave the highest release rate among all the matrices formulated. A hydrophobic additive, Beeswax, however showed biphasic release kinetics comparable to PLGA control matrices, but delayed the onset of the Phase II by 4 days. The morphological evaluation of matrices by SEM suggests that the water-soluble additives are leachable and thus generate a highly porous structure in the matrices. The matrix pore configuration (e.g., interconnected or closed) created with different additives determined the mechanism of drug release kinetics from the various matrix formulations.

Jager-Lezer et al. (121) examined the release kinetics of a water-soluble drug from two different W/O/W multiple emulsions prepared with two lipophilic surfactants at different concentrations. The study of the kinetics under both iso-osmotic and hypo-osmotic conditions allowed the author to distinguish between two possible release mechanisms, swelling-breakdown or facilitated diffusion. The results obtained indicate that water-soluble drug release occurs by a mechanism of swelling followed by a breakdown of the oil globules, in which the lipophilic surfactant is a decisive factor. It appears that the globule's swelling capacity is considerably increased when the lipophilic surfactant concentration increases, and the more the oil globule swells, the less the water-soluble drug releases. It seems that the stability could be improved by increasing the lipophilic surfactant concentration which could strengthen the interfacial film. In contrast, an excess of hydrophilic surfactant destabilized the emulsion.

Laugel et al. (122) studied the efficiency of suitable tracer incorporation in the aqueous inner phase for multiple emulsion studies. The use of dihydralazine as tracer allowed the evaluation of both the yield of preparation and the stability of eight multiple emulsions. In these, concentrations of several components were optimized, e.g., oil, lipophilic and hydrophilic emulsifiers, coemulsion and viscosity increasing agents. From entrapment data and droplet breakdown curves calculated from the dihydralazine chromatographic data, one emulsion was selected to study the release of some encapsulated moisturizing solutes such as urea, chitosan, and poly(ethylene glyco). Dihydralazine proved of value to discriminate between the two mechanisms responsible for the solute release, i.e., the breakdown of the multiple droplets and the diffusion of the solute through the oil layer. Diffusion curves were obtained from the levels of moisturizing substance in the outer aqueous phase, corrected by the amounts liberated by the droplet breakdown, calculated through dihydralazine levels. The lipophilicity of the solutes measured under conditions similar to those partitioning in the emulsions correlated with the diffusional route of solute transfer. Thus, the partition coefficient was an efficient parameter to predict the importance and the rate of the diffusion.

A mathematical model was developed by Li et al. (123) for the formation of PLGA microspheres loaded with a peptide using solvent extraction/evaporation methods. Intrinsic variables, such as solvent–polymer interaction parameters, and extrinsic variables, such as dispersed phase/continuous phase ratio, temperature and dispersed phase composition, were evaluated. A mathematical model based on mass transfer was developed by incorporating these variables and, by superimposing with the state of phase transition, the model was used to predict the microsphere

properties. The mass transfer in the dispersed phase was based on diffusion theory and was a function of the driving force of chemical potential gradient and transport parameters. The solvent removal process involved solvent diffusion out of the dispersed phase followed by evaporation at the continuous phase–air interface, a process which can be facilitated by forced convective flow. Mathematically, the process can be expressed by coupling the equations for mass transfer in the dispersed phase and first order evaporation from the continuous phase. Two phase transitions, the viscous and glassy boundaries, were used to represent the phase transitions in the polymer solution. The phase transition can be superimposed on the composition profile in the dispersed phase; the solidification of microsphere can be evaluated from such a treatment (123).

Izumikawa et al. (124) studied the physiochemical properties of progesterone-loaded poly(L-lactide) microspheres prepared by the solvent evaporation method. The solvent evaporation process was found to govern the physical characteristics of microspheres. Solvent removal at atmospheric pressure yielded microspheres of crystalline polymer matrices, whereas faster solvent removal under a reduced pressure gave microspheres of amorphous polymer matrices. The crystallinity of the polymer matrices was closely correlated with the morphology and physical properties of microspheres, and affected the drug release rate. The microspheres of crystalline polymer matrices had rough surfaces with large surface areas, and exhibited a rapid drug release, whereas the amorphous microspheres provided a slower drug release. The results of X-ray powder diffraction, differential scanning calorimetry (DSC), and Fourier-transform infrared (FTIR) spectroscopy suggested that progesterone formed a molecular dispersion in the amorphous polymer matrices.

COMPLEX COACERVATION: GELATIN AND GUM ARABIC

When oppositely charges polyelectrolytes with a relatively low charge density are mixed at an appropriate temperature, pH, and concentration, a liquid polyelectrolyte complex called a complex coacervate is formed (11,22,32,80) The first commercial microencapsulation process used complex coacervates formed by acid precursor gelatin and gum arabic. Figure 11 is a schematic diagram of this encapsulation process.

The first step is to form a solution of gelatin ($\approx$11 wt %) in 45–55°C water and gum arabic (11 wt %) in 45–55°C water. Distilled or deionized water must be used to avoid problems with solution. In most cases, high bloom strength (250–300 bloom) acid precursor gelatins were used, although lower bloom strength gelatins (150–225 bloom) can also be used. Bloom strength is a measure of how strong a gelatin sample forms and is indirectly related to gelatin molecular weight. High bloom strength gelatins tend to produce high molecular weight gelations and low bloom strength gelations tend to produce low molecular weight gelations, though there is not a direct correlation between bloom strength and molecular weight.

Once the gelatin and gum arabic solutions are prepared, the drug being encapsulated is emulsified or dispersed in

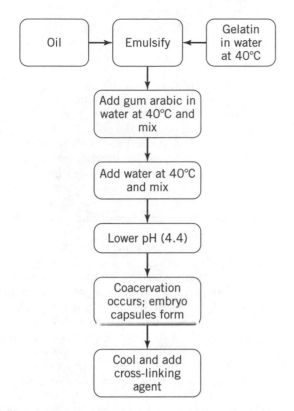

Figure 11. Microencapsulation by complex coacervation.

Rabiskova and Valaskova (32) encapsulated drugs that are often applied as solutions in plant oils. The encapsulation of the oils in the complex coacervate microcapsules can be improved by the addition of surfactants. Rabiskova used soybean, olive, and peanut oils as the representatives of plant oils. Using complex coacervation of gelatin and acacia they have found that when the surfactants with HLB values from 1.8 to 6.7 were used, the amount of encapsulated oil was high (65–85%). A significant decrease of the oil content in the microcapsules was found when Tween® 61 (HLB = 9.6) had been added to the mixture. No oil was found inside the microcapsules from the coacervate emulsion mixture containing Tween® 81 (HLB = 10) and Tween® 80 (HLB = 15), respectively.

ORGANIC PHASE SEPARATION: COACERVATION

Two chemically different polymers dissolved in a common solvent are usually incompatible. Thus, such a mixture separates into two phases. One phase is rich in one polymer, whereas the second phase is rich in the second polymer. As long as the phase containing the desired coating polymer preferentially wets or adsorbs on the surface of the core phase or drug, then embryo microcapsules spontaneously form which can be isolated and dried.

Figure 12 is a schematic diagram of a typical encapsulation process based on polymer–polymer incompatibility (58,125). The polymer that is to serve as the capsule wall

the 45–55°C gelatin solution. The drug is kept at the same temperature as the gelatin solution when the emulsion is made. The emulsion when formed should be above 45°C. Once the drug/gelatin emulsion or dispersion is formed, it is diluted by addition of a known volume of 45–55°C distilled (or deionized) water and 11 wt % gum arabic solution (45–55°C). The pH of the resulting mixture is adjusted to 3.8–4.4 by addition of acetic acid. The concentration of the acetic acid used can range from 10% (v/v) to glacial.

After the pH is adjusted, the system is allowed to cool slowly to room temperature. The system is stirred gently throughout this cooling period. Once room temperature is reached, the encapsulation mixture is cooled below 10°C and at this point, glutaraldehyde is added to cross-link the polymers. The pH of the system can then be raised to 9–10 with aqueous sodium hydroxide. The system is finally allowed to increase slowly to room temperature and the glutaraldehyde reaction proceeds for at least several hours (an overnight reaction is usually most convenient).

Slow cooling from 45 to 55°C to room temperature is essential to the success of the GGA encapsulation process. During this cooling process, the liquid coacervate slowly deposits around the core agent thereby forming embryo microcapsules. If the system is cooled too quickly, much of the GGA coacervate does not deposit around the active agent, but remains as discrete coacervate drops. (Such drops are called free coacervate and contain no active agent). Free coacervate is very undesirable, because coating material located in free coacervate drops is coating material not deposited around the active agent being encapsulated.

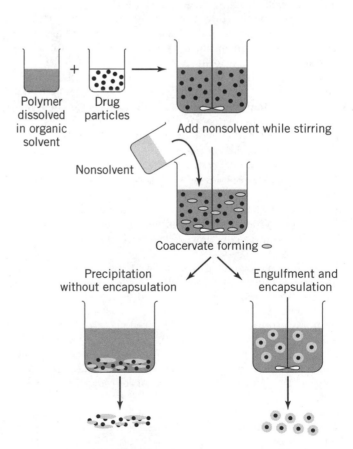

Figure 12. Microencapsulation by coacervation.

material is dissolved in an organic solvent. The material to be encapsulated is then added to this solution and an emulsion or dispersion is formed. To this emulsion a second polymer, or nonsolvent, that is incompatible with the capsule wall material is added. In Figure 12 it is nonsolvent but it could be cottonseed oil, silicone oil, low molecular weight polybutadiene, or any of a number of other materials. This second polymeric material is called the phase inducer and causes the coating material to phase separate. As long as the coating phase adsorbs on the core material, embryo capsules are formed. The system is then cooled and the embryo capsule walls are chemically cross-linked. Chemical cross-linking makes it possible to isolate the capsules as a free-flowing powder.

One of the polymers used to form the capsule wall could be Elvax® 40, a Dupont ethylene vinyl acetate copolymer that contains 40 wt % vinyl acetate. Fifty percent of the vinyl acetate units are hydrolyzed to form vinyl alcohol units. The latter are the units which react and could form a cross-linked or network polymer.

Many researchers have used triangular phase diagrams to describe microencapsulation by coacervation (60,126–129). Madan used phase diagrams to illustrate the coacervate region for several gelatin coacervation processes. He showed that the coacervation inducer could alter the area of coacervate formation on the phase diagram. Benita and Donbrow (60) used a phase diagram to describe the effect of polyisobutylene concentration on the coacervation of ethylcellulose microcapsules. They indicated that a minimum concentration was necessary for the formation of coacervate droplets while a relatively high polyisobutylene concentration prevented phase separation. Phase diagrams have also been used to describe the effect of polyisobutylene on the formation of Eudragit RS microcapsules. Namely, the two liquid phase regions which occurred prior to wall formation may be described, as well as changes in the phase diagrams that were related to occurrences in the microencapsulation process. Phase diagrams have been used to show how various surfactants affected the microencapsulation regions of cellulose acetate phthalate and of cellulose acetate trimellitate (129). Phase diagrams also have been used to describe coacervation as affected by coating polymer concentration, solvent amount, nonsolvent amount, and additives; however, they have not been used to identify potential solvent systems for microcapsule formation or to predict release rates from the microcapsules.

Membrane technology has shown that solubility parameters can be used to select solvents for membrane preparation. Klein and Smith (130) used Hansen's parameters for polarity and hydrogen bonding to form two-dimensional plots for ethylcellulose and cellulose acetate. These plots were then used to predict solvent systems for the formation of asymmetric membranes. Using Hansen's polarity parameters and hydrogen bonding parameters, Chawla and Chang (131) plotted the solubility of cellulose acetate. Several membranes were formed and shown to behave in a predictable fashion based on the solubility parameter of the solvent system. Shen and Cabasso (132) used Hansen's parameters to investigate their solvent systems and a phase diagram to describe how their ethylcellulose membranes were formed. This discussion suggests that potentially useful solvent systems for microcapsule membrane formation could also be chosen using solubility parameters.

Robinson (133) has suggested the use of the solubility parameter, the polymer–solvent interaction parameter and the polymer–solvent interaction parameter for the identification of potentially useful solvents for microcapsule preparation. He determined the solubility of ethylcellulose and plotted the solvent fractional polarity on a two-dimensional map versus the solubility parameter of the system that should be near the limit of the ethylcellulose solubility region for coacervation to occur. Robinson, however, did not report the preparation of microcapsules based on his findings.

Solubility parameters may provide a predictive method by which solvent systems can be chosen for the formation of microcapsules. As shown by the work in membrane technology, it may be possible to predict general structural characteristics of the microcapsule coat, thereby allowing the microcapsules to be formed with desired release rates.

Moldenhauer and Nairn (25) employed a coacervation method using an ethylcellulose and ion-exchange resin–drug complex to show that solubility parameters of the microencapsulation system can be correlated with morphological characteristics and release rates. Microcapsules prepared using solvent mixtures, which had a solubility parameter in the area of a two-dimensional solubility parameter map, usually exhibited similar release rates and morphological characteristics. The ability of polyisobutylene to promote mononucleated microcapsules decreased as the dispersive solubility parameter decreased. Three of the microencapsulation solvent systems were also analyzed using phase diagrams. It was found that the solubility parameter map provided predictive methods of solvents selection for microencapsulation, whereas the phase diagram provided information about the solvent and nonsolvent, with which the phase diagram are formed.

The phase separation of PLGA solutions in methylene chloride induced by the addition of a silicone oil in order to promote protein microencapsulation was studied by Nihant et al. (29). Because the process is very fast, the system was out of equilibrium at all times studied. The effect of the main processing parameters on the microencapsulation process has been analyzed and has highlighted that the kinetics of the main encapsulation steps have a great effect on the characteristics of the final microspheres. These results have been discussed on the basis of a physicochemical study of coacervation.

Ethylcellulose microcapsules containing theophylline were prepared by Sa et al. (134) by the phase separation coacervation process. To induce phase separation a nonsolvent and a variable amount of polyisobutylene were used. Results indicated that the overall release was governed by a diffusion controlled process. No statistical difference was evident between the different sized microcapsules with respect to their drug content, wall thickness, and in vitro drug dissolution profiles. Polyisobutylene was, however, found to influence the release profiles of drug to a great extent. An increase in polyisobutylene concentration retarded the release of theophylline from the microcapsules due to the formation of small and spheroidal co-acervate droplets in larger volumes, which resulted in the formation of more evenly coated microcapsules. Although the release of theophylline from the microcapsules was found to fit both the first-order and diffusion-controlled release processes, differential rate treatment indicated that the overall release was governed by diffusion controlled process (134).

In a different study Bachtsi and Kiparissides (59) developed oil-containing PVA microcapsules that were prepared by the simple coacervation method followed by the chemical cross-linking of the coacervated PVA membrane with glutaraldehyde. The effect of various parameters such as the microcapsule size, the degree of cross-linking of the coacervated polymer membrane, the amount of the desolvating agent, the surfactant concentration, and the ionic strength of the aqueous release medium on the release rate of the oil from the microcapsules into a model surfactant solution was experimentally investigated. It was shown that the oil release rate exhibited first-order kinetics. The permeability coefficient of the santosol oil the PVA coacervated/cross-linked membrane was found to vary from 10^{-4} to 10^{-6} cm/s and was strongly dependent on both the environmental conditions of the release medium and the physical and morphological characteristics of the microcapsules (59).

INTERFACIAL POLYMERIZATION

When two reactive monomers are dissolved in immiscible solvents (e.g., water and an alkane), the monomers diffuse to the oil–water interface where they react to form a polymeric membrane. This phenomenon has been used to form a range of microcapsules. Figure 13 is a schematic diagram of microencapsulation using an interfacial polymerization reaction. The interfacial reaction occurs rapidly and is

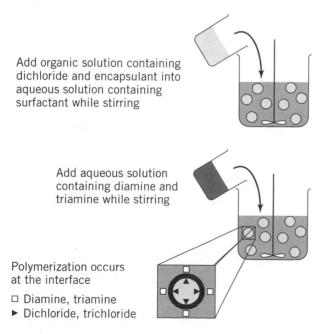

Add organic solution containing dichloride and encapsulant into aqueous solution containing surfactant while stirring

Add aqueous solution containing diamine and triamine while stirring

Polymerization occurs at the interface

□ Diamine, triamine
▶ Dichloride, trichloride

Figure 13. Microencapsulation by interfacial polymerization.

therefore considered a rapid means of preparing microcapsules. It was, however, found to be incorrect for some systems and long reaction times were needed to get strong microcapsules. The preferred acid chloride has relatively long carbon chains between the acid chloride groups, because such acid chloride hydrolyzes slowly at an oil–water interface. The acid chlorides are always added to the oil phase, whereas the amines are always added to the water phase. Isocyanates can be used rather than (or as a partial substitute for) acid chlorides (135). A base could be added to the aqueous phase to neutralize the HCl byproduct formed by reaction of an acid chloride with an amine.

The yield and quality of the membrane of the microcapsules obtained by interfacial polymerization may be controlled by a number of factors, some of which have been listed by Morgan (136). Specifically, in microencapsulation systems the chemical natures of the chloride and amine components and of the solvent, and the conditions under which the polycondensation reaction is performed, determines the nature and molecular weight of the polymer as well as its degree of cross-linking and crystallinity, and whether or not the membrane is porous. Experimental parameters likely to be of importance are the concentrations of the monomers, the temperature, the rate of mixing, and the reaction time. Cohen and Mathiowitz (44) determined the effect of the chemical nature of the monomer components; all reaction parameters were kept constant except for the monomer concentrations and reaction time. During these studies it became clear that the properties of the membrane vary after the initial formation of the microcapsules. There was much evidence that after the formation of the "premembrane" the polymerization proceeds via diffusion of the amine through the membrane where it reacts with the chloride at the inner face of the microcapsule wall. The effective amine concentration at the reaction site is then very much less than in the bulk aqueous solution (44).

Microcapsules were fabricated by preparing an aqueous solution of water and PVA as a surfactant (Fig. 13), and in some cases silane was added as a coupling agent (137). To this solution an organic solution containing the dichloride was added while stirring. After the correct emulsion size was obtained an aqueous solution of diamine was added. The polycondensation reaction which ensued was allowed to continue for different lengths of time. In several cases the silane was added to the chloride suspension prior to the addition of the amine solution. In this way there was an initial formation of a premembrane, resulting from the reaction between the chloride and the amine groups of the silane. After this step the amine was added, in solution, which underwent polycondensation with the chloride. The length of time for the reaction varied with the type of monomer. (For each system the disappearance of the dichloride monomer was followed by thin-layer chromatography.) The time required for the concentration of acid chloride to decrease by 0.5% is called the maturation time. After maturation the microcapsules were separated by decantation, repeatedly washed with distilled water, and dried by rapid washing with acetone (44,137).

Table 8 lists the amine and chloride components used, and Table 9 summarizes the compositions of the monomer mixtures employed. In different attempts the amine/

Table 8. Monomers Used for Preparation of Polyamide Microcapsules

Amine monomers

Ethylene diamine (EDA)	$NH_2(CH_2)_2NH_2$
Diethylene triamine (DETA)	$NH_2(CH_2)_2NH(CH_2)_2NH_2$
Mixtures of the above two amines	
Hexamethylene diamine (HMDA)	$NH_2(CH_2)_6NH_2$
Hexamethylene diamine/diethylene triamine mixtures	
Triethylene tetramine (TETRA)	$NH_2CH_2CH_2(NHCH_2CH_2)_2NH_2$
Tetraethylene pentamine (TEPTA)	$(NH_2CH_2CH_2NHCH_2CH_2)_2NH$
Bis-hexamethylene triamene (BHMT)	$NH_2(CH2)_6NH(CH_2)NH_2$
BHMT in HMDA mixture	

Chloride monomers

Terephthaloyl dichloride (Tr)	$1,4\text{-}C_6H_4(COCl)_2$
Trimesoyl chloride (Tm)	$1,3,5\text{-}C_6H_3(COCl)_3$

Table 9. Compositions of Monomer Mixtures Used for Preparation of Microcapsules

Name of batch	Amine:chloride (re. eq.)	Triamine:diamine (rel. eq.)
(EDA,Tr)	30	—
(DETA,Tr)	30	—
(HMDA,Tr)	30	—
(EDA + DETA,Tr)b	30	4:1
(HMDA + DETA,Tr)b	30	4:1
(HMDA + DETA,Tr)b	30	4:1
(EDA, Tm)	30	—
(HMDA, Tm)	30	—

chloride ratio was kept constant (30:1 or 15:1, in equivalent units) in order to avoid effects due to the diminishing monomer concentrations. For cases where the amine:chloride ratio was 30:1, the concentrations were 5.62 and 0.197 mole eq/L, respectively. Because these concentrations were constant, the main variable parameter was the character of the monomer. Note that from the list in Table 8 one could select monomers which are bifunctional or monomers which are of functionality three or higher. The polymer from two bifunctional monomers was linear and when one or both monomers had a functionality of three or higher, the resulting polymer was cross-linked (44).

It can be seen from Table 9 that Cohen and Mathiowitz (44) used an amine:chloride ratio of 15 or 30:1. This is near the upper limit of, or greater than, the ratio used by Morgan. These authors suggested that for amines with partition coefficients of between 14 and 180, amine:chloride ratios of 3 to 17:1 are optimal for obtaining high molecular weight polymers. They measured the partition coefficients for some amines and found values of 22 for HMDA and 27 for DETA, whereas that of EDA must be very high because of its low solubility in the organic phase. Thus the ratios are much higher than those required by Morgan's rule (44).

Reaction time in microcapsule preparation is extremely important in determining the time at which that capsules have attained their maximum impermeability. Consider microcapsules from (EDA,Tr), for, example; these are observed to form very rapidly (44). However, microcapsules separated from the reaction vessel after very short periods proved to be extremely fragile and collapsed even during the drying process. Further, analysis of the Tr content (of the core material; microcapsules were removed from the reaction vessel after various times) showed that an appreciable period is required for complete consumption of this monomer. When EDA was replaced by an amine monomer of higher molecular weight and functionality, it was found that the time required for full maturation was appreciably longer. For example, the approximate maturation times determined were (EDA,Tr) 5 min, (HMDA,Tr) 10 min, (DETA,Tr) 180 min, and (TEPTA,Tr) 240 min (44).

Thermal gravimetric analysis (TGA) is a often-used technique for characterizing polymer thermal stability, but Mathiowitz and Cohen have introduced this technique to determine the mechanical strength of microcapsules and also to study the maturation of the microcapsules immediately after preparation. This method is particularly useful because it enables examination of the individual microencapsulation and thus provides information about the reproducibility of the rate of release amongst a population of microcapsules. This in turn helped us to develop a mathematical model for photochemical rupture (47).

The effect of the reaction time on the thermal behavior of microcapsules from DETA is illustrated in Figure 14. The "immature" capsules released their contents at low temperatures, whereas the mature ones are stable until they reach a sharp rupture temperature. This may be due to more rapid diffusion of the core contents through thinner walls of immature capsules.

The time required for maturation was determined by the diffusion of the amine from the bulk aqueous solution through the membrane to the organic phase. The rate of this diffusion, which is low when compared with the reaction rate of the monomers in solution, is determined by the permeability of the membrane. The permeability, in turn, depends on factors such as the molecular weight of the polymer and the extent of its cross-linking. The growth of the membrane, which accompanies maturation, can be

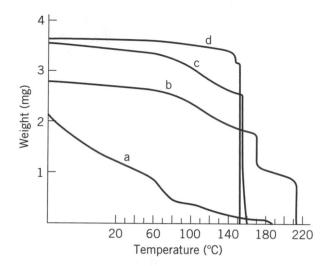

Figure 14. Effect of reaction time on thermal behavior of (DETA,Tr)S microcapsules as measured by TGA: (a) 1, (b) 4, (c) 10, (d) 100 minutes after starting the polymerization reaction. *Source:* With permission from Ref. 45.

seen clearly in electron micrographs (data not shown). After 1 minute the internal side had a smooth internal surface. After 4 minutes, small spheres of polymer were found to be formed on this surface and subsequently grow and cover the whole inner face of the membrane. The results suggest that, throughout the formation of the membranes of linear polymers, the diffusion rate of amine is constant. For the cross-linked polymers, however, there appear to be channels though which diffusion is more rapid. These channels could be voids or could contain a high proportion of polymer which is not cross-linked (44).

An indication of the stability of the membranes to heat can be obtained from TGA measurements. The membranes were prepared either by direct interfacial polymerization or by rupturing microcapsules and were carefully dried before use. In this way it was found that (EDA,Tr), (DETA + EDA,Tr) and (DETA,Tr) all begin to lose weight at 220–230°C, whereas (HDMA,Tr) does so only above 300°C.

Dry membranes were investigated also by DSC. The DSC curve for (DETA,Tr) shows no structure; at about 230°C, where weight loss starts, there was a slight change of slope and as the temperature rises, there was a continuously increasing heat loss. There is no sign of melting up to 450°C. This type of behavior is typical of cross-linked polymers. Visually, one observed that the material chars on heating. By contrast, the DSC curve for (EDA,Tr) shows a melting temperature at 450°C and the glass temperature at 225°C. (EDA + DETA,Tr) membranes also show an endotherm at 70°C, but no melting was observed. Repeated measurements suggest that $T_g \cong 260$°C. Above this temperature the polymer starts to decompose.

FTIR spectra can be very helpful in providing information on the bonding state of polyamides. What prominent features may we expect in these spectra? If there are any residual NH_2 groups present which have not reacted during the polymerization, one expects to see the absorp-

tions corresponding to the stretching modes of NH_2. In both primary amines and primary amides these modes are known to give an intense doublet around 3,450 and 3,225 cm^{-1}. The N-H stretch of secondary amines and amides gives a single strong absorption band near 3,335 cm^{-1}. Amide vibrational spectra are characterized by two intense bands, called amide I and amide II. The first of these is largely due to C = O stretching and is found at 1,665–1,640 cm^{-1}. The amide II band, at about 1,540 cm^{-1}, is due to a coupling of vibrations of C-N and of N-H, when the H is *trans* to the C = .

The FTIR results indicate that during the polycondensation reaction the doublet structure associated with the $-NH_2$ of the amine monomer (Figs. 15a,b,c) disappears and is replaced by an intense singlet (compare Figure 15a with 15d,f, and 15b with 15e,f). In many cases this latter band has a shoulder on the high frequency side. This structured band is undoubtedly the N-H stretch of the secondary amines and amides. It has been found also in other polyamides, and the main peak and shoulder have been assigned to a superposition of "free" and hydrogen-bonded N-H.

On this basis it was concluded that little or no unreacted NH_2 was present in the polymer. However, because of the breadth of the N-H adsorption, it was not possible to conclude that there was none present.

The X-ray powder diffraction patterns of a number of dried membrane materials were recorded for membranes of the (EDA + DETA,Tr) series. There were differences in crystallinity, with (EDA,Tr) > (EDA + DETA,Tr) > (DETA,Tr), and with the last membrane being essentially amorphous. Also, membranes of (HMDA + DETA,Tr) are of higher crystallinity than (DETA,Tr) ones (44). Thus, addition of one of the bifunctional amines EDA of HMDA to the trifunctional DETA in the preparation of the microcapsules leads to membranes of higher crystallinity than those membranes we have shown to be appreciably cross-linked. Morphological studies of microcapsules by SEM and transmission electron microscopy (TEM) were done on each sample. The external and internal faces and a cross section of the membrane wall was evaluated. Preparation for TEM required embedding the samples and cutting by microtome, the latter being difficult because of the fragility of the materials. Most membranes were stained with uranyl acetate which attaches to free amino groups and increases the resolution. Figure 16 capsules of (DETA,Tr) are seen from the external side (some capsules full, some ruptured). The structure is homogeneous and "closed." In fact, most of the membranes we studied looked similar at the external face, but there were differences in the internal faces. The internal faces and membrane cross-sectioning (Fig. 16) of (DETA,Tr) also show quite closed structures. The internal face is hilly, suggesting that the interfacial polymerization takes place in the organic phase. TEM studies (Fig. 16f) of the cross section provide a similar picture, with the polymer density apparently lower in the hills than in the other regions of the membranes. The thickness of the membrane of the (DETA,Tr) microcapsules was 2 μm, as measured by SEM.

Microcapsules of (EDA,Tr) appear nonporous under the optical and scanning electron microscopes. However, SEM

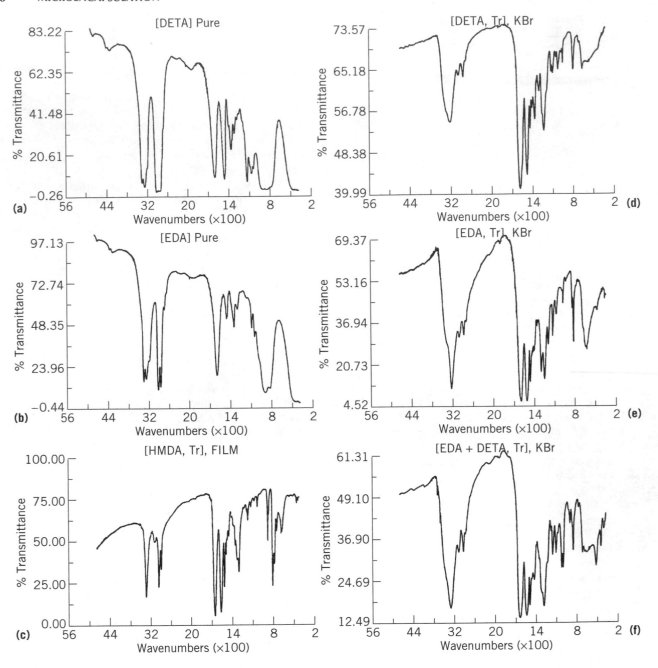

Figure 15. FTIR spectra of some amines and Tr membranes.

examination of the internal face and cross section of the membranes reveal a very porous structure (Fig. 17a,b). This membrane is clearly of the "skinned" type: one side has a closed structure, but the membrane is full of voids. This is shown also in the TEM pictures of the cross section (Fig. 17e). Note that the long axes of the pores lie parallel to the faces of the membrane. These pores are less than 1 μm in diameter, which classifies the membrane as microporous.

Figures 17c and 17d, show the internal face and cross section of such membranes with a double relative concentration of Tr. Here the number of pores is fewer and the internal face more homogeneous, but the structure is still porous.

In Figure 18a we see the internal face of capsule from (EDA + DETA(1:1.5),Tr). The structure is less porous than is (EDA,Tr), as was confirmed by the cross section (not shown). This membrane after silanation is shown in Figure 18b and its cross section in Figure 18e. Such treatment appears to decrease the porosity. An increase of the proportion of triamine further decreases the porosity, as shown for the internal face and cross section of a membrane from (EDA + DETA(1:4),Tr) in Figures 18a,b. In this case the wall thickness was 2.5 μm. In additional papers the use of those microspheres as swelling-controlled, diffusion-controlled, and photochemically controlled delivery systems were studied separately (46–48).

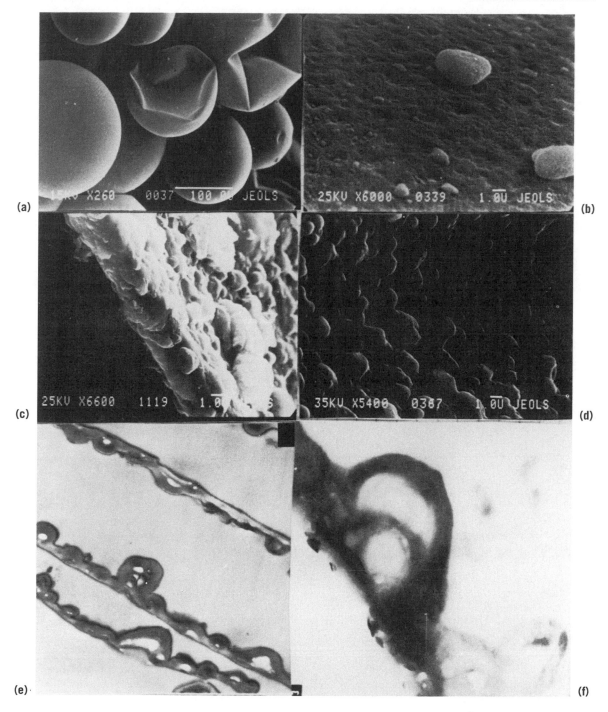

Figure 16. (DETA,Tr) MC: (**a**) SEM of external face; (**b**) SEM of external face; (**c**) SEM of cross section of membrane; (**d**) SEM of internal face; (**e**) TEM of cross section stained with uranyl acetate, ×10,000 (**f**) TEM of cross section, unstained, ×20,000. *Source:* With permission from Ref. 44.

Interfacial Coacervation

The first example of a phase separation process is an extreme case of polymer adsorption used to prepare small capsules (49). In this process Chang dissolved a polymer in the organic phase, and this polymer migrated to the water–organic liquid interface where it precipitated spontaneously from solution to form a membrane. This process is called interfacial coacervation (135). Phase separation

in this case is not induced by addition of a nonsolvent, change in temperature, or the presence of incompatible polymers, instead occurring spontaneously at the interface. A good example of this process is the emulsification of an aqueous protein solution in diethyl ether using a nonionic surfactant that is soluble in oil. Sorbitan trioleate (Span® 85) is a good surfactant. The emulsification process gives microcapsules that can easily be separated from the

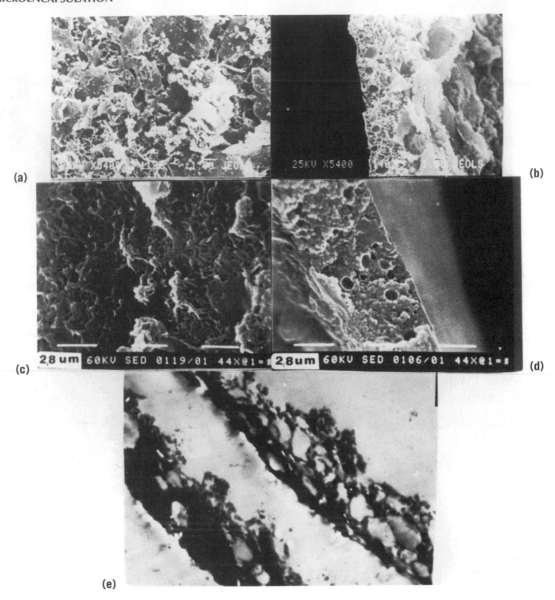

Figure 17. (EDA,Tr) MC: (**a**) SEM of internal face; (**b**) SEM of cross section of same membrane; (**c**) SEM of internal face of (EDA,Tr)x MC; (**d**) SEM of cross section of same membrane; (**e**) TEM of (EDA,Tr) MC shown in (**b**), ×10,000. *Source:* With permission from Ref. 44.

ether suspending medium and resuspended in *n*-butyl benzoate. Chang often used collodian (nitrocellulose) as a wall material, but emphasized that microcapsules can also be formed by interfacial coacervation or precipitation of other polymers using other solvents.

THERMAL DENATURATION

A number of water-soluble proteins are sensitive to heat and can denature when heated. The denaturation process causes the protein chain to unfold and become chemically cross-linked. This insolubilizes the protein and creates a convenient method of forming protein microspheres. Figure 19 is a schematic flow diagram of a process for forming protein microspheres. A relatively concentrated aqueous

protein solution (e.g., 20 wt %) is emulsified in an aliquot of oil at room temperature. This emulsion is then poured into an excess of agitated hot oil (120–200°C), which denatures the protein while simultaneously driving off the water. The product is a solid protein microsphere which can be isolated from the oil by a series of settling and decantation steps. The higher the temperature of the hot oil bath, the more thoroughly the microspheres are cross-linked. Proteins suitable for this process include serum albumin and egg albumin.

Jameela et al. (138) produced chitosan microspheres in the following manner. A 4% solution of chitosan in 5% acetic acid containing 2% sodium chloride was prepared. Six grams of this viscous solution was weighed, mixed with progesterone (20% by weight of chitosan) and dispersed in a mixture of 35 mL of liquid paraffin and 25 mL of petro-

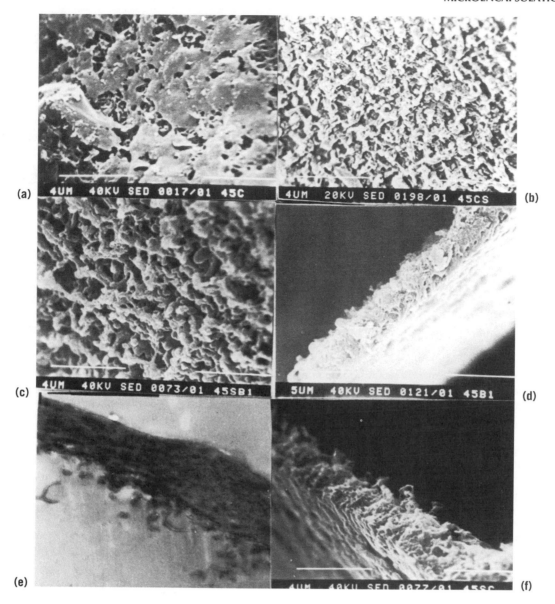

Figure 18. (EDA + DETA,Tr) MC: (**a**) SEM of internal face of (EDA + DETA,Tr)c MC; (**b**) SEM of internal face of (EDA + DETA,Tr)cS MC; (**c**) SEM of internal face of (EDA + DETA,Tr)bS MC; (**d**) SEM of cross section of same MC; (**e**) TEM of same MC shown in (**b**), ×10,000; (**f**) SEM of cross section of MC shown in (**b**). *Source:* With permission from Ref. 44.

leum ether containing 0.85 g of sorbitan sesquioleate, in a 100-mL round-bottomed flask at room temperature (27°C). The dispersion was stirred at 2,000 rpm for 5 min, and then 10 mL of glutaraldehyde-saturated toluene was introduced into the flask and the stirring continued. Microspheres were prepared using different amounts of glutaraldehyde saturated toluene for cross-linking. Highly cross-linked microspheres were prepared by adding 1 mL aqueous glutaraldehyde at the end of 30 min, in addition to 10 mL of glutaraldehyde-saturated toluene which was introduced initially. The cross-linking reaction was allowed to proceed for a total of 1.5 hours. The hardened microspheres were then separated by centrifugation, washed four times with petroleum ether, once with acetone, once with a 5% solution of sodium metabisulphite, three times

with water, centrifuged, vacuum-dried at room temperature and stored in a desiccator. Progesterone content in the microspheres was measured by extracting 5 mg of powdered microspheres with three 5 mL portions of ethanol, filtering the solution through a 0.45 μm filter and assaying spectrophotometrically at 247 nm. Particle size analysis of the microspheres was done using standard test sieves. Particles that passed through one sieve, but retained on the other were collected and weighed in an analytical balance, and the percent weight distribution was plotted against size (138).

The extent of drug release had a remarkable dependence on the cross-linking density of the microspheres, the highly cross-linked spheres releasing only around 35% of the incorporated steroid in 40 days compared to 70% from

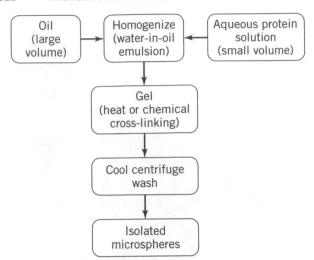

Figure 19. Thermal denaturation process.

spheres lightly cross-linked. Determination of the in vivo bioavailability of the steroid from microsphere formulation by intramuscular injection in rabbits showed that a plasma concentration of 1 to 2 ng/mL was maintained up to 5 months without a high "burst effect." Data obtained suggest that the cross-linked chitosan microspheres would be an interesting system for long term delivery of steroids (139).

Modena et al. (139) investigated hyaluronidase injectable microparticles. The goal of these researchers was to obtain a sustained release preparation of hyaluronidase or to use the enzyme as drug carrier. Microspheres were prepared by emulsification of the protein and were cross-linked either by thermal or chemical means. Results show that hyaluronidase microspheres with good morphological characteristics can be obtained by this preparation method.

Heelan and Corrigan (140) used whey protein (WPI) microspheres containing hydrochlorothiazide, eosin, blue violet, and sodium salicylate. The release of these compounds from WPI microspheres occurred rapidly, with at least 70% of the incorporated material released for all systems within the first 20 minutes. Release of microsphere contents was essentially complete within one hour. The degree of glutaraldehyde cross-linking was found to have no effect on the release profile, for durations of cross-linking up to 24 hours. Out of a range of release equations examined, the experimental release data was best described by a biexponential equation, and this agrees with the work of others for the release of drugs from albumin microspheres. Swelling of the microsphere systems was examined as this may contribute to the rapid release of drug from these systems.

Akbuga and Bergisadi prepared cross-linked chitosan microspheres containing 5-fluorouracil (5-FU). Variables included drug and chitosan concentrations, the cross-linking process, the type of oil, stirring rate, and additives. Initial 5-FU concentration, the type and concentration of chitosan, the viscosity of oil phase and glutaraldehyde concentration affected drug release for chitosan microspheres.

5-FU release from cross-linked chitosan microspheres is characterized by an initial rapid release of drug. Addition of substances such as alginic acid, chitin, agar, sodium caprylate, and stearic acid changed the release properties of 5-FU microspheres.

Monodisperse albumin microspheres were prepared by Muramatsu and Nakauchi (142) Uniform-sized emulsion droplets were successfully obtained by passing an albumin solution through the membrane and into kerosene at appropriate, applied pressures. After heating the emulsion monodisperse albumin microspheres were prepared. The heat-denaturing process itself did not affect the monodispersity once uniform emulsion droplets had been prepared. The shape and size of the albumin microspheres were strongly dependent on the concentration of the albumin solution and the heat denaturing temperature. Lower albumin concentrations produced nonspherical particles and higher denaturing temperatures made the particles smaller. Incorporated riboflavin released quite rapidly from the albumin microspheres, and increases in both albumin concentration and denaturing temperature caused the drug release to be sustained, presumably because a rigid and dense matrix was formed within the albumin microspheres.

Chitosan microspheres containing phenobarbitone were successfully prepared by glutaraldehyde cross-linking of an aqueous acetic acid dispersion of chitosan in light liquid paraffin containing sorbitan mono-oleate as a stabilizing agent. Uniform and spherical microspheres, with a loading efficiency up to 57.2%, could be fabricated, depending on the conditions. The main parameters which affected the preparation and performance of the microspheres were the molecular weight and concentration of chitosan as well as the concentration of the stabilizing agent. The incorporation of citric acid into the microspheres was found to increase the formation of a water-soluble gel when the microspheres come in contact with the dissolution medium, increasing the rate of drug release. The particle size was shifted toward smaller diameters with increased concentration of chitosan (1% w/v) and chitosan with low molecular weight. Rapid initial release (20–30% of the incorporated drug) was exhibited in all the prepared microspheres followed by slow release of the remaining drug. The release rate of the drug from the microspheres of high molecular weight chitosan was slow in comparison with that prepared from medium and low molecular weight chitosan. High concentrations of sorbitan mono-oleate increased the rate of the drug release (143). Lim and Wan (63) prepared chitosan microspheres by preparing a W/O emulsion comprising a mixture of light and heavy liquid paraffins containing sodium dioctyl sulphosuccinate as the oil phase and a chitosan solution as the aqueous phase. Pentasodium trypolyphosphate was included as a counterion. The chitosan microspheres obtained showed a high degree of aggregation. This was markedly reduced by the incorporation of magnesium stearate in the dispersed phase. The resultant microspheres were discrete and spherical with smooth surfaces. Additionally, with an increasing magnesium stearate content, larger-sized microspheres were produced. The DSC analysis data suggested that the magnesium stearate was converted to stearic acid during the preparation process. Chitosan microspheres containing propranolol hydrochloride were similarly prepared, but their surface was convoluted and their shape was not well defined. Unlike the microspheres without drug, the size of the drug-loaded microspheres decreased with increasing magnesium stearate content. The release of propranolol hydrochloride from the microspheres was fast, irrespective of the content of magnesium stearate. Drug encapsulation efficiency was enhanced when a greater amount of magnesium stearate was used (63).

GELATION: ALGINATE

One of the most important and useful properties of alginates is the ability to form gels by reaction with calcium salts (Fig. 20). These gels, which resemble a solid in retaining their shape and resisting stress, consist of almost 100% water (normally 99.0–99.5% water and 0.5–1.0% alginate). A gel, in classical colloid terminology, is defined as a system which owes its characteristic properties to a cross-linked network of polymer chains which form at the gel point. A considerable amount of research has been carried out in recent years to elucidate the nature of the cross-links and determine the structure of alginate gels.

It had been suggested that the cross-links were caused either by simple ionic bridging of two carboxyl groups on adjacent polymer chains via calcium ions or by chelation of single calcium ions by hydroxyl and carboxyl groups on each of a pair of polymer chains. Although these bonds may play a role in the gelation mechanism, they are not sufficiently energetically favorable to account for the gelation of alginate. It has been shown on the basis of fiber diffraction data and model-building calculations that the shape of both polymannuronic acid segments and the polyguluronic acid segments of alginic acid is ribbon-like and extended, and that these extended ribbons can stack together in sheets. On the basis of these data and the properties of gels, it has been suggested that the cooperative association of either polymannuronic acid segments or polyguluronic acid segments is involved in the formation of the cross-linked network of polymer chains.

Lim et al. developed a method of enclosing viable cells, tissues, and other labile biological substances within a semipermeable membrane. Preliminary in vitro studies of several types of microencapsulated cells and tissues (red blood cells, sperm cells, hepatoma cells, hepatocytes, pancreatic endocrine tissues, and islets) were described by Lim (19). Essentially, the process involves suspending the living cells or tissues in sodium alginate solution.

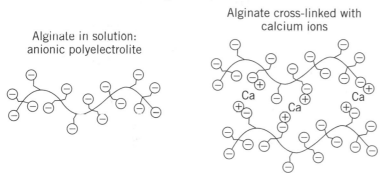

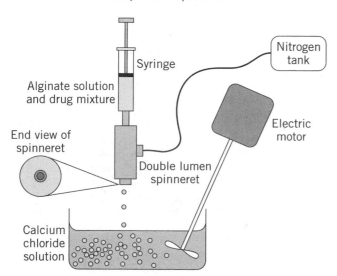

Figure 20. Sodium alginate gelation process.

The cell or tissue suspension is extruded through a microdroplet-forming device producing microdroplets which fall into a $CaCl_2$ solution and form gelled microbeads with the cells or tissues entrapped (Fig. 20). These cell-containing, gel microbeads are next treated with a solution of polylysine which displaces the surface layer of calcium ions and forms a permanent polysalt shell or membrane. Finally, the interior calcium alginate gel is "liquefied," either to stay in or to come out (depending on molecular weight and size of the starting alginate) of the capsule with a calcium sequestrant such as buffered citrate solution (19).

Diclofenac sodium is an ideal candidate for incorporation in a controlled release device to diminish its adverse effects after oral administration. Gohel et al. prepared microspheres by using sodium alginate as a polymer and $CaCl_2$ as a cross-linking agent. In this investigation, 3 full factorial design was used to investigate the joint influence of three variables: the stirring speed (X_1), concentration of $CaCl_2$ (X_2), and percent of heavy liquid paraffin in a blend of heavy and light liquid paraffin in the dispersion medium (X_3) on the time required for 80% drug dissolution (t_{80}). Potential variables such as concentration of sodium alginate and drug:sodium alginate ratio were kept constant. A statistical model with significant interaction terms is derived to predict t_{80}. The results of multiple linear regression analysis and F-statistics revealed that, for obtaining controlled drug release, the microspheres should be prepared using relatively lower stirring speed, higher interactions were found to be statistically significant in nature. A response plot was presented to show the effects of X_1, X_2, and X_3 on t_{80}. The drug was released by diffusion of anomalous type. A model was validated for accurate prediction of drug release profile (70,71).

Stable membranes were formed around alginate beads using a transacylation reaction between polysaccharidic esters, namely propylene glycol alginate (PGA) or pectin, and various proteins (human serum albumin [HSA], ovalbumin, bovine hemoglobin, lactoserum proteins). In a standard procedure, two reagents formed by dropwise addition into a calcium solution. Then the transacylation reaction was started by alkalization of the bead suspension. A membrane was formed around the beads made of a protein directly bound to a polysaccharide through amide linkages. The thickness of the membranes and the lysis time in trypsin were increased by raising the amount of NaOH used in the transacylation step. In a modified procedure, coated beads were obtained, incorporating PGA in the initial Na-alginate solution, and HSA in the transacylation bath. Activated charcoal was encapsulated in HSA-PGA beads, giving particles with adsorption properties toward creatinine. Assays were performed using PGA associated with alkaline phosphate as the membrane-forming protein. Stable beads were obtained having a relative activity of 39.3% as compared with free enzyme (73).

Lee et al. (72) developed a sustained release formulation which delivers melatonin (MT). MT is a pineal hormone of clinical value because of its short half-life, for those who have disordered circadian rhythm. The purpose of the study was to prepare MT-loaded microspheres by the emulsion melting/cooling method using stearyl alcohol (SA) and also dual-walled chitosan and sodium alginate beads, and to evaluate the release characteristics in simulated gastric and intestinal fluid. The MT-loaded microspheres were spherical, ranging in diameter from about 250 to 750 μm. When poly(ethylene glycol) 4000 (PEG) as a water-soluble additive, or aluminum tristearate (AT) as a water-insoluble additive, was incorporated, the surface roughness was further reduced resulting in a smooth matrix structure. The dual-walled chitosan and sodium alginate beads entrapping small MT-loaded microspheres were not spherical in structure. As the additive incorporated into SA microspheres increased, the drug content decreased. The release profiles of the MT-loaded microspheres were independent of pH. When the melted SA solution was cooled rapidly (in 10 minutes) to 25°C, the drug content increased but the release rate of MT-loaded microspheres decreased. The release rate of drug decreased as the amount of SA increased but an increase of agitation speed and amount of AT and PEG resulted in increased release rates. The release rate of drug from dual-walled chitosan beads increased slightly, but was retarded in the case of dual-walled alginate beads, when compared with MT-loaded microspheres. The emulsion melting/cooling method used to prepared MT-loaded microspheres using SA is simple and inexpensive, and may provide an alternative for the preparation of an oral sustained release dosage form of MT without using harmful organic solvents. The dual-walled chitosan and sodium alginate beads may also provide a convenient way to control the release of drugs (72).

Calcium alginate microspheres were prepared by an emulsification process (68). The effects of two copolymers, namely poly(vinylpyrrolidone) (PVP) and ethylcellulose, on the properties of the microspheres were studied. Microspheres prepared with and without PVP exhibited a better flow property but the drug content was lower and the drug release rate higher. The method of incorporating PVP was found to significantly affect the size distribution and drug content of the microspheres. Ethylcellulose produced marked aggregation of the microspheres which also showed a lower drug content, but a slower drug release. The retardation in drug release was attributed to the formation of aggregated microspheres with a less permeable matrix. The addition of triethylcitrate, which is a water-soluble plasticizer, was found to increase the rate of drug release, whereas the use of a higher viscosity grade of ethylcellulose produced the opposite effect. Ethylcellulose improved the flowability of the microspheres to a greater extent than PVP (68).

Porous microspheres were formed by the gelation of two polysaccharides, a polyanionic sodium alginate and a polycationic chitosan, followed by lyophilization which creates the porous structure (74). Porous microspheres were also formed by gelation of sodium alginate with $CaCl_2$ and gelation of sodium alginate with polylysine. FITC-BSA was incorporated into the microspheres by mixing the protein with the polysaccharide solution prior to gelation. Interleukin-2 (IL-2) was incorporated into the preformed microspheres by diffusion from an external aqueous solution of IL-2. Sustained release of the proteins from porous alginate/chitosan microspheres is of longer duration than from alginate/CaCl$_2$, or from alginate/polylysine microspheres. Activity of the released IL-2 was investigated by determining the induction of cytotoxic T lymphocytes (CTL) when incubated with tumor cells and lymphocytes. It was found that the IL-2 remained active in the alginate/chitosan microspheres because the released IL-2 triggered induction of CTL more efficiently than free IL-2. Tumor-killing specific activity of CTL was the same whether induced by the sustained released IL-2 or by the addition of free IL-2 (74).

Microspheres of theophylline were prepared by ionotropic gelation method. The objective of this study was to investigate the influence of variables such as stirring speed, concentration of CaCl$_2$, and composition of the dispersion medium on the characteristics of the microspheres. A 3^3 randomized full factorial design was used to study the effect of the selected variables on the time for 90% drug dissolution (t_{90}). A linear model with interactive terms was generated using the multiple linear regression approach. F-statistics were carried out to evolve the reduced model. Significant interactions were not detected between the selected variables and good agreement was observed between the predicted and experimental checkpoint. The microspheres were evaluated during in vivo studies in dogs and the pharmacokinetic parameters were estimated by performing nonlinear regression analysis. The Wagner-Nelson method was adopted to compute the percentage drug absorbed. A good correlation was observed between the in vitro and in vivo results (70).

Chitosan microspheres were prepared by Berthold et al. (144) by a novel precipitation process using sodium sulfate as a precipitant. Low, medium, and high molecular weight chitosan was chosen for the formulation of microspheres. The extent of precipitation was controlled by the concentration of sodium sulfate and monitored by turbidity measurement. The amount of sodium sulfate required for the preparation of the microspheres depended on the molecular weight of chitosan. The particle size was determined by photon correlation spectroscopy and centrifugal sedimentation. The morphological characteristics were examined using SEM. The surface charge was measured by microelectrophoresis. After preparation the loading property with various antiinflammatory drugs was investigated using spectrophotometry. The influence of surface adsorption on the drug modification was controlled by DSC. Drug liberation was tested in vitro using side-by-side diffusion cells with dialysis membrane made of cellulose acetate. The highest loading (up to 30.5% relative to the polymer mass) was achieved with prednisolone sodium phosphate. The adsorbed drug was present in an amorphous form. The drug release from the microspheres was dependent on the drug/polymer ratio (144).

GELATION AGAROSE

Agarose is a water-soluble, nonionic polysaccharide that self-associates in water to form a gel (145). Thus, it can be used to fabricate spherical gel particles in which an active agent is entrapped. Figure 21 contains a flow diagram of

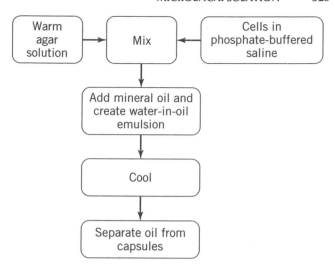

Figure 21. Microencapsulation by gelation using agarose.

recently developed fabrication procedure. The first step in the process consists of forming a molecularly dispersed solution of agarose in water. This requires heating an agarose-water mixture above 70°C, which is the melting point of agarose gels. The resulting solution is cooled to 40°C at which point the core material solidifies, thereby setting up the agarose gel structure and converting the aqueous droplets to spherical gel particles. The mineral oil is separated away from the gel particles by decantation and washing.

This procedure uses the large difference in gelation and melting temperatures of agarose. Agarose samples that gel at low temperatures (15–20°C) exist, but these gels, once formed, do not melt until 70°C. Thus, agarose can be completely dissolved in water at an elevated temperature, and then the solution obtained can be cooled to a reasonable temperature (i.e., above 25°C) without gelation occurring. At temperatures of 25–40°C, heat-sensitive core materials (e.g., live cells) can be added to the agarose solution. The agarose gel structure is then formed by cooling the mixture to 5–10°C. Significantly, the obtained gel particle has a matrix structure and is not a microcapsule with a continuous membrane surrounding a continuous core.

HOT MELT MICROENCAPSULATION

Hot melt is a process developed in the 1970s for photographic applications. In this process the melted polymer is mixed with drug, which can be encapsulated as solid or liquid particles. The mixture is then suspended in a immiscible solvent that is heated 5°C above the melting point of the polymer and stirred continuously using an overhead stirrer and a four blade impeller. Once the emulsion is stabilized (Fig. 22), it is cooled until the core material has solidified. The solvents used in this process could be silicon and olive oil. The low solubility of various drugs in these organic solvents makes them effective. It is recommended to sieve the drug, but in general, drug particle size is less than 50 μm. Using drugs with small particles sizes was

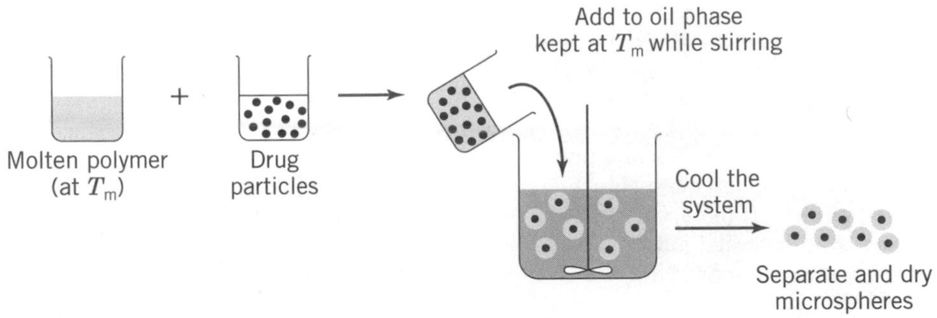

Figure 22. Microencapsulation by hot melt. Note that the dark dots represent drug particles; however, when the drug is water-soluble, an additional step may be required to prepare a water-in-oil emulsion, which is later encapsulated as shown here.

found to improve the drug distribution within microspheres. After cooling, the microspheres are washed by decantation with petroleum ether to give a free-flowing powder. Then they are sieved, dried, and stored in a freezer (when biodegradable polymers are used). Size distribution can be controlled by the stirring rate and the yield of encapsulation is 70–90%. This microencapsulation procedure is reproducible with respect to yield and size distribution, but the disadvantage of this approach is the moderate temperatures to which the drug must be exposed.

One way to overcome this problem is to synthesize polymers with lower melting points. This can be achieved by changes in the backbone of the polymer (i.e., in polyanhydrides), or using polymers that have a low melting point. When more stable drugs are involved the temperature, as well as the type of the polymer used, may be more versatile. Mathiowitz and Langer used this method to prepare polyanhydride microspheres (81). Surface morphology of the polyanhydride microspheres was studied via stereo microscopy and SEM and was performed immediately after preparation and after different periods of degradation. Both external and internal faces were examined. The microspheres were mounted on metal stubs, cut with a blade, and sputter-coated with gold-palladium. SEM of the poly(CPP-SA) are shown in Figure 23a. Microspheres are spherical, and the external surfaces appear smooth and crenellated. The crenellated surface is a typical result of this method. It is possible that the external surface is loaded with spherulites which formed during the slow cooling. No traces of drug or dye are found on the outer surfaces and cross sections reveal a dense internal structure, as seen in Figure 23b. Morphological studies made after 24 hours of in vitro degradation show that only the surface of the microsphere was attacked. The surface possessed small cracks and an irregular structure, whereas the internal face remains intact the same microspheres (Fig. 23c). A well-defined degrading zone, characterized by a spherical shape appeared and moved progressively from the surface towards the center of the microsphere. The erosion zone is composed of monomers (macromolecules). Figure 24d shows the same microspheres after 20 days of in vitro degradation. The microspheres show a weak structure (composed of monomers) which collapses easily (again these are insoluble monomers). The weight of this material is 5–10% of the initial weight; after 4 weeks the microspheres completely disintegrated. Figure 23of demonstrate a case where the drug loading of the microsphere was too

high (70%) resulting in high amounts of drug on the surface of the microsphere.

A good correlation was achieved when comparing weight loss of degrading samples with the production of the degradation products (81,83). These observations suggest that these microspheres display surface erosion. Incorporating hydrophilic molecules such as acid orange (M_W 364) at high loadings (30%) changes the degradation rate of the polymer. Release experiments were conducted in 10–50 mL of 0.1M, pH 7.4 phosphate buffer at 37°C in small columns. The release of acid orange was almost complete in 200 min and the degradation of the polymer lags behind the dye (81). Actually the release kinetics are affected more by the water uptake of the dye than by the degradation process. The influence of loading on the release profile was more pronounced when the loading is about 2%. Here release was controlled by polymer erosion. Except for the small burst effect at the beginning, the dye and polymer were released simultaneously. At higher loadings, the dye was released much faster than the polymer eroded. At high loadings of hydrophilic drugs, the release rate is not controlled by polymer erosion. Instead the polymer degradation is faster than that of a pure microsphere, and the drug is released faster than polymer dissolves. The reason for this is that the polymer starts to degrade from inside as well. The hot melt fabrication technique produces spheres with density independent of size. The study was confined to low loadings, that is, 2–5%, and the particles of the drug were mostly of small size (less than 50 μm) and for acid orange the size was less than 50 μm. The results demonstrate that the smaller the microspheres, the faster the release rate. It should be noted, however, that as the size of the microspheres approaches that of the incorporated drug particles, dissolution- or diffusion-controlled release may also occur due to particles touching the surface of the microspheres. Such a phenomenon may be occurring in the smallest microspheres. Incorporating insulin in microspheres changes the (release) degradation profile (81,83). In this case, drug release corresponds closely to polymer degradation. One explanation is the fact that zinc insulin has a low solubility in water (0.22 mg/dL) so that diffusional escape and osmotic swelling are diminished, which helps to achieve erosion-controlled release. Alternatively, it is possible that the small size of the insulin particles entrapped in the microspheres enabled good dispersion inside the polymer. The release of insulin in bioactive form was evident from the in vivo experiments. A possible mech

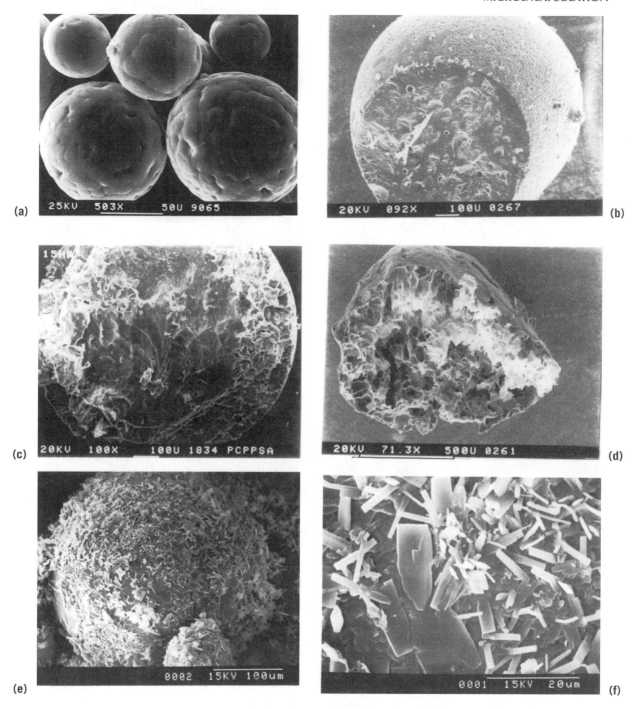

Figure 23. SEM of polyanhydride microspheres (**a**) external surface; (**b**) cross section; (**c**) cross section after 24 hours in buffer; (**d**) cross section after 20 days in buffer; (**e**) microsphere with 70% loading of salicilic acid; (**f**) higher magnification of same capsule.

anism describing these observations is that the release from polyanhydride microspheres loaded this low levels of drug involved two main steps. When microspheres are immersed in a buffer solution, the degradation process starts. A particle of drug, which is very close to the surface, dissolves and is released. As the degrading zone, which is composed of monomers, advances toward the center, all the hydrophilic drugs are released. Fewer hydrophilic drugs,

however, may be entrapped in the polymer, until the polymer completely dissolves. The latter phenomenon was observed for insulin.

The effect of in vivo performance of Zn/insulin-loaded (15% W/W) poly(CPP-SA) 20:80 microcapsules prepared by hot melt microencapsulation and implanted in diabetic rats, was sustained normoglycemia for up to 4 days (81) with no deaths due to insulin overdose. This stands in

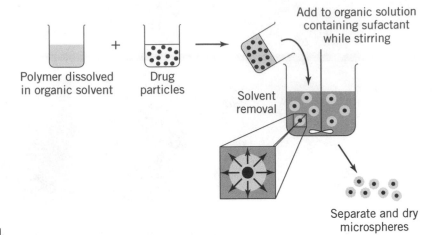

Figure 24. Microencapsulation by solvent removal.

sharp contrast to the microspheres made by solvent evaporation which caused short-lived, often fatal hypoglycemia (see "Solvent Evaporation").

SOLVENT REMOVAL

This method is a modification of organic phase precipitation (15) which, in specific situations, offers significant advantages. The fabrication occurs at room temperature and totally in organic solvents, an important consideration because for hydrolytically labile polymers such as polyanhydrides the avoidance of aqueous solutions is particularly important. Mathiowitz et al. (82,146) used this method to develop an improved technique of encapsulating insulin. In this example the polymer was dissolved in methylene chloride, the desired amount of drug was added and then the mixture was suspended in silicone oil containing Span® 85 and methylene chloride. After pouring the polymer solution into the silicone oil, petroleum ether was added and the mixture was stirred until the methylene chloride was extracted into the oil solution and sufficient microcapsule hardening was achieved. The resulting microspheres were isolated by filtration, washed with petroleum ether and dried overnight under vacuum (Fig. 24). The size of microspheres was always smaller than 300 μm. The best correlation between the expected and achieved loadings (82,83) was obtained with the hydrophilic substances myoglobin, acid orange, and insulin. This is understandable because the microencapsulation occurred in an organic solvent, preventing the loss of drug by diffusion.

The difference between solvent removal and organic phase separation is evident when comparing Figure 24 and Figure 12. In solvent removal the polymeric solution is introduced into the continuous phase, an emulsion is formed first and then the organic solvent is extracted to the continuous phase. In organic phase separation the polymer is dissolved in the continuous phase, a phase inducer is introduced, a coacervate is formed and, finally, encapsulation of drug occurs.

SEM of microspheres made from polymer without drug are shown in Figure 25. The amorphous, poly(CPP-SA) 50:50 microspheres are spherical with smooth and dense surfaces (Fig. 25a and 25b), whereas the crystalline poly(SA) (poly[sebacic acid]) microspheres display a very rough morphology containing fractures extending throughout the entire structure (Fig. 25c). The microspheres of poly(CPP-SA) 20:80 (Fig. 25d) and poly(CPP-SA) 50:50 exhibited a less porous internal structure (82,83), but the external dense layer was always present. A cross section of the poly(carboxyphenoxyhexane-co-sebacic acid) 50:50 microspheres reveals a very porous structure surrounded by a dense layer near the surface (Fig. 25d). When microspheres containing drugs were prepared, no change was observed in the external surface, for drug loadings up to 16.5%. Above that level, some crystals appeared on the surface (83).

The dense external structure and the porous core are typical of most of the microspheres produced by this method, especially the less crystalline polymers. A closer inspection of the physical events occurring during microsphere formation may help in understanding their performance. A schematic representation of the process is described in Figure 24 and a description of the process taking place is proposed. The polymer solution is introduced into the oil phase followed by rapid diffusion of the methylene chloride into the oil phase. The concentration of the polymer near the wall is high, which explains why precipitation of the outer shell occurs first (82,83), leaving high concentrations of polymer dissolved in methylene chloride inside the core. This organic solvent can be later removed by addition of a nonsolvent or by applying high vacuum. The process of microencapsulation is presumably diffusion controlled—at least during the first stages where the difference in concentration of methylene chloride between the two phases (silicone and polymer solution) is significant. After precipitation begins, the process becomes more complicated. It involves diffusion of methylene chloride, both in the polymer solution and in the already precipitated polymer. The first precipitation occurs in the external area of the forming sphere, and this layer slows subsequent diffusion of methylene chloride into the oil phase. This dense external structure and porous internal core are presumably obtained because during precipitation of the microspheres the external surface precipitates first, thus making it difficult for the microsphere to shrink. The re-

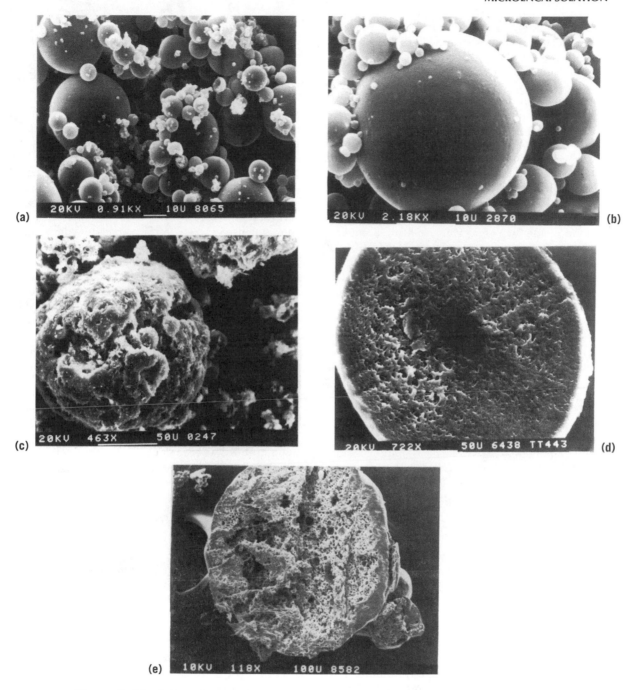

Figure 25. Morphology of microspheres made by solvent removal: (**a**) external surface of poly(CPP-SA) 50:50 microspheres; (**b**) higher magnification of (**a**); (**c**) external surface of poly(SA); (**d**) cross section of poly(CPP-SA) 20:80; (**e**) cross section of poly(CPH-SA) 50:50 microsphere.

mainder of the solvent then diffuses out of the microsphere leaving a porous structure.

In the more crystalline poly(SA) microspheres, there was no formation of a dense external layer, but a quick precipitation of the entire polymer emulsion led to a very porous structure. In other cases in the literature (84,146). The rate of precipitation may also be a key to understanding the type of microspheres which were obtained. The rough surface of the poly(SA) microspheres may be due to the faster precipitation of poly(SA) compared with

poly(CPP-SA) 50:50. Thus precipitation occurred in the poly(SA) microspheres before a stable emulsion could form. In contrast, in slower precipitating systems—poly(CPP-SA) 50:50, for example—there is first the formation of an emulsion and then precipitation. This "two-step" process during microencapsulation can be further controlled using different surface-active compounds to stabilize the emulsion. It should be noted that all experiments were done with the same organic solvents, because different solvents may lead to different external morphologies.

DSC and X-ray analysis of the polymers, dyes, and drug-loaded microspheres were performed in order to characterize the physical state of the polymers and dyes after microencapsulation (82,146). In cases where the drug formed a dispersion in the first stage of microencapsulation, we would expect that, at the end of the process, crystalline drug particles would be dispersed in the polymer matrix. In such a system DSC would display two endotherms, each relating to the melting point of either drug or polymer. In cases where the drug is dissolved in the organic polymeric solution, solvent removal causes the drug to either dissolve in the polymer or crystallize out and form a dispersion. In the latter case DSC would again display two endotherms. In the former case, where the drug forms a solution inside the polymer, no separate event relating to the melting of the drug would occur. However, some changes in the melting of the polymer might occur, provided the concentration of the drug in the polymer phase is high enough to cause changes exceeding the sensitivity of DSC. Mathiowitz thus monitored melting points of the dyes and polymer before and after encapsulation. A sharp endotherm was observed for free acid orange, p-nitroaniline and methyl red (119.4, 149.8, 181.2°C, respectively) corresponding to the melting phase transitions. The "blank" microspheres displayed a sharp endotherm at 78°C corresponding to the melting of the crystalline regions of the polymer (83).

In loaded microspheres (up to 16% loading), no melt corresponding to the acid orange appeared around 121°C (83). These facts may imply that the dye forms a solution inside the polymer (at loadings lower than 23%). However, the absence of the thermal event at low loadings does not always indicate that this is the case. In order to verify this point X-ray diffraction was used and indicates that acid orange was dispersed as crystals in the microspheres (data not shown) (82,146).

X-ray diffraction analysis of methyl red–loaded microspheres indicated no crystalline diffraction related to the dye, nor did the DSC show any endotherm related to the melting of the dye. However, the melting point of the polymer had slightly decrease compared to blank microspheres. X-ray diffraction displayed the typical diffraction pattern of pure poly(SA), but the crystallinity decreased from 55% to about 40% (82,146). However, the change in the melting point and the decrease in crystallinity suggested that the drug may be soluble in the polymer. It is quite possible that the dye, being soluble in the amorphous state, hindered the crystallization of the polymer and thus decreased the degree of crystallinity.

Similar experiments were performed with poly-(CPP-SA) 50:50 microspheres loaded with the same substances. Both DSC and X-ray diffraction confirmed that acid orange was dispersed as crystals in the polymer, whereas the hydrophobic dyes formed solutions inside the polymer (82,146).

Blank poly(CPP-SA) 50:50 microspheres prepared by solvent removal were implanted subcutaneously in rats. The spheres were smaller than 300 μm and were injected as an aqueous suspension. After 10 days of implantation several spherical microsphere remnants were found among the remains of degraded microspheres in tissue samples taken from the implantation site. These remnants were composed of the same polymer degradation products as seen in the nonintact remnants (as judged by infrared spectroscopy) and eventually disappeared from the implantation area. Although the appearance of external remnants might, at first glance, appear to contradict other evidence supporting surface erosion, the SEM analysis of microspheres already presented suggests a possible explanation based on polymer density. Cross sections of microspheres during release show an outer zone in which degradation has already occurred but the degradation products have not yet disappeared. In addition, cross-sectional views of undegraded microspheres formed by both solvent removal and hot melt microencapsulation show a dense external surface and a less dense inner core (82,83,146). It is quite plausible that during degradation the external surface erodes completely, leaving behind a dense but permeable layer of degradation products that must dissolve and diffuse away. Meanwhile, erosion continues into the core, where the degraded material is less dense and is able to more easily dissolve and diffuse out. The fact that the remnants disappear after a longer time in vivo is further evidence that solubilization of the degradation products may be the controlling step in the disappearance of the microspheres, but not in the release of the drug.

Histological studies of both samples revealed a moderate acute inflammatory response that peaked at day 3. Histological examination of tissue removed at day 40 from the implantation site revealed a layer of amorphous fibril material within the subcutaneous tissue, a remnant of the implanted polymer. There was no evidence of tissue reaction to this material within the subepidermis.

An in vivo study with insulin-loaded microspheres prepared by solvent removal demonstrated more successful serum and urine glucose control than previously seen with microspheres made by solvent evaporation. Five diabetic rats were implanted with 200 mg of insulin-loaded (10%) microspheres. The results demonstrate near-zero urine glucose levels and serum glucose control. A similar experiment with 200 mg of 5% (W/W) loaded microspheres decreased urine glucose effectively for 3 days and resulted in only 1 day of normoglycemia, whereas 100 mg of 10% (W/W) loaded microspheres showed 3 days of lowered urine glucose and 2 days of serum glucose control. For comparison, urine and blood glucose levels for both diabetic control and healthy control rats (5 rats in each group) were measured. As expected, glucose was never found in the urine of healthy rats and the untreated diabetic rats showed no significant lowering of blood or urine glucose levels (82).

Atkins et al. (144) prepared spherical, monolithic, poly(DL-lactide-co-glycolide) (PLGA) 50:50 and PLGA 75:25 microspheres with a honeycomb-like internal architecture, composed of and containing a range of vancomycin loadings. Microspheres were prepared using W/O emulsification, except that Span® 40 was used as the continuous oil phase surfactant. In a typical fabrication the organic polymer phase was prepared by the ultrasonication (100 W bath) of 1 g of either 75:25 or 50:50 PLGA together with either 1, 0.333, or 0.1 g vancomycin in 30 mL acetonitrile at 35°C for 15 minutes, providing theoretical percentage loadings of 50, 16.7, and 5% vancomycin, respectively. This organic phase was maintained at 55°C in a water bath. The continuous oil phase consisted of 125 g light mineral oil containing 2% (W/W) Span® 40 maintained at 55°C. The organic polymer phase was slowly added to the continuous phase and emulsified at 55°C using a high shear head at 3,000 rpm for 30 minutes. Droplet formation was monitored by light microscopy and the final emulsion was stirred at 440 rpm with a three-blade impeller in an off-center position for a further 60 minutes at 55°C to facilitate solvent evaporation. The emulsion was cooled to just above 35°C to prevent the precipitation of Span® 40, and left for 1 hour to allow the microspheres to harden. The microspheres were separated by vacuum filtration using solvent resistant polypropylene-backed PTFE filters (1 μm pore size) and washed with excess petroleum ether at 55°C to remove the Span® 40. The resultant microspheres were air-dried and weighed to determine percentage yield. The free-flowing preparation of grey/white microspheres were stored desiccated, under vacuum at room temperature (147). In a way, this method is a combination of solvent evaporation and solvent removal, because some of the solvent is removed by the organic phase and some is evaporated by the applied heat.

Porous salmon calcitonin-loaded PLGA microspheres (size range 35–140 mm) of varying matrix characteristics were prepared by an aqueous emulsification process using either a temperature gradient (Tmp) or dilution (Dil) of the continuous phase. The Tmp technique resulted in microspheres with a hollow internal core and a porous wall. The core size and thickness of the porous wall were dependent on the temperature gradient used. A rapid ramp in temperature from 15 to 40°C resulted in a large core and a thin wall, whereas a gradual temperature rise resulted in a smaller core. The Dil technique produced microspheres with a uniform, honeycomb-like pore structure without a core where pore size was dependent on the dilution volume used. The specific surface area was higher and bulk density lower for microspheres prepared by the Tmp technique, whereas there was no significant difference in the peptide load (3.2–4.5%) between both techniques. A rapid removal of CH_2Cl_2 was observed in the case of the Tmp technique while the Dil technique facilitated a slower and gradual CH_2Cl_2 removal. Residual CH_2Cl_2 was approximately <10–20 ppm for microspheres prepared by the Tmp technique, whereas the levels were 20–130 ppm for microspheres produced by the Dil technique. Higher retention of methanol (~15–20%) was observed in the droplet formation stage with the Tmp technique, subsequent removal of which affected the core size. In the Dil technique, very low levels of methanol (<2%) were retained in the droplets soon after dispersion resulting in a uniform porous structure without core. Slower removal of methanol from the microspheres was partly responsible for the core formation (148).

The use of supercritical solvents as an extraction method to prepare microspheres is an interesting approach. The aerosol solvent extraction system (ASES) uses a supercritical gas as nonsolvent for an organic solution of drug and polymer in order to form microparticles by a floc-culation process. Due to the miscibility of organic solvent and supercritical gas phase, microparticles with residual organic solvents below 30 ppm are formed. This principle was tested to encapsulate model drugs such as hyoscine butylbromide, indomethacin, piroxicam and thymopentin. As a carrier, the polymer poly(L-lactide) was used. The resulting microparticles were investigated with regard to particle formation, morphology, particle size, size distribution, and drug loading. The lower the polarity of incorporated drug, the greater the extraction, which reduced the drug loading of the microparticles. The extraction capacity of the gas phase depends on temperature and pressure which determines density and polarity of the gas. The obtained results show that the production conditions have to be optimized for each drug/polymer combination. Totally nonpolar drugs are completely extracted together with the organic solvent; however, polar drugs (especially peptides and proteins) are easy to incorporate with the ASES process (149).

Poly(L-lactide) microspheres containing a low molecular weight pharmaceutical agent were prepared using the precipitation with a compressed antisolvent (PCA) process with supercritical carbon dioxide as the antisolvent. Gentamycin, naloxone, and naltrexone were solubilized in methylene chloride using hydrophobic ion pairing (HIP) to stoichiometrically replace polar counter ions with an anionic detergent, aerosol OT (AOT, sodium bis-2-ethylhexyl sulfosuccinate). Through HIP complexation, solubilities in excess of 1 mg/mL were attainable in methylene chloride, allowing levels of direct incorporation that are not possible with other PCA approaches. The drug/polymer particles were spherical in shape and between 0.2 and 1.0 μm in diameter, as determined by SEM. Drug incorporation efficiencies were determined and in vitro release profiles measured. At 37°C, the release of the ion-paired drugs into phosphate-buffered saline displays minimal burst effects and exhibits release kinetics that are approximately linear with the square root of time, indicating matrix diffusion control of drug release. For gentamycin, linear release from the poly(L-lactide) microspheres was observed for more than 7 weeks, even at a drug loading of near 25% (W/W). Naltrexone exhibits similar release characteristics, although more drug was found on the surface of the microspheres. Conversely, rifampin, which was not ion-paired, was poorly encapsulated (150).

SPRAY-DRYING

Spray-drying is a method for preparing microspheres that is reproducible, rapid, and easy to scale up. Mathiowitz et al. (151) used this fabrication technique to examine its influence on crystallinity (by X-ray and DSC), external morphology (by SEM) and release kinetics of polyanhydrides. Model drugs, including the dyes, acid orange 8 and methyl red, and the protein, bovine somatotropin (STH), were examined with a variety of polyanhydride homo- and copolymers.

The following polymers were studied poly(sebacic anhydride) (PSA), copolymers of 1,3 bis-(carboxyphenoxypropane) (CPP) and sebacic acid (SA) having molar ratios of 20:80 and 50:50, copolymers of 1,6 bis-(carboxyphenoxy hexane) (CPH) and sebacic acid (SA) having a molar ratio of 50:50, copolymers of fumaric acid (FA) and sebacic acid (SA) having a molar ratio of 20:80, and poly(valeric anhydride) (PCPV).

In order to create a delivery system using spray-drying it is essential to dissolve the polymer in a volatile liquid. Polyanhydrides degrade in aqueous solutions, and therefore it is preferable to process them in organic solvents. With volatile solvents such as methylene chloride it possible to encapsulate various heat-sensitive drugs, including proteins, at low temperature. For this particular study only polymer that was soluble in methylene chloride was used. The polymer is first dissolved in methylene chloride, and the drug can be either dissolved (e.g., methyl red) or suspended as particles (e.g., acid orange 8 and STH). Because the spray-dryer nozzle was 0.5 mm in diameter, it was important to obtain very small particles of the insoluble drug. Particle size reduction, via spray-drying a dilute, aqueous, acid orange solution, resulted in raisin-shaped particles, 1 to 5 μm in size. These particles were subsequently suspended in the polymer solution and sprayed-dried as already described. STH (the pure drug) had a narrow size distribution (1 to 2 mm). Methyl red was soluble in the organic solvent and was sprayed dried as a solution. Throughout this work, the conditions of spraying were kept identical: the same organic solvent and the same polymer concentration were used. This fact allowed us to correlate the morphology of a series of polymers, spray-dried under the same conditions. In general, it was possible to spray dry the crystalline polymers PSA, P(CPP-SA) 20:80, P(FA-SA) 20:80, and P(FA-SA) 50:50. However, each polymer displayed a different morphology as judged by SEM. When using more hydrophobic polymers—P(CPP-SA) 50:50, P(CPH-SA) 50:50, and PCPV—some aggregation occurred during spraying. This could have been a result of the more viscous solutions of these polymers as well as their low glass transition.

SEM of black microspheres made of PSA are shown in Figure 26a. The microspheres are spherical in shape with few aggregates and display a rough external structure. Some of the polymer precipitated as long rods, which could be a result of fast precipitation that is typical of the PSA polymer. Microspheres made of P(CPP-SA) 20:80 polymers exhibited a crenellated external surface (Figure 26b) and sizes ranging from 1 to 5 μm. The same external surface appeared when acid orange-loaded (3%) P(CPP-SA) microspheres were examined. When methyl red was encapsulated, the external surfaces of the individual microspheres were spherical in shape with few pores on the surfaces. In this particular preparation some of the spheres accumulated in the spray-dryer trap.

The STH-loaded P(CPP-SA) 20:80 microspheres were spherical with smooth external surfaces, but with a few pores on the surface of some of the capsules. In this case, the drug was supplied as fine particles, 1 to 2 μm in size. It is possible that some of the spheres were single particles of drug encapsulated by a continuous polymer membrane. P(FA-SA) 20:80 was the next crystalline polymer that was studied. In this case, the microspheres were spherical and smaller than 10 μm (Figure 26c). High magnification reveals a highly porous structure. This porous structure was

typical of all spray dried fumaric polymers—both blank and loaded microspheres.

The external surfaces of the amorphous P(CPP-SA) 50:50 and P(CPH-SA) 50:50 microspheres were smooth and dense. However, the microspheres tended to fuse before the final drying. The same phenomenon was observed with PCPV microspheres (Figure 26d). This aggregation can be prevented by lowering the concentration of the polymer solution. However, the glass transitions of these polymers are very low, and this may have been the main reason for the high degree of fusion during spray-drying (151).

DSC and X-ray analyses of the spray-dried polymers loaded with dyes and drugs were performed in order to characterize the physical state of the polymers after microencapsulation. By monitoring the melting points of the dyes and the polymer before and after encapsulation it was possible to determine when a solution or phase separated system was obtained. A sharp endotherm was observed for free acid orange and methyl red (119.4 and 181.2°C, respectively) corresponding to the melting phase transitions. The "blank" spray-dried PSA microspheres displayed a sharp endotherm at 81°C, corresponding to the melting of the crystalline regions of the polymer. The crystallinity of the PSA microspheres was lower than the crystallinity of the original polymer (decrease of 7.6 cal/g). However, the crystallinity was not completely destroyed, and the typical powder diffraction of the PSA units was still retained. After acid orange is incorporated, the crystallinity of the polymer remains almost unchanged. To further study the behavior of the spray-dried microspheres, the P(CPP-SA) 20:80 microspheres were analyzed by DSC. A dramatic decrease was seen in the melting point of the blank microspheres (58.5°C) compared with the pure polymer (72°C). The melting was broad, and the numbers reported represent the peak maxima. This was true for microspheres loaded with acid orange (56.6°C), methyl red (56.2°C), and STH (58°C). The decrease in melting point could be a result of residual solvent (up to 5% by weight) in the microspheres, which acts as a diluent. There was also a pronounced decrease in the heat of fusion, which directly reflects a decrease in crystallinity. X-ray diffractions of two different loadings of acid orange in P(CPP-SA) 20:80 microspheres are shown in Figure 27. The four well-defined diffraction patterns, which correspond to the P(CPP-SA) 20:80 (152) are hardly seen and are replaced by broad bands, indicating a profound decrease in the degree of crystallinity. The blank microspheres seemed to be less crystalline than the loaded spheres, as judged by X-ray diffraction (Fig. 28). A comparison of blank P(CPP-SA) 20:80 microspheres to microspheres loaded with acid orange, as well as methyl red, is shown in Figure 28. As mentioned previously, the polymer still retains some crystallinity, but the fine structures of the crystalline areas are gone. The lower degree of crystallinity is more pronounced in the methyl red sample and is also supported by the lower heat of fusion (83,151). Previous publications, describing different encapsulation systems, indicated that methyl red may form solutions with polyanhydrides, resulting in a lower degree of crystallinity (83).

P(FA-SA) 20:80 behaved differently. The melting point, as well as the heat of fusion, was lowered for both loaded

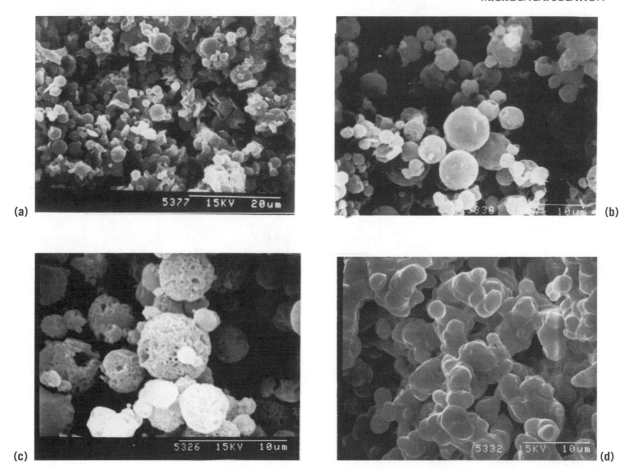

Figure 26. SEM of spray-dried microspheres: (**a**) blank poly(SA): (**b**) blank poly(CPP-SA) 20:80; (**c**) blank poly(FA-SA) 20:80; and (**d**) PCPV microspheres.

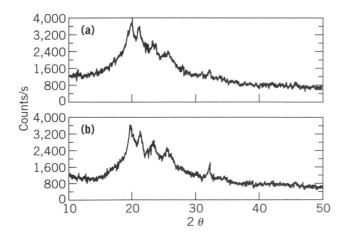

Figure 27. X-ray diffraction of P(CPP-SA) 20:80 spray-dried microspheres (**a**) loaded with 3% acid orange and (**b**) loaded with 10% acid orange. *Source:* With permission from Ref. 151.

and unloaded microspheres. However, the fine structure of the P(FA-SA) 20:80 polymer was retained (Fig. 29). This indicates that the polymers crystallized during the spray-drying process.

It was evident from the X-ray powder diffraction, as well as from thermal studies, that the polymers tend to lose their degree of crystallinity during spray-drying. This phenomenon is known in spray-drying of both polymers as well as small molecules (152,153). The fast drying process provides very short times for the polymer to precipitate, resulting in a more amorphous structure. Addition of drugs, especially those soluble in the organic solvents, further decreases the degree of crystallinity.

The release of acid orange from P(CPP-SA) 20:80 occurred over a period of 15 hours, and the polymer degraded completely over 24 hours. Similar release rates were observed in P(FA-SA) 20:80 microspheres, where polymer degradation was more closely correlated to release rates. In this case, both the porous structure and the good solubility of the degradation products resulted in a better correlation between the release and degradation products. Release of STH (Fig. 30) lasted over 24 hours and resulted in the release of about 90% of the drug. The short release rates (24 hours) that were obtained are expected. First, the degradation time of P(CPP-SA) 20:80 polymer is very fast (81). In addition, the size of the microspheres is very small (1–5 mm). This type of delivery system may find applications in cases where fast release is needed, for example, in oral delivery systems.

The release of the incorporated material can occur via two independent processes. The first is diffusion of the drug through fluid-filled pores formed by the dissolution of

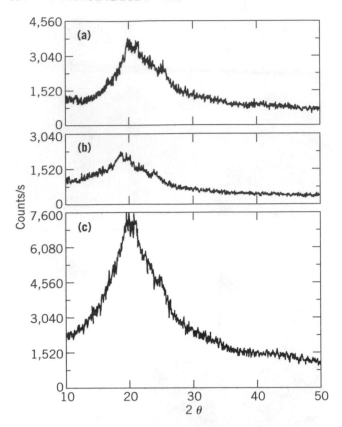

Figure 28. X-ray diffraction of P(CPP-SA) 20:80 spray-dried microspheres: (**a**) blank; (**b**) loaded with methyl red; and (**c**) loaded with acid orange. *Source:* With permission from Ref. 151.

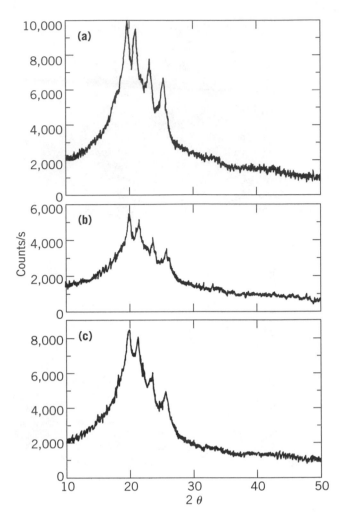

Figure 29. X-ray diffraction of P(FA-SA) 20:80 spray-dried microspheres: (**a**) blank; (**b**) loaded with acid orange; and (**c**) loaded with methyl red. *Source:* With permission from Ref. 151.

the incorporated drug particles; the second is via erosion of the polymer matrix as the anhydride bonds are hydrolyzed. The total release of drug is the sum of these two release rates.

For most of the polymer types used, the erosion of the polymer is less than 15% over the first four hours. During this time period, cumulative drug release is in the range of 60–70%. Thus, to compare the effect of different polymers and drug loadings, the release over this early time period was modeled as a diffusion process, since the release due to erosion is low. The following mass balance applies for the drug within the microspheres:

$$\frac{\partial C}{\partial t} = D_e \nabla^2 C \tag{21}$$

where C is the concentration of the drug in the particle, t is the time, D_e is the effective diffusion of the drug in the polymer matrix, and ∇^2 is the Laplacian.

The first equation can be integrated, and the cumulative fraction of the drug released as a function of time can be computed as follows:

$$\frac{M_t}{M_\infty} = -\frac{6}{\pi^2} \sum_{n=1}^{\infty} \frac{1}{n^2} \exp\left(-n^2\pi^2 D_e \frac{t}{r_0^2}\right) \tag{22}$$

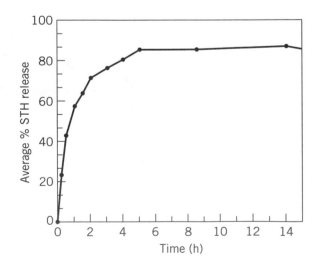

Figure 30. STH released from P(CPP-A) 20:80 microspheres. *Source:* With permission from Ref. 151.

where

$$\frac{M_t}{M_\infty} \qquad (23)$$

is the cumulative fraction released, and r_0 is the sphere radius.

The effective diffusion coefficient is governed by the fabrication parameters, such as the quantity of drug loaded, the size of the drug particles loaded, the crystallinity of the polymer, and the porosity of the system. The release curves are fitted to the second equation using a least squares fitting method and an estimate of the effective diffusion coefficient (D_e) is obtained. Knowing the diffusion coefficient of the drug in saline D_s, a retardation factor can be calculated as follows: $R = D_s/D_e$.

The degree of retardation provides information as to whether the drug or dye was successfully encapsulated. Diffusion coefficients were calculated for the 20:80 polymer for both acid orange and STH. The diffusion coefficients in saline for acid orange and STH (D_s) were estimated as 1×10^{-5} cm2/s and 1×10^{-6} cm^2/s, respectively. The estimated effective diffusion coefficients and the net retardation factors are summarized in Table 10.

The microspheres produced have approximately the same diameter as the drug particles that were incorporated. Thus, it is likely that only a single drug particle is contained within each microsphere. The retardation factors for acid orange and STH are on the same order of magnitude, despite the large difference in molecular weight. This supports the notion that the individual drug particles are completely entrapped within the polymers as the initial release is not a function of the characteristic properties of the drug.

Kreitz (154) studied the degradation of spray-dried PLGA microspheres for a period of up to three months using FTIR and SEM. Briefly, 10 g of PLGA 50:50 (35,000 M_w) were dissolved in methylene chloride, producing a 5% (w/v) polymer solution. This solution was spray-dried at 40°C, and the resultant microspheres were lyophilized. Fifty milligrams of the microspheres and 1 mL of buffer were added to separate microcentrifuge tubes for each time point (1 and 3 days and 1, 2, 3, 4, 6, 8, 10, 12, 16, and 20 weeks), and were placed in a 37°C water bath. At the specified time points the buffer was removed from a tube, the polymer was washed with distilled water and then lyophilized. SEM and FTIR were performed on each of the degradation samples and on preliminary (nondegraded) samples.

In the SEMs (Fig. 31) the degradation of the microspheres over three weeks is shown. In Figure 31a (day zero), the spheres are seen as 0.5–5 μm-diameter distinct particles with porous, crenellated surfaces. After only 1 day in 37°C buffer (Fig. 31b) the microspheres have lost their original surface features. They now appear smooth and have started to coalesce, indicating a drop in the glass-transition temperature due to degradation. At 3 days (Fig. 31c) the coalescence has proceeded but the original morphology remains discernible. At 7 days (Fig. 31d) the continuing degradation induces agglomeration from individual spheres, and at 2 weeks (Fig. 31e) the polymer appears as an amorphous mass, the original morphology now gone. The samples at 3 weeks (Fig. 31f) and subsequent time points were viscous liquids, having undergone extensive degradation.

The FTIR spectra of the microspheres' degradation over 12 weeks are shown in Figure 32, from 2,000 cm^{-1} to 600 cm^{-1}. The most apparent changes in the progression are seen in the peak at 1,760 cm^{-1}, which represents the carbonyl bond of the polyester, and in the peak triplet around 1,400 cm^{-1}, which represents the bonds between the lactide-lactide (L-L, 1,456 cm^{-1}), glycolide-glycolide (G-G, 1,425 cm^{-1}), and lactide-glycolide (L-G, 1,398 cm^{-1}) mer units of the polymer. The spectra remain fairly constant over the first week of degradation. At 2 weeks the carbonyl peak is broader, possibly due to the transition of some crystalline regions to amorphous regions. The peak triplet at 2 weeks shows no distinct change. At 3 weeks the L-L (left) peak in the triplet appears to have receded slightly relative to the G-G and L-G peaks, suggesting greater degradation of this bond relative to the other two types of ester bonds present in this polymer. Also, the carbonyl peak is slightly broader than that of 2 weeks indicating further crystalline-to-amorphous transition. At 4 weeks the carbonyl peak appears sharper and all three peaks of the triplet have decreased relative to the peak of the carbonyl bond. The carbonyl peak's sharpness may be the result of the amorphous regions' partial degradation and dissolution, leaving behind the more crystalline regions. The reduction in the triplet peak at this stage indicates a general progression of the polymer degradation via hydrolysis of the ester bonds. At 6 weeks the carbonyl peak appears unchanged from that of 4 weeks while the triplet peaks have decreased extensively. The peaks of the G-G and L-G bonds have decreased to a greater extent than that of the L-L peak. At 8 weeks the carbonyl peak's sharpness indicates continued degradation and dissolution of oligomers from the polymer. The G-G peak is the only one of the triplet which remains, a finding that continues to the last measurement at 12 weeks. This may be due to the degradation resistance of oligomer blocks consisting mostly of glycolide mers.

In the present Luck et al. studies the influence of the polymer composition and the production method of microspheres on the in vitro plasma protein adsorption were investigated using two-dimensional electrophoresis. Microparticles were prepared from poly(L-lactide) (L-PLA), (PLGA), and ABA triblock copolymers containing hydrophilic poly(oxyethylene) (B-block) domains connected to hydrophobic polyesters (A-blocks). Two different microencapsulation methods were employed, namely the W/O/W emulsion solvent evaporation method and the spray-drying technique. It could be demonstrated that the polymer composition and, especially, the encapsulation technique, influenced the interactions with plasma proteins

Table 10. Diffusion Coefficients D_s, (Salin), D_e (Polymer), and Retardation Factors for P(CPP SA) 20:80 Microspheres

Drug	D_s cm^2/s	D_e cm^2/h	R
Acid orange	1.0×10^{-5}	6.3×10^{-9}	5.7×10^6
STH	1.0×10^{-6}	8.0×10^{-10}	4.5×10^6

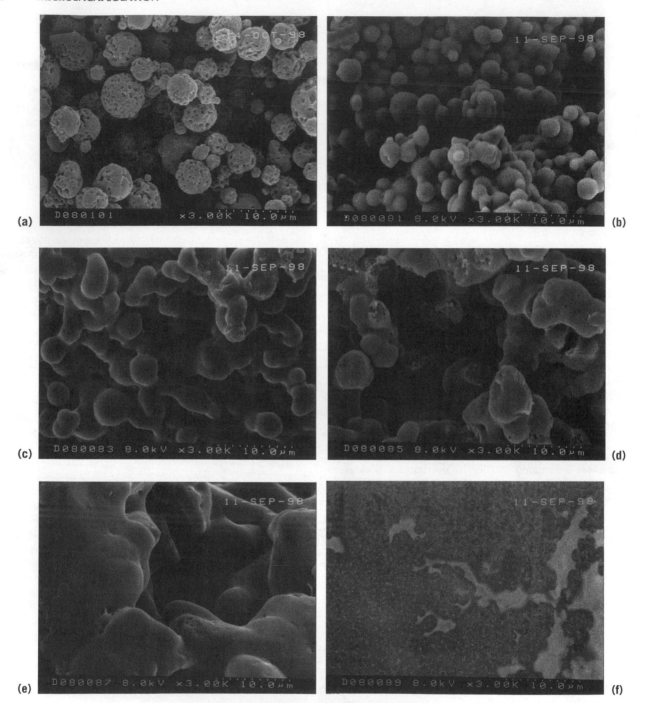

Figure 31. SEM series showing the procession of PLGA microsphere degradation at (**a**) time zero, (**b**) 1 day, (**c**) 3 days, (**d**) 2 weeks, and (**f**) 3 weeks.

significantly. For example, the percentages of several apolipoproteins in the plasma protein adsorption patterns of spray-dried PLGA and L-PLA particles were distinctly higher when compared with the adsorption patterns of the particles produced by the W/O/W technique. Some adsorbed proteins were found to be characteristic or even specific for particles produced by the same method or consisting of identical polymers. PVA used as stabilizer in the W/O/W technique may decisively influence the surface prop-

erties relevant for protein adsorption. The plasma protein adsorption on particles composed of ABA copolymers was drastically reduced when compared to microspheres made from pure polyesters. The adsorption patterns of ABA particles were dominated by albumin. The plasma protein adsorption patterns detected on the different microspheres are likely to affect their in vivo performance as parenteral drug delivery systems (155). It is known that the hydrophobicity of a surface can influence protein adsorption, i.e.,

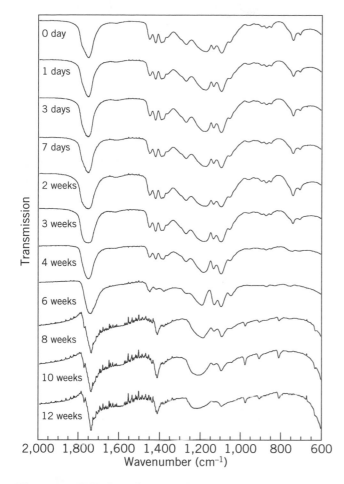

Figure 32. FTIR degradation studies on the same microspheres as shown in Figure 31.

parameters was observed in spray-dried microparticles. Polymer degradation was heterogeneous in L-PLA and DL-PLGA 75:25 microparticle and was not influenced by the presence of the drug at a nominal loading of 1% (W/W), when prepared by the three methods (note that with ASES, only L-PLA could be used for microencapsulation). In batches made of DL-PLGA 50:50 (M_w 52,600), the degradation rate decreased slightly with increased drug loading. Only for the case of DL-PLGA 50:50 (M_w 14,500) was the polymer degradation rate for spray-dried microparticles higher than that of microparticles prepared by the W/O/W solvent evaporation method. Generally, the degradation rates of the different microparticles followed the expected order: L-PLA < DL-PLGA 75:50 < DL-PLGA 50:50 (M_w 52,600) < DL-PLGA 50:50 (a mixture of M_w 52,600 and M_w 3,400). Polymer degradation was homogenous in DL-PLGA 50:50 microparticles. Decreasing the molecular weight of DL-PLGA 50:50 from 52,600 to 14,500 did not result in accelerate polymer degradation (156).

ONE-STEP FORMATION OF DOUBLE-WALLED MICROSPHERES

With the increasing complexity of therapeutic regimens, drug delivery systems may become more sophisticated. There are many approaches to achieving long-term release of pharmacologic agents using microspheres, but this technology is not without problems. One drawback to this sort of system is the initial "burst" effect caused by the rapid release of the drug particles trapped on the surface during manufacturing. One solution to this problem that was developed was to prepare multilayered microspheres consisting of concentric spheres of polymer. Traditional methods to form such delivery systems (e.g., pan- or dip-coating and air suspension coating) require multiple steps, which decreases process yield (157–159). First, the core would be formed, and then each of the coating layers was added in separate steps. More recently, Mathiowitz et al. have developed a method to manufacture multilayered microspheres in a single step (84,101,160–162). This process combines the natural tendency of polymers to phase separate as solution concentration increases with the microencapsulation process of solvent evaporation. Moreover, it is a one-step process for creating double-layered microspheres and has advantages over other methods for coating microspheres. In the dip-coating process, the coating is usually nonuniform in both coverage and thickness (Fig. 33). Also, each coating adds an additional step to the manufacturing process, increasing quality control problems at each stage, and further decreasing the yield. Coating processes involving fluidized beds have produced microspheres with a uniform coating, but fluidized beds are difficult to design for particle sizes of less than 100 μm.

✓The one-step process described here combines the phenomenon of phase separation with emulsion theory and can be used to produce spheres of diameters less than 20 μm and up to 1,000 μm. The basic difference between this process and organic phase separation or coacervation is that two polymers are used to cause the phase separation and that both are used in high concentration. Thus the

hydrophobic surfaces favor protein adsorption. Therefore, the hydrophobicity of films made of the polymers used for the microparticle formation was characterized using contact angle measurements. The measurement of contact angles gave the following rank order of hydrophobicities as a function of contact angles: L-PLA>PLGA>ABAI>ABAII (155). The most striking difference between the two particle types was the strong adsorption of the apolipoproteins on the spray-dried particles (155).

Three methods were used, namely spray-drying, W/O/W solvent evaporation and ASES, for the preparation of microparticles having the same size range, to study the influence of the preparation method on polymer degradation in vitro (phosphate-buffered saline, 37°C, one month). The following five polymers of the biodegradable PLA and PLGA groups were selected to prepare blank and drug-loaded microparticles: L-PLA (M_w 81,200); DL-PLGA 75:25 (M_w 64,300); DL-PLGA 50:50 (M_w 52,600); DL-PLGA 50:50 (M_w 14,500); and DL-PLGA 50:50 (M_w 3,400). Tetracosactide was selected as the model peptide. When microparticles were prepared by solvent evaporation, the mean diameter and, more markedly, the drug encapsulation efficiency decreased with decreasing molecular weight and an increasing proportion of glycolic acid in the polymer. In contrast, no direct influence of the polymer nature on these

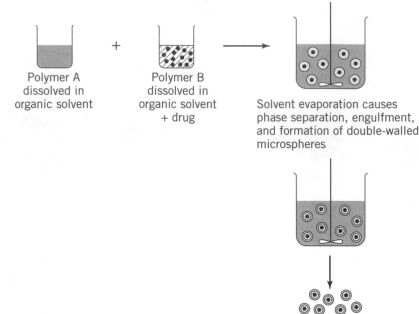

Figure 33. Formation of one-step double-walled microspheres.

final product, unlike coacervation, is the formation of two layers each containing two separate polymers.

The section entitled "Interfacial Phenomenon" and Figure 8 describe the tendency of a liquid to spontaneously spread across a solid or liquid surface in terms of the surface and interfacial tensions of the components. It can be modified to represent a system in which two dissimilar phases are dispersed within a third by substituting the appropriate interfacial tensions for the surface tensions in Harkin's equation (163):

$$\lambda_{AB} = \gamma_{BS} - \gamma_{AS} - \gamma_{AB} \qquad (24)$$

where γ_{AS} and γ_{BS} are the interfacial tensions of the solvent and polymer A or B, respectively, and γ_{AB} is the interfacial tension between polymers A and B. For positive values of λ_{AB}, polymer A spontaneously spreads on polymer B. The actual configuration of the two dissimilar phases (A and B) depends on the values of the three possible spreading coefficients and can be described as complete engulfing, partial engulfing, and nonengulfing (see Fig. 8).

Combination of the emulsion theory described here with the phenomenon of phase separation provides a novel approach for preparing double-walled polymer microspheres. By introducing a two-polymer solution into a continuous phase, a stable emulsion is created in which phase separation occurs within each drop. The phase separation can be engineered such that one polymer engulfs the others, forming double-walled microspheres in a single step. Each of the configurations shown in Figure 8 can be visualized using SEM (Fig. 33). Figure 34a shows a cross section of a double-walled sphere of polyanhydride and PLA exhibiting phase separation and complete engulfment. Figure 34b shows a nonengulfing, chaotic structure formed from PLA and polystyrene when precipitation occurred after phase separation but before engulfment. And Figure 34c shows a high-magnification SEM photo of the wall material in

Figure 34a indicating that some of the core phase is entrapped in the wall.

The microspheres were formed by first preparing separate solutions (10–20% w/v) of the two polymers in a volatile organic solvent (see Fig. 33). The drug or protein was added to the appropriate polymer solution at this stage and dispersed evenly. Then the two polymer solutions were mixed and dripped into a stirred bath of 0.5% PVA in water. As the solvent evaporated, the polymer solution concentration increased to the point where they were no longer mutually soluble and began to separate. If allowed enough time before hardening, the two phases configured themselves according to the modified Harkin's equation. There was only one thermodynamic equilibrium configuration of polymer A spreading on polymer B, but the extent of spreading was determined by the rate of polymer precipitation, as controlled by the rate of solvent evaporation. Therefore, two scenarios to produce double-walled microspheres were possible and achieved by balancing the thermodynamic and kinetic factors. In the first, polymers for which Harkin's equation predicts complete engulfment were given sufficient time during the evaporation process for the polymers to reach thermodynamic equilibrium. In this case, complete engulfment was the most stable thermodynamically, and the kinetic factors were minimized by slowing the rate of polymer precipitation. In the second scenario, the completely engulfed configuration was a transient intermediate in the progression from a non–phase separated system toward equilibrium, and the precipitation rate was manipulated such that the polymers were trapped in this configuration, thus allowing the formation of double-walled microspheres when not predicted by the modified Harkin's equation. Once the microspheres had hardened, they were filtered, washed with water, and freeze-dried in preparation for storage and further characterization by optical microscopy with or without cross-polarized light, ODM, TEM, FTIR spectroscopy and DSC.

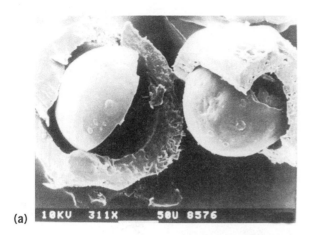
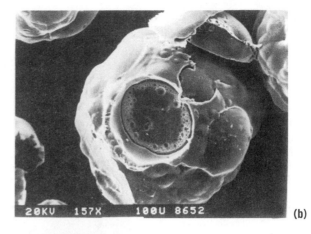

(a)

(b)

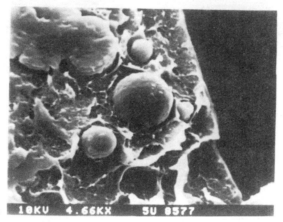

(c)

Figure 34. SEM of (**a**) double-walled microsphere; (**b**) multiphase microspheres; (**c**) higher magnification of the external layer in (**a**).

Optical microscopy proved to be a useful tool to study the microspheres as they were hardening. Cross-polarized light allowed the different polymers to be identified as they crystallized, and fluorescently labeled proteins aided in determining in which layer the protein has been trapped (84,101,162).

In a series of two papers (160,161) a more detailed description of the degradation of double-walled microspheres with a core of poly(CPP-SA) 20:80 and a coat of PLLA is given. The first paper presents the in vitro degradation, whereas the second paper discusses the in vivo degradation of these double-walled microspheres implanted subcutaneously and intramuscularly in rats. The second paper also correlates the degradation of the microspheres in the two environments, a critical step in the development of polymeric delivery systems for drugs or therapeutic proteins. Single polymer (SW) microspheres of PLLA, also made by solvent evaporation, were included in the study for comparison.

The general trends observed for double-walled microspheres of an inner core of poly(CPP-SA) 20:80 and outer layer of PLLA was that the inner core degraded first, becoming more granular in appearance as the polyanhydride broke down into short chain oligomers and then finally monomers. These monomers were insoluble in chloroform and were therefore not detectable by GPC or FTIR spec-

troscopy. DSC (Fig. 35) and SEM analyses of intact microspheres clearly showed their presence out to 6 months after being introduced to the buffer solution (161). The GPC data shows that the SW PLLA microspheres degraded significantly over the 6 months of in vitro degradation, despite the minimal morphologic changes seen by SEM. The PLLA of the double-walled microspheres degraded slightly faster than did the PLLA in the SW microspheres. At the early time points, the molecular weights of the two polymers could be calculated separately, showing that the poly(CPP-SA) 20:80 initially maintained a polymeric molecular weight, but after 2 weeks was no longer detectable.

FTIR also showed the disappearance of the anhydride bonds over the first two weeks of degradation (Fig. 36). DSC confirmed this, showing a decrease in size of the melting transition for the poly(CPP-SA) 20:80 polymer with the emergence of an intermediate peak due to the oligomers and monomers of the degraded polyanhydride. The SW PLLA microspheres remained dense and smooth in appearance throughout the study, and the FTIR spectra remained constant. The melting temperature of the PLLA decreased over the 6-month study due to the drop in molecular weight, which was confirmed by GPC.

Selected samples of the SW microspheres implanted subcutaneously were analyzed by SEM, and the micrographs are shown in Figure 37. After 1 week, the implant

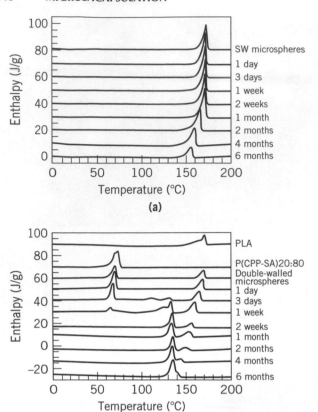

(a)

(b)

Figure 35. DSC thermogram of microspheres degraded in vitro. (a) SW PLLA and (b) Double-walled PLLA and poly(CPP-SA) 20:80. *Source:* With permission from Ref. 160.

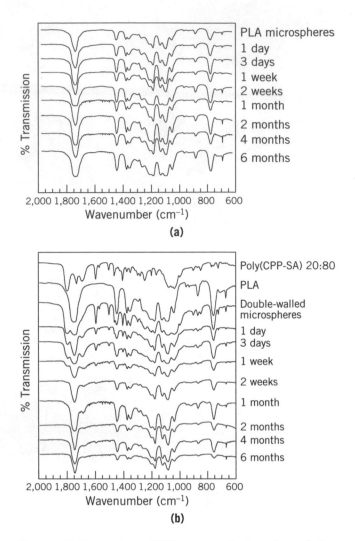

(a)

(b)

Figure 36. Transmission FTIR spectra of microspheres before and after in vitro degradation: (a) SW PLLA microspheres and (b) double-walled PLLA and poly(CPP-SA) 20:80. *Source:* With permission from Ref. 160.

site was slightly inflamed and the implant was filled with some excess fluid, resulting in a gap in the center of the implant seen after cross-sectioning (Fig. 37). This inflammation had cleared after 2 weeks. Even out to 6 months of degradation in vivo, the PLLA still appeared very dense. SW PLLA microspheres implanted intramuscularly degraded similarly to those implanted subcutaneously (data not shown).

Selected SEM micrographs of double-walled microspheres implanted subcutaneously are shown in Figure 38. Figure 38a shows the subcutaneous implant site after 1 week, revealing the empty center that was filled with fluid upon explantation. Higher magnification of the spheres after 1 week showed the degradation of the polyanhydride core (Fig. 38b). A higher magnification of the interface shows the differences in the rates of degradation of the two polymers (Fig. 38c). The PLLA coating was still relatively intact. After 1 and 6 months of degradation, the inner core continued to degrade and disappear, shrinking in size (Figures 38d, 38e, and 38f).

The degradation of the microspheres showed the same trends in vitro as in vivo. Microscopy showed no differences in the pattern or kinetics of the degradation. Physical characterization showed more differences between the degradation in vitro and in vivo, but the separate extraction step

required for the in vivo sampling may have skewed these results. The M_w of the microspheres degraded in vitro decreased faster than did the M_w of those degraded in vivo. In both cases and at all time points, the M_w of the double-walled microspheres was lower than that of the SW microspheres. FTIR spectroscopy and DSC analyses of the double-walled microspheres degraded in vivo identified PLLA as the only polymer present in the extracted sample at all time points. No differences were seen by these two methods between the samples degraded in vitro and in vivo.

Degradable, multilayered microspheres such as those described in this article could serve as complex delivery vehicles for therapeutic agents. The applications for such microspheres within the field of drug delivery are numerous, and a well-characterized degradation profile, both in vitro and in vivo, will aid in the development of a clinically useful delivery system.

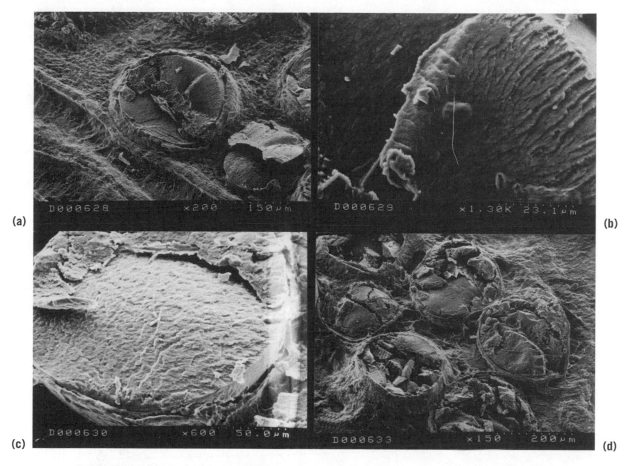

Figure 37. SEM of SW PLLA microspheres degraded at subcutaneous sites in vivo. (**a**) After 1 week, (**b**) higher magnification of interface after 1 week of degradation. (**c**) after 1 month, and (**d**) 6 months of degradation. *Source:* With permission from Ref. 161.

NOVEL ENCAPSULATION TECHNIQUES

One of the most interesting methods is being used for scale-up preparation of the injectable Prolease microsphere product, manufactured by Alkermes. The process is based on solvent extraction in nonaqueous solutions and, in addition, it is produced under cryogenic conditions. These two facts ensure high encapsulation efficiency of the drug while maintaining its integrity. A good review on the process, as well as approaches to scale it up, have been discussed by Tracy (164).

Mathiowitz et al. group has recently develop a new method to produce microspheres and nanospheres in the range of 0.2 to 30 μm, called the PIN (phase inversion microencapsulation) method (165). This process is based on the spontaneous formation of microspheres in an environment of a nonsolvent. Here the challenge is in developing oral delivery systems for proteins and genes, and the PIN system has been used to successfully deliver small molecules, insulin, and plasmid DNA by the oral route. The method is very gentle and thus the activities of very sensitive bioactive molecules and proteins such as IL-2 are not destroyed (166; N.K. Egilmez et al., unpublished data). Encapsulation of IL-2, PEG-modified IL-2 (PEG/IL-2), and interleukin-12 (IL-12) using the PIN technique resulted in

release of bioactive cytokines for up to one month in vitro (Y.S. Jong et al., unpublished data). The in vivo bioactivity of IL-2 released from PIN microspheres was demonstrated in a human tumor xenograft/SCID mouse model (166). Subcutaneous coinjection of IL-2 microspheres and tumor cells resulted in complete suppression of tumor engraftment in 80% of the animals. More recently, IL-12 releasing PIN microspheres were shown to be similarly effective in a mouse head and neck tumor model (M.A. Kuriakose et al., unpublished data) indicating the versatility of the PIN technique for functional encapsulation and release of different proteins.

APPLICATIONS OF MICROENCAPSULATION

With the vast array of encapsulation techniques currently available, nearly any active agent can be successfully incorporated into a microparticulate formulation. The limiting factors in applying these processes are imagination and, ultimately, cost. Encapsulation is a fairly standard practice in both the food, consumer product, and cosmetics industries. Flavors have been encapsulated since the 1930s, vitamins since the 1940s, and ink for carbonless paper since 1956 (167). The main purpose behind encap-

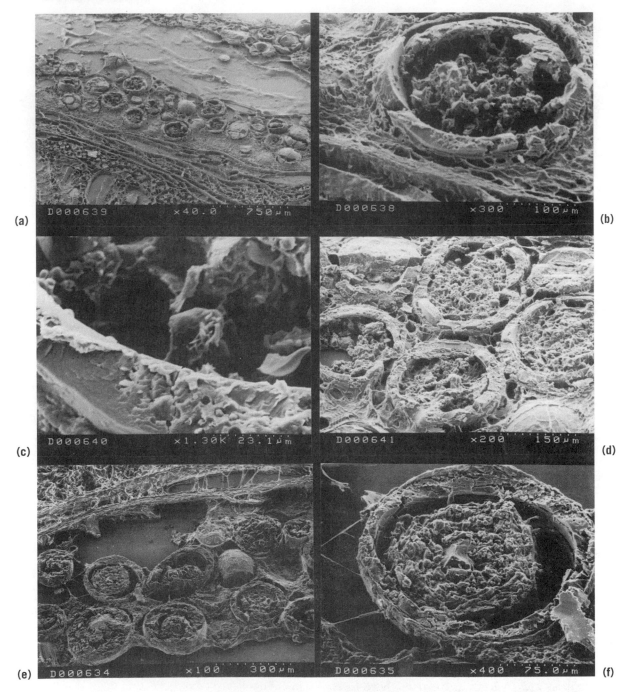

Figure 38. SEM of double-walled microspheres degraded subcutaneously in vivo. (**a**) After 1 week, showing gap in center of implant due to inflammation, (**b**) after 1 week, (**c**) higher magnification after 1 week of degradation, (**d**) after 1 month, (**e**) after 6 months, and (**f**) after 6 months of degradation. *Source:* With permission from Ref. 161.

sulating these materials was often for their protection and enhanced stability, as in foods and vitamins. The release of the active agent was triggered by drastic environmental changes in going from a dry to a wet environment or by physical trauma to the capsules in grinding or chewing. Encapsulated ink for carbonless paper is actually a triggered release device, where the trigger is the physical force that ruptures the capsule and releases the ink.

Encapsulation in the Food, Consumer Products, and Cosmetics Industries

For most products in the foods and consumer products industries, encapsulation must be accomplished on a very large scale and cannot add a significant cost to the product either in materials, processing, or labor. Even with these limiting factors, the majority of these products currently on the market have at least one component encapsulated. The most common techniques for encapsulating materials are spray-drying, extrusion, molecular inclusion, and coacervation (167). Of these, spray-drying and coacervation are true microencapsulation processes which have been discussed earlier in this article.

Spray-drying is often used to convert an oil or other liquid into a solid for easier handling and increased shelf life. This stability is dependent upon the wall materials used as well as the microcapsule porosity and the presence of any trace prooxidants or antioxidants. In general, spray-drying may be accomplished at a low cost and appropriate equipment is readily available. The resulting particles can be small and a variety of edible, soluble, and degradable wall materials may be used. Coacervation will usually give larger particles (20 μm and larger) and can also be made at a fairly low cost. A high loading can be achieved if the material to be encapsulated and the wall material are immiscible. Both liquids and solids have been encapsulated using coacervation with wall materials such as wax, protein, fat, carbohydrate, and gelatin.

Many of the same polymers used for pharmaceutical and medical applications are also used for cosmetic formulations, including polysaccharides, polypeptides, acrylates, and methacrylates (168). Most encapsulated ingredients in cosmetics products are in the nanoparticle size range. These nanoparticles usually contain cosmetic hydrophilic components which are designed to modulate the release in and onto the skin (169). Nanocapsules for cosmetic applications usually contain a lipophilic active substance which should be protected from the environment by encapsulation and release the active agent slowly over time. One of the key components in Lacome's Primordial is nanoencapsulated vitamin E.

Applications of Encapsulation for Agricultural Products

Encapsulated products with controlled release behavior can have significant advantages in the use of pesticides (59). Along with the traditional advantage of more constant release over extended periods of time, encapsulated pesticides can also show reduced mammalian toxicity, reduction of evaporative losses, and reduction in flammability of liquids. Most encapsulated pesticide materials are produced by interfacial polymerization or phase separation. The most widely used shell materials for interfacial polymerization are polyamides polyurea and polyurethane. For a variety of formulations, including Penncap M (encapsulated diazinon by Pennwalt), Penncaptrin (encapsulated permethrin by Pennwalt), Antifly (encapsulated pyrethrins by Kedem Chemicals), and Empire (encapsulated chlorpyriphos by Dow), the toxicity of the encapsulated material is no more than one-tenth that of the unencapsulated material with a longer efficacy and without a reduction in activity. The greatest advantage of the phase separation technique of encapsulation is the tremendous range of natural polymers, synthetic elastomers, and other synthetic polymers which may be used as the particle wall material. Markus has compiled a table of 46 different polymers that have been used in phase separation encapsulation and also provides examples of processes to encapsulate biological pesticides (59).

Applications and Opportunities for Encapsulation to Enhance Human Health

Although most of the current applications that have been realized using encapsulation are undoubtedly useful, they do not directly address the field of human health insofar as life-threatening conditions are concerned. Encapsulation has been used for decades for vitamins and other drugs, but only one product is currently on the market which uses microencapsulation to deliver a life-saving drug over 4 weeks. This is the Lupron Depot®, from Tap Pharmaceuticals, which contains leuprolide acetate, a LHRH agonist, gelatin, PLGA, and D-mannitol (135). This therapy results in inhibition of the growth of certain hormone dependent tumors.

Many of the formulations mentioned earlier in this article are being studied to treat the wide range of diseases and conditions which would respond well to controlled drug delivery. Other possible medical uses of encapsulation include artificial red blood cells, treatment of acute poisoning and kidney failure using encapsulated adsorbents and immunoadsorbents, encapsulation of living cells as well as encapsulation of enzymes for treatment of phenylketonuria, histidenemia, and other conditions (170). It is the hope of all working in this field that the Lupron Depot® is only a beginning and that medical science can embrace the opportunities that encapsulation can provide with the same enthusiasm that the consumer products and cosmetics fields have already shown.

BIBLIOGRAPHY

1. P. Becher, *Encyclopedia of Emulsion Technology*, Dekker, New York, 1983.

2. S. Cohen and H. Bernstein, *Microparticulate Systems for the Delivery of Proteins and Vaccines*, Marcel Dekker, New York, 1996.

3. C. Amiet-Charpentier, P. Gadille, B. Digat, and J.P. Benoit, *J. Microencapsul.* **15**, 639–659 (1998).

4. M.R. Baichwal and I.A. Abraham, *Indian J. Pharm. Sci.* **42**, 48–51 (1980).

5. J.A. Bakan and J.A. Anderson, in L. Lachman, H.A. Lieberman, and J.L. Kanig, eds., *Theory and Practice of Industrial Pharmacy*, Lea & Febiger, Philadelphia, 1976.

6. R.L. Broughton, F.V. Lamberti, and M.V. Sefton, *Proc. Int. Symp. Controlled Release Bioact. Mater.* **9**, 124 (1982).

7. R. Cadorniga, J.L. Lastres, and P. Frutos, *Boll. Chim. Farm.* **118**, 380 (1979).

8. P.B. Deasy, M.R. Brophy, B. Ecanow, and M.M. Joy, *J. Pharm. Pharmacol.* **32**, 15–20 (1980).

9. A.V. Deshpande and A.P. Njikam, *Indian J. Pharm.* **39**, 76 (1977).

10. D.L. Gardner and D.J. Fink, in E.S.E. Hafez and W.A.A. van Os, eds., *Biodegradable and Delivery Systems for Contraception*, MTP Press, Lancaster, England, 1980, Chapter 3.

11. A.A. Kassem and A.A. El-Sayed, *Bull. Fac. Pharm. Cairo Univ.* **12**, 77 (1975).

12. P.M. John, H. Minatoya, and F.J. Rosenberg, *J. Pharm. Sci.* **68**, 475 (1979).

13. A.P. Jarvis, Jr. and T.A. Gardina, *BioTechniques* **1**, 22 (1983).

14. L. Genc, M. Demirel, E. Guler, and N. Hegazy, *J. Microencapsul.* **15**, 45–53 (1998).

15. S.V. Lamberti, M.A. Wheatley, R.A. Evangelista, and M.V. Sefton, *Polym. Prepr.* **24**, 75 (1983).

16. T. Kato, R. Nemoto, H. Mori, and I. Kumagai, *Cancer (Philadelphia)* **46**, 14 (1980).

17. F. Lim, *J. Pharm. Sci.* **70**, 351 (1981).

18. M.L. Lorenzo-Lamosa, C. Remunan-Lopez, and M.J.A. Vila-Jato, *J. Controlled Release* **52**, 109–118 (1998).

19. F. Lim, *Biomedical Applications of Microencapsulation*, CRC Press, Boca Raton, Fla., 1984.

20. J. Lukaszczyk and P. Urbas, *J. Microencapsul.* **15**, 609–620 (1998).

21. L.A. Luzzi, *J. Pharm. Sci.* **56**, 634 (1967).

22. P.L. Madan, L.A. Luzzi, and J.C. Price, *J. Pharm. Sci.* **61**, 1586 (1972).

23. P.L. Madan, in T. Kondo, ed., *Microencapsulation: New Techniques and Applications*, Techno, Inc., Tokyo, 1979.

24. J.W. MiGinity, A.B. Combs, and A.N. Martin, *J. Pharm. Sci.* **64**, 889 (1975).

25. M.G. Moldenhauer and J.G. Nairn, *J. Controlled Release* **22**, 205–218 (1992).

26. S. Motycka and J.G. Nairn, *J. Pharm. Sci.* **68**, 211 (1979).

27. B.S. Nath, *Indian J. Pharm.* **35**, 26 (1973).

28. B.S. Nath, K. Satyanarayana, and K.N. Bao, *Indian J. Pharm.* **35**, 131 (1973).

29. N. Nihant, C. Grandfils, R. Jerome, and P. Teyssie, *J. Controlled Release* **35**, 117–125 (1995).

30. J.R. Nixon, ed., *Microencapsulation*, Dekker, New York, 1976.

31. J.R. Nixon, *J. Pharm. Sci.* **70**, 376 (1981).

32. M. Rabiskova and J. Valaskova, *J. Microencapsul.* **15**, 747–751 (1998).

33. D.A. Wood, T.L. Whateley, and A.T. Florence, *Int. J. Pharmacol.* **8**, 35 (1981).

34. G. Weiss et al., *J. Microencapsul.* **15**, 335–346 (1998).

35. A. Watanabe and T. Hayashi, in J.R. Nixon, ed., *Microencapsulation*, Dekker, New York, 1976, Chapter 2.

36. D. Vanichtanunkul, P. Vayumhasuwan, and U. Nimmannit, *J. Microencapsul.* **15**, 753–759 (1998).

37. M.I. Ugwoke and R. Kinget, *J. Microencapsul.* **15**, 273–281 (1998).

38. T. Dappert and C. Thies, *J. Membr. Sci.* **4**, 99 (1978).

39. C. Thies, *Polym.—Plast. Technol. Eng.* **5** (1975).

40. Y. Takeda, N. Nambu, and T. Nagai, *Chem. Pharm. Bull.* **29**, 264 (1981).

41. N.N. Salib, M.A. El-Menshawy, and A.A. Ismail, *Pharm. Ind.* **40**, 1230 (1978).

42. S.J. Risch and G.A. Reineccius, *Flavor Encapsulation*, American Chemical Society, Washington, D.C., 1988.

43. L. Brannon-Peppas, *Int. J. Pharm.* **116**, 1–9 (1995).

44. E. Mathiowitz and M.D. Cohen, *J. Membr. Sci.* **40**, 1–26 (1989).

45. E. Mathiowitz and M.D. Cohen, *J. Membr. Sci.* **40**, 27–41 (1989).

46. E. Mathiowitz and M.D. Cohen, *J. Membr. Sci.* **40**, 55–65 (1989).

47. E. Mathiowitz and M.D. Cohen, *J. Membr. Sci.* **40**, 67–86 (1989).

48. E. Mathiowitz and M.D. Cohen, *J. Membr. Sci.* **40**, 43–54 (1989).

49. T.M.S. Chang, *Artificial Cells*, Thomas, Springfield, Ill., 1972.

50. T. Kondo, in E. Matijevic, ed., *Surface and Colloid Science*, Plenum, New York, 1978, pp. 1–41.

51. A.F. Kydonieus, *Controlled Release Technologies: Methods, Theory, and Applications*, CRC Press, Boca Raton, Fla., 1980.

52. A. Kondo, *Microcapsule Processing and Technology*, Dekker, New York, 1979.

53. P.I. Lee and W.R. Good, *Controlled-Release Technology: Pharmaceutical Applications*, American Chemical Society, Washington, D.C., 1987.

54. A. Rolland, *Pharmaceutical Particulate Carriers: Therapeutic Applications*, Dekker, New York, 1993.

55. E. Mathiowitz and R. Langer, in M. Donbrow, ed., *Microcapsules and Nanoparticles in Medicine and Pharmacy*, CRC Press, Boca Raton, Fla., 1993, pp. 99–123.

56. S.S. Davis, L. Illum, J.G. McVie, and E. Tomlinson, *Microspheres and Drug Therapy*, Elsevier, New York, 1984.

57. G.R. Somerville and J.T. Goodwin, in A.F. Kydonieus, ed., *Controlled Release Technologies: Methods, Theory, and Applications*, CRS Press, Boca Raton, Fla., 1980, Chapter 8.

58. A. Markus, in S. Benita, ed., *Microencapsulation: Methods and Industrial Applications*, Dekker, New York, 1996, pp. 73–91.

59. A.R. Bachtsi and C. Kiparissides, *J. Controlled Release* **38**, 49–58 (1996).

60. S. Benita and M. Donbrow, *J. Colloid Interface Sci.* **77**, 102 (1980).

61. A.A. Kassem, A.A. Badawy, and A.A. El-Sayed, *Bull. Fac. Pharm. Cairo Univ.* **14**, 115 (1975).

62. S.A.H. Khalil, J.R. Nixon, and J.E. Carless, *J. Pharm. Pharmacoly* **20**, 215 (1968).

63. L.Y. Lim and S.C. Wan, *J. Microencapsul.* **15**, 319–333 (1998).

64. J.R. Nixon, S.A.H. Khalil, and J.E. Carless, *J. Pharm. Pharmacol.* **20**, 348 (1968).

65. R.E. Phares and G.J. Sperandio, *J. Pharm. Sci.* **53**, 515–518 (1964).

66. H. Takenaka, Y. Kawashima, and S.Y. Lin, *J. Pharm. Sci.* **69**, 513 (1980).

67. H.G. Bungenberg de Jong, in H.R. Kruyt, ed., *Colloid Science*, Elsevier, New York, 1949, Chapters 8 and 10.

68. L.W. Chan and P.W.S. Heng, *J. Microencapsul.* **15**, 409–420 (1998).

69. N.-H. Cho et al., *J. Controlled Release* **53**, 215–224 (1998).

70. M.C. Gohel et al., *J. Controlled Release* **45**, 265–271 (1997).

71. M.C. Gohel and A.F. Amin, *J. Controlled Release* **51**, 115–122 (1998).

72. B.-J. Lee, J.S. Choe, and C.-K. Kim, *J. Microencapsul.* **15**, 775–787 (1998).

73. M.C. Levy and F. Edwards-Levy, *J. Microencapsul.* **13**, 169–183 (1996).

74. L.-S. Liu et al., *J. Controlled Release* **43**, 65–74 (1996).

75. T. Uchida, K. Yoshida, and S. Goto, *J. Microencapsul.* **13**, 219–228 (1996).

76. E. Leo et al., *J. Microencapsul.* **15**, 421–430 (1998).

77. Z.G. Gao, K.H. Oh, and C.-K. Kim, *J. Microencapsul.* **15**, 75–83 (1998).

78. Y.-H. Cheng, L. Illum, and S.S. Davis, *J. Controlled Release* **55**, 203–212 (1998).

79. M.J. Blanco-Prieto et al., *J. Controlled Release* **43**, 81–87 (1997).

80. P. Benelli et al., *J. Microencapsul.* **15**, 431–443 (1998).

81. E. Mathiowitz and R. Langer, *J. Controlled Release* **5**, 13–22 (1987).

82. E. Mathiowitz et al., *J. Appl. Polym. Sci.* **35**, 755–774 (1988).

83. E. Mathiowitz, D. Kline, and R. Langer, *Scanning Microsc.* **4**, 329–340 (1990).

84. K. Pekarek, J. Jacob, and E. Mathiowitz, *Nature (London)* **367**, 258–260 (1994).

85. U.S. Pat. 5,611,344 (March 18, 1997), H. Benrstein, J. Straub, H. Brush, and R. Wing, (to Acusphere).

86. U.S. Pat. 5,853,698 (December 29, 1998), J. Straub, E. Mathiowitz, H. Bernstein, and H. Brush (to Acusphere).

87. U.S. Pat. 5,837,221 (July 29, 1996), H. Bernstein, J. Straub, H. Brush, and C. Church, (to Acusphere).

88. R.W. Baker and H.K. Lousdale, in A.C. Tanguary and R.E. Lacey, eds., *Controlled Release of Biologically Active Agents*, Plenum Press, New York, 1974, p. 15.

89. Y.W. Chien, in J.R. Robinson, ed., *Sustained and Controlled Release Drug Delivery Systems*, Dekker, New York, 1978, Chapter 4.

90. D.R. Paul in D.R. Paul and F.W. Harris, eds., *Controlled Release Polymeric Formulations*, American Chemical Society, Washington, D.C., 1976, Chapter 1.

91. T. Higuchi, *J. Pharm. Sci.* **52**, 1145 (1963).

92. A. Wade and P.J. Weller, *Hand Book of Pharmaceutical Excipients*, Pharmaceutical Press, London, 1994.

93. M.J. Schick, *Nonionic Surfactants: Physical Chemistry*, Dekker, New York, 1987.

94. J.T. Davies, *Proc. 2nd Int. Congr. Surf. Act.*, London, 1957, vol. 1, p. 426.

95. M.J. Schick, *Nonionic Surfactants*, Dekker, New York, 1989.

96. S. Geiger et al., *J. Controlled Release* **52**, 99–107 (1998).

97. P.J. Flory, *Principles of Polymer Chemistry*, Cornell University Press, Ithaca, N.Y., 1953.

98. A. Veis, *Biological Polyelectrolyles*, Dekker, New York, 1970.

99. J.Th.G. Overbeek and M.J. Voorn, *J. Cell. Comp. Physiol.* **49**, 7–26 (1957).

100. S. Torza and S.J. Mason, *J. Colloid Interface Sci.* **33**, 67–83 (1970).

101. K.J. Pekarek et al., *J. Controlled Release* **40**, 169–178 (1996).

102. H. Okada, Y. Ogawa, and T. Yashiki, *Prolonged Release Microcapsule and Its Production*, Tokyo, Takeda Chemical Industries, 1987, pp. 1–20.

103. Y. Ogawa et al., *Chem. Pharm. Bull.* **3**, 1095–1103 (1988).

104. H. Okada, T. Heya, Y. Ogawa, and T. Shimamoto, *J. Pharmacol. Exp. Ther.* **244**, 744–750 (1988).

105. H. Okada, Y. Doken, Y. Ogawa, and H. Toguchi, *Pharm. Res.* **11**, 1199–1203 (1994).

106. H. Okada, Y. Doken, Y. Ogawa, and H. Toguchi, *Pharm. Res.* **11**, 1143–1147 (1994).

107. D.T. Birnbaum et al., *Proc. Top. Conf. Biomater. Carriers Drug Delivery Scaffolds Tissue Eng.*, November 17–19, 1997, pp. 138–140.

108. D.T. Birnbaum, J.D. Kosmala, and L. Brannon-Peppas, *Polym. Prepr.* **38**, 600–601 (1997).

109. C. Schugens et al., *J. Controlled Release* **32**, 161–176 (1994).

110. W.I. Li, K.W. Anderson, R.C. Mehta, and P.P. DeLuca, *J. Controlled Release* **37**, 199–214 (1995).

111. T. Kidchob, S. Kimura, and Y. Imanishi, *J. Controlled Release* **54**, 283–292 (1998).

112. M.S. Reza and T.L. Whateley, *J. Microencapsul.* **15**, 789–801 (1998).

113. F.W. Okumu, J.L. Cleland, and R.T. Borchardt, *J. Controlled Release* **49**, 133–140 (1997).

114. A. Matsumoto et al., *J. Controlled Release* **48**, 19–27 (1997).

115. J.L. Cleland et al., *J. Controlled Release* **47**, 135–150 (1997).

116. H. Sah, *J. Controlled Release* **47**, 233–245 (1997).

117. W.W. Thompson, D.B. Anderson, and M.L. Heiman, *J. Controlled Release* **43**, 9–22 (1997).

118. R.V. Diaz et al., *J. Controlled Release* **43**, 59–64 (1997).

119. H. Rafati et al., *J. Controlled Release* **43**, 89–102 (1997).

120. C.X. Song, V. Labhasetwar, and R.J. Levy, *J. Controlled Release* **45**, 177–192 (1997).

121. N. Jager-Lezer et al., *J. Controlled Release* **45**, 1–13 (1997).

122. C. Laugel et al., *J. Controlled Release* **38**, 59–67 (1996).

123. W.-I. Li, K.W. Anderson, and P.P. DeLuca, *J. Controlled Release* **37**, 187–198 (1995).

124. S. Izumikawa, S. Yoshioka, Y. Aso, and Y. Takeda, *J. Controlled Release* **15**, 133–140 (1991).

125. U.S. Pat. 3,674,704 (July 4, 1972), R.G. Bayless, C.P. Shank, R. Botham, and D.W. Werkmeister.

126. P.L. Madan, *Drug. Dev. Ind. Pharm.* **4**, 95–116 (1978).

127. M. Donbrow, A. Hoffman, and S. Benita, *J. Microencapsul.* **7**, 1–15 (1990).

128. J.W. Beyger and J.G. Nairn, *J. Pharm. Sci.* **75**, 573–578 (1986).

129. S.P. Sanghvi and J.G. Nairn, *J. Pharm. Sci.* **80**, 394–398 (1991).

130. E. Klein and J.K. Smith, *Ind. Eng. Chem. Prod. Res. Dev.* **11**, 207–210 (1972).

131. A.S. Chawla and T.M.S. Chang, *J. Appl. Polym. Sci.* **19**, 1723–1730 (1975).

132. T.C. Shen and I. Cabasso, in R.B. Seymour, ed., *Macromolecular Solutions: Solvent-Property Relationships in Polymers*, Pergamon Press, New York, pp. 108–117.

133. D.H. Robinson, *Drug. Dev. Ind. Pharm.* **15**, 2597–2620 (1989).

134. B. Sa, A.K. Bandyopadhyay, and B.K. Gupta, *J. Microencapsul.* **13**, 207–218 (1996).

135. T.L. Whateley, in S. Benita, ed., *Microencapsulation: Methods and Industrial Applications*, Dekker, New York, 1996, pp. 349–375.

136. P.W. Morgan, *Condensation Polymers by Interfacial and Solution Methods*, Interscience, New York, 1965.

137. E. Mathiowitz, A. Raziel, M.D. Cohen, and E. Fischer, *J. Appl. Polym. Sci.* **26**, 809–822 (1981).

138. S.R. Jameela, T.V. Kumary, A.V. Lal, and A. Jayakrishnan, *J. Controlled Release* **52**, 17–24 (1998).

139. T. Modena et al., *J. Microencapsul.* **15**, 85–92 (1998).

140. B.A. Heelan and O.I. Corrigan, *J. Microencapsul.* **15**, 93–105 (1998).

141. J. Akbuga and N. Bergisadi, *J. Microencapsul.* **13**, 161–168 (1996).

142. N. Muramatsu and K. Nakauchi, *J. Microencapsul.* **15**, 715–723 (1998).

143. A.A. Al-Helw, A.A. Al-Angary, G.M. Mahrous, and M.M. Al-Dardari, *J. Microencapsul.* **15**, 373–382 (1998).

144. A. Berthold, K. Cremer, and J. Kreuter, *J. Controlled Release* **39**, 17–25 (1996).

145. K. Nilsson et al., *Nature (London)* **302**, 629 (1983).

146. E. Mathiowitz, P. Dor, C. Amato, and R. Langer, *Polymer* **35**, 547, 755 (1990).

147. T.W. Atkins, S.J. Peacock, and D.J. Yates, *J. Microencapsul.* **15**, 31–44 (1998).

148. R. Jeyanthi, B.C. Thanoo, R.C. Metha, and P.P. DeLuca, *J. Controlled Release* **38**, 235–244 (1996).

149. J. Bleich and B.W. Muller, *J. Microencapsul.* **13**, 131–139 (1996).

150. R. Falk et al., *J. Controlled Release* **44**, 77–85 (1997).

151. E. Mathiowitz et al., *J. Appl. Polym. Sci.* **45**, 125–134 (1992).

152. E. Mathiowitz, E. Ron, G. Mathiowitz, and R. Langer, *Macromolecules* **23**, 3212–3218 (1990).

153. E. Ron et al., *Macromolecules* **24**, 2278–2282 (1991).

154. M.R. Kreitz, Ph.D. Thesis, Brown University, Providence, R.I., 1999.

155. M. Luck et al., *J. Controlled Release* **55**, 107–120 (1998).

156. C. Witschi and E. Doelker, *J. Controlled Release* **51**, 327–341 (1998).

157. G.O. Fanger and J.E. Vandergaer, *Proc. 166th Annu. Meet. Am. Chem. Soc.*, Chicago, 1973.

158. E.S. Nuwayser et al., in G.I. Zatuchni, A. Goldsmith, J.D. Shelton and J.J. Sciarra, eds., *Long-Acting Contraceptive Delivery Systems*, Harper & Row, Philadelphia, 1984, pp. 64–76.

159. E.L. Parrot, *Pharmaceutical Technology*, Burgess, Minneapolis, Minn., 1970.

160. K. Leach-Pekarek, S. Takahashi, and E. Mathiowitz, *Biomaterials* **19**, 1981–1988 (1998).

161. J. Leach-Pekarek and E. Mathiowitz, *Biomaterials* **19**, 1973–1980 (1998).

162. K. Pekarek, J. Jacob, and E. Mathiowitz, *Adv. Mater.* **6**, 684–687 (1994).

163. W.D. Harkin, *The Physical Chemistry of Surface Films*, Reinhold, New York, 1952.

164. M. Tracy, *Biotechnol. Prog.* **14**, 108–115 (1998).

165. E. Mathiowitz et al., *Nature (London)* **386**, 410–416 (1997).

166. N.K. Egilmez et al., *Cancer Immunol. Immunother.* **46**, 21–24 (1998).

167. L. Brannon-Peppas, in M. El-Nakaly, D.M. Piatt, and B.A. Charpentier, eds., *Polymeric Delivery Systems, Properties and Applications*, American Chemical Society, Washington, D.C., 1993, pp. 42–52.

168. C.G. Gebelein, T.C. Cheng, and V.C. Yang, in C.G. Gebelein, T.C. Cheng, and V.C. Yang, eds., *Cosmetic and Pharmaceutical Applications of Polymers*, Plenum, New York, 1991, pp. 1–7.

169. S. Benita, M.-C. Martini, and M. Seiller, in S. Benita, ed., *Microencapsulation: Methods and Industrial Applications*, Dekker, New York, 1996, pp. 587–631.

170. *Physicians' Desk Reference*, Medical Economics Data Production Company, Montvale, N.J.; 1994, pp. 2385–2388.

See also COATINGS; LIPOSOMES; MICROENCAPSULATION FOR GENE DELIVERY; NANOPARTICLES.

MICROENCAPSULATION FOR GENE DELIVERY

ERIC KAI HUANG
YONG SHIK JONG
Brown University
Providence, Rhode Island

KEY WORDS

DNA vaccination
Gene therapy
Microencapsulation
Nonviral
Plasmid DNA
Polymer
Vector

OUTLINE

INTRODUCTION

Since Watson and Crick's determination of DNA structure, advances in molecular biology and recombinant DNA technologies have had an enormous impact on biological sciences. DNA-based diagnostics and recombinant pharmaceuticals have emerged as important additions to medical research and treatment methods. Gene therapy, however, has yet to provide similar tangible benefits. Nonetheless, it is often heralded as a panacea, the ultimate application of recombinant DNA research.

Gene therapy is based on the premise that a disease is the failed expression of a gene or expression of a defective one, which can be treated by the transfer of genes into specific cells of patients rather than through conventional pharmaceutical means. Gene transfer can be used to restore and/or supplement defective functions or interfere with the expression of aberrant genes. Currently, there are three categories of gene therapy (1). The ex vivo approach involves the removal of patient cells from the body, the transduction of these cells using an appropriate vector, and the subsequent return of the genetically altered cells to the patient. The in situ approach involves injecting the vector directly into the affected tissues. Finally, the in vivo approach uses the bloodstream to transport the vector to the affected tissues and/or cells.

Clinical success has been limited to genetic diseases caused by a single gene defect such as adenosine deaminase deficiency (2). However, advances in molecular biology are rapidly leading to the identification of defective genes and an increased understanding of the regulation of gene expression. Gene transfer constitutes the sine qua non of gene therapy. In fact, the application of human gene therapy is limited more by the lack of effective delivery methods for gene transfer. The December 1995 Report and Recommendations issued by NIH states that "Given the central role of vectors for delivering genes to somatic cells for therapeutic purposes, the Panel endorses *vigorous* and *expanded* research aimed at developing improved vectors" [our emphasis]. Thus, the development of both viral and nonviral gene transfer methods has come to the forefront of gene therapy research.

Viral-vector-mediated gene transfer makes use of the evolutionary advances by viruses to deliver genetic information into the cells they infect (3). Viral vectors are commonly recombinant animal viruses that contain exogenous information in their genome. They are usually replication-defective to prevent the occurrence of a pathological condition. There are four main types of viral vectors currently used in clinical trials: retrovirus, adenovirus, adeno-associated virus, and herpes-simplex virus (4). The advantages and disadvantages of each are described in Table 1. Generally viral vectors are more efficient than nonviral vectors, but do not have much in the way of capacity to deliver large expression cassettes (5). There is also the possibility of recombination into a replication-competent virus. However, viruses remain the most resourceful in entering cells and will probably be included in the next generation of hybrid vectors containing viral components expressly for this purpose. The basic scheme for viral transduction is as follows. An expression cassette is inserted into a replication-defective viral vector. This virus is inserted into a packaging cell, which produces all the necessary viral proteins necessary to package the virus. Target cells are then infected with these vectors (either in

vitro or in vivo), thus allowing the viruses to transmit the genetic information. What happens to the information then depends on the type of virus as well as the type of target cell.

Nonviral vectors rely on chemical or physical means to facilitate cellular uptake and intracellular transport of plasmid DNA without viral packaging (6). These vectors including liposomes, gene gun, ligand-mediated polylysine complexes, direct injection, and others. Table 2 summarizes the main nonviral vector approaches employed for gene therapy. These vectors contain plasmid DNA; circular double stranded DNA which exists extrachromosomally in bacteria. Nonviral vectors are considered to be more safe than viral vectors (no risk of infection or tumor formation), have no limit to the expression cassette size carried, and are easier to manufacture and purify (1). Their main drawbacks are low transfer efficiency and transient gene expression (7). With the exception of the gene gun, where adsorbed DNA can be shot directly into nucleus, nonviral vectors have generally been designed to enhance endosomal escape, cytoplasmic transport, and/or nuclear uptake of plasmid DNA. Strategies include inclusion of ligands for specific targeting, adenoviral attachment for endosomal escape, and other numerous modifications (8,9). However, it should be noted that some tissues have the intrinsic ability to internalize and express exogenous plasmid DNA. For example, in muscle tissue, the use of viral or chemical nonviral vectors to enhance gene transfer has been shown to be less efficient than injecting purified, plasmid DNA alone (10).

The goal of this article is not to present a review of all available viral and nonviral vectors. An excellent review by Nakanishi provides a comprehensive discussion of the various vector systems, both viral and nonviral, as well as their applications in human gene therapy (11). This article focuses on one specific emerging technology, vectors based on thermoplastic microencapsulation of plasmid DNA. A variety of polymers have been used for DNA delivery, including liposomes (DOTMA/DOPE), hydrogels (chitosan, alginate, poly[vinylpyrrolidone]), dendrimers (polyamidoamine), and water-soluble polymers (polylysine), which provides for either DNA condensation, charge neutralization, or binding/complexation (6,12–14). Some of these sys-

Table 1. Viral Vectors Used for Gene Therapy

Viral vector system	Advantages	Disadvantages
Retrovirus	Stable, long-term expression	Requires mitogenic cells for infection
	Can infect wide range of cell types	Small expression cassette (~9 kb)
		Possibility of insertional mutagenesis
		Difficult to concentrate/purify
Adenovirus	Can infect nondividing cells	Strongly immunogenic
	Capable of high expression levels	Small expression cassette (~7.5 kb)
	Easy to concentrate/purify	Significant risk of recombination into replication-competent
Adeno-associated virus	Can infect nondividing cells	Very small expression cassette (~5 kb)
	Does not cause any known human pathologies	Requires coinfection with helper virus
	Site-specific integration	System still not well characterized
Herpes-simplex virus	Ability to establish lifelong latent infections	Wild type virus is cytotoxic
	High titre stocks	Reactivation of wild-type virus is possible
	Large expression cassette capacity	High prevalence of seropositivity in general population

Table 2. Nonviral Vectors Used for Gene Therapy

Nonviral vector system	Advantages	Disadvantages
Cationic lipids and liposomes	Simple procedure Large expression cassette capacity Low immunogenicity/toxicity	Low transfection efficiency Transient expression Unstable complex formation Nonspecific targeting
Ligand-mediated polylysine complex	Specific targeting possible Low toxicity	Weak gene expression Low transfection efficiency May be immunogenic
Direct injection of DNA	No carrier molecules needed Minimum contaminants Low immunogenicity	Cannot be applied to cultured cells Low efficiency Transient expression Mechanism of entry not well-understood

tems are described in other articles. The particular vectors described in this article focus on the use of water-insoluble, thermoplastic, biodegradable polymers to encapsulate plasmid DNA. These polymers differ in that they do not interact with DNA (chemically or electrostatically) and serve simply to physically entrap DNA uniformly within a matrix structure. Once hydrated, plasmid DNA is released from the matrices in its "naked" form, via diffusion (through preexisting pores), which is enhanced by the actual hydrolytic degradation of the matrix itself (Fig. 1). The use of these types of systems has not been limited to plasmid DNA; whole viruses and oligonucleotides have also been successfully encapsulated within these polymer matrices for a number of different applications (15,16). However, the focus of this review is the use of these encapsulation systems specifically for applications in DNA vaccination.

BACKGROUND

DNA Vaccination

DNA vaccination can be defined as the induction of an immune response to antigen expression by cells in situ, following direct gene transfer of the antigen encoding DNA. Mechanistically, DNA vaccination is somewhat analogous

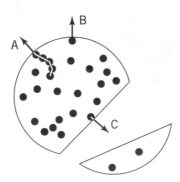

Figure 1. Macromolecule release from degrading matrix-type controlled release microsphere. (A) Diffusion of molecules from within the polymer matrix following the formation of interconnecting pores. (B) Diffusion of surface localized molecules. (C) Diffusion of molecules from within the polymer matrix following degradation of encapsulating polymer material.

to the use of live attenuated viral vaccines, as both result in intracellular production of antigenic proteins. However, it is inherently a subunit vaccine and the immune response is directed toward specific components instead of the whole virus. First, the antigen expressing plasmid DNA is administered into the host animal, most commonly via direct injection of the plasmid DNA in a buffer. Second, transfected cells begin expression of the antigen, which in some cases is actively secreted. Third, the host animal develops a specific immune response against the expressed antigen. Interest in DNA vaccination stems primarily from its ability to induce both cytotoxic T cell and antibody responses, with low DNA doses, for long periods of time (17,18). Antigens are produced de novo in its native form and thus compared to administration purified recombinant antigens, result in efficient presentation of both Class I and Class II major histocompatibility complex (MHC) (19). Moreover, DNA vaccination protocols require significantly less (up to 1,000-fold less) protein compared to the protein doses required for the more classical subunit vaccine approaches (20). Although there are some potential risks (tolerance, autoimmunity, integration), experimental studies to date indicate they are unlikely and the primary disadvantage appears to be the fact that DNA vaccination is limited to protein antigens.

Much of the work with DNA vaccination has focused on the use of direct injection of plasmid DNA. Direct injection of plasmid DNA was first demonstrated as a viable gene transfer technique in 1990 (21). This form of gene transfer uses purified bacterial DNA constructs without any additional chemical or biological agents, often referred to as naked DNA. Although transfection efficiencies are generally low, this technique has been used successfully in a number of different animal models. Subsequently, it was shown that direct gene transfer with plasmid DNA could provoke an immune response against the encoded protein antigen (19,22) heralding this revolutionary new approach to vaccine development. A number of excellent reviews have been written regarding DNA vaccination. Interested readers should access "The DNA Vaccine Web" by Robert Whalen (http://www.genweb.com/Dnavax/dnavax.html), which provides a comprehensive overview of DNA vaccination, including an extensive bibliography of related research and review articles.

Researchers have devised a number of strategies to improve the efficacy of DNA vaccination. The first involves the selection of the plasmid construct. In addition to the promoter, enhancer, and intron sequences, inclusion of palindromic single-stranded immunostimulatory sequences, specifically the unmethylated cytosine motif adjacent to a guanine residue (CpG) can dramatically upregulate the immune response (23). The same study demonstrated that the location of these sequences within the plasmid construct is important as well. It appears that these sequences increase the immune response through increased proliferation and cytokine release of B and T lymphocytes. The second is the selection of the inoculation site. Direct injection of plasmid DNA is most effective in muscle tissue both in terms of transfection efficiency and transgene expression. However, it has been demonstrated that other tissue such as the epidermis, which is much less permissive to direct injection vectors, can provide for more efficient vaccination (24,25). This apparent dichotomy has been attributed to the fact that the epidermis contains a rich population of specialized "professional" antigen presenting cells (APCs), that are absent in normal muscle tissue. In fact, it is thought that immune responses generated following intramuscular injection of DNA may be due primarily to APCs migrating into the injection site (26,27). It is important to note that the increased vaccine efficacy does not necessarily imply transfection of APCs themselves as it has been shown that transfected muscle cells can transfer antigens to APCs to trigger an immune response (28). The third strategy lies in the selection of the vector system. A number of vectors have been developed to increase transfection efficiency and provide alternative innoculation sites where naked plasmid DNA is ineffective (e.g., the oral route). The inoculation site is especially important as the type of immune response generated is modulated in part by the site of antigen exposure and lymphoid tissue targeted (29). Specialized vectors have been developed for intradermal, intranasal, intraperitoneal, and oral plasmid DNA delivery through the use of liposomes, gene guns, microbes, and cochleates (30) to increase the versatility of DNA vaccination protocols.

Microencapsulation for DNA Vaccination

The primary rationale for thermoplastic microencapsulation of plasmid DNA for DNA vaccination is based on the exploitation of two biological phenomenon, gastrointestinal (GI) tissue uptake and microsphere phagocytosis.

Although the extent of uptake remains somewhat controversial, particle uptake along the GI tract is an established biological phenomenon (31,32). It is thought that the uptake phenomenon is primarily due to a size effect; particles smaller than 10 μm in diameter can cross the GI barrier (33). The study of GI uptake of particles has focused on the possibility of targeting gut-associated lymphoid tissue or Peyer's patches known to be important in mounting the mucosal immune response (34,35). As delivery of purified unencapsulated antigens alone to this mucosal site is difficult, a major focus of GI uptake has been the development of effective oral vaccines. Thus, delivery systems have been designed to protect labile antigens from degradation within the harsh environment of the GI tract and to transport them across the "M" cell barrier for pre-

sentation to cells of the immune system (B cell follicular regions, interfollicular T cell zones, and APCs). Antigens derived from the simian immunodeficiency virus, influenza, staphylococcal enterotoxin, and others have been delivered orally via microsphere systems to generate both systemic and localized mucosal immunity (36).

Uptake can occur via paracellular as well as transcellular routes (37) and thus does not necessarily imply cellular internalization. In contrast, phagocytosis is defined as direct cellular internalization, a process primarily exhibited by antigen processing cells of the immune system such as macrophages and neutrophils. A form of endocytosis, phagocytosis refers specifically to internalization of soluble and insoluble macromolecules greater than 250 nm in size. The phagocytic capabilities of APCs are astounding, as it has been estimated that macrophages phagocytose 10^{11} senescent red blood cells on a daily basis. The intrinsic ability of APCs for phagocytosis of microspheres combined with their immunoregulatory function provides a potential passive targeting mechanism for efficient delivery therapeutic molecules to the immune system (38–40).

Advanced controlled release systems provides an alternative approach to the standard oral, intravenous, or intramuscular delivery of pharmaceutical agents. Controlled release systems have traditionally been designed to deliver drugs in a localized, prolonged manner through a sustained depot effect (41,42). These systems can be designed to locally administer drugs to any site in the body. Furthermore, in the case of labile drugs, they can provide protection from rapid in vivo degradation and more efficient dosing. Microencapsulation constitutes one approach for fabrication of matrix-based polymer controlled release systems in microsphere geometry. Microencapsulation of drugs within polymer materials can allow for control of the release rate and duration of delivery to enhance the pharmacokinetics of drugs compared with traditional dosage forms. A detailed review of microencapsulation and drug delivery is reviewed elsewhere in this encyclopedia.

Given that plasmid DNA degrades rapidly in vivo, on the order of minutes (43,44), controlled release systems designed for DNA delivery and gene transfer offer similar advantages. Most importantly for DNA vaccine applications, fabrication of these systems into small microsphere form offers the added possibility of targeting specific tissue; in the case of oral administration, the Peyer's patch, and for parental injections, the APCs. Conceptually, DNA would be released extracellulary within the Peyer's patch or the parental injection site upon administration. Internalization of DNA released from microspheres by adjacent cells is not thought to be facilitated and is assumed to follow the same pathway as direct injection of naked plasmid DNA. In the case where cells have successfully phagocytosed microspheres, DNA would be released intracellularly and serve to facilitate translocation of encapsulated DNA across the cellular membrane, the first barrier for naked plasmid DNA. It should be noted that although there are numerous reports of cytoplasmic internalization, there are no reports regarding nuclear internalization of microspheres. The two pathways are not mutually exclusive, as plasmid DNA release in these systems occurs immediately following hydration and is not specifically triggered to occur upon cytoplasmic entry.

FABRICATION TECHNIQUES

Physiochemical Properties of Plasmid DNA

Plasmid DNA exhibits a number of distinct physiochemical characteristics which present a number of challenges distinct from peptide or protein encapsulation (45). Plasmid DNA is an extremely large, negatively charged macromolecule with molecular weights in the millions of daltons; at least an order of magnitude higher than proteins. Moreover, plasmid DNA can exist in three different conformations (supercoiled, open circular, and linear), each with different hydrodynamic characteristics. Gene transfer is most effective with the supercoiled form (46,47) and thus delivery systems must optimize the encapsulation and release of this particular fraction. Although plasmids appear stable in organic solvents and are thermally stable (on the order of years), they are extremely sensitive to physical manipulation such as sonication, a processing step crucial for most microencapsulation techniques (48). In addition, aqueous DNA solutions are extremely viscous at relatively low concentrations, providing challenges for both loading and dispersion during the fabrication stage.

Manipulation of Plasmid DNA

Generally, fabrication steps involve (1) dispersion of plasmid DNA within the polymer solution, (2) formation of desired geometry, and (3) removal of solvent. The primary difficulty in encapsulation of DNA through traditional microencapsulation techniques is dispersion of DNA within the polymer matrix. Lyophilized solutions of DNA form macroaggregates, resembling a ball of cotton, which cannot be milled or otherwise physically micronized without shearing DNA strands. Although DNA can be spray-dried into particles (49), most techniques disperse DNA in solution to form an emulsion of DNA droplets dispersed in a continuous polymer–solvent phase. Once dispersed, techniques generally follow traditional "double emulsion" microencapsulation protocols designed for peptides and proteins. Formation of the initial emulsion has been achieved via vigorous vortex, homogenization, or sonication. A homogenous emulsion is critical for minimizing microsphere size distribution as well as reducing variability in drug loading (50). However, the principal limitation of this process stems from the physical sensitivity of DNA, which requires that both the duration and magnitude of agitation must be minimized (51). Thus an optimal emulsion, in terms of decreasing droplet size, is difficult to achieve. Although Adami et al. have reported that condensation of plasmid DNA with a peptide allowed for sonication at 100 W for up to 60 seconds, uncondensed, naked plasmid DNA was fragmented in less than 15 seconds (52).

Encapsulation Techniques for Plasmid DNA

A number of fabrication techniques have been used for encapsulation of plasmid DNA for various therapeutic applications (Table 3). However, only two techniques, solvent

Table 3. Fabrication Techniques for Plasmid DNA Encapsulation

Technique	Reference	Polymer
Solvent evaporation	53,54	PLGA
	40	PLGA
	55	PLGA
	56	PLGA
Phase inversion nanoencapsulation	37	P(FA:SA)
Heat extrusion	57	EVAc
Solvent cast coating	58	Proprietary
	59	PLGA

evaporation and phase inversion nanoencapsulation, have been used to fabricate microsphere formulations for DNA vaccination.

Solvent evaporation is one of the most common techniques used to produce matrix-type delivery systems in microsphere geometry (53,60). Briefly, the polymer is dissolved in an organic solvent is emulsified with the drug of choice in an aqueous solution to produce a dispersed phase of drug/water within a continuous phase of polymer/solvent. The emulsion is subsequently dripped into a stirred aqueous bath for removal of solvent. Due to the limited miscibility between the organic solvents used and the aqueous bath, solvent is gradually removed from the polymer matrix via evaporation over a period of hours.

Jones et al. first reported encapsulation of plasmid DNA in poly(lactide-co-glycolide) (PLGA) microspheres using solvent evaporation (53,54). Microspheres were reported as $1 \sim 2 \mu m$ in diameter with an encapsulation efficiency of 25%. The in vitro bioactivity of released plasmid DNA was determined to be 25% compared to unencapsulated plasmid controls using bacterial transformation assays and luciferase expression in tissue culture transfection assays. A second group reported using solvent evaporation for encapsulation of plasmid DNA in PLGA-based microspheres (40,51). The volume percent analysis of microsphere size indicated 85% of the microspheres were between 1.1 μm and 10 μm in diameter with a theoretical loading of 0.45% (w/w). In vitro coincubation of microspheres containing a luciferase reporter plasmid DNA with a macrophage cell (P388D1) resulted in engulfment and luciferase expression at 24 hours postengulfment, confirming release and bioactivity of the encapsulated plasmid DNA. The conformation of plasmids released from microspheres, as reported by both groups, showed that there was a partial conversion from supercoiled DNA to open circular DNA, which Hedley et al. attributed to the fabrications conditions during solvent evaporation.

Phase inversion nanoencapsulation (PIN) is a recently developed microencapsulation technique which has been used to encapsulated small drugs, proteins, and genes (37). In this method, nanosized microspheres are fabricated by the spontaneous phase inversion of dilute polymer solutions, which are then quickly dispersed into an excess of nonsolvent for the polymer. This method differs from existing methods of encapsulation in that no stirring or agitation of the nonsolvent bath is required. Most traditional microencapsulation techniques required the formation of a polymeric emulsion using stirrers, sonicators, air-jet, etc., and the final size of the particles is determined by the rate of stirring. In the PIN technique, as solvent leaves the polymer solution and enters the bulk nonsolvent phase, polymer instantaneously precipitates into the form of microspheres in what appears to be a self-assembling system.

A reporter plasmid DNA encapsulated into poly-(fumaric acid-co-sebacic acid) (P(FA:SA), 20:80, Mw 2k) microspheres (0.1 ~ 5.0 μm) via the PIN technique was reported by Mathiowitz et al. (37). Extraction analysis of microspheres following encapsulation showed a DNA loading of 0.1% (w/w) which retained a large fraction of the supercoiled form following fabrication (Fig. 2). Furthermore, in vitro release studies indicated that plasmid DNA was released from PIN microspheres in supercoiled and open circular conformation up to a period of 4 days.

IN VIVO APPLICATIONS

Microsphere Uptake and Gene Delivery

The feasibility of using microsphere uptake to deliver genes into the Peyer's patch for functional gene transfer was first demonstrated by Mathiowitz et al. (37). Using PIN, a reporter plasmid was encapsulated in microspheres composed of P(FA:SA). P(FA:SA) is an extremely bioadhesive polyanhydride that degrades rapidly via hydrolytic degradation (61). The authors selected P(FA:SA) upon the theory that increased bioadhesion can promote particle uptake in the gastrointestinal tract. In vivo light and transmission electron microscopy studies of GI tissue sections, following oral feeding of P(FA:SA) microspheres, indicated traversal of microspheres across both the mucosal epithelium and the follicle-associated epithelium covering the lymphatic elements of Peyer's patches (37).

Analysis of small intestinal tissue, five days after a single dose (50 mg microspheres encapsulating 50 μg pCMV/βgal) to rats, revealed functional expression of the encapsulated reporter gene product β-galactosidase. Whole tissue X-gal histological staining of the Peyer's patch areas revealed transfection of cells primarily in the serosal surface of Peyer's patch area. Control animals receiving a much higher dose (500 μg) of unencapsulated plasmid DNA

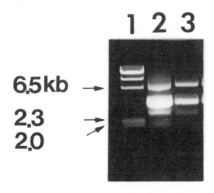

Figure 2. Agarose gel electrophoresis analysis of encapsulated pCMV/βgal plasmid DNA. (1) λ *Hind* III; (2) unencapsulated stock pCMV/βgal; (3) pCMV/βgal extracted from microspheres.

did not show any expression in the Peyer's patch. Analysis of frozen cross sections showed that the majority of transfected cells were located in the muscularis mucosae and the adventitia below the Peyer's patches. The general localization of transfected cells was consistent with previous observations using fluorescently tagged microspheres, which suggests that the serosal tissue layer acts as a sieve to trap appropriately sized microspheres that have passed through the mucosal barrier (62).

Microsphere-Based Oral DNA Vaccination

The efficacy of inducing an immune response, following oral administration of microspheres containing the antigen encoding plasmid DNA, was demonstrated by Jones et al. (53,54). Solvent evaporation was used to encapsulate luciferase reporter plasmid DNA in PLGA microspheres (~2 μm) and a 50 μg DNA dose fed to mice. Although neither luciferase expression nor PLGA uptake was evaluated, induction of luciferase specific serum IgA, IgG, and IgM responses were evident from 3 to 9 weeks following a single dose indicating successful gene transfer. A dose response study of 1, 5, 20, and 50 μg doses suggested increased titres with increasing dose. Interestingly, even the 1 μg dose was sufficient to induce the humoral response. Moreover, analysis of fecal extracts showed significant levels of IgA antibodies, which was detectable up to 16 weeks, illustrating that the oral route is effective in inducing mucosal as well as systemic immune responses.

In addition to oral administration (O), these same studies reported comparative data regarding delivery of encapsulated plasmid DNA via intramuscular (IM) and intraperitoneal (IP) injections. Analysis of serum IgG titres following a single dose (IP, IM, O) of 50 μg of encapsulated plasmid DNA indicated that the IP route provoked the strongest IgG response at both 3 and 6 weeks following administration. IP injections of unencapsulated small hepatitis B surface antigen plasmid DNA alone does not induce a cellular and humoral immune response (63) indicating improved transfection with microencapsulation at this site. In contrast, animals given the encapsulated plasmid DNA via O administration showed the highest levels of fecal IgA levels, reflecting the importance of the delivery site in modulating the immune response. In both IP and O administration, animals receiving the encapsulated plasmid DNA showed enhanced serum IgG levels compared to the unencapsulated naked DNA controls. Somewhat surprisingly, animals receiving naked unencapsulated plasmid DNA orally also developed specific IgG titres, albeit at lower levels. Although other reports indicated that direct oral administration of plasmid DNA was ineffective (64), this observation suggests the intriguing possibility that plasmid DNA may have some ability to bypass the enzymatic and mucosal barrier of the GI tract.

Microsphere-Based Parental DNA Vaccination

A parental DNA vaccine application based on microsphere phagocytosis has been reported by Hedley et al. (40). In an effort to target APCs in a parental inoculation site, a microsphere system was evaluated to enhance vaccination efficacy. The authors hypothesized that successful delivery of a single antigen expressing DNA construct could be more efficient than direct delivery of the synthetic antigen, as it has been shown previously that an APC expressing a peptide gene construct results in over 10,000 Class I MHC associated peptide molecules (65).

Using solvent evaporation, plasmid DNA was encapsulated in PLGA microspheres. Subsequently, plasmid DNA (VSV N_{52-59}) encoding for a peptide derived from the vesicular stomatitis virus (VSV), was encapsulated in PLGA microspheres (1.1~10 μm). Both intraperitoneal and subcutaneous immunization of mice with encapsulated VSV N_{52-59} plasmid DNA produced significant cytotoxic T lymphocyte (CTL) responses, which were more pronounced when compared with a subcutaneous injection of purified VSV N_{52-59} peptide alone. Moreover, comparison of intraperitoneal or subcutaneous injections of 2~5 μg VSV N_{52-59} plasmid DNA generated stronger CTL responses compared with an intramuscular injection of a much larger 200 μg of unencapsulated VSV N_{52-59} plasmid DNA. The increased immune response was attributed to decreased degradation of the administered plasmid DNA dose as well as increased uptake of plasmid DNA, via microsphere phagocytosis, by APCs.

CONCLUSION

At the time of this review, there are over 270 approved human gene transfer protocols approved by the Office of Recombinant DNA Activities (see website at http://www.nih.gov/od/orda/protocol.htm). Currently, the three major targets are infectious disease, monogenic disease, and cancer. Due to the diverse nature of these categories, there is most likely no "perfect" vector. The most effective vectors will need to be tailored to the disease. Application of gene therapy to target vaccine development has recently provided an alternative approach to vaccination. DNA vaccination is an entirely new area of research which will require specialized vector systems for optimal therapeutic efficacy. While still in the very early stages, with further development, microencapsulation techniques may find a niche for specific applications in DNA vaccination.

BIBLIOGRAPHY

1. W.F. Anderson, *Nature (London)* **392**(Suppl.), 25–30 (1998).
2. R.M. Blaese et al., *Science* **270**, 475–480 (1995).
3. W.H. Gunzburg and B. Salmons, *Mol. Med. Today* **1**(9), 410–417 (1995).
4. P.D. Robbins, H. Tahara, and S.C. Ghivizzani, *Trends Biotechnol.* **16**(1), 35–40 (1998).
5. P.C. Watt, M.P. Sawicki, and E.J. Passaro, *Am. J. Surg.* **165**(3), 350–354 (1993).
6. F.D. Ledley, *Hum. Gene Ther.* **6**, 1129–1144 (1995).
7. G. Romano, P.P. Claudio, H.E. Kaiser, and A. Giordano, *In Vivo* **12**(1), 59–67 (1998).
8. F.L. Cosset and S.J. Russell, *Gene Ther.* **3**(11), 946–956 (1996).
9. P. Yeh and M. Perricaudet, *FASEB J.* **11**(8), 615–623 (1997).
10. H.L. Davis et al., *Hum. Gene Ther.* **4**, 733–740 (1993).
11. M. Nakanishi, *Crit. Rev. Ther. Drug Carrier Syst.* **12**(4), 263–310 (1995).
12. R. Riessen et al., *Hum. Gene Ther.* **4**(6), 749–758 (1993).
13. K. Anwer et al., *Hum. Gene Ther.* **9**(5), 659–670 (1998).
14. R.J. Mumper, J. Wang, J.M. Claspell, and A.P. Rolland, *Proc. Int. Symp. Controlled Release Bioact. Mater.* **22**, 178–179 (1995).
15. S. Akhtar and K.J. Lewis, *J. Cell. Biochem.* **17E**(Suppl.), 205 (1993).
16. E.R. Edelman, M. Simons, M.G. Sirois, and R.D. Rosenberg, *Circ. Res.* **76**(2), 176–182 (1995).
17. J.B. Ulmer, J.J. Donnelly, and M.A. Liu, *Curr. Opin. Invest. Drugs* **2**(9), 983–989 (1993).
18. J.B. Ulmer et al., *Vaccine* **12**(16), 1541–1544 (1994).
19. J.B. Ulmer et al., *Science* **259**, 1745–1749 (1993).
20. S. Lu et al., *Virology* **209**, 147–154 (1995).
21. J.A. Wolff et al., *Science* **247**, 1465–1468 (1990).
22. D.C. Tang, M. Devit, and S.A. Johnston, *Nature (London)* **356**, 152–154 (1992).
23. Y. Sato et al., *Science* **273**, 352–354 (1996).
24. E.F. Fynan et al., *Proc. Nat. Acad. Sci. U.S.A.* **90**, 11478–11482 (1993).
25. I. Nakano et al., *J. Virol.* **71**, 7101–7109 (1997).
26. R.E. Spier, *Vaccine* **14**, 1285–1288 (1996).
27. M. Corr, D.J. Lee, D.A. Carson, and H. Tighe, *J. Exp. Med.* **184**, 1555–1560 (1996).
28. T.M. Fu et al., *Mol. Med.* **3**(6), 362–371 (1997).
29. N.F. Pierce and J.B. Kaper, *J. Immunol.* **124**, 307–311 (1980).
30. G. Gregoriadis, *Pharm. Res.* **15**(5), 661–670 (1988).
31. E. Sanders and C.T. Ashworth, *Exp. Cell Res.* **22**, 137–145 (1961).
32. A.T. Florence, *Pharm. Res.* **41**(12), 809–812 (1997).
33. J.H. Eldridge et al., *Adv. Exp. Med. Biol.* **251**, 191–202 (1989).
34. M.E. LeFevre and D.D. Joel, *Life Sci.* **21**(10), 1403–1408 (1977).
35. A. Florence and P.U. Jani, *Drug Saf.* **10**, 233–266 (1994).
36. N. Santiago, S. Haas, and R.A. Baughman, in M.F. Powell and M.J. Newman, eds., *Vaccine Design: The Subunit and Adjuvant Approach*, Plenum, New York, 1995, pp. 413–438.
37. E. Mathiowitz et al., *Nature (London)* **386**, 411–414 (1997).
38. Y. Tabata and Y. Ikada, *Adv. Polym. Sci.* **94**, 107–141 (1990).
39. C. Scheicher, M. Mehlig, H.P. Dienes, and K. Reske, *Eur. J. Immunol.* **25**, 1566–1572 (1995).
40. M.L. Hedley, J. Curley, and R. Urban, *Nat. Med.* **4**(3), 365–368 (1998).
41. R. Langer, *Science* **249**, 1527–1533 (1990).
42. R. Langer, *Nature (London)* **392**(Suppl.), 5–10 (1998).
43. M. Manthorpe et al., *Hum. Gene Ther.* **4**, 419–431 (1993).
44. D. Lew et al., *Hum. Gene Ther.* **6**, 553–564 (1995).
45. C.R. Middaugh, R.K. Evans, D.L. Montgomery, and D.R. Casimiro, *J. Pharm. Sci.* **87**(2), 130–146 (1998).
46. A.H. Wyllie and A.J. Strain, *Biochem. J.* **218**, 475–482 (1984).
47. J.A. Wolff et al., *Hum. Mol. Genet.* **1**(6), 363–369 (1992).
48. H.I. Elsner and E.B. Lindblad, *DNA* **8**, 679–701 (1989).
49. D.J. Freeman and R.W. Niven, *Pharm. Res.* **13**(2), 202–209 (1996).
50. R. Krishnamurthy and J.A. Lumpkin, *BioPharm*, January, pp. 32–36 (1998).
51. U.S. Pat. 5,783,567 (July 21, 1998). M.L. Hedley, J.M. Curley, and R.S. Langer (to Pangaea Pharmaceuticals, Inc.).
52. R.C. Adami et al., *J. Pharm. Sci.* **87**(6), 678–683 (1998).

53. D.H. Jones et al., *Vaccine* **15**(8), 814–817 (1997).

54. D.H. Jones, J.C.S. Clegg, and G.H. Farrar, *Dev. Biol. Stand.* **92**, 149–155 (1998).

55. D. Wang, D. Robinson, G. Kwon, and J. Samuel, *Keystone Symp. Mol. Cell. Biol.*, Keystone, Colo., January 19–25, 1998.

56. H. Cohen et al., *Proc. Int. Symp. Controlled Release Bioact. Mater.* **25**, 374–375 (1998).

57. Y.S. Jong et al., *J. Controlled Release* **47**, 123–134 (1997).

58. V. Labhasetwar et al., *J. Pharm. Sci.* **87**(11), 1347–1350 (1998).

59. V. Labhasetwar et al., *Proc. Int. Symp. Controlled Release Bioact. Mater.* **25**, 372–373 (1998).

60. L.R. Beck et al., *Fertil. Steril.* **31**(5), 545–551 (1979).

61. D.E. Chickering and E. Mathiowitz, *J. Controlled Release* **34**, 251–261 (1995).

62. P.U. Jani, G.W. Halbert, J. Langridge, and A.T. Florence, *J. Pharm. Pharmacol.* **42**, 821–826 (1990).

63. W. Bohm, T. Mertens, R. Schirmbeck, and J. Reimann, *Vaccine* **16**, 949–954 (1998).

64. E. Manickan, K.L. Karem, and B.T. Rouse, *Crit. Rev. Immunol.* **17**, 139–154 (1997).

65. L.C. Anton, J.W. Yewdell, and J.R. Bennink, *J. Immunol.* **158**, 2535–2542 (1997).

ADDITIONAL READING

M.T. Aguado, *Vaccine* **11**, 596–597 (1993).

T. Alexakis et al., *Appl. Biochem. Biotechnol.* **50**, 93–106 (1995).

J. Cohen, R.A. Siegel, and R. Langer, *J. Pharm. Sci.* **73**(8), 1034–1037 (1984).

S. Cohen, M.J. Alonso, and R. Langer, *Int. J. Technol. Assess. Health Care* **10**, 121–130 (1994).

J. Fang et al., *Proc. Nat. Acad. Sci. U.S.A.* **93**, 5753–5758 (1996).

M. Kanke et al., *Parenter. Sci. Technol.* **42**, 157–165 (1988).

T.J. Smith, *BioPharm*, April, pp. 54–55 (1994).

See also LIPOSOMES; POLYMERIC SYSTEMS FOR GENE DELIVERY, CHITOSAN AND PINC SYSTEMS.

MUCOSAL DRUG DELIVERY, BUCCAL

WENDY WEBBER
Brown University
Providence, Rhode Island

KEY WORDS

Biodegradable

Buccal mucosa

Epithelium

Local delivery

Peptides

Periodontal disease

PLGA

Sublingual delivery

Sublingual mucosa

Systemic circulation

OUTLINE

Although often thought of under the umbrella term of buccal delivery, drug delivery via the membranes of the oral cavity is traditionally divided into three categories: (*1*) buccal delivery, which infers drug administration through the lining of the cheek to the systemic circulation; (*2*) sublingual, the administration of drug via membranes of the floor of the mouth or the underside of the tongue to the systemic circulation; and (*3*) local delivery to the mouth, which involves treatment of conditions within the oral cavity by administration to the affected mucosal tissues. These sites for delivery differ in both structure and composition, as well as in degree of permeability and, therefore, also vary in their ability to retain a delivery device for a desired length of time. The following article provides a chronologically oriented overview of the various methods and technologies that exist or have been attempted in the utilization of the oral mucosae for applications in buccal delivery, sublingual delivery and local drug delivery to the mouth. Table 1 summarizes some of the specific drugs delivered to the oral mucosa.

THE STRUCTURE OF THE ORAL MUCOSAE

In general terms, the oral mucosae is made up of an outermost layer of stratified squamous epithelium, which is covered with mucus and consists of a stratum distendum, stratum filamentosum, stratum suprabasale, and a stratum basale. Below this lies a basal lamina, the lamina propria, and the submucosa (Fig. 1). The epithelium serves as the mechanical barrier that protects underlying tissues, whereas the lamina propria acts as a mechanical support and also carries the blood vessels and nerves. Some regions of the oral mucosa are keratinized, whereas others are not (Fig. 2). The nonkeratinized regions, such as buccal mucosa, are more permeable than the keratinized regions. This is due, to some extent, to the composition of intercellular lipids comprising the particular region. Whereas keratinized regions contain predominantly neutral lipids (ceramides), nonkeratinized areas are composed of a glycosyl ceramide that appears to be derived from membrane-coating granules that differ morphologically from the lamellate membrane-coating granules of keratinized tissue.

Table 1. Drugs Delivered via Oral Mucosae

Type of delivery	Drug	Reference	Year
Systemic, Buccal	Verapamil	Davis and Johnson (1)	1979
	Insulin	Ishida et al. (2)	1981
		Nagai (3)	1985
	Glyceryl trinitrate	Davis et al. (4)	1983
	Ketobemidone	Hansen et al. (5)	1991
	Diclofenac sodium	Cassidy et al. (6)	1993
	Buprenorphine	Guo (7)	1994
		McQuinn et al. (8)	1995
	Diltiazem	Ahuja et al. (9)	1995
	LHRH	Lee and Chien (10)	1995
	Testosterone	Kim et al. (11)	1995
	Nitroglycerin	Iga and Ogawa (12)	1996
	Progesterone	Voorspoels et al. (3)	1997
	Peptides	Veillard et al. (14)	1987
		Merkle et al. (15)	1986
		Harris and Robinson (16)	1990
Sublingual	Nitrates	Field (17)	1858
		Riseman et al. (18)	1958
		Pimlott and Addy (19)	1985
		Thadani and Lipicky (20)	1994
		Abrams (21)	1995
	Lidocaine	Bergman et al. (22)	1968
	Buprenorphine	Edge et al. (23)	1979
		Brewster et al. (24)	1981
	Temazepam	Russell et al. (25)	1988
Local	Lidocaine	Nagai and Konishi (26)	1987
	Prostaglandin	Nagai and Konishi (26)	1987
	Fluoride	Bottenberg et al. (27)	1991
	Miconazole nitrate	Reading et al. (28)	1981
		Bouckaert et al. (29)	1992
	Nystatin	Encarnacion and Chin (30)	1994
	Hydrocortisone	Fabregas and Garcia (31)	1995
	Chlorhexidine	Soh et al. (32)	1982
		Coventry and Newman (33)	1982
		Soskolne et al. (34)	1983
		Addy et al. (35)	1988
		Steinberg et al. (36)	1990
	Tetracycline	Goodson et al. (37)	1983
		Addy et al. (35)	1988
		Tonetti et al. (38)	1990
		Heijl et al. (39)	1991
		Baker et al. (40)	1988
		Minabe et al. (41)	1989
		Heller et al. (42)	1989
		Deasy et al. (43)	1989
		Eckles et al. (44)	1990
		Roskos et al. (45)	1995
		Maze et al. (46)	1995
		Webber et al. (unpublished data)	1997
	Metronidazole	Loesche et al. (47)	1987
		Addy et al. (36)	1988
	Doxycycline	Larsen (48)	1990
	Growth factors	Lynch et al. (49)	1991
	BMPs	Wozney (50)	1995
		Sigurdsson et al. (51)	1995

In general, it appears that the patterns of epithelial differentiation observed in the oral mucosa vary to produce a surface layer that sufficiently meets the demands placed upon that particular tissue (54,55). Furthermore, in dealing with drug delivery, the amount of a certain drug absorbed through the buccal mucosa are determined by many factors, including the pKa of the base, the rate of partition of the unionized form of the drug, the lipid–water partition coefficient of that particular drug, and lastly, on the pH of the solution (56).

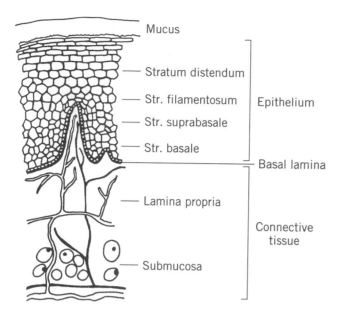

Figure 1. Schematic cross section through the oral mucosa showing the epithelium, basal lamina, and connective tissue. *Source:* From Ref. 52.

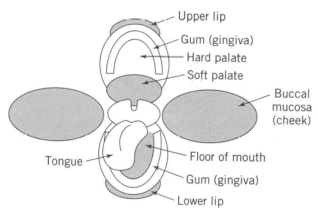

Figure 2. Schematic representation of the "open" oral cavity, showing keratinized (white) and nonkeratinized (shaded) regions of the mouth. *Source:* From Ref. 53.

DELIVERY TO THE SYSTEMIC CIRCULATION

Via Buccal Mucosa

Administration of a drug via the buccal mucosa (the lining of the cheek) to the systemic circulation is defined as buccal delivery. Though the buccal mucosa is significantly less permeable than the sublingual mucosa and usually not able to provide rapid drug absorption or good bioavailabilities, it is more permeable than skin and also boasts other advantages over alternative delivery routes. The fact that the buccal mucosa is less permeable than the sublingual makes it a more desirable site for sustained release delivery. The oral mucosa itself provides a protective covering for the underlying tissues, acting as a physical barrier against toxins and microorganisms. Patient compliance is high with buccal delivery due to the accessibility of the cheek lining and lack of invasive measures. In the case of an adverse reaction, administration of drug can be stopped at any time by device removal. Most importantly, however, drugs administered via the buccal mucosa directly enter the systemic circulation, thereby avoiding enzymatic degradation in the gastrointestinal tract as well as first-pass metabolism in the liver. Furthermore, peptides and proteins are not only susceptible to the acidic environment of the stomach, but they are generally high in molecular weight and are hydrophilic in nature, and therefore cannot permeate the intestinal mucosa as easily as they can the buccal tissues. For these reasons, buccal delivery is being researched with increasing intensity as a route of administration for the increasing number of peptide drugs currently on the market.

Applications in Buccal Delivery

Due to the buccal mucosae being more permeable than the skin, as well as the other advantages already mentioned, the buccal mucosae have been increasingly used as a route of drug delivery. Evidence of a biexponential absorption curve suggests that the buccal membrane can also act as a storage area for certain drugs before they are passed into the bloodstream. In studies by Davis and Johnston in 1979, in which occurrence of the antianginal agent verapamil in biological fluids and tissues was assayed fluorometrically, the buccal absorption of verapamil was found to occur in a biphasic manner (1). Despite this fact, interest in the buccal mucosa as a route for delivery led Ishida et al. in 1981 (2) to attempt to develop an oral dosage form that would solve the problem of insulin administration via injection. The system was a core of cacao butter, insulin, and additive surrounded by a layer of hydroxypropyl cellulose-H and Carbopol-934 (a polyacrylic acid) that adhered to the oral mucosa of beagle dogs for up to 6 hours. Furthermore, a decrease of blood sugar levels was maintained at over 70% for 3 hours. The amount of insulin absorbed in this manner, however, was found to be only 0.5% of the amount absorbed when given as an intramuscular insulin injection (2).

Release of glyceryl trinitrate from modified hydroxypropylmethylcellulose (Synchron) matrix tablets via the buccal route was accomplished in 1983 by Davis and his colleagues. The matrix tablets look like conventional tablets, but contain a drug that is entrapped in a slowly eroding, nondisintegrating Synchron and lactose base. The Synchron formulation showed sustained release of a model drug in excess of 3 hours, whereas normally dissolving tablets had completed release within 20 minutes (4).

Nagai et al. published a good deal of research in the 1980s, a portion of which was concerning oral mucosal adhesive tablets for the administration of insulin. They used a combination of hydroxypropylcellulose and Carbopol to prepare tablets that would turn into a gel-like substance in the swollen state. This gel would adhere firmly to the oral mucosa for extended periods of time, releasing the insulin in a controlled manner (26). The bioavailability was about 0.5% of that observed in intramuscular administration in dogs, but has recently been improved to 0.75% by using Witepsol® as the core base in place of cocoa butter (57). The adhesive tablets were then developed into a system releasing triamcinolone acetonide ointment to treat aphthous stomatitis. The product, Aftach®, is a small, thin, double-layered tablet and is now commercially available (3). The upper layer consists of lactose and serves as a supporting layer; the triamcinolone acetonide is dispersed in the lower lydroxypropylcellulose and Carbopol 934 adhesive layer (57).

Ketobemidone is a powerful narcotic analgesic that is traditionally administered perorally or rectally and, therefore, has a low and variable bioavailability. In 1991, Hansen et al. began studies in which they synthesized various carboxylic acid and carbonate esters of ketobemidone. The goal was to improve the bioavailability of the drug by using the buccal approach. However, due to the limited lipophilicity of the compound, the drug did not permeate the oral mucosa. To improve penetration of the drug across the oral mucosa, Hansen and her colleagues developed more lipophilic prodrugs of ketobemidone, which are converted back to the active parent drug during or after absorption across the mucosa (5). The esters synthesized were, in fact, found to have increased lipophilicity over the parent drug and are potentially more capable of crossing the buccal mucosal barrier.

Buccal delivery of the nonsteroidal antiinflammatory drug diclofenac sodium (Voltaren) from a hydrogel disk was studied in humans by Cassidy et al. (6). The 1-cm^2 hydrogel disks were formulated with 80 wt% hydroxyethyl methacrylate and 20 wt% hydrophobic difunctional macromolecular cross-linker. A 50 wt % solution of diclofenac sodium in 85.5% (v/v) methanol:water was loaded into the dry disks over a period of 48 hours. Patients had the hydrogel device affixed to their buccal mucosa for 4 hours, and blood samples were taken at regular intervals for diclofenac sodium quantification. Results were compared with intravenous infusion of the drug into the same patients for 4 hours at 3 mg/hour. The study demonstrated that diclofenac was readily transported across the buccal mucosa, with a steady-state flux of 2.1 mg/cm^2-hr. (6).

Carbopol 934, polyisobutylene (PIB), and polyisoprene (PIP) formed by a two-roll milling process and loaded with buprenorphine was formulated for controlled drug delivery by researchers at 3M Pharmaceuticals. Guo noted that the surface properties of the buccal patches were dependent upon the Carbopol 934 content as well as the existing polymeric ratio. Polymer patches with higher Carbopol content, or higher PIB:PIP ratios, had higher water uptake capacity, which led to increased swelling and more buprenorphine release (7). The analgesic buprenorphine was delivered safely and effectively over a 12-hour period to the upper gum or lip from these thin, noneroding, ethylcellulose-backed, mucoadhesive polymeric disks. However, this period only accounted for release of 15% of the drug load, which indicates that an extended application time could result in prolonged buprenorphine release. Evaluation of the 3M Transmucosal Drug Delivery System was discussed by Benes et al. in the June 1995 3M Delivery newsletter. Results demonstrated that the 3M system, named CYDOT®, is also comfortable and acceptable to the wearer of the device (58). Pharmacologically relevant serum concentrations of buprenorphine were attained using these devices and sustained for 12–24 hours in humans in 1995 (8). Greater drug delivery was achieved from patches applied to the gum rather than the lip, most likely because of the superior mucoadhesion present at this site.

In 1995, it was reported by Ahuja et al. that diltiazem, a calcium channel blocker commonly used in the treatment of cardiovascular disorders, could be formulated into polymeric buccal tablets that achieved up to an 86% in vitro release of the diltiazem obtained from a dissolution study after 4 hours. The multilayered tablets were comprised of a cap layer of Carbopol 934 combined with either hydroxypropyl cellulose, hydroxypropylmethyl cellulose, or poly(vinyl pyrrolidone) compressed using a die punch set around an already compressed core of drug. In vitro release data was compiled using bovine cheek pouch membrane in a Franz diffusion cell (9).

Lee and Chien developed a method of controlling transmucosal delivery of luteinizing hormone-releasing hormone (LHRH) from a bilayer system composed of a fast-releasing layer containing a polypyrrolidone (PVP (K-30)) and a sustained-release layer formulated from Carbopol 934 and PVP (K-90). The delivery device also contains an enhancer, sodium cholate, which promotes the transmucosal permeation of LHRH and a stabilizer, cetylpyridinium chloride, which stabilizes LHRH from degradation by the oral microflora. Simulation of the system in vivo involves adhering the film to the alveolar mucosa, with the other side facing the buccal mucosa in a specially designed device holder. Results demonstrated a burst release of LHRH from the fast-release layer, thereby providing a rapid delivery of the hormone, and a prolonged release of LHRH from the sustained-release layer. Therefore, varying the formulation of the device can result in modulation in the rate of LHRH transmucosal permeation (10).

Buccal delivery of testosterone was achieved in 1995 by Kim et al. The buccal matrix was comprised primarily of a blend of water-soluble polymers that melt near body temperature. Testosterone (T) was dispersed in the polymer matrix. When introduced into the buccal cavity, the polymer matrix melts and disperses within 5 minutes, exposing mucosal tissues to the testosterone. A single 10-mg transbuccal dose of the testosterone was found to induce a prompt rise in testosterone levels in the serum as well as dihydrotestosterone (DHT) concentrations. Furthermore, the method of administration was associated with a more normal DHT:T ratio than other preparations. The serum testosterone levels remained elevated above baseline for 24 hours. Therefore, transbuccal delivery of testosterone seems promising due to its simplicity, acceptability, reversibility, lack of toxicity, and protection from hepatic first-pass metabolism (11).

Two types of sustained release buccal dosage forms were prepared by Iga and Ogawa for nitroglycerin and isosorbide dinitrate (12). One device is a slowly disintegrating plain tablet, whereas the other is a slowly disintegrating polyethylene film-covered tablet, which has a single hole on the top surface through which disintegration and drug release can occur. The plain tablets disintegrated in 3–6 hours, whereas the film-covered tablets resulted in an almost constant plasma drug level for both drugs for over 10 hours until the tablet was removed. The tablets achieved almost complete bioavailabilities for both nitroglycerin and isosorbide dinitrate, which is in contrast to the near negligible bioavailabilities achieved when delivering these drugs orally, indicating that this type of sustained release buccal dosage form could be of importance in increasing the bioavailabilities of rapidly eliminating drugs and prolonging their absorption times (12).

The buccal delivery possibilities of progesterone were investigated in 1997 by Voorspoels et al. using a slow release degradable bioadhesive tablet in dogs. The bioadhesive tablet consisted of micronized progesterone, drum-dried waxy maize starch, Carbopol 974P, and sodium stearylfumarate compressed into a tablet. The tablet was placed above the right upper canine in the oral cavity. Delivery of progesterone involves release of the drug from the bioadhesive tablet, which is erosion controlled, followed by dissolution of the progesterone into the saliva, and finally, absorption of the drug into the buccal mucosa. The mean residence time of the drug was measured as well as the absolute bioavailability. Results indicated that buccal delivery may be useful, as mean residence time was dramatically improved by the administration of a bioadhesive tablet compared with intravenous formulations (13).

Applications in Peptides. Due to the emergence of peptides as a major class of future drugs, the buccal epithelium is being closely scrutinized as a possible route of peptide delivery. Initial studies of peptide absorption and permeability through the buccal mucosa were performed by Veillard et al., and preliminary results showed that although a higher drug dosage was administered via the buccal route than intravenously, corresponding plasma levels were much lower from buccal delivery than by direct intravenous injection (14). Therefore, penetration enhancers may be needed to achieve the desired activity when using the buccal route for peptide delivery.

Further studies on peptide delivery by Merkle and his colleagues in 1986 closely followed those by Veillard. Hydroxyethylcellulose patches containing the tripeptide protirelin and backed with an impermeable laminate were designed as buccal patches (15). Protirelin has a molecular weight of 362 and was readily absorbed across the buccal mucosa, as shown by increases in pituitary thyrotropin and prolactin levels, whereas calcitonin with a molecular weight of 3,500 could not permeate the buccal mucosa at all. However, after 30 minutes of contact with the mucosa between 48% and 72% of the protirelin was still found in the patches, indicating that a large portion of the drug was unable to be absorbed within this short contact time. This was most likely due to the high viscosity of the polymer, as much more drug was released when a lower viscosity polymer was used.

Via Sublingual Mucosa

Sublingual delivery traditionally involves systemic administration of drug via membranes of the floor of the mouth or the ventral surfaces of the tongue. The sublingual mucosa is relatively permeable due to the thin membrane and large veins, allows rapid absorption and acceptable bioavailabilities of many drugs, and is a convenient and easily accessible location. Furthermore, the sublingual mucosa is a smooth surface, not furred like the top of the tongue, and is free of mucus and undigested food, unlike the stomach.

Applications in Sublingual Delivery

The history of sublingual delivery dates back to 1858 when A. G. Field first realized that nitroglycerin dropped on the tongue was readily absorbed through the membranes (17). But it was not until a century later that Riseman et al. noted that many nitrates are highly effective in treating patients with angina pectoris when administered from either hypodermic injection, inunction, buccally or sublingually. Of the six nitrates tested to treat angina pectoris, including nitroglycerin, erythrol tetranitrate, pentaerythritol tetranitrate, mannitol hexanitrate, triethenolamine trinitrate, and sodium nitrate, the erythrol tetranitrate administered buccally or sublingually had the greatest prophylactic impact (18). However, it appears that the prolonged duration of action of the tablets may be due to their prolonged duration of tablet dissolution, directly leading to a prolonged period of absorption into the bloodstream. Therefore, another study by the group was undertaken to determine if, in fact, the prolonged dissolution time was essential for the prolonged therapeutic effect, as well as to assess the effect of varying the dosage of the erythrol tetranitrate. Results showed that the erythrol tetranitrate is absorbed more rapidly and uniformly from the sublingual route than from the buccal pouch. However, the prolonged beneficial effects of erythrol tetranitrate are not dependent upon prolonged absorption. The effects are long lasting even following sublingual administration of erythrol tetranitrate with rapid dissolution time (59).

Research in 1985 by Pimlott and Addy measured the absorption of isosorbide dinitrate (ISDN) into the systemic circulation after application of tablets to the buccal, palatal, and sublingual mucosal sites. For the buccal and sublingual sites, maximum plasma levels of ISDN were achieved at 5 minutes, after which levels fall gradually. Concentrations of ISDN were about 1.2 ng/mL after 30 minutes from either the sublingual or buccal route. On the other hand, plasma levels of ISDN were undetectable at all times from the palatal mucosa (19).

Another study involving oral nitrate treatment for patients with angina pectoris was completed by Thadani and Lipicky in 1994. It is currently accepted that intermittent use of short-acting oral nitrates used to terminate an attack of angina as well as provide prophylaxis for anticipated activity, and intermittent use of long-acting oral nitrates to provide prophylaxis for anticipated activity are both valid and successful therapies. However, tolerance presents a problem in limiting multiple dosing regimens of most oral long-acting nitrates and continual prophylaxis has not yet been achieved by any long-acting oral nitrate. Here, nitroglycerin spray and sublingual tablets of isosorbide dinitrate were used to successfully relieve an established attack of angina, and infrequent use of such substances is not associated with the development of tolerance (20).

Studies evaluating the use of sublingual buprenorphine in patients following surgery and comparing its effects with intramuscularly administered morphine were done by Edge et al. in 1979. Each patient received either a tablet of 0.4 mg buprenorphine and an injection of 5% dextrose in 1 mL, or a dummy tablet and an injection of 10 mg morphine in 1 mL. A pain "score" was obtained from the patients by means of a visual linear analog. Results indicated a slower onset of action by the buprenorphine, but a much longer duration than the morphine (23).

Temazepam is one of the shorter acting membranes of the 1,4 benzodiazepine group of drugs that is commonly prescribed for short-term therapy for adult insomnia. The pharmacokinetics of a new 10 mg sublingual temazepam tablet were compared with the currently marketed 10 mg oral gelatin capsule by Russell et al. in 1988 (25). Evidence shows the sublingual formulation to have a 98.4% bioavailability relative to the oral capsule, and the mean maximum plasma concentrations were similar. Therefore, it seems that the sublingual tablet is an acceptable alternative to the currently used oral capsule.

Although most sublingual delivery is accomplished via mouthwashes, oral sprays, or topical gels, controlled release tablets are currently being investigated as the most promising future technology for delivery drug sublingually.

LOCAL DELIVERY TO THE MOUTH

The classification of local delivery to the mouth includes any system that is applied to the oral mucous membranes in order to treat conditions of the mouth such as periodontal disease, gingivitis, oral candidiasis, and other chronic lesions or topical fungal infections. Traditional methods of delivery to the diseased site have involved chewing gums, mouthwashes, ointments, and gels. However, these methods share a common disadvantage in that they all have relatively short residence times and, therefore, fail to maintain therapeutic concentrations long enough to affect the bacterial population. Furthermore, drug is lost in the saliva (i.e., with swallowing), and patients on these treatments often have low patient compliance due to the need for frequent drug application. Current technology, however, is attempting to prolong residence time and increase patient compliance by using sustained release drug delivery systems.

Applications in Local Delivery

One of the earlier controlled release products to go through clinical trials was the Orabase system by Kutscher et al. composed of a finely ground pectin, gelatin, and carboxymethyl cellulose in a polyethylene–mineral oil gel base. This vehicle, in which therapeutics could be incorporated, has the ability to adhere to the site of application without causing any deleterious effects on the underlying tissue. Results varied with duration of maintenance ranging anywhere between 15 and 152 minutes, depending on the site in the oral cavity to which the device was adhered (60).

A device by Nagai et al. similar to that described earlier to deliver insulin systematically was also fabricated of hydroxypropyl cellulose and Carbopol, yet loaded with lidocaine for the local treatment of toothache. Unfortunately, lidocaine was not absorbed and remained in the dosage form for up to 6 hours. Nagai and Konishi, known for their work in the buccal delivery field, also formulated an adhesive gingival plaster that is loaded with prostaglandin $F_{2-\alpha}$ for the facilitation of tooth movement in the orthodontic process (26). A minimum of 70% of the drug load was released within the first 6 hours. In vivo studies in monkeys showed that application of the plaster to the gingiva did, in fact, accelerate tooth movement and, therefore, decrease movement time.

Bottenberg and his colleagues researched the possibility of using various bioadhesive polymers as fluoride-containing, slow-release tablets for oral use, specifically in the war against dental caries. Modified starch, poly(acrylic acid) (PAA), poly(ethylene glycol) (PEG) and sodium carboxymethylcellulose were the bioadhesive polymers investigated. A modified maize starch tablet containing 5% (w/w) PAA and PEG with a 300,000-dalton molecular weight proved to be the most successful formulation. Two formulations were then tested in vivo, including a drum-dried waxy maize and a PEG. Tablets were placed on the attached gingiva in the upper canine region, held for 30 seconds, and then moistened with the tongue. After insertion of the tablets, saliva samples were taken at regular intervals. In vivo, fluoride levels between 150 and 1,000 μg/mL were maintained for up to 8 hours, which is significantly longer than levels obtained with the administration of 4 times the amount of fluoride in a fluoride toothpaste. A patent for the application of modified starch as a bioadhesive slow-release drug carrier was applied for in 1991 (27).

A miconazole-loaded oral gel was tested in a study by Reading et al. for its efficacy against erythema, plaques, and perlèche in children with oral candidiasis. After one week, the gel boasted a 100% clinical cure rate for both plaques and perlèche. It showed a 97% cure rate for erythema (28). Buccal gels loaded with miconazole nitrate are also used for the treatment of topical fungal infections such as oral candidiasis. These gels are traditionally applied several times a day. Immediately following each application, the salivary miconazole nitrate concentration is at its maximum and then is rapidly cleared from the oral cavity. In an effort to prolong residence time of the drug, Bouckaert et al. formulated a bioadhesive tablet of modified starch and 5% PAA. Although a drug amount sixfold lower than that existing in the gel was released from the tablet, the salivary miconazole nitrate concentrations produced by the tablet were higher than by the gel and remained at a therapeutic level for over 10 hours. In vivo, a mean adhesion time of the tablet to the mucosa was in excess of 9.5 hours. The polymer tablets eventually eroded completely, and none had to be removed due to irritation to the mucosa. Furthermore, erosion seems to play an important role in the drug release rate from these systems. Although further investigation is required, variability in drug level appears to be due to tablet erosion by soft tissue movements and the individual movement patterns occurring within the mouth (29).

Mucosal Oral Therapeutic System (MOTS) is a controlled nystatin-releasing osmotic system based on an osmotic technique for delivering highly water-soluble or insoluble drugs that was developed by Encarnacion and Chin at the Alza Corporation in California (31). Nystatin is an antibiotic that exerts both a fungistatic and fungicidal effect for the treatment of oral candidiasis. Salivary concentrations of nystatin produced by the MOTS exceeded those produced by a nystatin pastille for all time points beyond 30 minutes. Release continued for at least 2 hours. The higher sustained concentration produced by the MOTS would hopefully decrease the duration of therapy and thereby increase patient compliance.

Buccoadhesive matrix tablets have also been used for delivery of hydrocortisone hemisuccinate in the treatment of aphthous stomatitis and other gingival ulcers. The polymers used included hydroxypropylcellulose, hydroxypropylmethycellulose, polycarbophil, and modified maize starch. The maize starch formulation, which proved to have the optimal gingival tolerance, was found to deliver hydrocortisone in vitro for up to 24 hours, dissolve, and eventually result in the complete erosion of the tablet (31).

Local Delivery to Treat Dental Disease. Much of the local delivery research is geared toward the treatment of periodontal disease and gingivitis. Periodontal disease is a disease of the supporting structures of the teeth, namely the periodontal ligament, cementum, alveolar bone, and the tissue components of the gingiva (see Fig. 1). Abundant evidence implicates the microorganisms in the dental plaque as the primary causative agent of various forms of periodontal disease. In fact, there exists a strong correlation between the presence and amount of plaque and calculus on the teeth and the severity of disease. When microflora are allowed to build up in the moist, warm, anaerobic, ecologically ideal environment of the sulcus, the bacteria proliferate and produce an excess of enzymes and toxins that diffuse through the gum epithelium and cause inflammation. This condition, known as gingivitis, leads to an increase in polymorphonuclear neutrophil (PMN) migration into the sulcus. The PMNs destroy bacteria but also release enzymes, such as collagenase, that cause the breakdown of collagen. The sulcus deepens, forming a periodontal pocket into which plaque can migrate. Plaque then colonize the cementum, causing it to break down. Macrophages invade to fight the infection, releasing interleukin I, a substance inducing osteoclast stimulation, which in turn leads to bone resorption. Alveolar bone resorption hallmarks the breakdown of the structural support system and leads to eventual tooth loss (61).

A healthy periodontal situation appears to be associated with a primarily facultative gram-positive organism located almost entirely supragingivally on the tooth's surface. Normally, the host's defense mechanisms, including saliva, crevicular fluid, and PMNs, provide the necessary protection to the dentogingival area. The constant contact between saliva and the oral mucosa serves as a flushing action, ridding the mouth of excess bacteria. Saliva also contains substances that not only interfere with bacterial adhesion and growth, but actually phagocytose the bacteria. The crevicular fluid is formed in the gingival connective tissue as a result of extraction from the microcirculation, then unidirectionally flushes through the tissues and

junctional epithelium into the gingival crevice. The flushing action serves to minimize bacterial colonization of the crevice and increases in relation to the level of inflammation in the gingival tissues. The crevicular fluid also contains protective components such as complement proteins, antibodies, and nonspecific opsonins. Many bacteria harbored in the gingival crevice turn on the host's immune response, activating the complement cascade (61). PMNs are also thought to play an integral role in the protection of the gingival tissues from bacteria. When plaque builds up in the gingival sulcus, the PMNs provide a barrier by preventing direct contact between the bacteria and the epithelial cells. PMNs in the gingival sulcus proceed to phagocytose the bacteria, in an effort to save the tissues from bacterial attack (62). Therefore, the onset of gingivitis and periodontal disease occurs when the bacterial composition of the mouth is imbalanced and plaque growth is allowed to flourish. Due to the fact that the primary cause of these dental diseases is bacterial overgrowth, antibiotics are frequently used in their treatment. Common local microbial therapies evaluated include chlorhexidine, tetracycline, and metronidazole.

A study in 1982 by Soh et al. investigated the effect of direct application of chlorhexidine to periodontal pockets (32). After 28 days it was found that chlorhexidine treatment had significantly reduced periodontal inflammation, whereas further deterioration had occurred in the placebo cases.

In an effort to prolong residence time of chlorhexidine in the periodontal pocket, Coventry and Newman in 1982 attempted the slow release of 20% chlorhexidine gluconate from Cuprophan (cellulose-based) hollow fiber dialysis tubing inserted in the periodontal pocket. The tubing had been loaded with the drug solution via capillary action, heat sealed, and then cut to a length suitable for the periodontal pocket. The devices were retrieved after only one week, at which time significant reduction in disease manifestations were noted (33).

In 1983, Soskolne et al. examined release kinetics of chlorhexidine from two formulations of sustained release devices, including a faster-releasing ethyl cellulose system or a slower-releasing ethyl cellulose–PEG system. Data confirmed the kinetics of chlorhexidine release in vivo to be diffusion controlled, as expressed by the Higuchi model. The effects of the drug on the bacterial flora within the periodontal pockets was also noted. Data shows release of up to 80% of the chlorhexidine within 3 days from the fast release devices, whereas the slow release devices had a release of about 50% of the drug after 6 days. The microbial floral content was examined in 16 pockets from 6 patients. All chlorhexidine-treated pockets had a decreased relative amount of motile rods and spirochetes, as well as a corresponding increase in nonmotile organisms in comparison with the placebo-treated pockets and to the flora present prior to chlorhexidine treatment (34).

A partially cross-linked soluble Byco protein, obtained from Croda Colloids in England, was used for the sustained release of chlorhexidine in 1990. Steinberg et al. found that the release kinetics of the degradable films were affected by the chlorhexidine loading, the cross-link density of the polymer, and the particular chlorhexidine salt used (36). Highly cross-linked films exhibited antibacterial activity for over 24 days, whereas low cross-linked films maintained therapeutic levels for only 10 days. This was an improvement over earlier versions, such as the degradable films made of hydroxypropylcellulose in 1988. All of the drug from these films was released within 24 hours (63).

In 1990, Larsen prepared some acrylic strips as described by Addy et al. (35) to examine release of doxycycline in vitro from three other bioabsorbable materials to compare with release from the acrylic strips. The bioabsorbable materials used were a hemostatic gauze made of oxidized regenerated cellulose, a collagen wound dressing, and a fibrin sealant. Results indicated that only the hemostatic gauze and the fibrin sealant may be capable of prolonged doxycycline release in vivo due to the rapid dissolution of the other devices or low levels of concentration and residual activity remaining in these devices after only a few days (48).

Controlled release of another antibiotic, tetracycline, was attempted by Goodson et al. in 1983 from monolithic fibers of various polymeric compositions for use in periodontal therapy. Fibers made of polyethylene, polypropylene, polycaprolactone, polyurethane, and cellulose acetate released 100% of their drug load within the first 24 hours. Ethylene vinyl acetate fibers, however, achieved sustained release of tetracycline for up to 9 days (37). The monolithic fibers were prepared by the melt extrusion process, in which 25% tetracycline and 75% ethylene vinyl acetate was heated to 214°C and extruded as a 0.5 mm fiber. Goodson and his colleagues continued the research to find, in 1985, that these monolithic fibers released 57% of the drug into the periodontal pocket within the first 9 days. Furthermore, immediately following treatment, the total bacterial counts (spirochetes, motile rods, and nonmotile rods) were significantly reduced in the periodontal pockets (64). This research went one step further when the team declared the release of drug into the periodontal pocket from these fibers to be zero-order. This can be explained by the structure of the device. The fiber delivery system is composed of a polymeric matrix loaded with tetracycline hydrochloride powder. After extrusion, some of the tetracycline crystallites end up on the fiber surface. Upon device insertion into the periodontal pocket, the crystallites dissolve, forming pores on the surface. In turn, these pores allow solvation of deeper particles, resulting in zero-order drug delivery (38). This contrasts with the nonlinear release pattern of the fiber observed previously in vitro by Goodson et al. (37). In addition, fiber therapy alone was determined to be more effective than scaling alone, based on the degree of elimination of causative bacteria, amount of reduction in total viable counts, degree of elimination of bleeding on probing, and the amount of reduction in gingival index. It was, however, shown that combining scaling and fiber therapy is the most effective treatment (39).

In vitro studies by Baker et al. in 1988 used tetracycline-loaded biodegradable microparticles prepared by solvent evaporation with between 5 and 30 wt% of drug and suspended in a carrier gel to accomplish release of up to 3 days. The prepared formulation was injected into the periodontal pocket via syringe and needle. Such in vitro results typically correspond to about 10 or more days of release in vivo considering the low rate of crevicular fluid exchange within the periodontal pocket (40). Although nonbiodegradable polymers tried in this microparticle formulation included polysulfone, polystyrene, and polycarbonate, the biodegradable polymer of choice was a lactic acid–glycolic acid copolymer that tends to degrade in 4–12 weeks in an aqueous environment. Patents were obtained by Baker in both 1988 and 1990 (patent numbers 4,780,320 and 4,919,939, respectively) for these formulations of drug-containing microparticles suspended in a fluid carrier medium for the treatment of periodontal disease. The poly(lactide-co-glycolide) (PLGA) system was found to deliver tetracycline for a period of 25 hours, although the authors estimate this to be the equivalent of up to 10 to 20 days of release in vivo (65,66).

Investigators Minabe et al. in 1989 administered cross-linked processed collagenic film preparations loaded with tetracycline to the periodontal pocket to halt excessive growth of periodontopathogenic bacteria. They found that they could control the amount of drug release somewhat by adjusting the original drug loading and the time of the cross-link process. It was also found that an amount of drug exceeding the therapeutic dose was present in the gingival crevicular fluid of the periodontal pocket for up to 10 days postinsertion (41).

An intracrevicular application of 40% tetracycline HCl in a white petrolatum carrier gel was compared to scaling and root planing by Eckles et al. (44) in the treatment of periodontitis. Results indicated that biologically effective tetracycline was released from the gel into the gingival crevicular fluid for at least 3 days. Posttreatment analysis indicated that reduced probing pocket depths and bleeding on probing relative to baseline measurements remained for 8–12 weeks. Reduced percentages of spirochetes and motile rods, as well as the increase in cocci that accompanies this phenomenon, lasted for 2–8 weeks (44). However, similar effects seen in scaled and root-planed sites lasted longer and, therefore, led to the conclusion that the subgingival application of tetracycline cannot replace conventional treatment methods, but only supplement them.

A new type of poly(ortho ester) was prepared by Heller et al. in 1989 by the condensation of a triol and an alkyl ortho ester. This reaction produces a viscous paste at room temperature, despite molecular weights in excess of 50,000 daltons. This is beneficial for mixing in therapeutic agents without using solvents, as well as for application into the periodontal pocket. Furthermore, such materials may be useful in drug delivery because rates of release can be altered by adding small amounts of basic or acidic excipients to the polymer (42). For example, the system was loaded with tetracycline and injected into periodontal pockets using a blunt needle. Complete release occurred within 24 hours. However, when 0.5 wt% of the basic excipient $Mg(OH)_2$ was incorporated into the polymer, release was extended to about 10 days (45). This was based on the knowledge that poly(ortho esters) contain a pH-sensitive linkage in their backbone. Therefore, hydrolysis of the polymer chain can be sped up by the addition of acidic excipients to the environment, or retarded by the incorporation of basic excipients.

Deasy et al. delivered tetracycline hydrochloride or metronidazole from degradable polyhydroxybutyric acid strips for the treatment of periodontal disease. The system components were physically mixed using a mortar and pestle, then aliquots of the mixture were compressed under 106 kg cm^{-2} of force into strips 0.5 mm in thickness. In vitro studies were performed in simulated gingival fluid and revealed that increasing the loading of tetracycline resulted in increased drug release, whereas at a constant drug loading of 25%, metronidazole was released much faster. In vivo, the strips loaded with tetracycline produced the greatest results. The strips were inserted into periodontal pockets at 4-day intervals for 16 days, reducing the plaque index, gingival index, and pocket depths significantly when compared with untreated controls. The microflora of the treated pockets was altered favorably, increasing the proportion of cocci and decreasing the numbers of gram-negative rods, fusiforms, and spirochetes. Unfortunately, the clinical improvements resulting from the treatment were not maintained upon the conclusion of the treatment (43).

In 1995, Maze et al. achieved 10-day controlled release of tetracycline hydrochloride from biodegradable PLGA film strips in periodontitis patients. Films were prepared by film casting a dispersion of the antibiotic in a 85:15 solution of the polymer dissolved in methylene chloride. All films were γ-irradiated and secured in the periodontal pockets via a suture/cement technique. Results indicated that film-treated pockets caused significant probe depth reduction for 26 weeks, a clinical attachment level gain for 12 weeks, lower percentages of spirochetes for 4 weeks, decreased levels of motile rods for 8 weeks, and a corresponding increase in cocci levels for 4 weeks. Furthermore, when compared with scaling and root planing, the films appear to have an enhanced antibacterial effect (46).

Webber et al., in 1997, successfully modulated the release of tetracycline from degradable PLGA films to achieve release over a 30-day period. The incorporation of soluble salt excipients in the polymer films changed the release kinetics of the system dramatically. The classical triphasic PLGA release curve involving the initial release due to diffusion of the drug, a lag phase, and then the second release due to degradation of the polymer is no longer apparent. Instead, the salt-loaded systems achieve continuous release of drug for 30 days. Figure 3 depicts the release curves for the five experimental systems. All of the films were fabricated via the solvent casting technique using 1 g of PLGA polymer (Boehringer Ingelheim, Resomer RG503, lot #223808, M_r = 34,000) dissolved in 1 mL of methylene chloride (Fisher Scientific) per film. The films contained either 0% (control films), 1%, 5%, or 25% loadings (w/w) of sodium chloride that was predissolved in 200 μL of distilled water and sonicated into the polymer solution. One system contained a blend of 75% PLGA (Boehringer Ingelheim, Resomer RG503, lot #223808, M_r = 34,000) and 25% PLGA (Polysciences, lot #85761, M_r = 5,000) as well as 25% NaCl. All systems also contained a 5% loading (w/w) of tetracycline HCl also predissolved in 100 μL of distilled water and sonicated into the polymer solution.

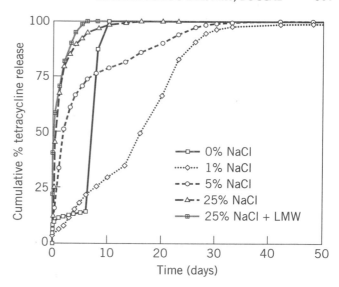

Figure 3. Comparison of tetracycline release from PLGA solvent cast films loaded with different amount of NaCl. *Source:* W. Webber, unpublished data.

This approach to modulating release of therapeutics from the PLGA matrix was unique in that the degradation of the polymer was not altered during the process of modulation. Figures 4 and 5 show degradation trends as monitored by gel permeation chromatography readings of molecular weight and differential scanning calorimetry measurements of glass-transition temperatures, respectively. In both cases, the salt-loaded films degrade at the same rate as the control (or 0% NaCl) film. Therefore, mod-

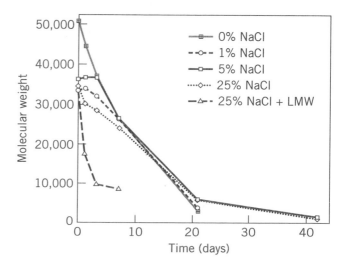

Figure 4. A measure of molecular weight of the various PLGA systems over time as measured by gel permeation chromatography. The similar decreasing trend in the control and salt-loaded systems shows that the salt is not speeding up the degradation process. The last system containing some low molecular weight polymer, however, does decrease in molecular weight faster than the other systems. In this case, the low molecular weight excipient is acting as a plasticizer and speeding up the polymer degradation. *Source:* W. Webber, unpublished data.

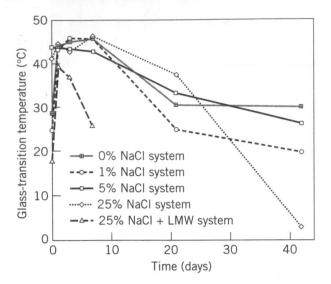

Figure 5. A measure of glass-transition temperature of the various PLGA systems over time as measured by differential scanning calorimetry. Again, the similar decreasing trend in the control and salt-loaded systems shows that the salt is not speeding up the degradation process. The last system containing some low molecular weight polymer, however, does decrease in molecular weight faster than the other systems. These results correlate well with the molecular weight data seen in Figure 4. *Source:* W. Webber et al., unpublished data.

ulation of tetracycline release is most likely caused by pore formation occurring where the salt particles are located. Further experimentation has shown that the systems are swelling and the water is being trapped within the polymer matrix, causing the tetracycline to be released at a constant rate for an extended period of time (W. Webber et al., unpublished data).

Studies by Loesche et al. in 1987 evaluated ethylcellulose films containing 20% metronidazole for their ability to reduce the proportionate levels of spirochetes in periodontal pockets. Though the films were brittle and unable to remain fixed within the pocket, they did succeed in reducing levels of plaque and spirochetes. It was also found that the use of films over a one-week period in conjunction with scaling and root planing had more of an impact clinically than the use of scaling and root planing alone (47).

Release of three antimicrobials, including chlorhexidine, tetracycline, and metronidazole, occurred from acrylic resin vehicles in which the drugs were polymerized into the acrylic strips and placed into periodontal pockets. Strips were changed on a weekly basis over a period of 14 weeks (35). All drug treatments produced immediate improvements based on reduced bleeding, reduced crevicular fluid flow, increased percentage of cocci, and decreased total motiles in comparison with the control groups. The study showed that sole use of antimicrobial drugs could achieve results similar to those reached by conventional mechanical debridement techniques, but the combination of root planing followed by metronidazole strip treatment appeared to be the most effective.

Polypeptide growth factors are an important class of potent biologic mediators which have recently been found to significantly enhance regeneration of both hard and soft tissue components of the periodontium. Studies by Lynch et al. demonstrate the effectiveness of short-term application of a combination of platelet-derived growth factor B (PDGF-B) and insulin-like growth factor one (IGF-1) on periodontal attachment apparatus formation during the early phases of postsurgical wound healing (67). Following conventional periodontal surgery in 13 beagle dogs, a methylcellulose gel containing a combination of 3 μg of recombinant PDGF-B and IGF-1 was applied. More than 96% of the protein was cleared by 96 hours, and none of it could be detected at 2 weeks postapplication. However, histological analyses at 2 and 5 weeks revealed 5 to 10-fold increases in new bone and cementum in the treated sites compared with the control sites (49).

Bone morphogenetic proteins (BMPs) represent a unique family of proteins that induce new bone formation at the site of implantation without affecting the growth rate of preexisting bone. Studies show that recombinant human BMP-2 (rhBMP-2) induces ectopic bone formation in vivo and can cause mesenchymal precursor cells to differentiate into cartilage- and bone-forming cells in vitro (50). RhBMP-2 has been tried and proven to repair bony defects in animal models of bone loss due to periodontal disease. Sigurdsson et al. suggest that implantation of a rhBMP-2 containing device not only regenerates original alveolar bone height, but also additional periodontal attachment apparatus. In Sigurdsson's research, defects were treated with polypropylene-reinforced expanded poly(tetrafluoro ethylene) membranes. The membranes are supposed to maintain the necessary space required for successful reconstruction of periodontal architecture. Histologically, the membrane-treated defects showed significant alveolar bone and cementum regeneration as well as some periodontal ligament fibers forming between the new bone and cementum. Supraalveolar defects treated with rhBMP-2 revealed bone and cementum regeneration to average 95% and 40% of the defect height, respectively, whereas control defects achieved only 20% and 10%, respectively. Therefore, the space provision membranes offer a significant, natural potential for bone and cementum regeneration, whereas the rhBMP-2 filler offers an unlimited regeneration potential for alveolar bone and a noteworthy regeneration potential for cementum (51).

Due to its high permeability, natural protective barrier against toxins and microorganisms, and high patient treatment compliance, the oral mucosal tissues have been the site of delivery for a variety of drugs in numerous therapies. Controlled release from polymeric systems allows for increased device residence time and therefore achieves longer delivery of drug. Although more immediate delivery of substances is possible through the sublingual mucosa, buccal mucosa is permeable to larger molecular weight species such as peptides and proteins and has the potential for achieving sustained delivery for up to many weeks.

BIBLIOGRAPHY

1. B.J. Davis and A. Johnston, *Br. J. Clin. Pharmacol.* **7**, 434–435 (1979).

2. M. Ishida, Y. Machida, N. Nambu, and T. Nagai, *Chem. Pharm. Bull.* **29**, 810–816 (1981).

3. T. Nagai, *J. Controlled Release* **2**, 121–134 (1985).

4. S.S. Davis et al., *Adv. Pharmacother.* **1**, 17–25 (1983).

5. L.B. Hansen, L.L. Christrup, and H. Bundgaard, *Acta Pharm. Nord.* **3**, 77–82 (1991).

6. J. Cassidy et al., *Pharm. Res.* **10**, 126–129 (1993).

7. J.-H. Guo, *J. Pharm. Pharmacol.* **46**, 647–650 (1994).

8. R.L. McQuinn et al., *J. Controlled Release* **34**(3BR273), 243–250 (1995).

9. A. Ahuja, M. Dogra, and S.P. Agarwal, *Indian J. Pharm. Sci.* **57**, 26–30 (1995).

10. Y. Lee and Y.W. Chien, *J. Controlled Release* **37**, 251–261 (1995).

11. S. Kim, W. Snipes, G.D. Hodgen, and F. Anderson, *Contraception* **52**, 313–316 (1995).

12. K. Iga and Y. Ogawa, *Proc. Int. Symp. Controlled Release Bioact. Mater.* **23**, 155–156 (1996).

13. J. Voorspoels, F. Comhaire, W.D. Sy, and J.P. Remon, *Proc. Int. Symp. Controlled Release Bioact. Mater.* **24**, 185–186 (1997).

14. M. Veillard, M. Longer, T.W. Martens, and J.R. Robinson, *J. Controlled Release* **6**, 123–131 (1987).

15. H.P. Merkle, R. Anders, J. Sandow, and W. Schurr, *Delivery Syst. Pept. Drugs*, 159–175 (1986).

16. D. Harris and J.R. Robinson, *Biomaterials* **11**, 652–658 (1990).

17. A.G. Field, *Med. Times Gaz.* **16**, 291 (1858).

18. J.E.F. Riseman, G.E. Altman, and S. Koretsky, *Circulation* **17**, 22–39 (1958 January).

19. S.J. Pimlott and M. Addy, *Oral Surg., Oral Med. Oral Pathol.* **59**, 145–148 (1985).

20. U. Thadani and R.J. Lipicky, *Cardiovas. Drugs Ther.* **8**, 611–623 (1994).

21. J. Abrams, *Arch. Intern. Med.* **155**, 357–364 (1995).

22. S. Bergman, I.A. Siegel, and S. Ciancio, *J. Dent. Res.* **47**, 1184 (1968).

23. W.G. Edge, G.M. Cooper, and M. Morgan, *Anaesthesia* **34**, 463–467 (1979).

24. D. Brewster, M.J. Humphrey, and M.A. McLeavy, *J. Pharm. Pharmacol.* **33**, 500–506 (1981).

25. W.J. Russell, N.R. Badcock, D.B. Frewin, and L.N. Sansom, *Eur. J. Clin. Pharmacol.* **35**, 437–439 (1988).

26. T. Nagai and R. Konishi, *J. Controlled Release* **6**, 353–360 (1987).

27. P. Bottenberg et al., *J. Pharm. Pharmacol.* **43**, 457–464 (1991).

28. J.H. Reading, P.D. Clifford, R.W. Coles, and N. Rajagopolan, *Curr. Ther. Res.* **30**, 605–610 (1981).

29. S. Bouckaert et al. *Eur. J. Clin. Pharmacol* **43**, 137–140 (1992).

30. M. Encarnacion and I. Chin, *Eur. J. Clin. Pharmacol.* **46**, 533–535 (1994).

31. J.L. Fabregas and N. Garcia, *Drug Dev. Ind. Pharm.* **21**, 1689–1696 (1995).

32. L.L. Soh, H.N. Newman, and J.D. Strahan, *J. Clin. Periodontol.* **9**, 66–74 (1982).

33. J. Coventry and H.N. Newman, *J. Clin. Periodontol.* **9**, 129–133 (1982).

34. A. Soskolne, G. Golomb, M. Friedman, and M. Sela, *J. Periodontal Res.* **18**, 330–336 (1983).

35. M. Addy et al., *J. Periodontol.* **59**, 557–564 (1988).

36. D. Steinberg, M. Friedman, A. Soskolne, and M.N. Sela, *J. Periodontol.* **61**, 393–398 (1990).

37. J.M. Goodson et al., *J. Periodontol.* **54**, 575–579 (1983).

38. M. Tonetti, M.A. Cugini, and J.M. Goodson, *J. Periodontal Res.* **25**, 243–249 (1990).

39. L. Heijl et al., *J. Clin. Periodontol.* **18**, 111–116 (1991).

40. R.W. Baker, E.A. Krisko, and F. Kochinke, *Proc. Int. Symp. Controlled Release Bioact. Mater.* **15**, 238a–238b (1988).

41. M. Minabe et al., *J. Periodontol.* **60**, 113–117 (1989).

42. J. Heller, S.Y. Ng, B.K. Fritzinger, and K.V. Roskos, *Biomaterials* **11**, 235–237 (1989).

43. P.B. Deasy, A.E.M. Collins, D.J. MacCarthy, and R.J. Russell, *J. Pharm. Pharmacol.* **41**, 694–699 (1989).

44. T.A. Eckles et al., *J. Clin. Periodontol.* **17**, 454–462 (1990).

45. K.V. Roskos et al., *Biomaterials* **16**, 313–317 (1995).

46. G.I. Maze et al., *J. Clin. Periodontol.* **22**, 860–867 (1995).

47. W.J. Loesche et al., *J. Periodontal Res.* **22**, 224–226 (1987).

48. T. Larsen, *J. Periodontol.* **61**, 30–34 (1990).

49. S.E. Lynch et al., *J. Periodontol.* **62**, 458–467 (1991).

50. J.M. Wozney, *J. Periodontol.* **66**, 506–510 (1995).

51. T.J. Sigurdsson, D.N. Tatakis, M.B. Lee, and U.M.E. Wikesjo, *J. Periodontol.* **66**, 511–521 (1995).

52. M.E. deVries, *Dev. Drug Delivery* (1991).

53. M.E. deVries, Ph.D. Thesis, University of Leiden, Leiden, The Netherlands, 1991.

54. P.W. Wertz and C.A. Squier, *Crit. Rev. Ther. Drug Carrier Syst.* **8**, 237–269 (1991).

55. N. Chidambaram and A.K. Srivatsava, *Drug Dev. Ind. Pharm.* **21**, 1009–1036 (1995).

56. A.H. Beckett and E.J. Triggs, *J. Pharm. Pharmacol.* **19** (Suppl.), 31s–41s (1967).

57. T. Nagai and Y. Machida, *Pharm. Int.* **6**, 196–200 (1985).

58. L. Benes et al., *7th Int. Symp. Recent Adv. Drug Delivery Syst.*, Salt Lake City, Utah, 1995.

59. G.E. Altman, J.E.F. Riseman, and S. Koretsky, *Am. J. Med. Sci.* **240**, 100–110 (1960).

60. A.H. Kutscher et al., *Oral Surg. Oral Med. Oral Pathol.* **12**, 1080–1089 (1959).

61. R.A. Seymour and P.A. Heasman, *Drugs, Diseases an the Periodontium*, Oxford University Press, New York, 1992.

62. S.S. Socransky, *J. Periodontol.* **48**, 497–504 (1977).

63. T. Noguchi, M. Fukuda, and I. Ishikawa, *Adv. Den. Res.* **2**, 401–404 (1988).

64. J.M. Goodson, S. Offenbacher, D.H. Farr, and P.E. Hogan, *J. Periodontol.* **56**, 265–272 (1985).

65. U.S. Pat. 4,780,320 (October 25, 1988).

66. U.S. Pat. 4,919,939 (April 24, 1990).

67. S.E. Lynch et al., *J. Clin. Periodontol.* **16**, 545–548 (1989).

See also BIOADHESIVE DRUG DELIVERY SYSTEMS; MUCOSAL DRUG DELIVERY, INTRAVITREAL; MUCOSAL DRUG DELIVERY, NASAL; MUCOSAL DRUG DELIVERY, OCULAR; MUCOSAL DRUG DELIVERY, VAGINAL DRUG DELIVERY AND TREATMENT MODALITIES.

MUCOSAL DRUG DELIVERY, INTRAVITREAL

Suzanne Einmahl
Arati A. Deshpande
Cyrus Tabatabay
Robert Gurny
University of Geneva
Geneva, Switzerland

KEY WORDS

Biodegradable polymers

CMV retinitis

Endophthalmitis

Intraocular disease

Intravitreal

Iontophoresis

Liposomes

Microspheres

Nonbiodegradable polymers

Ocular drug delivery

Prodrugs

Proliferative vitreoretinopathy

Sustained release

OUTLINE

INTRODUCTION

Drug delivery to the posterior segment is a major challenge in ophthalmology. Treatment of vitreoretinal diseases has so far been limited to conventional forms of drug administration, that is, topical instillation, subconjunctival injection, or systemic (oral and parenteral) administration. Unfortunately, owing to the anatomical and physiological barriers that exist, in most cases these routes have not proved to be efficient for treating vitreoretinal disorders because the intravitreal or retinal levels of drugs achieved were too low.

The topical route of drug delivery severely limits the access of most drugs to the vitreoretinal tissues. In general, approximately 1% or less of an applied dose is absorbed across the cornea and reaches the anterior segment tissues, and only a tiny fraction of this absorbed dose will then move to the posterior segment of the eye (1). This is due to the existence of protective mechanisms in the eye that are essential for its normal visual function; those include solution drainage, lacrimation, diversion of exogenous substances into the systemic circulation via the conjunctiva, and the structure of the cornea itself, which is relatively impermeable to most drugs (1).

Subconjunctival injections represent an attempt to increase intraocular drug levels while minimizing the frequency of dosing. However, with this technique, higher drug concentrations are generally achieved in the anterior chamber rather than in the posterior segment tissues. Drug delivery to the eye after systemic administration depends on the ocular vascular circulation for transport to the targeted area. The inner two-thirds of the retina are perfused by the central retinal artery. The capillary walls are quite permeable to many substances (1). However, for most drugs, the concentrations achieved in the vitreous humor are much lower than the corresponding serum concentrations unless the eye is inflamed. In this latter case, drug concentrations in the posterior segment can reach as high as 10% of the serum drug levels. The blood–retinal barrier (BRB) plays a major role in restricting drug coming from the choriocapillaries and entering the vitreoretinal compartment as well as restricting drug elimination from this space. This barrier is characterized by the *zonulae occludentes* between the contiguous cells of the retinal vessels and the retinal pigmented epithelium, which prevent the flow of substances by the paracellular pathway, thereby diverting them to a highly selective transcellular route. The ability of a drug to penetrate the BRB is related to its lipid solubility. Furthermore, some substances are transported out of the vitreous body by an active transport system that is inhibited by probenecid, a situation similar to that in the kidney tubular epithelial cells (2). Circumstances that may alter the BRB, inducing its breakdown, include posttraumatic inflammation; viral, bacterial, or fungal infection; and iatrogenic causes such as vitrectomy (3).

Because of these constraints in delivering drugs to their site of action in the vitreoretinal tissues in such a way as to achieve therapeutic levels, it appears then that the only way to attain therapeutic concentrations is by intravitreal injection (4). The vitreous humor is a hydrophilic gel containing 99% water and 1% organic substances such as collagen and hyaluronic acid through which drugs diffuse freely as they would in water (5). After injection into the vitreous body, drugs may be eliminated by diffusion into the aqueous humor of the posterior chamber with subsequent removal by the normal egress of fluid from the anterior chamber. This pathway is limited by the small surface available for diffusion. Drugs eliminated by this route generally have half-lives in the range of 20 to 30 h (6). The other possible elimination pathway from the vitreous is through the retina via penetration of the BRB: this is the so-called posterior route. Drugs eliminated by this way typically exhibit half-lives in the range of 5 to 10 h (6).

Lipophilic drugs are eliminated more rapidly for the same reason: They pass into the vitreoretinal compartment more readily after systemic administration. The elimination of an intravitreally administered drug is influenced by infection and inflammation. Infection tends to accelerate the rate of clearance, whereas the effect of inflammation on vitreous pharmacokinetics is drug dependent. In general, the half-life of nontransported drugs, such as aminoglycosides, is reduced in the presence of ocular inflammation, whereas the half-life of carbenicillin, an actively transported drug, is slightly increased. Intravitreal dosage route was initially reserved primarily for the treatment of endophthalmitis; nowadays this route is also occasionally used for the treatment of diseases such as proliferative vitreoretinopathy (PVR), viral retinitis, and uveitis. Intravitreal injection allows high intraocular drug levels to be reached rapidly, thus resolving the problems of conventional application. Unfortunately, successful treatment of most vitreoretinal diseases requires multiple injections to maintain therapeutically effective drug concentrations in the vitreous for a desired period of time. Additionally, even if repeated drug injections into an already compromised eye improve the ocular condition, this strategy can cause several complications, such as increased risk of ocular infection, intraocular hemorrhage, retinal detachment, and cataract. Moreover, the initial peak level of drug achieved immediately after a bolus intravitreal injection may result in toxicity to the retina and other ocular tissues.

Because of the rapid clearance of drugs from the eye and the variable toxicity encountered in previous studies, researchers have thus been encouraged to develop new systems of drug delivery to the posterior segment that would sustain a therapeutic level of the drug over an extended period of time. Thus, the "peak and valley" effects could be minimized, and drug concentrations could be maintained at an effective therapeutic level for a prolonged period of time. Several delivery systems with a slow-release feature have been developed, including polymeric matrices (biodegradable or not), colloidal systems (liposomes and microspheres), and other delivery systems such as iontophoresis or the prodrug approach.

This article first provides an overview of the vitreoretinal disorders amenable to intraocular drug therapy such as PVR, viral retinitis, endophthalmitis, and uveitis and then discusses the various systems of sustained drug delivery for treatment of these diseases.

VITREORETINAL DISEASES

Proliferative Vitreoretinopathy

Among the severe and blinding diseases of the posterior segment of the eye, many are pathophysiologically characterized by a proliferation of one or more cell types and are therefore referred to as proliferative disorders.

PVR is a pathologic condition occurring as a complication of retinal detachment in 5–10% of the cases (7) in which benign cells proliferate in the vitreous cavity, resulting in the formation of membranes on both surfaces of the detached retina. It is the most common cause of failure following retinal reattachment surgery (8). There are some risk factors that increase susceptibility to the development of PVR: repeated procedures (such as failure of previous surgery), damaged retinal surface (retinal folds or holes), treatment modality (vitrectomy, cryotherapy), and preoperative vitreous hemorrhage (9).

First described in 1939, PVR was formerly known as "massive vitreous retraction," "massive preretinal retraction," and "massive periretinal proliferation." In 1983, the Retina Society introduced the new terminology to reflect the pathologic changes in the vitreous and the retina (7). They also established a standardized classification to determine the different stages of the disease so as to compare and evaluate methods of treatment and clinical results. This classification has since been revised many times (10).

The pathogenesis (11) of PVR is related to the loss of integrity of the vitreoretinal structures. The first important step of the disease process is the disruption of the BRB, allowing serum components to penetrate into the vitreous cavity (12). Serum, a stimulus to migration, exerts chemotaxis to retinal pigmented epithelial (RPE) cells, glial cells, and Müller cells, which migrate into the vitreous cavity through retinal holes. Fibronectin and platelet-derived growth factors promote cellular adhesion to the vitreous collagen and fibroblast proliferation, leading to membrane formation. The presence of contractile elements in these epiretinal membranes, mainly composed of myofibroblasts, provokes cell contraction, which can distort or redetach the retina. The epiretinal membranes formed are stabilized by the collagen of the extracellular matrix. An inflammatory response is often provoked, as evidenced by the presence of various white blood cells such as macrophages and lymphocytes (13). Even though the mechanism that triggers certain cells or cell types to proliferate is still obscure, many attempts have been made to find a pharmacological cure for the disease.

The development of suitable treatments for PVR has been assisted by experimental animal models, produced by intravitreal injection of autologous (14) or heterologous fibroblasts (15) or by the injection of macrophages, which mimics the development of PVR from its initial stage onwards (16).

The pharmacological treatment of PVR consists in the inhibiting progression of the disease at various stages (Table 1). PVR parallels the wound-healing process and follows a course that can be divided into three phases: inflammation, cellular proliferation, and regeneration (Fig. 1) (26). The time course of PVR development is important in the selection of particular drugs. In the initial stage, that is, the inflammatory phase, long-effect steroids are more suitable. In the proliferative phase, antiproliferative drugs can be used. Because inflammatory factors may still continue to act in this stage, better control may be achieved if the antiproliferative drugs are combined with steroids.

Drugs such as corticosteroids and nonsteroidal antiinflammatory agents (NSAIs) prevent the breakdown of the blood–retinal barrier (17). As they act early in the disease process, they are particularly effective in reducing the incidence of PVR in experimental models (26). Corticosteroids were the first drugs investigated to treat PVR (27). Their major mechanism of action is the reduction of the inflammatory response in the eye, thereby moderating the

Staphylococcus aureus, Pseudomonas aeruginosa, Proteus, and coliform species, with increasing incidence of *Staphylococcus epidermidis* (80). An anaerobic species, *Bacillus*, is associated with penetrating ocular trauma, most often in rural areas (81). All these microorganisms cause exogenous endophthalmitis; the agents invade the eye from outside, for example, during ophthalmic surgery or penetrating injury. Sometimes, however, endophthalmitis can be endogenous, or blood borne. Endogenous endophthalmitis is most often mycotic, caused by *Candida albicans*. The frequency of endogenous infections, though three times less frequent than exogenous infections, is now increasing in both immunocompromised patients and patients under prolonged treatment with antibiotics, corticosteroids, or antimetabolites (82).

The symptoms of acute endophthalmitis are ocular pain and decreased visual acuity, with edematous lids, conjunctival hyperemia and chemosis, and corneal edema. On the other hand, patients with chronic endophthalmitis (caused by organisms of low virulence) do not present many clinical signs other than photophobia.

An early diagnosis and the beginning of an optimal therapy are both important to increase the chance of getting rid of the microorganisms and enhancing the visual prognosis. At this stage, the intravitreal injection of an antibiotic and eventually vitrectomy plays a very important role, not only in removing the infectious microorganisms, their associated toxins, and the inflammatory components, but also in capturing the infecting organism(s) for a microbiological identification (83) and proper antibiotic selection.

Before the use of intravitreal injections of antibiotics, the treatment of endophthalmitis had poor results (84). Indeed, the eye is an organ extremely susceptible to inflammation; it has poor defense mechanisms, and most antibiotics penetrate very poorly into the ocular cavity. There are actually two crucial parameters to note when treating such a disease: the drug must achieve sufficient levels in the vitreous, above the ID_{50}, and it must do so over a prolonged period of time. That is why topical, systemic, and subconjunctival administration of antibiotics failed to adequately treat endophthalmitis. In a series of experiments over the past 20 years, Peyman and coworkers as well as D'Amico et al. attempted to determine the toxic levels of various antibiotics by clinical, histological, and electroretinographic examination; to measure the clearance of nontoxic doses from the intraocular fluids after intravitreal injection; and to compare the effectiveness of intravitreal injection with systemic or subconjunctival administration in treating experimentally induced endophthalmitis (Table 2).

Experimental endophthalmitis was produced by injecting various organisms into the animal eye, with or without vitrectomy. Those studies in rabbits or monkeys showed that intravitreal administration of antibiotics is the most effective way of achieving high and immediate intravitreal drug levels without retinal toxicity (108,109).

Current therapeutic strategy for presumed endophthalmitis includes the intravitreal injection of a single or, more frequently, a combination of broad-spectrum antibiotics (110). These antibiotics are used at the highest possible nontoxic dose. Besides antibiotics, intravitreal corticosteroids such as dexamethasone play an important role in the management of bacterial endophthalmitis because of their beneficial effect in reducing the inflammation that accompanies the infection. Adjunctive treatment of endophthalmitis is the systemic administration of another antibiotic, especially in the case of endogenous endophthalmitis, to provide extraocular coverage and to maintain some intravitreal levels, with steroids used to reduce the inflammatory response.

Therapy for fungal endophthalmitis is similar to that for bacterial endophthalmitis except that antifungals, rather than antibacterials, are administered. The recommended therapeutic strategy is the direct intravitreal administration of amphotericin B. If the treatment fails, miconazole may be used (1). Systemic antifungal treatment is also employed.

Posterior Uveitis

Posterior uveitis, whether it is endogenous and chronic or associated with systemic diseases such as Behçet's disease, is a pathology characterized by vitreal inflammation and retinal vasculitis. In the majority of patients, the etiologic agent is not known. It has been postulated that in many cases uveitis may be autoimmune in origin. Uveitis usually has a low response to treatments with steroids or cytotoxic drugs, and it may require long-term chronic treatment. If untreated, the outcome is generally severe, eventually leading to progressive blindness.

The immunomodulating drug cyclosporin was investigated and found effective in treating experimental autoimmune uveitis (111) and acute inflammation unresponsive to usual treatment (112). Cyclosporin A is a cyclic polypeptide composed of 11 amino acids that effectively inhibits the development of experimentally induced uveitis (113). It acts by inhibiting the synthesis of interleukin 2 by the T helper lymphocytes (114). Cyclosporin A has been shown in several human clinical trials to be effective in treating chronic uveitis, especially that associated with Behçet's disease (115). Unfortunately, its systemic administration causes severe complications, such as renal toxicity, hypertension, and immunosuppression, which limit its use. Topical administration, on the other hand, resulted in nondetectable levels of the drug in all the intraocular structures because of its poor ocular bioavailability (116). To avoid these toxic effects and to achieve sufficient levels in the vitreous, cyclosporin was injected intravitreally and prevented experimental autoimmune uveitis (117). Grisolano and Peyman found no toxic effects in rabbits treated with 100 μg of intravitreal cyclosporin (118).

An adjunct to immunosuppressive treatment for noninfectious inflammation of the posterior segment is the use of corticosteroids. They are frequently employed to reduce intraocular inflammation and are currently the mainstay in the treatment of uveitis. Local steroid injections are preferred so as to avoid the side effects associated with systemic steroid administration. It is possible that a combination of drugs, attacking different targets in the immune response system, might work synergistically and thus would allow effective treatment with lower doses and presumably fewer side effects.

Table 2. Management of Endophthalmitis: Peak Concentrations and Half-Lifes of Various Drugs in the Vitreous Following Intravitreal Injection

Class of drugs	Dose (mg)	Concentration (μg/mL)	Half-life (h)	Ref.
Penicillins				
Ampicillin	5	900	6	85
Carbenicillin	1	270	10	86
Methicillin	2	632–2,000	3–5	87
Oxacillin	0.5	200	6	88
Penicillin G	2,000 U	500–1,000	3	89
Cephalosporins				
Cefazolin	1	330	7	86
Cefotetan	1	670	7.5	90
Ceftazidime	0.2	91.9	7.4	91
Ceftriaxone	2	1,345	12	92
Cephalotin	2	380–550	—	93
Moxolactam	2	130	20	94
Aminoglycosides				
Amikacin	0.25	110	24	95
Gentamicin	0.1	18	33	86
Gentamicin	0.1	100	32	96
Kanamycin	0.5	330	18	97
Netilmicin	0.25	167	24	98
Tobramycin	0.5	383	16	99
Miscellaneous				
Aztreonam	0.1	62	7.5	100
Chloramphenicol	2	60	10	101
Ciprofloxacin	0.1	80	2.2	102
Clindamycin	1	235	7–8	103
Erythromycin	0.5	250	10	104
Lincomycin	1.5	900	10	105
Vancomycin	1	786	38.5	106
Corticosteroids				
Dexamethasone	0.4	267	3	107

Source: Adapted from Ref. 6.

DRUG DELIVERY SYSTEMS

Biodegradable Polymers

Systems that control and prolong the action of therapeutic agents have grown in importance during the recent years with the development of biodegradable polymers. They are particularly important in the case of implants, because their use eliminates the step of removing the implant after the drug has been released, which, in some applications, can represent a significant advantage over other systems.

Biodegradable polymers gradually dissolve by hydrolytic or enzymatic cleavage of the polymeric structure or by simple dissolution. Heller (119) defined three mechanisms of polymer erosion (Fig. 2). Mechanism I concerns polymers that are made water insoluble by their hydrolytically unstable cross-links. These polymers, such as crosslinked gelatin, collagen, or poly(vinyl alcohol), provide highly hydrophilic matrices. Thus, substances with low

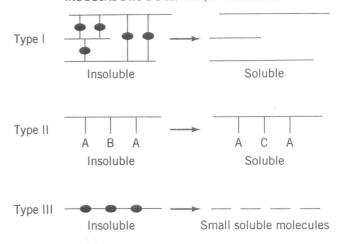

Figure 2. Schematic representation of three different breakdown mechanisms. ●, hydrolitically unstable bonds; A, hydrophobic substituent; B → C, hydrolysis, ionization, protonation. *Source:* Adapted from Ref. 119.

molecular weight and high water solubility diffuse rapidly through the polymeric network independently of the rate of erosion of the matrix. These polymers are mainly used for the release of sparingly water-soluble drugs and for macromolecules such as enzymes and antigens (120).

Mechanism II includes polymers that are initially water insoluble and are solubilized by hydrolysis, ionization, or protonation of a pendent group yet lack backbone cleavage. This mechanism has the feature of not causing any significant change in the molecular weight of the polymer. These polymers, such as poly(vinyl methyl ether/maleic anhydride), cannot therefore be used for implants because of the difficulty of their elimination.

Mechanism III refers to hydrophobic polymers that are converted to small soluble molecules by backbone cleavage. As long as these breakdown products are not toxic, these polymers, for example, polyanhydrides, polycaprolactones, poly(ortho ester)s, poly(lactic acid)s (PLA), poly(glycolic acid)s (PGA), and their copolymers, are suitable as implantable carriers for the administration of drugs to any organ. They offer a wide range of applications in the ophthalmic field, whether applied on the surface of the eye or as intraocular implants.

The breakdown of polymers does not necessarily proceed through one mechanism only, and erosion occurs by a combination of these mechanisms (Table 3).

Poly(vinyl alcohol). Poly(vinyl alcohol) (PVA) is used in ophthalmology as a viscosifier for collyria and also as an intravitreal drug delivery carrier. PVA is synthesized by the polymerization of vinyl acetate to poly(vinyl acetate), which is then hydrolyzed to PVA. Its solubility in water will depend on the extent of hydrolysis and the degree of polymerization (122).

In a recent study, Hainsworth et al. evaluated various methods of sustained delivery to achieve therapeutic levels of ciprofloxacin (123). He compared in vitro two devices made either of PVA or of the bioerodible PLA. He found that the release of ciprofloxacin from the PVA matrix was very fast; over 90% of the drug was released within the

Table 3. Classification of Biodegradable Polymers Following the Heller Terms

Polymer	Mechanism of erosion	Chemical structure
Poly(vinyl alcohol)	Type I	$\left[\begin{array}{c}CH-CH_2\\ |\\ OH\end{array}\right]_n$
Gelatin	Type I	Mixture of purified protein fractions obtained by hydrolysis of animal collagen
Collagen	Types I and III	Protein extracted from animal tissues such as skin, sinews, and bones
Polyanhydrides	Type III	$\left[\begin{array}{c}O \quad\quad O\\ \| \quad\quad \|\\ R-C-O-C\end{array}\right]_n$
Polycaprolactone and its copolymers	Type III	$\left[\begin{array}{c}O-(CH_2)_5-C\\ \|\\ O\end{array}\right]_n$
Poly(ortho ester)s	Type III	$\left[\begin{array}{c}R \quad O\\ O \quad O-R'\end{array}\right]_n$
Poly(lactic acid)s, poly(glycolic acid)s, and their copolymers	Type III	$\left[\begin{array}{c}CH-C\\ |\quad \|\\ R \quad O\end{array}\right]_n$

Source: Ref. 121.

first 24 h, and this release showed a square-root dependence of time, whereas release from PLA matrices followed a similar but slightly slower pattern.

On the other hand, as an intravitreal administration, PVA is most frequently coupled with ethylene vinyl acetate (EVA) in nonbiodegradable implants. These devices will be discussed later in this article.

PLA, Poly(glycolic acid), and Their Copolymers. Initially, poly(α-hydroxy acid)s were developed as synthetic, bioresorbable sutures in the 1960s. As a result of their good histocompatibility (124), this family of polyesters now includes the most-investigated biodegradable polymeric carriers for drug delivery systems. The principal polymers of this class are homo- and copolymers derived from lactic and glycolic acids: PLA, PGA, and its copolymers (PLGA).

Poly(α-hydroxy acids) are generally synthesized by a condensation reaction at high temperatures. The ring-opening polymerization of cyclic glycolic and lactic acid diesters is an efficient method to produce high-molecular-weight polymers. The simple step-growth polymerization method leads only to low-molecular-weight polymers with poor mechanical properties (125). The presence of an asymmetric carbon in lactic acid makes it possible to obtain levorotatory (L), dextrorotatory (D), or racemic (D,L) forms of the corresponding polymer, which can have different physicochemical properties.

The mechanism of degradation of these polyesters is a homogeneous erosion of the core. The polymeric chains are first cleaved by hydrolysis and then by an enzymatic chain scission process, thereby releasing acidic monomers that are rapidly eliminated by a physiological pathway. PGA is

far too sensitive to hydrolysis to be considered useful as a carrier for sustained drug delivery (126). PLA degrades more slowly than PLGA; it also shows less initial burst of the drug than PLGA.

Drug delivery from PLGA matrices appears to follow biphasic kinetics (127). A mechanism to explain this profile would include a delayed increase in the permeability of PLGA arising from different factors, such as a reduction of the glass-transition temperature (T_g), an increase in the degree of hydration of the polymer, or a delayed onset of polymer weight loss by a bulk process (127). Kunou et al. studied the in vitro release pattern of plugs made with different types of PLA and PLGA and containing various percentages of ganciclovir as a model drug (128). The in vitro release of ganciclovir was shown to follow a triphasic process: (1) initial burst, (2) diffusional stage, and (3) final burst due to swelling and disintegration of the polymeric matrix (Fig. 3). The initial burst is certainly due to the rapid release of the drug located on the surface and in the water channels of the polymeric matrix. During the second phase, the drug is slowly released, controlled by the degradation rate of the polymer. In general, the release rate decreases with increasing molecular weight of PLA and PLGA and lactide content of PLGA. On the other hand, an increase in ganciclovir loading results in a higher release rate (128). During this second phase, a significant weight loss is observed. However, drug release from the implant is more rapid than the polymer weight loss. This observation suggests that the drug can diffuse through channels in the polymeric matrix during biodegradation but that the weight of the polymer does not change until a moment in hydrolysis when oligomers are produced by a random chain-scission mechanism, small enough to be soluble in

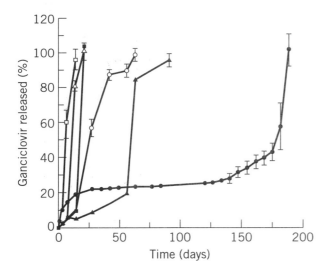

Figure 3. Effects of the molecular weight and lactic acid/glycolic acid ratio of PLA (PLGA) on in vitro release from scleral implants loaded with 10% ganciclovir. ○, PLA-20,000, ●, PLA-100,000, △, PLGA (75/25)-20,000; ▲, PLGA (75/25)-121,000; □, PLG(50/50)-20,000; ■, PLGA(50/50)-95,000. *Source:* Reproduced from Ref. 128 with permission.

water. The third phase of release occurs when the polymeric bulk swells and disintegrates.

The degradation rate can be varied by many factors in addition to the composition and configuration of the polymer or copolymer used, its porosity, and also the physicochemical properties of the incorporated drug.

The in vivo applications of poly(α-hydroxy acids) in the field of ophthalmology are mainly as topical and intraocular drug delivery systems, and as implants as well as microspheres. Besides microspheres, which will be discussed later in this article, implantable biodegradable polymeric matrices have been developed as new drug delivery systems in the vitreous. These implants are generally in the form of small cylinders that can be implanted in the eye by means of a syringe with a conventional needle (19- or 20-gauge) (129). Table 4 summarizes the different studies using these polyesters.

Rubsamen et al. (129) investigated PLGA-based rods containing 5-FU to treat experimental PVR in rabbit eyes. The devices can deliver therapeutic levels of 5-FU for almost 3 weeks and reduce the incidence of tractional retinal detachment. No adverse mechanical or toxic effects were apparent during the time of the study. However, because these devices were not fixed in the vitreous cavity, they might move and come into contact with the retina. Consequently, a stable localization of the device in the vitreous base through a suture fixation or an alternative mode of fixation at the site of implantation might be desirable.

In 1994, Hashizoe and coworkers designed a new device that is implanted at the *pars plana* and releases drugs directly into the vitreous (134). These scleral plugs, made of PLGA (40 kDa), were charged with 1% doxorubicin. The scleral plug gradually released doxorubicin in a concentration maintained within the therapeutic level for 1 month without any notable toxicity to the retina. In another study, Hashizoe et al. (131) demonstrated that the implantation of a scleral plug composed of PLA (20 kDa) and 1% doxorubicin effectively inhibited intravitreal proliferation of fibroblasts and could be a very effective way to treat PVR. Compared to the release of doxorubicin from the PLGA scleral plug (134), the authors observed that the PLA plugs have a longer period of drug release and showed less initial burst. Kunou and coworkers (128) investigated the use of scleral plugs to release ganciclovir for the treatment of CMV retinitis. The concentration of ganciclovir was maintained within the therapeutic range for over 3 months in the vitreous and for over 5 months in the retina and the choroid. A modulated release could be obtained with the scleral implant by varying the ratio and composition of the polymers, the molecular weight, and the drug concentration. Hashizoe et al. (137) further investigated the retinal toxicity of these plugs containing ganciclovir. At 3 months after implantation, only slight inflammatory changes occurred around the plug; the authors concluded that the biocompatibility of the device might be clinically acceptable. One of the advantages of scleral plugs is that the device becomes swollen during hydrolysis and seals the sclerotomy from inside. Fixation on the sclera is easy and requires no sutures. The same observations were made when other drugs were incorporated into the scleral plug, such as fluconazole (136), adriamycin (133), or betamethasone (135).

Table 4. Use of PLA–PLGA Implants for Intravitreal Administration

Polymer	Drug	Implant form	Animal model	Duration (weeks)	Year	Author (et al.)	Ref.
PLA	Fluorescein-Na	Implant	Rabbit	4	1994	Kimura	130
PLA	Ciprofloxacin	Disc	Rabbit	4	1996	Hainsworth	123
PLA	Doxorubicin	Scleral plug	Rabbit	>4	1995	Hashizoe	131
PLA, PLGA	Ganciclovir	Scleral plug	Rabbit	>20	1995	Kunou	128
PLGA	5-Fluorouracil	Cylinder	Rabbit	3	1994	Rubsamen	129
PLGA	5-Fluorouridine, dexamethasone	Cylinder	Pig	several	1996	Foster	132
PLGA	Adriamycin	Scleral plug	Rabbit	>4	1993	Hashizoe	133
PLGA	Doxorubicin	Scleral plug	Rabbit	>4	1994	Hashizoe	134
PLGA	Betamethasone	Scleral plug	Rabbit	>4	1996	Kunou	135
PLGA	Fluconazole	Scleral plug	Rabbit	3	1997	Miyamoto	136
PLGA	Ganciclovir	Scleral plug	Rabbit	12	1997	Hashizoe	137

On the other hand, it would be interesting to develop an injectable liquid-polymer drug delivery system that would solidify in the vitreous cavity and might overcome some disadvantages of the current solid implants. Indeed, the problem with polyesters is their very high melting point, above 170°C (138). Davis et al. reasoned that a family of injectable poly(α-hydroxy acid)s would provide an important therapeutic alternative to implants that require surgical procedures (139). They formulated a polymer system called Meltamer composed of block copolymers that are solid at 37°C but melt at various temperatures above 42°C and resolidify at body temperature. In vivo screening in rabbit eyes demonstrated that the heated polymer can be easily and safely injected into various ocular sites. The biocompatibility was excellent for more than 5 weeks, and the polymer completely degraded after that period of time (140).

Polycaprolactones. Other polymers from the polyesters family have been evaluated as long-term drug delivery systems. Poly-ϵ-caprolactone (PCL) was used in 1973 as a subdermal delivery system for contraceptive steroids under the trademark Capronor (141).

PCL is synthesized by a ring-opening polymerization of the monomer ϵ-caprolactone. It is semicrystalline, rather hydrophobic compared to poly(α-hydroxy acid)s, and has a high molecular weight. However, because of the great interest for low-molecular-weight polymers due to their controllable degradation profile and their low melting point, low-molecular-weight (LMW) polycaprolactones were prepared by means of hydrolytic degradation of high-molecular-weight (HMW) commercial PCL (142). Polymers of molecular weight from 4,000 to 10,000 were obtained without any structural changes. Comparison of the in vitro release rate of 5-FU as a model drug showed that the LMW PCL matrices exhibited more uniform drug release than the HMW devices. In a further study (143), Chin et al. mixed HMW and LMW PCL in different proportions, incorporated ganciclovir inside, and observed that the in vitro release rate of ganciclovir increased with the proportion of LMW. In general, these experiments demonstrated first-order kinetic release from matrices of PCL.

As with PLA and PLGA, PCL hydrolyzes by random chain scission through hydrolytic cleavage of ester groups to ϵ-hydroxycaproic acid, leading to a continual decrease of the molecular weight without any significant loss of weight. Enzyme catalysis is excluded in this first phase, because the diffusion of such HMW substances is impossible in the polymer bulk. When the molecular weight reaches about 5,000, the cleavage of the chain is catalyzed by enzymes and accompanied by a loss of weight resulting from the diffusion of small polymeric fragments from the matrix, which subsequently fragments and undergoes phagocytosis (141).

Concerning the application of PCL in the ophthalmologic field, many investigations have been made concerning the use of topical instillation of colloidal PCL-nanoparticles for the administration of β-blocking agents or indomethacin.

Intraocular application of polycaprolactone-based delivery systems has been investigated by Borhani et al.

(144,145). They mixed HMW and LMW polycaprolactones in different proportions with 5-FU, and the pellets obtained showed, as expected, a faster release rate when the proportion of LMW polycaprolactone increased (144). In an in vivo study in rabbits (145) with 5-FU (10% or 20%) and HMW PCL, Borhani et al. demonstrated that these devices permit a slow release of 5-FU and thus increase the efficacy by providing a constant concentration of drug during the active period of PVR. An inflammatory cell reaction was found in the sclera near the implant site; however, in a study of biocompatibility and toxicity of PCL, no implant-related inflammation was observed (145).

Peyman and associates (146) have developed a PCL-based biodegradable porous implant for sustained and constant drug delivery. Nontoxic water-soluble inorganic salts such as NaCl or KCl were used as pore-forming agents and incorporated into PCL by a melting process. Biodegradable porous reservoir devices were prepared and loaded with different substances, for example, 5-FU, ganciclovir, foscarnet, and the dye carboxyfluorescein. During the in vitro release of the drug, the inorganic salts dissolved in water, leaving pores in the PCL devices. As the percentage of inorganic salt increases, a higher density of pores was observed in the devices. The porous reservoir devices provided a constant release of the drugs, depending on the pore size of the polymer. A concentration gradient across the wall of the polymer was created that forced the flow of the drug from the inner reservoir system to the surrounding aqueous medium. The release pattern followed zero-order kinetics without any initial burst, and the release lasted more than 6 months (Fig. 4) (146). This PCL reservoir device can be produced with various ratios of HMW polymer, allowing the device to degrade very slowly and therefore dissolving only after all the drug is released.

Polyanhydrides. Polyanhydrides were first investigated in the 1930s as substitutes for polyesters in textile applications, but because of their hydrolytic instability, the idea was soon abandoned, and attention turned to their use as

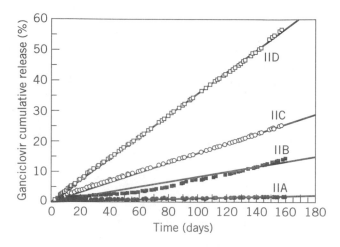

Figure 4. Cumulative release of ganciclovir over time from porous reservoir. IIA, 0% of porogen; IIB, 20% of porogen; IIC, 30% of porogen; IID, 40% of porogen. *Source:* Reproduced from Ref. 146 with permission.

biomaterials. Their very rapid hydrolysis is due to the lability of the anhydride links. The rate of hydrolysis of the polymeric chains on their surface is much faster than the penetration of water into the core of the matrix; this so-called heterogeneous surface erosion enables a zero-order kinetic profile and a good control over the rate and the duration of the release (147).

The most frequently investigated ocular matrix carrier consists of 1,3-bis(carboxyphenoxy) propane (PCPP) and its copolymers with sebacic acid (SA), a more hydrophilic monomer. Previous studies also described carriers with other 1,3-bis(carboxyphenoxy) alkanes with SA (148). Pure PCPP has an extremely long life (over 3 years) (147,149), whereas after copolymerization with 80% of SA, this is reduced to a few days. The ratio of the two monomers plays an important role in the rate of hydrolysis of the resulting polymer: When the proportion of SA increases, the hydrophobicity of the polymer decreases, resulting in a faster rate of hydrolysis of the polymeric chains at the surface. It should also be noted that polyanhydrides are pH-sensitive; they undergo faster breakdown at high pH and are more stable in acidic media.

Because of their surface erosion and excellent biocompatibility (149), polyanhydrides have been particularly useful for the controlled delivery of antimetabolites for the postsurgical treatment of glaucoma (121).

In a recent study (150), Lewis et al. reported the use of polyanhydride as an intravitreal bioerodible vehicle for 5-FU in the treatment of proliferative vitreoretinopathy. PCPP-SA loaded with 20% of 5-FU was compressed into a T-shaped device and sutured to a sclerotomy. Sustained release of 5-FU decreased the short- and long-term rate of retinal detachment in experimental PVR in rabbits. Alonso and coworkers described (151) the use of 1,3-bis(carboxyphenoxy) butane and SA to study the intraocular biocompatibility and in vitro kinetics of gentamicin. The implants were well tolerated in the vitreous body of rabbit eyes, and continuous levels of gentamicin were released in vitro.

Poly(ortho ester)s. The predominant mode of drug release from the previously mentioned hydrophilic systems such as PLA and PLGA is diffusion, with poor correlation between the rate of polymer erosion and the rate of drug release. For this reason, the development of new polymers that contain pH-labile linkages in their backbone has been proposed. Under certain conditions, the hydrolysis of such hydrophobic polymers can be confined predominantly to the outer surface. The resultant heterogeneous surface erosion allows excellent control of the release kinetics. Poly(ortho ester)s (POEs), as well as the previously described polyanhydrides, are polymers whose main characteristic is a release of the drug by surface erosion, following zero-order kinetics.

Since the late 1970s, four generations of POEs have been synthesized to produce bioerodible carriers for drug delivery (Table 5). The first was synthesized at ALZA Corp. in California; it was a hydrophobic solid polymer whose hydrolysis was catalyzed in acidic media (actually by the acidic coproducts released by the breakdown of the polymer). Various potential applications were described by

Choi and Heller in their patents, but none concerned ophthalmic use (152).

The second generation of POEs was also a solid. The backbones of these polymers contain acid-labile linkages that are stable in alkaline media, hydrolyze slowly in pH 7.4 phosphate buffer, and degrade at increasing rates as the acidity of the medium increases. To produce drug delivery devices with lifetimes ranging from hours to months, studies were carried out by different investigators who incorporated acidic or basic excipients into hot-molded samples to modify erosion rates (152).

Recently, a new polymer has been described (153) and characterized by Merkli and coworkers (152). This viscous ointmentlike material allows the incorporation of drugs by simple mixing into the polymer at room temperature without the use of a solvent. This characteristic is of considerable interest with respect to peptide and protein delivery as well as for other thermolabile drugs. This third generation of POEs can be injected using a syringe with an appropriate hypodermic needle without any other surgical intervention, which is a significant advantage when compared with solid bioerodible devices that must be placed either with a trocar or through a surgical procedure. It is the only POE up to now that has been used in ophthalmic formulations. It has been investigated as an injectable bioerodible polymeric implant for controlled subconjunctival release of antimetabolites such as 5-FU and mitomycin C after glaucoma filtration surgery (154). The release of drugs from this semisolid POE occurs via a combined erosion and diffusion mechanism. For a LMW POE, the degradation rate is relatively fast, and the diffusion component is almost absent. On the other hand, for an HMW POE, the degradation rate of the polymer is slower, so the effect of drug diffusion through the flexible polymeric chains is more noticeable. The semisolid POE exhibits Newtonian behavior (152), and its viscosity is related to polymeric chain rigidity. In semisolid POE with low viscosity, high-chain flexibility facilitates hydrolysis. The first step of the reaction is the rapid hydrolysis of the labile orthoester bonds. This initial reaction is followed by a slower hydrolysis that produces a carboxylic acid and a triol. For more viscous polymers, where the chains are less flexible, water penetration is severely hindered, and the rate of initial hydrolysis is slowed. Consequently, to obtain drug release over an extended period of time, it is necessary to synthesize HMW polymers, but the major concern with these POEs is their very high viscosity, which makes their injection through a hypodermic needle very difficult.

A number of parameters have been shown to be important in controlling the release rate of drugs incorporated in POEs (155). Among these are the hydrophilicity of the drug, the particle size, and the amount incorporated. The influence of acidic excipients added to the system is directly proportional to their concentration, solubility, and pK_a. The use of highly water-soluble acids characterized by a low pK_a value leads to a fast polymer degradation where the drug is released principally by polymer erosion. For POEs stabilized with a basic excipient such as magnesium hydroxide, the release of the therapeutic agent is principally determined by diffusion and can be controlled by the amount of base incorporated into the polymer. The

Table 5. Chemical Structures of the Four Generations of Poly(ortho ester)s

Generation	Chemical structure

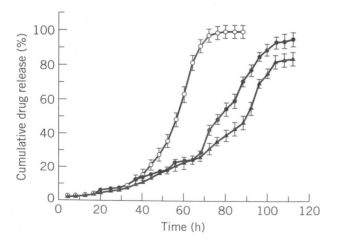

First

$R = -(CH_2)_6-$

or

$R = -CH_2-\langle \text{cyclohexyl} \rangle-CH_2-$

Second

$R = -(CH_2)_6-$

or

$R = -CH_2-\langle \text{cyclohexyl} \rangle-CH_2-$

Third

$R = -CH_3$

$R' = -(CH_2)_4-$ or $-(CH_2)_8-$

Fourth

$R = -H$ or $-CH_3$

---

concomitant release of 5-FU and dexamethasone has been investigated by Zignani and coworkers (unpublished data). The addition of dexamethasone phosphate, a hydrophobic steroidal antiinflammatory agent, to the highly hydrophilic and basic POE prolongs the release of the hydrophilic antimetabolite 5-FU while minimizing inflammation due to the polymer (Fig. 5). This system is promising for a subconjunctival application following glaucoma filtration surgery or intravitreally for the management of PVR.

Figure 5. Cumulative in vitro release of 5-fluorouracil (1%) and dexamethasone sodium phosphate (1%) from POE in PBS at 37°C. ○, 5-FU (1%); ●, 5-FU (1%) in the presence of dexamethasone phosphate (1%); ▲, dexamethasone phosphate (1%) in the presence of 5-FU (1%). *Source:* Zignani et al., unpublished data.

The biotolerance of the semisolid biodegradable POE was investigated subcutaneously and with the cage-implant system (156); the biocompatibility appeared to be acceptable. The subconjunctival biocompatibility was studied by Bernatchez et al. (157). The acute inflammation resolved rapidly, and no chronic inflammation developed. After further purification of the polymer and using an aseptic preparation method, Zignani (158–160) further improved the biocompatibility of the polymer. After extensive testing, the same authors reported that the initial monomers and intermediate degradation products induced only a slight to moderate inflammatory reaction and no chronic response. As a matter of fact, aseptic preparation is up to now the only way to obtain sterile preparations because it has been shown that irradiation procedures produce degradation of the polymer and induce free radical formation (161–163).

A new family of POE, a self-catalyzed polymer, has been developed by Ng et al. (164). These POEs are similar to the second generation in that they contain short dimer segments of α-hydroxy acids in their backbone. Because POEs are susceptible to acid-catalyzed degradation, polymer hydrolysis can be controlled by the amount of incorporated α-hydroxy acids, and no acidic excipient has to be added (165). Concerning the in vitro drug release (166), it was found that the acidic 5-FU was released much faster than the weakly basic mitomycin C. These polymers appear to be very promising candidates for ophthalmic applications.

Nonbiodegradable Polymers

Ethylene Vinyl Acetate. The EVA copolymers are a family of materials with a number of promising advantages.

EVA, a thermoplastic lipophilic polymer, is mainly used as a membrane in reservoir systems and is quite permeable to certain lipophilic substances such as pilocarpine but is sufficiently hydrophobic to be relatively impermeable to hydrophilic drugs as well as water. The intrauterine progesterone contraceptive system Progestasert® (167) and the pilocarpine ocular insert Ocusert® produced by ALZA Corporation in Palo Alto, California (168), are examples of commercially introduced sustained-release systems based on EVA. In both cases, EVA is the constituent of a membrane that controls the rate of release of the drug, keeping it almost constant over several days.

In 1992, Ashton and coworkers developed an implantable sustained-release device to treat chronic disorders of the eye (169). This device consists of a central core of drug entirely coated in PVA, a permeable polymer. The surface area available for release, and consequently the release rate, is, then controlled by additional layers of EVA, which is impermeable to the drugs used, and PVA (Fig. 6). Water diffuses into the device and dissolves part of the pellet, forming a saturated drug solution. The drug then diffuses from the device, and as long as the solution inside the device is saturated, the release rate is constant. This is a so-called reservoir system (170). This device has been implanted intravitreally in animal and human eyes (Fig. 7) for the treatment of various vitreoretinal disorders (Table 6). As it is nondegradable, this system is almost devoid of any intraocular inflammatory response. However, it has to

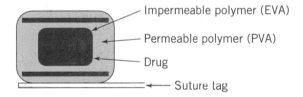

- Impermeable polymer (EVA)
- Permeable polymer (PVA)
- Drug
- Suture tag

Figure 6. Diagram of the implantable sustained-release device. *Source:* Reproduced from Ref. 170 with permission.

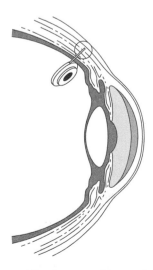

Figure 7. Position of the device in the eye. *Source:* Reproduced from Ref. 170 with permission.

be removed or replaced to prevent any risk of fibrous encapsulation.

The first device was developed by Smith et al. in 1992 to treat CMV retinitis with ganciclovir (170). We have seen before that the treatment of CMV retinitis requires repeated intravitreal injections of ganciclovir to maintain therapeutic levels in the eye and to prevent relapse. Because of the severe complications associated with these frequent injections and the short intravitreal half-time of ganciclovir, this drug is a good candidate for a local sustained-release delivery system. Pellets of ganciclovir were thus prepared as described earlier and implanted intravitreally into rabbit eyes. Sustained levels of ganciclovir could be maintained in the vitreous of rabbits for more than 80 days after implantation of the polymeric device, and both the device and the resulting chronic low concentrations of ganciclovir appeared to be well tolerated (170). Ashton et al. compared the pharmacokinetics data of a ganciclovir implant in healthy rabbit eyes and in diseased human eyes. The rabbit eye was found to be a good model for studying the intravitreal pharmacokinetics of ganciclovir, suggesting a common elimination mechanism (178). Sanborn et al. (171) implanted devices releasing ganciclovir at a steady rate over approximately 4–5 months in patients with AIDS-associated CMV retinitis and found that the progression of the disease was first halted out and subsequently reversed, with all patients eventually being free of retinitis.

In 1993, Anand and associates reported the cumulative experience with this device: 30 eyes from 22 patients received the intraocular device and were followed up for a median of 125 days (172). Conventional intravenous therapy had failed in these patients; however, 5 patients had no history of intravenous therapy. The authors reported initial stabilization of the disease in 90% of eyes, with a mean time to disease progression of 133 days. In 1994, a new implant was developed, characterized by a slower release rate and a longer life span (8 months). In a randomized controlled clinical trial conduced by Martin et al. (173), this implant was found to be effective with a median time to progression of retinitis of 226 days, compared with 15 days for untreated patients. The devices were well tolerated intraocularly and did not experience significant biodegradation. Furthermore, Anand et al. (179) as well as Charles and Steiner (180) reported the histopathologic and electron microscopic features of some of the human eyes treated with the device and were encouraged by the relative lack of toxicity of the ganciclovir-containing intraocular devices and the fact that they are effective in sustaining clinical nonprogression of CMV retinitis. This ganciclovir device was approved by the U.S. Food and Drug Administration (FDA) in 1996 and is commercially available under the name Vitrasert™ (Chiron Vision Corporation), each implant containing a minimum of 4.5 mg of ganciclovir and being designed to release the drug over a 5- to 8-month period of time.

The life span of the device is an important factor influencing the therapeutic outcome and the potential costs and risks of repeated implantation procedures. In many reported cases, progression of disease in patients with intraocular devices has been attributed to depletion of drug

Table 6. Use of the EVA–PVA Devices for Intravitreal Administration

Drug	Model	Duration (weeks)	Year	Author (et al.)	Ref.
		CMV retinitis			
Ganciclovir	Rabbit	>11	1992	Smith	170
Ganciclovir	Human	20–25	1992	Sanborn	171
Ganciclovir	Human	19	1993	Anand	172
Ganciclovir	Human	33	1994	Martin	173
		Uveitis			
Cyclosporin	Rabbit	10 years	1996	Pearson	174
Cyclosporin, dexamethasone	Rabbit	>10	1996	Enyedi	175
Dexamethasone	Rabbit	>18	1995	Cheng	176
Dexamethasone	Rabbit	>18	1996	Hainsworth	177

from the device. When the device becomes depleted, it then has to be replaced. Morley and associates (181) described their initial surgical experience in replacing ganciclovir implants in patients with AIDS-associated CMV retinitis. Most patients retained good vision after ganciclovir implant replacement; however, the implants were occasionally difficult to extract because they were fibrosed into the scleral wound. Furthermore, in four of nine eyes that received a second implant, a retinal detachment developed. The purpose of a very recent study by Chen and Ashton (182) was to investigate various factors affecting in vitro release rate and to develop an implantable intraocular device providing sustained release of ganciclovir over 2 years. Pellets of ganciclovir were coated in a solution of PVA and then partially coated in films of the impermeable EVA, leaving a diffusion pore to allow release. The assembly was coated in PVA and heat treated. A slower release rate was obtained by decreasing the size of these pores and by increasing the heating temperature during the manufacturing process. On the other hand, increasing the percentage amount of PVA added to the pellet enhanced the release, while coating the device one more time, even in 5% PVA solution, significantly slowed down the release. Finally, a release rate of approximately 1.5 μg/h was achieved. Thus, these devices have a theoretical life span of over 600 days (183).

Treatment of posterior chronic uveitis with these EVA–PVA devices was also investigated. Cyclosporin devices were prepared by Pearson et al. (174). No significant decrease of cyclosporin level in the core of the device could be measured after intravitreal implantation in rabbit eyes during the 6 months of the study. Data suggest that owing to the high potency of cyclosporin and the very slow release rate of the device, these implants would provide sustained intravitreal levels of the drug for about 10 years (174). A second series of devices was prepared containing cyclosporin and dexamethasone (175). These two drugs might be beneficial in diseases such as uveitis and also proliferative vitreoretinopathy. Based on the fact that cyclosporin and corticosteroids reduce inflammation by different mechanisms, a device containing both drugs in combination would be more effective than a device containing either agent alone. These devices maintained therapeutic levels of both cyclosporin and dexamethasone in the vit-

reous over 10 weeks, and the presence of dexamethasone did not seem to change the release characteristics for cyclosporin (175). In an experimental model of PVR, the device containing both drugs lessened the severity of the disease and delayed the onset of neovascularization, but addition of cyclosporin to a device containing dexamethasone did not enhance efficacy (184). Devices were also prepared, containing dexamethasone alone for the treatment of PVR (177) and uveitis (176). Dexamethasone was released continuously for 3–4 months at an effective concentration in both cases. Furthermore, the devices were well tolerated, with no indication of toxicity or inflammation.

Polysulfone. Polysulfone is a water-impermeable polymer. A polysulfone capillary fiber (PCF) has been investigated as a slow-release delivery system. It is an anisotropic ultrafiltration fiber mainly developed for cell culture purposes by Amicon Corporation. PCF has the following important features: (1) it has deep macrovoids in its outer membrane, which increases the surface area for drug diffusion and release; (2) it seems to be permeable to lipophilic as well as hydrophilic compounds; (3) the PCF–drug device can be readily sterilized; (4) the device prevents dispersion of drug formulations, such as liposomes or microspheres, in the vitreous, and (5) most importantly, the bioactivity of the drug is unchanged by utilizing the PCF device because the fabrication process does not require chemical reaction, heat, or solvent exposure. The obvious disadvantage of this device is the need for surgical removal of the drug-depleted device because it is not a biodegradable system.

Rahimy and coworkers found that the PCF system is capable of maintaining a relatively constant intravitreal level of the hydrophilic dye carboxyfluorescein (CF) for up to 45 days (185). The in vitro CF release profile appears to be biphasic: The device releases about 50% of its CF content during the first 10 days; from day 10 to day 30, it exhibits slower release with approximately zero-order kinetics. From this standpoint, the PCF device can be classified as a reservoir diffusion-controlled system. Dye diffusion through the PCF membrane is mainly driven by the concentration gradient between the PCF core and the incubation medium. The transport of dye molecules across the PCF membrane remains constant if the core is maintained in a saturated state, such as a solid or suspension form. However, such a state is difficult to maintain in this case because the drug used is highly water soluble. As a result, it can be expected that during the second phase of the release, the rate would decrease as the concentration in the core drops below the saturation value. Intravitreal implantation of this device into rabbit eyes showed sustained-release kinetics. The in vivo time-course study showed CF levels for up to 45 days in the vitreous cavity. Furthermore, both clinical and histopathological data demonstrated that the PCF device is well tolerated by rabbit eyes (185).

Promising results have been obtained with daunomycin-charged PCF, as studied by Rahimy and coworkers, for the treatment of PVR (186). This device was implanted intravitreally in rabbit eyes, and the results demonstrated that the device could prolong the release of daunomycin at a therapeutic concentration in the vitreous for at least 21 days. At the doses of daunomycin used, the device prevented tractional retinal detachment in an experimental model of PVR and was well tolerated without causing toxicity to ocular tissues.

Silicone. Silicone oil is a highly hydrophobic polymer of dimethylsiloxane showing transparency, good tolerance, and properties similar to the vitreous humor concerning the refractive index and the viscoelasticity. These characteristics have led to its use in vitreoretinal surgery; silicone oil is most frequently used as an intraocular tamponade after vitrectomy (187). It can serve as a long-term tamponade, preventing recurrent retinal detachment. However, owing to many complications such as emulsification, keratopathy, increased intraocular pressure, and cataract formation, its use is restricted to specific applications like repair of retinal detachment with proliferative vitreoretinopathy (188).

Most of the antiproliferative drugs are water soluble and thus cannot be used with silicone oil. However, lipophilic drugs, such as carmustine (also known as BCNU), can be dissolved in silicone oil, which in turn acts as a depot material and releases the drug gradually into the vitreous cavity, thus prolonging its activity (189). High doses of BCNU can be loaded in the oil without increasing its toxicity, because the effective dose gradually released to the tissues is much smaller. However, silicone oil does not dissolve and does not have sustained-release properties itself.

Another antiproliferative lipophilic drug used in association with silicone oil is retinoic acid. Araiz (50) concluded that retinoic acid given in a single intravitreal administration in solution with silicone oil produces a significant and lasting reduction in cellular proliferation in an experimental model of PVR.

Nanoparticles, Microspheres and Liposomes

Nanoparticles and Microspheres. Microparticles and nanoparticles are colloidal drug carriers in the micron and submicron size range. These systems were first developed to resolve solubility problems of poorly soluble drugs as well as for long acting injectable formulations and im-

proved drug targeting. These carriers have been evaluated as ophthalmic drug delivery vehicles over the past 15 years. An important potential use for these systems was to improve the classical aqueous eye drop formulations, which have several disadvantages such as a rapid elimination of the drugs from the precorneal site. Consequently, colloidal suspensions were designed to combine ophthalmic sustained action with the ease of application of eyedrop solutions (190).

Nanospheres have a diameter between 10 and 1,000 nm and are monolithic particles made of a porous or solid polymeric matrix, whereas nanocapsules consist of a solid or liquid drug reservoir surrounded by a polymeric membrane. Nanoparticles are usually prepared by the emulsion polymerization method, with synthetic polymers such as polyalkylcyanoacrylates (PACA), polyacrylamides, and polymethylmethacrylates. PACA has certain advantages over the two others polymers; it is biodegradable and has no adverse toxic profile (191).

Concerning the ophthalmic potential applications of nanoparticles, they are mainly used as a topical treatment for glaucoma, inflammation, or external infections of the eye because they are administered as drops and provide sustained action. However, only a few studies have been conducted concerning the intravitreal application of nanoparticles. El-Samaligy and coworkers (192) described the intravitreal injection of acyclovir and ganciclovir nanoparticles made of biodegradable polymers, such as bovine serum albumin (BSA), polyethylcyanoacrylate (PECA), and chitosan. All of these polymers exhibited interesting characteristics during in vitro evaluation (drug-loading capacity, particle size, homogeneity of nanosphere formation, and drug release). PECA was chosen for in vivo studies in rabbits because it demonstrated the best drug loading and the smallest particle size. Therapeutic levels of ganciclovir were detected in the vitreous for up to 10 days following injection of the nanospheres. Lens opacification and vitreous turbidity appeared after the PECA–nanospheres injection, most certainly due to the drug formulation, a colloidal opaque dispersion.

Microparticles have a particle size above 1 μm and comprise microspheres and microcapsules. Microspheres are polymeric drug combinations in which the drug is homogeneously dispersed in the polymer matrix. The polymers used for the preparation of microspheres are mainly based on PLA and PLGA. These bioerodible systems present the advantage that the microspheres degrade after delivering the drug; they do not have to be removed. Following administration of the suspension in the eye, the particles remain at the delivery site and the drug is released from the polymeric matrix through diffusion, polymer degradation, erosion, or a combination of these processes.

So far, it seems difficult for biodegradable polymer microspheres to encapsulate hydrophilic drugs and obtain satisfactory release profiles without burst effects (193,194). When using the conventional method of preparation of the microspheres, microcrystals of the hydrophilic substance may form in the matrix with a nonhomogeneous distribution. These microcrystals create pores in the microspheres, which in return increase the surface area of the matrix and by this means induce a faster degradation and release of the drug by diffusion. The near-linear release of drugs has been correlated with a corresponding linear decrease of molecular weight of the polymer and to the fast progression in pore formation. Diffusion of the drug from the deeper layers of the microspheres to the surface might partially explain the faster release from the lower-molecular-weight polymers. For hydrophobic drugs, the most important mechanism of release seems to be the degradation of the polymer matrix.

The factors affecting biodegradation are therefore the following: (1) LMW polymers and copolymers with a medium to high content of glycolide have faster degradation time (with 50:50 PLGA having the shortest half-life), (2) smaller-size microspheres show faster degradation, (3) the presence of drug may affect degradation time, and (4) vitrectomized eyes show faster clearance times compared to normal eyes (195).

Besides topical ophthalmic applications, which have been widely studied (191), some authors have investigated microspheres for subconjunctival (194,196,197) as well as intravitreal injections to provide sustained release of drugs (Table 7). In 1991, Khoobehi et al. (193) investigated the intravitreal injection of microspheres as a sustained-delivery system. Microspheres were made of different combinations of PLA and PLGA and contained fluorescein as a drug model. After intravitreal injection in the rabbit eye, high concentrations of the dye were detected within 24 h; they gradually decreased after 5 days, and lower concentrations were still measurable for 16 days. The in vitro and in vivo release rates from PLGA microspheres were faster than from PLA (193).

Moritera and associates (198) entrapped 5-FU in PLA and PLGA microspheres and injected it intravitreally in rabbits. The drug was released over a period up to 7 days, and the release profile was accelerated by using lower-molecular-weight polymers or copolymers. The microspheres were observed as a white mass in the vitreous cavity and were completely cleared out, on average after 48 days. Administration of microspheres had no adverse effects on the ocular tissues, even though the degradation products of PLA and PLGA are acidic. Moritera also injected PLA microspheres with adriamycin in rabbits (199). This drug, 50 times more potent than 5-FU, was released at a continuous rate for over 14 days, was effective in preventing the rate of retinal detachment after 4 weeks in an experimental model of PVR, and showed no toxicity to the retina even at a relatively high dose. Peyman and associ-

ates (200) demonstrated the efficacy of microspheres in increasing the half-life of encapsulated antimetabolites when injected intravitreally in primate eyes. Both cytosine arabinoside (ara-C) and 5-FU were entrapped in PLGA microspheres. ara-C and 5-FU released from microspheres were still detectable in the eye 11 days after injection, and the clearance kinetics were similar for both drugs. The release patterns for all these hydrophilic drugs showed an initial burst. On the other hand, Giordano et al. (201) entrapped retinoic acid, a highly hydrophobic drug, in PLGA microspheres and obtained a constant release of the drug. This system could provide therapeutic levels of retinoic acid for 40 days (Fig. 8) and avoids the use of silicone oil as a reservoir; neither does it require surgery to implant or remove the drug delivery system. Veloso and coworkers (202) recently reported the use of PLGA microspheres loaded with ganciclovir for the treatment of experimental CMV retinitis in rabbits. Using a new preparation technique, the authors obtained a very high loading of the drug, and the microspheres released ganciclovir within the therapeutic range for at least 42 days. The progression of the retinitis decreased after 3 days. Neither retinal toxicity nor adverse tissue reaction were observed after 8 weeks. Acyclovir was also investigated as a candidate for microsphere incorporation for chronic treatment of herpes simplex infections or acute retinal necrosis syndrome (140). In vitro release of acyclovir was slower when higher-molecular-weight PLA, higher-lactide-content PLGA, and larger microspheres were used. After intravitreal injection in rabbit eyes, acyclovir levels were sustained for 14 days after microsphere injection, whereas no more acyclovir was detected 3 days after administration of raw drug (140).

A biocompatibility study was conducted by Giordano and coworkers (195); following intravitreal injection of empty microspheres of relatively low molecular weight PLGA, a mild, localized, nonprogressive foreign-body reaction was observed. The choroid and retina were normal, and no clinical inflammatory signs were observed 4 days postoperatively and thereafter.

Liposomes. Liposomes were first investigated in the 1960s as a membrane model. They have been studied for many years since as a potential drug delivery system. Liposomes are microscopic vesicles composed of membrane-like lipid bilayers surrounding aqueous compartments. These lipid layers are composed of natural phospholipids such as egg lecithin or synthetic phospholipids, for example, dipalmitoylphosphatidylcholine. Cholesterol is usually

Table 7. Intravitreal Injection of Microspheres

Polymer	Drug	Animal model	Duration (days)	Year	Author (et al.)	Ref.
PLGA/PLGA	Fluorescein Na	Rabbit	16	1991	Khoobehi	193
PLA/PLGA	5-FU	Rabbit	7	1991	Moritera	198
PLA	Adriamycin	Rabbit	14	1992	Moritera	199
PLGA	5-FU, ara-C	Monkey	11	1992	Peyman	200
PLGA	Retinoic acid	Rabbit	40	1993	Giordano	201
PLA/PLGA	Acyclovir	Rabbit	14	1997	Conti	140
PLGA	Ganciclovir	Rabbit	42	1997	Veloso	202
PLGA	Fluconazole	Rabbit	21	1992	Kimura	203

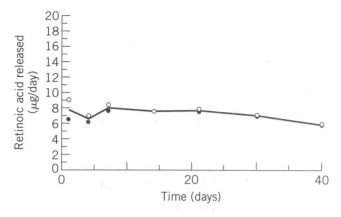

Figure 8. In vitro release rate of retinoic acid. Solid and open circles represent two different sets of experiments. The line represents the average of two measurements. *Source:* Reproduced from Ref. 201 with permission.

included in the formulation to stabilize the liposomal membrane and to minimize leaching out of the encapsulated water soluble drug. Substances such as α-tocopherol are added to decrease liposome permeability (204).

Liposomes may be classified as multi- or unilamellar depending on the number of concentric, alternating layers of phospholipids and aqueous spaces. Small unilamellar vesicles (SUV) have a diameter less than 100 nm. LUV refers to large unilamellar vesicles; and MLV, to multilamellar vesicles.

The rate of drug release from liposomes will depend upon the quality of the liposomes as well as the property of the drugs and the state of the eye. The drugs escape either by leakage through the membranes of intact liposomes or by diffusion from degraded or destabilized liposomes. Barza et al. (204) examined the effect of the size and composition of liposomes on their pharmacokinetic disposition following intravitreal injection. LUV liposomes have a longer retention time in the eye than SUVs. Concerning the components of liposomes, cholesterol stabilizes liposomal membranes, so in this case the rate of drug release is determined by the clearance of the liposome itself, whereas for non-cholesterol-containing vesicles, it is determined by the rate of leakage of the drug from the liposome. The physicochemical properties of the encapsulated drug determine its rate of release. Hydrophilic drugs are captured in the aqueous phase of liposomes, whereas lipophilic drugs, such as amphotericin B, are usually bound to the lipid bilayer or dissolved in the lipid phase. Such drugs will thus not leach out as readily as hydrophilic compounds to the external water phase. The state of the eye is also a major factor; liposomes showed a higher clearance rate in infected eyes, maybe due to an enhanced rate of diffusion of the liposome, an increased rate of flow from the vitreous to the anterior chamber, an augmented uptake by fixed or mobile phagocytes, or a breakdown of the blood–retinal barriers.

The pharmacokinetics of liposomally encapsulated drugs is not yet fully understood. Following intravitreal injection of liposomes, several processes begin simulta-

neously; intact as well as degraded liposomes clear from the vitreous body, the vesicles leak their contents in the vitreous humor, and these contents are eliminated. The mode of elimination of liposomes themselves from the vitreous remains unclear. The liposomes may egress by diffusion via the anterior route, or they may be removed by phagocytosis, for example, by pigmented epithelial cells or by degradation in situ as well as by other mechanisms or a combination of these processes (204). The state of the blood–retinal barrier and the structural integrity of the vitreous body may markedly affect the pharmacokinetic behavior of intravitreal liposomes. The liposomes are more rapidly cleared in vitrectomized eyes (205), and the breakdown of the blood–retinal barrier induced by inflammation allows the liposomes to egress and the drug to leak more easily from the vitreous.

Liposomes have been administered by practically every conceivable route. Some degree of success has been achieved for the topical and parenteral routes; a prolongation of plasma half-lives with liposome-encapsulated drugs has been reported. The development of liposomes for ocular drug delivery has been studied for various approaches of administration. Topical instillation is the most convenient and frequently used means of administration for ophthalmic therapy (206). Liposome encapsulation enhances the corneal penetration of topically applied drugs. It provides a convenient way to retard their release from a relatively inert depot without changing the intrinsic characteristics of the agents and to increase the duration of therapeutic levels. Some investigators have also experimented with the subconjunctival and intravitreal injection of liposomally entrapped drugs. Others have attempted to target ocular tissues by a systemic route of administration (207) (Table 8).

Antibiotics for the treatment of endophthalmitis were the first drugs to be encapsulated into liposomes and injected intravitreally in rabbit eyes. As early as 1986, Fishman and associates (208) incorporated gentamicin in MLV. The authors observed a lower peak value of gentamicin in the vitreous, which would presumably result in a decrease of toxic effects on the intraocular structures. However, enhanced toxicity from liposome-entrapped drugs arising from longer exposure may still be possible. Nevertheless, the release profile was significantly improved, and liposome encapsulation was thought very promising for sustained intravitreal drug administration. Another antibiotic, clindamycin, was studied by Fiscella (209) and Rao (210). The clearance of encapsulated clindamycin was 10 hours, compared to 3 hours for nonencapsulated clindamycin. Furthermore, this treatment was successful and efficacious in treating an experimental model of *S. aureus* endophthalmitis. Tobramycin, an antibiotic with marked inhibitory action against many gentamicin-resistant strains of bacteria, such as *P. aeruginosa*, was encapsulated in liposomes by Kim and Kim (211) and allowed to reduce the initial burst of the drug so as to prolong its action in the vitreous (Fig. 9) and to prevent any retinal toxicity. Zeng and associates (212) prepared liposomes with amikacin, a more effective antibiotic than gentamicin. The duration of therapeutic concentrations was generally prolonged. They observed that liposomes were more rapidly

Table 8. Applications of Liposomes for Intravitreal Administration

Drug	Type	Animal model	Duration (days)	Year	Author (et al.)	Ref.
Endophthalmitis						
Gentamicin	MLV	Rabbit	8	1986	Fishman	208
Clindamycin	MLV	Rabbit	2	1987	Fiscella	209
Clindamycin	LUV	Rabbit	N.A.	1989	Rao	210
Tobramycin	MLV	Rabbit	18	1990	Kim	211
Amikacin	MLV	Rabbit	9	1993	Zeng	212
Amphotericin B	SUV	Rabbit	35	1985	Tremblay	213
Amphotericin B	SUV	Monkey	N.A.	1985	Barza	214
Amphotericin B	LUV	Rabbit	N.A.	1989	Liu	215
CMV retinitis						
Trifluorothymidine	LUV	Rabbit	28	1987	Liu	216
Ganciclovir	LUV	Rabbit	28	1987	Peyman	217
Ganciclovir	MLV	Rabbit	14	1992	Díaz-Llopis	218
Ganciclovir	LUV	Human	24	1994	Akula	219
Ganciclovir	LUV	Rabbit	60	1996	Le Bourlais	220
2' nor-cyclic GMP	MLV	Rabbit	N.A.	1993	Shakiba	221
Foscarnet	LUV	Rabbit	3	1997	Grümbel	222
Cidofovir	MLV	Rabbit	240	1995	Besen	223
Cidofovir	MLV	Rabbit	120	1996	Kuppermann	224
Uveitis						
Cyclosporin	LUV	Rabbit	16	1988	Alghadyan	225
PVR						
5-fluorouracil	LUV	Rabbit	N.A.	1988	Joondeph	226
ara-C, FUMP	MLV	Rabbit	14	1991	Assil	227
FUMP	MLV	Rabbit	N.A.	1994	Gariano	228
5-fluorouridine	MLV	Rabbit	N.A.	1997	García-Arumí	229
Cytarabine	LUV	Rabbit	N.A.	1989	Liu	230
Fluoroorotate	+ + +	Rabbit	N.A.	1989	Heath	231
Daunomycin	LUV	Rabbit	14	1993	Hui	16

Notes: N.A., nonavailable; LUV, large unilamellar vesicles; MLV, multilamellar vesicles; SUV, small unilamellar vesicles; + + +, various types of vesicles.

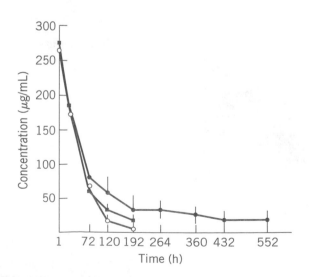

Figure 9. Tobramycin concentrations in the vitreous following intravitreal injection of liposome-encapsulated tobramycin (LET), tobramycin in PBS (TS), and tobramycin in empty liposome (TEL) in rabbits. ●, LET; ○, TS; ■, TEL. *Source:* Reproduced from Ref. 211 with permission.

cleared in vitrectomized eyes and in severely infected eyes. This is probably due to damage of the blood–retinal barrier and therefore an enhanced elimination of the drug. They concluded, however, that in severe endophthalmitis the intravitreal injection of liposomes alone could not suppress the inflammation.

Amphotericin B is a hydrophobic drug that showed different behavior from the other antibiotics described above. In a study in 1986 by Tremblay and coworkers (213), it was shown that liposome encapsulation of amphotericin B noticeably reduced its toxicity in rabbit eyes (Fig. 10) but without enhancing the therapeutic levels compared to nonencapsulated amphotericin B. The toxicity of this drug was also reduced in primate eyes (214). Indeed, unlike water-soluble molecules, which are trapped in the aqueous phase of the liposomes, amphotericin B is presumably intercalated in the liposomal bilayers. Because amphotericin B binds to sterols, this protective effect of the liposomes may result from competition for drug binding between cholesterol in the liposome and in the host's cellular membranes, reducing the acute interaction between amphotericin B and the sterol receptors. Liu and coworkers (215) further investigated the efficacy of liposomally bound amphotericin B for the treatment of experimental fungal en-

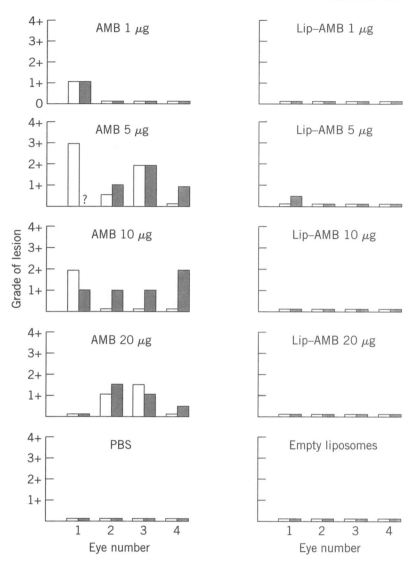

Extent of vitreal band formation and retinal damage observed ophthalmoscopically 5 weeks after injection of commercial amphotericin B (AMB) or liposomal amphotericin B (lip–AMP) in the indicated dosage in pigmented rabbits. Each bar is the result in one eye using the following score system:

Grade	Vitreal bands	Retinal damage
0	None	None
1+	Minimal	Silvery sheen or atrophy of the retina occupying 0.5–1 whole field visible at one time
2+	Moderate	Retinal sheen or atrophy of the retina occupying >1 field visible at one time
3+	Severe	More extensive than above (no such lesions actually found)

Control eyes receive phosphate-buffer saline (PBS) or empty (drug-free) liposomes.

Figure 10. Gross toxicity of intravitreal amphotericin B. □, vitreal bond formation; ■, retinal damage. *Source:* Reproduced from Ref. 213 with permission.

dophthalmitis in rabbit eyes. Liposomal amphotericin B eradicated the infection in only 40% of the eyes treated, whereas the same dosage of free drug eradicated 100% of the infection. This reduction of efficacy might be due to the membrane-stabilizing effect of cholesterol and, consequently, the reduced availability of the drug against infec-

tive organisms or to competition between liposomal membrane cholesterol and fungal ergosterol. As a result, it appears that intravitreal liposomal preparations are not ideal for treating acute clinical conditions, such as endophthalmitis, that require initially high doses of antibiotics. Liposomes may, however, be advantageous for chronic disorders for which a persistent low concentration of drug is necessary. In this latter case, liposomal preparations not only avoid the initial toxicity of the drug but also reduce the need for repeated intravitreal injections.

A disease such as CMV retinitis requires frequent intravitreal injections and long-term treatment. In 1987, the first antiviral compound, trifluorothymidine, was tested for liposomal encapsulation. Liu et al. (216) found that a substantial amount of drug remained in the vitreous 28 days after intravitreal injection, an effective concentration against most HSV types and CMV. Ganciclovir, the highly efficacious antiviral drug, has been extensively studied. Peyman et al. were the first to encapsulate it into LUV (217). The injection of liposome-entrapped ganciclovir appeared as a whitish suspension located in the inferior part of the vitreous body. This haze disappeared after 4 weeks, a period of time during which the total concentration of ganciclovir was within the therapeutic range to treat different viral strains. Díaz-Llopis et al. (218) further compared liposomal ganciclovir to a free ganciclovir solution. Liposomally encapsulated ganciclovir increased the time period required for reinjection in the treatment of CMV retinitis. The results reported are comparable to those of Peyman (217), but Díaz-Llopis used a simplified production procedure. The first clinical study performed in human eyes was undertaken by Akula et al. (219) in 1994. Intravitreal injection of liposomal ganciclovir formed a whitish suspension located in the inferior part of the vitreous cavity that gradually disappeared over 2 weeks and allowed the retention of ganciclovir for up to 24 days. Finally, Le Bourlais and coworkers (220) managed to obtain sustained release from liposomal ganciclovir for up to 60 days without toxic effects on the retina. A cyclic phosphate derivative of ganciclovir, 2'-nor-cyclic GMP, anionic in nature at neutral pH, proved an ideal candidate for encapsulation into MLV (221). This drug is as potent as ganciclovir and has a long-lasting antiviral effect, thus requiring less frequent dosing. The liposomal incorporation of 2'-nor-cyclic GMP allowed the half-life to be prolonged up to 1,000 h, more than 75 times that of ganciclovir, without any toxic signs. Finally, cidofovir was recently investigated by Besen (223) and Kuppermann (224). This compound has a different mechanism of action from ganciclovir and foscarnet; it might be beneficial for viral strains resistant to usual therapy. Cidofovir is 10 times more potent and more selective than ganciclovir and requires only short exposure time for antiviral action. Being polar and water soluble, it is highly suitable for liposomal encapsulation. Liposomal cidofovir was present in the vitreous 90 days after injection at a concentration 10 times above the ID_{50} of CMV. The efficacy of a single injection of this liposomal formulation of cidofovir may thus prevent reactivation of retinitis for more than 8 months. Kuppermann and coworkers used a lower, more appropriate dose of cidofovir (224). This system possessed a potent antiviral effect lasting up to 4 months.

PVR is a clinical condition that requires a sustained delivery of antiproliferative drugs, thus prolonging the duration of the therapeutic effect while minimizing the toxic side effects of a high initial dose. Liposome-encapsulated 5-FU was investigated by Joondeph et al. (226). This formulation allowed higher intraocular levels of 5-FU over a prolonged period after injection of a dose that, when given in the free form, is indeed toxic to the retina. Antimetabolites such as ara-C and 5-fluorouridine-5'-monophosphate (FUMP) were encapsulated by Assil and coworkers (227) and investigated for the treatment of experimental PVR in rabbits. The half-lives of both drugs were significantly prolonged. ara-C was found to be less effective than FUMP in reducing tractional retinal detachment, probably because of its lower potency (227). Liposomal FUMP was found very efficacious by increasing exposure time of fibroblasts to the drug from 1 to 72 hours, resulting in a 20-fold increase in efficacy. FUMP was further investigated by Gariano and coworkers (228) to evaluate its retinal toxicity when entrapped in MLV. It was found nontoxic at doses sufficient to inhibit PVR. García-Arumí and coworkers (229) encapsulated 5-fluorouridine in collagen-coated liposomes, knowing that this protein is the most important constituent of the extracellular matrix of epiretinal membranes in PVR and that cells involved in this process have specific receptors for collagen. This coating may increase the affinity of the target cells for the surface of liposomes. In an electron microscopy study, these authors confirmed that intravitreally injected liposomes bind extensively to the internal limiting lamina of the retina without entering the retina, thus potentially decreasing retinal toxicity. Liposomal ara-C has also been shown to be nontoxic to the retina when encapsulated into liposomes (230). Heath et al. selected a so-called liposome-dependent drug, fluoroorotate, a compound that seems not to enter cells unless bound to liposomes (231). Heath demonstrated the in vitro antiproliferative and anticontractile effects of fluoroorotate, properties that are essential for the treatment of PVR. The liposome drug complex was delivered to epiretinal membranes within the rabbit eye while minimizing toxicity to underlying tissues such as the retina. A single injection of liposomal fluoroorotate effectively inhibited retinal detachment in an experimental model of PVR (231). Finally, in a study by Hui et al. (16), daunomycin was encapsulated into liposomes and investigated in an experimental model of PVR. A prolonged half-life and minimized toxicity were reported following the encapsulation process.

Another approach of delivering local concentrations of a drug while lessening toxic effects at other sites is to administer liposomally encapsulated drugs by a systemic route. Various strategies have been attempted to target the released contents of liposomes. One approach has been to formulate liposomes that release their contents in response to hyperthermia (heat of 40–42°C). These liposomes are called "temperature-sensitive" and have been studied since 1984; Khoobehi et al. (232) delivered carboxyfluorescein and ara-C from temperature-sensitive liposomes, using a noninvasive microwave generator as an external trigger. Liposomes prepared from synthetic phospholipids rapidly released their contents at a phase-transition temperature of 41°C; however, in the presence of serum, the transition temperature decreased to approximately 40°C. The amounts of dye and drug released were different owing to the different physicochemical characteristics of both substances. Khoobehi et al. (233) further investigated the release of drugs from temperature-sensitive liposomes, ara-C, and 5-fluorouridine. A microwave-generated hyperthermia was applied to the rabbit eye, and the intravitreal release of the drugs was measured. The amounts were all higher in the heated eyes. The application of heat did not cause any damage to the ocular tissues. Ogura and co-workers (234) managed to deliver a model substance, carboxyfluorescein, to selective areas of the retina. As penetration of the drug into the retinal tissue is significantly restricted by intercellular tight junctions between vascular endothelial cells, retinal pigmented epithelial cells, and photoreceptors that form the blood–retinal barrier, the authors induced a breakdown of this barrier by laser pulses. The drug encapsulated in temperature-sensitive liposomes, situated in the lumen of the vessels, could then penetrate into the retina through areas where the barrier was disrupted. Liposomal encapsulation prevented any retinal toxicity compared with injection of the free drug. No evidence of retinal injury after laser exposure was found.

In summary, data generated in the last two decades clearly demonstrate that liposomes have great potential as novel drug delivery systems. The following advantages can be mentioned (207). First of all, liposomes can incorporate both hydrophilic and lipophilic compounds; therefore, even water-insoluble constituents can be administered in a liquid dosage form in which the therapeutic agent is dissolved. Composed of lipids similar to those present in biological membranes, liposomes are expected to be biocompatible and biodegradable. Liposomes can provide slow or controlled release and consequently prolonged action of encapsulated drugs. As long as the drug is incorporated within the liposomes, it cannot be metabolized. The rate of drug release can be influenced by selecting appropriate lipid components of the liposomal membrane, such as cholesterol or hydrogenated phospholipids. Finally, there is considerably reduced retinal toxicity of intravitreally injected drugs when they are encapsulated within liposomes.

Drug delivery using liposomes may be useful for the treatment of posterior segment diseases; however, there are also inherent problems encountered with these methods. One of the major problems limiting the widespread use of liposomes is both chemical and physical stability. Chemical instability may be due to hydrolysis or oxidation of the lipid components; physical instability may be caused by drug leakage from the vesicles and/or aggregation or fusion of the vesicles into larger particles. All these processes influence the bioavailability of encapsulated drugs. Some of these stability problems can be overcome by lyophilization; if the finished product is preserved in a relatively more stable dry state, its shelf life is longer. Sterilization is often difficult because most methods are unsuitable for liposomal products; phospholipids are thermolabile and sensitive to sterilization procedures involving the use of heat, radiation, and/or chemical sterilizing agents. The method available for sterilization of liposomes is filtration through 0.22-μm membranes; however, filtration is not suitable for LUV and does not remove viruses or pyrogens (207). Finally, intravitreally administered liposomes tend to spread diffusely within the vitreous cavity and cause cloudiness, interfering with the patient's visual acuity and the ability of the ophthalmologist to examine

the fundus until complete biodegradation of the formulation has occurred (217,235).

Iontophoresis

Iontophoresis, from the Greek *ionto*, ion, and *phoresis*, to bear, is a process that allows increased penetration of ionized molecules across or into tissues by application of a low electric current (mA) (236). The drug is applied with an electrode carrying the same charge as the drug, while the ground electrode, which is of the opposite charge, is placed elsewhere on the body to complete the electric circuit (236) (Fig. 11).

The factors governing the penetration of drugs by iontophoresis have been studied by Hughes and Maurice (238); the penetration of a drug is proportional to the current and to the duration of its application, whereas the concentration of the drug solution does not seem to be an important factor (239). Other factors are the design of the electrode and the physicochemical properties of the drug, such as its charge (it should be ionized at a physiological pH and soluble in water) and its size (the drug should have a relatively small molecular size, <600 Da [24]).

Two types of iontophoresis are performed in the eye, namely, transcorneal and transscleral iontophoresis (237). Although transcorneal iontophoresis is capable of producing high and sustained levels of drug in the cornea and the aqueous humor, thus allowing the treatment of anterior segment diseases, only meager concentrations are achieved in the vitreous humor. This is due to the iris–lens diaphragm, which limits the penetration of the drug into the vitreous cavity. Incidentally, significant drug concentration levels were achieved in aphakic eyes, as reported by Fishman and colleagues (241). To circumvent the iris–lens barrier, transscleral iontophoresis is applied through the pars plana rather than the cornea. Because it is as effective in phakic as in aphakic eyes, it provides therapeutic vitreous drug levels to treat posterior segment disorders. Transscleral iontophoresis may thus replace or supplement intravitreal injections. This procedure has gained interest as a local drug delivery system for sub-

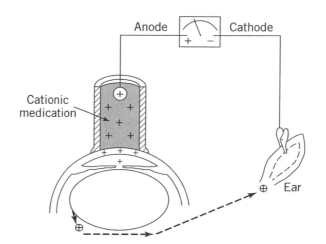

Figure 11. Ocular iontophoresis in the rabbit. *Source:* Reproduced from Ref. 237 with permission.

stances that are not amenable to topical delivery and require repeated administration over an extended period of time, such as antibiotics, antifungal, antiviral, antimetabolite, and steroid drugs (242) (Table 9).

The first application of transscleral iontophoresis was carried out by von Sallman as early as 1943; atropine and scopolamine were introduced in the vitreous humor by using an electrode circling the sclera (243). Since that time, iontophoretic delivery of antibiotics has been successful in providing vitreal therapeutic levels of drugs. Burstein et al. (243) administered gentamicin to rabbit eyes by means of transscleral iontophoresis. After the application of current for 3 minutes, a depot of gentamicin was introduced into the vitreous humor, which allowed therapeutic levels to be maintained in the adjoining ocular tissues for more than 24 h. Grossman and coworkers (245) compared transcorneal and transscleral iontophoresis of gentamicin to each other and with respect to subconjunctival injection. The highest intravitreal levels were achieved by transscleral iontophoresis, 53.4 μg/mL after 16 h, whereas the peak level achieved through transcorneal iontophoresis was 0.5 μg/mL after 30 min, and through subconjunctival injection, 2.6 μg/mL after 30 min. The vitreal levels remained within the therapeutic range for 24 h. Barza et al. (239) delivered iontophoretically three antibiotics, cefazolin, ticarcillin, and gentamicin, to rabbit eyes. Three hours after application of a current for 10 min over the *pars plana*, mean vitreal concentration of the antibiotics reached 94 to 207 μg/mL. Drug penetration showed a correlation with the current intensity and the duration of iontophoresis but not with the concentration of the drug solution. The procedure caused focal damage to the retina, for example, hemorrhagic necrosis, edema, and infiltration by polymorphonuclear cells, but the authors supposed that such an amount of injury is no greater than that caused by

an intravitreal injection or surgical implantation of a sustained-release drug delivery device. Transscleral iontophoresis of gentamicin was also found effective in monkeys (244). Vitreal levels achieved were similar to those obtained in rabbit eyes with a lower current (239). The procedure was well tolerated, and the small burns produced by the electric current were over the *pars plana*, an area of the eye not critical for vision. The authors concluded that transscleral iontophoresis could be applied in humans with topical anesthesia only. Vancomycin is an antibiotic compound bearing two positive charges and having a relatively high molecular weight of 1,448 Da. It is very effective against gram-positive bacteria and *Bacillus* species. After application of 3.5 mA for 10 min, vitreal levels of vancomycin were well above the minimal therapeutic concentration of 5 μg/mL 8 h after treatment (240). Ciprofloxacin, a zwitterionic molecule, was investigated by Yoshizumi et al. (246). After transscleral iontophoresis, higher vitreal concentrations were achieved when the negatively charged form of ciprofloxacin was used rather than the positively charged form. However, aqueous levels were higher than vitreous levels, which were under the MIC$_{90}$ of several organisms commonly causing endophthalmitis.

Grossman and Lee (247) attempted to deliver ketoconazole, an antifungal agent, to the vitreous of rabbits by transscleral iontophoresis. The water solubility of this drug is relatively low. The peak concentration achieved in the vitreous was not sufficient for therapeutic fungicidal activity. Transscleral iontophoresis is consequently not an effective means to deliver this antifungal drug for the treatment of endogenous endophthalmitis.

Lam and coworkers (248) performed transscleral iontophoresis of dexamethasone sodium phosphate into rabbit eyes and obtained high and long-lasting therapeutic

Table 9. Ocular Iontophoretic Drug Delivery

Drugs	Current (mA)	Duration (min)	Peak level (μg/mL)	Animal model	Year	Author (et al.)	Ref.
Endophthalmitis							
Gentamicin	2.0	3	20.0	Rabbit	1985	Burstein	243
Gentamicin	1.5	10.0	28.0	Monkey	1987	Barza	244
Gentamicin	2.0	10.0	53.4	Rabbit	1990	Grossman	245
Gentamicin	2.0	10.0	207.0	Rabbit	1986	Barza	239
Cefazolin	2.0	10.0	119.0	Rabbit	1986	Barza	239
Ticarcillin	2.0	10.0	94.0	Rabbit	1986	Barza	239
Vancomycin	3.5	10.0	13.4	Rabbit	1988	Choi	240
Ciprofloxacin	5.0	15.0	0.2	Rabbit	1991	Yoshizumi	246
Ketoconazole	4.0–6.0	15.0	0.1	Rabbit	1989	Grossman	247
Uveitis							
Dexamethasone	1.6	25.0	139.3	Rabbit	1989	Lam	248
Dexamethasone	0.4	4.0	N.A.	Rat	1997	Behar-Cohen	249
CMV retinitis							
Ganciclovir	1.0	15.0	74.0	Rabbit	1994	Lam	250
Foscarnet	1.0	10.0	200.0	Rabbit	1993	Sarraf	251
Foscarnet	1.0	10.0	203.0 μM[a]	Rabbit	1996	Yoshizumi	252

Notes: N.A., nonavailable.
[a]Given as a supplementation of intravenous foscarnet.

concentrations of this antiinflammatory drug, maybe owing to pools of dexamethasone that would have accumulated in the different ocular tissues. In an experimental model of uveitis, Behar-Cohen et al. (249) investigated iontophoresis of dexamethasone by applying the electrode on both sclera and cornea of rat eyes. This procedure allowed the reduction of inflammation in both anterior and posterior segments of the eye as efficiently as systemic corticotherapy without any clinical or histological damages to the eyes.

Transscleral iontophoresis of antiviral agents such as ganciclovir could be useful for the treatment of CMV retinitis. Lam et al. (250) showed that a single iontophoretic application of ganciclovir over the *pars plana* may deliver a therapeutic dose of this drug into the vitreous, resulting in significant levels even 3 days after its administration. Foscarnet was also successfully delivered by transscleral iontophoresis (251). The peak concentration achieved 4 h after the administration of the current was below the concentration reported to cause retinal toxicity, and therapeutic levels could be maintained up to 60 h after iontophoresis.

The advantages of iontophoresis include the minimization of systemic exposure to the drug; the delivery of high concentrations of the drug directly to the targeted site; a minimal discomfort for the patient, only under topical anesthesia; and improved consistency in the penetration of the drug (238). It is a noninvasive procedure that may replace or supplement intravenous therapy or intravitreal injection of drugs (252).

Nevertheless, iontophoresis is not a harmless procedure. Transscleral iontophoresis might be associated with damage to the retina and the choroid, as described by Maurice (253). He observed destruction of most of the layers of the retina, with an engorgement of the choroid. Barza et al. (240,245) noticed hemorrhagic necrosis; edema; inflammatory infiltration of the retina, the choroid, and the ciliary body; and retinal burns. Lam and coworkers (254) presented a detailed description of the pathologic features occurring after transscleral iontophoresis. The pathologic changes varied with the duration of application. In contrast to the extensive retinal changes caused by 2 to 25 min of transscleral iontophoresis, a short application period (≤ 1 min) did not result in histopathologic changes. Although the mechanism of retinal damage caused by transscleral iontophoresis is not known, it is suspected to be produced by heat or by the directly applied electrical current. On the other hand, during iontophoresis, electrolysis takes place in the electrode chamber, and the pH of the solution is sharply raised (or decreased, depending on the polarity of the electrode). Hence, negatively charged hydroxide ions may be driven into the vitreous and accumulate in the vicinity of the area undergoing iontophoresis toward the end of the procedure, causing chemical burns.

Prodrugs and Codrugs

The term *prodrug* was first introduced in 1958 by Albert (255) to describe an inactive compound, formed by linking a drug to an inert chemical, namely, the promoiety, by a covalent bond that could be broken in vivo by any mechanism, spontaneously or enzymatically, to yield the active drug substance. Furthermore, the prodrug should possess better delivery properties than the parent drug molecule (256). The use of prodrugs for ocular delivery has been reviewed by Lee and Li (257). Prodrugs are mainly used topically to increase corneal drug absorption to enhance efficacy, reduce the incidence of systemic side effects by lowering the required dose, and prolong the duration of action and thereby improve patient compliance. In the case of intravitreal delivery, the main advantage of prodrugs is that they prolong the action of drugs that are rapidly cleared out from the vitreous when administered in a conventional dosage form.

Steffansen and coworkers (258) developed a drug delivery system of 5-FU prodrugs suspended in silicone oil to maintain therapeutic intravitreal levels of 5-FU over several days for the treatment of PVR. They synthesized several lipophilic N-alkoxycarbonyl derivatives of 5-FU, with alkyl chain lengths ranging from 6 to 18 carbon units. All prodrugs hydrolyzed quantitatively to the parent 5-FU in aqueous buffer. Hydrolysis was accelerated in the presence of plasma or rabbit vitreous, which exhibited an enzymatic contribution, but in all cases the reaction followed first-order kinetics. The release rate of 5-FU depended on the alkyl chain length; the more lipophilic the prodrug, the more sustained the release rate.

Taskintuna and associates (259) investigated a lipid prodrug, acyclovir diphosphate dimyristoylglycerol (ACVDP-DMG). ACVDP-DMG represents the combination of acyclovir with cytidine diphosphate diacylglycerol (Fig. 12), a naturally occurring phospholipid, and it is very active against HSV and CMV. ACVDP-DMG is the prototype of a class of liposome prodrugs that the authors term *prosomes*. This compound makes up part of a liposome wall together with naturally occurring phospholipids, as opposed to conventional liposomes in which the drug is placed inside the liposomes. This prosome was found superior to both ganciclovir and acyclovir in a rabbit model of HSV retinitis. The ACVDP-DMG seemed to be specifically absorbed by the retina following intravitreal injection in rabbits, because the liposome walls seemed to fuse with the retinal cell membranes, allowing incorporation and progressive release of the drug into the retinal cells. This system did not seem to cause any toxic effects to the retina or the lens. In a pharmacokinetic study (260), liposomal ACVDP-DMG provided therapeutic levels of acyclovir for 18 days.

The use of a conjugate drug, a so-called codrug, is a novel approach that allows sustained release of two drug entities. These two drugs become relatively insoluble when covalently linked, and hydrolysis of the chemical bond allows both drugs to be released slowly in equimolar quantities. The codrug has a distinct advantage over the use of either drug alone because it incorporates the properties of both parent compounds while allowing a sustained delivery over an extended period of time. Consequently, a controlled release is achieved without recourse to more traditional polymeric drug delivery systems, some of which have been shown to induce a mild, localized foreign-body reaction with glial proliferation and inflammation.

A study by Berger and coworkers (261) was designed to evaluate the efficacy of two codrugs in preventing the de-

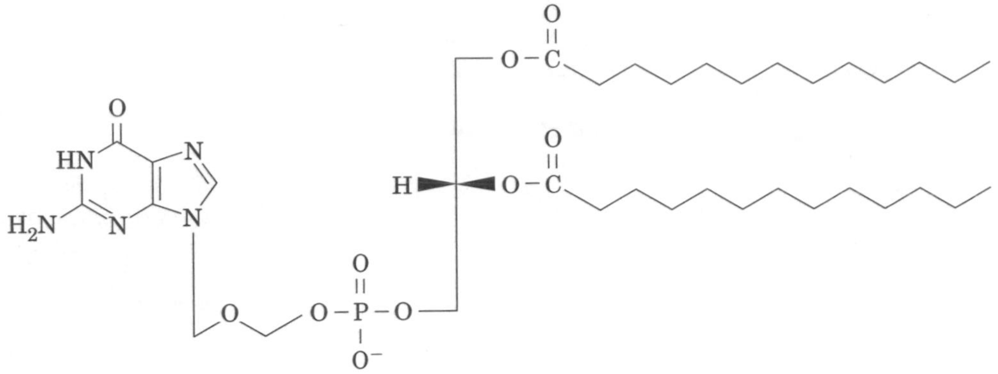

Figure 12. Structure of acyclovir diphosphate dimyristoylglycerol. *Source:* Ref. 261.

velopment of PVR in a rabbit model. The codrugs are composed of an antimetabolite, 5-FU, covalently linked to a corticosteroid, dexamethasone (DEX) or triamcinolone acetonide (TA), by a carbonate bond (Fig. 13). After synthesis of the codrugs by chemical reaction, the authors prepared pellets by direct compression of the DEX–5-FU powdered codrug and a suspension of the TA–5-FU codrug. The DEX–5-FU pellet released the drugs over 1 week in vitro. Using an experimental model of PVR in rabbits, the authors implanted the pellet intravitreally and observed a reduction of the incidence of retinal detachment from 70 to 20% until day 13, after which by day 20 the retinal detachment was up to 40%. The TA–5-FU codrug in suspension is more hydrophobic and provided considerably longer sustained release in vitro than the more soluble DEX–5-FU codrug. The TA–5-FU suspension reduced the incidence of retinal detachment from 89 to 30% from day 14 until day 28. Corelease occurs in two steps. The first step, codrug dissolution, is determined by the solubility of the compound and is the rate-determining step. The second step, codrug hydrolysis, occurs rapidly. This may explain why the more hydrophobic drug was the more effective in inhibiting experimental PVR.

In another investigation by Guo (262), an intravitreal device composed of the prodrug acyclovir–flurbiprofen was developed for the treatment of acute retinal necrosis (ARN), a disease that is accompanied by severe vasculitis. Treatment of inflammation can cause difficulty as steroids may induce a flare of viral activity. In AIDS-associated ARN, patients frequently respond poorly to systemic acyclovir, necessitating intravitreal injections. However, the damaged blood–retinal barrier enhances the clearance of acyclovir, requiring more frequent drug administration. A system capable of maintaining sustained therapeutic levels of acyclovir and flurbiprofen would thus be a real advantage. Pellets of codrug released both parent drugs in vitro following a zero-order kinetics. The release rate increased in the presence of proteins and enzymes. Bearing in mind that inflammation can elevate ocular protein concentrations by a factor of 10, this would result in accelerated drug release from this codrug system. The codrug delivery system may therefore form the basis of a disease-regulated delivery system, increasing release rate to match the severity of the condition and then decreasing to preserve the life span of the device (262).

CONCLUSION

In the past, most intraocular diseases, including sight-threatening endophthalmitis, devastating CMV retinitis, proliferative vitreoretinopathy, and uveitis, were treated by systemic and subconjunctival administration of drugs. These routes of treatment led, in the majority of cases, to the loss of the eye owing to the poor penetration of the various drugs into the vitreous cavity. This can be explained by the tight junctional complexes that interconnect cells of the retinal pigment epithelium and also tightly bind together the endothelial cells forming the walls of the retinal capillaries. These surfaces form the so-called blood–retinal barrier and prohibit passage of substances across the cells. In diseases such as endophthalmitis, the inflammation breaks down this barrier, but at this stage of the disease the retina has already been irreversibly damaged. The means of bypassing physiological and anatomical barriers and achieving high vitreous concentrations is through intravitreal administration. The use of intraocular drugs had formerly been restricted to the treatment of endophthalmitis. Nowadays, it is also considered for disorders that have been described in this article such as CMV retinitis, proliferative vitreoretinopathy, and uveitis. All these clinical conditions require frequent and repeated intravitreal injections of drugs, which may cause severe complications such as retinal detachment, vitreous hemorrhage, or intraocular infections. That is why sustained delivery systems have been developed recently to prolong the therapeutic levels of these drugs in the vitreous and thus diminish the frequency of the injections. This article has reviewed some of these systems (Table 10).

Biodegradable polymers have an advantage over other controlled-release systems in obviating the need to surgically remove the drug-depleted device. Potentially, biodegradable matrix systems also enjoy a number of other advantages in terms of simplicity in design and predictability of release if the latter is controlled solely by the erosion of the matrix. In many cases, however, the release occurs also by diffusion through the matrix, making the process more difficult to control—particularly if the matrix is hydrophilic and thereby absorbs water, promoting degradation in the interior of the matrix. To maximize control over the release process, it is desirable to have a polymeric system

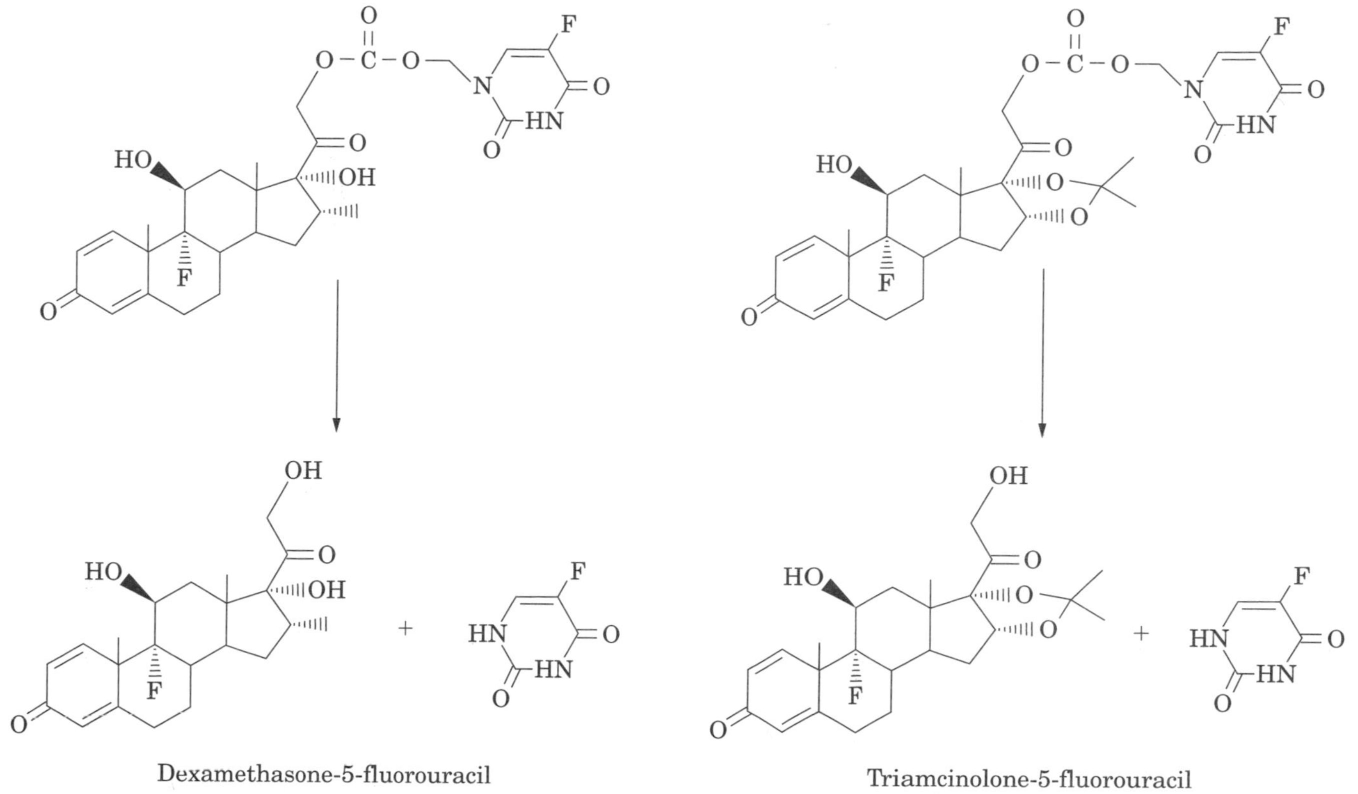

Figure 13. Chemical structures of dexamethasone–5-fluorouracil and triamcinolone–5-fluorouracil codrugs and hydrolysis to the parent drugs. *Source:* Ref. 261.

that degrades only from the surface and delays the permeation of drug molecules. Achieving such a heterogeneous degradation requires the rate of hydrolytic degradation on the surface to be much faster than the rate of water penetration into the bulk. The ideal polymer would have a hydrophobic backbone but with a water-labile linkage. Many classes of polymers have been designed with these considerations in mind. Among them, polyanhydrides and POEs erode from surface. Taking advantage of the pH dependence of the rate of ortho ester cleavage, preferential hydrolysis at the surface is obtained by either addition of basic substances to suppress degradation in the bulk or incorporation of acidic catalysts to promote degradation on the surface.

Devices that are not biodegradable such as the EVA–PVA implants are of clinical utility for chronic, sight-threatening diseases such as CMV retinitis and uveitis. These conditions are likely to require long-term drug therapy; therefore, any device may need to be replaced once depleted of drug. On the other hand, in diseases such as PVR, which requires relatively short-term therapy (weeks or months), a biodegradable system is clearly more desirable.

Microspheres and liposomes have been shown to increase the efficacy, reduce the toxicity, prolong the activity, and provide site-specific delivery for many drugs when administered to the eye. However, liposomes tend to have a short shelf life and to migrate within the eye (possibly to unwanted locations) following intraocular injection. Fur-

thermore, the intravitreal injection of a liposome preparation always disturbs the patient's vision. Microspheres are more stable, their production is reproducible, and the release rate is controllable; but the injection of microspheres in the vitreous is always followed by an impairment of the visual acuity.

Transscleral iontophoresis has proved to be fast and painless and in most cases results in the delivery of a high and long-lasting vitreal concentration of the drug. However, several authors have noticed damage to the retina such as burns and disorganization of the retinal cell layers. These lesions are probably as harmful as those created by an intravitreal injection or surgical implantation of a sustained-release drug delivery device.

The prodrug or codrug approach, on the other hand, is a good method of providing sustained release of one or more drugs. The main advantage of this system is the absence of any polymeric material that might cause problems of biocompatibility.

The ideal drug release system should then fulfill the following criteria: (*1*) the systems should provide a sustained therapeutic concentration of drug in a reliable and predictable way over an adequate period to obtain the desired clinical response: inhibition of the inflammation or prevention of proliferation and contraction of epiretinal membranes in the case of proliferative vitreoretinopathy; (*2*) the concentration of drug should be relatively uniform over the administration period, with no early or late excessive release of the drug; (*3*) the device should be easily

Table 10. Advantages and Drawbacks of the Drug Delivery Systems Described in this Article

Pros	Cons
Biodegradable polymeric systems	
No need to be removed	Possible toxicity of breakdown products
No impairment of the clarity of ocular media	Rapid degradation
For *short-term* therapy (weeks to months)	Often sterilization problems
Controllable release rates	
Eventually injectable through a needle	
Nonbiodegradable polymeric systems	
No degradation products	To be removed after depletion
No impairment of the clarity of ocular media	Risk of encapsulation
For *long-term* therapy (months to years)	
Controllable release rates	
Nanoparticles, microspheres	
Injectable through needle	Vitreal haze after injection
Long shelf life	Initial burst effect
Good control over release	
Liposomes	
Good biocompatibility	Vitreal haze after injection
Reduction of drug toxicity	Short shelf life
Injectable through needle	Difficult to sterilize
Iontophoresis	
Noninvasive	For ionized drug
	Damages to the eye (burns)
Prodrugs and codrugs	
Concomitant equimolar release of both drugs from the codrug	No tailored release from the codrug
No need for polymeric carrier material	
Good tolerance	

implantable or injectable but must remain stable and non-migratory within the eye; (*4*) the device should be totally biodegradable to avoid the need for explantation at a later date; (*5*) the device should have a long shelf life, should be easily handled by surgeons and operating room personnel, and should be easily sterilized; and (*6*) there should be no toxic effect from sustained exposure to the drug or degradation products of the device.

None of the sustained-delivery systems introduced to date fulfill all these criteria. Yet all of the exciting approaches described in this article may lead to the improvement of vision in patients with severe posterior segment diseases.

ACKNOWLEDGMENTS

This work was supported by Swiss National Science Foundation grants #32.46795.96 and #32.35925.92

BIBLIOGRAPHY

1. V.H.L. Lee, K.J. Prince, D.A. Frambach, and B. Martini, in S.J. Ryan, ed., *Retina*, Mosby, St. Louis, Mo., 1989, pp. 483–498.

2. J.G. Cunha-Vaz and D.M. Maurice, *J. Physiol. (London)* **191**, 467–486 (1967).

3. D.M. Maurice and S. Mishima, in M.L. Sears, ed., *Pharmacology of the Eye*, Springer-Verlag, Berlin, 1984, pp. 19–116.

4. G.A. Peyman and R. Herbst, *Arch. Ophthalmol. (Chicago)* **91**, 416–418 (1974).

5. D.M. Maurice, *J. Physiol. (London)* **137**, 110–125 (1957).

6. T.S. Lesar and R.G. Fiscella, *Drug Intell. Clin. Pharm.* **19**, 642–654 (1985).

7. The Retina Society Terminology Committee, *Ophthalmology* **90**, 121–125 (1983).

8. W.F. Rachal and T.C. Burton, *Arch. Ophthalmol. (Chicago)* **97**, 480–483 (1979).

9. M. Cowley et al., *Arch. Ophthalmol. (Chicago)* **107**, 1147–1151 (1989).

10. C. Claes, H.M. Freeman, and F.I. Tolentino, in H.M. Freeman and F.I. Tolentino, eds., *Proliferative Vitreoretinopathy (PVR)*, Springer-Verlag, New York, 1988, pp. 3–11.

11. P.A. Campochiaro, *Arch. Ophthalmol. (Chicago)* **115**, 237–241 (1997).

12. P.A. Campochiaro, J.A. Bryan, B.P. Conway, and E.H. Jaccoma, *Arch. Ophthalmol. (Chicago)* **104**, 1685–1687 (1986).

13. D.G. Charteris, P. Hiscott, I. Grierson, and S.L. Lightman, *Ophthalmology* **99**, 1364–1367 (1992).

14. D.B. Chandler, F.A. Quansah, T. Hida, and R. Machemer, *Graefe's Arch. Clin. Exp. Ophthalmol.* **224**, 86–91 (1986).

15. A. Ophir, M.S. Blumenkranz, and A.J. Claflin, *Am. J. Ophthalmol.* **94**, 450–457 (1982).

16. Y.N. Hui et al., *Graefe's Arch. Clin. Exp. Ophthalmol.* **231**, 109–114 (1993).

17. J.H. Stahl, D.B. Miller, B.P. Conway, and P.A. Campochiaro, *Graefe's Arch. Clin. Exp. Ophthalmol.* **225**, 418–420 (1987).

18. M. Lemor, S. de Bustros, and B.M. Glaser, *Arch. Ophthalmol. (Chicago)* **104**, 1223–1225 (1986).

19. C. Verdoorn et al., *Arch. Ophthalmol. (Chicago)* **104**, 1216–1219 (1986).

20. R.L. Avery and B.M. Glaser, *Arch. Ophthalmol. (Chicago)* **104**, 1220–1222 (1986).

21. M. Gonvers, *Am. J. Ophthalmol.* **100**, 239–245 (1985).

22. M.K. Hartzer et al., *Exp. Eye Res.* **48**, 321–328 (1989).

23. L.J.B. McGuigan et al., *Invest. Ophthalmol. Visual Sci.* **29**, 112–118 (1988).

24. N.D. Radtke, A.D. Weinsieder, and R.J. Ballou, *Graefe's Arch. Clin. Exp. Ophthalmol.* **224**, 230–233 (1986).

25. A.R. Irvine, H.W. Flynn, D. Miller, and S.C. Pflugfelder, *Arch. Ophthalmol. (Chicago)* **110**, 1450–1454 (1992).

26. M.S. Blumenkranz and M.K. Hartzer, in S.J. Ryan, ed., *Retina*, Mosby, St. Louis, Mo., 1989, pp. 401–411.

27. Y. Tano, G. Sugita, G. Abrams, and R. Machemer, *Am. J. Ophthalmol.* **89**, 131–136 (1980).

28. M.S. Blumenkranz, A.J. Claflin, and A.S. Hajek, *Arch. Ophthalmol. (Chicago)* **102**, 598–604 (1984).

29. Y. Tano, D.B. Chandler, and R. Machemer, *Am. J. Ophthalmol.* **90**, 810–816 (1980).

30. D.B. Chandler et al., *Graefe's Arch. Clin. Exp. Ophthalmol.* **225**, 259–265 (1987).

31. A. Barrada et al., *Ophthalmic Surg.* **14**, 845–847 (1983).

32. J.A. Leon et al., *Invest. Ophthalmol. Visual Sci.* **31**, 1709–1716 (1990).

33. A. Ophir, *Ophthalmic Res.* **23**, 128–132 (1991).

34. M.S. Blumenkranz, A. Ophir, A.J. Claflin, and A.S. Hajek, *Am. J. Ophthalmol.* **94**, 458–467 (1982).

35. M.S. Blumenkranz, E. Hernandez, A. Ophir, and E.W.D. Norton, *Ophthalmology* **91**, 122–130 (1984).

36. G. Jarus, M.S. Blumenkranz, E. Hernandez, and N. Sossi, *Ophthalmology* **92**, 91–96 (1985).

37. W.H. Stern et al., *Am. J. Ophthalmol.* **96**, 33–42 (1983).

38. M.S. Blumenkranz, M.K. Hartzer, and A.S. Hajek, *Arch. Ophthalmol. (Chicago)* **105**, 396–399 (1987).

39. P. Wiedemann et al., *Graefe's Arch. Clin. Exp. Ophthalmol.* **220**, 233–235 (1983).

40. U.H. Steinhorst et al., *Invest. Ophthalmol. Visual Sci.* **34**, 1753–1760 (1993).

41. M.A. Sunalp, P. Wiedemann, N. Sorgente, and S.J. Ryan, *Exp. Eye Res.* **41**, 105–115 (1985).

42. P. Wiedemann, K. Lemmen, R. Schmiedl, and K. Heimann, *Am. J. Ophthalmol.* **104**, 10–14 (1987).

43. J.A. Khawly, P. Saloupis, D.L. Hatchell, and R. Machemer, *Graefe's Arch. Clin. Exp. Ophthalmol.* **229**, 464–467 (1991).

44. M. Kirmani et al., *Retina* **3**, 269–272 (1983).

45. M. Santana et al., *Graefe's Arch. Clin. Exp. Ophthalmol.* **221**, 210–213 (1984).

46. F.M. van Bockxmeer, C.E. Martin, D.E. Thompson, and I.J. Constable, *Invest. Ophthalmol. Visual Sci.* **26**, 1140–1147 (1985).

47. M. Lemor, J.H. Yeo, and B.M. Glaser, *Arch. Ophthalmol. (Chicago)* **104**, 1226–1229 (1986).

48. C. Davidson, W.R. Green, and V.G. Wong, *Invest. Ophthalmol. Visual Sci.* **24**, 301–311 (1983).

49. A.A. Deshpande, C. Tabatabay, and R. Gurny, *J. Controlled Release* **48**, 115–129 (1997).

50. J.J. Araiz et al., *Invest. Ophthalmol. Visual Sci.* **34**, 522–530 (1993).

51. M. Nakagawa et al., *Invest. Ophthalmol. Visual Sci.* **36**, 2388–2395 (1995).

52. G.A. Peyman et al., *Ophthalmic Surg.* **15**, 844–846 (1984).

53. G.A. Peyman et al., *Ophthalmic Surg.* **15**, 411–413 (1984).

54. D.E. Henderley, W.R. Freeman, D.M. Causey, and N.A. Rao, *Ophthalmology* **94**, 425–434 (1987).

55. R.F. Sison et al., *Am. J. Ophthalmol.* **112**, 243–249 (1991).

56. J.A. Schulman et al., *Jpn. J. Ophthalmol.* **30**, 116–124 (1986).

57. J.A. Schulman et al., *Ophthalmic Surg.* **17**, 429–432 (1986).

58. G.N. Holland et al., *Ophthalmology* **94**, 815–823 (1987).

59. D.A. Jabs, C. Newman, S. de Bustros, and B.F. Polk, *Ophthalmology* **94**, 824–830 (1987).

60. H.L. Hennis, A.A. Scott, and D.J. Apple, *Surv. Ophthalmol.* **34**, 193–203 (1989).

61. D.A. Jabs, C. Enger, and J.G. Bartlett, *Arch. Ophthalmol. (Chicago)* **107**, 75–80 (1989).

62. G.N. Holland et al., *Arch. Ophthalmol. (Chicago)* **107**, 1759–1766 (1989).

63. D.J. D'Amico et al., *Arch. Ophthalmol. (Chicago)* **104**, 1788–1793 (1986).

64. J.S. Pulido, G.A. Peyman, T. Lesar, and J. Vernot, *Arch. Ophthalmol. (Chicago)* **103**, 840–841 (1985).

65. M.H. Heinemann, *Arch. Ophthalmol. (Chicago)* **107**, 1767–1772 (1989).

66. I. Cochereau-Massin et al., *Ophthalmology* **98**, 1348–1355 (1991).

67. P. Lehoang et al., *Ophthalmology* **96**, 865–874 (1989).

68. M.A. Jacobson and J.J. O'Donnell, *J. AIDS* **4**, S11–S15 (1991).

69. W.L. Drew et al., *J. Infect. Dis.* **163**, 716–719 (1991).

70. M. Diaz-Llopis et al., *Am. J. Ophthalmol.* **114**, 742–747 (1992).

71. P. Berthe et al., *Invest. Ophthalmol. Visual Sci.* **35**, 1038–1045 (1994).

72. D.R. Guyer et al., *Arch. Ophthalmol. (Chicago)* **107**, 868–874 (1989).

73. L.S. Kirsch et al., *Ophthalmology* **102**, 533–543 (1995).

74. D.A. Jabs, *Arch. Ophthalmol. (Chicago)* **115**, 785–786 (1997).

75. E. Chavez de la Paz et al., *Ophthalmology* **104**, 539–544 (1997).

76. T.P. Margolis et al., *Am. J. Ophthalmol.* **112**, 119–131 (1991).

77. J.H. Yeo et al., *Ophthalmology* **93**, 1418–1422 (1986).

78. D.A. Jabs et al., *Retina* **7**, 9–13 (1987).

79. T.A. Meredith, in S.J. Ryan, ed., *Retina*, Mosby, St. Louis, Mo., 1989, pp. 183–188.

80. C.A. Puliafito, A.S. Baker, J. Haaf, and C.S. Foster, *Ophthalmology* **89**, 921–929 (1982).

81. H.C. Boldt et al., *Ophthalmology* **96**, 1722–1726 (1989).

82. A. Tarkkanen, V. Tommila, O. Valle, and I. Raivio, *Br. J. Ophthalmol.* **51**, 188–192 (1967).

83. R.K. Forster, R.L. Abbott, and H. Gelender, *Ophthalmology* **87**, 313–319 (1980).

84. M. Neveu and A.J. Elliott, *Am. J. Ophthalmol.* **48**, 358–373 (1959).

85. G.A. Peyman, D. Sanders, and M. Goldberg, *Advances in Uveal Surgery, Vitreous Surgery, Treatment of Endophthalmitis*, Appleton-Century-Crofts, New York, 1975.

86. M. Barza, A. Kane, and J.L. Baum, *Invest. Ophthalmol. Visual Sci.* **24**, 1602–1606 (1983).

87. M.J. Daily, G.A. Peyman, and G. Fishman, *Am. J. Ophthalmol.* **76**, 343–350 (1973).

88. R.T. Kasbeer and G.A. Peyman, *Graefe's Arch. Clin. Exp. Ophthalmol.* **196**, 279–287 (1975).

89. J.P. Duguid et al., *Br. J. Ophthalmol.* **31**, 193–211 (1947).

90. W. Philipp et al., *Graefe's Arch. Clin. Exp. Ophthalmol.* **228**, 475–480 (1990).

91. K. Mochizuki et al., *Ophthalmic Res.* **24**, 150–154 (1992).

92. R.K. Shockley et al., *Arch. Ophthalmol. (Chicago)* **102**, 1236–1238 (1984).

93. J.J. Rutgard, R.A. Berkowitz, and G.A. Peyman, *Ann. Ophthalmol.* **10**, 293–298 (1978).

94. N.H. Leeds, G.A. Peyman, and B. House, *Ophthalmic Surg.* **13**, 653–656 (1982).

95. P. Nelsen, G.A. Peyman, and T.O. Bennett, *Am. J. Ophthalmol.* **78**, 82–89 (1974).

96. L.M. Cobo and R.K. Forster, *Am. J. Ophthalmol.* **92**, 59–62 (1981).

97. G.A. Peyman, D.R. May, E.S. Ericson, and D. Apple, *Arch. Ophthalmol. (Chicago)* **92**, 42–47 (1974).

98. H. Sloane, G.A. Peyman, M. Raichand, and S. West, *Can. J. Ophthalmol.* **16**, 22–26 (1981).

99. T.O. Bennett and G.A. Peyman, *Graefe's Arch. Clin. Exp. Ophthalmol.* **191**, 93–107 (1974).

100. M. Barza and M. McCue, *Antimicrob. Agents Chemother.* **24**, 468–473 (1983).

101. J. Koziol and G.A. Peyman, *Can. J. Ophthalmol.* **9**, 316–321 (1974).

102. P.A. Pearson, D.P. Hainsworth, and P. Ashton, *Retina* **13**, 326–330 (1993).

103. J.T. Paque and G.A. Peyman, *Ophthalmic Surg.* **5**, 34–39 (1974).

104. H. Meisels and G.A. Peyman, *Ann. Ophthalmol.* **8**, 939–943 (1976).

105. A.G. Schenk and G.A. Peyman, *Graefe's Arch. Clin. Exp. Ophthalmol.* **190**, 281–292 (1974).

106. M.A. Smith et al., *Ophthalmology* **93**, 1328–1335 (1986).

107. R.O. Graham and G.A. Peyman, *Arch. Ophthalmol. (Chicago)* **92**, 149–154 (1974).

108. G.A. Peyman, in I.K. Reddy, ed., *Ocular Therapeutics and Drug Delivery. A Multi-disciplinary Approach*, Technomic Publishing, Basel, 1996, pp. 265–282.

109. J.A. Schulman and G.A. Peyman, in A.K. Mitra, ed., *Ophthalmic Drug Delivery Systems*, Dekker, New York, 1993, pp. 383–425.

110. G.A. Peyman and S.S. Bassili, *Ophthalmic Surg.* **26**, 294–303 (1995).

111. R.B. Nussenblatt et al., *Arch. Ophthalmol. (Chicago)* **100**, 1146–1149 (1982).

112. R.B. Nussenblatt, A.G. Palestine, and C.C. Chan, *Am. J. Ophthalmol.* **96**, 275–282 (1983).

113. G. Striph, B. Doft, B. Rabin, and B. Johnson, *Arch. Ophthalmol. (Chicago)* **104**, 114–117 (1986).

114. R.B. Nussenblatt and A.G. Palestine, *Surv. Ophthalmol.* **31**, 159–169 (1986).

115. R.B. Nussenblatt et al., *Am. J. Ophthalmol.* **115**, 583–591 (1993).

116. D. BenEzra, G. Maftzir, C. de Courten, and P. Timonen, *Br. J. Ophthalmol.* **74**, 350–352 (1990).

117. R.B. Nussenblatt et al., *Arch. Ophthalmol. (Chicago)* **103**, 1559–1562 (1985).

118. J. Grisolano and G.A. Peyman, *Ophthalmic Surg.* **17**, 155–156 (1986).

119. J. Heller, *Biomaterials* **1**, 51–57 (1980).

120. A.A. Deshpande, J. Heller, and R. Gurny, *Crit. Rev. Ther. Drug Carr. Sys.* **15**, 381–420 (1998).

121. A. Merkli, C. Tabatabay, and R. Gurny, *Eur. J. Pharm. Biophys.* **16**, 51–283 (1995).

122. N.A. Peppas, in N.A. Peppas, ed., *Hydrogels in Medicine and Pharmacy*, CRC Press, Boca Raton, Fla., 1987, pp. 1–48.

123. D.P. Hainsworth et al., *J. Ocul. Pharmacol.* **12**, 183–191 (1996).

124. H. Kobayashi, K. Shiraki, and Y. Ikada, *J. Biomed. Mater. Res.* **26**, 1463–1476 (1992).

125. M. Vert, P. Christel, F. Chabot, and J. Leray, in G.W. Hastings and P. Ducheyne, eds., *Macromolecular Biomaterials*, CRC Press, Boca Raton, Fla., 1984, pp. 119–142.

126. M.B. Sintzel, S.B. Bernatchez, C. Tabatabay, and R. Gurny, *Eur. J. Pharm. Biophys.* **42**, 358–374 (1996).

127. S.S. Shah, Y. Cha, and C.G. Pitt, *J. Controlled Release* **18**, 261–270 (1992).

128. N. Kunou et al., *J. Controlled Release* **37**, 143–150 (1995).

129. P.E. Rubsamen et al., *Arch. Ophthalmol. (Chicago)* **112**, 407–413 (1994).

130. H. Kimura et al., *Invest. Ophthalmol. Visual Sci.* **35**, 2815–2819 (1994).

131. M. Hashizoe et al., *Curr. Eye Res.* **14**, 473–477 (1995).

132. R.E. Foster et al., *Invest. Ophthalmol. Visual Sci.* **37**, (Abstr.) S196 (1996).

133. M. Hashizoe et al., *Invest. Ophthalmol. Visual Sci.* **34**, (Abstr.) 1489 (1993).

134. M. Hashizoe et al., *Arch. Ophthalmol. (Chicago)* **112**, 1380–1384 (1994).

135. N. Kunou et al., *Invest. Ophthalmol. Visual Sci.* **37**, (Abstr.) S41 (1996).

136. H. Miyamoto et al., *Curr. Eye Res.* **16**, 930–935 (1997).

137. M. Hashizoe et al., *Curr. Eye Res.* **16**, 633–639 (1997).

138. R. Gurny et al., *Eur. J. Hosp. Pharm.* **3**, 15–19 (1993).

139. P. Davis, K. Kiss, J.M. Parel, and S.W. Cousins, *Invest. Ophthalmol. Visual Sci.* **33**, (Abstr.) 727 (1992).

140. B. Conti et al., *Eur. J. Pharm. Sci.* **5**, 287–293 (1997).

141. C.G. Pitt and A. Schindler, in G.I. Zatuchni, A. Goldsmith, J.D. Shelton, and J.J. Sciarra, eds., *Long-acting Contraceptive Delivery Systems*, Harper & Row, Philadelphia, 1984, pp. 48–63.

142. D. Yang, M.H. Rahimy, and G.A. Peyman, *Invest. Ophthalmol. Visual Sci.* **34**, (Abstr.) 1493 (1993).

143. S. Chin, M.H. Rahimy, and G.A. Peyman, *Invest. Ophthalmol. Visual Sci.* **34**, (Abstr.) 1490 (1993).

144. H. Borhani, M.H. Rahimy, and G.A. Peyman, *Invest. Ophthalmol. Visual Sci.* **34**, (Abstr.) 1488 (1993).

145. H. Borhani, G.A. Peyman, M.H. Rahimy, and H. Thompson, *Int. Ophthalmol.* **19**, 43–49 (1995).

146. G.A. Peyman et al., *Ophthalmic Surg. Lasers* **27**, 384–391 (1996).

147. K.W. Leong, B.C. Brott, and R. Langer, *J. Biomed. Mater. Res.* **19**, 941–955 (1985).

148. D.A. Lee et al., *Ophthalmology* **94**, 1523–1530 (1987).

149. K.W. Leong, P. D'Amore, M. Marletta, and R. Langer, *J. Biomed. Mater. Res.* **20**, 51–64 (1986).

150. H. Lewis, S. Schwartz, D. Lee, and K. Leong, *Invest. Ophthalmol. Visual Sci.* **32**, (Abstr.) 1047 (1991).

151. J.I. Alonso et al., *Invest. Ophthalmol. Visual Sci.* **32**, (Abstr.) 1293 (1991).

152. A. Merkli, J. Heller, C. Tabatabay, and R. Gurny, *J. Biomater. Sci., Polym. Ed.* **4**, 505–516 (1993).

153. J. Heller, S.Y. Ng, B.K. Fritzinger, and K.V. Roskos, *Biomaterials* **11**, 235–237 (1990).

154. A. Merkli, J. Heller, C. Tabatabay, and R. Gurny, *J. Controlled Release* **29**, 105–112 (1994).

155. A. Merkli, J. Heller, C. Tabatabay, and R. Gurny, *J. Controlled Release* **33**, 415–421 (1995).

156. S.B. Bernatchez et al., *J. Biomed. Mater. Res.* **27**, 677–681 (1993).

157. S.B. Bernatchez et al., *J. Biomed. Mater. Res.* **28**, 1037–1046 (1994).

158. M. Zignani et al., *J. Controlled Rel.* **48**, 115–129 (1997).

159. M. Zignani et al., *J. Biomed. Mater. Res.* **39**, 277–285 (1998).

160. M. Zignani, T. Le Minh, C. Tabatabay, and R. Gurny, *Proceed. Int. Symp. Control. Rel. Bioact. Mater.* **24**, 907–908 (1997).

161. A. Merkli, J. Heller, C. Tabatabay, and R. Gurny, *Pharm. Res.* **11**, 1485–1491 (1994).

162. M.B. Stinzel, A. Merkli, C. Tabatabay, and R. Gurny, *Drug Dev. Ind. Pharm.* **23**, 857–878 (1997).

163. M.B. Stinzel et al., *Int. J. Pharm.* **175**, 165–176 (1998).

164. S.Y. Ng, T. Vandamme, M.S. Taylor, and J. Heller, *Macromolecules* **30**, 770–772 (1997).

165. M.B. Stinzel et al., *Biomater.* **19**, 791–800 (1998).

166. M.B. Stinzel et al., *J. Controlled Release* **55**, 213–218 (1998).

167. B.B. Pharriss et al., *J. Reprod. Med.* **17**, 91–97 (1976).

168. R.L. Friederich, *Ann. Ophthalmol.* **6**, 1279–1274 (1974).

169. P. Ashton et al., *J. Ocul. Pharmacol.* **10**, 691–701 (1994).

170. T.J. Smith et al., *Arch. Ophthalmol. (Chicago)* **110**, 255–258 (1992).

171. G.E. Sanborn et al., *Arch. Ophthalmol. (Chicago)* **110**, 188–195 (1992).

172. R. Anand et al., *Arch. Ophthalmol. (Chicago)* **111**, 223–227 (1993).

173. D.F. Martin et al., *Arch. Ophthalmol. (Chicago)* **112**, 1531–1539 (1994).

174. P.A. Pearson et al., *Arch. Ophthalmol. (Chicago)* **114**, 311–317 (1996).

175. L.B. Enyedi, P.A. Pearson, P. Ashton, and G.J. Jaffe, *Curr. Eye Res.* **15**, 549–557 (1996).

176. C.K. Cheng et al., *Invest. Ophthalmol. Visual Sci.* **36**, 442–453 (1995).

177. D.P. Hainsworth, P.A. Pearson, J.D. Conklin, and P. Ashton, *J. Ocul. Pharmacol.* **12**, 57–63 (1996).

178. P. Ashton et al., *J. Ocul. Pharmacol.* **8**, 343–347 (1992).

179. R. Anand, R.L. Font, R.H. Fish, and S.D. Nightingale, *Ophthalmology* **100**, 1032–1039 (1993).

180. N.C. Charles and G.C. Steiner, *Ophthalmology* **103**, 416–421 (1996).

181. M.G. Morley, J.S. Duker, P. Ashton, and M.R. Robinson, *Ophthalmology* **102**, 388–392 (1995).

182. J. Chen and P. Ashton, *Proc. Int. Symp. Controlled Release Bioact. Mater.* **24**, 619–620 (1997).

183. J. Chen et al., *Invest. Ophthalmol. Visual Sci.* **37**, S41 (1996).

184. P.A. Pearson, L.B. Enyedi, G.J. Jaffe, and P. Ashton, *Invest. Ophthalmol. Visual Sci.* **35**, (Abstr.) 1923 (1994).

185. M.H. Rahimy et al., *J. Drug Target.* **2**, 289–298 (1994).

186. M.H. Rahimy et al., *J. Ocul. Pharmacol.* **10**, 561–570 (1994).

187. P.A. Cibis, B. Becker, E. Okun, and S. Canaan, *Arch. Ophthalmol. (Chicago)* **68**, 590–599 (1962).

188. Q.H. Nguyen et al., *Opthalmology* **99**, 1520–1526 (1992).

189. M.H. Arroyo et al., *Retina* **13**, 13, 245–250 (1993).

190. A. Zimmer and J. Kreuter, *Adv. Drug Delivery Rev.* **16**, 61–73 (1995).

191. A. Joshi, *J. Ocul. Pharmacol.* **10**, 29–45 (1994).

192. M.S. El-Samaligy et al., *Drug Delivery* **3**, 93–97 (1996).

193. B. Khoobehi, M.O. Stradtmann, G.A. Peyman, and O.M. Aly, *Ophthalmic Surg.* **22**, 175–180 (1991).

194. D. Khoobehi, M.O. Stradtmann, G.A. Peyman, and O.M. Aly, *Ophthalmic Surg.* **21**, 840–844 (1990).

195. G.G. Giordano, P. Chevez-Barrios, M.F. Refojo, and C.A. Garcia, *Curr. Eye Res.* **14**, 761–768 (1995).

196. H. Kimura et al., *Invest. Ophthalmol. Visual Sci.* **33**, 3436–3441 (1992).

197. C.A. Harper et al., *Int. Ophthalmol.* **17**, 337–340 (1993).

198. T. Moritera et al., *Invest. Ophthalmol. Visual Sci.* **32**, 1785–1790 (1991).

199. T. Moritera et al., *Invest. Ophthalmol. Visual Sci.* **33**, 3125–3130 (1992).

200. G.A. Peyman, M. Conway, B. Khoobehi, and K. Soike, *Int. Ophthalmol.* **16**, 109–113 (1992).

201. G.G. Giordano, M.F. Refojo, and M.H. Arroyo, *Invest. Ophthalmol. Visual Sci.* **34**, 2743–2751 (1993).

202. A.A.S. Veloso, Q. Zhu, R. Herrero-Vanrell, and M.F. Refojo, *Invest. Ophthalmol. Visual Sci.* **38**, 665–675 (1997).

203. H. Kimura et al., *Invest. Ophthalmol. Visual Sci.* **33**, (Abstr.) 1013 (1992).

204. M. Barza, M. Stuart, and F. Szoka, *Invest. Ophthalmol. Visual Sci.* **28**, 893–900 (1987).

205. W.H. Stern et al., *Invest. Ophthalmol. Visual Sci.* **28**, 907–911 (1987).

206. V.H.L. Lee, P.T. Urrea, R.E. Smith, and D.J. Schanzlin, *Surv. Ophthalmol.* **29**, 335–348 (1985).

207. D. Meisner and M. Mezei, *Adv. Drug Delivery Rev.* **16**, 75–93 (1995).

208. P.H. Fishman, G.A. Peyman, and T. Lesar, *Invest. Ophthalmol. Visual Sci.* **27**, 1103–1106 (1986).

209. R.G. Fiscella, G.A. Peyman, and P.H. Fishman, *Can. J. Ophthalmol.* **22**, 307–309 (1987).

210. V.S. Rao, G.A. Peyman, B. Khoobehi, and S. Vangipuram, *Int. Ophthalmol.* **13**, 181–185 (1989).

211. E.K. Kim and H.B. Kim, *Yonsei Med. J.* **31**, 308–314 (1990).

212. S. Zeng et al., *Ophthalmology* **100**, 1640–1644 (1993).

213. C. Tremblay et al., *Invest. Ophthalmol. Visual Sci.* **26**, 711–718 (1985).

214. M. Barza et al., *Am. J. Ophthalmol.* **100**, 259–263 (1985).

215. K.R. Liu, G.A. Peyman, and B. Khoobehi, *Invest. Ophthalmol. Visual Sci.* **30**, 1527–1534 (1989).

216. K.R. Liu et al., *Ophthalmology* **94**, 1155–1159 (1987).

217. G.A. Peyman et al., *Retina* **7**, 227–229 (1987).

218. M. Diaz-Llopis et al., *Doc. Ophthalmol.* **82**, 297–305 (1992).

219. S.K. Akula et al., *Br. J. Ophthalmol.* **78**, 677–680 (1994).

220. C. Le Bourlais et al., *J. Microencapsul.* **13**, 473–480 (1996).

221. S. Shakiba et al., *Invest. Ophthalmol. Visual Sci.* **34**, 2903–2910 (1993).

222. H.O.C. Gümbel et al., *2nd Int. Symp. Exp. Clin. Ocul. Pharmacol. Pharm.* Munich, Germany, September 11–14, 1997, p. 16.

223. G. Besen et al., *Arch. Ophthalmol. (Chicago)* **113**, 661–668 (1995).

224. B.D. Kuppermann et al., *J. Infect. Dis.* **173**, 18–23 (1996).

225. A.A. Alghadyan et al., *Int. Ophthalmol.* **12**, 109–112 (1988).

226. B.C. Joondeph, B. Khoobehi, G.A. Peyman, and B.Y. Yue, *Ophthalmic Surg.* **19**, 252–256 (1988).

227. K.K. Assil et al., *Invest. Ophthalmol. Visual Sci.* **32**, 2891–2897 (1991).

228. R.F. Gariano et al., *Retina* **14**, 75–80 (1994).

229. J. Garcia-Arumi et al., *Ophthalmologica* **211**, 344–350 (1997).

230. K.R. Liu et al., *Ophthalmic Surg.* **20**, 358–361 (1989).

231. T.D. Heath, N.G. Lopez, G.P. Lewis, and W.H. Stern, *Invest. Ophthalmol. Visual Sci.* **28**, 1365–1372 (1987).

232. B. Khoobehi et al., *Ophthalmology* **95**, 950–955 (1988).

233. B. Khoobehi, G.A. Peyman, M.R. Niesman, and M. Oncel, *Jpn. J. Ophthalmol.* **33**, 405–412 (1989).

234. Y. Ogura et al., *Invest. Ophthalmol. Visual Sci.* **32**, 2351–2356 (1991).

235. G.A. Peyman et al., *Int. Ophthalmol.* **12**, 175–182 (1988).

236. D. Sarraf and D.A. Lee, *J. Ocul. Pharmacol.* **10**, 69–81 (1994).

237. J.M. Hill, R.J. O'Callaghan, and J.A. Hobden, in A.K. Mitra, ed., *Ophthalmic Drug Delivery Systems*, Dekker, New York, 1993, pp. 331–354.

238. L. Hughes and D.M. Maurice, *Arch. Ophthalmol. (Chicago)* **102**, 1825–1829 (1984).

239. M. Barza, C. Peckman, and J. Baum, *Ophthalmology* **93**, 133–139 (1986).

240. T.B. Choi and D.A. Lee, *J. Ocul. Pharmacol.* **4**, 153–164 (1988).

241. P.H. Fishman et al., *Invest. Ophthalmol. Visual Sci.* **25**, 343–345 (1984).

242. V. Baeyens et al., *Adv. Drug Deliv. Rev.* **28**, 335–361 (1997).

243. N.L. Burstein, I.H. Leopold, and D.B. Bernacchi, *J. Ocul. Pharmacol.* **1**, 363–368 (1985).

244. M. Barza, C. Peckman, and J. Baum, *Invest. Ophthalmol. Visual Sci.* **28**, 1033–1036 (1987).

245. R.E. Grossman, D.F. Chu, and D.A. Lee, *Invest. Ophthalmol. Visual Sci.* **31**, 909–916 (1990).

246. M.O. Yoshizumi et al., *J. Ocul. Pharmacol.* **7**, 163–167 (1991).

247. R. Grossman and D.A. Lee, *Ophthalmology* **96**, 724–729 (1989).

248. T.T. Lam, D.P. Edward, X.A. Zhu, and M.O.M. Tso, *Arch. Ophthalmol. (Chicago)* **107**, 1368–1371 (1989).

249. F.F. Behar-Cohen et al., *Exp. Eye Res.* **65**, 533–545 (1997).

250. T.T. Lam et al., *J. Ocul. Pharmacol.* **10**, 571–575 (1994).

251. D. Sarraf et al., *Am. J. Ophthalmol.* **115**, 748–754 (1993).

252. M.O. Yoshizumi et al., *Am. J. Ophthalmol.* **122**, 86–90 (1996).

253. D.M. Maurice, *Ophthalmology* **93**, 128–131 (1986).

254. T.T. Lam, J. Fu, and M.O.M. Tso, *Graefe's Arch. Clin. Exp. Ophthalmol.* **223**, 389–394 (1991).

255. A. Albert, *Nature* **182**, 421–423 (1958).

256. L.L. Christrup, J. Moss, and B. Steffansen, in J. Swarbrick and J.C. Boylan, eds., *Encyclopedia of Pharmaceutical Technology*, Dekker, New York, 1996, pp. 39–70.

257. V.H.L. Lee and V.H.K. Li, *Adv. Drug Delivery Rev.* **3**, 1–38 (1989).

258. B. Steffansen, P. Ashton, and A. Buur, *Int. J. Pharm.* **132**, 243–250 (1996).

259. I. Taskintuna et al., *Retina* **17**, 57–64 (1997).

260. S. Shakiba et al., *Antimicrob. Agents Chem.* **39**, 1383–1385 (1995).

261. A.S. Berger et al., *Invest. Ophthalmol. Visual Sci.* **37**, 2318–2325 (1996).

262. H. Guo et al., *Invest. Ophthalmol. Visual Sci.* **35**, 1907 (1994).

See also BIOADHESIVE DRUG DELIVERY SYSTEMS; MUCOSAL DRUG DELIVERY, BUCCAL; MUCOSAL DRUG DELIVERY, NASAL; MUCOSAL DRUG DELIVERY, OCULAR; MUCOSAL DRUG DELIVERY, VAGINAL DRUG DELIVERY AND TREATMENT MODALITIES.

MUCOSAL DRUG DELIVERY, NASAL

PAOLO COLOMBO
University of Parma
Parma, Italy

KEY WORDS

Butorphanol

Calcitonin

Desmopressin

Drug delivery

Enhancer

Inhalation

Insufflator

Insulin

Nasal route

Particle size

Powder

Spray

Sumatriptan

OUTLINE

Introduction

Nasal Delivery: Historical and Behavioral Use

Anatomy and Physiology of the Nose

Toxicological Considerations

Dosage Forms and Materials

Metering and Insufflators

Qualitative and Quantitative Aspects of Nasal Dose Delivery

INTRODUCTION

This article intends to update the state of the art of nasal drug delivery from a pharmaceutical and technological point of view. Many important contributions can be found in literature on the subject, focusing on different aspects of interest to researchers, such as the Proctor edited book (1), the edited and directly contributed books of Chien (2,3), and the reviews of Illum (4), Wilson (5), Edman (6), Merkus (7), Gizurarson (8), Duchene (9), Harris (10), Buri (11), and Alpar (12).

A Nasal Drug Delivery Focus Group, organized in an American Association of Pharmaceutical Scientists section (13), has also been constituted as well as an Open Forum for free exchange and information in all R and D areas ranging from the formulation to the marketing of nasal preparations.

NASAL DELIVERY: HISTORICAL AND BEHAVIORAL USE

New materials and new technologies have stimulated pharmaceutical researchers to identify and use alternatives to the classical oral and injectable routes. One of the routes currently being studied is the nasal way, even though the physiological evolution of the nose followed the olfactive and respiratory necessity to provide humid, warmed, and filtered air for the lungs. In fact, nasal mucosa evolved in order to have a wide surface, large blood supply, and efficient filtering system. Because the mucosa is often affected by various diseases that alter its functionality, the first nasal drug delivery system was for restoring normal nasal conditions. Man discovered the possibility of using nasal mucosa for absorbing substances giving systemic effects. Unfortunately, the most convincing examples of systemic effects obtained by administering active principles inside the nose were those which misused the nose, such as the behavioral habit of sniffing cocaine or tobacco. An instructive behavioral employment of the nose for drug absorption, usually in order to have hallucinations or more general mental effects, is the religious rite of the Amazonian population of Yanomamo to assume *epenà*, that, is a powdered mixture of different plant parts like *Mimosa acacioides*, *Piptadenia peregrina*, and others not identified (14). The interest of this rite for pharmaceutical researchers is linked to the administration devices the natives use

in order to deposit the powdered drug in the nose (Fig. 1). The devices consist of an insufflator having the form of a long linear pipe activated by an assistant or, alternatively, a Y-shaped curved tube which allows for self-administration. These "medical devices" focalize the typical aspect of nasal delivery that is the need for a nebulizer or an insufflator for depositing solid or liquid formulations into the nose.

All these uses, or misuses, of the nose for systemic drug delivery have provided a lot of important information as to the employment of the nasal route for therapeutically drug delivery. The effects, and in particular, the toxicity manifested by the mucosa in response to drug deposition are of paramount importance for setting the therapeutical delivery of drugs in terms of safety and efficacy. From these experiences it is worthwhile underlining some aspects that are particularly useful for the design of therapy and dosage form for the nose. The rapid onset of the effect is linked to high mucosa permeability and indicates using the nose for therapies requiring prompt response. Then, the maniacal use of the nose because of the effects involving the brain opens the possibility of directly reaching the brain after deposition on the olfactory mucosa. Finally, the fact that drugs are successfully administered in powder form increases the formulation possibilities for designing the appropriate dosage form.

ANATOMY AND PHYSIOLOGY OF THE NOSE

The nose is characterized by two nasal cavities, separated by a septum and divided into three main regions: vestibule (nostril), atrium (or preturbinate region), and turbinate region (15). The last region is composed of an olfactory upper part and of two respiratory medium and lower parts that join together in the rhinopharynx. The turbinate region is characterized by cornets and meati, gaps situated between cornets and the nasal external part. The nostrils are the entry of the nasal cavity.

The nose presents sensitive, vegetative, and sensorial nervous conduction. The trigeminal nerves respond to al-

Figure 1. Yanomano Indian tribe using the insufflator pipe for *epenà* nasal administration.

lergic stimulus causing sneezing; the vegetative system provides secretory and vasomobility functions, and particular elements of the olfactory mucosa control the activity of sensorial nerves.

Nasal cavities are covered by respiratory mucosa that, within the nostrils, is characterized by a stratified, squamous and keratinized epithelium, with hairs, called vibrissae. Beyond the limen nasi, the epithelium loses its keratin cover and becomes the respiratory mucosa with pluristratified cylindrical epithelium. It is provided with vibratile cilia and other mucus secreting cells. Goblet cells and submucosa glands produce a high amount of mucus, which is the protective barrier against external agents. The continuous film of mucus is structured in two layers: the lower one is smooth with low viscosity, the upper one is more viscous and elastic and moves following the cilia movements.

The nose, which has an extensive vascular network, has two main functions: the sense of smell given by the olfactory mucosa and the inspired air conditioning by purification, heating, and moisture regulation. The greatest particles are removed by the vibrissae of the vestibule. Other particles are removed by the anatomic structures of the nasal cavities. The combined action of the cilia and mucus layer is called mucociliary clearance, an important defense mechanism against inhaled dust, allergens, and microorganisms. The coordinated beating of the cilia results in the movement of the upper mucus layer towards the nasopharynx, where it is swallowed. Finally, there is an air flow control because the respiratory air volumes are monitored by the cornets, which alternatively change their volume, giving a variable resistance to the breathed air.

TOXICOLOGICAL CONSIDERATIONS

The poor nasal bioavailability of many substances (in particular, peptide and protein drugs) can be substantially improved by the use of absorption enhancers. The acceptability of these enhancers is not only dependent on their promoting effect but also on their safety profile for systemic and local adverse effects (16–21). Nasal drug formulations must not alter the histology and physiology of the nose in the sense that the mucosa must retain its functionality as a barrier toward external substances and microorganisms. In any case, damage induced must be reversible. The histological toxicity refers to the alteration of mucosa, including membrane protein removal, cell loss, excessive mucus discharge, ciliotoxicity, and disturbance of the normal enzymatic balance (22,23). In addition, the dosage form and its components should not interfere with the mucociliary clearance.

Various methods have been used to test the toxicity of drugs and additives on the nasal mucosa and the mucociliary system. Traditionally, histopathological examination of a prefixed membrane specimen by light and scanning electron microscopy is regarded as the indicator of cytotoxicity. These methods suffer from inspector subjectivity and the impossibility of highlighting subtle changes in nasal mucosa and do not provide the nasal sensitivity tolerance measurement in response to a particular formulation.

Therefore, in order to determine minute changes occurring in the mucosal tissue due to exposure to formulations, a biochemical approach has been developed (24). The extent of the release of total proteins, although not very specific as to the type of damage, provides a general indication about the extent of irritation.

The release of enzymes lactate dehydrogenase (LDH) and 5′nucleotidase (5′-ND), directly indicate the extent of damage suffered by the mucosa. Membrane-bound 5′-ND release in the nasal perfusate gives an indication of the level of membrane perturbation, whereas the cytosolic enzyme LDH indicates cell leaching and/or lysis (25).

Mucociliary transport and clearance interferences can be measured in vivo (26,27) or in vitro (28). Determination of ciliary beat frequency in vitro has been carried out on explants of ciliated mucosa from human adenoid tissue (29), from the trachea of different animal species (30,31), or from chicken embryo trachea (32). The frog palate preparation as an ex vivo model for the mucociliary transport velocity study has also been proposed for the indication of topical tolerability of different substances (33). Effects on the ciliary beat frequency detected in vitro may be more pronounced than the influence in vivo. In vitro experiments directly expose ciliated epithelia to test solution, whereas in vivo the cilia are protected by mucus (34). Therefore, in vitro ciliary beat frequency tests should be used as indicators for potential damage to nasal epithelium, rather than proof of such damage occurring in the in vivo situation. One of the best known in vivo tests is the saccharin transit time, i.e., the time required for the subject to taste a saccharin particle placed on the inferior turbinate of the naris (35). However, the most powerful method used for measuring the deposition and clearance of drugs in the nasal cavity remains scintigraphy.

DOSAGE FORMS AND MATERIALS

Nasal dosage forms consist of preparations containing dispersed or dissolved drugs, filled in a container designed to be squeezed or spray activated (36). The aim of delivery is to deposit the formula on the mucosa and coat the available surface, in particular the respiratory part, which is the major absorption site for drugs. Other therapeutic situations must require a localized accumulation of the product in certain districts of the nasal cavity. This can be achieved through an appropriate design of the insufflator and of the formulation to produce a fine dispersion of droplets or particles capable of sticking to the mucosa (37). This avoids the coalescence of the mist with a backflow of product and limits a fast transport to the pharynx by mucociliary clearance. Therefore, dispersion pattern and bioadhesion are the two key factors to be considered during the development phase of the formulation.

At present, the application of the product by spraying is very elegant and accepted. Therefore, the objective of formulation design is to obtain an aerosol useful for inspiration and deposition in the upper airways. In the past, drops were often instilled in the nose, but the advancement of insufflator technology has made this form obsolete and limited to pediatric use or to patients less able to perform the insufflative maneuvers. Liquid preparations are common dosage forms for nasal delivery. Because the nasal epithelium is essentially a lipophilic transport barrier, transnasal transport is related to the nasal mucosa tissue–water partition coefficient, suggesting also an important role of the stereochemical conformation during membrane transport (38). Therefore, aspects such as formula pH, ionic strength, surface active agents, viscosity, and drug concentration have to be considered in order to facilitate the transport (39). However, from a technological point of view, the liquid preparations present problems linked to formula stability, low drug concentration at the absorption site, and short residence time in nasal cavity.

These drawbacks accelerated the development of nasal powders as alternative nasal dosage forms with improved chemicophysical and microbiological stability. Furthermore, drug dissolution on nasal mucosa provides elevated drug concentration at the deposition site, giving rise to a high flux of active ingredient. In many cases the superiority of nasal powder compared with nasal liquid was demonstrated, in particular with peptidic drugs (40–42). Administration of powders requires a nasal insufflator for dose emission and deposition of particles in the nose. It has been assessed that the site and pattern of inhalatory powder deposition in the respiratory tract are affected by the aerodynamic properties of the powder (43). Moreover, the formalities of dose delivery control the deposition mechanisms, i.e., inertial impacting, sedimentation, and diffusion. It could be postulated that efficient nasal delivery of powder from a spraying device requires impacting with adhesion and/or sedimentation of particles on nasal mucosa; therefore, powder properties such as particle size, shape, surface, density, and flow must be optimized to activate the proper mechanism for therapeutic treatment. The number of drugs directly administrable to the nose in powder form is limited because of unsuitable characteristics such as large particle size, low solubility, poor absorption, and irritability. These limits can be overcome through the use of a suitable solid excipient as carrier. Such a carrier must be compatible, hydrophilic, soluble, and of an aerodynamic particle size favorable to nasal deposition. The most common material used are sugars, β-cyclodextrin, cyclodextrin derivatives, phospholipids, starches, cellulose derivatives, poly(vinylpyrrolidone) and others. Swellable polymers proved very useful as nasal carriers, because the swelling phenomenon was added as a transport enhancing effect. Particle size is the main parameter affecting nasal drug delivery. It was found that powders around 100 μm in size are efficiently delivered in terms of amount and type of delivery, when an insufflator device using a gelatin capsule as reservoir was used (44). In the particle size range between 150 and 50 μm there was an evident change in the insufflation behavior: for size over 150 μm, the spray pattern suggested more favorable conditions for impacting the nasal mucosa; below 50 μm, a more uniform deposition by sedimentation is expected, but the possibility of particle respirability can increase as well. Other formulations used for nasal delivery involve nasal gels; one example is vitamin B_{12} gel, which provides a superior bioavailability compared with oral delivery (45). A scopolamine gel is expected to be filed soon for approval (46).

METERING AND INSUFFLATORS

Devices for nasal delivery differ according to the formulation to be dispensed. Liquid solutions are delivered using metered atomizing pumps, metered-dose pressurized nasal inhalers, rhinal tubes for variable volume delivery, and plastic spray or squeeze bottles (47). Pumps and squeeze bottles operate by mechanical actuation to sample a liquid volume from a reservoir and to produce a mist cloud having the shape of an inverse cone or of a sagittal plume. The use of these devices is usually extensively explained in the product leaflets, and the intervention of a pharmacist for assembling the nasal spray device is often requested.

Quantity dispensed and reproducibility are the major points to be assessed. Pumps, both mechanically or gas actuated, are very precise and accurate in delivery, provided that they are primed according to the indications of the producer. The delivery rate is very fast because emission is usually completed in less that one second. The size of droplets produced with these devices prevents the entrance of the preparation into the lung, and their size and velocity provide an impacting on the nasal mucosa with a distributed deposition. The multidose preparations require preservatives in the solution that can alter the mucosa. Metered unidose insufflator devices are the technological solution to avoiding preservative use. An example of these is reproduced in Figure 2. However, considering that there are two nostrils and that deposition carried out in both nostrils doubles absorption, bidose devices have been developed and marketed both by the Pfeiffer (48) and Valois (49) companies.

Powder delivery requires different types of insufflators, which can be mechanically or respiratory actuated. The user requests are for a small-sized portable device, with high spraying performance and visible feedback, moisture protected and easy to handle. The mechanically designed devices consist of a rubbery bulb connected through the dose reservoir to a nasal adapter (Fig. 3). The squeezing of the rubbery bulb provides a stream of air capable of emitting the appropriately loaded powder in the insufflator. The insufflators designed to be used by breathing through

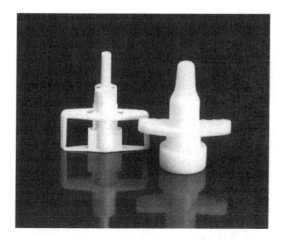

Figure 2. Monospray systems for nasal administration of monodose of liquid formulation (Valois Pharm, France).

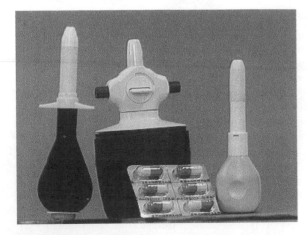

Figure 3. Different insufflators for nasal administration of powdered formulations. From left to right: Rinoflatore® (Fisons, Rome, Italy), Miat Nasal Insufflator® (Miat, Milan, Italy), Puvlizer® (Teijin, Tokyo, Japan).

the nose are a nose adapted version of the dry powder inhalers, designed for lung delivery. With both types of devices, the drug unidose is loaded in a gelatin capsule that is pierced just before activation. Because the capsule is located between the air jet producer and the nose adapter, the air stream that flows through creates a turbulence inside the capsule, capable of aerosolizing and emitting the amount of powder contained. This phenomenon, called "dancing cloud" by the Hovione company (50), causes a complete, gradual, and efficient emission of the powder content of the motionless capsule. The devices loaded with gelatin capsule can deliver different amounts of powder without adversely affecting their behavior (51).

QUALITATIVE AND QUANTITATIVE ASPECTS OF NASAL DOSE DELIVERY

Nasal delivery of a drug requires metering of the dose and its emission by means of a device capable of producing an aerosol suitable for deposition on nasal mucosa. The words *cloud, plume,* or *puff* are used indifferently for indicating the nasal aerosol. The goal of puff production is to appropriately deposit the drug according to the pathology to be treated, which could be for localized or systemic effects. For example, a disease such as rhinitis requires a deposition on the total area of the mucosa, whereas a targeting to the brain would require localized deposition at the roof of the nose. Other therapeutic possibilities require the adaptation of the puff for deposition at different sites.

In any case, nasal delivery of drug involves both qualitative and quantitative aspects of drug delivered. The qualitative aspect refers to the aerodynamic behavior of the cloud produced and is described by the spray pattern and the cloud geometry, whereas the quantitative aspect is linked to the dose of drug sprayed per puff. The qualitative aspect is assessed by photographic technique in order to obtain the sequence of dose emission from the pump or insufflator and to collect information on spray pattern and geometry. Plume shape, height, area, density, particle

size, and velocity are the parameters involved in the spray pattern and geometry determination.

In the case of liquid preparations, the qualitative aspect is primarily dependent on the device used for insufflation. The spray geometry in the case of pump metered-dose insufflators or squeeze plastic bottles is totally different. It is not surprising to find that different geometry can result in different bioavailability of the drug. This is probable not only when comparing two different types of nasal insufflators but also in the case of the same type manufactured by different producers. As an example, Figure 4 shows two mists of the same liquid formulation produced using two similar pumps manufactured by different producers. The two preparations were not bioequivalent, because delivery with one pump gave a bioavailability 30% lower than the reference (C. Vecchio and R. Bettini, University of Parma, Department of Pharmacy, personal communication, 1998). Registrative health authorities require for droplet size distribution determination using two different methods, such as laser scattering and cascade impactor. In addition, the spray pattern and plume geometry must be compared for bioequivalence studies.

In the case of nasal powder, the powder cloud, which looks like a plume emerging from a chimney, grows in dimension during emission, with a maximum height and width depending on the characteristics of the product sprayed and the device used. The cloud aspect is mainly dependent on the formulation's characteristics and, particularly, on the fundamental (size and shape) and derived (packing and flow) properties of the powder (44). Using a rubbery bulb insufflator, the clouds originating from small particle size powder are fluffy and homogeneous in density, whereas the clouds obtained from large particle size powders are characterized by visible individual particle trajectories (Fig. 5). The rate of particle delivery decreased with decreasing size, whereas the time needed to completely emit the dose through the nose adapter of the insufflator increased with decreasing size. For nasal impacting, the powder cloud should remain as compact as possible to

Figure 4. Nasal puffs obtained by spraying the same desmopressin nasal solution through two different metered-dose pumps. Puff (**a**) provided a superior bioavailability compared with puff (**b**). The amounts emitted were not significantly different.

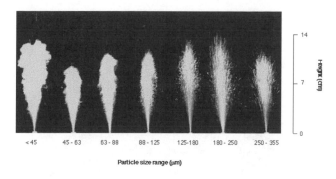

Figure 5. Influence of nasal powder particle size on the puff appearance (Miat Nasal Insufflator).

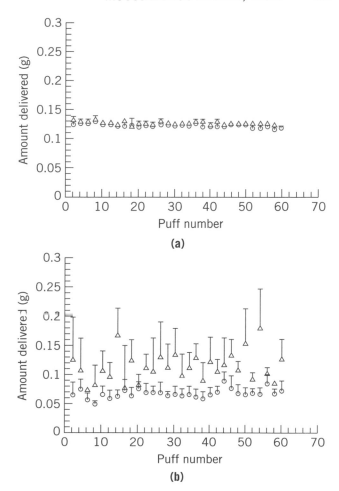

Figure 6. Differences between women (○) and men (△) in delivering the same xylometazoline nasal solution from (**a**) metered-dose pump and (**b**) squeeze bottle.

achieve an efficient shot of powder to the nasal mucosa, whereas for sedimentation a larger cloud would be preferred. The measurement of the expansion area of the axial section of the clouds during emission evaluates the packing of the cloud: as the particle size decreased below 100 μm, the area of the puff increased (44). Serum progesterone levels following nasal administration in rabbits of two powder mixtures containing co-ground progesterone-β-cyclodextrin or co-lyophilized progesterone and β-cyclodextrin showed rapid increase (52). Progesterone co-grounded powder exhibited a significantly higher extent of bioavailability, without a significant difference in rate compared with the co-lyophilized powder. The progesterone-β-CD co-ground powder was ejected by the insufflator at higher speed and as a compact cloud.

The quantitative aspect of nasal delivery is different according to the physical state of the preparation, i.e., liquid or solid, and it is largely dependent on the type of device used for spraying. In the case of liquid preparations, there are obviously different delivery behaviors according to the device used. Metered pumps are designed for delivering a very precise and accurate amount of nasal solution. The alternative, the squeeze bottle, suffers from a strong dependence on the energy used in squeezing the bottle in order to emit the dose. Therefore, the device affects the accuracy of delivery. As an example, a solution of xylometazoline was delivered in different amounts from squeeze bottle by different patients. Figure 6 shows the behavior of successive sprays performed by male or female patients: it is evident that the males exert more strength in spraying than females, because they sprayed out more product per shot. The same solution charged in a metered pump device is less dependent on the varying strength of the patient, as Figure 6 shows as well. Finally, metered pumps are regularly used in prescription preparations, and the squeeze bottle is the choice for over-the-counter preparations.

The quantitative aspect of a nasal solution filled in multidose reservoir is first tested by the labeled number of sprays that must be available using the preparation completely. It is also required that the number of priming operations to be performed before the device is ready for use should be declared. After this preliminary characteristic, the content uniformity per spray is a regulatory requisite. This must be checked from dose to dose, from container to container, and from batch to batch, considering that the accepted variability is established between 85 and 115% of the labeled dose.

Nasal inhalation powders are delivered using insufflators that generally work on a unidose basis. The drug is dosed in a hard gelatin capsule and the capsule is loaded and pierced in the insufflator. The production of the puff is done by squeezing the rubbery bubble that produces the air stream necessary for nebulizing the powder. The dimension of the rubbery bubble determines the amount of the emitted powder and the complete delivery of the dose from the capsule. This aspect is strictly dependent on the properties of the formulation inside the capsule. Successive generations of powder insufflators were proposed with the aim of allowing depositing the dose in the two nostrils. This quantitative problem was solved by using insufflators that have a small bubble, so determining the need to squeeze the bubble many times to completely emit the amount loaded into the capsule, alternating the nostril involved in the insufflation. The amount of dose emitted by this sequence of insufflation is reported in Figure 7, where it can be appreciated that the successive squeezing allow sharing the amount deposited in the two nostrils and the delivery depends on particle size of powder.

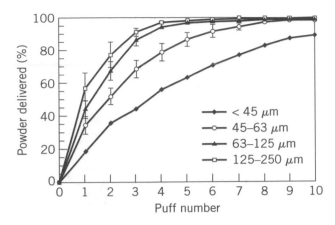

Figure 7. Cumulative percentage of nasal powder delivered from Puvlizer nasal insufflator as a function of the puff number (powder loaded; 25 mg).

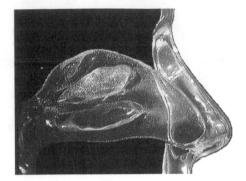

Figure 8. Powder deposition in the left section of the artificial nasal cavity showing a large coating of atrium and superior cornet.

Deposition of emitted dose in the nasal cavity was studied using various techniques both in vivo and in vitro. Scintigraphic techniques are the most powerful for determining the site of dose deposition and were used to show the influence of dosage form and device. One of the first papers published on the subject compared in vivo the sites of deposition and the patterns of clearance following intranasal administration of nasal spray and nasal drops. It was found that spray was deposited anteriorly in the nasal cavity, with little dose reaching the turbinates, whereas drops dispersed the drug throughout the length of the cavity. A substantial difference was also observed in terms of clearance, evidentiating that the spray was cleared more slowly (53).

Technological tests of pattern deposition have been suggested by health authorities and consist of spraying the product against a flat surface, such as a Kieselgel sheet, to highlight the printing of the droplets sprayed by the pump. This test is requested as quality control and must be effected using the same device at two distances from the sheet, in order to have a printing of the distribution of droplets at different levels of cloud. In vitro studies were also done using a cast of the human nose. A significant difference was observed among the deposition of liquid solution applied by a drop bottle, a squeeze bottle, a metered pump, and a pressurized inhaler. This study also provided indications on the method of delivery, because it was observed that in the case of pressurized aerosols, a double delivery in each nostril effected in different directions provided better distribution of the product (54).

Few data are available concerning the deposition of powder in the nose (55). The requisite particle size for nasal deposition has been stated as less than 10 μm (1). An unpublished work correlated the deposition pattern in a silicone cast of the human nose with the particle size of the powder sprayed. It was found that atrium deposition was predominant independently of particle size (Fig. 8). Other authors have investigated the use of a glass model of the nasal cavity, without the turbinate presence, to estimate nasal deposition (56, 57). Recently, using a silicone model including the turbinate structure, good nasal deposition

was obtained despite the fact that the particle size measured with aerodynamic methods was less than optimal. The model with turbinates gave higher deposition in the nasal cavity, as well as reducing the fraction penetrating the nose (58).

PENETRATION ENHANCERS AND BIOADHESION

A drug given by the nasal route is absorbed very quickly, entering the bloodstream similarly to an injection. Therefore, the nasal route must be primarily considered for rapid effect. However, this effect is also transient, because the efficient clearance mechanisms of the nose rapidly activate as well, so limiting the absorption time. Therefore, employing nasal delivery for prolonged release requires the development of particular strategies in order to keep the substance on the mucosa for a long time without altering the functionality of the nose.

Mucociliary clearance is the most significant physiological factor that affects nasal drug absorption, because it determines the time a drug remains at the absorption site. Some pathophysiological conditions, such as rhinitis, the common cold, hay fever, sinusitis, asthma, and nasal polyposis, may affect the retention of drugs in the nasal cavity. Environmental factors such as humidity, temperature, airborne toxins and chemicals, and many pharmaceutical excipients may also affect the clearance (59, 60). In order to achieve high absorption with only minimal effects on the mucociliary mechanism, the absorption process must be rapid, preferably within the first 15 minutes after administration (61). If the rate of clearance could be slightly decreased or halted in a reversible manner, then such retardation would be useful in increasing the contact time between the active drug and nasal mucosa, thereby increasing bioavailability.

Nasal mucosa allows effective absorption of a variety of lipophilic drugs and hydrophilic drugs, such as peptides and proteins (62). The major difficulty in administering those drugs intranasally is their low nasal bioavailability due to enzymatic degradation, mucociliary clearance, and poor mucosal membrane permeability. The attempts made to overcome these problems include coadministration of absorption enhancers and/or mucoadhesive substances.

The influence of the enhancers on the absorption of the drug across the nasal membrane is related to a direct effect on the drug and/or to an influence on the mucosa. For some drugs the solubilizing or stabilizing effect is of major importance. With regard to mucosa, enhancers may act by altering the properties of the mucus layer, by opening the tight junctions between epithelial cells, increasing membrane fluidity, creating disorders in the phospholipid of membrane, and facilitating the leaking of proteins and lipids from the membrane. The improvement of peptide and protein absorption is probably due to one or a combination of these mechanisms.

The most evaluated compounds as enhancers are surfactants (laureth-9), bile salts (glyco-taurocholate, deoxycholate), chelators (EDTA, citric acid), fatty acid salts (oleic, caprylic, capric, and lauric), phospholipids (L-α-lysophosphatidylcholine [DDPC], didecanoyl-PC), fusidates (sodium taurodihydrofusidate, STDHF), glycyrrhetinic acid derivatives (carbenoxolone, glycyrrhizinate), cyclodextrins (α-, β-, γ-cyclodextrins), hydroxypropyl-β-cyclodextrin and dimethyl β cyclodextrin (DMβCD), randomly methylated β-cyclodextrin (RAMEB), chitosan, and particulate carriers (microcrystalline cellulose, starch microspheres, and liposomes).

Nasal absorption enhancers differ substantially in efficacy and safety. Bile salts, surfactants, Ca^{2+} chelators and STDHF have been assumed to increase nasal drug transport, but they have shown morphological damage and severe inhibition of nasal ciliary movement. In vivo laureth-9 and sodium deoxycholate are associated with nasal irritation, and STDHF leads to painful stinging and lacrimation (1). Calcium chelators penetrate into the cells where they interact with intracellular Ca^{2+}, causing severe damage or even cell death. Therefore, research has been focusing on new classes of promoters of nasal drug absorption. Controlled studies in humans using medium-chain phospholipid DDPC as insulin enhancer have shown that nasal mucosal physiology was unaffected after intranasal administration, but that insulin bioavailability was low, despite intranasal doses about 20 times higher than subcutaneous doses (63). Cyclodextrins (CDs) are cyclic oligosaccharides showing a polar outer surface and an apolar interior cavity able to include lipophilic guest molecules. CDs can enhance lipophilic drug absorption by solubilization and protection against physicochemical and enzymatic degradation. Thus, CDs are also able to enhance hydrophilic drug absorption by the extraction of specific lipids from biological membranes, leading to an increase in membrane permeability and fluidity. The extent of protection and absorption enhancement seems to depend strongly on the nature of the drug used as well as on the CD used. For example, in vivo studies in rats have demonstrated that the addition of 5% α-CD to a nasal preparation of insulin resulted in an absolute bioavailability of approximately 30%; on the contrary, β- and γ-CDs did not affect insulin absorption. However, DMβCD gave rise to a large increase in insulin absorption, with a bioavailability of 100%. In contrast to the result obtained in rats, experiments in rabbits and human volunteers showed no absorption-enhancing effect of CDs for insulin, with a bioavailability of approximately 3–5% (64). Studies in rabbits

have concluded that α-CD is able to increase nasal absorption of human growth hormone (hGH). In fact, it has been seen that the presence of 30% α-CD in a powder formulation of hGH raises the nasal bioavailability from 8% to 23–25% (65). RAMEB enhanced dihydroergotamine (DHE) nasal absorption when administered by liquid and powder formulations including CD (RAMEB:DHE ratio 10:1), showing a bioavailability of 50% and 56%, respectively (66).

New compounds recently studied, chitosans are biodegradable high weight cationic polysaccharides. Their mechanism of transport enhancement is a combination of bioadhesion and transient opening of the tight junctions in the membrane. The cell-binding activity of chitosans is related to electrostatic interactions between cell surfaces charged negatively and the cationic polyelectrolyte structure. Chitosans have no arresting effect on the mucociliary clearance, and they do not cause significant changes in nasal mucosa histology. Medium molecular weight chitosans are able to enhance the nasal absorption in animals and human volunteers of polypeptides and other polar drugs, such as insulin, salmon calcitonin, and morphine metabolites (67). Because rapid mucociliary clearance decreases the time of drug contact with the absorbing regions of nasal mucosa, the use of compounds having bioadhesion properties has been revealed as very efficient in overcoming this problem. It has been shown that formulations including bioadhesive materials are retained in the nasal cavity with half-life clearance of 3 h or longer, compared with 15–20 minutes for usual formulations (68). Mucoadhesives are synthetic or natural polymers that interact with the mucus layer. Recently, bioadhesive microspheres based on materials such as starch, albumin and Sephadex, with particle sizes of 40–60 μm, have been developed. Starch microspheres are able to increase considerably the nasal absorption of insulin in rats and sheep, and of hGH and salmon calcitonin in sheep (69,70). The absorption enhancement by starch microspheres is not only related to their mucoadhesive properties but also to their capability of opening tight junctions by the dehydration of mucosal cells. The use of degradable starch microspheres as a nasal delivery system for hGH resulted in an increase of plasma peak height from 1.0 to 9 ng/mL and of area under the curve (AUC) from 28 to 892 ng min/mL, with a relative bioavailability of 2.7%.

Other bioadhesive polymeric systems have also been used in nasal peptide drug delivery (71). Microcrystalline cellulose was suggested to provide prolonged residence time due to its insolubility (41). Recent studies concluded that the absorption-enhancing effect of particulate carriers correlates directly with their Ca^{2+} binding capacity. In fact, the opening of the tight junctions may also be explained by a local decrease in Ca^{2+} concentration (72). There are many ongoing investigations to improve nasal bioavailability by a combination of microcrystalline cellulose (MCC) with permeation enhancers (sodium taurocholate [ST], ammonium glycyrrhizinate [AG], and glycyrrhetinic acid [GA]). Insulin absolute bioavailability from a 1.5% w/v suspension resulted in 1.96%. The presence of ST, AG, and GA in the MCC suspension provided bioavailabilities of 8.36, 7.83, and 2.15%, respectively. Thus, the combination of a bioadhesive polymer and permeation relatively nontoxic enhancers can be of promising potential for developing a nasal spray formulation for peptide drugs (73).

Finally, liposomes are attracting considerable interest for drug delivery to nasal mucosa. In fact, they are known to sustain the release of the entrapped drugs and to decrease the mucociliary clearance of the drugs due to their surface viscosity. Their action on nasal mucosa is related to the incorporation of phospholipids in the membrane, opening "new pores" in the paracellular tight junction (74). Proliposomes, i.e., a free-flowing powder immediately forming a liposomal dispersion on adding water, have also been manufactured for nasal delivery with the intention of sustaining the delivery of propanolol through nasal mucosa (75).

DRUGS DEVELOPED FOR NASAL ADMINISTRATION

Nasal preparations for local effect have been available over-the-counter for a long time. Recently the nose was considered for delivering drugs with systemic effects, and appropriate products were marketed. The products described here, delivered under prescription, are examples of systemic effect nasal preparations and include also some relevant products for topical effect. Oxytocin and nafarelin nasal sprays have not been reviewed.

Butorphanol

Butorphanol is a potent synthetic mixed agonist-antagonist opioid analgesic. Butorphanol is well absorbed orally, but due to extensive first-pass metabolism, oral bioavailability is very low. Alternative nonparenteral routes of administration, such as transnasal, sublingual, and buccal have been developed. The biopharmaceutical evaluation of the transnasal formulation discovered significant advantages over sublingual and buccal formulations (76). Butorphanol administered intranasally showed linear pharmacokinetics for doses ranging from 1 to 4 mg; the bioavailability and the maximum concentration were higher than those found after administering the drug via sublingual and buccal routes. Because both sublingual and buccal dosage forms are physically placed in the mouth, some portion of the dose is swallowed, absorbed orally, and subject to first-pass metabolism. In contrast, little butorphanol can escape from the sinus cavity after nasal administration, so that the majority of the dose is absorbed through the desired route. Therefore, butorphanol intranasal administration is a useful tool for the treatment of moderate to severe pain. The most frequently reported adverse effects with butorphanol administered nasally were congestion and insomnia.

Butorphanol for nasal administration is marketed as Stadol NS Nasal Spray (Bristol Myers Squibb Co.) (77). It is an aqueous solution of butorphanol tartrate for nasal administration as a metered spray. Each bottle contains 2.5 mL of a 10 mg/mL solution of butorphanol tartrate with sodium chloride, citric acid, and benzethonium chloride in purified water, with pH 5.0. Stadol NS is used in postoperative analgesia, mainly in the treatment of migraine pain. Onset of analgesia, which is within a few minutes for intravenous administration and within 10–15 minutes for intramuscular injection, is within 15 minutes for the nasal spray doses. Peak analgesic activity occurs within 30–60 minutes following intravenous and intramuscular administration and within 1–2 hours following nasal spray administration. Compared with the injectable form, Stadol NS has a longer duration of action (4–5 hours). Mean peak blood levels of about 1 ng/mL occur at 30–60 minutes after 1 mg dose administered nasally. The absolute bioavailability of Stadol NS is 60–70% and does not change in patients with allergic rhinitis. The fraction of Stadol NS absorbed is unaffected by the concomitant administration of a nasal vasoconstrictor, but the rate of absorption is decreased. Therefore, a slower onset can be anticipated if Stadol NS is administered concomitantly with or immediately following a nasal vasoconstrictor.

The patient should be instructed on the proper use of Stadol NS. The pump reservoir must be fully primed prior to initial dose. After priming, each metered spray delivers an average of 1.0 mg of butorphanol tartrate, and the 2.5 mL bottle delivers an average of 14–15 doses of Stadol NS. If not used for 48 hours or longer, the unit must be reprimed.

Calcitonin

Calcitonin is a 32 amino acid polypeptide hormone secreted by the parafollicular cells of thyroid glands. It provides the right bone growth by regulating Ca^{2+} turnover in cells. Nowadays it can be successfully employed in the treatment of osteoporosis and in Paget's desease, characterized by abnormal bone formation. The synthetic salmon calcitonin is currently formulated in several ways. Oral administration is contraindicated because the hormone is subjected to digestive degradation. Injectable calcitonin has been available on the market since 1984. Because of injection inconvenience to patients, intranasal administrations seemed to be more attractive. Many studies have been carried out to demonstrate the efficiency of nasal delivery, and the benefits have been compared with the parenteral route. The drug has been delivered as snuff, drops, and nebulized sprays. In late 1995 a new nasal spray was approved by the U.S. FDA.

Data obtained in experiments comparing the nasal with subcutaneous administrations have shown an equivalence, because both preparations were capable of alleviating pain and reducing bone disorder in the population of osteoporotic patients (78). Nasal calcitonin delivery is safe, preventative, and may increase bone mass of the lumbar spine. Fracture efficacy data are not yet available, although preliminary results are promising. Nasal calcitonin may be an analgesic to bone and of benefit in glucocorticoid-induced osteoporosis (79). The dose of nasal calcitonin for the treatment of established osteoporosis is 200 international units daily.

Although compliance problems are bypassed, by nasal administration low bioavailability increases the amount of dose administered. Results regarding the bioavailability of calcitonin nasal spray (Miacalcin®, Sandoz) have shown a great variability. Miacalcin is rapidly absorbed by nasal mucosa, and the plasma concentration peak appears after

31–39 minutes, which is twice as long as the 16–25 minutes found for the parenteral route. In volunteers approximately 3% of nasal dose, compared with intramuscular injection, is available (data ranged between 0.3 and 30.6%) (80). Adverse effects, which include nausea, rhinitis, and nasal discomfort, are generally mild and transient and always less common than others related to parenteral formulations. The nasal spray has been reported as having no serious adverse reactions associated with high doses. An increase in the bioavailability may be obtained using enhancers and proteolitic enzyme inhibitors (81), which improve the transport of the hormone through the nasal epithelium.

The delivery device is basically a pump system, which must be primed before the first use. The pump is activated once a faint spray is emitted, and it does not need to be reactivated before each successive use.

Dihydroergotamine

DHE is an ergot alkaloid used for the treatment of orthostatic hypotension and mainly for the prophylactic therapy of migraine. DHE was mainly available in parenteral dosage forms. The oral route is not suitable due to very low bioavailability (1%) caused by incomplete absorption and, particularly, to a high first-pass effect by the liver. However, alternative routes of administration that result in plasma levels comparable to the intramuscular route have been investigated (82). It has been demonstrated that intranasal administration provides a feasible delivery of DHE into systemic circulation. In fact, pharmacokinetic studies performed on humans show that DHE administered intranasally presents rapid absorption with a bioavailability, relative to intramuscular injection, of approximately 38%. A linear kinetics in the dosage range of 1 to 4 mg was observed (83). Another important pharmacokinetic result, concerning the reliability of this route of administration of DHE for the treatment of migraine, was that the vasomotor phenomena which could affect the nasal mucosa during a migraine attack, rhinitis, or the simultaneous administration of a local vasoconstrictor, had little or no influence on the bioavailability of DHE administered intranasally.

The first nasal solution consisted of an ampoule with DHE methanesulfonate salt at 4 mg/mL, and caffeine as enhancer. The ampoule had to be placed into a nebulizer when the migraine attack occurred, and after it was opened, it had to be used within 24 hours due to limited pharmaceutical and microbiological stability. Furthermore, the low concentration of DHE required large volumes to be sprayed into the nostrils, causing a spillage of solution from the nose. To overcome these drawbacks and to improve the nasal formulation, a pharmaceutically more stable nasal spray of higher concentration of DHE, able to administer a intranasal dose in a much smaller spray volume, was developed. Recently, the nasal spray (Migranal, Novarti's) was approved by the FDA (84). In two recent clinical trials of nasal spray, patients experienced headache relief as early as 30 minutes after treatment. Up to 60% of patients had responded within 2 hours, and up to 70% within 4 hours, following a single 2 mg treatment.

An interesting work in rabbits was carried out comparing two different formulations, liquid and lyophilized powder, containing a concentration of DHE of 10 mg/mL and RAMEB (66). It was assessed that the amount of RAMEB in liquid sprays did not affect the bioavailability of DHE. Nevertheless, by adding RAMEB to liquid, DHE solubility was increased. This allowed for more concentrated formulations and made possible administering higher doses in one puff, avoiding the spillage of liquid from the nasal cavity. Furthermore, the presence of RAMEB also increased the stability of the drug. Different results have been obtained from powdered formulations in which the DHE absorption was dependent of the amount of β-cyclodextrin and of the powder volume. The addition of CD seemed to improve absorption by enabling a rapid dissolution in the mucus layer of the DHE powder sprayed into the nostril.

Sumatriptan

Sumatriptan is a serotonin receptor agonist used in the treatment of migraine and cluster headache. It is available in a subcutaneous injection form or as tablets for oral dosage, but recently also as a nasal spray. The rationale of the nasal form is that the subcutaneous form is difficult to be self-administered for several patients, the oral route provides low bioavailability (14%), and administration during nausea or vomiting due to migraine may be unpleasant. The nasal spray is generally well tolerated; the most frequently reported events are transient disturbance of taste and nausea or vomiting.

The nasal formulation (Imigran, Glaxo Wellcome) is a solution of sumatriptan hemisulphate (10 mg/250 μL), buffered at pH 5.5, considering this pH within the normal range of nasal secretions. The solution is hypertonic. A high concentration is required for administering the dose in a small volume, suitable for spraying into the nostrils. Because of the low solubility of sumatriptan succinate used in the subcutaneous form, the hemisulphate salt has been preferred for the nasal form. Sumatriptan is a basic compound (pK$_a$ 9.63), so it is almost completely ionized at pH 5.5. The good absorption at this pH supports the hypothesis of a paracellular mechanism driving the absorption (85).

The bioavailability and the rate of absorption are intermediate between the values observed after subcutaneous and oral administration. The times to peak plasma concentrations are 12 min for a 6 mg subcutaneous dose, 2 h after a 100 mg oral dose, and 1 h for a 20 mg intranasal dose. Following the latter route, sometimes a secondary peak was observed after 1.5–2 h. It is likely that part of the dose runs out of the back of the throat and is swallowed with the saliva, becoming a second oral dose. After 2 h from a 20 mg dose, more than 50% of the patients reported headache relief. A second administration at this time is effective in two-thirds of the nonresponders (86).

Desmopressin

Desmopressin, the synthetic analogue of the naturally occurring antidiuretic hormone, vasopressin, has for many years been the drug of choice in the treatment of diabetes insipidus. Traditionally, it has been delivered by the intranasal route using the rhinyle catheter method, and was one of the first examples of a peptide that could be given systematically by the nasal route. Desmopressin solution was administered intranasally as a spray, using a metered-dose pump, or as drops, using a rhinyle catheter. Plasma levels showed that desmopressin was absorbed to a greater extent after administration of the spray, with a two- to three-fold increase in the relative bioavailability compared with the drops. Moreover, the use of an intranasal spray device can deposit well-controlled doses within the nasal cavity, which remain there sufficiently long to provide a clear enhancement in absorption and bioavailability (26).

DDAVP® Nasal Spray (desmopressin acetate) or DDAVP® Rhinal Tube (Rhône-Poulenc Rorer Pharmaceutical, Inc.) are available as aqueous solution for intranasal use (87). Each milliliter contains desmopressin acetate 0.1 mg, chlorbutanol, and sodium chloride. Intranasal DDAVP provides a prompt onset of antidiuretic action with a long duration after each administration. Its antidiuretic effect is about one-tenth that obtained with an equivalent dose administered by injection.

Cromolyn Sodium

Cromolyn sodium is indicated for the prevention and treatment of the symptoms of allergic rhinitis, because it inhibits the degranulation of sensitized mast cells and the release of histamine. The available product is a nasal solution (Nasalcrom® Nasal Solution, FISONS Pharmaceuticals) (88). Each milliliter of Nasalcrom contains 40 mg cromolyn sodium in purified water with benzalkonium chloride to preserve and EDTA to stabilize the solution.

Cromolyn sodium is poorly absorbed from the gastrointestinal tract. After instillation of Nasalcrom, less than 7% of the total dose administered is absorbed and is rapidly excreted unchanged in the bile and urine. The remainder of the dose is either expelled from the nose or swallowed and excreted via the alimentary tract.

Another nasal dosage form of cromolyn available on the market is formulated as nasal powder (Lomudal®, Fison Italchimici). It is presented as capsules containing 20 mg powder cromolyn sodium. The nasal powder administration requires the use of a special insufflator called Rinoflatore (see Fig. 3).

Steroid Drugs

Oral biavailability of steroid drugs is extremely low due to extensive elimination by hepatic first-pass metabolism. Nasal absorption of steroids, including progesterone, estradiol, and testosterone, has resulted in systemic bioavailability comparable with intravenous administration in rats and rhesus monkeys. For example, progesterone oral systemic bioavailability was approximately 7.9%, which is significantly less than the bioavailability achieved by nasal route (72–82%). The results demonstrate that nasal delivery can result in as much as a 10-fold reduction in the hepatogastrointestinal first-pass elimination of progesterone (89).

Other steroid drugs (i.e., glucocorticoids), such as budesonide, dexamethasone, flunisolide, fluticasone pro-

prionate, triamcinolone acetonide, and beclomethasone dipropionate are administered in the nasal cavity to obtain a local effect. Budesonide is an antiinflammatory glucocorticosteroid marketed as Rhinocort® Nasal Inhaler (Astra) (90). It is a metered-dose pressurized aerosol unit containing a suspension of micronized budesonide, indicated for the management of symptoms of seasonal or perennial allergic rhinitis in adults and children. A 3-week clinical study with placebo in seasonal rhinitis, comparing Rhinocort and orally ingested budesonide in 98 patients with allergic rhinitis due to birch pollen, demonstrated that the therapeutic effect of budesonide can be attributed to its topical effects. Only about 20% of an intranasal dose from the Rhinocort inhaler reached the systemic circulation. Biopsies of the nasal mucosa of 50 adult patients after 12 months of treatment and of 10 patients after 3–5 years of therapy showed no histopathological evidence of adverse effects. Rhinocort Nasal Inhaler is supplied in a 7 g canister containing 200 metered doses, provided with a metering valve and nasal adapter, together with patient's instructions for use. Each activation delivers approximately 32 μg of micronized budesonide to the patient.

Beclomethasone diproprionate (BDP) is another antiinflammatory steroid. Beconase® AQ Nasal Spray (Glaxo Wellcome, Inc.) or Vancenase® AQ nasal spray (Schering Plough Corp.) is a metered-dose, manual pump spray unit containing a suspension of BDP in an aqueous medium containing microcrystalline cellulose, carboxymethylcellulose sodium, dextrose, benzalkonium chloride, polysorbate 80, and phenylethyl alcohol (91). After initial priming (3–4 activations) each activation of the pump delivers from the nasal adapter 100 mg of suspension containing 42 μg of BDP. Beconase AQ Nasal Spray is indicated for the relief of the symptoms of seasonal or perennial allergic and nonallergic (vasomotor) rhinitis. The mechanism of the aerosolized drug's action in the nose is unknown. When given by nasal inhalation, the drug is deposited primarily in the nasal passages. Only about 20–25% of the dose is absorbed. A portion of the drug is swallowed. Biopsies of nasal mucosa obtained during clinical studies showed no histopathologic changes. Rino Clenil® (Chiesi Farmaceutici) is another metered-dose pressurized aerosol containing BDP 0.01 g, sorbitan trioleate, and propellant.

THE INSULIN CASE AND FUTURE DEVELOPMENTS: VACCINES AND BRAIN TARGETING THROUGH THE NOSE

Intranasal administration of drugs is likely to gain further importance in time. A large number of experiments on nasal drug delivery have used insulin as a model drug. The high interest in this drug itself makes it a suitable molecule to check the efficacy of nasal formulation. Despite the fact that insulin nasal delivery is not yet a reality, a very important challenge in the field of nasal drug delivery is the total or partial substitution of insulin daily injections with an intranasal therapy for diabetes mellitus. Up to now, several trials with different intranasal formulations have resulted in low and variable bioavailability and in uncertainty about long-term safety. Therefore, an intranasal therapy is not likely to be available in the near future (63). Moreover, considerations exist as to whether the oral form of insulin would be more convenient. The reasons are based on the fact that the intestinal administration of insulin showed that the drug is absorbed via the liver. This is the same as insulin produced by the pancreas and is different from the injected or inhaled insulin that goes directly into the circulation. Obviously, an ideal diabetes mellitus therapy should be capable of simulating the profile of normal insulin secretion (92,93). As mentioned earlier, high and predictable bioavailability and long-term safety are the main conditions for an intranasal formulation to be introduced into therapeutic practice. At present, neither a liquid nor a solid dosage form can assure both. We refer to the review of Merkus et al. (64) for a deeper evaluation of the mechanisms by which the adjuvants improve absorption of insulin.

New results are expected in the fields of vaccination and brain targeting (94). The first effective immunizations by this route were demonstrated in the late 1920s. Immune reactions develop in two different ways depending on the site of the first contact with the antigen. If the antigen directly enters the bloodstream, B-lymphocytes are primed to express specific antibodies and to release them into systemic circulation. If otherwise the infective agent (or the exogenous substance) is contacted by a mucosal surface, a different mechanism is activated. The antigen is picked up by specific M-cells of the epithelium and presented to T- and B-lymphocytes located in follicles forming the so-called mucosal associated lymphoid tissue (MALT). Thereafter, the primed lymphocytes migrate from the original MALT (e.g., the nasal associated lymphoid tissue) to the regional lymph nodes; here they get into further differentiation and then reach, by means of the systemic circulation, all the other mucosal surfaces, where both humoral and cellular immunity is provided. Vaccination by parenteral injection provides effective systemic immunity, but also implies high costs, low patient compliance, and several side effects. Some of these disadvantages could be avoided by immunization via mucosal surfaces. Future vaccination must be inexpensive, easy to distribute and administer. These are exactly the possibilities offered by intranasal vaccination. For the time being, no intranasal vaccine has yet been licensed. However, a wealth of studies have been undertaken in this direction. In particular, intranasal vaccines against the influenza virus have been found to be highly effective in several experiments in humans. Very interesting results have been obtained in the research for a vaccine against human immunodeficiency virus (HIV). In experiments on mice, intranasal immunization was superior to vaginal, gastric, or rectal immunization for the induction of systemic and mucosal anti-HIV antibody responses (95). Other investigations have been devoted to herpes virus, *Helicobacter pylori*, *Streptococcus pneumoniae*.

Finally, the nasal mucosa is also a very suitable site for the administration of peptides and small proteins to the brain that do not diffuse through the blood-brain barrier. An interesting summary on this subject has been reported by Sakane et al. (96). Many studies have demonstrated the presence of a particular transport mechanism from the olfactory mucosa to the brain, exploiting an easier access to the cerebrospinal fluid (CSF). The nerves coming from the olfactory bulb spread out in bundles close to the cribriform plate (the part of the ethmoid bone constituting the roof of the anterior cranial fossa). The bundles cross this bony wall and enter the nasal cavity, ending in many small protrusions of the mucosal surface. Each nervous bundle is surrounded by supporting cells and by a space containing CSF; this space is probably an extension of the subarachnoid space, and its presence provides a reliable explanation of the high rate of absorption from the olfactory region to the CSF.

As demonstrated by Gizurarson et al. (97), after instillation to the olfactory region of the nasal cavity, a significantly higher concentration of insulin reaches the brain as compared to subcutaneous administration. The relative bioavailability (intraolfactory versus subcutaneous) was 370%, with high differences between the administration techniques used. Based on these results, peptides and small proteins are the most interesting molecules for drug delivery to the brain exploiting intranasal administration.

ACKNOWLEDGMENTS

This article has been made possible thanks to the collaborative work of the young researchers active in nasal delivery studies at the Pharmaceutical Department of the University of Parma: Daniela Cocconi, Elena Pasini, Angela Armanni, Stefano Cagnani, Monica Sala, and Stefano Bonfante. Professor Dimitri Rekkas of the University of Athens must to be thanked as well for his helpful suggestions.

BIBLIOGRAPHY

1. D.F. Proctor and I. Anderson, *The Nose: Upper Airway Physiology and the Atmospheric Environment*, Elsevier, Amsterdam, 1982.

2. Y.W. Chien, *Transnasal Systemic Medications*, Elsevier, Amsterdam, 1985.

3. Y.W. Chien, K.S.E. Su, and S.F. Chang, *Nasal Systemic Drug Delivery*, Dekker, New York, 1989.

4. L. Illum, *S.T.P. Pharmacol.* 3(7), 594–598 (1987).

5. C.G. Wilson and N. Washington, in M.H. Rubinstein, ed., *Physiological Pharmaceutics Biological Barriers to Drug Absorption*, Ellis Horwood, Chichester, 1989, pp. 139–154.

6. P. Edman and E. Bjork, *Adv. Drug Delivery Rev.* 8, 165–177 (1992).

7. J.C. Verhoef and F.V.H.M. Merkus, in A.G. de Boer, ed., *Drug Absorption Enhancement*, Harwood Academic Publishers, Chur, Switzerland, 1994, pp. 119–154.

8. S. Gizurarson, *Adv. Drug Delivery Rev.* 11, 329–347 (1993).

9. D. Duchene and G. Ponchel, *Drug Dev. Ind. Pharm.*, 19(1 and 2), 101–122 (1993).

10. A.S. Harris, *J. Drug Target.* 1, 101–116 (1993).

11. P. Buri and A.L. Cornaz, *Eur. J. Pharm. Biopharm.* 40(5), 261–270 (1994).

12. A.J. Almeida and H.O. Alpar, *J. Drug Target.* 3, 455–467 (1996).

13. American Association of Pharmaceutical Scientists, available at: *http://www.aaps.org*

14. E. Biocca, *Viaggi tra gli Indi: Alto Rio Negro—Alto Orinoco: Appunti di un Biologo*, Consiglio Nazionale delle Ricerche, Roma, Italy, 1965, vol. 2, pp. 235–239.

15. N. Mygind and R. Dahl, *Adv. Drug Delivery Rev.* **29**, 3–12 (1998).

16. V.H.L. Lee, A. Yamamoto, and U.B. Kompella, *Crit. Rev. Ther. Drug Carrier Syst.* **8**, 91–192 (1991).

17. K. Overgaard et al., *J. Clin. Endocrinol. Metab.* **72**, 344–349 (1991).

18. L. Illum and S.S. Davis, *Clin. Pharmacokinet.* **23**, 30–41 (1992).

19. F.W.H.M. Merkus et al., *J. Controlled Release* **24**, 201–208 (1993).

20. H. Critchley, S.S. Davis, F. Farraj, and L. Illum, *J. Pharm. Pharmacol.* **46**, 651–656 (1994).

21. N.G.M. Schipper, J.C. Verhoef, S.G. Romeijn, and F.W.H.M. Merkus, *Calcif. Tissue Int.* **56**, 280–282 (1995).

22. S.G. Chandler, L. Illum, and N.W. Thomas, *Int. J. Pharm.* **76**, 61–70 (1991).

23. S.G. Chandler, N.W. Thomas, and L. Illum, *Pharm. Res.* **11**, 1623–1630 (1994).

24. Z. Shao and A.K. Mitra, *Pharm. Res.* **9**, 1184–1189 (1992).

25. Z. Shao, R. Krishnamoorthy, and A.K. Mitra, *Pharm. Res.* **9**, 1152–1163 (1992).

26. A.S. Harris, I.M. Nilsson, Z.G. Wagner, and U. Alkner, *J. Pharm. Sci.* **75**, 1085–1088 (1986).

27. H.J.M. van de Donk, A.G.M. van den Heuvel, J. Zuidema, and F.W.H.M. Merkus, *Rhinology* **20**, 127–137 (1982).

28. S. Gizurarson, C. Marriot, G.P. Martin, and E. Bechgaard, *Int. J. Pharm.* **65**, 243–247 (1990).

29. W.A.J.J. Hermens, P.M. Hooymans, J.C. Verhoef, and F.W.H.M. Merkus, *Pharm. Res.* **7**, 144–146 (1990).

30. L. Jian and A.L.W. Po, *Int. J. Pharm.* **95**, 101–104 (1993).

31. A.R. Khan, B. Bengtsson, and S. Lindberg, *Eur. J. Pharmacol.* **130**, 91–96 (1986).

32. H.J.M. van de Donk, I.D. Muller Plantema, J. Zuidema, and F.W.H.M. Merkus, *Rhinology* **18**, 119–133 (1980).

33. P.C. Braga, G. Piatti, M. Dal Sasso, and A. Bernini, *J. Pharm. Pharmacol.* **44**, 938–940 (1992).

34. E. Marttin, N.J.M. Skipper, J.C. Verhoef, and F.W.H.M. Merkus, *Adv. Drug Delivery Rev.* **29**, 13–38 (1998).

35. I. Andersen et al., *Am. Rev. Respir. Dis.* **110**, 301–305 (1974).

36. C.R. Behl et al., *Adv. Drug Delivery Rev.* **29**, 89–116 (1998).

37. C.R. Behl et al., *Adv. Drug Delivery Rev.* **29**, 117–133 (1998).

38. D.C. Corbo, J.C. Liu, and Y.W. Chien, *J. Pharm. Sci.* **79**, 202–206 (1990).

39. A.A. Hussain, *Adv. Drug Delivery Rev.* **29**, 39–49 (1998).

40. N.G.M. Schipper, S.G. Romeijn, J.C. Verhoef, and F.W.H.M. Merkus, *Pharm. Res.* **5**, 682–686 (1993).

41. T. Nagai et al., *J. Controlled Release* **1**, 15–22 (1984).

42. D. Provasi et al., *Proc. Int. Symp. Controlled Release Bioact. Mater.* **19**, 421–424 (1992).

43. M.T. Vidgren, A. Karkkainen, P. Karjalainen, and J. Nuutinen, *Int. J. Pharm.* **42**, 216–221 (1988).

44. A. De Ascentiis et al., *Pharm. Res.* **13**, 734–738 (1996).

45. *Physicians' Desk Reference,* Medical Economics Data Production Company, Montvale, N.J., 1996, p. 1792.

46. *SCRIP* **2300**, 23 (1998).

47. H. Kublik and M.T. Vidgren, *Adv. Drug Delivery Rev.* **29**, 157–177 (1998).

48. Pfeiffer, Compiser system 101573,1611.

49. Valois Pharm., available at *http://www.cosmeticindex.com/ci/val/index.html*

50. Hovione, available at: *http://www.hovione.com/hovione.htm*

51. A. De Ascentiis, Ph.D. Thesis, University of Parma, Department of Pharmacy, 1994.

52. D. Provasi et al., *Eur. J. Pharm. Biopharm.* **40**, 223–227 (1994).

53. J.G. Hardy, S.W. Lee, and C.G. Wilson, *J. Pharm. Pharmacol.* **37**, 294–296 (1985).

54. N. Mygind and S. Vesterhauge, *Rhinology* **11**, 79–88 (1978).

55. I. Gonda, *Adv. Drug Delivery Rev.* **29**, 179–184 (1998).

56. G.W. Halloworth and J.M. Padfield, *J. Allergy Clin. Immunol.* **77**(2), 348–353 (1996).

57. K.D. Ostrander et al., *Pharm. Tech.*, 98–106 (September, 1995).

58. S. Leung, D. Velasquez, and D. Schultz, *Pharm. Res.* **14**(11), Suppl. (November 1997).

59. W.A. Lee, R.E. Ennis, and L.C. Foster, *Proc. Int. Symp. Controlled Release Bioact. Mater.* **15**, 77 (1988).

60. W.A.J.J. Hermens and F.W.H.M. Merkus, *Pharm. Res.* **4**, 445–449 (1987).

61. S. Gizurarson, S.N. Rasmussen, and F. Larsen, *J. Pharm. Sci.* **80**, 505–506 (1991).

62. A.E. Pontiroli, *Adv. Drug Delivery Rev.* **29**, 81–87 (1998).

63. F.W.H.M. Merkus, N.G.M. Schipper, and J.C. Verhoef, *J. Controlled Release* **41**, 69–75 (1996).

64. F.W.H.M. Merkus, J.C. Verhoef, S.G. Romeijn, and N.G.M. Schipper, *Pharm. Res.* **8**, 588–592 (1991).

65. C. Vermehren, H.S. Hansen, and M.K. Thomsen, *Int. J. Pharm.* **128**, 239–250 (1996).

66. E. Martin, S.G. Romeijn, J.C. Verhoef, and F.W.H.M. Merkus, *J. Pharm Sci.* **86**, 802–807 (1997).

67. L. Illum, N.F. Farraj, and S.S. Davis, *Pharm. Res.* **11**, 1186–1189 (1994).

68. L. Illum, N. Farraj, H. Critchley, and S.S. Davis, *Int. J. Pharm.* **46**, 261–265 (1988).

69. E. Björk and P. Edman, *Int. J. Pharm.* **47**, 233–238 (1988).

70. L. Illum et al., *Int. J. Pharm.* **63**, 207–211 (1990).

71. L. Pereswetoff-Morath, *Adv. Drug Delivery Rev.* **29**, 185–194 (1998).

72. C.R. Oechslein, G. Fricker, and T. Kissel, *Int. J. Pharm.* **139**, 25–32 (1996).

73. P. Dondeti, H. Zia, and T.E. Needham, *Int. J. Pharm.* **122**, 91–105 (1995).

74. L. Illum, *3rd Ann. Meet. Nasal Drug Delivery Focus Group, Am. Assoc. Pharm. Sci.*, Boston, November 5, 1997.

75. B. Ahn, S. Kim, and C. Shim, *J. Controlled Release* **34**, 203–210 (1995).

76. W.C. Shyu et al., *Biopharm. Drug Dispos.* **14**, 371–379 (1993).

77. *Physicians' Desk Reference*, Medical Economics Data Production Company, Montvale, N.J., 1996, pp. 775–778.

78. B. Combe, C. Cohen, and F. Aubin, *Calcif. Tissue Int.* **61**, 10–15 (1997).

79. S. Silverman, *Am. J. Med. Sci.* **313**(1), 13–16 (1997).

80. *Physicians' Desk Reference*, Medical Economics Data Production Company, Montvale, N.J., 1996, pp. 2275–2276.

81. K. Morimoto and M. Kakemi, *Int. J. Pharm.* **113**, 1–8 (1995).

82. D.T.-W. Lau et al., *Pharm. Res.* **11**(11), 1530–1534 (1994).

83. H. Humbert, M.D. Cabiac, C. Dubray, and D. Lavene, *Clin. Pharm. Ther.* September, pp. 265–275, (1996).

84. *SCRIP* **2294** (December 19), 21 (1997).

85. A. Barrow et al., *Biopharm. Drug Dispos.* **18**(5), 443–458 (1997).

86. P. Fowler et al., *Cephalgia* **15**(Suppl. 14), 238 (1995).

87. *Physicians' Desk Reference*, Medical Economics Data Production Company, Montvale, N.J., 1996, pp. 2017–2018.

88. *Physicians' Desk Reference*, Medical Economics Data Production Company, Montvale, N.J., 1996, pp. 994–995.

89. D.C. Corbo, Y.C. Huang, and Y.W. Chien, *Int. J. Pharm.* **46**, 133–140 (1988).

90. *Physicians' Desk Reference*, Medical Economics Data Production Company, Montvale, N.J., 1996, pp. 556–558.

91. *Physicians' Desk Reference*, Medical Economics Data Production Company, Montvale, N.J., 1996, pp. 1076–1078.

92. J.A. Galloway and R.E. Chance, *Horm. Metab. Res.* **26**, 591–598 (1994).

93. J. Hilsted et al., *Diabetologia* **38**, 680–684 (1995).

94. A.J. Almeida and H.O. Alpar, *J. Drug Target.* **3**, 455–467 (1996).

95. H.F. Staats, S.P. Montgomery, and T.J. Palker, *AIDS Res. Hum. Retroviruses* **13**(11), 945–952 (1997).

96. T. Sakane, S. Yamashita, T. Nadai, and H. Sezaki, *S.T.P. Pharmacol. Sci.* **7**(1), 98–106 (1997).

97. S. Gizurarson, T. Thorvaldsson, P. Sigurdsson, and E. Gunnarsson, *Int. J. Pharm.* **140**, 77–83 (1996).

See also BIOADHESIVE DRUG DELIVERY SYSTEMS; MUCOSAL DRUG DELIVERY, BUCCAL; MUCOSAL DRUG DELIVERY, INTRAVITREAL; MUCOSAL DRUG DELIVERY, OCULAR; MUCOSAL DRUG DELIVERY, VAGINAL DRUG DELIVERY AND TREATMENT MODALITIES.

MUCOSAL DRUG DELIVERY, OCULAR

O. FELT
V. BAEYENS
M. ZIGNANI
P. BURI
R. GURNY
University of Geneva
Geneva, Switzerland

KEY WORDS

Bioadhesion

Eyedrops

Hydrogels

Inserts

Liposomes

Microparticles

Nanoparticles

Ocular delivery systems

Ocular pharmacokinetics

Pseudo-latexes

Residence time

Thermosetting gels

Tolerance

INTRODUCTION

Historically, the use of topical devices for eye treatment is mentioned in Assyrian medical texts. Vegetable drugs (e.g., caraway, cassia, onions) were commonly prescribed and were applied as powders, ointments, or washes mixed with water, milk, wine, or oil (1). As an example, it was suggested to treat purulent conjunctivitis with "a local application of tanner's verdigris on vellum with copper dust, arsenic and yellow sulphide of arsenic mixed in curd" (1).

Actually, topical delivery of eyedrops into the lower cul-de-sac is the most common method for the administration of therapeutic agents in the treatment of ocular diseases and in diagnostics. However, one of the major problems encountered with solutions is the rapid and extensive elimination of drugs from the precorneal lachrymal fluid by solution drainage, lachrymation, and nonproductive absorption by the conjunctiva or the nasal mucosa, which may cause undesirable side effects (2,3) (Fig. 1). It must be noted that this high drainage rate is due to the tendency of the eye to maintain its residence volume at 7–10 μL permanently, whereas volumes topically instilled range from 20 to 50 μL. In fact it has been demonstrated in vivo that 90% of the dose was cleared within 2 min for an instilled volume of 50 μL and, within 4 min for an instilled volume of 10 μL (4). Consequently, the ocular residence time of conventional solutions is limited to a few minutes, and the overall absorption of a topically applied drug is

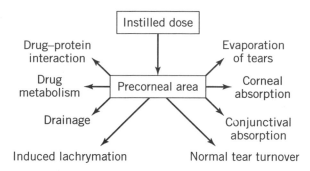

Figure 1. Drug elimination pathways from the precorneal area.

limited to 1–10% (5,6). Drug uptake occurs as a massive pulse entry, followed by a rapid decline, which means a short initial period of overdosing, followed by a long period of underdosing (7).

Initial attempts to overcome the poor bioavailability of topically instilled drugs typically involved the use of ointments based on mixtures of white petrolatum and mineral oils (8,9) and suspensions (10,11). Ointments ensure superior drug bioavailability by increasing the contact time with the eye, minimizing the dilution by tears, and resisting nasolachrymal drainage. Because these vehicles have the major disadvantage of providing blurred vision, they are nowadays mainly used for either nighttime administration or for treatment on the outside and edges of the eyelids (12). Use of suspensions as ophthalmic delivery systems relies on the assumption that particles may persist in the conjunctival sac. The efficiency of suspensions has shown high variability, which occurred as a result of inadequate dosing, probably mainly due to the lack of patient's compliance in adequately shaking the suspension before administration (13). These disadvantages have led to other approaches being investigated. One of the common methods to optimize prolonged precorneal residence time is to use hydrogels (14,15), liposomes (16), micro- and nanocarrier systems (16–19), and inserts (20,21). In comparison with traditional formulations, these systems have the following advantages:

- Increased contact time
- Prolonged drug release
- Reduction of systemic side effects
- Reduction of the number of applications
- Better patient compliance

A rapid overview of the most common diseases, e.g., ocular inflammations, glaucoma, and dry eye syndrome, treated with the ophthalmic dosage forms reviewed in this article is briefly provided here. Ocular inflammations are triggered by trauma, viral or bacterial infections, immunorelated phenomena, or corneal ulceration. Depending on the etiologic agent, the treatment of ocular inflammations consists of a topical steroidal therapy (dexamethasone) in combination with nonsteroidal antiinflammatory drugs (diclofenac), immunosuppressive agents (azathioprine), antimicrobial agents (tobramycin), and mydriatic-cycloplegic drugs (pilocarpine) (22).

Glaucoma results from the impairment of the aqueous humor flow and is characterized by an elevation of the intraocular pressure, progressive optic neuropathy, visual impairment, and eventually blindness (22). The most frequent drug therapy is based on the use of parasympathomimetics (pilocarpine), with or without adrenergic agonists (epinephrine) or β-blockers, including timolol, betaxolol, carteolol, and metipranolol.

Dry eye syndrome and keratoconjunctivitis sicca (KCS) are ocular surface pathologies concerned with reduction and unstability of the precorneal tear film. KCS is associated with local symptoms such as irritation, photophobia, foreign body sensation, and burning (23). The treatment of this disease relies on the use of artificial tear formulations

able to fulfill the physicochemical role of normal tear including lowering the surface tension of the tear film, forming a hydrophilic layer compatible with adsorbed mucin, and enhancing the tear volume when necessary (23).

The aim of the following article is to describe the various polymeric systems used to achieve prolonged contact time of drugs with the cornea and increase their bioavailability. Advantages and shortcomings of the different systems reviewed are discussed as well as their characteristics and their in vivo applications.

HYDROGELS

Definition and Classification

The most common way to improve drug retention on the corneal surface is undoubtedly by using polymers to increase solution viscosity. Previous studies on rabbits by Robinson et al. (24,25) established that the rate of drainage from the eye of an instilled solution is markedly reduced as the viscosity of the solution is increased. More recently, the approach to improve precorneal retention is based on the use of mucoadhesive polymers. The principle for use of bioadhesive vehicles relies on their ability to interact with the mucin coating layer present at the eye surface (26).

Kim et al. (27) define hydrogels as polymers endowed with the ability to swell in water or aqueous solvents and induce a liquid–gel transition. However, in ophthalmology the limit between actual hydrogels and highly viscosified solutions is not clearly established. According to Plazonnet et al. (28), aqueous gels are at the upper limit of viscous preparations, and they are formed when high molecular weight polymers or high polymer concentrations are incorporated in the formulations.

Currently, two groups of hydrogels are distinguished, namely preformed and in situ forming gels (Fig. 2). Preformed hydrogels can be defined as simple viscous solutions which do not undergo any modifications after administration. In situ forming gels are formulations, applied as

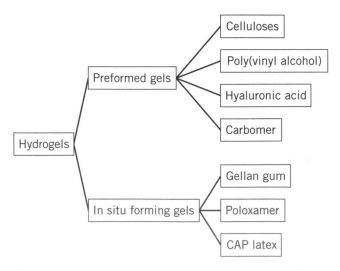

Figure 2. Classification of ophthalmic hydrogels. *Source:* Adapted from Ref. 29.

solutions, sols, or suspensions, that undergo gellation after instillation due to physic-chemical changes inherent to the eye (29).

The polymers chosen to prepare ophthalmic hydrogels should meet some specific rheological characteristics. It is generally well accepted that the instillation of a formulation should influence tear behavior as little as possible (6). Because tears have a pseudoplastic behavior, pseudoplastic vehicles would be more suitable as Newtonian formulations, which have a constant viscosity independent of the shear rate, whereas pseudoplastic solutions exhibit decreased viscosity with increasing shear rate, thereby offering lowered viscosity during blinking and stability of the tear film during fixation. The importance of the rheological properties of topical semisolid preparations regarding ocular tolerance and thus, good efficacy, has been reviewed by Zignani et al. (30).

Preformed Hydrogels

Preformed hydrogels for topical administration in the eye can be based on natural, synthetic, or semisynthetic polymers. Some characteristics of the more commonly used polymers are listed in Table 1.

Cellulose Derivatives. Because pure cellulose is not water soluble due to its relatively high crystallinity, cellulosic derivatives have been used for a long time as viscosifiers in collyria. Methylcellulose (MC) was first introduced in ophthalmic formulations in the 1940s as a mean of decreasing their fluidity (31). Some years later, Mueller and Deardorff (32) showed in man that solutions of homatropine hydrobromide exhibited enhanced cycloplegic and mydriatic activity in the presence of MC. Further promising results were obtained in 1962 by Haas and Merrill (33), who reported a lowered intraocular pressure in man after administration of pilocarpine incorporated in an MC vehicle. Since then, cellulosic polymers have been extensively studied as vehicle for ocular drug delivery. Currently, a large number of commercial formulations contain cellulosic viscosifiers, including Adsorbotear® (Alcon, Fort Worth, Texas) and Tears Naturale (Alcon, Fort Worth, Texas).

The cellulosic derivatives most commonly used in ophthalmology are:

- Methylcellulose (MC)
- Hydroxyethylcellulose (HEC)
- Hydroxypropycellulose (HPC)
- Hydroxypropylmethylcellulose (HPMC)
- Sodium carboxymethylcellulose (CMC Na)

The boundary between viscous solutions and gels for cellulosic derivatives is particularly difficult to define, because data regarding the hydrocolloid concentration or the viscosity of the final formulation are not always available. Therefore, some studies listed in Table 2 deal more with viscous solutions than with actual hydrogels.

Comparing the performance of three different cellulosic derivatives, namely HEC, HPC, and HPMC, Ludwig et al. (41) reported that HEC solutions were the most effective in reducing the elimination rate of sodium fluorescein from the cornea, probably due to a better tolerance. In fact, HEC was rated as the most comfortable by the volunteers, whereas HPC and HPMC gave rise to complaints of irritation and blurred vision. Several studies have clearly demonstrated the efficacy of cellulosic polymers in increasing ocular availability of numerous drugs when compared with simple saline solutions by decreasing the drainage rate from the eye (25,40,44). For example, Chrai and Robinson (25), using MC as the viscosity-inducing polymer, found a 10-fold decrease in the drainage rate constant for a 100-fold change in viscosity. However, they reported that increasing the viscosity above 15–20 cps, which appeared as the optimum viscosity, did not lead to a proportional improvement.

Subsequent advances in the polymers field with respect to ocular drug delivery have led to the use of poly(vinyl alcohol) (PVA); sodium hyaluronate, and carbomer, which often give better results (35,38,44,47) than celluloses.

Poly(vinyl alcohol). PVA is a synthetic polymer commercially obtained by polymerization of vinylacetate to poly(vinyl acetate) and subsequent hydrolysis to PVA (49).

Table 1. Characteristics of Polymers Used To Prepare Preformed Hydrogels for Ophthalmic Applications

Polymer	Origin	Characteristics
Cellulosic derivatives	Semisynthetic	Good tolerance Optical clarity Newtonian behavior Similar refractive index as the cornea
Poly(vinyl alcohol)	Synthetic	Newtonian behavior Wetting agent
Sodium hyaluronate	Skin, connective tissues, muscles, tendon, vitreous body, aqueous humor	Biocompatible Mucoadhesive Pseudoplastic behavior Viscoelastic behavior
Carbomer	Synthetic	Good tolerance Bioadhesion Possibility to be neutralized by the active compound in its basic form

Table 2. Preformed Hydrogels Containing Cellulosic Derivatives for Ophthalmic Administration

Polymer	Concentration (%)	Therapeutic agent	Refs.
MC	N.A.	Pilocarpine nitrate	25
MC	N.A.	Pilocarpine hydrochloride	34
MC	1.0	None	35
MC	0.6	Antazoline hydrochloride Pilocarpine hydrochloride	36
HEC	1.1–3.4	Sodium fluorescein	37
HEC	12.0	Pilocarpine	38
HEC	1.1	Sodium fluorescein	39
HEC	0.325; 0.50	Pilocarpine nitrate	40
HEC	1.1; 1.7	Sodium fluorescein	41
HEC	0.2–0.50	L-653,328	42
HEC	2.0	Naphazoline atenolol	43
HPC	5.5	Pilocarpine	38
HPC$_{LMw}$	4.5	Tropicamide	44
HPC$_{MMw}$	1.40	Tropicamide	44
HPC	1.8; 3.4	Sodium fluorescein	41
HPC	0.35; 1.8	Sodium fluorescein	39
HPC$_{LMw}$	5.0	Pilocarpine nitrate	45
HPC$_{MMw}$	1.2	Pilocarpine nitrate	45
HPMC	0.36; 0.60	Sodium fluorescein	39
HPMC	0.36; 0.64	Sodium fluorescein	41
HPMC	0.5	None	46
CMC Na	4.0	Pilocarpine	47
CMC Na	4.0	Acetazolamide	48
CMC Na	1.63	Tropicamide	44
EHEC	5.0	Pilocarpine	38

Note: MC, methylcellulose; HEC, hydroxyethylcellulose; HPC, hydroxypropylcellulose; HPC$_{LMw}$, low molecular weight hydroxypropylcellulose; HPC$_{MMw}$, medium molecular weight hydroxypropylcellulose; HPMC, hydroxypropylmethylcellulose; CMC Na, sodium carboxymethylcellulose; EHEC, ethylhydroxyethylcellulose.

PVA was introduced in the early 1960s (50) and has been reported to have corneal contact time superior to MC when tested on rabbits. Conflicting results were obtained by Linn and Jones (51), who found that PVA exhibited a significantly shorter elimination time than another cellulosic derivative, namely HPMC (Fig. 3). Numerous authors (46,52,53) reported quite similar results in favor of 0.5%

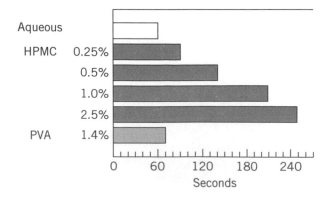

Figure 3. Lachrymal excretion time of various vehicles. Average of 20 separate instillations of each vehicle. *Source:* Adapted from Ref. 51 with permission.

MC over 1.4% of PVA in rabbits or humans. These last findings seemed more reasonable than those of Krishna and Brow (50) because 0.5% MC solutions exhibit significantly greater viscosity compared with 1.4% solutions based on PVA. Patton and Robinson (24) highlighted those presuming contradictory results. By testing solutions based on MC and PVA, the authors concluded that two vehicles exhibiting or at least approximating to Newtonian behavior in the same viscosity range could not have significantly different effects on ocular drug bioavailability. Moreover, they established that an optimal viscosity range (12–15 cps) also existed for PVA as demonstrated for MC (25).

Since then, numerous studies have been conducted, mostly comparing celluloses with PVA in an effort to determine the ideal ophthalmic vehicle. Some drugs tested in formulations containing PVA as well as the subsequent observations are listed in Table 3.

Lachrymal drainage evaluations of PVA formulations by γ scintigraphy (35,54) have demonstrated a significant delay of the drainage in man and rabbits, when compared with a saline solution. Hardberger et al. (35) have reported that the average $T_{1/2}$ for saline was markedly shorter (4.2 minutes) than for 1.4% PVA solutions (24 minutes).

Some commercial products, particularly for the treatment of dry eye, are based on PVA, including HypoTears® (IOLAB Corp., Claremont, California) and Liquifilm® (Allergan, Irvine, California).

Sodium Hyaluronate. The sodium salt of hyaluronic acid (SH) is a high molecular weight biological polymer composed of repeating disaccharide units of glucuronic acid and *N*-acetylglucosamine, a specific ultrapure fraction being patented as Healon® (Kabi Pharmacia, Sweden) by Balazs (57) in 1979. Its use as a vehicle in ocular drug delivery has been extensively reviewed by Bernatchez et al. (58). The efficacy of SH to increase precorneal residence time of ophthalmic formulations in humans has been investigated by several authors using different methods summarized in Table 4.

γ scintigraphic data of Snibson et al. (60) pointed out a very interesting phenomenon. They demonstrated that the residence times of 0.2% and 0.3% SH solutions on the cornea were significantly longer for patients having dry eye syndrome than in healthy subjects. The rationale for such a result was that the alteration of tear mucin in dry eyes might have modified the interaction of SH with the ocular surface.

An extended residence time is one of the factors used to select artificial tears for the therapy of KCS. At present, the therapeutic schedule in the treatment of dry eye implies frequent instillations, which lead to two major shortcomings: patient discomfort and side effects due to preservatives used in multiple dosage forms such as benzalkonium chloride, well known for their potential toxicity to the corneal epithelium. Because SH can protect against damages caused by benzalkonium chloride (62), it has been frequently proposed as a vehicle of choice in tear substitutes (61,63–65) and all the studies reported improvement of several symptoms associated with KCS, such as blurred vision, pain, photophobia, with this kind of

Table 3. Ophthalmic Formulations Based on PVA

PVA (%)	Drug	Species[a]	Effects[b]	Reference
0.0–10.0	Pilocarpine nitrate	R	1–3%: optimum concentrations range 10%: probably obstruction of the lachrymal duct	24
1.4	Tracer ^{99m}Tc	R/H	Diminution of the drainage rate	35
1.2	Pilocarpine nitrate	R/H	Improvement of the miotic response	45
3.0–6.5	Tracer ^{99m}Tc	R/H	Significant corneal retention within the first 20–50 s	54
1.4–4.2	Fluorescein	H	1.4–4.2%: Diminution of tear constant elimination 4.2%: discomfort, blurred vision	55
6.0	Pilocarpine	R	Improved precorneal retention Improved bioavailability	56

[a]H; human; R; rabbit.
[b]Comparative conclusions are made toward saline solutions.

Table 4. Effect of SH on the Precorneal Residence Time of Topical Solutions

Tracer	n^a	HA concentration (%)	Half-life (s)	Refs.
Fluorescein	4	0	96	37
		0.10	144	
		0.19	138	
		0.25	>240	
^{99m}Tc	7	0	96	59
		0.125	168[b]	
		0.250	>1200	
^{99m}Tc	6	0	36	60
		0.2	279[b]	
		0.3	437[b]	
	12 KCS[c]	0	40	
		0.2	468	
		0.3	909	
^{99m}Tc	6 KCS[c]	0.2	321	61

[a]Number of healthy individuals unless mentioned otherwise
[b]Not significantly different from the control.
[c]Keratoconjunctivitis sicca.
Source: Adapted from Ref. 58.

treatment. A further advantage of SH in this application is its pseudoplastic behavior.

The ability of SH to prolong drug release by increasing precorneal drug residence time has been studied (mostly in animals) for several ophthalmic compounds such as pilocarpine (66–71) or, more recently, gentamicin (72). Residence time of gentamicin in humans was found to be 2.23-fold superior when instilled in 0.25% SH formulations than in an isotonic phosphate buffer solution, and drug bioavailability was significantly improved for at least 10 minutes.

Carbomer. Cross-linked poly(acrylic acid) of high molecular weight, commercially available as Carbopol® (B.F. Goodrich Chemical Company, Cleveland, Ohio), is widely used in ophthalmology to enhance precorneal retention to the eye.

Preparation of Carbopol hydrogels is simply based on the dispersion of the polymer in water at room temperature, followed by a neutralization process with agents such as sodium hydroxide, triethanolamine, or directly with ac-

tive basic compounds. The maximal viscosity is obtained at neutral pH.

Carbopol offers the advantage of exhibiting excellent mucoadhesive properties when compared with others polymers (e.g., cellulose derivatives, PVA and SH). The mechanisms involved in the mucoadhesion ability of Carbopol have been investigated previously (73,74). Four mechanisms of interaction between mucin and poly(acrylic acid) have been described (73,74):

- Electrostatic interaction
- Hydrogen bonding
- Hydrophobic interaction
- Interdiffusion

These mechanisms can be explained by the similar features of the mucus network and the cross-linked poly(acrylic acid):

- Macromolecular expanded network
- Negative charges
- Significant hydratation in aqueous media
- Significant number of carboxyl groups

The efficacy of Carbopol in enhancing precorneal residence time has been extensively studied by incorporating tracers such as sodium fluorescein (75) or active compounds such as pilocarpine or prednisolone (47,76–78). Some in vivo studies on rabbits or humans are reported in Table 5.

Comparing different types of poly(acrylic acid) (Carbopol 940, 934, 941, and 910), Unlü et al. (81) concluded that Carbopol 940 showed superior appearance and clarity. The results reported in these studies showed the superiority of poly(acrylic acid) as a sustained release agent over reference solutions (77,82) or over some hydrogels (47,56,79). However, the majority of authors avoided tolerance evaluations. Only Ludwig et al. (75) noted some differences in acceptability of Carbopol formulations (0.1 and 0.2%) from one patient to another; some volunteers complained of blurred vision. This result was confirmed by a clinical trial in human by Amin et al. (83), who observed a slight irritation after administration of Carbopol 940 gel, whereas the Draize test on rabbits showed no ocular irritation.

Table 5. Preformed Ophthalmic Hydrogels Based on Carbopol

Carbopol type	Concentration (%)	Drug	Reference
Carbopol 934	N.A.	Prednisolone sodium phosphate	77
Carbopol 940		Prednisolone acetate	
Carbopol 940	1.0–6.0	Pilocarpine	47
Carbopol 941			
Carbopol 940	1.0–4.0	Flurbiprofen	79
Carbopol 940	0.3	Tropicamide	80
Carbopol 934	0.49	Pilocarpine nitrate	56

A large number of commercial ophthalmic preparations contain Carbopol, including tear substitutes such as Lacrigel® (Europhta, Monaco), Lacrinorm® (Chauvin, Montpellier, France) or formulations containing active compounds such as Iduviran® (Chauvin, Montpellier, France) and Pilopine® (Alcon, Fort Worth, Texas).

Other natural or synthetic polymers have also been evaluated as potential vehicles to prolong the residence time of drugs at the surface of the eye but are currently being further investigated. Therefore, they are not extensively discussed in this article but are principally mentioned here for reference: chondroitin sulfate (63,67), xanthan gum (40,83,84), poly(vinylpyrrolidone) (44,85,86), and chitosan (87). Briefly, xanthan gum and chitosan are both polysaccharides of natural origin, being respectively obtained by an aerobic fermentation of a carbohydrate with *Xanthomonas campestris* and by deacetylation of chitin. An important difference between the two polymers is the anionic character of xanthan gum, whereas chitosan exhibits positive charges. Xanthan gum has been proposed as a material for artificial tears preparations (83) as well as vehicle for drug delivery (40,84). The possible advantage of chitosan over xanthan gum lies in the presence of positive charges at physiological pH on the sugar backbone of chitosan, which are supposed to interact with the negative charges of the mucus, thereby confering a bioadhesive property to this polysaccharide. Therefore, chitosan has attracted attention for topical ophthalmic applications, for example to enhance tobramycin delivery to the eye (87). γ scintigraphic evaluations have shown that the presence of chitosan was efficient to prolong precorneal residence time of formulations based on this polysaccharide, when compared with a commercial solution (87).

In Situ Forming Gels

The use of preformed hydrogels still has drawbacks that can limit their interest for ophthalmic drug delivery or as tear substitutes. They do not allow accurate and reproducible administration of quantities of drugs and, after administration, they often produce blurred vision, crusting of eyelids, and lachrymation. A new approach is to try to combine advantages of both solutions and gels, such as accuracy and facility of administration of the former and prolonged residence time of the latter. Thus, in situ hydrogels can be instilled as eyedrops and undergo an immediate gelation when in contact with the eye. The liquid to semisolid phase change can be triggered by:

- Increased temperature
- Increased pH
- Ionic strength of the tear film

Thermoreversible Hydrogels. These hydrogels are liquid at room temperature (20–25°C) and undergo gelation when in contact with body fluids (35–37°C), due to an increase in temperature.

Different thermal setting gels have been described in the literature, including for example acrylic acid copolymers (84,88) and *N*-isopropylacrylamide derivatives (89,90). However, specific requirements inherent to ophthalmic administration such as tolerance have limited the choice of such polymers.

Poloxamers, commercially available as Pluronic® (BASF-Wyandotte, USA), are the most commonly used thermal setting polymers in ophthalmology. They are formed by a central hydrophobic part (polyoxypropylene) surrounded by hydrophilic part (ethylene oxide). Depending on the ratio and the distribution along the chain of the hydrophobic and hydrophilic subunits, several molecular weights are available, leading to different gelation properties. Pluronic F-127, which gives colorless and transparent gels, is the most commonly used polymer in pharmaceutical technology. Briefly, hydrogels based on Pluronic are commonly prepared (91,92) by solubilization of the polymer in cold water (5–10°C) followed by gelation upon warming to ambient temperature.

Three principal mechanisms have been proposed to explain the liquid–gel phase transition after an increase in temperature, including the gradual desolvation of the polymer, increased micellar aggregation, and the increased entanglement of the polymeric network (93–95). Furthermore, Miller and Drabik (93) have suggested that intramolecular hydrogen bonds might promote gelation. The importance of the entanglement process in the gelation phenomenon of poloxamers has been confirmed by Gilbert et al. (96), who used a fluorescent probe technique to evaluate the hydration and diffusion processes in Pluronic F-127 solutions. A schematic representation of the gelation process, proposed by Waring and Harris (95) is shown in Fig. 4. The mucomimetic property of poloxamers is supposed to be due to their hydrophobic and hydrophilic sequences simulating mucin action by adsorption of the aqueous layer of tears on the hydrophobic epithelium (Fig. 5). Owing to their protective and mucomimetic action, poloxamers have also been evaluated for the treatment of dry eye (95,97). For example, Flow Base® (95), containing 18% of poloxamer 407, sodium chloride, and potassium chloride

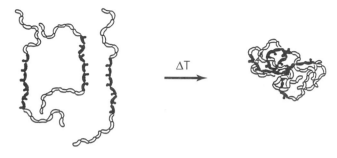

Figure 4. Liquid–gel transition of formulations based on poloxamers. *Source:* From Ref. 95 with permission.

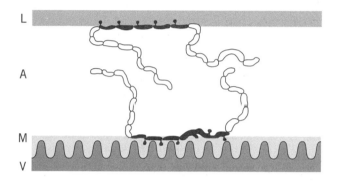

Figure 5. Model of the supposed action of poloxamers as tear substitutes. L, lipophilic phase; A, aqueous phase; M, mucus; V, villosities. *Source:* From Ref. 95 with permission.

has been shown to possess clinically advantageous properties as a tear substitute. The major drawback of this product is the formation of solid residues on the eyelids after instillation of 50 μL of solution, this problem being overcome by instillation of smaller volumes.

Poloxamers have also been widely investigated as ocular drug delivery systems. Miller and Donovan (98) reported enhanced activity of pilocarpine in poloxamers 407 gels when compared with a simple solution, whereas Dumortier et al. (99) have shown that a thermoreversible gel does not improve the kinetic profile of morphine over a reference solution. It must be noted that in both investigations the same polymer was used but not at the same concentrations (25% (98) and 20% (99), respectively), which might explain the discrepancies of the results.

Studying the influence of some parameters on the release rate of solutes from Pluronic F-127 hydrogels in vitro, Gilbert et al. (100) pointed out that increasing polymer concentration decreased the release rate of the drug, whereas increasing drug lipophilicity decreased the release rate. A recent γ scintigraphic study (101) on a semi-interpenetrating network based on poloxamer and poly(acrylic acid), Smart Hydrogel™, has been shown to remain significantly longer at the surface of the eye than a reference solution ($t_{50\%}$ about 25-fold higher).

Some applications of thermoreversible hydrogels in ophthalmology refer to the use of other polymers, the poloxamines, which are copolymers of poly(ethylene oxide) and poly(propylene oxide) obtained from a precursor, commercialized as Tetronic® (102).

Despite all the promising results obtained with thermoreversible gels, there remains an important drawback associated with the use of these hydrogels; the risk of gelling before administration by an increase in the ambient temperature during packaging or storage.

Pseudolatexes: pH-Induced Gelation. El-Aasser (103) defined pseudolatexes as artificial latexes prepared by the dispersion of a preexisting polymer in an aqueous medium. In situ gelling pseudolatexes for ophthalmic use can be described as aqueous colloidal dispersions of polymer, which become viscous gels after instillation in the conjunctival cul-de-sac due to modification of the pH (104).

Pseudolatexes are obtained by dispersion of an organic solution of a preformed polymer in an aqueous medium, leading to an O/W emulsion. Solvents from the internal phase are then evaporated to obtain a fluid dispersion of polymeric particles with a size generally smaller than 1 μm (104). Two principal methods are commonly used to prepare ophthalmic pseudolatexes, the solvent evaporation process (105–107) and the salting out process (106,108,109). Both methods allow the production of a lyophilized and easily redispersible powder. Thus, pseudolatexes have the advantage of ensuring the physical stability of the latex as well as the stability of active compounds such as pilocarpine, which is sensitive to aqueous media. In addition, such systems represent an interesting technological alternative that avoids the use of organic solvents, which can cause problems such as toxicity and pollution. Bioactive materials can be added into these systems at various times of the preparation: in the aqueous or in the organic phases during preparation or by adsorption on the final latex (105).

Ibrahim has listed (104) some prerequisites necessary for an optimal formulation of ophthalmic pseudolatex:

- Solubility of the polymer selected in organic solvents as well as insolubility in water
- Existence on the macromolecule of ionizable groups, which can react with the electrolytes of the lachrymal fluid
- Use of a high molecular weight polymer
- Rapid coagulation process after instillation to avoid precorneal drainage of the instilled formulation before the phenomenon of gelation appears
- Compatibility of the different components of the colloidal dispersion with precorneal tissues

First preliminary investigations of pH-sensitive nanoparticulate systems (latex) for ophthalmic administration began in the early 1980s (110) and have been extensively studied by Boye (19). He proposed the preparation of latexes containing pilocarpine with cellulose acetate phthalate (CAP). The choice of this polymer was determined by the compatibility of the polymer with the active compound, the ability of the CAP latex to be a free-running solution at pH 4.2 and a gel at 7.2, and finally, the latex stability at relatively low pH which is a prerequisite to ensuring the stability of pilocarpine.

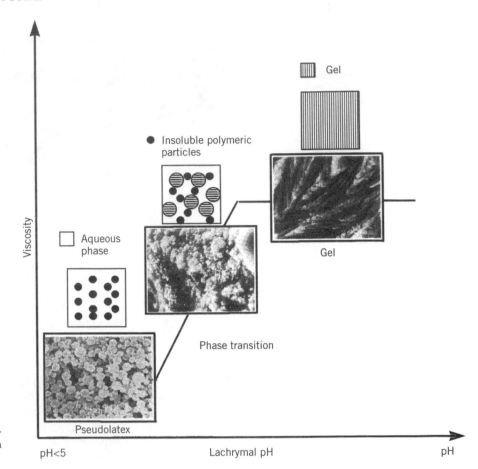

Figure 6. Transformation of the colloidal dispersion in gel. *Source:* From Ref. 111 with permission.

The principle of the sol–gel transition of the polymer CAP is shown schematically in Fig. 6. The gelation capacity of CAP latexes has been visualized in vitro by scanning electron microscopy and in vivo in rabbits by incorporating methylene blue in the ophthalmic formulations (106).

The efficacy of a preparation based on a pseudolatex has been evaluated by measuring pharmacological responses (19,105) and precorneal residence time by γ scintigraphy (19,111). This technique has clearly demonstrated the superiority of CAP latex over a solution to prolong the corneal residence time of pilocarpine, as shown in Fig. 7.

Finally, it is important to note that irritation tests (19) on rabbits including examination of the cornea, the iris and the conjunctiva have demonstrated that the investigated pseudolatexes did not induce visible irritation. However, a sensation of discomfort seems to be unavoidable after the coagulation of the solution in the conjunctival cul-de-sac as is the case for any semisolid preparation.

Ionically Induced Gelation: Gellan Gum. Gellan gum is an anionic exocellular polysaccharide produced by the bacterium *Pseudomonas elodea*, having the characteristic property of cation-induced gelation (112,113). The acetylated form is commercially available as Gelrite® (Kelco Division of Merck and Co, USA). The sol–gel transition process is induced by the presence of monovalent or divalent ions such as Na^+ and Ca^{2+}. Some other parameters influence the phase transition, e.g., the concentration of poly-

saccharide, the temperature of the preparation, and the nature and the concentration of cations. Kang et al. (114) have determined that divalent ions such as magnesium or calcium were superior to monovalent cations in promoting the gelation of the polysaccharide (Fig. 8). However the concentration of sodium in tears (2.6 g/L) is quite sufficient to induce the gelation (115). Because the presence of lach-

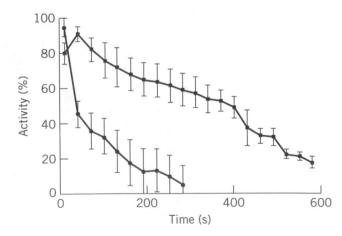

Figure 7. Corneal residence time of the pH-triggered 2% pilocarpine hydrochloride preparation (■), compared to a 2% solution (●). *Source:* From Ref. 111 with permission.

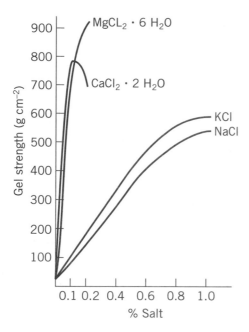

Figure 8. Effects of cations on gel strength of deacetylated gellan gum. *Source:* From Ref. 114 with permission.

the cornea than HEC, whereas a contradictory observation was noted in rabbits (119). This result is explained by the lower basal turnover and the slower blink rate in rabbits compared with man.

Efficacy of gellan gum has been also evaluated by measuring pharmacokinetic parameters (115) and pharmacological response (40,120). Rozier et al. (115) found an increased ocular bioavailability of timolol maleate when incorporated in Gelrite formulations versus the commercial Timoptic® solution. This result was confirmed by Vogel et al. (120), who observed a twofold decrease of the intraocular pressure of patients after administration of Gelrite-containing timolol.

Sanzgiri et al. (14) proposed a mechanism of drug release in vitro from gellan matrices of methylprednisolone (MP). The data suggested that MP release was influenced by the dissolution of the drug, its diffusion from the matrix, and possibly by erosion of the matrix; the combination of the three processes resulting in overall diffusion-controlled release kinetics as shown by the release index of the drug.

Exceptional rheological properties of gellan gum such as thixotropy, pseudoplasticity, and thermoplasticity (116) are further advantages for its use in ophthalmology: the fluidity of the solution can be increased simply by shaking or slightly warming the preparation.

Recently two other natural polymers believed to be able to form in situ gels by interacting with the lachrymal fluid have been evaluated as potential adjuvants in ophthalmic formulations (121,122). Carrageenans, a group of water-soluble sulphated galactans extracted from red seaweed, showed similar features to gellan gum regarding their rheological behavior, gelling properties (114), and tolerance. This suggested that they could be interesting polymers for prolonging the residence time of topical ocular formulations (121). Some alginates, rich in guluronic acid residues, have been demonstrated to exhibit reversible liquid–gel transition after administration and to be efficient in reducing intraocular pressure when carrying pilocarpine (122).

DISPERSED SYSTEMS

Liposomes

Liposomes are microscopic vesicles composed of alternating aqueous compartments and lipid bilayers (mainly

rymal fluid is required to induce gel formation, accidental gelation during storage does not occur as with thermoreversible gels. The gelling mechanism is based on a modification of the conformation of the polysaccharide. It corresponds to the formation of double-helical junction zones in the presence of cations, followed by aggregation of the double-helical segments, leading to a three-dimensional network (116).

Corneal contact time of formulations based on gellan gum has been investigated using two main methods, which are fluorometry (117,118) and γ scintigraphy (40,119). Both techniques have demonstrated improved residence times with Gelrite when compared with saline or various commercial solutions. Gelrite has also provided corneal residence times superior to those of other hydrogel preparations based on polymers such as cellulosic derivatives or xanthan gum (Fig. 9) (40). A γ scintigraphic study by Greaves et al. (119) analyzing three formulations has pointed out the defectiveness of the gel in rabbits. In the case of humans, Gelrite showed longer contact time with

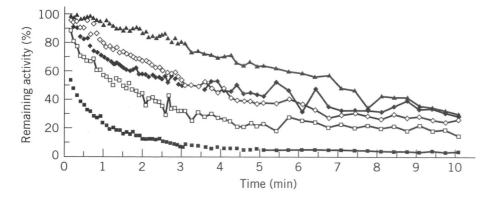

Figure 9. Precorneal drainage of ^{99m}Tc-DTPA incorporated in various formulations containing pilocarpine nitrate 2%. (■) Reference solution ($n = 13$), (□) HEC 0.325% ($n = 9$), (♦) HEC 0.5% ($n = 8$), (◇) xanthan gum 0.3% ($n = 9$), (▲) Gelrite 0.6% ($n = 9$). *Source:* From Ref. 40 with permission.

phospholipids and cholesterol). Liposomes are classified in three categories according to their size and the number of bilayers: (1) small unilamellar vesicles (SUV), (2) large unilamellar vesicles (LUV), and (3) multilamellar vesicles (MLV). Depending on their composition liposomes can have a positive, negative, or neutral surface charge.

The efficacy of liposomes in ophthalmic therapy depends on several parameters, including (1) the drug encapsulation efficiency, (2) the size and the charge of the vesicles, (3) the distribution of the drug in the liposomes, (4) the stability of the liposomes after instillation, (5) the residence time of the liposomes in the conjunctival sac, and finally, (6) the affinity of the liposomes for the cornea (123). Of these, a major factor affecting ocular drug bioavailability is the unstability of liposomes to the proteins in the conjunctival sac. Tall et al. (124) reported that proteins exert a destabilizing effect on the integrity of liposomes. However, Stratford et al. (125) have studied in vitro the effect of tears proteins on the release of epinephrine and inulin from liposomes. They reported only a slight increase of drug concentration in the release medium containing the simulating composition tears (126) when compared with a simple phosphate buffer solution.

The use of liposomes as ocular delivery systems was first reported by Smolin et al. (127) and Schaeffer and Krohn (128). Animal studies by Smolin et al. (127) demonstrated that entrapping idoxuridine in liposomes was more effective than the free drug in the treatment of acute and chronic herpetic keratitis. Studying the corneal uptake of penicillin G and indoxole with different types of liposomes, Schaeffer and Krohn (128) reported that corneal uptake of drugs was largely increased with positively charged liposomes. This suggests that the interaction between the cornea and liposomes is probably based on an electrostatic interaction, owing to the negatively charged epithelium at physiological pH. This in vitro study determined that the degree of association of liposomes with the corneal surface is decreasing as follows: $MLVs^+ > SUVs^+ > MLVs^- > SUVs^- > MLVs = SUVs$. Fitzgerald et al. (129) similarly reported that positively charged egg lecithin MLVs were retained markedly longer in the precorneal region than neutral or negative MLVs. However, γ scintigraphy experiments have demonstrated that vesicle retention occurred mainly in the inner canthus as well as in other extraocular regions, but not on the corneal surface where significant absorption takes place (129).

Various investigations concerning different liposome–ophthalmic drug combinations are reported in Table 6. The various studies concerning the use of liposomes in ophthalmic field have been also extensively reviewed by Lee et al. (123) and Mezei and Meisner (130,131).

Contradictory results were obtained from the studies listed in Table 6, suggesting high entrapment efficacy of lipophilic drugs in liposomes compared with hydrophilic compounds. Singh and Mezei (141) have tested triamcinolone acetonide and dihydrostreptomycin sulfate as lipophile and hydrophile model drugs, respectively. Concentrations of triamcinolone acetonide in different ocular tissues were markedly increased with liposomes, compared with a control suspension. On the other hand, the hydrophilic drug dihydrostreptomycin sulfate showed reduced ocular

concentrations when associated with liposomes. Meisner et al. (135) also reported that atropine salt was less promising than free base to achieve a long-acting drug delivery. Schaeffer and Krohn (128) obtained a 10-fold enhancement of the corneal penetration of the hydrophilic penicillin G entrapped in liposomes over polysorbate 80 solutions. This can be explained, in part, by the amphiphilic behavior of penicillin G, which is not completely internalized in the aqueous phase but intercalates into liposomal membranes by insertion of its hydrophobic moiety.

More recently, the use of polymer-coated liposomes, which are expected to achieve superior precorneal retention time when compared with uncoated vesicles, has been investigated. Surprisingly, both cationic and anionic mucoadhesive polymers, namely chitosan (137) and Carbopol (142), failed to improve the corneal retention (137) or the drug bioavailability (142).

The ocular irritability of neutral and positive liposomes has been assessed by Draize test, histological examination, and rabbits blinking test (143,144). The two former methods indicated that irritation induced by each type of liposome might be considered as negligible, whereas the blinking method of Tanaka et al. (144) confirmed the safety of neutral liposomes but demonstrated that positive liposomes may cause pain or discomfort.

The use of liposomes in ocular drug delivery is still at an experimental stage and no liposomal ocular commercial products are available. This is due to a number of remaining limitations to their routinal use. Several shortcomings are inherent to liposomes such as their short shelf life, their limited drug loading capacity, as well as sterilization difficulties, because most of the methods can cause irreversible damage to the liposomes (123,131). Furthermore, the improvement of liposomes as drug carrier systems in ophthalmology requires a good understanding of the mechanisms involved in their interaction with the cornea. For instance, endocytosis is considered by most investigators as the dominant mechanism of interaction between liposomes and cells over fusion, adsorption, or lipid exchange processes (145). However, the cornea has been shown to exhibit only slight phagocytic activity (146), and endocytosis is probably not the main mechanism of interaction of the vesicles with corneal cells. Therefore, adsorption or lipid exchange is believed to be the major mechanism of interaction between the liposomes and the corneal cells (147).

Microparticles and Nanoparticles

Microparticles and nanoparticles are colloidal drug carriers in the micrometer and submicrometer range, which have been evaluated for ophthalmic drug delivery purposes over the past 15 years (148). Micro- or nanoparticles are divided in two groups, micro- or nanospheres and micro- or nanocapsules. Microspheres are monolithic particles possessing a porous or solid polymer matrix, whereas microcapsules consist of a polymeric membrane surrounding a solid or a liquid drug reservoir (148). Practically, the term nanoparticles is applied to nanospheres and nanocapsules because it is often difficult to determine if they are real capsules or matrix-type particles.

Table 6. Ocular Liposomal Formulations for Topical Application

Drug	Liposomal characteristics		Subject	Parameter(s) examined	Refs.
	Type	Size			
Acetylcholinesterase	MLV, MLV$^-$, MLV$^+$	0.2–4.0 μm	Rabbit	Prophylactic antimiotic efficacy	133
Acyclovir	SUV	N.A.	Mouse cornea	Binding ability Antiviral efficacy	134
Atropine base and sulfate	MLV, MLV$^-$, MLV$^+$	0.4–4.2 μ 0.4–4.2 μm 0.4–4.2 μm	Rabbit	Mydriasis	135
Dexamethasone and esters derivatives	MLV	1 μm	Rabbit cornea	Corneal steroid absorption	136
Dihydrostreptomycin sulfate	MLV, LUV, LUV$^+$ SUV, SUV$^+$	N.A.	Rabbit	Ocular drug disposition	137
Epinephrine	MLV	1.5 μm	Rabbit	Ocular drug concentration	125,138
Idoxuridine	MLV	0.2 μm	Rabbit	Antiviral efficacy	139
	N.A.	N.A.	Rabbit	Corneal penetration of ^{125}I-labeled drug	
Indoxole	MLV, MLV$^-$, MLV$^+$	N.A.	Rabbit cornea	Drug corneal interaction and penetration	128
	SUV, SUV$^-$, SUV$^+$		Rat		
Inulin	MLV	1.5 μm	Rabbit	Ocular drug concentration	125,138
Penicillin G	MLV, MLV$^-$, MLV$^+$	N.A.	Rabbit cornea	Drug corneal interaction and penetration	128
	SUV, SUV$^-$, SUV$^+$		Rat		
Pilocarpine base and hydrochloride	MLV, MLV$^-$, MLV$^+$	0.1–0.2 μm	Rabbit	Miosis, intra ocular pressure	140
Triamcinolone acetonide	MLV	5.0 μm	Rabbit	Ocular drug concentration	141
Tropicamide	MLV	0.3–1.2 μm	Rabbit	Precorneal clearance and bioavailability	142

Source: Adapted from Refs. 123 and 132.

The application of such systems in the ophthalmic field has been extensively reviewed by Kreuter and colleagues (148–150). Upon topical instillation of a particulate suspension in the cul-de-sac, the drug is slowly released in the lachrymal pool by dissolution and mixing, diffusion, or mechanical disintegration or erosion of the polymeric matrix (149). The upper size limit for microparticles for ophthalmic administration is about 5–10 μm. The ophthalmic administration of particles of higher size can result in an itching sensation and can induce lachrymation, with the possible consequence of reducing drug bioavailability.

The manufacturing methods used to produce micro- and nanoparticulate carriers are numerous, such as interfacial polymerization (151,152), desolvatation (153,154), or aggregation by pH adjustment and heat treatment (155). Nanoparticles for ophthalmic drug delivery have been mainly produced by emulsion polymerization and are based on several synthetic or natural biocompatible polymers, as shown in Table 7. The active compound can be dissolved, trapped, encapsulated, adsorbed or linked to these colloidal systems (148). The various fabrication processes have been extensively reviewed in specialized books or reviews (156–158) and in the chapter NANOPARTICLES of this encyclopedia.

As shown in Table 7, the principal materials used so far to prepare colloidal systems for ophthalmic drug delivery have been synthetic biodegradable polymers belonging to the group of poly(alkyl cyanoacrylate). These polymers can be degraded following two concomitant metabolization pathways, which are the erosion of the polymer backbone leading to the formation of formaldehyde (187) or the cleavage of the ester inducing the formation of a water-soluble polymer backbone and the corresponding alcohol (188). In vivo, the presence of enzymes favors the second pathway, which is quite convenient because it reduces the production of the toxic formaldehyde under physiological conditions. The nontoxicity of nanoparticles based on some polymers has been demonstrated in vivo, i.e., poly(isobutyl cyanoacrylate) and poly(hexyl cyanoacrylate) were found to be well tolerated after topical application in rabbits (148) and empty poly(butyl cyanoacrylate) nanoparticles in saline did not induce adverse effect in humans (189).

Drug release from poly(alkyl) cyanoacrylate nanoparticles can occur by different isolated or concomitant mechanisms (29):

- Degradation of the polymer (rate depending on the length of the alkyl chain)
- Desorption of the active compound adsorbed from the surface of the nanoparticles
- Diffusion through the polymeric matrix

Precorneal elimination and penetration of particles in the cornea have been evaluated using various labeling methods with radioactive tracers such as ^{141}Ce (190), ^{99m}Tc (183), ^{14}C (191,192), ^{111}In (193), or ^{3}H (165), or with fluorescent probes (194–196). Initial attempts to evaluate res-

Table 7. Micro- and Nanoparticles as Drug Delivery Systems for Topical Ocular Application

Drug	Polymer	Refs.
Acyclovir	Chitosan	159
Amikacin	Poly(butyl cyanoacrylate)	160
Betaxolol	Poly(ϵ-caprolactone)	161
	Poly(isobutyl cyanoacrylate)	161,162
	Poly(lactide-*co*-glycolide)	161
Carteolol	Poly(ϵ-caprolactone)	163
Chloramphenicol	Poly(lactic acid)	164
Hydrocortisone	Albumin	165
Indomethacin	Poly(ϵ-caprolactone)	166
	Poly(ϵ-caprolactone) coated with chitosan	167,168
	Poly(ϵ-caprolactone) coated with poly(L-lysine)	167,168
Metipranolol	Poly(ϵ-caprolactone)	17
Pilocarpine	Albumin	169–172
	Gelatin	169
	Poly(butyl cyanoacrylate)	18,173–177
	Poly(hexyl cyanoacrylate)	174,177
	Poly(lactic acid)	178
	Poly(methyl methacrylate-*c*-acrylic acid)	11,179–181
	Poly(methyl methacrylate)	174
	Polyamide	182
	Polyphthalamide	183
Progesterone	Poly(hexyl cyanoacrylate)	184
	Poly(butyl cyanoacrylate)	185
Timolol	Poly(alkyl cyanoacrylate)	186

Source: Adapted from Ref. 147.

idence time were made in the early 1980s by Sieg and Triplett (190), who labeled polystyrene microspheres of 3 μm and 25 μm diameter with ^{141}Ce. They found that precorneal elimination of smaller particles was dependent on the volume instilled, unlikely for the 25 μm diameter particles. The washout phase was greatly enhanced after administration of 50 μL of 3 μm particles instead of 25 μL. Hence, this indicated that there was a lower limit for particle-size retention in the eye, in addition to the well-recognized upper size limit for preventing the onset of irritation. The study of Wood et al. (191), evaluating the disposition of poly(hexyl cyanoacrylate) nanoparticles, showed that colloidal particles were rapidly removed from the precorneal area in a similar way to aqueous solutions but were better retained, which was attributed to mucin binding or buoyancy of the nanoparticles.

Diepold et al. (192) and Zimmer et al. (165) have reported that the residence time of nanoparticles was significantly higher in inflamed ocular tissues than in healthy eyes. The increased retention of nanoparticles is probably due to some peculiar physiological modifications accompanying the inflammatory process. One can cite as possible causes an increased cell permeability (165), a secretion in the precorneal area of substances (e.g., albumin, fibrin) that can bind with nanoparticles, and a partial blockade of the nasolachrymal duct due to the swollen conjunctival tissue (192). These studies suggest that colloidal carriers could considerably improve the therapeutic index of some antiinflammatory, antibacterial, or antiviral drugs (150).

Calvo et al. (196), using confocal laser scanning microscopy, have observed ex vivo and in vivo that poly(ϵ-caprolactone) (PCL) nanocapsules penetrated the corneal epithelial cells by an endocytic mechanism. Furthermore, PCL nanocapsules (196) exhibited a selectivity for the cornea versus the conjunctiva, which means that such systems could reduce systemic absorption. This result was in accord with the in vivo data of Losa et al. (17), who found reduced cardiovascular side effects of metipranolol when incorporated in PCL nanocapsules.

Most applications of drug-loaded ophthalmic delivery systems involve glaucoma therapy, using either cholinergic agonists like pilocarpine (11,18,169,174,181) or β-blockers such as betaxolol (161–163) or carteolol (163). Zimmer et al. (171), evaluating miotic response and intraocular pressure (IOP) of rabbits after administration of pilocarpine-loaded microspheres and nanospheres based on albumin, reported a great improvement of the bioavailability of the drug, when compared with a reference solution. These particles increased the ocular bioavailability by 50–90% when considering the miotic response and by 50–70% when considering the IOP-lowering effect. Furthermore, the authors have shown that this result could be improved by coadministering these particles with bioadhesive polymers such as hyaluronic acid, mucin, sodium carboxymethylcellulose, or poly(acrylic acid) (172).

INSERTS

Definition

This section is devoted to solid devices delivering drugs to the anterior segment of the eye that are denoted by the general name *insert*, originating from the Latin *inserere*, to introduce. Historically, the first solid medication precursors of the present insoluble inserts were described in the nineteenth century. They consisted of squares of dry filter paper, previously impregnated with drug solutions (e.g., atropine sulfate, pilocarpine hydrochloride) (197); small sections were cut and applied under the eyelid. *Lamellae*, the precursors of the present soluble inserts, consisted of glycerinated gelatin containing different ophthalmic drugs (197). However, the use of lamellae ended when more stringent requirements for sterility of ophthalmic preparations were enforced. Nowadays, ophthalmic inserts are again provoking great interest, as evidenced by the increasing number of publications in the field in recent years. Table 8 gives an overview of the different drugs applied with inserts.

The uses of ocular inserts have been extensively reviewed by Bawa (198), Saettone (197), Saettone and Salminen (199), Khan and Durrani (200), and Shell (201,202). Gurtler and Gurny (203) have reviewed ophthalmic inserts in the patent literature, and Baeyens et al. (22) have described inserts as ocular drug delivery devices in veterinary medicine.

Ophthalmic inserts are defined as preparations with a solid or semisolid consistency, the size and shape of which are especially designed for ophthalmic application (i.e., rods or shields) (203). These inserts are placed in the lower fornix and, less frequently, in the upper fornix or on the cornea. They are usually composed of a polymeric vehicle containing the drug and are mainly used for topical therapy.

Further advantages of inserts over other drug delivery systems discussed already are (22):

- accurate dosing
- absence of preservatives
- increased shelf live, due to the absence of water

However, they have one significant disadvantage, their solid consistency, which means that they are perceived by patients as a foreign body in the eye (199). Besides the initial discomfort, other potential disadvantages arising from their solid state are possible movement around the eye, occasional inadvertent loss during sleep or while rubbing the eyes, interference with vision, and difficult placement (and removal for insoluble types) (199). Most of the ongoing research is therefore dedicated to improving ocular retention and to ensure an easy placement by the patient, while reducing the foreign body sensation in the eye. Ophthalmic inserts are generally classified according to their solubility behavior and their possible bioerodibility (203) (Fig. 10).

Soluble Inserts

Soluble inserts are the most frequently investigated class of ophthalmic inserts (see Table 8). Their main advantage relies on their complete solubility compared with their insoluble counterparts, so that they do not need to be removed from the eye after deposition. They are usually divided into two categories according to their polymer composition. The first type is based on natural polymers whereas the second is derived from synthetic or semisynthetic polymers.

Natural Polymers. Natural polymers include collagen, which was the first ophthalmic insert excipient described in the literature. Inserts containing collagen were first developed by Fyodorov (198,240) as corneal bandages following surgical operations and eye disease. Later, collagen shields as drug carriers were suggested by Bloomfield et al. (223). As described for contact lenses, the therapeutic agents are generally absorbed by soaking the collagen shield in a solution containing the drug and, once placed in the eye, the drug is gradually released from the interstices between the collagen molecules, as the collagen dissolves. Accordingly, the residence time of drugs (241) such as antibacterials (222,242), antiinflammatory agents (234,236), antivirals (239,243), or combination drugs (230) was increased when compared with traditional eye drops (see Table 8). However, as observed for contact lenses, most drugs are released quite rapidly by a diffusion process, whereas dissolution requires a much longer time. The corneal shields, currently available for clinical use, do not contain drugs but are designed as disposable therapeutic corneal bandages (199). For example, Bio-Cor® (developed by Bausch and Lomb, Clearwater, Florida) is made of porcine scleral collagen, whereas Medilens® (developed by Chiron Ophthalmics, Irvine, California) and ProShield® (devel-

oped by Alcon Surgical, Forth Worth, Texas) are prepared from bovine corium tissue (243–245).

The main advantages of collagen shields over contact lenses is their solubility and that they do not need to be removed. However, collagen may cause an inflammatory response in the ocular tissues. Also, if shields are not used in association with antibacterials, a secondary infection may occur (239). Nowadays, these devices have the further disadvantage of not being well accepted by the authorities, because of possible prion-based infection.

Synthetic and Semisynthetic Polymers. Ophthalmic inserts containing synthetic, i.e., poly(vinyl alcohol) (205, 233), and semisynthetic, i.e., cellulose based (204,205,208, 209,216,225,233), polymers are frequently described in the literature (see Table 8). This stems in part from their advantage of being based in products well adapted for ophthalmic use and their ease of manufacture by conventional methods, including extrusion (225), compression (204), and compression molding (246). Drug release from such systems is generally characterized by two phases (203,247). The first corresponds to the penetration of tear fluid into the insert, which induces a rapid diffusion of the drug and forms a gel layer around the core of the insert. This external gelification induces the second phase corresponding to a decreased release rate, again controlled by diffusion. The major problems of these soluble inserts are the rapid penetration of the lachrymal fluid into the device, the blurred vision caused by the solubilization of insert components, and the glassy constitution of the insert increasing the risk of expulsion. Ethylcellulose, a hydrophobic polymer, can be used to decrease insert deformation and therefore prevent blurred vision (225,228,233). Regarding the risk of expulsion, several authors (217,218,225,228) have incorporated carbomer, which is at low concentrations a strong, but well-tolerated bioadhesive polymer. Recently, Baeyens et al. (226,228) and Gurtler et al. (225,248) have used CAP in combination with gentamicin sulfate to decrease drug solubility. Prolonged release of the drug above the minimal inhibitory concentration (MIC) was obtained for more than 50 h, whereas gentamicin incorporated without CAP was released for less than 24 h. Subsequently, a new insert providing release of gentamicin and dexamethasone at different rates was developed. The prolonged release of gentamicin—an antibacterial agent—is combined with the immediate release of dexamethasone—an antiinflammatory agent—against structural damage that can be caused by the infection (Fig. 11). The release rate can also be decreased by using Eudragit as an insert coating agent (204,205,216). This polymer is normally used for enteric coating, and Saettone et al. (204) have observed in rabbits that Eudragit-coated inserts containing pilocarpine induced a miotic effect of longer duration, compared with the corresponding uncoated products.

Lacrisert® is a soluble insert that was successfully commercialized by Merck Sharp and Dohme in 1981 (198). The device weighs 5 mg, measures 1.27 mm in diameter with a length of 3.5 mm, and is composed of HPC and is useful in the treatment of dry eye syndrome. The device is placed in the lower fornix where it slowly dissolves over 6–8 h to stabilize and thicken the tear film (249).

Table 8. Currently Available Inserts for Ocular Drug Delivery

Drugs	Type of insert	Carrier	Assays	Refs.
Antiglaucoma				
Pilocarpine	Soluble	HPC/D-lactose/glyceryl palmito-stearate/Eudragit® RS	in vitro release in vivo miotic response	204
Pilocarpine	Soluble	PVA/XG/HPMC/HA/GB/Eudragit RS 30 D	in vitro release in vivo miotic response	205,206
Pilocarpine	PVP		in vitro release in vivo miotic response	207
Pilocarpine	Soluble	Alginate; MC	in vitro release in vivo miotic response	208
Pilocarpine	Soluble	HPC; PVM/MA	in vivo release in vitro release in vivo release	209
Pilocarpine	Soluble	HA; HAE	in vitro mucoadhesion in vitro retention in vivo miotic response	68
Pilocarpine	Bioerodible	PVMMA	in vitro release in vivo release	209
Pilocarpine	Bioerodible	Gelatin	in vitro release in vivo miotic response	210
Pilocarpine	Insoluble (diffusion)	Ethylene vinyl acetate, alginate	in vivo release	211
Pilocarpine	Insoluble (contact lens)	HEMM/EGDM	in vivo miotic response	212
Pilocarpine	Insoluble (contact lens)	MOPTSS/TEGDM/CHM/MA/MM	in vitro release	213,214
Pilocarpine/epinephrine	Insoluble (osmotic)	Ethylene vinyl acetate	in vitro release	215
Timolol	Soluble	HPC/Eudragit RS	in vitro release	216
Timolol	Soluble/bioerodible	HPC; PVA; PVMMA; PVA/Carbopol 940	in vitro release in vivo release	217
Timolol and prodrugs of timolol	Soluble/bioerodible	PVA; HPC; PVMMA; PVA/Carbopol 940	in vitro release in vivo release	218
Tilisolol	Soluble	HPM	in vitro release in vivo release	219

Antibacterial

Drug	Type	Material	Study	Ref.
Chloramphenicol	Soluble	PVA	in vivo release	206
Erythromycin	Soluble	Copolymers of N-vinylpyrrolidone	in vitro release	220,221
Gentamicin	Soluble	Collagen	in vitro release	222
Gentamicin	Soluble	Collagen	in vivo release	223
Gentamicin	Soluble	Collagen	in vitro release	224
Gentamicin	Soluble	HPC/EC/Carbopol 934P	in vivo retention and release; in vivo release	225,226
Gentamicin	Bioerodible	Gelatin	in vitro release	227
Gentamicin and dexamethasone	Soluble	HPC/EC/Carbopol 934P	in vivo release	228,229
Gentamicin and dexamethasone	Soluble	Collagen	in vitro release	230
Tobramycin	Soluble	Collagen	in vivo release; in vitro release	231
Tobramycin	Soluble	Collagen	in vivo treatment	
Tetracycline or chloramphenicol	Insoluble (contact lens)	PMM	in vivo efficacy; in vitro release; in vivo efficacy	232

Antiinflammatory

Drug	Type	Material	Study	Ref.
Dexamethasone	Soluble	PVA; HPC; EC; CAP; Eudragit	in vivo release	233
Dexamethasone	Soluble	Collagen	in vivo release	234
Dexamethasone	Bioerodible	Gelatin	in vivo release	233
Prednisolone	Insoluble (contact lens)	HEM/n-vinyl 2-pyrrolidone	in vitro release	235
Prednisolone acetate	Soluble	Collagen	in vivo release	236
Hydrocortisone	Insoluble (osmotic)	Ethylene vinyl acetate	in vitro release	237

Antiviral

Drug	Type	Material	Study	Ref.
Idoxuridine	Bioerodible	Polypeptide	in vivo treatment	238
Trifluorothymidine	Soluble	Collagen	in vivo release	239

CAP, cellulose acetate phthalate; CHM, cyclohexane methacrylate; EC, ethylcellulose; EGDM, ethylene glycol dimethacrylate; GB, glyceryl behenate; HA, hyaluronic acid; HAE, ethyl ester hyaluronic acid; HEM, 2-hydroxyethylmetacrylate; HEMM, hydroxyethyl methyl metacrylate; HPC, hydroxypropylcellulose; HPM, hydroxypropyl methacrylate; HPMC, hydroxypropylmethylcellulose; MA, methacrylic acid; MC, methylcellulose; MM, methyl methacrylate; MOPTSS, metacryloxypropyl tris(trimethylsiloxy) silane; PAA, polyacrylic acid; PMM, poly(methyl methacrylate); PVA, poly(vinyl alcohol); PVM/MA, poly(methyl vinyl ether/maleic acid); PVMMA, n-butyl half ester of poly(methyl vinyl ether/maleic anhydride); PVP, poly(vinyl pyrrolidone); TEGDM, triethylene glycol dimethacrylate; XG, xanthan gum.

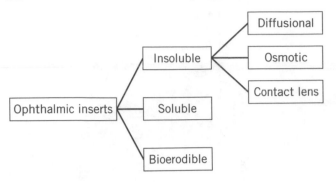

Figure 10. Classification of ophthalmic inserts. *Source:* Adapted from Ref. 203.

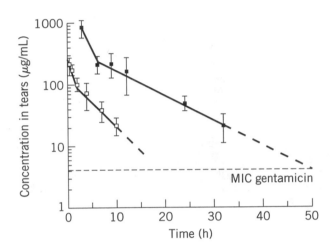

Figure 11. Combined release of gentamicin sulfate (■) and dexamethasone phosphate (□) at different release rates from a single insert containing 5.0 mg of gentamicin sulfate (25.0% w/w) and 1.0 mg of dexamethasone phosphate (5.0% w/w) (tested in rabbit, mean ± S.E.M., $n = 6$). *Source:* Adapted from Ref. 228.

New Ophthalmic Delivery System (NODS®), originally patented by Smith & Nephew Pharmaceuticals, Ltd., in 1985, consists of a medicated flag (4 mm × 6 mm, thickness 20 μm, weight 0.5 g) that is attached to a paper-covered handle by means of a short (0.7 mm) and thin (3–4 μm) membrane (Fig. 12) (206). All components (flag, membrane, and handle) are made of the same grade water-

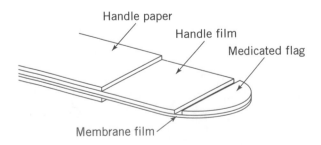

Figure 12. Schematic representation of the NODS system. *Source:* Adapted from Ref. 198.

soluble poly(vinyl alcohol). For use, the flag is touched onto the surface of the lower conjunctival sac. The membrane dissolves, rapidly releasing the flag, which swells and dissolves in the lachrymal fluid, delivering the drug. When evaluated in humans, NODS produced an increase in bioavailability for pilocarpine and chloramphenicol with respect to standard eyedrop formulations (206).

Insoluble Inserts

Insoluble inserts can be classified into three categories (203): diffusional and osmotic systems, and hydrophilic contact lenses. Each class of insert shows a different drug release profile. Diffusional and osmotic systems contain a reservoir that is in contact with the inner surface of the drug rate controller to which its supplies the drug. The reservoir contains, respectively, a liquid, a gel, a colloid, a semisolid, a solid matrix, or a carrier containing drug. Carriers are made of hydrophobic, hydrophilic, organic, natural, or synthetic polymers. The third category, contact lenses, is a particular group of insoluble ophthalmic devices. However, the main disadvantage of these devices is their insolubility, because they need to be removed from the eye after treatment.

Diffusional Inserts. Diffusional inserts consist of a central reservoir of drug enclosed in specially designed semipermeable or microporous membranes allowing the drug to diffuse from the reservoir at a precisely determined rate. Drug release from such a system is controlled by the lachrymal fluid permeating through the membrane until a sufficient internal pressure is reached to drive the drug out of the reservoir. These diffusional systems prevent a continuous decrease in release rate by the use of a barrier membrane of fixed thickness, resulting in a zero-order release pattern.

Ocusert® (developed by Alza Corporation, Palo Alto, California) is undoubtedly the most commonly described insoluble insert in the literature (199,202,211,250–256) (Fig. 13). This flat, flexible, elliptical device consists of a pilocarpine reservoir with alginic acid, a mixture surrounded on both sides by a membrane of ethylene-vinyl acetate copolymer. The device is encircled by a retaining ring impregnated with titanium dioxide. The dimensions of the elliptical device are: major axis, 13.4 mm; minor axis, 5.7 mm; thickness, 0.3 mm. Two types of Ocusert are available for humans: the Pilo-20® and Pilo-40®, providing two different release rates for pilocarpine (20 μg/h and 40 μg/h, respectively) over a period of seven days (211).

Osmotic Inserts. The osmotic inserts are mostly described in the patent literature, and in vivo tests are rarely reported (203). They are generally made up of a central core surrounded by a peripheral component. The central part can consist of a single reservoir or two distinct compartments (Fig. 14). The single reservoir contains the drug, with or without an additional osmotic solute dispersed through a polymeric matrix, so that the drug is surrounded by the polymer as discrete small deposits. If the central part is made up of two compartments, the drug and the osmotic solute are placed in separate chambers, the drug

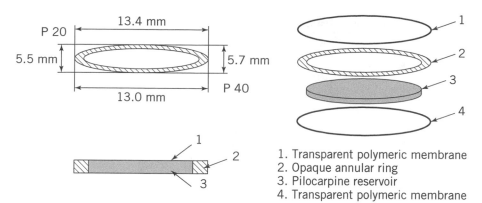

1. Transparent polymeric membrane
2. Opaque annular ring
3. Pilocarpine reservoir
4. Transparent polymeric membrane

Figure 13. Schematic representation of the Ocusert system. *Source:* Adapted from Ref. 198.

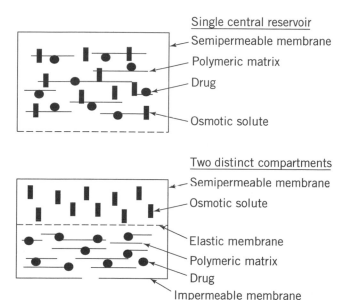

Figure 14. Schematic representation of the two types of osmotic inserts.

reservoir being surrounded by an elastic impermeable membrane, and the osmotic solute reservoir by a semipermeable membrane. The peripheral part of these osmotic inserts comprises in all cases a covering film made of an insoluble semipermeable polymer.

The majority of patents deal with systems having a unique central reservoir (215,237). The release of drug from these inserts can occur via two distinct release mechanisms: an osmotic and a diffusional release (203). When the insert is placed in the ocular environment, this starts the osmotic release, meaning tear fluid diffuses to the peripheral deposits through the semipermeable polymeric membrane, wets them, and induces their dissolution. The solubilized deposits generate a hydrostatic pressure against the polymer matrix triggering its rupture in the form of pores releasing the drug. This osmotic part of the release is characterized by a zero-order release profile. Ideally, the drug is continuously released from the osmotic insert by the increasing formation of apertures in the device forming a lattice of composition dispensing paths in the polymer on all sides of the inserts. In fact, these paths

are interconnected, forming tortuous microchannels of irregular shapes and size causing a second drug release corresponding to a diffusional nonconstant release.

The release of drug from systems having a central reservoir subdivided into two compartments (257,258) starts as soon as the device is placed in the eye. Tears diffuse into the osmotic compartment, inducing osmotic pressure that stretches the elastic membrane and contracts the compartment containing the drug, so that the active compound is forced through the single drug release aperture. Thus, these systems are characterized by two distinct compartments and a single aperture having a very small diameter.

Contact Lenses. The initial use of contact lenses was for vision correction. The use of contact lenses has been extended as potential drug delivery devices by presoaking them in drug solutions. The main advantage of this system is the possibility of correcting vision and releasing drug simultaneously. Contact lenses are composed of a hydrophilic or hydrophobic polymer that swells by absorbing water. The swelling, caused by the osmotic pressure of the polymer segments, is opposed by the elastic retroactive forces arising along the chains as cross-links are stretched until a final swelling (equilibrium) is reached.

Refojo (259) has proposed a subdivision in five groups of contact lenses, namely rigid, semirigid, elastomeric, soft hydrophilic, and biopolymeric. Rigid contact lenses have the disadvantage of being composed of polymers (e.g., PMMA) hardly permeable to moisture and oxygen. Moreover, these systems are not suitable for prolonged delivery of drug to the eye and their rigidity makes them very uncomfortable to wear. The permeability problem was resolved using gas permeable polymers such as cellulose acetate butyrate. However, the discomfort associated with the foreign object and long adaptation period remain the shortcomings of rigid contact lenses. For this reason, soft hydrophilic contact lenses were developed for prolonged release of drugs such as pilocarpine (212), chloramphenicol and tetracycline (232), and prednisolone sodium phosphate (235) (see Table 8). The most commonly used polymer in the composition of these types of lenses is HEMM copolymerized with PVP or EGDM. PVP is used for increasing water of hydration, whereas EGDM is used to decrease the water of hydration.

Shell and Baker (247) have shown that drug release from presoaked contact lenses was extremely rapid, with

Table 9. Advantages and Shortcomings of Some Topical Ocular Drug Delivery Systems

Drug delivery system	Advantages	Shortcomings
Hydrogels	Reduction of the number of applications Good compliance Better tolerance than ointments	Slight blurred vision No true sustained release effect
Liposomes	Accurate dosing Improved bioavailability for lipophilic drugs	Insufficient stability Short shelf life Limited drug loaded capacity
Micro- or nanoparticles	Accurate dosing Slight increased ocular bioavailability	Too slight improvement for heavy processes of fabrication
Inserts	Accurate dosing Absence of preservatives Increased shelf life, due to the absence of water	Difficulty of placement Foreign body sensation

an in vivo residence time in general not longer than 24 h (200). In addition, preservatives, such as benzalkonium chloride, cannot be avoided and they have greater affinity with the hydrophilic contact lens material than for the aqueous drug solution (198). Bawa has described other approaches to decrease drug release rate from contact lenses. These include the introduction of the drug into the monomer mixture followed by polymerization of the monomers in the presence of the drug. This procedure removes the need for preservatives and consequent eye sensitization, because the drug is added in the matrix as a solid (213,214). However, the main problem associated with all contact lenses is their high cost of manufacture, and the difficulty of incorporating a precise amount of drug into the matrix. Disposable contact lenses have been commercially available for many years already, and the continued progress made in polymer chemistry should facilitate the development of this type of inserts.

Bioerodible Inserts

These inserts are formed by bioerodible polymers, i.e., materials that undergo hydrolysis of chemical bonds and hence dissolution (cross-linked gelatin derivatives, polyester derivatives) (209,211,233,238,260). The great advantage of these inserts is the possibility of modulating their erosion rate by modifying their final structure during synthesis, and by addition of anionic or cationic surfactants. However, erodible systems can have significantly variable erosion rates based on individual patient physiology and lachrymation patterns, whereas degradation products and residual solvents used during the polymer preparation can cause inflammatory reaction.

In conclusion, the majority of therapeutic agents can be delivered using inserts which are a promising alternative administration route, because of their various advantages compared with classical dosage forms. However, only few of these compounds have been commercialized. This can be attributed to the reluctance of ophthalmologists and patients to replace the traditional ophthalmic solutions as well as the cost and the need to train both the prescribers and the patients to place the inserts correctly in the eyes.

In the future, the use of ophthalmic inserts will certainly increase because of the development of new polymers, the emergence of new drugs having short biological half-lives or systemic side effects, and the need to improve the efficacy of ophthalmic treatments by ensuring an effective drug concentration in the eye for several days.

CONCLUSION

Although the various systems described in this article have been generally demonstrated to be successful approaches for prolonged ocular therapy, they all fall short of the ideal for a variety of reasons (Table 9). For example, the use of hydrogels remains associated with possible blurring vision, liposomes are often insufficiently stable after sterilization, and inserts are subject to a lack of patient compliance, due to their difficulty of placement in the eye (particularly for the elderly) and the sensation in the eye of foreign body. For these reasons, new polymers are currently under investigation to improve such systems and new approaches are being developed. Some authors have proposed the incorporation of lectins (261) or cyclodextrins (262,263) in ophthalmic formulations, or the use of codrugs (264) and prodrugs. Lectins have shown to bind to corneal and conjunctival surfaces as well as to the constituents of the tear film. Therefore, they are currently being investigated in the formulation of drug carrier complexes, where they could anchor the dosage form to the epithelial surfaces. The principle of using cyclodextrins in ophthalmic formulations relies on their ability to solubilize water-insoluble drugs and on capacity to reduce local drug irritation in the eye, which could, in turn, result in an improved bioavailability.

BIBLIOGRAPHY

1. S. Duke-Elder, in S. Duke-Elder, ed., *System of Ophthalmology*, Henry Kimpton, London, 1962, pp. 461–479.

2. V.H.L. Lee and J.R. Robinson, *J. Pharm. Sci.* **68**, 673–684 (1979).

3. L. Salminen, *J. Ocul. Pharmacol.* **6**, 243–249 (1990).

4. S.S. Chrai and J.R. Robinson, *J. Pharm. Sci.* **62**, 1112–1121 (1973).

5. V.H.L. Lee, *Pharm. Int.* **6**, 135–138 (1985).

6. M. Van Ooteghem, in P. Edman, ed., *Biopharmaceutics of Ocular Drug Delivery*, CRC Press, Boca Raton, Fla., 1993, pp. 27–42.

7. V. Baeyens and R. Gurny, *Pharm. Acta Helv.* **72**, 191–202 (1997).

8. M.F. Saettone, B. Giannaccini, F. Barattini, and N. Tellini, *Pharm. Acta Helv.* **2**, 3–11 (1982).

9. J.L. Greaves, C.G. Wilson, and A.T. Birmingham, *Br. J. Clin. Pharmacol.* **35**, 188–192 (1993).

10. R.N. Weinreb et al., *Am. J. Ophthalmol.* **110**, 189–192 (1990).

11. Z. Mazor, U. Ticho, U. Rehany, and L. Rose, *Br. J. Ophthalmol.* **63**, 58–51 (1979).

12. N.K. Gangrade, N.B. Gaddipati, M.G. Ganesan, and I.K. Reddy, in I.K. Reddy, ed., *Ocular Therapeutics and Drug Delivery*, Technomic Publishing, Lancaster, Pa., 1996, pp. 377–403.

13. O. Olejnik, in A.K. Mitra, ed., *Ophthalmic Drug Delivery Systems*, Dekker, New York, 1993, pp. 177–197.

14. Y.D. Sanzgiri et al., *J. Controlled Release* **26**, 195–201 (1993).

15. S. Kumar, B.O. Haglund, and K.J. Himmelstein, *J. Ocul. Pharmacol.* **10**(1), 47–56 (1994).

16. D.M. Maurice, *Int. Ophthalmol. Clin.* **33**, 81–91 (1993).

17. C. Losa et al., *J. Ocul. Pharmacol.* **8**, 191–198 (1992).

18. R. Diepold et al., *Graefe's Arch. Clin. Exp. Ophthalmol.* **227**, 188–193 (1989).

19. T. Boye, Ph.D Thesis, No. 2176, University of Geneva, School of Pharmacy, Geneva, Switzerland (1986).

20. S.R. Nadkarni and S.H. Yalokowsky, *Pharm. Res.* **10**, 109–112 (1993).

21. J.L. Greaves et al., *Br. J. Clin. Pharmacol.* **33**, 603–609 (1992).

22. V. Baeyens et al., *Adv. Drug Delivery Rev.* **28**, 335–361 (1997).

23. S.P. Kulkarni et al., *Drug Dev. Ind. Pharm.* **23**, 465–471 (1997).

24. T.F. Patton and J.R. Robinson, *J. Pharm. Sci.* **64**, 1312–1316 (1975).

25. S.S. Chrai and J.R. Robinson, *J. Pharm. Sci.* **63**, 1218–1222 (1974).

26. R. Krishnamoorthy and A.K. Mitra, in A.K. Mitra, ed., *Ophthalmic Drug Delivery Systems*, Dekker, New York, 1993, pp. 199–221.

27. S.W. Kim, Y.H. Bae, and T. Okano, *Pharm. Res.* **9**, 283–290 (1992).

28. B. Plazonnet et al., in M.F. Saettone, M. Bucci, and P. Speiser, eds., *Ophthalmic Drug Delivery; Biopharmaceutical, Technological and Clinical Aspects*, Liviana Press/Springer-Verlag, Padova and Berlin, 1987, pp. 117–139.

29. P. Buri and F. Gurtler, in P. Buri et al., eds., *Les préparations ophtalmiques*, Lavoisier, Paris, 1995, pp. 127–215.

30. M. Zignani, C. Tabatabay, and R. Gurny, *Adv. Drug Delivery Rev.* **16**, 51–60 (1995).

31. K.C. Swan, *Arch. Ophthalmol. (Chicago)* **33**, 378–380 (1945).

32. W.H. Mueller and D.L. Deardorff, *Am. J. Pharm. Assoc.* **45**, 334–341 (1956).

33. J.S. Haas and D.C. Merrill, *Am. J. Ophthalmol.* **54**, 21–25 (1962).

34. S.P. Loucas and H.M. Haddad, *Metab. Ophthalmol.* **1**, 27–34 (1997).

35. R. Hardberger, C. Hanna, and C.M. Boyd, *Arch. Ophthalmol. (Chicago)* **93**, 42–45 (1975).

36. C. Melis-Decerf and M. Van Ooteghem, *J. Pharm. Pharmacol.* **31**, 12–15 (1979).

37. A. Ludwig and M. Van Ooteghem, *J. Pharm. Belg.* **44**, 391–397 (1989).

38. R.D. Schoenwald, R.L. Ward, L.M. DeSantis, and R.E. Roehrs, *J. Pharm. Sci.* **67**, 1280–1283 (1978).

39. A. Ludwig and M. Van Ooteghem, *S. T. P. Pharmacol. Sci.* **2**, 81–87 (1992).

40. G. Meseguer et al., *Int. J. Pharm.* **95**, 229–234 (1993).

41. A. Ludwig, N.J. Van Haeringen, V.M.W. Bodelier, and M. Van Ooteghem, *Int. Ophthalmol.* **16**, 23–26 (1992).

42. J. Grove, M. Durr, M. Quint, and B. Plazonnet, *Int. J. Pharm.* **66**, 23–28 (1990).

43. M. Dittgen, S. Oestereich, and D. Eckhardt, *S. T. P. Pharmacol. Sci.* **2**, 93–97 (1992).

44. M.F. Saettone et al., *Int. J. Pharm.* **20**, 187–202 (1984).

45. M.F. Saettone et al., *J. Pharm. Pharmacol.* **34**, 464–466 (1982).

46. J.H. Trueblood, R.M. Rossomondo, W.H. Carlton, and L.A. Wilson, *Arch. Ophthalmol. (Chicago)* **93**, 127–130 (1975).

47. S.G. Deshpande and S. Shirokolar, *J. Pharm. Pharmacol.* **41**, 197–200 (1989).

48. S.S. Tous and K. Abd-El Nasser, *S. T. P. Pharmacol. Sci.* **2**, 125–131 (1992).

49. N.A. Peppas, in N.A. Peppas, ed., *Hydrogels in Medicine and Pharmacy*, CRC Press, Boca Raton, Fla., 1987, pp. 1–37.

50. N. Krishna and F. Brow, *Am. J. Ophthalmol.* **57**, 99–106 (1964).

51. M.L. Linn and L.T. Jones, *Am. J. Ophthalmol.* **65**, 76–78 (1973).

52. F.C. Bach et al., *Am. J. Ophthalmol.* **68**, 659–662 (1970).

53. S.R. Waltman and T.C. Patrowicz, *Invest. Ophthalmol. Visual Sci.* **9**, 966–973 (1970).

54. I. Zaki, P. Fitzgerald, J.G. Hardy, and C.G. Wilson, *J. Pharm. Pharmacol.* **38**, 463–466 (1986).

55. A. Ludwig and M. Van Ooteghem, *Drug Dev. Ind. Pharm.* **14**, 2267–2284 (1988).

56. N.M. Davies, S.J. Farr, J. Hadgraft, and I.W. Kellaway, *Pharm. Res.* **8**, 1039–1043 (1991).

57. U.S. Pat. 4,141,973 (1979), E.A. Balazs.

58. S.F. Bernatchez, O. Camber, C. Tabatabay, and R. Gurny, in P. Edman, ed., *Biopharmaceutics of Ocular Drug Delivery*, CRC Press, Boca Raton, Fla., 1993, pp. 105–120.

59. R. Gurny et al., *Graefe's Arch. Clin. Exp. Ophthalmol.* **228**, 510–518 (1991).

60. G.R. Snibson et al., *Eye* **5**, 594–602 (1990).

61. G.R. Snibson et al., *Cornea* **11**, 288–293 (1992).

62. Y.S. Wysenbeek, N. Loya, and I. Ben Sira, *Invest. Ophthalmol. Visual Sci.* **29**, 194–199 (1988).

63. M.B. Limberg, C. McCaa, G.E. Kissling, and H.E. Kaufman, *Am. J. Ophthalmol.* **103**, 194–197 (1987).

64. C. Tabatabay, *J. Fr. Ophthalmol.* **8**, 513 (1985).

65. J.G. Orsoni et al., *Ophthalmologie* **2**, 355–357 (1988).

66. O. Camber, P. Edman, and R. Gurny, *Curr. Eye Res.* **6**, 779–784 (1987).

67. M.F. Saettone, D. Monti, M.T. Torracca, and P. Chetoni, *J. Ocul. Pharmacol.* **10**(1), 83–92 (1994).

68. M.F. Saettone et al., *Int. J. Pharm.* **51**, 203–212 (1989).

69. M.F. Saettone et al., *Int. J. Pharm.* **72**, 131–139 (1991).

70. R. Gurny et al., *J. Controlled Release* **6**, 367–373 (1987).

71. O. Camber and P. Edman, *Curr. Eye Res.* **8**, 563–567 (1989).

72. S.F. Bernatchez, C. Tabatabay, and R. Gurny, *Graefe's Arch. Clin. Exp. Ophthalmol.* **231**, 157–171 (1993).

73. S.S. Leung and J.R. Robinson, *J. Controlled Release* **5**, 223–231 (1988).

74. H. Park and J.R. Robinson, *Pharm. Res.* **4**, 457–464 (1987).

75. A. Ludwig, N. Unlü, and M. Van Ooteghem, *Int. J. Pharm.* **61**, 15–25 (1990).

76. R.C. Allen et al., *Am. J. Ophthalmol.* **97**, 723–729 (1984).

77. R.D. Schoenwald and J.J. Boltralik, *Invest. Ophthalmol. Visual Sci.* **18**, 61–66 (1979).

78. M.F. Saettone, B. Giannaccini, A. Guiducci, and P. Savigni, *Int. J. Pharm.* **31**, 261–270 (1986).

79. S. Mengi and S.G. Deshpande, *S. T. P. Pharmacol. Sci.* **2**, 118–124 (1992).

80. M.F. Saettone, B. Giannaccini, P. Savigni, and A. Wirth, *J. Pharm. Pharmacol.* **32**, 519–521 (1980).

81. N. Unlü, M. Van Ooteghem, and A.A. Hincal, *Pharm. Acta Helv.* **67**, 5–10 (1992).

82. N. von der Ohe, M. Stark, H. Mayer, and H. Brewitt, *Graefe's Arch. Clin. Exp. Ophthalmol.* **234**, 452–456 (1996).

83. P.D. Amin, C.P. Bhogte, and M.A. Deshpande, *Drug Dev. Ind. Pharm.* **22**, 735–739 (1996).

84. M. Albasini and A. Ludwig, *Farmaco* **50**, 633–642 (1995).

85. M.F. Saettone, in A.A. Hincal, H.S. Kasand, and M. Sumnu, eds., *New Approaches to Controlled Drug Delivery*, Editions de Santé, Paris, 1991, pp. 192–200.

86. A.H. Abd-El-Gawad, E.M. Ramadan, and U.A. Seleman, *Pharm. Ind.* **54**, 977–980 (1992).

87. O. Felt, P. Buri, and R. Gurny, *2nd Int. Symp. Exp. Clin. Ocul. Pharmacol. Pharm.*, 1997, p. 22.

88. A.S. Hoffman, A. Afrassiabi, and L.C. Dong, *J. Controlled Release* **4**, 213–222 (1986).

89. A.S. Hoffman, *J. Controlled Release* **6**, 297–305 (1987).

90. T.G. Park and A.S. Hoffman, *Proc. Int. Symp. Controlled Release Bioact. Mater.* **17**, 112–113 (1990).

91. I.R. Schmolka, *J. Biomed. Mater. Res.* **6**, 571–582 (1972).

92. *Technical Data on Pluronic® Polyol Gels*, Publ. No. 0-513, I.C. BASF Wyandotte Corp., Wyandotte, Mich., 1979.

93. S.C. Miller and B.R. Drabik, *Int. J. Pharm.* **18**, 269–276 (1984).

94. M. Vadnere, G. Amidon, S. Lindebaum, and J.L. Haslam, *Int. J. Pharm.* **22**, 207–218 (1984).

95. G.O. Waring and R.R. Harris, in I.H. Leopold and R.P. Burns, eds., *Symposium on Ocular Therapy*, Wiley, New York, 1979, pp. 127–140.

96. J.C. Gilbert, C. Washington, M.C. Davies, and J. Hadgraft, *Int. J. Pharm.* **40**, 93–99 (1987).

97. M.A. Lemp, *Int. Ophthalmol. Clin.* **13**, 221–223 (1973).

98. S.C. Miller and M.D. Donovan, *Int. J. Pharm.* **12**, 147–152 (1982).

99. G. Dumortier et al., *S. T. P. Pharmacol. Sci.* **2**(1), 111–117 (1992).

100. J.C. Gilbert, J. Hadgraft, A. Bye, and L.G. Brookes, *Int. J. Pharm.* **32**, 223–228 (1986).

101. P. Gilchrist et al., *137th Br. Pharm. Conf.*, Scarborough, September 15–19, 1997.

102. C. Koller and P. Buri, *S. T. P. Pharmacol. Sci.* **3**, 115–124 (1987).

103. M.S. El-Aasser, *Adv. Emulsion Polymer. Latex Technol.*, 10 *Annu. Short Course,* Lehigh University, Bethlehem, Pa., 1979, pp. 1–13.

104. H. Ibrahim, Ph.D Thesis, No. 2369, University of Geneva, School of Pharmacy, Geneva, Switzerland (1989).

105. R. Gurny, T. Boye, H. Ibrahim, and P. Buri, *Proc. Int. Symp. Controlled Release Bioact. Mater.* **12**, 300–301 (1985).

106. H. Ibrahim, R. Gurny, C. Bindschaedler, and P. Buri, *5th Congr. Int. Technol. Pharm.*, APGI, Paris, 1989, pp. 70–76.

107. H. Ibrahim et al., *Int. J. Pharm.* **77**, 211–219 (1991).

108. H. Ibrahim et al., *4th Eur. Congr. Biopharm. Pharmacokinet.*, April 17–19, 1990.

109. H. Ibrahim et al., *Int. J. Pharm.* **87**, 239–246 (1992).

110. R. Gurny, *Pharm. Acta Helv.* **56**, 130–132 (1981).

111. R. Gurny, H. Ibrahim, and P. Buri, in P. Edman, ed., *Biopharmaceutics of Ocular Drug Delivery*, CRC Press, Boca Raton, Fla., 1993, pp. 81–90.

112. P. Jansson and B. Lindberg, *Carbohydr. Res.* **124**, 135–139 (1983).

113. M.A. O'Neill, R.R. Selvendran, and V.J. Morris, *Carbohydr. Res.* **124**, 123–133 (1983).

114. K.S. Kang et al., *Appl. Environ. Microbiol.* **43**, 1086–1091 (1982).

115. A. Rozier, C. Grove, C. Mazuel, and B. Plazonnet, *Proc. Int. Symp. Controlled Release Bioact. Mater.* **16**, 109–110 (1989).

116. P.B. Deasy and J. Quigley, *Int. J. Pharm.* **73**, 117–123 (1991).

117. Aust. Pat. 63189/86 (September 26, 1986), C. Mazuel and M. Friteyre (to Merck Sharp and Dohme Chibret).

118. D.M. Maurice and S.P. Srinivas, *J. Pharm. Sci.* **81**, 615–619 (1992).

119. J.L. Greaves et al., *Curr. Eye Res.* **9**, 415–420 (1990).

120. R. Vogel et al., *Invest. Ophthalmol. Visual Sci.* **31**, 404 (1990).

121. E. Verschueren, L. Van Santvliet, and A. Ludwig, *S. T. P. Pharmacol. Sci.* **6**, 203–210 (1996).

122. S. Cohen, E. Lobel, A. Trevgoda, and Y. Peled, *J. Controlled Release* **44**, 201–208 (1997).

123. V.H.L. Lee, P.T. Urrea, R.E. Smith, and D.J. Schanzlin, *Surv. Ophthalmol.* **29**, 335–348 (1985).

124. A.R. Tall, V. Hogan, L. Askinazi, and D.M. Small, *Biochemistry* **17**, 322–326 (1978).

125. R.E. Stratford, D.C. Yang, M.A. Redell, and V.H.L. Lee, *Curr. Eye Res.* **2**, 377–386 (1982).

126. F.J. Holly, *J. Colloid Interface Sci.* **49**, 221–231 (1974).

127. G. Smolin, M. Okumoto, S. Feiler, and D. Condon, *Am. J. Ophthalmol.* **91**, 220–225 (1981).

128. H.E. Schaeffer and D.L. Krohn, *Invest. Ophthalmol. Visual Sci.* **22**, 220–227 (1982).

129. P. Fitzgerald, J. Hadgraft, and C.G. Wilson, *J. Pharm. Pharmacol.* **39**, 487–490 (1987).

130. M. Mezei and D. Meisner, in P. Edman, ed., *Biopharmaceutics of Ocular Drug Delivery*, CRC Press, Boca Raton, Fla., 1993, pp. 91–104.

131. D. Meisner and M. Mezei, *Adv. Drug Delivery Rev.* **16**, 75–93 (1995).

132. N.M. Davies, I.W. Kellaway, J.L. Greaves, and C.G. Wilson, in A.K. Mitra, ed., *Ophthalmic Drug Delivery Systems*, Dekker, New York, 1993, pp. 289–306.

133. P.N. Shek and R.F. Barber, *Biochim. Biophys. Acta* **902**, 229–236 (1987).

134. S.G. Norley, D. Sendele, L. Huang, and B.T. Rouse, *Invest. Ophthalmol. Visual Sci.* **28**, 591–595 (1987).

135. D. Meisner, J. Pringle, and M. Mezei, *Int. J. Pharm.* **55**, 105–113 (1989).

136. K. Taniguchi et al., *J. Pharmacobio-Dyn.* **11**, 39–46 (1988).

137. I. Henriksen et al., *Int. J. Pharm.* **145**, 231–240 (1996).

138. R.E. Stratford, D.C. Yang, M.A. Redell, and V.H.L. Lee, *Int. J. Pharm.* **13**, 263–272 (1983).

139. S.K. Dharma, P.H. Fishman, and G.A. Peyman, *Acta Ophthalmol.* **64**, 298–301 (1986).

140. S. Benita et al., *J. Microencapsul.* **1**, 203–216 (1984).

141. K. Singh and M. Mezei, *Int. J. Pharm.* **16**, 339–344 (1983).

142. N.M. Davies, S.J. Farr, J. Hadgraft, and I.W. Kellaway, *Pharm. Res.* **9**, 1137–1144 (1992).

143. K. Taniguchi et al., *J. Pharmacobio-Dyn.* **11**, 607–611 (1988).

144. H. Tanaka et al., *J. Eye* **2**, 1127–1129 (1985).

145. R.I. Juliano, in R.I. Juliano, ed., *Drug Delivery Systems: Characteristics and Biomedical Applications*, Oxford University Press, New York, 1980, pp. 189–236.

146. S.E.G. Nilsson and S. Latkovic, *6th Congr. Eur. Soc. Ophthalmol.*, 1981, pp. 21–22.

147. K. Singh and M. Mezei, *Int. J. Pharm.* **19**, 263–269 (1984).

148. A. Zimmer and J. Kreuter, *Adv. Drug Delivery Rev.* **16**, 61–73 (1995).

149. A. Joshi, in I.K. Reddy, ed., *Ocular Therapeutics and Drug Delivery*, Technomic Publishing, Lancaster, Pa., 1996, pp. 441–460.

150. J. Kreuter, in A.K. Mitra, ed., *Ophthalmic Drug Delivery Systems*, Dekker, New York, 1993, pp. 275–287.

151. A. Duc-Mauger, J. Benoit, and F. Puisieux, *Pharm. Acta Helv.* **61**, 119–124 (1986).

152. U.S. Pat. 4,666,641 (1987), R. Fickat, S. Benita, and F. Puisieux.

153. J.J. Marty and R.C. Oppenheim, *Aust. J. Pharm. Sci.* **6**, 65–76 (1977).

154. U.S. Pat. 4,107,288 (1978), R.C. Oppenheim, J.J. Marty, and P. Speiser.

155. G.V. Taplin, D.E. Johnson, E.K. Dore, and H.S. Kaplan, *J. Nucl. Med.* **5**, 259–275 (1964).

156. J. Kreuter, *Pharm. Acta Helv.* **58**, 196–209 (1983).

157. J. Kreuter, in J.S. Boylan and J.C. Boylan, eds., *Encyclopedia of Pharmaceutical Technology*, Dekker, New York, 1994, pp. 165–190.

158. J. Kreuter, in *Colloidal Drug Delivery Systems*, Dekker, New York, 1994, pp. 219–342.

159. I. Genta et al., *J. Pharm. Pharmacol.* **49**, 737–742 (1997).

160. M.J. Alonso et al., *5th Congr. Int. Technol. Pharm.*, APGI, 1989, Paris, pp. 77–83.

161. L. Marchal-Heussler et al., *S. T. P. Pharmacol. Sci.* **2**, 98–104 (1992).

162. L. Marchal-Heussler et al., *Int. J. Pharm.* **58**, 115–122 (1990).

163. P. Maincent et al., *Proc. Int. Symp. Controlled Release Bioact. Mater.* **19**, 226–227 (1992).

164. U.S. Pat. 4,001,388 (January 4, 1977), J.W. Shell (to ALZA Corporation).

165. A.K. Zimmer, P. Maincent, P. Thouvenot, and J. Kreuter, *Int. J. Pharm.* **110**, 211–222 (1994).

166. V. Masson et al., *Proc. Int. Symp. Controlled Release Bioact. Mater.* **19**, 423–424 (1992).

167. P. Calvo, J.L. Vila-Jato, and M.J. Alonso, *Int. J. Pharm.* **153**, 41–50 (1997).

168. P. Calvo, J.L. Vila-Jato, and M.J. Alonso, *Proc. Int. Symp. Controlled Release Bioact. Mater.* **24**, 97–98 (1997).

169. S.E. Leucuta, *Int. J. Pharm.* **54**, 71–78 (1989).

170. A.K. Zimmer, J. Kreuter, M.F. Saettone, and H. Zerbe, *Proc. Int. Symp. Controlled Release Bioact. Mater.* **18**, 493–494 (1991).

171. A.K. Zimmer, H. Zerbe, and J. Kreuter, *J. Controlled Release* **32**, 57–70 (1994).

172. A.K. Zimmer et al., *J. Controlled Release* **53**, 31–46 (1995).

173. T. Harmia, P. Speiser, and J. Kreuter, *J. Microencapsul.* **3**, 3–12 (1986).

174. T. Harmia, P. Speiser, and J. Kreuter, *Int. J. Pharm.* **33**, 45–54 (1986).

175. T. Harmia et al., *Int. J. Pharm.* **33**, 187–193 (1986).

176. J. Kreuter, in M.F. Saettone, M. Bucci, and P. Speiser, eds., *Ophthalmic Drug Delivery*, Liviana Press Springer-Verlag, Padua and Berlin, 1987, pp. 101–106.

177. A. Zimmer et al., *Pharm. Res.* **11**, 1435–1442 (1994).

178. V. Vidmar, S. Pepeljnjak, and I. Jalsenjak, *J. Microencapsul.* **2**, 289–293 (1985).

179. C. Andermann, G. de Burlet, and C. Cannet, *J. Fr. Ophthalmol.* **5**, 499–504 (1982).

180. H.Z. Klein et al., *Am. J. Ophthalmol.* **99**, 23–26 (1985).

181. U. Ticho et al., *Br. J. Ophthalmol.* **63**, 45–47 (1979).

182. M.E. Evans, N.E. Richardson, and D.A. Norton, *J. Pharm. Pharmacol.*, 19 p. (1981).

183. M. Beal, N.E. Richardson, B.J. Meakin, and D.J.G. Davies, in Davis, Illum, McVie, and Tomlinson, eds., *Microspheres and Drug Therapy: Pharmaceutical Immunological and Medical Aspects*, 1984, pp. 347–348.

184. J. Kreuter et al., *Proc. Int. Symp. Controlled Release Bioact. Mater.* **12**, 304–305 (1985).

185. V.H.K. Li et al., *J. Microencapsul.* **3**, 213–218 (1986).

186. T. Harmia-Pulkinnen, A. Ihantola, A. Tuomi, and E. Kristoffersson, *Acta Pharm. Fenn.* **95**, 89–96 (1997).

187. W.R. Vezin and A.T. Florence, *J. Pharm. Pharmacol.* **30**, 5P (1978).

188. V. Lenaerts et al., *Biomaterials* **5**, 65–68 (1984).

189. J. Kreuter, in V. Lenaerts and R. Gurny, eds., *Bioadhesive Drug Delivery Systems*, CRC Press, Boca Raton, Fla., 1990, pp. 203–212.

190. J.W. Sieg and J.W. Triplett, *J. Pharm. Sci.* **69**, 863–864 (1980).

191. R.W. Wood, V.H.K. Li, J. Kreuter, and J.R. Robinson, *Int. J. Pharm.* **23**, 175–183 (1985).

192. R. Diepold, J. Kreuter, P. Guggenbuhl, and J.R. Robinson, *Int. J. Pharm.* **54**, 149–153 (1989).

193. P. Fitzgerald, J. Hadgraft, J. Kreuter, and C.G. Wilson, *Int. J. Pharm.* **40**, 81–84 (1987).

194. A. Zimmer, J.R. Robinson, and J. Kreuter, *Pharm. Res.* **7**, S114 (1990).

195. A. Zimmer, J. Kreuter, and J.R. Robinson, *J. Microencapsul.* **8**, 497–504 (1991).

196. P. Calvo et al., *Int. J. Pharm.* **103**, 283–291 (1994).

197. M.F. Saettone, in P. Edman, ed., *Biopharmaceutics of Ocular Drug Delivery*, CRC Press, London, 1993, pp. 61–79.

198. R. Bawa, in A.K. Mitra, ed., *Ophthalmic Drug Delivery Systems*, Dekker, New York, 1993, pp. 223–260.

199. M.F. Saettone and L. Salminen, *Adv. Drug Delivery Rev.* **16**, 95–106 (1995).

200. M.A. Khan and M.J. Durrani, in I.K. Reddy, ed., *Ocular Therapeutics and Drug Delivery*, Technomic Publishing, Lancaster, Pa., 1996, pp. 405–439.

201. J.W. Shell, *Drug Dev. Res.* **6**, 245–261 (1985).

202. J.W. Shell, *Surv. Ophthalmol.* **29**, 117–128 (1984).

203. F. Gurtler and R. Gurny, *Drug Dev. Ind. Pharm.* **21**(1), 1–18 (1995).

204. M.F. Saettone et al., *Acta Pharm. Technol.* **36**(1), 15–19 (1990).

205. M.F. Saettone et al., *Int. J. Pharm.* **86**, 159–166 (1992).

206. M.C. Richardson and P.H. Bentley, in A.K. Mitra, ed., *Ophthalmic Drug Delivery Systems*, Dekker, New York, 1993, pp. 355–367.

207. L. Salminen, A. Urtti, H. Kujari, and M. Juslin, *Graefe's Arch. Clin. Exp. Ophthalmol.* **221**, 96–99 (1983).

208. S.P. Loucas, M. Heskel, and M. Haddad, *Metab. Ophthalmol.* **1**, 27–34 (1976).

209. A. Urtti, L. Salminen, and O. Miinalainen, *Int. J. Pharm.* **23**, 147–161 (1985).

210. G.M. Grass, J. Cobby, and M.C. Makoid, *J. Pharm. Sci.* **73**, 618–621 (1984).

211. L. Sendelbeck, D. Moore, and J. Urqhart, *Am. J. Ophthalmol.* **80**, 274–283 (1975).

212. Y.T. Maddox and H.N. Bernstein, *Ann. Ophthalmol.* **4**, 789–802 (1972).

213. Eur. Pat. 219-207-A2 (April 22, 1987), R. Bawa (to Bausch and Lomb, Inc.).

214. Eur. Pat. 219-207-B1 (April 22, 1987), R. Bawa (to Bausch and Lomb, Inc.).

215. U.S. Pat. 4,190,642 (February 26, 1980), R.M. Gale, M. Ben-Dor, and N. Keller (to ALZA Corporation).

216. U.S. Pat. 5,145,884 (September 8, 1992), Y. Yamamoto, Y. Kaga, T. Yoshikawa, and A. Moribe (to Menicon Co.).

217. V.H.L. Lee et al., *J. Ocul. Pharmacol.* **10**, 421–429 (1994).

218. V.H.L. Lee et al., *Proc. Int. Symp. Controlled Release Bioact. Mater.* **18**, 291–292 (1991).

219. H. Sasaki, C. Tei, K. Nishida, and J. Nakamura, *J. Controlled Release* **27**, 127–137 (1993).

220. S. Hosaka, H. Ozawa, and H. Tanzawa, *Biomaterials* **4**, 243–247 (1983).

221. H. Ozawa, S. Hosaka, T. Kunitomo, and H. Tanzawa, *Biomaterials* **4**, 170–174 (1983).

222. R.B. Phinney, D. Schwartz, D.A. Lee, and B.J. Mondino, *Arch. Ophthalmol. (Chicago)* **106**, 1599–1604 (1988).

223. S.E. Bloomfield et al., *Arch. Ophthalmol. (Chicago)* **96**, 885–887 (1978).

224. D.H. Slatter, N.D. Costa, and M.E. Edwards, *Aust. Vet. J.* **59**, 4–6 (1982).

225. F. Gurtler, V. Kaltsatos, B. Boisramé, and R. Gurny, *J. Controlled Release* **33**, 231–236 (1995).

226. V. Baeyens et al., *J. Ocul. Pharmacol. Ther.* **14**, 263–272 (1998).

227. P.I. Punch, D.H. Slatter, N.D. Costa, and M.E. Edwards, *Aust. Vet. J.* **62**(3), 79–82 (1985).

228. V. Baeyens et al., *J. Controlled Release* **52**, 215–220 (1998).

229. V. Baeyens, E. Varesio, J.-L. Veuthey, and R. Gurny, *J. Chromatogr. B* **692**, 222–226 (1997).

230. J.K. Milani et al., *Am. J. Ophthalmol.* **116**, 622–627 (1993).

231. K.K. Assil, S.R. Zarnegar, B.D. Fouraker, and D.J. Schanzlin, *Am. J. Ophthalmol.* **113**, 418–423 (1992).

232. R. Praus, I. Brettschneider, L. Krejci, and D. Kalvodova, *Ophthalmologica* **165**, 62–70 (1972).

233. M.A. Attia, M.A. Kassem, and S.M. Safwat, *Int. J. Pharm.* **47**, 21–30 (1988).

234. D.G. Hwang, W.H. Stern, P.H. Hwang, and L.A. MacGowan-Smith, *Arch. Ophthalmol. (Chicago)* **107**, 1375–1380 (1989).

235. D.S. Hull, H.F. Edelhauser, and R.A. Hyndiuk, *Arch. Ophthalmol. (Chicago)* **92**, 413–416 (1974).

236. M.R. Sawusch, T.P. O'Brien, and S.A. Updegraff, *J. Cataract Refract. Surg.* **15**, 625–628 (1989).

237. Ger. Offen. P-26-33-987.7 (February 10, 1977), R.M. Gale (to ALZA Corporation).

238. D. Pavan-Langston, R.H.S. Langston, and P.A. Geary, *Arch. Ophthalmol. (Chicago)* **93**, 1349–1351 (1975).

239. J.R. Gussler, P. Ashton, W.S. VanMeter, and T.J. Smith, *J. Cataract Refract. Surg.* **16**, 719–722 (1990).

240. U.S. Pat. 4,913,904 (April 3, 1990), S.N. Fyodorov et al.,

241. M.L. Friedberg, U. Pleyer, and B.J. Mondino, *Ophthalmology* **98**, 725–732 (1991).

242. M.R. Sawusch, T.P. O'Brien, J.D. Dick, and J.D. Gottsch, *Am. J. Ophthalmol.* **106**, 279–281 (1988).

243. J.M. Hill, R.J. O'Callaghan, J.A. Hobden, and H.E. Kaufman, in A.K. Mitra, ed., *Ophthalmic Drug Delivery Systems*, Dekker, New York, 1993, pp. 261–273.

244. R.S. Shofner, H.E. Kaufman, and J.M. Hill, *Ophthalmol. Clin. North Am.* **2**, 15–23 (1989).

245. B.J. Mondino, *Am. J. Ophthalmol.* **112**, 587–590 (1991).

246. R.J. Harwood and J.B. Schwartz, *Drug Dev. Ind. Pharm.* **8**(5), 663–682 (1982).

247. J.W. Shell and R.W. Baker, *Ann. Ophthalmol.* **6**, 1037–1045 (1974).

248. F. Gurtler et al., *Pharm. Res.* **12**, 1791–1795 (1995).

249. D.W. Lamberts, D.P. Langston, and W. Chu, *Ophthalmology* **85**, 794–800 (1978).

250. J.R. Robinson, *S.T.P. Pharmacol. Sci.* **5**(12), 839–846 (1989).

251. B.G. Clerc and C. Robberechts, *Recl. Med. Vet.* **168**, 97–103 (1992).

252. S.M. Drance, D.W.A. Mitchell, and M. Schulzer, *Can. J. Ophthalmol.* **10**, 450–452 (1975).

253. M.F. Armaly and K.R. Rao, *Invest. Ophthalmol. Visual Sci.* **12**(7), 491–496 (1973).

254. I.P. Pollack, H.A. Quigley, and T.S. Harbin, *South Med. J.* **69**(10), 1296–1301 (1976).

255. R.L. Friederich, *Ann. Ophthalmol.* **6**, 1279–1284 (1974).

256. U.S. Pat. 4,014,335 (March 29, 1977), R.K. Arnold (to ALZA Corporation).

257. Eur. Pat. 262-893-A2 (December 18, 1988), S. Darougar (to Merck and Co., Inc.).

258. U.S. Pat. 5,147,647 (September 15, 1992), S. Darougar.

259. M.F. Refojo, *Curr. Eye Res.* **4**(6), 719–723 (1985).

260. P.I. Punch, D.H. Slatter, N.D. Costa, and M.E. Edwards, *J. Vet. Pharmacol. Ther.* **8**, 335–338 (1985).

261. T.J. Nicholls et al., *Int. J. Pharm.* **138**, 175–183 (1996).

262. T. Loftsson and E. Stefansson, *Drug Dev. Ind. Pharm.* **23**, 473–481 (1997).

263. N.M. Davies, G. Wang, and I.G. Tucker, *Proc. Int. Symp. Controlled Release Bioact. Mater.* **24**, 547–548 (1997).

264. H. Guo, G. De Witt, M. Wu, and P. Ashton, *Proc. Int. Symp. Controlled Release Bioact. Mater.* **24**, 617–618 (1997).

See also Bioadhesive drug delivery systems; Mucosal drug delivery, buccal; Mucosal drug delivery, intravitreal; Mucosal drug delivery, nasal; Mucosal drug delivery, vaginal drug delivery and treatment modalities.

MUCOSAL DRUG DELIVERY, VAGINAL DRUG DELIVERY AND TREATMENT MODALITIES

JONATHAN D. EICHMAN
University of Michigan Medical School
Ann Arbor, Michigan

MICHAEL J. RATHBONE
InterAg
Hamilton, New Zealand

JOSEPH R. ROBINSON
University of Wisconsin
Madison, Wisconsin

KEY WORDS

Animal vagina

Bioadhesives

Contraception

Drug delivery

Estrus cycle control

Hormones

Human vagina

Inserts

Vagina

Vaginal dryness

OUTLINE

INTRODUCTION AND OVERVIEW

Products for women are on the rise in part because of gender equality issues and in part because of new drugs and/ or delivery systems. Given the convenience of the oral route of administration, this is still the preferred route of drug delivery. However, many drugs are intended for local treatment and still other drugs are susceptible to first-pass metabolism; hence, the vaginal route of drug delivery is a more common site of drug application today than it was in the recent past.

Vaginal delivery of treatment modalities for local conditions is both understandable and expected whereas using the vaginal portal for systemic drug delivery carries with it both cultural and therapeutic issues. As will become clear in this article, the vaginal route is a very attractive route for drug delivery despite the presence of significant biological barriers.

A cartoon depiction of the reproductive organs is shown in Figure 1. Note the location of the vagina leading to the cervix. Dimensions of the vaginal cavity vary with age and tissue thickness and also varies with hormonal status. These changes present a challenge in the design of an appropriate drug delivery system that is effective across all age patients irrespective of their hormonal status.

VAGINAL ANATOMY AND PHYSIOLOGY

Premenopausal State

The vagina is a thin-walled, fibromuscular tube extending from the body exterior to the uterus. In the adult premenopausal female, the vagina is approximately 7 to 10 cm in length and 2 cm in width. The vagina may be segmented into the anterior wall (8 cm) and the posterior wall (11 cm), which combine to form two ridges of folds imparting a cross-sectional H-shaped appearance (1).

The vaginal wall consists of three principal layers: the epithelial layer, the muscular coat, and the tunica externa (adventitia). The inner mucosal layer may be further subdivided into the epithelium and lamina propria (2). The outermost epithelium is situated above the basement membrane and consists of noncornified, stratified squamous epithelium subdivided into four distinct layers: (*1*) a superficial layer consisting of large, flat cells with pyknotic nuclei; (*2*) an intermediate layer of larger and flatter nucleated cells; (*3*) a parabasal layer of polyhedral cells; and (*4*) a monolayer of cuboidal basal cells closely apposed to the basement membrane (3,4). A depiction of vaginal cell histology is shown in Figure 2. The first three cell categories are frequently exfoliated. Cuboidal cells are typically not sloughed off the vaginal wall unless undergoing extensive trauma. The epithelium overlies and is supported by the lamina propria, a region of dense connective tissue intertwined with a network of elastic fibers. The epithelium is drawn into numerous longitudinal and transverse muscular folds called rugae serving to increase the vaginal surface area (5). The vaginal wall does not contain mucus glands, but is continuously covered by a thin layer of protective moisture, some of which is obtained from Skene's and Bartholin's glands located near the vaginal orifice.

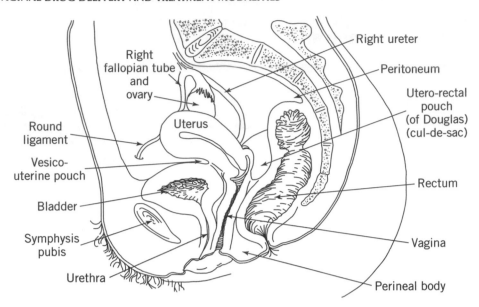

Figure 1. A depiction of the human reproductive system.

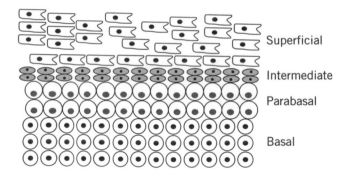

Figure 2. Depiction of vaginal histology.

Most vaginal secretions originate from cervical mucus glands and/or exuded fluid from the highly vascularized lamina propria (transudation) as well as cells sloughed off from the vaginal mucosa (3,6). Cervical mucus is a primary source of vaginal moisture and acts as a barrier layer protecting the underlying epithelium. During a woman's reproductive years, approximately 1 to 3 g/day of total fluid is secreted. Increased blood vessel dilation due to sexual stimulation leads to enhanced blood flow to the vaginal region and increases the production of this vaginal fluid. The volume and viscosity of cervical mucus undergoes significant changes during the menstrual cycle. Estrogen dominates during the first half of the cycle, which at ovulation induces large quantities of mucus secretion and is characteristically thin and alkaline. During the luteal phase, in which progesterone levels are high, mucus secretion decreases and is more viscous.

The muscular layer, lying distal to the epithelium, consists of smooth muscles and elastic fibers. The latter are primarily arranged in longitudinal fashion with a small inner portion of fibers arranged circularly. This organization imparts great elasticity to the vagina. The outer tunica adventitia consists of dense, loose connective tissue and provides a region of attachment of the vagina to surrounding organs.

Vaginal blood perfusion is supplied from uterine and pudendal arteries, which branch from the internal iliac arteries. Subsequently, these arteries form the cervicovaginal artery supplying the cervix and vaginal surfaces. The vaginal, uterine, and vesicle veins allow drainage of the rich plexus surrounding the vagina with eventual emptying into the internal iliac veins (3,7). Suffice it to say that the vagina is well endowed with a blood supply.

Vaginal fluid is acidic due to the presence of Döderlein's lactobacilli, which convert luminal carbohydrates such as glycogen secreted from exfoliated epithelial cells into lactic acid (8). A newborn child's vaginal pH ranges from 5.5 to 5.8, which is attributable to alkalinity of the amniotic fluid. During the first week of life, Döderlein's bacilli appear within the vaginal cavity dropping the pH to approximately 5.0. This value rises to neutrality within the first month and persists until puberty (9). During the years between the initial menstrual period (i.e., menarche) and menopause, pH for a healthy vagina drops to 4.0 to 5.0 with considerable fluctuation, dependent upon the menstrual cycle. The lowest pH values occur midcycle, whereas higher values are obtained during the period immediately prior to or preceding menstruation (9,10). A pH gradient also exists within the vagina, in which the lowest and highest values are obtained as one moves towards the cervix and vaginal vestibule, respectively (9). Sexual stimulation or enhanced blood flow stimulate an increase in vaginal pH.

The vaginal mucosa has been observed to undergo cytological changes influenced by the level and type of hormones present. Thus, due to a high concentration of maternal estrogen within the neonate, the vaginal epithelium is quite thick. Within three weeks, the epithelium flattens and remains relatively thin until puberty, at which time the epithelium thickens to normal levels ranging from 200 to 300 μm depending upon estrogen levels during the menstrual cycle.

Vaginal fluid consists primarily of cervical secretions and transudation from blood vessels through intercellular channels into the vagina. Thus, these secretions are dependent on blood flow rate. The weight of vaginal discharge in premenopausal women is 3–4 g/4 hours, whereas estrogen-deprived postmenopausal women have discharges that are 50% less. Table 1 shows typical vaginal discharges for women.

Peri- and Postmenopausal State

Perimenopause is the 3 to 5 years preceding menopause during which there is a reduction in estrogen levels. The perimenopause period typically begins during the midforties and is characterized by menstrual cycle irregularity (12). During a normal menstrual cycle, 6 to 12 follicles mature and proliferate in response to follicle-stimulating hormone (FSH) and luteinizing hormone (LH), but only a single follicle releases an ovum (13). The remaining follicles degenerate and by inception of menopause, a limited number of follicles are present in the ovary. During perimenopause, the reduction in functional follicles precipitates an alteration in ovary hormone secretion. Typically, the ovaries secrete high concentrations of estrogen during the follicular phase of the menstrual cycle. The menstrual cycle depends upon the presence of estrogen for development of theca and granulosa cells, which are involved in the production of estrone, estradiol-17 β, and also induce an LH surge required for ovulation (13,14). As the menstrual cycle becomes more irregular, the ovaries become unresponsive to higher FSH levels. By the end of perimenopause, estrogen production has declined 70–80% of its original concentration, leading to a subsequent decrease in estradiol production and thus removing an important negative feedback control to FSH production. The decline in estrogen levels also prevents LH production necessary for ovulation. Therefore, the initial clinical evidence of perimenopause is a shortened menstrual cycle precipitated by high FSH secretion creating rapid follicular development (14).

Menopause is defined as the last spontaneous episode of uterine bleeding in which the ovaries stop producing hormones (15). Histologically, the vaginal epithelium changes and returns to conditions similar to prepuberty. The epithelium thickness is reduced, corresponding to a shedding of the outer superficial and intermediate cell layers, in which vaginal smears of menopausal women primarily show the presence of basal cells and leukocytes (16). In premenopausal women, the vaginal mucosa may be as thick as 45 cell layers during the first half of the menstrual cycle. In comparison, the vaginal mucosa of postmenopausal women becomes fragile and may be composed of only three to four cell layers. Figure 3 represents a section of normal vaginal tissue compared with estrogen-deficient tissue. Along with epithelial thinning, there is a subsequent drop in glycogen and Döderlein's bacilli levels precipitating alterations in bacterial flora and an increased alkalinity to pH 7.0 (4). The pH change leads to an enhanced opportunity for bacterial and fungal infections due to the loss of acidic organisms within the vaginal cavity.

In postmenopausal women, there is a decrease in the size of the vagina in comparison to menstruating women. The average vaginal length and width decrease to 6.0 and 1.0 cm, respectively. The vagina also loses its elasticity and vascularity, the latter of which precipitates a reduction in vaginal secretions, which become increasingly watery after menopause (1).

DESIRABLE FEATURES OF A VAGINAL DRUG DELIVERY SYSTEM

An ideal vaginal drug delivery system must be functionally effective and aesthetically pleasing to the patient. From a functional point of view, its purpose is to deliver drug at an effective rate over a predefined period of time. Because of patient compliance issues for every route of administration, the dosing interval should be as long as possible and preferably not less than once daily. A longer interval would be preferable provided it is not so unusual as to be confusing to the patient. Drug metering from the vaginal delivery system is determined by the pharmacodynamic response but minimally the drug delivery system must be sufficiently flexible to accommodate different drugs and different rates of release.

The aesthetic or patient-related issues can be prominent and must be considered. Such factors as vaginal leakage of the system and staining of undergarments are important concerns. It also goes without saying that the

Table 1. Vaginal Discharge Rates

Subjects	Rate of Discharge	Refs.
Reproductive Age		
Including cervical secretions	3–4 g/4 h	11
Without cervical secretions	2.7 g/24 h	10
Postmenopausal, no estrogen supplement	1.7 g/4 h	11
Hysterectomized		
Ovarectomized	1.56 ± 0.05 g/24 h	10
Intact ovaries	1.89 ± 0.12 g/24 h	10
Ovarectomized with estrogen supplement	1.97 ± 0.05 g/24 h	10

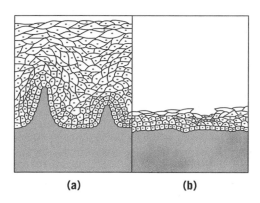

Figure 3. (**a**) Normal vaginal mucosa and (**b**) estrogen-deficient mucosa.

system must not be irritating or interfere with normal physiological processes.

A significant issue for chronically administered drugs is whether or not the system interferes with sexual intercourse. To this end, insoluble inserts, or bulky erodible systems, are likely to be less well accepted by the patient. Gels and creams must be odorless and not create a sticky sensation during sexual intercourse.

A concern for any product to be commercialized is the ease and cost of manufacturing. A unit dose system does not need a preservative but the microbial bioburden must be low. Methods to process the drug delivery system to ensure low bioburden are often limited by the physical nature of the system or the physicochemical stability of the system to sterilizing techniques. A multidose system does require a preservative, and this can require substantial development effort to find a suitable chemical preservative.

REPRODUCTIVE SYSTEM PATHOLOGIES AND TREATMENT

Vaginal Dryness

As the estrogen level begins to decline at the onset of menopause, subsequent vaginal anatomical and physiological changes occur such as vaginal atrophy and a lack of tissue hydration. A reduction in circulating estrogen levels precipitates vasoconstriction leading to less blood flow and consequently less fluid transudation to the vaginal tissue (6). Five years after the last menstrual period, only 25% of women complain of vaginal dryness, with the percentage of complaints increasing to 65% by 60 years of age. Vaginal dryness is more commonly a problem for postmenopausal women who are not sexually active or not undergoing drug therapy. The reduction of the epithelium to 4 or 5 cell layers and the lack of tissue hydration results in the vagina becoming predisposed to a greater likelihood of irritation with subsequent inflammation. Common complaints caused by vaginal dryness include a burning sensation, postcoital bleeding, purulent discharge, a decrease in lubrication with sexual arousal, and dyspareunia (6).

Vaginal dryness is typically not a serious problem and can often be treated with either hormone replacement therapy or topical lubricants. Estrogen replacement therapy has been shown to increase vaginal hydration to levels of the premenopausal state, but may be contraindicated in certain patients such as breast cancer patients who are likely also taking tamoxifen, an estrogen blocker. Therefore, the development of a nonhormonal therapeutic would be advantageous. A microparticulate system called Replens®, which incorporates a cross-linked bioadhesive polymer, polycarbophil, was introduced into the market. The topical moisturizer remains within the vagina for 3 to 4 days and has been shown to impart greater lubrication efficacy in comparison with other lubricants (17).

A study on breast cancer patients, a group for which estrogen replacement therapy is contraindicated, found that vaginal dryness was relieved with use of Replens as well as returning vaginal pH to premenopausal levels (6). Of 25 postmenopausal patients, the vaginal dryness index as described in Table 2 improved after the first month of treatment ($P < .001$). Other studies have also indicated

the safety and efficacy of Replens compared with local estrogen therapy. Nachtigall showed that in a randomized study of 30 women, over one year past their last menstrual period, Replens was an alternative therapy to estrogen vaginal cream (18). This therapy induced significant enhancement in vaginal moisture, lubrication, and vaginal elasticity with concomitant reduction in pH to premenopausal levels.

Bioadhesive gels induce tissue hydration by increasing localized vaginal blood flow by 25%, leading to an increase in vaginal fluid transudation. Estrogen induces similar vaginal blood flow enhancement when used alone. If combined with a bioadhesive gel, an increase in vaginal blood flow of 50% has been exhibited. The exact mechanism for the blood flow increase is unknown, but it has been postulated that the bioadhesive polyelectrolyte on the tissue surface creates ion movement into the tissue. Subsequently, greater blood flow is observed. This is similar to the mechanism of tissue hydration induced by the mucus layer lining epithelial surfaces (6).

Menopausal Stress Incontinence

Given that both vaginal and urethral blood flow increased following application of Replens, it is expected that the same product might be useful to treat patients with menopause-related stress incontinence. As with vaginal dryness, there are a number of women, such as breast cancer patients, who cannot use estrogen replacement therapy and thus a nondrug alternative is attractive.

The lower urinary tract contains the urethra, a tubular structure that allows urine to exit from the urinary bladder. The urethra is composed of estrogen-sensitive tissues similar to those found in the vagina, due to the presence of estrogen receptors located in the mucosa and connective tissue (20). Urethral cells, like vaginal mucosa, mature and proliferate upon estrogen exposure. During menopausal and postmenopausal years, the reduction in estrogen levels lead to marked changes in the urinary system such as the inability for effective urine control. Urinary stress incontinence is a condition resulting in urine leakage due to physical stress such as heavy lifting, coughing, or laughing. In postmenopausal years, the urethral mucosa atrophies to a state in which the urethra is primarily lined with immature parabasal cells (19). Additionally, the lack of estrogen promotes a weakening and relaxation of urethra musculature and ligaments, while also diminishing the level of blood flow to the region. These three factors combine to contribute to the loss of urinary continence inducing a 30% drop in urethral closure pressure in postmenopausal women (19). Studies have shown a significant correlation between menopause and the onset of urinary stress incontinence with 70% of postmenopausal women in one study suffering from incontinence due to the initiation of menopause (20,21).

Estrogen replacement therapy is the most common form of treatment for urinary stress incontinence. Increased estrogen levels cause thickening of the mucosa, increased blood supply, and enhanced muscle tone to the urethra. Recently, it has been shown that bioadhesive gels may provide not only an enhancement in vaginal blood flow, but

Table 2. Vaginal Health Index

	1	2	3	4	5
Elasticity	None	Poor	Fair	Good	Excellent
Fluid volume (pooling of Secretions)	None	Scant amount, vault not entirely covered	Superficial amount, vault entirely covered	Moderate amount	Normal amount
pH	6.1 or above	5.6–6.0	5.1–5.5	4.7–5.0	4.6 or below
Epithelial integrity	Petechiae noted before contact	Bleeds with light contact	Bleeds with scraping	Not friable-thin epithelium	Normal
Moisture (coating)	None, surface inflamed	None, surface not inflamed	Minimal	Moderate	Normal

Source: From Ref. 19.

also induce a doubling of suburethral blood flow leading to the elimination of urinary stress incontinence (6). This result has been substantiated in double-blind cross-over studies.

Bacterial Vaginosis

Trichomoniasis, candidiasis, and bacterial vaginosis are several forms of vaginitis that commonly occur within the female population. Bacterial vaginosis, formerly named nonspecific vaginosis or *Gardnerella*-associated vaginitis, is the most prevalent vaginal infection among women of childbearing age, 16–48 years (22,23). Bacterial vaginosis is not a true infection but a condition in which there is an alteration in the balance of vaginal bacteria without inflammation. Under normal conditions, the vagina is heavily populated with lactobacilli bacteria, which help to maintain vaginal acidity. Bacterial vaginosis is characterized by a reduction in lactobacilli concentration with subsequent increases in aerobic and anaerobic bacteria including, *Gardnerella vaginalis*, *Mycoplasma hominis*, *Ureaplasma urealyticum*, and *Bacteroides* species (24,25).

Women with bacterial vaginosis often have a fish-like vaginal odor, a thin milky-grey homogenous vaginal discharge, vaginal pH > 4.5, and a positive test for clue cells in the vaginal fluid. An increase in vaginal pH liberates amines such as putrescine, trimethylamine, and cadaverine leading to the fish-like odor. Because semen is also slightly alkaline, women with bacterial vaginosis commonly complain of an enhanced odor following sexual intercourse (26).

Bacterial vaginosis commonly occurs in sexually active women with no convincing evidence that it should be categorized as a sexually transmitted disease. It is more common in women who use nonbarrier contraceptive methods but less common in postmenopausal women and prepubescent girls (27,28). These observations led to the theory that hormonal factors play a role in the condition. However, hormones have never been associated with the disease, and in many cases, there are no obvious factors predisposing women to bacterial vaginosis.

Since 1978, metronidazole has been the treatment of choice for bacterial vaginosis. Various studies have shown that oral metronidazole (500 mg twice daily for 7 days) is the preferred treatment (24,29,30) but other regimens consisting of single-dose metronidazole (2 g), 2% clindamycin vaginal cream, and oral clindamycin are effective treatments (31). Other alternatives to metronidazole delivery systems are needed due to unpleasant side effects and contraindications during the first trimester of pregnancy.

Recently, increased interest in the development of localized drug delivery systems within the vaginal cavity has been shown due to the advantage of localized drug levels, which reduces dosing frequency, drug administration, and side effects (32). Treatment of bacterial vaginosis with bioadhesive gels with pH-reducing properties would be expected to eliminate the characteristically fishy odor within a short time period due to the conversion of polyamines to nonvolatile salt forms. Additionally, the return of the vaginal environment to acidic pH would favor a higher lactobacilli population (6).

In a double-blind, placebo, crossover study consisting of women with vaginal odor, the bioadhesive gel product was locally applied every third day. The study showed two effects upon application: (1) a reduction in vaginal pH and (2) a concomitant decrease in vaginal odor when compared with the placebo group. The bioadhesive gel is not an antimicrobial gel but it potentiates an unfavorable condition for continued microbial growth (6).

Recently, there has also been interest in the development of a metronidazole bioadhesive tablet. Studies were performed to determine the efficacy of treatment between a localized metronidazole bioadhesive and oral tablets for the treatment of bacterial vaginosis (32). In a double-blind study, patients were randomly given a bioadhesive tablet with or without 100 mg metronidazole. The bioadhesive consisted of a modified starch–polyacrylic acid combination. The two groups were compared with patients given two 500 mg doses of oral metronidazole for 7 days. Similar cure rates were obtained with the metronidazole bioadhesive tablet and oral treatment groups with only one-seventh of the dose given with localized treatment.

Sexually Transmitted Diseases

There are an estimated 333 million new cases of sexually transmitted diseases (STDs) that occur worldwide each year. The United States leads the industrialized world with an STD rate that is 50–100 times greater than other industrialized countries with an estimated 10 to 12 million new cases annually (33). Women, adolescents, young children, and substance abusers are most susceptible to the spread of STDs. Of the new cases, greater than 3 million occur in children and young adults 13 to 19 years of age. A recent Centers for Disease Control and Prevention (CDC) report indicated that of the common U.S. infectious diseases, 85% originated from sexual transmission (34).

Some of the most common STDs include chlamydia, gonorrhea, syphilis, human papillomavirus, genital herpes, and human immunodeficiency virus (HIV). Chlamydia is ranked by the CDC as the most prevalent with an estimated 4 million new cases annually. Gonorrhea is the next most prevalent with new cases occurring at a rate of 800,000 per year. In 20–40% of women who obtain inadequate treatment of chlamydia and gonorrhea, the disease leads to a more serious disease state, namely pelvic inflammatory disease. Inadequate treatment may also result in fatal ectopic pregnancies (34).

HIV infection has been reported in over 160 countries with 75% of the population infected via sexual transmission of the virus (35). Estimations are anywhere between 40,000 to 80,000 new HIV infections per year in the U.S. with an average of 500,000 to 2.3 million adult AIDS deaths worldwide between 1992 and 2000 (36).

Overcoming STDs is one of the greatest concerns and challenges facing the world today due to the health impact on infected individuals and the tremendous economic consequence associated with treatment. In the U.S. alone, STDs add between 15 and 18 billion dollars annually to the cost of the nation's health care system (34).

One potential method for controlling the spread of STDs is preventing the transmission of the infecting organism. Nonoxynol-9 (N-9) is a nonionic surfactant that exerts both spermicidal and antiviral/antibacterial activities by damaging cell membranes of spermatozoa and microorganisms. This agent is the only chemical currently used in the U.S. as the active substance in topically applied contraceptives. In vitro, N-9 has been shown to have activity against organisms responsible for STD pathogenicity such as *Neisseria gonorrhoeae*, *Trichomonas vaginalis*, *Treponema pallidum*, herpes simplex, *Chlamydia trachomatis*, and HIV (37–39). In vitro studies have indicated that 0.1–1.0% N-9 inactivates cell-free and cell-associated HIV (40). In concentrations of 5% or greater, N-9 kills lymphocytes containing the HIV virus. Because gonococcal, chlamydial, and trichomonal infections have been correlated with an increased risk of HIV transmission, the reduction in the spread of these diseases would also indirectly reduce the number of HIV infections.

Clinical trials have established that N-9 preparations can decrease the transmission of STDs such as gonococcal, chlamydial, and trichomonal infections (41–43). An N-9 film, when used in combination with condoms, in a single-blind randomized study of 343 women reduced the rate of cervical infections of *Chlamydia trachomatis* and *Neisseria gonorrhoeae* by 25% (40% if used in >75% coital acts). In a study by Rosenberg et al., N-9 (1.0 g) in a contraceptive sponge decreased the prevalence of gonorrhea and chlamydia infection in Thai women by 70% and 30%, respectively (36).

There is some controversy whether N-9 used in vivo is effective in HIV inactivation. A contraceptive vaginal sponge containing N-9 (1.0 g) did not protect women prostitutes against being infected with HIV (10). However, in a second study using an N-9 suppository with a lower N-9 dose (150 mg), there was evidence of a protective effect against HIV infection among women prostitutes (44).

One of the problems associated with N-9 administration is the potential for N-9 toxicity to the genital tract epithelium when frequently administered or used in high doses. Under these conditions, the vaginal mucosa may become irritated increasing the risk for women to be infected with HIV due to small lesions or disruptions within the vaginal lining.

The use of a bioadhesive gel in combination with N-9 would be advantageous particularly due to the fact that the spermicide would remain localized within the vaginal cavity for 1 to 3 days providing localization of N-9 for greater time periods in addition to a reduced N-9 concentration within the vaginal cavity. The gel allows intimate contact with the tissue with preferential binding to damaged tissue enabling an additional use as a barrier to systemic invasion of HIV viruses. The complex of N-9 and bioadhesive polymer has also been shown to increase N-9's antiviral and spermicidal activity. The Today Sponge and other nonbioadhesive topical spermicidal preparations contain anywhere between 1.0 g and 100–200 mg N-9, respectively. The combined bioadhesive spermicidal preparation contains a lower concentration of N-9 preventing cervical or vaginal epithelial ulceration while still having spermicidal, antiviral, and antimicrobial activity (45).

In studies at the Pasteur Institute in Paris, France, researchers have shown that N-9 can kill the free AIDS virus, but not when the virus is attached to a lymphocyte. If N-9 is combined with a bioadhesive, the bioadhesive attaches to the lymphocyte for a period of time allowing N-9 to kill the lymphocyte and subsequently the AIDS virus (44). However, clinical studies have yet to be performed that confirm these results.

Advantage 24, a topical contraceptive, contains N-9 in a bioadhesive gel composed of polycarbophil. The product adheres to the epithelium and remains localized allowing for once-a-day application. Advantage 24 forms a temporary barrier over the cervix and contains the lowest dose of N-9 (52.5 mg) of any product on the U.S. market (46). The frequency of sexual intercourse does not affect localization of the delivery system nor the dosing interval.

A randomized, placebo-controlled, double-blind crossover study of 60 female prostitutes in Mombasa, Kenya, was conducted to establish the safety and toxicity of Advantage 24 administration (47). Advantage 24 or a placebo gel was applied vaginally once daily for 2 weeks. The study concluded that Advantage 24 did not induce epithelial toxicity.

The Joint United National Programme on HIV/AIDS has recently announced that Advantage 24 was shown to inhibit STD transmission (HIV included) during intercourse (46). Due to the prospect that women may want to increase the N-9 dose or possibly decrease the potential for condom usage, the CDC will not accept N-9 as an alternative method for combating or preventing HIV/STD infection. Currently, additional Phase III studies of Advantage 24 for HIV are underway in Thailand and South Africa (46).

Endometriosis

The inner portion of the uterus is lined with endometrial tissue that responds to hormonal stimulation by proliferating prior to each menstrual period with subsequent shedding as menstrual flow during the latter portion of the menstrual cycle. Endometriosis is a benign disease in which the endometrial tissue migrates to areas outside the uterine cavity such as the ovaries, fallopian tubes, pelvic cavity, vagina, and large bowel (48). The invasive tissue is sensitive to hormonal stimulation with resultant breakdown and bleeding confined to a localized area with no outlet, leading to tissue irritation and inflammation (22,49). This may initiate scar tissue development with subsequent lesion, nodule, or growth formation resulting in pain or sexual discomfort.

Menstrual cramping (i.e., dysmennorrhea), an important diagnostic symptom, is the most frequently experienced pain associated with endometriosis. Endometriosis is found in 10–15% of menstruating women between the ages of 25 and 44 (50). Women may also experience pain associated with sexual activity (i.e., dyspareunia) and chronic midline pelvic pain (48,51). Bladder and large bowel lesions may cause pain upon defecation or abdominal bloating, or produce rectal bleeding (50). In 30–40% of cases, endometriosis may be severe enough to cause infertility (49). For women under 35 years of age, surgery may restore or maintain fertility in 25–50% of the cases. For women over 35, removal of the ovaries and uterus may be recommended.

There are various treatment options depending on the age, symptoms, desire for pregnancy, and disease extent. Typically, treatments include either drug therapy to suppress the growth and differentiation of the displaced tissue, surgery, or abdominal hysterectomy (50).

Drug therapy is used as a means for palliation and is very often not a cure. The standard for drug therapy is danazol, a drug that decreases estradiol concentration by reducing the frequency of estradiol pulses. Disease recurrence occurs between 20 and 30% per year and side effects include nausea, weight gain, and hot flashes (51). Gonadotropin-releasing hormone agonists (e.g., nafarelin, leuprolide) are used to control the release of anterior pituitary hormones producing a state of reversible hypoestrogenemia (50). There are concerns over the long-term usage of these medications due to an increase in low density lipoprotein (LDL) levels and/or a greater chance of developing osteoporosis.

Progestin agents have been shown to decrease the risk of estrogen-precipitated endometrial hyperplasia by promoting the transformation of the endometrium into a secretory mucosa, but their use has been limited due to promotion of irregular vaginal bleeding, depression, and enhanced LDL levels (52).

In order to reduce these unwanted side effects, strategies were developed aimed at looking toward new delivery routes and using natural progesterone to reduce side effects. Natural progesterone is problematic when administered orally due to rapid prehepatic and hepatic metabolism leading to insufficient endometrial effects (53). The production of metabolites also leads to symptomatic side effects, in particular, drowsiness. Vaginal administration of natural progesterone induced higher plasma concentrations reached later after dosing and reduced side effects than when administered orally due to a reduction in prehepatic metabolism (21).

Crinone®, a biocompatible bioadhesive gel incorporating natural progesterone (90 mg), was developed as a delivery system to circumvent oral delivery problems. The bioadhesive gel adheres to the vaginal epithelium imparting prolonged release properties. The gel may be administered once daily with peak progesterone plasma levels occurring 6 hours after application (29). Crinone given every 48 hours induced an effective secretory endometrial transformation usually encountered with oral progesterone (300 mg) administration or with 150–600 mg vaginal tablets (37). The explanation for the effectiveness of Crinone is the bioadhesive vehicle allows for greater absorption of progesterone by promoting enhanced contact time with vaginal epithelium. Although not approved for endometriosis at this time, but approved for in vitro fertilization patients, Crinone has shown the potential for use of a vaginal bioadhesive delivery system providing prolonged release of progesterone at lower doses which results in fewer side effects, reduced dosing frequency, and improved patient compliance and acceptance.

TOPICAL CONTRACEPTIVES

Prevention of pregnancy, i.e., population control, is a global problem. Oral contraceptives have been the treatment of choice since their introduction in the 1950s. However, for many individuals, because of their inability to use hormone products, or the cost of such products, topical contraceptives are a reasonable alternative. For a topical contraceptive to be effective, its active ingredient, usually N-9, must be placed in the vaginal cavity to immobilize or destroy the approximately 40 million sperm in a typical ejaculate. If not destruction of these sperm then elimination of those sperm prevents them from the cervical canal (Figure 4). This is a formidable challenge.

Present topical contraceptives have label instructions to the patient that the product must be inserted 10 minutes before sexual intercourse. Presumably the clearing mechanisms of the vagina are sufficiently robust to remove applied material, which is a strong argument for using a bioadhesive product that may keep the product in place for 3–4 days.

The more difficult issue is how to place and maintain the spermicidal product at the opening of the cervical canal both during and after sexual intercourse. At midcycle, when the egg is available for fertilization, there is a change in consistency of cervical mucus and subsequent leakage of this material out through the opening of the cervical canal, i.e., the os. This flow of mucus will hinder retention of a liquid or semisolid material from remaining at the site of expected maximal need.

Current topical contraceptives are reasonably unreliable, as compared with oral contraceptives. The need to use the product 10 minutes before sexual intercourse and thus no overnight protection is a significant liability. A bioadhesive polymer can indeed provide extended duration of action and thus elevate the reliability of bioadhesive-

Table 4. Factors To Consider When Designing an Intravaginal Veterinary Drug Delivery System for Estrus Control

Factor	Objective	Reason
Size	Optimize: Length Diameter Width	Animal comfort Ease of insertion Ease of removal
Shape	Optimize: Overall spatial geometry	Impel retention characteristics Prevent animal discomfort and damage Impel a means for insertion and removal
Retention	Maintain device inside vagina for entire treatment period	Ensure continuity of drug delivery over required insertion period
Release characteristics	Meet clinical requirements	Maintain sufficiently high progestagen plasma levels to prevent ovulation
Removal	Ability to: Terminate delivery at will Remove easily	Impel sudden drop in progestagen levels to induce estrus
Adverse effects	Avoidance of: Damage to mucosa Damage to cervix Irritation to vaginal mucosa	Reduce discharge formation Eliminate membrane perforation

Table 5. Polymers, Drugs, Manufacturing Methods and in vitro and in vivo Release Characteristics of Commercially Available Controlled Release Intravaginal Veterinary Drug Delivery Systems

Delivery system	Drug	Polymer	Manufacturing technique	Type of delivery system	Release characteristics in vitro	Release characteristics in vivo
Sponge	FGA[a] MAP[b]	Polyurethane	Single application of drug dissolved in ethanol	Matrix	$t^{1/2}$ (21)	$t^{1/2}$ (142–144)
PRID	Progesterone	Silicone	Low temperature injection molding[c]	Matrix	$t^{1/2}$ (94)	$t^{1/2}$ (145)
CIDR-S	Progesterone	Silicone	High temperature (190°C) injection molding[d]	Matrix	Not reported	Not reported
CIDR-G	Progesterone	Silicone	High temperature (190°C) injection molding[d]	Matrix	$t^{1/2}$ (Personal results)	Not reported
CIDR-B	Progesterone	Silicone	High temperature (190°C) injection molding[d]	Matrix	$t^{1/2}$ (146)	Not reported

[a]PGA, Fluorogestone acetate
[b]MAP, Methyl acetoxy progesterone
[c]Progesterone/silicone mixture around a stainless steel sheet
[d]Progesterone/silicone mixture around a nylon spine

systems not being successful in these animals may include the excessive amount of discharge associated with sponges (which may be acceptable by sheep and goat farmers but not by owners of these other species) and poor retention rates. CIDR-G have been inserted into deer with success both in terms of estrus synchrony and suitability of the delivery system design with respect to animal comfort, retention, etc. (86–95). Both PRID and CIDR-B have been investigated in horses (100–103) and buffalo (104–109). The probable reason for these delivery systems not being completely successful in these animals is the inappropriate design for these species (i.e., overall dimensions), which results in either straining following insertion (100,101) or the need to adapt the dimensions of the device before insertion to improve retention characteristics (103).

Brief History

Controlled drug delivery has a long history in the animal reproduction field. Polyurethane sponges were first investigated in sheep in the early 1960s as a delivery system for the administration of synthetic progestagens to control the estrus cycle (110–112). T.J. Robinson successfully demonstrated the worth of this delivery system in large sheep trials under Australian farming conditions (110–112). Shortly afterwards, D.F. Wishart demonstrated that the sponge was equally effective in sheep farmed under British conditions (113–124). In the 1970s, J.F. Roche in collaboration with Abbott Laboratories developed the PRID device for use in cattle (116–123). In the 1980s, R.A.S. Welsh in collaboration with D. Miller developed the CIDR-S (124,125) and shortly afterwards the CIDR-G (for sheep and goats) (126–130). Rapid development resulted in the CIDR-G technology being extended to the design and development of a device for use in cattle called the CIDR-R (131–141). Interdispersed with these developments were conceptual approaches of Rajamahendran (cattle) (70–72), the Plasthyd Device (sheep) (73) and Kabadi and Chiens silicone sheets (sheep) (74–77).

DESIGN FACTORS IN CONTROLLED RELEASE INTRAVAGINAL VETERINARY DRUG DELIVERY SYSTEMS

A number of factors should be considered when designing a controlled release intravaginal veterinary drug delivery system (M.J. Rathbone et al., unpublished data, 1998). These are summarized in Table 4. Ease of insertion, retention characteristics, ease of removal, animal comfort, and achievement of clinical objectives (through release rates) are the key aspects that need to be considered and tailored to a particular animal species if an intravaginal veterinary drug delivery system is to be successfully developed.

INTRAVAGINAL VETERINARY DRUG DELIVERY SYSTEMS

Currently available intravaginal veterinary drug delivery systems are shown in Figure 5 together with their dimensions. A brief description of the delivery system, polymer used to manufacture it, and the type of release characteristics are given in Table 5.

FUTURE DEMANDS AND REQUIREMENTS OF INTRAVAGINAL VETERINARY DRUG DELIVERY SYSTEMS

The future demands for intravaginal veterinary drug delivery for animal health and production are dependent upon the perception in some circles for the need to eliminate the adverse and unwanted effects which intramuscular and subcutaneous injection cause on administration such as ulcer formation and hide damage. Alternate routes for drug administration may be necessary to limit the occurrence of these problems and the intravaginal route offers advantages for some compounds. Future demands on the intravaginal veterinary drug delivery scientist will be influenced by the extent to which this concept is pursued and the suitability of the physicochemical and pharmacokinetic properties of the drugs which need to be delivered. In addition intravaginal veterinary drug delivery system design will be influenced by the requirements of the reproductive physiologists and endocrinologists who are currently defining the types of drugs and their delivery patterns for "ideal" synchrony programs (55–58).

BIBLIOGRAPHY

1. D.G. Ferris et al., *J. Fam. Pract.* **41**, 443–449 (1995).
2. A. Forbes, *Crit. Pathol. AIDS Proj.* **31**, 19–20 (1996).
3. D.A. Grimes and W. Cates, Jr., in K.K. Holmes, P.A. Mardh, and P.F. Sparting, eds., *Sexually Transmitted Diseases*, McGraw-Hill, New York, 1990, pp. 1087–1099.
4. A.C. Guyton and J.E. Hall, *Textbook of Medical Physiology*, Saunders, Philadelphia, 1996, pp. 1017–1032.
5. L.H. Hill, H. Ruperalia, and J.A. Embil, *Sex. Transm. Dis.* **10**, 114–118 (1983).
6. C.S. Iosif and Z. Bekassy, *Acta Obstet. Gynecol. Scand.* **23**, 257–260 (1984).
7. M.R. Joesoef and G.P. Schmid, *Clin. Infect. Dis.* **20**, S72–S79 (1995).
8. R.W. Kistner, in E.S.E. Hafez, and T.N. Evans, eds., *The Human Vagina*, Elsevier/North-Holland Biomedical Press, Amsterdam, 1978, pp. 109–120.
9. K. Knuth, M. Amiji, and J.R. Robinson, R., *Adv. Drug Delivery Rev.* **11**, 137–167 (1993).
10. J. Kreiss et al., *J. Am. Med. Assoc. JAMA*, **268**, 477–482 (1992).
11. C. Landau, M.G. Cyr, and A.W. Moulton, *The Complete Book of Menopause*, The Berkley Publishing Group, New York, 1994, pp. 23–41.
12. P.-G. Larsson, *Int. J. STD AIDS* **3**, 239–247 (1992).
13. W.C. Louv et al., *J. Infect. Dis.* **158**, 518–523 (1988).
14. R.I.J. MacDermott, *Br. J. Obstet. Gynaecol.* **102**, 92–94 (1995).
15. Y. Machida et al., *Chem. Pharm. Bull.* **27**, 93–100 (1979).
16. H.L. Martin et al., *Sex. Transm. Dis.* **24**, 279–283 (1997).
17. S.M. McKinlay, *Maruritas* **23**, 137–145 (1996).
18. H. Moi, *Int. J. STD AIDS* **1**, 86–94 (1990).
19. L.E. Nachtigall, *Fertil. Steril.* **61**, 178–180 (1994).
20. K. Morimoto, T. Takeeda, Y. Nakamoto, and K. Morisaka, *Int. J. Pharm.* **12**, 107–111 (1982).
21. K. Nahoul, L. Dehennin, M. Jondet, and M. Roger, *Maturitas* **16**, 185–202 (1993).
22. M.E. Niatas, *U.S. Pharmacist* **21**, 6 (1996).
23. S. Niruthisand, R.E. Roddy, and S. Chutivongse, *Lancet* **339**, 1371–1375 (1992).
24. M. Nisolle and J. Donnez, *Peritoneal, Ovarian, and Rectovaginal Endometriosis. The Identification of Three Separate Diseases*, Parthenon Publishing Group, New York, 1997.
25. T. O'Dowd, *Practitioner* **239**, 538–541 (1995).
26. E.W. Page, C.W. Villee, and D.B. Villee, *Human Reproduction; Essentials of Reproductive and Perinatal Medicine*, Saunders, Philadelphia, 1981.
27. W. Platzer, S. Poisel, and E.S.E. Hafez, in E.S.E. Hafez and T.N. Evans, eds., *The Human Vagina*, Elsevier/North-Holland Biomedical Press, Amsterdam, 1978, pp. 39–53.
28. B. Polsky et al., *Lancet*, **1**, 1456 (1988).
29. J.L. Pouly et al., *Hum. Reprod.* **11**, 2085–2089 (1996).
30. C.J.F. Priestley and G.R. Kinghorn, *Br. J. Clin. Pharmacol.* **50**, 331–334 (1966).
31. W.F. Rayburn et al., *Obstet. Gynecol.* **79**, 374–379 (1992).
32. H. Rekers, A.C. Drogendijk, H.A. Valkenburg, and F. Riphagen, *Maturitas* **15**, 101–111 (1992).
33. J.L. Richardson and L. Illum, *Adv. Drug Delivery Rev.* **8**, 341–366 (1992).
34. J.R. Robinson and W.J. Bologna, *Drug Store News / Inside Pharm.* (1990).
35. J.R. Robinson and W.J. Bologna, *J. Controlled Release* **28**, 87–94 (1994).
36. M.J. Rosenberg, W. Rojanaopithayakorn, P.J. Feldblum, and J.E. Higgins, *JAMA, J. Am. Med. Assoc.* **257**, 2308–2312 (1987).
37. D. Ross et al., *Am. J. Obstet. Gynecol.* **177**, 937–941 (1997).
38. M.M. Shaaban, *Maruritas* **23**, 181–192 (1996).
39. D. Sokai and P.L. Hermonat, *Am. J. Public Health* **85**, 737–738 (1995).
40. S.Z. Song, J.R. Cardinal, S.H. Kim, and S.W. Kim, *J. Pharm. Sci.* **70**, 216–219 (1981).
41. R.W. Steger and E.S.E. Hafez, in E.S.E. Hafez and T.N. Evans, eds., *The Human Vagina*, Elsevier/North-Holland Biomedical Press, Amsterdam, 1978, pp. 95–106.

42. P. Stratton and N.J. Alexander, *Infect. Dis. Clin. North Am.* **7**, 841–859 (1993).

43. A.V.G. Taylor, J. Boland, A.L. Bernal, and I.Z. MacKenzie, *Prostaglandins* **41**, 585–594 (1991).

44. C.A. Temple, *Nurs. Times* **90**, 42–43 (1994).

45. A.V.G. Taylor, J. Boland, and I.Z. MacKenzie, *Prostaglandins* **40**, 89–98 (1990).

46. R.W. Tureck, Ph.D. Thesis, University of Pennsylvania Health System, Philadelphia, 1997.

47. G. Wagner and R.T. Levin, in E.S.E. Hafez and T.N. Evans, eds., *The Human Vagina*, Elsevier/North Holland Biomedical Press, Amsterdam, 1978, pp. 121–138.

48. M.E. Watanabe, *Scientist* **11**, 1–4 (1997).

49. L. Zekeng, P.J. Feldblum, R.M. Oliver, and L. Kaptue, *AIDS* **7**, 725–731 (1993).

50. R. Berkow, *Endometriosis: The Merck Manual*, Merck Research Laboratories, Rahway, NJ, 1992, pp. 1809–1813.

51. L. Fedele et al., *Fertil. Steril.* **53**, 155–173 (1990).

52. F. Casanas-Roux et al., *Hum. Reprod.* **11**, 357–363 (1996).

53. H. Adlercreutz and F. Martin, *J. Steroid Biochem.* **13**, 231–244 (1980).

54. S.Z. Song, J.R. Cardinal, S.H. Kim, and S.W. Kim, *J. Pharm. Sci.* **70**, 216–219 (1981).

55. M.J. Rathbone, K.L. Macmillan, C.R. Bunt, and S. Burggraaf, *Adv. Drug Delivery Rev.* **28**, 363–392 (1997).

56. M.J. Rathbone et al., *J. Controlled Release* **53**, 274–282 (1998).

57. M.J. Rathbone et al., *Crit. Rev. Ther. Drug. Carrier Sys.* **15**, 285–380 (1998).

58. J.F. Roche, *Anim. Rep. Sci.* **1**, 145–154 (1978).

59. J.F. Roche and D.J. Prendiville, *Vet. Rec.* **102**, 12–14 (1978).

60. S.E. Curl, W. Durfey, R. Patterson, and D.W. Zinn, *J. Anim. Sci.* **27**, 1189 (1968).

61. J.N. Wiltbank et al., *J. Anim. Sci.* **33**, 600–606 (1971).

62. C.O. Woody and R.A. Pierce, *J. Anim. Sci.* **39**, 903–906 (1974).

63. C. Burrell, J.N. Wiltbank, D.G. LeFever, and G. Rodeffer, *J. Anim. Sci.* **34**, 915 (1972).

64. R.W. Whitman, J.N. Wiltbank, D.G. LeFever, and A.H. Denham, *Proc. West. Sect. Am. Soc. Anim. Sci.* **23**, 280–282 (1972).

65. C. Burrell, J.N. Wiltbank, D.G. LeFever, and G. Rodeffer, *Proc. West. Sect. Am. Soc. Anim. Sci.* **23**, 547–551 (1972).

66. C.O. Woody and F.B. Abenes, *J. Anim. Sci.* **41**, 1057–1064 (1975).

67. J.C. Spitzer, D. Miksch, and J.N. Wiltbank, *J. Anim. Sci.* **43**, 305 (1976).

68. J.C. Spitzer, D.L. Jones, E.D. Miksch, and J.N. Wiltbank, *Theriogenology* **10**, 223–227 (1978).

69. E.D. Miksch et al., *Theriogenology* **10**, 201–221 (1978).

70. R. Rajamahendran, P.C. Laguë, and R.D. Baker, *Anim. Reprod. Sci.* **3**, 271–277 (1980/1981).

71. R. Rajamahendran, P.C. Laguë, and R.D. Baker, *J. Anim. Sci.* **49**, 554–559 (1979).

72. R. Rajamahendran, L. Forgrave, P.C. Laguë, and R.D. Baker, *Can. J. Anim. Sci.* **55**, 787 (1975).

73. S.M.N. Mandiki, J.L. Bister, and R. Paquay, *Small Rumin. Res.* **15**, 265–272 (1995).

74. M.B. Kabadi and Y.W. Chien, *J. Pharm. Sci.* **73**, 1464–1468 (1984).

75. M.B. Kabadi and Y.W. Chien, *Drug Dev. Ind. Pharm.* **11**, 1271–1312 (1985).

76. M.B. Kabadi and Y.W. Chien, *Drug Devel. Ind. Pharm.* **11**, 1313–1361 (1985).

77. Y.W. Chien, in *Novel Drug Delivery Systems: Fundamentals, Developmental Concepts, Biomedical Assessments*, Y.W. Chien, ed., Marce Dekker, New York, 1982, pp. 413–463.

78. R.W. Kelly, K.P. McNatty, G.H. Moore, and M. Gibb, *J. Reprod. Fertil.* **64**, 475–483 (1982).

79. R.W. Kelly and G.H. Moore, *N. Z. Agric. Sci.* **11**, 179–181 (1977).

80. J.C. Haigh, M. Cranfield, and R.G. Sasser, *J. Zoo Anim. Med.* **19**, 202–207 (1988).

81. G.W. Asher et al., *J. Zool.* **215**, 197–203 (1988).

82. G.W. Asher, *J. Reprod. Fertil.* **75**, 521–529 (1985).

83. H.N. Jabbour et al., *Proc. N. Z. Soc. Anim. Prod.* **51**, 147–151 (1991).

84. H.N. Jabbour, G.W. Asher, J.F. Smith, and C.J. Morrow, *J. Reprod. Fertil.* **94**, 353–361 (1992).

85. G.W. Asher et al., *N. Z. Vet. J.* **40**, 8–14 (1992).

86. K.L. Macmillan and G.W. Asher, *Proc. N. Z. Soc. Anim. Prod.* **50**, 123–133 (1990).

87. G.H. Moore and G.M. Cowie, *Proc. N. Z. Soc. Anim. Prod.* **46**, 175–178 (1986).

88. M.W. Fisher et al., *Proc. N. Z. Soc. Anim. Prod.* **46**, 171–173 (1986).

89. G.W. Asher, J.L. Adam, R.W. James, and D. Barnes, *Anim. Prod.* **47**, 487–492 (1988).

90. C.J. Morrow, G.W. Asher, J.F. Smith, and F.A. Veldhuizen, *Proc. N. Z. Soc. Anim. Prod.* **53**, 417–421 (1993).

91. G.W. Asher et al., *Anim. Reprod. Sci.* **33**, 241–265 (1993).

92. H.N. Jabbour, F.A. Veldhuizen, G. Green, and G.W. Asher, *J. Reprod. Fertil.* **98**, 495–502 (1993).

93. G.W. Asher et al., *J. Reprod. Fertil.* **89**, 761–767 (1990).

94. G.W. Asher and J.G.E. Thompson, *Anim. Reprod. Sci.* **19**, 143–153 (1989).

95. C.J. Morrow, G.W. Asher, and K.L. Macmillan, *Anim. Reprod. Sci.* **37**, 159–174 (1995).

96. D.L. Thompson, S.I. Reville, D.J. Derrick, and M.P. Walker, *J. Anim. Sci.* **58**, 159–164 (1984).

97. J.E. Dinger, E.E. Noiles, and M.J.L. Bates, *Theriogenology* **16**, 231–237 (1981).

98. D.L. Thompson, R.A. Goodke, and T.M. Nett, *J. Anim. Sci.* **56**, 668–677 (1983).

99. M.A. Draincort and E. Palmer, *J. Reprod. Fertil.* **32**, 283–291 (1982).

100. M. Lübbecke, E. Klug, H.O. Hoppen, and W. Jöchle, *Reprod. Domest. Anim.* **29**, 305–314 (1994).

101. W. Jöchle, D. Hamm, H. Sieme, and H. Merkt, *Reprod. Domest. Anim.* **26**, 183 (1991).

102. K. Arbeiter, U. Barth, and W. Jöchle, *J. Equine Vet. Sci.* **14**, 21–25 (1994).

103. D.R. Rutten et al., *Vet. Rec.* **119**, 569–571 (1986).

104. A.R. Rao and C. Rao, *Vet. Rec.* **113**, 623–624 (1983).

105. R. Rajamahendran and M. Thamotharam, *Anim. Reprod. Sci.* **6**, 111–118 (1983).

106. R. Rajamahendran, K.N. Jayatilaka, J. Dharmawardena, and M. Thamotharam, *Anim. Reprod. Sci.* **3**, 107–112 (1980).

107. G. Singh, G.B. Singh, R.D. Sharma, and A.S. Nanda, *Theriogenology* **21**, 859–867 (1983).

108. G. Singh, G.B. Singh, R.D. Sharma, and A.S. Nanda, *Theriogenology* **19**, 323–329 (1983).

109. F.I. Hill et al., *Proc. N. Z. Soc. Anim. Prod.* **52**, 25–27 (1992).

110. T.J. Robinson, *Proc. Aust. Soc. Anim. Prod.* **5**, 47–52 (1964).

111. T.J. Robinson, *Nature (London)* **206**, 39–41 (1965).

112. T.J. Robinson, *The Control of the Ovarian Cycle in the Sheep*, Sydney University Press, Sydney, 1967.

113. D.F. Wishart, *Vet. Rec.* **79**, 356–357 (1966).

114. D.F. Wishart, *Vet. Rec.* **80**, 276–287 (1967).

115. D.F. Wishart and B.D. Hoskin, *J. Reprod. Fertil.* **17**, 285–289 (1968).

116. R.E. Mauer, S.K. Webel, and M.D. Brown, *Ann. Biol. Anim. Biochim. Biophys.* **15**, 291–296 (1975).

117. J.F. Roche, *J. Reprod. Fertil.* **43**, 471–477 (1975).

118. J.F. Roche, *Ann. Biol. Anim. Biochim. Biophys.* **15**, 301–302 (1975).

119. J.F. Roche, *J. Reprod. Fertil.* **43**, 471–477 (1975).

120. J.F. Roche, *J. Reprod. Fertil.* **46**, 253–255 (1976).

121. J.F. Roche, *J. Reprod. Fertil.* **46**, 341–345 (1976).

122. J.F. Roche, *Vet. Rec.* **99**, 184–186 (1976).

123. J.F. Roche, D.J. Prenderville, and W.D. Davis, *Vet. Rec.* **101**, 417–419 (1977).

124. R.A.S. Welch, Annual Report of Agricultural Research Division, New Zealand Ministry of Agriculture and Fisheries, 1982–1983, p. 64.

125. R.A.S. Welch et al., *Proc. 10th Int. Congr. Anim. Reprod. Artif. Insem.* 1984, p. 354.

126. A.J. Ritar, P. Ball, T.M. Black, and R.B. Jackson, *Proc. Aust. Soc. Reprod. Biol.* **19**, 26 (1987).

127. A.J. Ritar et al., *Proc. Aust. Soc. Reprod. Biol.* **19**, 27 (1987).

128. A.J. Ritar et al., *Proc. Aust. Soc. Reprod. Biol.* **19**, 28 (1987).

129. N.A. Holt, *Proc. Aust. Soc. Reprod. Biol.* **19**, 34 (1987).

130. D.R. Barnes, A.P. Oakley, K.L. Macmillan, and T.J. Braggins, *Proc. Aust. Soc. Reprod. Biol.* **19**, 62 (1987).

131. R.A.S. Welch, *Proc. Ruakura Farmers' Conf.* **37**, 105–107 (1985).

132. K.L. Macmillan, A.J. Peterson, D.R. Barnes, and S.M. Duncan, *Proc. Endocrinol. Soc. Aust.* **29**, E3 (1986).

133. K.L. Macmillan, V.K. Taufa, D.R. Barnes, and A.M. Day, *Proc. Asian / Aust. Assoc. Anim. Prod.* **4**, 220 (1987).

134. G.F. Duirs et al., *Proc. Aust. Soc. Reprod. Biol.* **19**, 59 (1987).

135. K.L. Macmillan et al., *Proc. Aust. Soc. Reprod. Biol.* **19**, 61 (1987).

136. K.L. Macmillan, V.K. Taufa, and A.M. Day, *Proc. 11th Int. Congr. Anim. Reprod.*, 1988, vol. 4, p. 444.

137. K.L. Macmillan and J.G.E. Pickering, *Proc. 11th Int. Congr. Anim. Reprod.*, 1998, vol. 4, p. 442.

138. S.P. Washburn, H.G. Howard, W. Jöchle, and K.L. Macmillan, *J. Anim. Sci.* **67**, 382 (1989).

139. A.J. Peterson and H.C. Henderson, *J. Reprod. Fertil. Suppl.* **43**, 315 (1990).

140. K.L. Macmillan, S.P. Washburn, H.V. Henderson, and S.F. Petch, *Proc. N. Z. Soc. Anim. Prod.* **50**, 471–472 (1990).

141. K.L. Macmillan and A.J. Peterson, *Anim. Reprod. Sci.* **33**, 1–25 (1993).

142. T.J. Robinson, *Aust. J. Agric. Res.* **21**, 783–792 (1970).

143. A.J. Allison and T.J. Robinson, *J. Reprod. Fertil.* **22**, 515–531 (1970).

144. J. Morgan, R.E. Lack, and T.J. Robinson, in T.J. Robinson, ed., *The Control of the Ovarian Cycle in the Sheep*, Sydney University Press, Sydney, 1967, pp. 195–207.

145. V.W. Winkler, S. Borodkin, S.K. Webel, and J.T. Mannebach, *J. Pharm. Sci.* **66**, 816–818 (1977).

146. C.R. Bunt, M.J. Rathbone, S. Burggraaf, and C. Ogle, *Proc. Int. Symp. Controlled Release Bioact. Mater.* **24**, 145–146 (1997).

See also BIOADHESIVE DRUG DELIVERY SYSTEMS; MUCOSAL DRUG DELIVERY, BUCCAL; MUCOSAL DRUG DELIVERY, INTRAVITREAL; MUCOSAL DRUG DELIVERY, NASAL; MUCOSAL DRUG DELIVERY, OCULAR.

NANOPARTICLES

Fanny De Jaeghere
Eric Doelker
Robert Gurny
University of Geneva
Geneva, Switzerland

KEY WORDS

Applications in therapeutics
Biodistribution
Drug carrier
Drug targeting
Freeze-drying
Long-circulating nanoparticle
Nanocapsule
Nanoparticle
Nanosphere
Physicochemical characterization
Polymer
Preparation methods
Purification
Sterilization
Surface modification

OUTLINE

The challenge of modern drug therapy is the optimization of the pharmacological action of drugs coupled with the reduction of their toxic side effects in vivo. One response is the use of colloidal drug carriers that can provide site-specific or targeted drug delivery combined with optimal drug release profiles. Among these carriers, liposomes and nanoparticles have been the most extensively investigated. In the late seventies, because liposomal formulations started to face some technological limitations including poor stability and low drug entrapment efficiency, polymeric nanoparticles were proposed as alternative drug carriers. Nanoparticles are solid colloidal particles ranging in size from 10 to 1,000 nm. They are made of a macromolecular material which can be of synthetic or natural origin. Depending on the process used for their preparation, two different types of nanoparticles can be obtained, namely nanospheres and nanocapsules. Nanospheres have a matrix-type structure in which a drug is dispersed, whereas nanocapsules exhibit a membrane-wall structure with an oily core containing the drug. Because these systems have very high surface areas, drugs may also be adsorbed on their surface. The general structure and drug association modes of nanoparticles are illustrated in Figure 1 (1).

MANUFACTURE OF NANOPARTICLES

Numerous methods exist for the manufacture of nanoparticles, allowing extensive modulation of their structure, composition, and physicochemical properties. The choice of the manufacturing method essentially depends on the raw material intended to be used and on the solubility characteristics of the active compound to be associated to the particles. Regarding the raw material, criteria such as biocompatibility, the degradation behavior, choice of the administration route, desired release profile of the drug, and finally, the type of biomedical application determine its selection. From these considerations, it is clear that nanoparticle formulation requires an initial and very precise definition of the needs and objectives to be achieved.

Historically, the first methods used to produce nanoparticles were derived from the field of latex engineering developed by polymer chemists. These methods were based on the in situ polymerization of a monomer in various me-

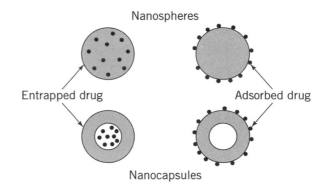

Figure 1. Various types of drug-loaded nanoparticles. *Source: From Ref. 1.*

dia. Pioneers in this field were Birrenbach and Speiser (2) who produced in the early seventies the very first polymerized nanoparticles for pharmaceutical use. Since that time, in situ polymerization-based methods have been widely developed, allowing a great diversity of nanoparticulate formulations to be obtained, as well as a better understanding of the mechanisms involved in these processes. In spite of real technological advances realized in this field, polymerization-based methods may present some drawbacks and limitations, which have made the development of new methods necessary. Thus, alternative methods based on the dispersion of well-characterized preformed polymers or natural macromolecules have been proposed, enlarging the field of possibilities for nanoparticulate formulations. As with polymerization-based methods, these new techniques allow the production of both nanospherical and nanocapsular systems. The most important milestones in the development of nanoparticulate systems are summarized in Table 1 (2–13).

In Situ Polymerization

Nanospheres. Two different approaches have been considered for the preparation of nanospheres by in situ polymerization, depending on whether the monomer to be polymerized is emulsified in a nonsolvent phase (emulsification polymerization), or dissolved in a solvent that is a nonsolvent for the resulting polymer (dispersion polymerization).

General Aspects of Emulsification Polymerization. Depending on the nature of the continuous phase in the emulsion, it is traditional to distinguish conventional emulsification polymerization from inverse emulsification polymerization. In the former case, the continuous phase is aqueous (o/w emulsion), whereas in the latter process it is organic (w/o emulsion). In both cases the monomer is

Table 1. Milestones in the Field of Nanoparticle Manufacture

Year	Milestone	Refs.
Nanoparticles formed by polymerization		
1976	Polyacrylamide nanospheres	2
1976	Poly(methyl methacrylate) nanospheres	3
1979	Poly(alkyl cyanoacrylate) nanospheres	4
1986	Poly(alkyl cyanoacrylate) nanocapsules	5
Nanoparticles from preformed polymers		
1972	Albumin nanospheres by heat denaturation	6
1978	Gelatin nanospheres by desolvation	7
1979	Albumin nanospheres by cross-linking	8
1981	Poly(lactic acid) nanospheres by emulsification-solvent evaporation	9
1986	Poly(lactic acid) nanospheres by direct precipitation	10
1987	Poly(lactic acid) nanocapsules by interfacial deposition	11
1988	Poly(lactic acid) nanospheres by salting-out process	12
1995	Poly(lactic acid) nanospheres by emulsification-diffusion	13

emulsified in the nonsolvent phase with surfactant molecules, leading to the formation of monomer-swollen micelles and stabilized monomer droplets. The polymerization reaction (consisting of a nucleation and a propagation stage) takes place in the presence of a chemical or physical initiator. The energy provided by the initiator creates free reactive monomers in the continuous phase which then collide with the surrounding unreactive monomers and initiate the polymerization chain reaction. The reaction generally stops once full consumption of monomer or initiator is achieved. The drug to be associated to the nanospheres may be present during polymerization or can be subsequently added to the preformed nanospheres, so that the drug can be either incorporated into the matrix or simply adsorbed at the surface of the nanospheres.

Far from being totally elucidated, the mechanism by which the polymeric particles are formed during emulsification polymerization is not as simple as it was first believed, being initially described as a simple polymerization within the stabilized monomer droplets (14). Indeed, it is well established that the particles obtained by emulsification polymerization are generally much smaller (100–300 nm) than the original stabilized monomer droplets in the continuous outer phase (1–10 μm) (15). Other mechanisms, involving sites of nucleation other than the monomer droplets, have been considered to explain the particle formation process (16–19). First, the so-called micellar polymerization mechanism was proposed, involving the swollen-monomer micelles as the site of nucleation and polymerization. Swollen micelles exhibit sizes in the nanometer range and thus have a much larger surface area in comparison with that of the monomer droplets. It was assumed that, once generated in the continuous phase, free reactive monomers would more probably initiate the reaction within the micelles. Being slightly soluble in the surrounding phase, the monomer molecules reach the micelles by diffusion from the monomer droplets through the continuous phase, thus allowing the polymerization to be pursued within the micelles. So, in this case, monomer droplets would essentially act as monomer reservoirs (Fig. 2).

A second mechanism, called the homogeneous nucleation and polymerization process, has been proposed (16–19). If the monomer is sufficiently soluble in the continuous outer phase, the nucleation and polymerization stages can occur directly in this phase, leading to the formation of primary polymer chains called oligomers. In this case, throughout polymer chain growth, both the micelles and the droplets play the role of monomer reservoirs (Fig. 3). When the oligomers have reached a certain length, they precipitate and form primary particles which are stabilized by the surfactant molecules provided by the micelles and the droplets. Depending on the bulk conditions and system stability, the end-product nanospheres are formed either by additional monomer input into the primary particles or by fusion of the primary particles.

Whatever the mechanism involved (droplet, micellar, or homogeneous polymerization) each terminal nanosphere formed by emulsification polymerization usually consists of a large number of polymeric chains (18,19).

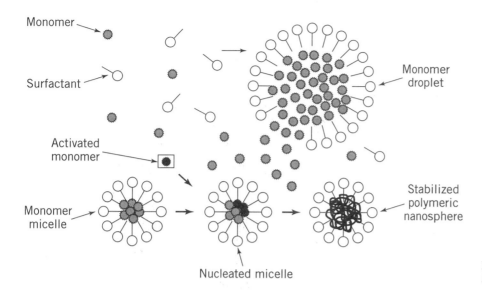

Figure 2. Micellar polymerization mechanism. *Source:* Adapted from Ref. 18.

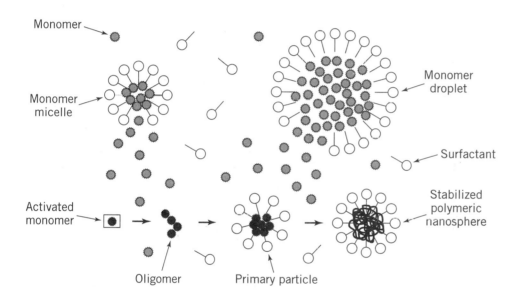

Figure 3. Homogeneous nucleation mechanism. *Source:* Adapted from Ref. 18.

Emulsification Polymerization in an Organic Continuous Phase. According to certain authors (2,20–22), the previously described mechanisms are only applicable when the polymerization process involves an aqueous continuous outer phase. It was assumed that in the case of inverse emulsification polymerization, in which the continuous phase is an organic one, the very water-soluble monomers used in this system cannot diffuse from the micelles through the organic phase because of their very low partition coefficient. As a result, particle formation would only result from the fusion of small nucleated micelles of constant size (Fig. 4). For this reason, this process is generally mentioned as an inverse "microemulsification" polymerization. The resulting nanospheres would contain fewer polymeric chains and a narrower distribution size, in contrast to the particles obtained by conventional emulsification polymerization (20–22). This theory has been debated by Kreuter (16) assuming that, whatever the partition co-

efficient of the monomer, the latter should still be slightly soluble in and diffuse through the organic phase. According to this author the mechanism of polymerization in an inverse emulsion is not qualitatively different from that in a conventional emulsion.

As previously mentioned, the first report concerning the use of nanoparticles for pharmaceutical applications was made by Birrenbach and Speiser in the seventies (2). These earliest nanoparticles were polyacrylamide nanospheres prepared by inverse emulsification polymerization and were intended to incorporate water-soluble antigenic material for vaccination purposes. Typically, water-soluble acrylamide monomers and human immunoglobulin G (IgG) were emulsified in *n*-hexane in the presence of a cross-linker (*N,N'*-methylene bisacrylamide) and large amounts of anionic surfactants (bis-(2-ethylhexyl)-sodium sulfosuccinate and poly(oxyethylene)-4-lauryl ether). The polymerization was initiated by γ-, ultraviolet, or visible light ir-

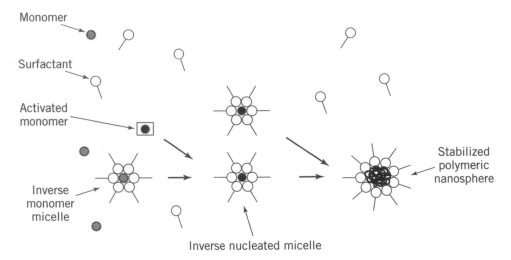

Monomer

Surfactant

Activated monomer

Inverse monomer micelle

Inverse nucleated micelle

Stabilized polymeric nanosphere

Figure 4. Mechanism of inverse emulsification polymerization. *Source:* Adapted from Ref. 18.

radiation, leading to the formation of IgG-loaded polyacrylamide nanospheres in the organic phase. Subsequently, several authors (20–25) used variants of this technique for the production of polyacrylamide nanospheres, but only a few produced nanospheres containing an active substance. Kopf et al. (23) succeeded in entrapping 96% of norephedrine HCl in polyacrylamide nanospheres. Labhasetwar and Dorle (25) produced polyacrylamide nanospheres incorporating metronidazole and primaquine but in this case the entrapment efficiency was low (<6%). In fact, these formulations have not been further developed for medical purpose, due, in particular, to the nonbiodegradable nature of this acrylic material. The use of polyacrylamide nanospheres as vaccine adjuvants is still being considered, but the large amounts of solvents and surfactants required for their production limit somewhat the interest of this application. However, these initial nanoparticle formulations allowed a better understanding of polymerization processes and opened up new prospects in the field of drug targeting.

The inverse emulsification polymerization process was rapidly adapted for the production of biodegradable poly(alkyl cyanoacrylate) (PACA) nanospheres (26–30). In these studies, the drug was dissolved in a small volume of water or hydrophilic solvent (methanol) and emulsified in an organic phase (e.g., isooctane, cyclohexane-chloroform, hexane) in the presence of large amounts of surfactants. Alkylcyanoacrylate monomers were then added directly or dissolved in an organic solvent to the preformed w/o emulsion under stirring. It was initially claimed that due to this subsequent addition of the monomers, particles with a shell-like wall (nanocapsules) were formed, resulting from the interfacial polymerization of monomers at the surface of the water-swollen micelles containing the drug. In fact, on the basis of transmission electron microscopy observations, it was later shown that the presence of nanocapsules was only occasional in the final nanoparticulate suspension and that most of the particles formed during this process were true nanospheres (19,26). Hydrophilic compounds such as doxorubicine (27,29,30), fluorescein (27),

and methylene blue (28), as well as lipophilic compounds such as triamcinolone acetonide (26), were efficiently incorporated into PACA nanoparticles using this technique. As with former polyacrylamide nanospheres, PACA nanoparticles were finally obtained in the form of an organic dispersion containing large amounts of potentially toxic surfactants. In view of their therapeutic use, a tedious and extensive washing of the particles was required, making the overall manufacturing procedure long and difficult. This drawback has placed this process at a disadvantage with respect to polymerization in an aqueous phase for the production of PACA nanospheres.

Emulsification Polymerization in an Aqueous Continuous Phase. A major improvement was the preparation of nanospheres by emulsification polymerization in an aqueous continuous phase using no, or very little, surfactant. In this process, the surfactant acts mainly as stabilizer of the polymerized particles rather than emulsifier. Emulsification polymerization in a continuous aqueous phase is actually the most important method for the production of nanospheres.

A simple emulsification polymerization procedure was proposed in 1982 by Couvreur et al. (4) for the production of biodegradable PACA nanospheres. Since that time, these nanospheres have been the object of the most extensive investigations in the field of submicroscopic polymeric carriers. PACA nanospheres are produced by emulsifying water-insoluble alkylcyanoacrylate monomers in an acidic aqueous phase containing the drug and nonionic surfactants (e.g., poloxamer 188, polysorbate 20) or steric stabilizers (e.g., dextran 70). An anionic micellar polymerization takes place after diffusion of the monomer molecules through the aqueous phase. Once the polymerization is fully completed, the particle suspension is neutralized with NaOH, brought to isotonicity by glucose, and filtered. In contrast to other polymerization systems requiring an energy input that can affect the stability of the incorporated drug, the polymerization here is spontaneously initiated at room temperature by the hydroxide ions present in water, under vigorous stirring. The pH of the medium determines the polymerization rate. The pH has to be acidic in order to prevent excessively rapid polymerization and enable the formation of monodispersed (nonagglomerated) nanoparticles. At pH values below 3, the size of the nanospheres obtained is approximately 200 nm with a narrow size distribution. Nanospheres with diameters as small as 30 nm can be produced by increasing the concentration of the surfactant or the pH of the polymerization medium in the pH range from 1 to 3 (31). Even smaller nanospheres can be obtained using sulfur dioxide as polymerization inhibitor (32). Among other parameters, the pH of the polymerization medium also has a major influence on the molecular weight of the polymer forming the nanospheres. This effect is generally described as being complex and is related to the antagonist action of initiator (OH^-) and terminator (H^+) during the polymerization process. As a result of the termination mechanism by H^+ ions, the molecular weights after anionic polymerization are generally very low and decrease with decreasing pH (33,34). To control the molecular weight of the polymer forming the nanospheres is important given the great influence of this parameter on the degradation rate of the particle, on the resulting drug release kinetic, as well as on the biodistribution of the particles. Consequently, optimization of the polymerization conditions (pH, temperature, stirring rate, type and concentration of monomer, surfactant, stabilizer, and acidifying agent) has been the object of very extensive investigations (33–36). It has been shown that such formulations were very reproducible in term of size and drug content, even after preparation at a semiindustrial level. Since the early patent of Couvreur et al. (4), a wide variety of drugs have been efficiently incorporated into PACA nanospheres. Most of them are hydrophilic and display cytostatic or antibiotic activities (1).

A major advantage of PACA nanospheres is their very rapid elimination from the body, within a few days, as a result of their very rapid degradation in vivo (37). The degradation mechanism of PACA nanospheres in biological conditions is complex. It involves at least two pathways, a chemical process (the so-called formaldehyde-producing pathway) and an enzymatic process, which was shown to be dominant and to occur through the hydrolysis of the ester side chains of the polymer (37–39). The incidence of the resulting degradation products (specially formaldehyde) in vivo is still a matter of debate. Toxic effects have been shown to occur toward a number of cells in vitro, with a clear relationship between the toxicity graduation and the alkyl chain length of the polymer (39–41). PACA nanospheres with long side chains (butyl, isobutyl, and isohexyl cyanoacrylates) generally exhibit a lower toxicity, which is attributed to their slower degradation, compared with nanospheres with short side chains (methyl and ethyl cyanoacrylates) (39,40). In addition, nanospheres with long alkyl chains are generally characterized by higher entrapment efficiencies and, as a result of slower degradation, slower drug release profiles (39). Although the bioacceptability of PACA nanospheres has to be considered carefully, they are actually considered as one of the most promising candidates for drug delivery in humans. A Phase I clinical trial using doxorubicin-loaded PACA nanospheres has been performed and revealed an improvement of the doxo-

rubicin therapeutic index, illustrating the potential of these formulations as drug delivery systems (42).

The acidic nature of the polymerization medium can represent a major drawback when the drug intended to be incorporated into PACA nanospheres is labile at low pH. This problem can be overcome by using slightly different monomers such as the methylidene malonate derivatives. Those monomers have been proposed for the production of nanospheres in polymerization media having higher pH values. Developed on the same basis as alkylcyanoacrylates, alkyl methylidene malonic acid esters present an alkyl oxycarbonyl group instead of a cyano group, which is less electrophilic and thus less reactive in the presence of nucleophilic hydroxide ions (43). Diethyl methylidene malonate monomers were successfully used for the production of nanospheres by anionic polymerization in aqueous media (pH 6.7 to 8.7) (43,44). Unfortunately, poly(diethyl methylidene malonate) nanospheres could not be considered as suitable systemic drug carriers given their demonstrated nonbiodegradability both in vitro and in vivo (43). A new methylidene malonate derivative, methylidene malonate 2.1.2. was designed to overcome the lack of degradation of the former polymeric derivative. Poly(methylidene malonate 2.1.2.) (PMM 2.1.2.) nanospheres could be produced through anionic polymerization at pH values from 4 to 9, with an excellent batch to batch reproducibility in the pH range from 5 to 6 (45,46). In addition to the fact that these newly developed nanospheres may be useful for the incorporation of acid labile drugs, they have also been shown to exhibit satisfactory degradability and erodability (46,47), low in vitro (46,47), and in vivo (48) toxicity as well as a satisfactory shelf life (49). Although the production of drug-loaded PMM 2.1.2. nanospheres has not been described yet, these formulations appear to be promising alternative tools for the intravenous delivery of drugs, as well as good candidates for targeting purposes (50).

Numerous other derivatives have been used to prepare polymerized nanospheres in situ. The production of polyglutaraldehyde, poly(vinyl pyridine), poly(acroleine) and polystyrene nanospheres has been described by different authors (19). Although the lack of biodegradability of these systems compromises their clinical use as drug carriers, they could be potentially useful as adjuvants in vaccines (19).

Dispersion Polymerization in Water for Production of Polymethacrylic Nanospheres. The term *emulsification polymerization* is used when the monomer is emulsified in a nonsolvent by mean of surfactants. In the case of dispersion polymerization, the monomer is no more emulsified but dissolved in an aqueous medium which acts as a precipitant for the polymer to be formed. The nucleation is directly induced in the aqueous monomer solution and the presence of stabilizers or surfactants is not absolutely necessary for the formation of stable nanospheres. This method was developed in the mid-seventies by Kreuter and Speiser (3) for the production of very slowly biodegradable poly(methyl methacrylate) (PMMA) nanospheres. The aim of these authors was to propose a simplified manufacturing procedure based on the method previously developed by Birrenbach and Speiser (2) but avoiding the use of large amounts of organic solvents and surfactants. In this method, water-soluble methyl methacrylate monomers are dissolved in an aqueous medium and polymerized by γ-irradiation (3,51) or by chemical initiation (ammonium or potassium peroxodisulfate) combined with heating to temperatures above 65°C (52,53). In the case of chemical initiation, the aqueous medium must be previously flushed with nitrogen for 1 h in order to remove its oxygen content, which could inhibit the polymerization by interfering with the initiated radicals. Whatever the type of initiation used, oligomers are formed and above a certain molecular weight precipitate in the form of primary particles which may or may not be stabilized by surfactant molecules. Finally, nanospheres are obtained by the growth or the fusion of primary particles in the aqueous phase (Fig. 5).

The possible production of PMMA nanospheres by surfactant-free polymerization is very advantageous because, as previously mentioned, the removal of detergents is generally very cumbersome. Being very slowly biodegradable and biocompatible (54), PMMA nanoparticles have been shown to be an optimal material for vaccination purposes. For this application, initiation by γ-irradiation can be useful for the production of PMMA nanospheres by polymerization in the presence of antigenic material, because it can be carried out at room temperature or below, thus preventing the destruction of these heat-sensitive substances (51). Antigens may be present during polymerization (3,55) but can also be added to the preformed nanospheres (3,53,55,56). The antigenic materials used to produce nanoparticulate PMMA adjuvants were influenza virions (3,55), influenza subunit antigens (53), bovine serum albumin (52,53), and more recently HIV-1 and HIV-2 antigens (56,57). For the particles produced in the presence of influenza virions, a shell-like structure was proposed (55,58). Because of their large dimension ($\sim$80 nm), the virions are more probably coated by a shell of polymerized monomers initially adsorbed at their surface, than strictly incorporated in a polymeric matrix.

Besides PMMA nanospheres, copolymer methacrylic nanospheres can also be produced by the dispersion polymerization process using blends of methyl methacrylate with one or several other acrylic acid derivatives (e.g., hydroxyethyl methacrylate, methacrylic acid, ethylene glycol dimethacrylate, sulfopropylmethacrylate) (53,59–61).

These copolymer nanospheres were developed with the intention of modifying the surface properties of the nanospheres, namely the hydrophilicity but also the charge (61) which are important parameters governing the body distribution of the particles.

Various types of drugs have been linked to PMMA and polymethacrylic nanospheres (1). Rolland (62) performed extensive investigations with doxorubicin-loaded polymethacrylic nanospheres suggesting that, in spite of their very low biodegradability, these particles could be used in humans for cancer treatment using a monthly intravenous injection protocol. Nevertheless, compared with some other colloidal systems, the use of such practically nonbiodegradable particles appears to be very limited, if not precluded when regular therapeutic administration is desired. Essentially suitable as adjuvants for vaccination purpose, PMMA and polymethacrylic nanospheres are also of great value for fundamental studies on the in vitro and in vivo behavior of particles remaining intact in biologic media over extended time periods (59,63–66). In providing general information about the interactions of the nanospheres with cells or opsonins, their biodistribution and bioelimination, these studies allow a better understanding of the mechanisms regulating the biological fate of nanoparticulate drug carriers.

Nanocapsules

PACA Nanocapsules. On the basis of the method proposed by Couvreur et al. (4) for preparing PACA nanospheres, Al Khouri-Fallouh et al. (5) developed a new method leading to the production of nanocapsules, a new type of colloidal carrier with a capsular structure consisting of a polymeric envelope surrounding an oily central cavity. The aim was to produce a nanoparticulate formulation with high entrapment efficiency for lipophilic drugs. This could be hardly achieved with PACA nanospheres prepared by anionic emulsion polymerization because this method required dissolution of the drug in an aqueous polymerization medium, precluding the incorporation of poorly water-soluble compounds.

In the procedure described by Al Khouri-Fallouh et al. (5), the monomer (isobutyl cyanoacrylate) and a lipophilic drug (lomustine, progesterone) are dissolved in an ethanolic phase containing an oil (Myglyol®, Lipiodol®) or a non-

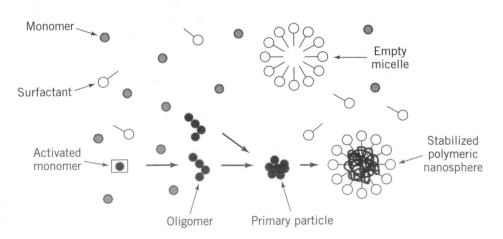

Figure 5. Mechanism of dispersion polymerization. *Source:* Adapted from Ref. 18.

miscible organic solvent (benzylic alcohol). This mixture is slowly injected through a needle into a magnetically stirred aqueous phase (pH 4–10) containing an nonionic surfactant (poloxamer 188). The mixture immediately becomes milky and nanocapsules with a mean diameter of 200–300 nm with a narrow polydispersity are formed. The colloidal suspension can then be concentrated by evaporation under reduced pressure and filtered through sintered glass before redilution with a physiological buffer. Examination by transmission electron microscopy, after negative staining of the particles, demonstrated the existence of a polymeric wall with a mean thickness of about 3 nm (5,67). On the basis of these observations, it was assumed that formation of nanocapsules resulted from the so-called interfacial polymerization mechanism. This mechanism was described as a spontaneous and rapid process: upon mixing with the aqueous phase, ethanol rapidly diffuses out of the organic phase giving rise to spontaneous emulsification of the oil/monomer/drug mixture. Due to their interfacial properties (67), the monomer molecules spontaneously locate at the surface of the oil nanodroplets and, upon contact with aqueous hydroxide anions, immediately polymerize at the water–oil interface, leading to the formation of solid wall-structured particles. The speed of magnetic stirring has no influence on the particle size, which depends solely on the nature and the volume of the oil, and on the volume of the diffusing organic phase (68). The presence of surfactant in the aqueous phase is not necessary for the successful formation of nanocapsules but does guarantee the physical stability of the preparation. For efficient encapsulation, the lipophilic drug must have a partition coefficient which favors its location in the oil, and the oil must then be chosen accordingly (68). Since the early description of this new process, numerous workers have used it as such or with slight modifications to produce nanocapsules incorporating a wide variety of lipophilic drugs with high entrapment efficiencies (1).

Extensive investigations have been performed to determine the influence, on PACA nanocapsule morphology and structure, of parameters such as the nature and pH of the aqueous phase, composition of the organic phase (solvent, oil, monomer), surfactant and emulsification conditions (67,69–72). In particular, in a very interesting study employing freeze-fracture electron microscopy, Fresta and Puglisi (71,72) showed that, depending on the type of organic solvent used for the nanocapsule preparation, heterogeneous systems consisting of a mixture of nanocapsules and nanospheres could be obtained. When protic water-miscible organic solvents such as ethanol, *n*-butanol, or isopropanol were used in the preparation, both types of particles were formed in the suspension, whereas when aprotic water-miscible organic solvents such as acetone and acetonitrile were used, only true nanocapsules were obtained. It was assumed that protic solvents, with a certain nucleophilic character, could give rise to the polymerization of the monomer molecules initially in the organic mixture, before emulsifying it in the aqueous phase. Evidence of initial polymerization in an organic protic phase was supported by the fact that when the monomer was dispersed, for example, in pure ethanol, cloudy suspensions were observed, whereas when it was added to ac-

etone or acetonitrile the resulting solutions remained absolutely clear. On the basis of these observations, Fresta and Puglisi (71,72) assumed that upon contact with the aqueous phase, oligomers, preformed in the protic organic phase, may precipitate and lead to the formation of nanospheres in the final suspension. As to the nanocapsules, they may be formed according to two different mechanisms: (1) by normal polymerization of the monomers at the water–oil interface and (2) by deposition at the interface of the preformed oligomers present in the organic phase (interfacial deposition of a preformed polymer theory). When an aprotic solvent is used, only interfacial polymerization may occur, allowing the production of true nanocapsule suspensions. Accordingly, the use of acetone was shown to provide high-quality nanocapsules, with regular wall thickness and homogeneous size distribution (32).

Slightly different theories have been proposed by other investigators to explain the presence of both nanospheres and nanocapsules in the suspensions prepared with nucleophilic solvents (73,74). Whatever the real nature of the mechanism involved, it clearly appears that when the production of a true nanocapsule formulation is desired, the most suitable conditions of preparation have to be established, especially with regard to the organic solvent to be chosen. In addition, a selective characterization of the resulting particles should be systematically conducted in order to assess the real homogeneity of the system. In good accordance with these considerations, Chouinard et al. (69) described the preparation of poly(isohexyl cyanoacrylate) nanocapsules using an ethanolic oily phase. In order to prevent immediate polymerization in ethanol, the monomer was initially saturated with a polymerization inhibitor (sulfur dioxide) prior to mixing with the ethanolic oily phase. Upon contact with the aqueous phase, sulfur dioxide rapidly diffuses into water, allowing interfacial polymerization to occur and nanocapsules to be formed. Evidence of the homogeneous capsular morphology of the particles was assessed by freeze-fracture microscopy, as well as by density measurements (69).

Several authors have reported the production of nanocapsules by interfacial polymerization of cyanoacrylate monomers using a inverse emulsification polymerization procedure. This technique was used to encapsulate hydrophilic compounds such as doxorubicin (27,29,30), fluorescein (27), or methylene blue (28), as well as the lipophilic drug triamcinolone acetonide (26). In this procedure, the drug was dissolved in a small volume of water (or methanol in the case of triamcinolone acetonide) and emulsified in an organic external phase (e.g., isooctane, hexane) containing a surfactant. Then, an organic solution of cyanoacrylate monomers was added to the preformed w/o emulsion. It was generally assumed that, using this procedure, nanocapsules were formed, resulting from an interfacial polymerization process around the nanodroplets. However, it was showed by Krause et al. (26) by transmission electron microscopy that, in fact, following this procedure, a mixture of nanospheres and nanocapsules was formed, with a predominance of nanospheres. A rational explanation for the formation of nanocapsules is that the polymerization process in some cases is so rapid that an impermeable polymer wall may be formed at the interface, preventing the diffusion of further monomers into the interior of the particles. However, in most cases, the interior of the particles is also polymerized and solid monolithic nanospheres are formed (19). For this reason, this particular technique is sometimes classified in the literature with other related methods allowing the preparation of PACA nanospheres by inverse emulsification polymerization (1,19).

Poly(N^α,N^ϵ-L-lysinediethylterephthaloide) Nanocapsules by Interfacial Polycondensation Using Electrocapillarity Emulsification. Arakawa and Kondo (75) proposed an original technique for the preparation of blood hemolysate–loaded nanocapsules. These hemoglobin containing nanoparticles were intended to be used as artificial red blood cells. Poly(N^α,N^ϵ-L-lysinediethylterephthaloide) nanocapsules containing sheep hemolysate are prepared by interfacial polycondensation of L-lysine with terephthaloyl dichloride in an emulsion made by electrocapillarity. A water phase containing the hemolysate and L-lysine is slowly injected into an organic solution of terephthaloyl dichloride containing a surfactant. During the injection, an electrical potential difference is applied between the two phases. When this potential reaches a certain value (850 V), the interfacial tension is reduced to zero and spontaneous emulsification occurs. The polycondensation between the monomers should be expected to occur exclusively at the water–oil interface, leading to the formation of wall-type nanoparticles. However, formation of true nanocapsules still remains to be proven by electron microscopy analysis (19). In addition, as for other preparation methods implying a w/o emulsion, these particles must be subsequently transferred to an aqueous phase by successive washings.

Dispersion of a Preformed Polymer

As described already, since the early description of polymerization processes for the production of latex in the polymer industry, extensive efforts have been made to adapt this technology for the production of polymeric colloids that meet pharmaceutical requirements. Although real technological advances have been achieved, allowing for example the fulfillment of the submicroscopic size criteria, most of the polymeric carriers prepared by polymerization still encounter major drawbacks (74). With the exception of PACA and recently developed PMM 2.1.2. nanoparticles, most of the carriers produced by polymerization have inadequate biodegradability properties precluding their use for regular therapeutic administration. Only for vaccination purposes can very slowly biodegradable PMMA systems be considered as being suitable adjuvants when achievement of a very prolonged immune response is desired. In addition, due to the multicomponent nature of the polymerization media, it is generally very difficult to predict the molecular weight of the resulting polymerized material. This is a major drawback because the molecular weight greatly influences the biodistribution and release behavior of the polymeric carrier. Another drawback is the possible inhibition of drug activity due to interactions with activated monomers or with the numerous H^+ ions present in anionic polymerization processes. Finally, the main limitation to the use of polymerized carriers is related to the

presence of toxic residues, namely the unreacted monomer, initiator, and surfactant molecules whose elimination requires time-consuming and not always efficient procedures.

In order to circumvent those limitations and extend the manufacturing possibilities for the achievement of biodegradable, well-characterized, and nontoxic nanoparticles, new methods involving the use of already polymerized materials have been developed. These materials include natural macromolecules (biopolymers) and synthetic polymers.

Nanospheres Prepared From Natural Macromolecules. Among the natural macromolecules available for the manufacture of nanospheres, proteins such as albumin, gelatin, legumin, or vicilin, as well as polysaccharides like alginate or agarose have been evaluated (Table 2). These macromolecules have attracted wide interest as biomaterials due to their intrinsic properties of biodegradability and biocompatibility. Of the previously mentioned macromolecules, albumin and gelatin have been the most extensively used. Two main manufacturing techniques have been reported to produce nanospheres from natural macromolecules. The first technique is based on the formation of a w/o emulsion and subsequent heat denaturation or chemical cross-linking of the macromolecule. The second approach involves a phase separation process in an aqueous medium that may be followed by chemical cross-linking (see Table 2). The term cross-linking is used to describe the formation of covalent bonds between the lysine amino groups of proteins and an aldehydic compound, leading to the hardening and stabilization of the formed particles.

Emulsification-Based Methods. The emulsification technique was initially introduced by Scheffel et al. (6) for the production of albumin nanospheres and was later optimized by Gallo et al. (76). In this process, an aqueous solution of albumin is emulsified at room temperature in a vegetal oil (cottonseed oil) and homogenized either by mean of a manual (6) or mechanical high pressure homogenizer (77) or by mean of ultrasonication (76). Once a high degree of dispersion is achieved, the emulsion is added dropwise to a large volume of preheated oil (>120°C) under stirring. This leads to the immediate vaporization of the water contained in the droplets and to the irreversible denaturation of the albumin which coagulates in the form of solid nanospheres (18) (Fig. 6). The suspension is then allowed to cool down at room temperature or in an ice bath. Subsequently, the particles are submitted to several washings using large amounts of organic solvent (e.g., ether, ethanol, acetone) for complete removal of the oil. This purification step represents a main drawback in terms of manufacturing wastes, especially in view of large scale particle production. In addition, the hardening step by heat denaturation may be harmful to heat-sensitive drugs. To circumvent this latter problem, the use of a cross-linking agent was proposed by Widder et al. (8) for the chemical hardening of the albumin nanodroplets. Surprisingly, although the cross-linking agent (2,3-butanedione or formaldehyde) was added only after the washing and resuspension of the system in ether, no coalescence of the soft

Table 2. Main Methods for the Production of Nanospheres from Natural Macromolecules

Macromolecule	Production principle	Hardening procedure[a]	Reference
Albumin	w/o emulsification	HD	6,76
	w/o emulsification	CL	8,78,79
	Phase separation in an aqueous medium		
	By addition of a desolvating agent	CL	7
	By modification of the pH	CL	83
Gelatin	w/o emulsification	CG + CL	80
	Phase separation in an aqueous medium		
	By addition of a desolvating agent	CL	7
	By modification of the temperature	CL	84
Vicilin, legumin	Phase separation in an aqueous medium by modification of the pH	CL	85,86
Alginate	Phase separation in an aqueous medium by addition of divalent cations	PC	82
Agarose	w/o emulsification	CG	81

[a]HD, heat denaturation; CL, cross-linking; CG, cold gelation; PC, polyelectrolytic complexation.

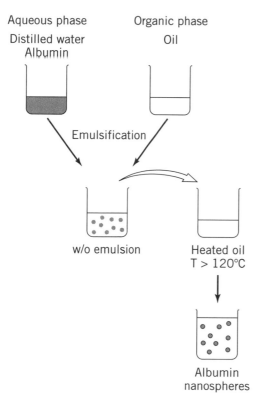

Figure 6. Preparation of nanospheres by thermal denaturation of albumin.

non-cross-linked albumin droplets was reported during these experiments (16).

Another method for preparing cross-linked albumin nanospheres has been proposed using a polymeric phase (ethylcellulose in toluene or hydroxypropylcellulose in chloroform) instead of an oily dispersing phase (78,79). It was asserted that, after purification and drying, the resulting particles were more easily redispersed and also exhibited narrower size distributions compared with particles produced with an oily dispersing phase (79). Nevertheless, with this particular method, the elimination of the polymeric dispersing agent still remains a problem, requiring several washings with large amounts of organic

solvent (78,79), and thus it does not offer any advantage over the previously described techniques.

Gelatin and, more recently, polysaccharidic agarose nanospheres have been produced using an emulsification-based method involving the gelation of the macromolecule (80,81). In this process, the w/o emulsion was cooled (0–5°C) below the gelation temperature of the macromolecule, leading to the complete gelation of the macromolecule droplets. The resulting hydrogel nanospheres were further stabilized by cross-linking (80) or directly washed with an organic solvent (81).

Phase Separation-Based Methods in an Aqueous Medium. As previously mentioned, the main disadvantage of emulsification methods is that large amounts of organic solvents are required to obtain nanospheres free of any oil or dispersing agent residues. Another disadvantage is that it is very difficult to produce small nanospheres (<500 nm) with narrow-size distributions, due to the intrinsic instability of the emulsion prior to hardening by heat or cross-linking (19). Coacervation or controlled desolvation methods have been developed to circumvent these problems. In this case, the particles are formed in an aqueous medium by a phase separation process and are subsequently stabilized by cross-linking with glutaraldehye.

A now traditional method was proposed by Marty et al. (7), based on the desolvation and resolution properties of proteins. In this process, gelatin and albumin nanospheres can be produced by the slow addition of a desolvating agent (neutral salt or alcohol) to the protein solution. Upon this addition, a progressive modification of the protein tertiary structure is induced leading, when a certain degree of desolvation is obtained, to the formation of protein aggregates. The nanospheres are obtained by subsequent cross-linking of these aggregates with glutaraldehyde. To obtain small and monodispersed particles, it is important to maintain the system at a point just before coacervation is initiated (7,16). The addition of the desolvating agent is monitored by turbidimetry measurements of the system and must be stopped as soon as the turbidity increases, otherwise aggregates that are too large will be formed. Alternatively and for optimal monitoring of the process, the system can be desolvated until the coacervation state is reached, and then rapidly reverted to the precoacervated

drug loadings can be achieved, depending on the solubility of the drug in acetone and on the nature of the salting-out agent used. For instance, savoxepine, a neuroleptic drug (pK_a 8.3), was loaded in PLA nanospheres either in the form of a free base or as a salt, the salt being much less soluble in acetone. Two different salting-out agents, magnesium chloride and magnesium acetate, were used, providing an acidic or a basic aqueous phase, respectively (95). The highest entrapment efficiency (95%) was achieved with the formulation involving savoxepine base and a basic aqueous phase (pH 8). Having minimal affinity for the aqueous phase under these conditions, the drug remains within the organic phase, leading to very efficient entrapment in the resulting nanospheres.

Although the salting-out process has proved suitable for the production of large quantities of highly drug-loaded nanospheres, the use of acetone and large amounts of salts may raise some concern about recycling of the salts and about compatibility with active compounds. Recently, Leroux et al. (13) developed a new method called emulsification-diffusion, which involves the use of benzyl alcohol as organic solvent. The originality of this method is based on the partial miscibility of benzyl alcohol with water. An aqueous phase containing a stabilizing agent (PVA or gelatin) is added to a solution of polymer in benzyl alcohol under mechanical stirring. Because benzyl alcohol is only miscible at a ratio of 1:25 (m/v) with water, a two-phase system is formed and an o/w emulsion is obtained upon complete addition of the aqueous phase. Then, the emulsion is diluted with a large amount of pure water in order to overcome the 1:25 miscibility ratio of benzyl alcohol. The precipitation of the polymer occurs as a result of the diffusion of benzyl alcohol into water, leading to the formation of nanospheres. By increasing the percentage of PVA in the external phase, it was possible to produce nanoparticles as small as 70 nm in diameter, whereas with gelatin the smallest nanoparticles obtained had an average size of 700 nm. The polymers used were PLA, PLGA, PCL, and methacrylic acid copolymer Eudragit® S100. Chlorambucil, a cytostatic drug with a very slight water solubility, was successfully entrapped into PLA nanospheres (13). In a recent study, the potential use of other partially water-soluble solvent and stabilizing agents was investigated, and a mechanism based on interfacial phenomena was proposed to explain the formation of nanospheres (96).

Direct Precipitation-Based Method. This technique, proposed by Fessi et al. (10), involves the use of an organic solvent that is completely miscible with the aqueous phase, typically acetone, but ethanol or methanol can also be used. This method allows nanospheres to be obtained without prior emulsification. In this case, the polymer precipitation is directly induced in an aqueous medium (containing or not a surfactant) by progressive addition under stirring of the polymer solution (Fig. 10). After nanoparticle formation, the solvent is removed by vaporization under reduced pressure. The usefulness of this method is limited to drugs that are highly soluble in polar solvents, but only slightly soluble in water (e.g., indomethacin), to avoid extensive loss of the drug during the solvent diffusion (87). In fact, the main limitation of this method is that it is not easy to choose a polymer/

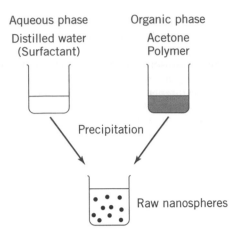

Figure 10. Direct precipitation method.

drug/solvent/nonsolvent system allowing high entrapment efficiencies and production yields. In general, this method has to be carried out with low concentrations of polymer in the organic phase. In this case, polymer dispersion and small particle size can be obtained easily. In contrast, when it is necessary to increase the amount of polymer in the organic phase (e.g., for the preparation of large-scale batches), large aggregates tend to form, resulting in poor production yields (97). Recently, it was shown that changing the nature of the organic phase could reduce the polymer loss. For example, the use of mixtures of acetone and water instead of acetone alone was shown to favor the dispersion of the polymer and to increase the production yield (97).

Nanocapsules Prepared From Synthetic Polymers. Nanocapsules can be produced from synthetic polymers by a very similar procedure to that already described. This method was also proposed by Fessi et al. (11) and is generally called the interfacial deposition technique. It differs from the nanosphere preparation method by the introduction of an oily component into the polymer organic solution. First, the polymer is dissolved in acetone, then a phospholipid mixture (e.g., Epikuron®) and benzyl benzoate are added to this solution. The resulting organic solution is poured into an aqueous phase containing a surfactant (e.g., poloxamer 188) under moderate stirring. Acetone diffuses immediately into the aqueous phase, inducing the deposition and the precipitation of the polymer around the oily droplets (Fig. 11). Once the nanocapsules are formed, acetone is eliminated under reduced pressure. Drugs intended to be encapsulated by this method must have a high solubility in the organic-oily phase, otherwise they diffuse from the oily solution and precipitate in the aqueous medium during particle formation (11,98). For example, as a result of the poor solubility of indomethacin in organic-oily phases, very poorly loaded PLA nanocapsules (0.25% w/v) could be produced with this drug (11). The production of cyclosporin A–loaded nanocapsules made of PCL was recently reported (98). Under optimized conditions, drug loadings as high as 50% could be obtained, but because no data about production yields were provided, it is not clear

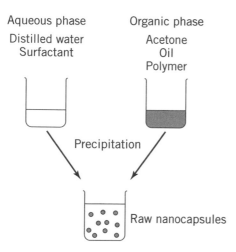

Aqueous phase
Distilled water
Surfactant

Organic phase
Acetone
Oil
Polymer

Precipitation

Raw nanocapsules

Figure 11. Interfacial deposition technique.

whether this procedure is suitable for the production of large-scale batches.

Pharmaceutical Aspects

Because nanoparticles are intended to be used as pharmaceutical dosage forms in humans, among other requirements, they are required (1) to be free of any potentially toxic impurities, (2) to be easy to store and to administer, and finally (3) to be sterile if parenteral use is envisaged.

Purification. Depending on the preparation method, various potentially toxic impurities can be found in the nanoparticulate suspensions including organic solvents, residual monomers, polymerization initiators, electrolytes, surfactants, stabilizers, and large polymer aggregates. The necessity for and degree of purification are dependent on the final purpose of the formulation developed. For example, the stabilizer PVA, frequently used to prepare polyester nanoparticles, is not acceptable for parenteral administration, whereas it is not so critical for oral and ocular administration (87). Although polymer aggregates can be easily removed by simple filtration through sintered glass filters, the removal of other impurities requires more sophisticated procedures. The most commonly reported procedures are gel filtration, dialysis, and ultracentrifugation (7,69,99–101). However, these methods are not entirely satisfactory because they are restricted to the laboratory scale or they are incapable of eliminating molecules with high molecular weight (Table 3). The necessity of finding an efficient purification technique that can be scaled up from an industrial standpoint led to the development of the cross-flow filtration method. In this technique, first used by Allémann et al. (99), the nanoparticle suspension is filtered through membranes, with the direction of the fluid being tangential to the surface of the membranes. In contrast to perpendicular filtration modes, the clogging of the filters is thereby avoided (Fig. 12). Depending on the type of membrane used, either microfiltration or ultrafiltration can be performed. The suspension is submitted to several filtration cycles, while the filtrate, containing components smaller than the pores of the membrane as well as soluble

impurities, is discarded. First, concentration of the suspension is achieved. Then, pure water is added to the system at the same rate as the filtration rate, thus allowing the circulation volume to remain constant (diafiltration step). Simple to use, this technique allows the fast purification of large amounts of nanoparticles with no alteration of their size. For example, it was shown that by using a microfiltration membrane (porosity of 100 nm), approximately 6 g of PLA nanoparticles produced by the salting-out process could be purified in less than 3 hours, with complete removal of the salts and PVA macromolecules (99). In addition, scale-up is feasible by enlarging the filtering surface.

Freeze-drying. If nanoparticles are stored as aqueous suspensions, degradation and/or solubilization of the polymer, drug leakage, drug desorption, and/or drug degradation may occur. Freeze-drying (lyophilization) probably represents one of the most useful methodologies to ensure the long-term conservation of polymeric nanoparticles (102). This technique involves the freezing of the suspension and the subsequent elimination of its water content by sublimation under reduced pressure. After complete desiccation, nanoparticles are obtained in the form of a dry powder that is easy to handle and to store. Freeze-dried nanoparticles are usually readily redispersible in water without modification of their physicochemical properties (1). Because nanoparticles are usually produced with surfactants or stabilizers (e.g., polysorbate, poloxamer, PVA), the residual presence of these compounds generally favors the redispersion of the particles. However, in some specific cases, full redispersion of the system may be difficult to achieve. For example, nanocapsules composed of an oily core surrounded by a tiny polymeric wall tend to aggregate during the freeze-drying process (67,102). Similarly, aggregation problems have been reported with nanospheres made of various materials (102–104). This problem can be circumvented by desiccating these systems in the presence of an appropriate lyoprotective agent such as mono- or disaccharides (e.g., trehalose, sucrose, glucose) (102,104). The mechanisms by which sugars protect nanoparticles during freeze-drying are frequently referred to as "poorly understood" in the literature. However, very detailed and useful information about these mechanisms can be found in a number of articles dealing with lyoprotection and cryoprotection of liposomes and proteins (105,106). In these studies, it is commonly suggested that during freeze-drying sugars may interact with the solute of interest (e.g., liposome, protein) through hydrogen-bonding. As a result, the solute might be maintained in a "pseudo-hydrated" state during the dehydrating step of freeze-drying, and would therefore be protected from damage during dehydration and subsequent rehydration. Such a protective interaction is made possible by the ability of sugars to remain amorphous during freeze-drying (105,106). It has to be kept in mind that the addition of sugar may affect the isotonicity of the final nanoparticulate suspension, and that a subsequent step of tonicity adjustment may be required prior to any parenteral or ocular administration.

Sterilization. Nanoparticles intended to be used parenterally are required to be sterile and apyrogenic. Surpris-

when it was shown that hydrophilicity alone could not provide antiphagocytic effect. Indeed, highly hydrophilic macromolecules or polymers such as dextran, gelatin, or PVA failed to prevent the massive capture of colloidal carriers by phagocytic cells of the MPS (110). It has been proposed that besides hydrophilicity, high flexibility of the coating chains is another major requirement to provide effective protection against opsonization. Among the nonionic hydrophilic polymers fulfilling this criteria, poly(ethylene oxide) (PEO), also commonly named poly(ethylene glycol), has been the most successful synthetic materials used to alter the opsonization process. The protein-resistant nature of PEO chains is attributed to their unique solution properties and molecular conformation in aqueous solutions. Highly hydrated PEO chains produce a surface which is in a liquid-like state and thereby minimizes the tendency to make hydrophobic interactions (117). The considerable flexibility and mobility of the chains result in the sampling of a large number of possible conformations at the particle surface. This highly dynamic state may prevent interactions with approaching opsonins (111,117).

The surface modification of particles using PEO derivatives has been achieved using two main approaches. In a first attempt, preformed particles were modified by physical adsorption of amphiphatic PEO-based compounds including commercially available ethoxylated surfactants and, more recently, new block copolymers with a tailored composition and a R-PEO structure (where R is a synthetic polymer similar to the polymer forming the particle core). In this first approach the PEO moieties are maintained around the particle through intermediate hydrophobic interactions of noncovalent nature. The main concern was to ensure the coating stability, which through the adsorption process was shown to be somewhat limited. As a result, a second approach was recently developed involving use of the previously mentioned R-PEO copolymers and leading to PEO-grafted nanoparticles.

PEO-Coated Nanoparticles. The adsorption approach was initially based on the use of commercially available PEO-based surfactants, such as ethoxylated nonyl phenol (Antarox®), polysorbates (Tween®), PEO-24-laurylether (Brij® 35), perethoxylated castor oils (Cremophor®) (110,118), or different PEO homopolymers (119,120).

However, during the last decade, the most popular and promising coating surfactants have been ethylene oxide (EO) and propylene oxide (PO)-based copolymers, the so-called poloxamers and poloxamines. In contrast to the previously mentioned compounds, these surfactants are available in a very wide range of molecular weights and hydrophilicity, allowing a real modulation of the surface modification and an optimal efficacy in terms of steric stabilization. Poloxamers are linear ABA block copolymers with the general structure $(EO)_n$-$(PO)_m$-$(EO)_n$, where n and m are the numbers of (EO) and (PO) units, respectively. Poloxamines are also ABA block copolymers, but instead of being linear, they present a branched tetrafunctional structure with a central ethylene diamine bridge: $\{(EO)_n$-$(PO)_m\}_2$-N-CH_2-CH_2-N-$\{(EO)_n$-$(PO)_m\}_2$. Due to their original structure, these amphiphatic surfactants attach themselves onto the surface of nanoparticles through their central hydrophobic portion (i.e., $(PO)_m$ or $(PO)_m$ ethylene

diamine, respectively), whereas the hydrophilic $(EO)_n$ portions protrude into the surrounding medium, forming a brush-like coat around the particle. The adsorption of surfactant molecules onto the particles is generally performed by 24 hours' incubation of equal volumes of nanoparticle suspension (2.5%) with a coating solution of the relevant surfactant (0.05–2.5% w/w) (121).

Within the poloxamer and poloxamine series, only polymers with a certain optimal molecular weight and n/m ratios have an ability to provide efficient protection against phagocytosis (121,122). The length of the protruding $(EO)_n$ chains determines the coating layer thickness around the particle and their ability to cover the hydrophobic $(PO)_m$ anchoring parts. Another prerequisite is a sufficient length of the anchoring $(PO)_m$ block to preclude the desorption/displacement of the coat upon contact with dynamic biological environments. In this respect, poloxamer 407 (69 PO and 2×98 EO), poloxamer 338 (54 PO and 2×128 EO) and poloxamine 908 (4×17 PO and 4×119 EO) were shown to be the most efficient products in diverting model polystyrene or PMMA nanoparticles from the liver and in providing extended circulation times after intravenous administration in different animal models (112,122). In some cases, the foregoing polymers led not only to the decrease of particle uptake by liver macrophages but also to the redirection of the nanoparticles to other organs such as the bone marrow, spleen, and lymph nodes (112,122). In addition to the intrinsic properties of the coating material, other parameters such as the particle size (curvature) and the surface characteristics have been shown to strongly influence the final conformation of the adsorbed polymer and thereby its ability to alter the biological fate of the particles (111,121,122). Although the correlations between these different factors have not been clearly established yet, particle size has been shown to affect the adsorbed amount of polymer, the coating layer thickness, as well as the mobility of the protruding PEO chains (111,121,122). Together with the particle size, the nature of the surface to be coated also determines the final conformation of the coating polymer. Until recently, the promising in vivo results achieved with poloxamer- and poloxamine-coated polystyrene and PMMA particles could not be transferred to biodegradable drug carriers. In general, the surface of biodegradable particles is distinctly less hydrophobic than that of nonbiodegradable model particles, leading to no or weak adsorption of poloxamer and poloxamine surfactants to the particle surface (110). In the latter case, a rapid desorption of the coating layer can be expected to occur upon contact with biological media, or even before when a washing procedure is performed to remove excess of free surfactant molecules prior to biological testing. In addition, the production of biodegradable nanoparticles frequently involves the use of a hydrophilic stabilizer (e.g., dextran or PVA) whose residual presence on the particle surface can further inhibit surfactant adsorption (123,124). As a result, attempts to provide a steric protection to biodegradable particles using poloxamers and poloxamines have usually failed (111,123,124). Recently, these surfactants were used to stabilize PLGA nanoparticles prepared by a emulsifier-free nanoprecipitation method (125,126). In vitro, different particle uptake and protein resistance abilities were observed between PLGA and polystyrene model nanoparticles modified in the same manner. This was attributed to distinct conformations of the coating layer on the two different surfaces. However, following intravenous administration to rats, PLGA-coated nanoparticles were shown to exhibit slightly prolonged circulation times and reduced accumulation in liver and spleen, comparable, surprisingly, to that obtained with polystyrene nanoparticles tested in parallel that had been modified in the same manner. Furthermore, when the PLGA-coated particles were washed of excess surfactant before intravenous administration, prolonged circulation times, although slightly reduced, were still observed. A relative stability of the coatings could obviously be achieved in this study. Although this point was not discussed by the authors, this might be partly explained by the absence of emulsifier in the preparation process.

New amphiphilic R-PEO diblock copolymers were recently proposed for the advantageous replacement of the surfactants previously used. The advantage of the R-PEO copolymers over the poloxamers and poloxamines is in replacing the poly(propylene oxide) (POP) moiety of the latter polymers with a biodegradable and biocompatible R chain. Indeed, the R moiety can be chosen among the family of the hydrophobic polymers generally used to produce biodegradable nanoparticles. In addition to its safe nature, the R part of the R-PEO copolymers is expected to be a better anchor group when adsorbed onto a surface of a similar nature. These polymeric materials are generally synthesized by ring-opening polymerization or by melt condensation, with tailored molecular weights and R/PEO ratios (127,128). In a recent study, a PLA-PEO block copolymer was adsorbed onto both PLGA and polystyrene nanoparticles (129). Following intravenous administration into rats, the PLGA modified particles were shown to exhibit extended circulation levels, whereas the coated polystyrene particles, after one hour of effective blood circulation, were suddenly massively taken up by the MPS. These distinct behavior patterns of the two systems have been attributed to a difference in the stability of the PLA-PEO coatings on polystyrene and PLGA nanoparticles, the affinity of the PLA anchor moiety presumably being higher for the PLGA surface than for that of polystyrene.

PEO-Grafted Nanoparticles. It is evident from results with both model nonbiodegradable and biodegradable systems that the stability of the coating layer is an essential feature in modifying particle interaction with the biological environment. Although the adsorption approach undoubtedly provided information on the in vivo behavior of sterically stabilized nanoparticles, the relative unreliability of the resulting steric barrier was soon considered a limitation, especially in terms of interpreting the results. Theoretically, whatever the affinity between the surface and the coating material, the desorption of the latter is always possible in vivo.

The introduction of novel R-PEO block copolymers provided a very interesting alternative to the adsorption approach for surface modification. As a matter of fact, due to their peculiar amphiphatic structure and composition, these copolymers can be used as the main material to produce, in a single-step procedure, nanoparticles with the R

blocks forming the central core and the PEO blocks forming a hydrophilic shell covalently linked to the core. Recently, several authors reported the production of PEO-grafted nanoparticles using emulsification-solvent evaporation, direct precipitation, or the salting-out process. In these procedures, the R-PEO copolymer is dissolved in an organic phase which is subsequently mixed with an aqueous phase. Due to their high affinity for the aqueous phase, the PEO blocks are presumed to migrate to the water interface, whereas the hydrophobic R blocks remain within the nanodroplets and subsequently form the solid core of the particles after organic solvent removal. So far the copolymers used have been PLA-, PLGA-, PCL- and poly(sebacic acid)-PEO diblock copolymers (104,115,128,130–136). The resulting PEO-grafted nanoparticles exhibited sizes between 100 and 300 nm. It has to be emphasized that, in most studies, the particle size was determined directly after purification of the raw nanoparticle suspensions, avoiding the possible effects of a freeze-drying step on the resuspension ability of the PEO surface-modified nanoparticles. It was shown recently that the presence of PEO at the nanoparticle surface could severely impair the redispersion of the freeze-dried particles after rehydration (104). This effect may be attributed to the well-known tendency of PEO to crystallize during freeze-drying (106,137) and can be circumvented using an appropriate lyoprotectant additive (e.g., trehalose) (104,106,137). It appears that the use of a lyoprotectant additive should be systematically considered when PEO surface-modified nanoparticles are intended to be freeze-dried.

The blood clearance and biodistribution of the R-PEO based systems have been studied (Table 4). It was demonstrated that the protective effect of PEO depends on both the chain length and the surface density of the PEO chains, although it is still not clear which parameter is the most dominant (104,111). Nevertheless, results from the literature indicate that, above a certain threshold, increase of the PEO density no longer prevents phagocytosis (111,133). Similarly, there appears to be an optimal chain length (around 2,000 Da) that is necessary to achieve efficient protection (111,129). To further improve the performance of PEO-coated nanoparticles, new copolymers presenting more than one PEO block have been recently proposed (128,138). These so-called R-(PEO)$_n$ multiblock copolymers would allow the production of nanospheres with optimal PEO surface-densities.

Various drugs were successfully entrapped into PEO-grafted nanospheres such as lidocaine (128,131), prednisolone (128), ibuprofen (115), as well as oligonucleotides (139). The entrapment efficiency and in vitro drug-release patterns were shown to depend strongly on the chemical nature of the hydrophobic core, as well as the molecular weight and surface density of the hydrophilic PEO chains (128). The fact that the PEO chains might be involved in the release process was unexpected for the authors. However, some studies performed on various PLA/PLGA-PEO copolymers have shown that the PEO segments can greatly influence the physical properties of the polymer, such as its degradation behavior and its degree of swelling and permeability in water (140,141). Therefore, depending

Table 5. Principal Techniques for the Physicochemical Characterization of Nanoparticles

Parameter	Technique	Reference
Particle size and morphology	Transmission electron microscopy	19,110,149
	Scanning (electron, force, tunneling) microscopy	19,131,149,151
	Freeze-fracture electron microscopy	19,72,128,149
	Photon correlation spectroscopy	19,110,149
Drug content		19,149
In vitro drug release		19,149,150
Molecular weight	Gel permeation chromatography	19,149,152
Crystallinity	X-ray diffraction	19,131,149
	Differential scanning calorimetry	19,128,131,149
Surface charge	Zeta potential measurement	19,60,110,143,149
Surface hydrophobicity	Hydrophobic interaction chromatography	19,60,110,143
	Contact angle measurement	19,110,153
	Rose Bengal binding	60,110
Surface chemical analysis	Secondary ion mass spectrometry	19,110,149
	X-ray photoelectron spectroscopy	19,128,149,152
	Nuclear magnetic resonance	128,143,152
	Fourier transform infrared spectroscopy	143
Protein adsorption	Two-dimensional polyacrylamide gel electrophoresis	126,154,155

and *Salmonella typhimurium* infections has been demonstrated in numerous studies, both in cell cultures and in mouse models (19,156). The effective uptake of ampicillin-loaded nanoparticles was demonstrated in murine macrophages by confocal and transmission electron microscopy studies. In addition, the authors reported that the nanoparticles were localized in the same vacuoles as the infecting bacteria (158).

Nanoparticles also hold promise as drug carriers for the treatment of parasitic infections such as visceral leishmaniasis. This infection is caused by *Leishmania donovani*, an intracellular parasite of the MPS. Most of the drugs usually used to treat this infection (e.g., primaquine, dehydroemetine) exert, apart from the desired activity, very toxic and adverse side effects. The binding of these drugs to various types of nanoparticles was shown to significantly increase their therapeutic index as a result of passive targeting to the MPS (19,159). Surprisingly, it was shown that unloaded PACA nanoparticles exhibited a significant antileishmanial activity on their own. In fact, it appeared that PACA nanoparticles could induce an activation of the respiratory burst in macrophages leading to the production of toxic oxygen metabolites (19,156). It is reasonable to think that this immunomodulation activity of plain nanoparticles may open interesting perspectives not only in the field of parasitic infections, but also in the treatment of other infectious or tumoral diseases.

In the field of viral infections, a very important challenge is the targeting of human immunodeficiency virus (HIV)-infected macrophages. Indeed, it is now well established that macrophages of the MPS play an important role in the immunopathogenesis of HIV infection by acting as a reservoir for the virus and its dissemination throughout the body (19). Therefore, nanoparticles represent an interesting system for the specific transport of antiviral agents displaying poor selectivity and/or short plasma half-life. Recently, PACA nanoparticles loaded with the protease inhibitor saquinavir were shown to be effective in HIV-infected human macrophage cultures (160). In another

study, azidothymidine bound to PACA nanoparticles was successfully targeted into macrophage-rich organs in rats (161). These initial promising results suggest that new perspectives in the treatment of HIV-related diseases may be open. Substances whose development has been halted because of their unfavorable pharmacokinetic properties could be made efficient and available, using nanoparticulate technology.

Peroral Administration

Delivery of Poorly Absorbed Drugs. Some authors have supported the idea that nanoparticles may improve the bioavailability of peptide or protein drugs administered orally. The rationale for this approach is that nanoparticles can protect these labile drugs from extensive enzyme degradation in the gastrointestinal tract (GIT) and enhance their absorption (1) by optimizing their interaction with the absorption site in the gut wall or (2) by directly transporting them through the intestinal mucosa to the systemic circulation.

Precursors in this field, Maincent et al. (162) reported that the relative peroral bioavailability of vincamine in rabbits was considerably increased when this drug was associated with PACA nanoparticles. Later, Michel et al. (163) found that insulin encapsulated in PACA nanocapsules reduced glycemia by 50–60%, whereas free insulin did not affect glycemia when administered orally to diabetic rats. This effect was attributed to the protection of insulin from proteolytic degradation. It was also suggested that this effect could result from the retarded passage of intact nanocapsules through the rat mucosa (163). Although experimental evidence of such a mechanism was found in rodents, whether or not it plays a significant role in increasing the bioavailability of drugs is still a controversial issue. In fact, in many studies, the passage of nanoparticles across the gastrointestinal mucosa was shown to be very low (2–3% of the injected dose), leading to the conclusion that only very potent drugs would be able to exert their activity by this specific route (1,164). In fact, the most probable mechanisms by which nanoparticles increase the oral bioavailability of drugs is by protecting them against degradation and by releasing them in the GIT in a way that favors their absorption. For example, in a study by Lenaerts et al. (165), the peroral efficacy of PACA nanoparticles loaded with vincamine was attributed to the bioadhesive behavior of the particles, allowing the slow release of the drug close to its absorption window and its subsequent diffusion into the vascular compartment. Similarly, Mathiowitz et al. (166) reported enhanced oral bioavailability for model proteins and gene (insulin, dicumarol, plasmid DNA) encapsulated into biologically adhesive nanoparticles made of polyanhydride copolymers of fumaric acid and sebacic acid. The latest developments in the field of bioadhesive particulate systems, involving for example the use of lectins as specific bioadhesive moieties, are described in the literature (167,168). Recently, it was demonstrated by our group that pH-sensitive nanoparticles could significantly increase the bioavailability of poorly water-soluble HIV-protease inhibitors in mice and dogs (169). These formulations are made of polymethacrylic copolymers which rapidly dissolve and release the poorly water-soluble drug at a specific level of the GIT. It was suggested that this rapid and specific release, combined with the very high level of dispersion provided by the nanoparticulate formulation, favored the solubilization of the drug in the intestinal fluid, resulting in a positive impact on drug absorption.

Delivery of Vaccines. As previously mentioned, although restricted, particulate uptake does take place in the intestinal mucosa (164). This uptake was shown to occur mainly in the lymphoid regions of the intestine called the Peyer's patches, through the action of specialized epithelial cells, called M cells. These cells play a determining role in the sampling and transport of luminal antigens into lymphoid tissues for immunologic surveillance and initiation of appropriate immunologic response. It is generally accepted that limited doses of antigen are sufficient to induce an efficient immunization. Thus, it has been postulated that the use of nanoparticles would be profitable for the oral delivery of antigens, because of their ability to control the release of proteins and to protect them from enzymatic degradation in the GIT. Biodegradable PACA nanoparticles have been shown to enhance the secretory immune response after their oral administration in association with ovalbumin in rats (170). PMMA nanoparticles appear to be promising nanoparticulate systems for this application. The very slow degradation rate (30–40% per year) of these particles seems to be particularly appropriate for vaccine purposes, because prolonged contact between the antigen and the immunocompetent cells favors the persistence of immunity. Factors affecting the efficacy of the immunoparticles include particle size, hydrophobicity, and the presence or absence of surface ligands. Indeed, by associating targeting agents such as MAb specific from M cells, it may be possible to increase the levels of absorption of nanoparticle vaccines and therefore the immune response (171). Coupled with advances in molecular biology, immunology, and virology, controlled delivery nanoparticulate systems may be the next generation of effective vaccines in the field of oral immunization.

Other Routes of Administration

Besides the previously described main applications, nanoparticles can be considered for the intramuscular and subcutaneous routes. Although these routes have been so far rarely employed with nanoparticles, they may present some advantages in the attempt to prolong the plasma level of drugs, to protect them from enzymatic degradation or to reduce their irritant effect when applied intramuscularly. Depending on the rate of release which is desired for the drug, PACA or polylactide (PLA, PLGA) nanoparticles appear to be particularly suitable for these routes, due to their particular and controllable degradation properties (1,172–174). Due to their very slow biodegradation rate, PMMA nanoparticles are very attractive for vaccine purposes using the intramuscular or subcutaneous routes. These nanoparticles were shown to exhibit very powerful adjuvant properties for a number of antigens either trapped in the polymer or adsorbed onto the particle surface (175) (see also "Dispersion Polymerization in Water for Production of Polymethacrylic Nanospheres").

Another possible route of administration for nanoparticles is their topical application to the eye. The use of nanoparticles by the ocular route has been investigated for the treatment of chronic diseases such as glaucoma, following the observation that various types of nanoparticles tend to adhere to the ocular epithelial surface. As a result, several authors have tried to take advantage of this prolonged residence time of nanoparticles, because most of the conventional ophthalmologic formulations failed so far in providing sufficient drug bioavailability (176). The polymers that seem to have the best potential for this application are PACA, PLGA, and PCL. They have been used in the form of either nanospheres or nanocapsules. Because of their low viscosity in suspension, these systems can be administered as easily as eye-drops with the advantage of having a reservoir-like behavior, that is, able to deliver the drug progressively (176–178, as well as MUCOSAL DRUG DELIVERY, OCULAR).

CONCLUSION

Nanoparticles represent very promising drug delivery systems which can be considered for a very wide range of applications. Optimization of earlier polymerization procedures combined with the development of new procedures using well-characterized and biodegradable polymeric materials has enabled the development of nanoparticulate systems with increased acceptance and potential. Although the entrapment of hydrophilic compounds (e.g., proteins, DNA, oligonucleotides) still faces some limitations, the many possible variations in structure and type of nanoparticles allow the efficient entrapment of a great number of molecules. The technology of nanoparticles being now quite well mastered, the main objective is the improvement of their targeting properties following intravenous administration. Although the massive uptake of nanoparticles by the MPS can be very advantageous for the treatment of diseases associated to this system, the targeting to sites other than the MPS remains an exciting and major challenge. Several strategies have been developed to achieve this goal, relying on the considerable progress made in the field of nanoparticle characterization and the growing understanding of their in vivo behavior. The strategy that is actually gaining a widespread interest is based on the design of nanoparticules with tailored surface characteristics. More than ever, the achievement of pharmaceutical nanoparticle formulations for human use depends on the successful exploitation of multidisciplinary knowledge.

BIBLIOGRAPHY

1. E. Allémann, R. Gurny, and E. Doelker, *Eur. J. Pharm. Biopharm.* **39**, 173–191 (1993).
2. G. Birrenbach and P.P. Speiser, *J. Pharm. Sci.* **65**, 1763–1766 (1976).
3. J. Kreuter and P.P. Speiser, *Infect. Immun.* **13**, 204–210 (1976).
4. U.S. Pat. 4,329,332 (May 11, 1982), P. Couvreur, M. Roland, and P. Speiser.
5. N. Al Khouri-Fallouh et al., *Int. J. Pharm.* **28**, 125–132 (1986).
6. U. Scheffel, B.A. Rhodes, T.K. Natarajan, and H.N. Wagner, *J. Nucl. Med.* **13**, 498–503 (1972).
7. J.J. Marty, R.C. Oppenheim, and P. Speiser, *Pharm. Acta Helv.* **53**, 17–23 (1978).
8. K. Widder, G. Flouret, and A.E. Senyei, *J. Pharm. Sci.* **68**, 79–82 (1979).
9. R. Gurny, N.A. Peppas, D.D. Harrington, and G.S. Banker, *Drug Dev. Ind. Pharm.* **7**, 1–25 (1981).
10. Fr. Pat. 2,608,988 (December 31, 1986), H. Fessi, J.P. Devissaguet, F. Puisieux, and C. Thies (to Centre National de la Recherche Scientifique).
11. H. Fessi et al., *Int. J. Pharm.* **55**, R1–R4 (1989).
12. U.S. Pat. 4,968,350 (November 6, 1990), C. Bindschaedler, R. Gurny, and E. Doelker (to the inventors).
13. J.C. Leroux, E. Allémann, E. Doelker, and R. Gurny, *Eur. J. Pharm. Biopharm.* **41**, 14–18 (1995).
14. D.P. Durbin, M.S. El-Aasser, G.W. Poehlein, and J.W. Vanderhoff, *J. Appl. Polym. Sci.* **24**, 703–707 (1979).
15. J.W. Vanderhoff and S. El-Aasser, in H.A. Lieberman, M.M. Rieger, and G.S. Banker, eds., *Pharmaceutical Dosage Forms: Dispersed Systems*, Dekker, New York, 1988, pp. 93–149.
16. J. Kreuter, *Pharm. Acta Helv.* **58**, 196–208 (1983).
17. J.W. Vanderhoff, *J. Polym. Sci., Polym. Symp.* **72**, 161–198 (1985).
18. C. Vauthier-Holtzscherer et al., *S. T. P. Pharma. Sci.* **1**, 109–116 (1991).
19. J. Kreuter, in J. Kreuter, ed., *Colloidal Drug Delivery Systems*, Dekker, New York, 1994, pp. 219–343.
20. F. Candeau and Z. Zekhnini, *Macromolecules* **19**, 1895–1902 (1988).
21. C. Holtzscherer, J.P. Durand, and F. Candeau, *Colloid Polym. Sci.* **265**, 1067–1074 (1987).
22. M.T. Carver et al., *J. Phys. Chem.* **93**, 4867–4873 (1989).
23. V.H. Kopf, R.K. Joshi, M. Soliva, and P. Speiser, *Pharm. Ind.* **39**, 993–997 (1977).
24. I. Sjöholm and P. Ekman, *J. Pharmacol. Exp. Ther.* **211**, 656–662 (1979).
25. V.D. Labhasetwar and A.K. Dorle, *J. Controlled Release* **12**, 113–119 (1990).
26. H.-J. Krause, A. Schwarz, and P. Rohdewald, *Drug Dev. Ind. Pharm.* **12**, 527–552 (1986).
27. M.S. El-Samaligy, P. Rohdewald, and H.A. Mahmoud, *J. Pharm. Pharmacol.* **38**, 216–218 (1986).
28. M.R. Gasco and M. Trotta, *Int. J. Pharm.* **29**, 267–268 (1986).
29. R. Carpignano, M.R. Gasco, and S. Morel, *Pharm. Acta Helv.* **66**, 28–32 (1991).
30. M.R. Gasco, S. Morel, and I. Viano, *Pharm. Acta Helv.* **66**, 47–49 (1991).
31. B. Seijo, L. Roblot-Treupel, and P. Couvreur, *Int. J. Pharm.* **62**, 1–7 (1990).
32. V. Lenaerts et al., *J. Pharm. Sci.* **78**, 1051–1052 (1989).
33. S.J. Douglas and S.S. Davis, *Br. Polym. J.* **17**, 339–342 (1985).
34. G. Puglisi et al., *J. Microencapsul.* **10**, 353–366 (1993).
35. S.J. Douglas, L. Illum, S.S. Davis, and J. Kreuter, *J. Colloid Interface Sci.* **101**, 149–158 (1984).
36. L. Vansnick, P. Couvreur, D. Christiaens-Leyh, and M. Roland, *Pharm. Res.* **1**, 36–41 (1985).
37. L. Grislain et al., *Int. J. Pharm.* **15**, 335–345 (1983).
38. V. Lenaerts et al., *Biomaterials* **5**, 65–68 (1984).
39. P. Couvreur and C. Vauthier, *J. Controlled Release* **17**, 187–198 (1991).
40. S. Maassen, E. Fattal, R.H. Müller, and P. Couvreur, *S. T. P. Pharma. Sci.* **3**, 11–22 (1993).
41. R. Zange and T. Kissel, *Eur. J. Pharm. Biopharm.* **44**, 149–157 (1997).
42. J. Kattan et al., *Invest. New Drugs* **10**, 191–199 (1992).
43. J. De Keyser, J.H. Poupaert, and P. Dumont, *J. Pharm. Sci.* **80**, 67–70 (1991).
44. T.K.M. Mbela, J.H. Poupaert, and P. Dumont, *Int. J. Pharm.* **79**, 29–38 (1992).
45. F. Lescure et al., *Proc. Int. Symp. Controlled Release Bioact. Mater.* **18**, 325–326 (1991).
46. F. Lescure et al., *Pharm. Res.* **11**, 1270–1277 (1994).
47. P. Breton et al., in G. Gregoriadis, ed., *Targeting of Drugs*, Plenum, New York, 1994, pp. 161–172.
48. P. Breton et al., *Proc. Int. Symp. Controlled Release Bioact. Mater.* **21**, 608–609 (1994).
49. D. Roy et al., *Int. J. Pharm.* **148**, 165–175 (1997).
50. P. Breton et al., *Eur. J. Pharm. Biopharm.* **43**, 95–103 (1996).
51. J. Kreuter and H.J. Zehnder, *Radiat. Eff.* **35**, 161–166 (1978).
52. J. Kreuter et al., *Vaccine* **4**, 125–129 (1986).
53. J. Kreuter et al., *Vaccine* **6**, 253–256 (1988).
54. J. Kreuter, *Methods Enzymol.* **112**, 129–138 (1985).
55. J. Kreuter and P.P. Speiser, *J. Pharm. Sci.* **65**, 1624–1627 (1976).
56. F. Stieneker, J. Kreuter, and J. Löwer, *AIDS* **5**, 431–435 (1991).
57. J. Kreuter, F. Stieneker, and J. Löwer, *Proc. Int. Symp. Controlled Release Bioact. Mater.* **18**, 211–218 (1991).
58. J. Kreuter, *Pharm. Acta Helv.* **58**, 242–250 (1983).
59. A. Rolland, B. Collet, R. Le Verge, and L. Toujas, *J. Pharm. Sci.* **78**, 481–484 (1989).

60. G. Lukowski, R.H. Müller, B.W. Müller, and M. Dittgen, *Int. J. Pharm.* **84**, 23–31 (1992).

61. K. Langer et al., *Int. J. Pharm.* **137** 67–74 (1996).

62. A. Rolland, *Int. J. Pharm.* **54**, 113–121 (1989).

63. A. Rolland et al., *J. Immunol. Methods* **96**, 185–193 (1987).

64. J.-Y. Cherng et al., *Pharm. Res.* **13**, 1038–1042 (1996).

65. S.D. Tröster et al., *J. Controlled Release* **20**, 247–260 (1992).

66. G. Borchard and J. Kreuter, *Pharm. Res.* **13**, 1055–1058 (1996).

67. N. Al Khouri et al., *Pharm. Acta Helv.* **61**, 274–281 (1986).

68. F. Puisieux et al., S. Dumitriu, ed., *Polymeric Biomaterials*, Dekker, New York, 1994, pp. 749–794.

69. F. Chouinard et al., *Int. J. Pharm.* **72**, 211–217 (1991).

70. F. Chouinard, S. Buczkowski, and V. Lenaerts, *Pharm. Res.* **11**, 869–874 (1994).

71. G. Puglisi, M. Fresta, G. Giammona, and C.A. Ventura, *Int. J. Pharm.* **125**, 283–287 (1995).

72. M. Fresta et al., *Biomaterials* **17**, 751–758 (1996).

73. M. Gallardo et al., *Int. J. Pharm.* **100**, 55–64 (1993).

74. P. Couvreur, G. Couarraze, J.P. Devissaguet, and F. Puisieux, in S. Benita, ed., *Microencapsulation, Methods and Industrial Applications*, Dekker, New York, 1996, pp. 183–211.

75. M. Arakawa and T. Kondo, *J. Pharm. Sci.* **70**, 354–357 (1981).

76. J.M. Gallo, C.T. Hung, and D.G. Perrier, *Int. J. Pharm.* **22**, 63–74 (1984).

77. S. Winoto-Morbach and W. Müller-Ruchholtz, *Eur. J. Pharm. Biopharm.* **41**, 55–61 (1995).

78. Y. Akasaka et al., *Drug Des. Delivery* **3**, 85–97 (1988).

79. M. Roser and T. Kissel, *Eur. J. Pharm. Biopharm.* **39**, 8–12 (1993).

80. T. Yoshioka, M. Hashida, S. Muranishi, and H. Sezaki, *Int. J. Pharm.* **81**, 131–141 (1981).

81. N. Wang and X.S. Wu, *Pharm. Dev. Technol.* **2**, 135–142 (1997).

82. M. Rajaonarivony et al., *J. Pharm. Sci.* **82**, 912–917 (1993).

83. W. Lin et al., *J. Drug Target.* **1**, 237–243 (1993).

84. M.S. El-Samaligy and P. Rohdewald, *J. Pharm. Pharmacol.* **35**, 537–539 (1983).

85. I. Ezpeleta, J.M. Irache, J. Gueguen, and A.M. Orecchioni, *J. Microencapsul.* **14**, 557–565 (1997).

86. T. Mirshahi, J.M. Irache, J. Gueguen, and A.M. Orecchioni, *Drug Dev. Ind. Pharm.* **22**, 841–846 (1996).

87. M.J. Alonso, in S. Cohen and H. Bernstein, eds., *Microparticulate Systems for the Delivery of Proteins and Vaccines*, Dekker, New York, 1996, pp. 203–242.

88. S.J. Holland, B.J. Tighe, and P.L. Gould, *J. Controlled Release* **4**, 155–180 (1986).

89. A. Göpferich, *Eur. J. Pharm. Biopharm.* **42**, 1–11 (1996).

90. U.S. Pat. 4,177,177 (December 4, 1979), J.W. Vanderhoff, M.S. El-Aasser, and J. Ugelstadt (to the inventors).

91. M.C. Julienne, M.J. Alonso, J.L. Gómez Amoza, and J.P. Benoit, *Drug Dev. Ind. Pharm.* **18**, 1063–1077 (1992).

92. M.D. Blanco and M.J. Alonso, *Eur. J. Pharm. Biopharm.* **43**, 287–294 (1997).

93. T. Niwa et al., *J. Controlled Release* **25**, 89–98 (1993).

94. E. Allémann, R. Gurny, and E. Doelker, *Int. J. Pharm.* **87**, 247–253 (1992).

95. E. Allémann, J.C. Leroux, R. Gurny, and E. Doelker, *Pharm. Res.* **10**, 1732–1737 (1993).

96. D. Quintanar-Guerrero, H. Fessi, E. Allémann, and E. Doelker, *Int. J. Pharm.* **143**, 133–141 (1996).

97. O. Thioune, H. Fessi, J.P. Devissaguet, and F. Puisieux, *Int. J. Pharm.* **146**, 233–238 (1997).

98. P. Calvo et al., *Pharm. Res.* **13**, 311–315 (1996).

99. E. Allémann, E. Doelker, and R. Gurny, *Eur. J. Pharm. Biopharm.* **39**, 13–18 (1993).

100. K. Langer, E. Seegmüller, A. Zimmer, and J. Kreuter, *Int. J. Pharm.* **110**, 21–27 (1994).

101. A. Rolland, D. Gibassier, P. Sado, and R. Le Verge, *J. Pharm. Belg.* **41**, 94–105 (1986).

102. M. Auvillain, G. Cavé, H. Fessi, and J.P. Devissaguet, *S.T.P. Pharma. Sci.* **5**, 738–744 (1989).

103. P. Sommerfeld, U. Schroeder, and B.A. Sabel, *Int. J. Pharm.* **155**, 201–207 (1997).

104. F. De Jaeghere et al., *Pharm. Res.* **16**, 864–871 (1999).

105. G. Strauss, P. Schurtenberger, and H. Hauser, *Biochim. Biophys. Acta* **858** 169–180 (1986).

106. J.F. Carpenter, S.J. Prestrelski, and T. Arakawa, *Arch. Biochem. Biophys.* **303**, 456–464 (1993).

107. V. Masson, F. Maurin, H. Fessi, and J.P. Devissaguet, *Biomaterials* **18**, 327–335 (1997).

108. C. Volland, M. Wolff, and T. Kissel, *J. Controlled Release* **31**, 293–305 (1994).

109. R.L. Juliano, *Adv. Drug Delivery Rev.* **2**, 31–54 (1988).

110. R.H. Müller, *Colloidal Carriers for Controlled Drug Delivery and Targeting*, CRC Press, Boca Raton, Fla., 1991.

111. S. Stolnik, L. Illum, and S.S. Davis, *Adv. Drug Delivery Rev.* **16**, 195–214 (1995).

112. G. Storm, S.O. Belliot, T. Daemen, and D.D. Lasic, *Adv. Drug Delivery Rev.* **17**, 31–48 (1995).

113. S.J. Douglas, S.S. Davis, and L. Illum, *Crit. Rev. Ther. Drug Carrier Syst.* **3**, 233–261 (1987).

114. D.V. Bazile et al., *Biomaterials* **13**, 1093–1102 (1992).

115. T. Verrcechia, G. Spcnlchaucr, and D.V. Bazile, *J. Controlled Release* **36**, 49–61 (1995).

116. J.-C. Olivier et al., *J. Controlled Release* **40**, 157–168 (1996).

117. J.H. Lee, J. Kopecek, and J.D. Andrade, *J. Biomed. Mater. Res.* **23**, 351–368 (1989).

118. J.C. Leroux et al., *Life Sci.* **57**, 695–703 (1995).

119. J.C. Leroux et al., *J. Controlled Release* **39**, 339–350 (1996).

120. E. Allémann et al., *Int. J. Cancer* **66**, 821–824 (1996).

121. R.H. Müller, D. Rühl, and K. Schulze-Forster, *Eur. J. Pharm. Sci.* **5**, 147–153 (1997).

122. S.M. Moghimi, *Adv. Drug Delivery Rev.* **16**, 183–193 (1995).

123. S.J. Douglas, S.S. Davis, and L. Illum, *Int. J. Pharm.* **34**, 145–152 (1986).

124. R.H. Müller and K.H. Wallis, *Int. J. Pharm.* **89**, 25–31 (1993).

125. S.E. Dunn et al., *J. Controlled Release* **44**, 65–76 (1997).

126. T.I. Armstrong, M.C. Davies, and L. Illum, *J. Drug Target.* **4**, 389–398 (1997).

127. R. Gref, Y. Minamitake, M.T. Peracchia, and R. Langer, in *Microparticulate Systems for the Delivery of Proteins and Vaccines*, Dekker, New York, 1996, pp. 279–306.

128. M.T. Peracchia et al., *J. Controlled Release* **46**, 223–231 (1997).

129. S. Stolnik et al., *Pharm. Res.* **11**, 1800–1808 (1994).

130. R. Gref et al., *Proc. Int. Symp. Controlled Release Bioact. Mater.* **20**, 131–132 (1993).

131. R. Gref et al., *Science* **263**, 1600–1603 (1994).

132. D. Labarre et al., *Proc. Int. Symp. Controlled Release Bioact. Mater.* **21**, 91–92 (1994).

133. D. Bazile et al., *J. Pharm. Sci.* **84**, 493–498 (1995).

134. R. Fernàndez-Urrusuno et al., *Pharm. Res.* **12**, 1385–1387 (1995).

135. M. Vittaz et al., *Biomaterials* **17**, 1575–1581 (1996).

136. H. Sahli et al., *Biomaterials* **18**, 281–288 (1997).

137. K.-I. Izutsu, S. Yoshioka, and S. Kojima, *Pharm. Res.* **12**, 838–843 (1995).

138. R. Gref et al., *Adv. Drug Delivery Rev.* **16**, 215–233 (1995).

139. C. Emile et al., *Proc. 1st World Meet. APGI/APV*, 1995, vol. 1, pp. 461–462.

140. K.J. Zhu, L. Xiangzhou, and Y. Shilin, *J. Appl. Polym. Sci.* **39**, 1–9 (1990).

141. P. Ferruti et al., *Biomaterials* **16**, 1423–1428 (1995).

142. S.E. Dunn et al., *Pharm. Res.* **11**, 1016–1022 (1994).

143. M.T. Peracchia, C. Vauthier, F. Puisieux, and P. Couvreur, *J. Biomed. Mater. Res.* **34**, 317–326 (1997).

144. B.G. Müller and T. Kissel, *Pharm. Pharmacol. Lett.* **3**, 67–70 (1993).

145. L. Illum, P.D.E. Jones, and S.S. Davis, in S.S. Davis, L. Illum, J.G. McVie, and E. Tomlinson, eds. *MIcrospheres and Drug Therapy*, Elsevier, Amsterdam, 1984, pp. 353–363.

146. L. Illum, P.D.E. Jones, R.W. Baldwin, and S.S. Davis, *J. Pharmacol. Exp. Ther.* **230**, 733–736 (1984).

147. A. Rolland, D. Bourel, B. Genetet, and R. Le Verge, *Int. J. Pharm.* **39**, 173–180 (1987).

148. V.P. Torchilin and V.S. Trubetskoy, in S. Cohen and H. Bernstein eds., *Microparticulate Systems for the Delivery of Proteins and Vaccines*, Dekker, New York, 1996, pp. 243–277.

149. B. Magenheim and S. Benita, *S. T. P. Pharma. Sci.* **1**, 221–241 (1991).

150. C. Washington, *Int. J. Pharm.* **58**, 1–12 (1990).

151. M. Skiba, F. Puisieux, D. Duchêne, and D. Wouessidjewe, *Int. J. Pharm.* **120**, 1–11 (1995).

152. S.K. Das, I.G. Tucker, J.T. Hill, and N. Ganguly, *Pharm. Res.* **12**, 534–540 (1995).

153. S.D. Tröster and J. Kreuter, *J. Microencapsul.* **9**, 19–28 (1992).

154. J.C. Leroux et al., *J. Biomed. Mater. Res.* **28**, 471–481 (1994).

155. T. Blunk et al., *Eur. J. Pharm. Biopharm.* **42**, 262–268 (1996).

156. P. Couvreur and C. Vauthier, in A.G. de Boer, ed., *Drug Absorption Enhancement, Concepts, Possibilities, Limitations and Trends*, Harwood Academic Publishers, Chur, Switzerland, 1994, pp. 457–486.

157. J.C. Leroux, E. Doelker, and R. Gurny, in S. Benita, ed., *Microencapsulation Methods and Industrial Applications*, Dekker, New York, 1996, pp. 535–575.

158. H. Pinto-Alphandary et al., *Pharm. Res.* **11**, 38–46 (1994).

159. J.M. Rodrigues, Jr. et al., *Int. J. Pharm.* **126**, 253–260 (1995).

160. A.R. Bender et al., *Antimicrob. Agents Chemother.* **40**, 1467–1471 (1996).

161. R. Löbenberg, J. Maas, and J. Kreuter, *Proc. Int. Symp. Controlled Release Bioact. Mater.* **23**, 657–658 (1996).

162. P. Maincent et al., *J. Pharm. Sci.* **75**, 955–958 (1986).

163. C. Michel et al., in T.L. Whateley, ed., *Microencapsulation of Drugs*, Harwood Academic Publishers, Chur, Switzerland, 1992, pp. 233–242.

164. A.T. Florence, *Pharm. Res.* **14**, 259–266 (1997).

165. V. Lenaerts, P. Couvreur, L. Grislain, and P. Maincent, in V. Lenaerts and R. Gurny, eds., *Bioadhesive Drug Delivery Systems*, CRC Press, Boca Raton, Fla., 1990, pp. 93–104.

166. E. Mathiowitz et al., *Nature (London)* **386**, 410–414 (1997).

167. G. Ponchel et al., *Eur. J. Pharm. Biopharm.* **44**, 25–31 (1997).

168. E. Haltner, J.H. Easson, and C.-M. Lehr, *Eur. J. Pharm. Biopharm.* **44**, 3–13 (1997).

169. J.C. Leroux et al., *J. Pharm. Sci.* **84**, 1387–1391 (1995).

170. D.T. O'Hagan, K.J. Palin, and S.S. Davis, *Vaccine* **7**, 213–216 (1989).

171. J. Pappo and T.H. Ermak, *Clin. Exp. Immunol.* **76**, 144–148 (1989).

172. S.S. Guterres et al., *Proc. 1st World Meet. APGI/APV*, 1995, vol. 1, pp. 515–516.

173. C. Tasset et al., *J. Controlled Release* **33**, 23–30 (1995).

174. A. Sanchez and M.J. Alonso, *Eur. J. Pharm. Biopharm.* **41**, 31–37 (1995).

175. J. Kreuter, *Vaccine Res.* **1**, 93–98 (1992).

176. C.A. Le Bourlais et al., *Drug Dev. Ind. Pharm.* **21**, 19–59 (1995).

177. T. Harmia, P. Speiser, and J. Kreuter, *Pharm. Acta Helv.* **62**, 322–331 (1987).

178. A. Joshi, *J. Ocul. Pharmacol.* **10**, 29–45 (1994).

See also LIPOSOMES; MICROENCAPSULATION; MICROENCAPSULATION FOR GENE DELIVERY.

NONDEGRADABLE POLYMERS FOR DRUG DELIVERY

ROLAND BODMEIER
JÜRGEN SIEPMANN
Freie Universität Berlin
Berlin, Germany

KEY WORDS

Acrylic polymers
Aquacoat®
Cellulose esters
Coating
Ethyl cellulose
Eudragit®
Hydroxypropylmethyl cellulose
Implantable systems
Intravaginal systems
Matrix systems
Microencapsulation
Ocular systems
Poly(ethylene oxide)
Poly(ethylene vinyl acetate)
Silicones

OUTLINE

Ethyl Cellulose
    Coated Systems and Films
    Matrix Systems
    Microencapsulation
Cellulose Esters: Cellulose Acetate, Cellulose Acetate Butyrate, and Cellulose Acetate Propionate

Polymers play a dominant role as carrier materials in drug delivery systems. The selection of a particular carrier is primarily determined by the intended use and the desired release profile. The polymer should be inexpensive, readily available, and easily processed on a large scale. When applied to an animal or human, it must be biocompatible and nontoxic. The route of administration also plays a decisive role: Polymers for parenteral use have to satisfy different requirements than polymers for oral use. This article reviews the most important nondegradable polymers used in drug delivery systems. They include the cellulose derivatives ethyl cellulose, cellulose acetate, cellulose acetate butyrate, cellulose acetate proprionate, and hydroxypropylmethyl cellulose; various acrylic polymers; silicones; poly(ethylene vinyl acetate); and poly(ethylene oxides). The physicochemical properties of the polymers are briefly discussed, followed by a review of various drug delivery systems in which the polymers have been incorporated.

ETHYL CELLULOSE

Ethyl cellulose is a cellulose ether prepared by the reaction of alkali cellulose with ethyl chloride; its chemical structure is shown in Figure 1. Its properties and applications have been reviewed recently (1). Its glass transition temperature is 120°C (2). It is characterized by the degree of ethoxy substitution and the solution viscosity. Commercial grades of ethyl cellulose have a degree of substitution be-

tween 2.25 and 2.58 (44 to 50% ethoxyl content) per anhydroglucose unit. Ethyl cellulose polymers are sold under the trade name Ethocel® by the Dow Chemical Company. Ethocel is available in six grades from standard 4 to 100, the numbers representing the viscosity of 5% w/v solutions in toluene ethanol (80:20) in cP, with the 7 and 100 grades also being offered with a fine particle size for applications in which the polymer is not dissolved in organic solvents but is used as a dry powder. A similar range of ethyl cellulose products is also offered by Hercules. Ethyl cellulose is water insoluble but soluble in a variety of organic solvents/solvent mixtures (3). The desired use of ethyl cellulose will determine the choice of a particular grade, for example, lower-molecular-weight grades are used for coating, and higher-molecular-weight grades are used for microencapsulation. Different grades can also be blended to obtain films with special properties. The polymer is tasteless and odorless, physiologically inert, stable in a pH range between 3 and 11, and, because of its nonionic character, compatible with most drug substances.

Ethyl cellulose has been used by the pharmaceutical industry for almost 40 years for the coating of solid dosage forms (tablets, pellets, granules); in matrix systems, which are prepared by wet granulation or direct compression; or in microencapsulation processes. It has excellent film-forming properties. Besides the predominant use as controlled-release barriers, thin films have been used as a moisture barrier to improve the stability of hydrolytically unstable drug substances or for taste-masking purposes.

Coated Systems and Films

Ethyl cellulose is one of the most widely used water-insoluble polymers for the coating of solid dosage forms. It can be applied as an organic solution or as an aqueous colloidal polymer dispersion. Many studies have been performed with ethyl cellulose films to predict properties of the coatings, for example, mechanical or permeability properties.

Various factors of the spraying process with organic polymer solutions, such as spraying distance, flow rate, and atomizing air pressure, affected the mechanical and release properties of ethyl cellulose films (4). It was pointed out that the variables governing solvent evaporation and spreading of the organic polymer solution droplets during the coating process are very important to obtain films with the desired properties. The selection of a suitable organic solvent system has been facilitated through the determination of the dilute solution properties of ethyl cellulose, namely the intrinsic viscosity and the interaction constant (5). Methylene chloride and ethanol in a ratio of 60:40% w/w were found to be optimal. Water concentrations in excess of 10% resulted in uncontrolled situations (e.g., polymer precipitation) during solvent evaporation. Based on tensile tests and thermal analysis, dibutyl sebacate and Myvacet were the most efficient plasticizers for ethyl cellulose films cast from ethanolic solution (6). The permeability of the polymeric films can be controlled by the molecular weight of the polymer or polymer blends or by the inclusion of additives like plasticizers or pore formers. The mechanical stability of the polymeric films increases with

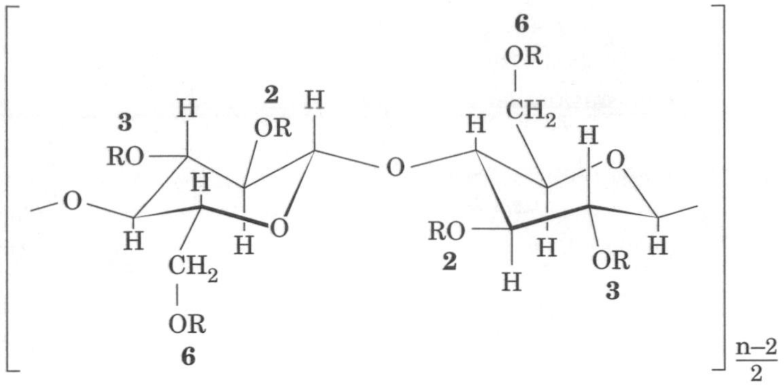

Figure 1. Structure of a section of two anhydroglucose units (cellobiose) in a cellulose derivative. *Source:* Adapted from Doelker (117) with permission from Springer-Verlag.

Cellulose derivative	Substituent R (other than H)
Ethyl cellulose	$-CH_2CH_3$
Cellulose acetate	$-COCH_3$
Cellulose acetate propionate	$-CH_2CH_3$, $-COCH_2CH_3$
Cellulose acetate butyrate	$-CH_2CH_3$, $-COCH_2CH_2CH_3$
Hydroxypropylmethyl cellulose	$-CH_2CH(CH_3)OH$, $-CH_3$

increasing molecular weight. The release of drug from ethyl cellulose/hydroxypropylmethyl cellulose (HPMC) (9:1)–coated pellets decreased with increasing molecular weight of ethyl cellulose and increasing diethyl phthalate (plasticizer) concentration for the lower-molecular-weight ethyl cellulose grades (7). Above a molecular weight of 35,000 Da, the addition of a plasticizer had no effect on the drug release. The rapid release with the lower-molecular-weight grades was attributed to the weak mechanical properties of the coating, reflected by cracks and flaws in the film.

A porous ethyl cellulose film was obtained by spraying an ethyl cellulose–ethanol–water ternary mixture (8–10). The film porosity increased with increasing water content of the coating solution as a result of a phase separation process. The film porosity was also affected by the temperature and the relative humidity but was only slightly affected by the concentration of the polymer and its molecular weight. The increased film porosity resulted in increased permeation rates.

Although coating with organic polymer solutions is still widespread, aqueous ethyl cellulose dispersions have been developed to overcome problems associated with organic solvents (11). Two aqueous ethyl cellulose pseudolatexes are commercially available, namely Aquacoat®, manufactured by FMC, and Surelease®, by Colorcon®. Aquacoat® (30% solids content) is prepared by a direct emulsification–solvent evaporation method (12), whereby an organic polymer solution is emulsified into water to form an emulsion. The pseudolatex is obtained after homogenization and solvent removal. Sodium lauryl sulfate and cetyl alcohol are used as emulsifier and coemulsifier. The polymer dispersion must be plasticized to reduce its minimum film formation temperature (MFT). For coating purposes, 20–30% plasticizer is added, and the dispersion is diluted to a solids content between 10 and 25%. Surelease® (25% solids content) is a fully plasticized dispersion and is prepared by a

phase inversion–in situ emulsification technique (13). Ethyl cellulose, dibutyl sebacate or fractionated coconut oil (plasticizer), and oleic acid (secondary plasticizer) are hot-melt extruded under pressure into water containing ammonia. Initially, a water-in-polymer dispersion is formed, which then inverts into a polymer-in-water dispersion. Ammonium oleate forms in situ as a stabilizer. Upon drying and film formation, ammonia evaporates, leaving oleic acid as an additional plasticizer within the film.

Various additives, which are present in the ethyl cellulose dispersions, will also be present in the final film or coating and can therefore affect film properties, such as mechanical properties or the permeability. Surfactants are necessary to physically stabilize the dispersion during preparation and storage. Plasticizers and antitacking agents or additives, which affect the permeability of the ethyl cellulose film (e.g., hydrophilic polymers such as HPMC), are added shortly before the application of the polymer dispersion.

Although a pH-independent drug release is expected with ethyl cellulose, several studies with Aquacoat®-coated beads showed a faster drug release in simulated intestinal fluid when compared to simulated gastric juice (14–17). This was caused by the presence of the anionic surfactant, sodium lauryl sulfate, which resulted in better wetting of the coated pellets in pH 7.4 buffer as indicated by contact-angle measurements (18) and not by residual acid/base groups in the ethyl cellulose polymer (19). Later, it was reported that the pH-dependent release could be circumvented by curing the coated dosage form above the glass-transition temperature of the plasticized polymer coating (20,21). During storage, sodium lauryl sulfate and cetyl alcohol were squeezed from the film, possibly changing the permeability (22). In addition, charged surfactants such as sodium lauryl sulfate could form insoluble complexes with cationic drugs present in the core (23,24).

Although the drug release from ethyl cellulose–coated multiparticulates such as pellets or granules is adequate, the release from tablets is often too slow. Water-soluble additives have therefore been incorporated into ethyl cellulose coatings to modify the drug release. They include low-molecular-weight materials including various sugars (e.g., sucrose, lactose, and sorbitol); salts (e.g., sodium chloride and calcium phosphate); surfactants such as sodium lauryl sulfate; or hydrophilic polymers including polyethylene glycol, polyvinyl pyrrolidone and, in particular, cellulose ethers (e.g., HPMC) (15,25–32). During dissolution studies, these additives leach from the coating membrane, or hydrate in the coating in the case of high-molecular-weight polymers, resulting in more permeable membranes and generally in a faster drug release. In addition, with thin coatings, hydrophilic polymers are added to increase the quantity of the coating to achieve a more uniform coating distribution on the pellet. Slight variations in the coating level will then not affect the release rate significantly.

The water-soluble high-molecular-weight polymers are usually not considered true pore-forming agents because they do not completely leach out from the coating to leave a well-defined pore structure. Ethyl cellulose/HPMC blends have shown phase separation with a limited degree of mixing between the polymers (33). Film studies revealed that HPMC-rich macroscopic polydispersed domains were dispersed within the ethyl cellulose–rich matrix. Complete leaching of HPMC was only observed at HPMC concentrations above 60% w/w; otherwise, some HPMC retention was observed. A critical HPMC concentration was identified below which very little polymer leached from the coating and no pores are formed. Above 24% HPMC, the polymer leaches from the ethyl cellulose films, resulting in pore formation and an increase in drug release (34,35). For the development of an osmotic system, the water permeability of pure ethyl cellulose was only about one-tenth of cellulose acetate but increased with HPMC in the film. At higher HPMC content, the initially semipermeable ethyl cellulose/HPMC film also became permeable for the drug (34). In an interesting experimental setup developed by the same research group, the permeability of ethyl cellulose/ HPMC increased with increasing HPMC content as was shown with a pressurized cell device in which the permeability was measured in dependence to an applied tensile stress (36). Pellets coated with an aqueous ethyl cellulose dispersion containing HPMC initially formed water-filled pores after extraction of the HPMC at the beginning of the release process in the aqueous medium (37). However, after 2 h, these pores closed irreversibly as a result of fusion at temperatures above the MFT. The release was then as slow as without HPMC. A decrease in acetaminophen release with increasing HPMC concentration was contributed to the lower solubility of the drug in the HPMC-containing Aquacoat® film (38).

During coating with the HPMC-containing ethyl cellulose dispersion (Aquacoat®), a sediment formed in the colloidal dispersion upon standing, indicating destabilization of the colloidal ethyl cellulose particles by HPMC (39,40). The addition of HPMC to the ethyl cellulose pseudolatex resulted in the flocculation of the colloidal polymer particles above a critical HPMC concentration. The observed flocculation phenomena could interfere with the film formation of the colloidal polymer dispersion upon removal of water and thus could affect the drug release from the polymer-coated dosage forms.

A pore-forming agent, urea, was dissolved in the ethyl cellulose pseudolatex, Aquacoat®, to increase the release rate of drugs from coated osmotically active tablets (41). The release rates varied as a function of coating thickness, pore-former level and plasticizer type, and concentration. Scanning electron microscopy revealed that the urea was eluted from the coating, leaving a porous coating.

The drug release could also be increased by incorporating drug powder in the coating formulation (30). Theophylline was incorporated in the coating and resulted in faster drug release due to an increase in film porosity after dissolving from the coating. A gradient matrix system has been developed that consisted of an ethyl cellulose film with acetaminophen and xylitol coated on a core (42,43). A constant release could be obtained by increasing the drug concentration toward the core and having an inverse concentration gradient for xylitol. The drug release occurred through water-filled pores. Both compounds were soluble in the polymer, with acetaminophen acting as a plasticizer. Above a critical concentration, both the drug and xylitol crystallized, and the plasticizing effect disappeared.

Besides water-soluble additives, insoluble ingredients such as magnesium stearate or talc help reduce agglomeration or sticking of the coated particles during the coating process (15). The pigment concentration has a strong influence on the final film properties such as mechanical strength and permeability. Care must be taken when incorporating coloring agents into Surelease®, an aqueous dispersion of high pH value, because the basicity of the dispersion will destroy the dye–substrate complex (44). Colorants such as aluminum lakes should be replaced with inorganic pigments such as titanium dioxide.

With aqueous colloidal polymer dispersions, the addition of plasticizers is required for polymer dispersions having an MFT above the coating temperature. Water-soluble plasticizers are dissolved in the aqueous dispersions, whereas water-insoluble plasticizers are emulsified. Iyer et al. determined the uptake of the water-insoluble plasticizer, dibutyl sebacate, into Aquacoat® by using an alkaline partition column to separate the unbound plasticizer and gas chromatography for the plasticizer assay (45). The uptake of dibutyl sebacate was found to be complete within 30 min irrespective of the amount used; the uptake rate was faster with increasing solids content of the pseudolatex or when smaller quantities of plasticizer were incorporated. However, a previous study reported the presence of visible dibutyl sebacate droplets in Aquacoat® after 1 week of mixing, indicating incomplete plasticization after such a long plasticization time (17). Factors influencing the rate and extent of the plasticizer uptake by the colloidal particles, such as type and concentration of the plasticizer and type and solids content of the polymer dispersion, were investigated with Aquacoat® (46–48). The distribution behavior of the water-soluble plasticizers, triethyl citrate and triacetin, within Aquacoat® was virtually not affected by the mixing time or degree of agitation. The water-insoluble plasticizers were not completely taken up by the colloidal polymer particles within a 24-h period. This may have important implications for the coating with aqueous polymer dispersions when compared to organic polymer solutions in which the plasticizer is completely dissolved. During coating, in addition to the plasticized polymer particles, the emulsified plasticizer droplets will be sprayed onto the solid dosage forms. This could result in an uneven plasticizer distribution within the film, potentially causing changes in the mechanical and especially release properties upon aging.

Plasticizers do not only affect the film formation from colloidal polymer dispersions or the mechanical properties of the resulting films; their choice will also affect the drug release from the coated dosage form (14,15,49). Increasing the concentration of dibutyl sebacate or triethyl citrate decreased the drug release from Aquacoat®-coated dosage forms (15), probably because of better fusion of the colloidal polymer particles. In general, water-insoluble plasticizers retard the drug release more than water-soluble plasticizers.

Process variables such as spray rate, droplet size, bed temperature, spray mode, chamber geometry, and so on can have a significant impact on the drug release (12–14,50). Dissolution data and morphological studies indicated differences in the nature of the coating, which was attributed to differences in particle motion in the bed, in particle distribution and density in the coating zone, and in the direction and distance the droplets had to travel prior to impinging on the particles (51). The coating temperature should be sufficiently high to achieve efficient water removal and subsequent particle coalescence. In general, it should be 10–20°C higher than the MFT of the polymer dispersion (52). The drug release with Surelease®-coated theophylline pellets decreased with increasing the product temperature from 32 to 48°C because of a more complete film formation. Coating at low product-bed temperatures prevents sufficient coalescence of the colloidal particles and promotes drug diffusion in the coating, resulting in a rapid release (53). Excessive temperatures resulted in porous films and poorly coalesced particles because of the high evaporation rate of water. Smaller nozzle diameters resulted in better coatings with fewer imperfections (54).

The coalescence of the colloidal ethyl cellulose particles into a homogeneous film is often incomplete after coating with aqueous polymer dispersions. As a consequence, changes in the drug release from the coated dosage form caused by further coalescence during storage have been observed as a function of storage temperature and time (12,16–18,55–57). A curing step or thermal treatment (storage of the coated dosage forms at elevated temperatures for short time periods) is often recommended to accelerate the coalescence of the ethyl cellulose particles prior to long-term storage. The storage temperature should be about 10°C above the MFT (16). Higher curing temperatures could cause excessive tackiness and agglomeration of the solid dosage forms. Curing was reported to be required with Aquacoat®-coated pellets but not with Surelease®-coated pellets (57).

Although curing at 40°C for 24 h was insufficient curing at either 50 or 60°C resulted in a significant reduction in drug release with Aquacoat®-coated pellets (18). The limiting drug-release pattern was approached after curing the beads for 1 h at 60°C. This value was also found by other authors (58). As an alternative to oven curing, Aquacoat®-coated beads have been cured directly in the fluidized bed after the coated beads have been applied with a thin layer of hydroxypropylmethyl cellulose (59). The hydrophilic overcoat prevented the sticking and agglomeration of the beads without altering the release profiles of the original coated pellets. The curing temperature had a more dramatic effect than curing time with Aquacoat®-coated pellets (60). An increase in drug release was observed with dibutyl sebacate, while a decrease was observed with tributyl citrate. The decrease was explained with a further gradual coalescence, while the increase was explained by either the plasticizer being squeezed from the coating or by drug being solubilized in the plasticizer at higher curing times. Although curing of the Aquacoat®-coated chlorpheniramine maleate beads produced a retarding effect in drug release, curing of ibuprofen beads coated with a comparable coating system resulted in more complex drug-release patterns (61). At curing times in excess of 4 h, the drug release increased. The increase in drug release (curing periods in excess of 4 h) could be explained by the migration of ibuprofen from the bead interior to the bead surface through the ethyl cellulose coating during the curing step. Large drug crystals could be observed throughout the coated surface by scanning electron microscopy. The drug–polymer affinity, coupled with the drug's low melting point, could thus serve as an explanation for the phenomenon of drug migration, a process that was accelerated at elevated temperatures. The diffusion of guaifenesin, another low-melting drug, through the vapor phase across the Aquacoat® coatings during storage of the coated beads has also been observed (17).

The ethyl cellulose pseudolatexes Aquacoat® and Surelease® resulted in very brittle films in the dry state and weak films in the wet state with low values for puncture strength and elongation (<5%) in both cases (62). In contrast, acrylic-based polymeric films were stronger and more flexible. Curing did not improve the mechanical properties of the Aquacoat® films. Ethyl cellulose films, when cast from organic solutions, were stronger (had higher puncture strength) in both the dry and wet state when compared with Aquacoat® films. However, the elongation values were still low. Interestingly, triethyl citrate leached almost completely from the pseudolatex-cast film, while more than 75% of the original plasticizer was still present in films cast from organic solutions. The higher leaching of triethyl citrate could have been the result of the anionic surfactant, sodium lauryl sulfate, being present in Aquacoat® films. The pseudolatex-cast films took up almost 43% water, compared with only 12% with the solvent cast films.

Most studies on the compaction of pellets coated with ethyl cellulose revealed a damage to the coating with a loss of the sustained release properties (63–69). This is not surprising because of the weak mechanical properties of ethyl cellulose.

Several articles discussed possible mechanisms by which drug release from multiparticulate dosage forms coated with water-insoluble polymers and in particular ethyl cellulose might occur (70,71). The mechanism of drug release will be determined by the physicochemical properties of the drug, the polymer, and the dosage form. The possible mechanisms included solution/diffusion through a continuous polymer phase, solution/diffusion through plasticizer channels, diffusion through aqueous pores, and release driven by osmotic effects (70). Ozturk reported the release from ethyl cellulose–coated dosage forms to be a combination of osmotically driven release and diffusion through the polymer and or aqueous pores. To determine if the drug release was driven by osmosis or occurred primarily by diffusion through the polymer, the drug release from pellets and the drug diffusion across cast films was measured in diffusion cells (62). Ibuprofen had a significantly higher solubility in ethyl cellulose films than chlorpheniramine maleate. Ibuprofen, the water-insoluble drug, was released from the coated beads and diffused across free films, while chlorpheniramine maleate, the water-soluble drug, was released from the beads but did not diffuse across the polymeric film. Ibuprofen was released primarily by solution/diffusion through the hydrophobic polymer. On the other hand, chlorpheniramine maleate, the water-soluble drug, was not released by a solution/diffusion mechanism from the beads because of its negligible diffusion across cast films. Chlorpheniramine maleate was released through aqueous (micro)channels caused by osmotic effects with subsequent rupturing of the weak polymeric membrane. As described earlier, Aquacoat® films were extremely weak in the wet state (% elongation <1%).

The mechanism of release was reported to be different with pellets with lower coating levels and pellets with higher coating levels coated with Aquacoat® or Surelease® from diffusion through water-filled pores to diffusion of the drug through the membrane (57). Drug release from incompletely coated beads at low coating levels followed the square-root-of-time model, whereas the drug release at higher coating levels was best described with zero-order release kinetics (72). As with a typical reservoir system, three phases, an initial lag time, a constant-release phase, and a final declining-release phase, were observed (73). The major mechanism for release was reported to be diffusion and not osmotic pumping. The constant-release rate was proportional to the size (surface area) of coated pellets for metoprolol salts of different solubility. The zero-order release phase was shorter for more water-soluble drugs from Aquacoat®-coated pellets (74). Free films were not permeable for the water-soluble drugs, while the drugs were released from pellets through water-filled channels. The channels were attributed to artifacts of the coating process and not to the formation during contact with dissolution media. Each pellet was described to work like a mini–osmotic pump with multiple orifices (pores).

In addition to the colloidal ethyl cellulose dispersions, a micronized ethyl cellulose powder with an average particle size of a few μm is available in Japan from Shin-Etsu (54,75). The polymeric powder is dispersed in water with the addition of relatively large amounts of plasticizer prior to use. A comparative coating study of aqueous ethyl cellulose suspensions and pseudolatex dispersion revealed that the pseudolatex required less plasticizer for film formation than the aqueous polymer suspension. The average diameter of the ethyl cellulose particles in the suspension was 5.6 μm.

Matrix Systems

Ethyl cellulose can be incorporated as a carrier material into matrix preparations either by solution granulation or direct compression. Ethyl cellulose solutions were used for the preparation of granules by wet granulation, whereby the drug release was controlled by the amount of ethyl cellulose or the addition of a hydrophilic polymer (e.g., HPMC) to the granulation fluid. Ethyl cellulose has been used for solvent granulation of water-sensitive drugs. The resulting tablets have good physical properties. Controlled release theophylline tablets were prepared by fluid bed granulation of the drug and excipients with the aqueous dispersion, Surelease®, followed by compression of the granules (13). Because of its thermoplastic nature, ethyl cellulose can also be used for extrusion granulation.

Various studies have evaluated ethyl cellulose as a directly compressible excipient (76–81). The compressibility of ethyl cellulose has recently been reported (80). With directly compressible systems, the particle size of ethyl cellulose affected the release rate and the tablettability. Ethyl cellulose matrix controlled release tablets containing pseudoephedrine HCl were prepared by direct compression of different viscosity grades of ethyl cellulose (76). The lower viscosity grades produced harder tablets. Compared to HPMC matrix systems, matrix systems based on ethyl cellulose will release the drug faster at higher drug loadings because of a diffusion/erosion vs leaching drug release mechanism.

Microencapsulation

Ethyl cellulose microparticles can be prepared by various microencapsulation processes (see MICROENCAPSULATION). Depending on the microstructure of the microparticles, microcapsules (reservoir system) or microspheres (matrix system) can be distinguished.

Ethyl cellulose was one of the first polymers used for the microencapsulation of water-soluble drugs by the classical organic phase separation process (82). Phase separation can be induced by a temperature change in a cyclohexane system, whereby the drug is dispersed in a heated ethyl cellulose solution in cyclohexane at 80°C followed by gradual cooling of this solution to form the polymer coacervate to enclose the drug particles. In addition to the temperature change, the coacervation can be further induced by the addition of incompatible polymers, such as low-molecular-weight polyethylene or polyisobutylene. Polyisobutylene also acts as a protective colloid. As with aqueous phase separation techniques, the phase separation of ethyl cellulose can also be induced by the addition of nonsolvents, for example, in an ethyl cellulose–dichloromethane (solvent)-n-hexane (incompatible solvent) system.

Although microcapsules are formed primarily with the organic phase separation techniques, ethyl cellulose microspheres have been prepared with the solvent evaporation method, whereby the polymer is dissolved in an organic solvent followed by emulsification of this polymer–

drug solution into an external phase (83,84). The microspheres are obtained after solvent diffusion in the external phase and solvent evaporation. Depending on the solubility of the drug, either an external aqueous or oily phase can be used. Various modifications of this method have been developed, including multiple-emulsion (water-in-oil-in-water, W/O/W) and cosolvent methods. Water-soluble drugs were entrapped, whereby an alcoholic ethyl cellulose solution containing the active drug was emulsified into liquid paraffin followed by solvent evaporation (85).

Indomethacin polymeric nanoparticles were prepared by microfluidization, whereby the drug-containing solution was emulsified into an aqueous phase followed by microfluidization (86). The nanoparticles formed after solvent diffusion in the aqueous phase and solvent evaporation. For the drug to be encapsulated, it had to have a high solubility in the polymeric matrix. Otherwise, unwanted drug crystallization was observed in the aqueous phase.

Ethyl cellulose microparticles can also be prepared by spray-drying of organic polymer solutions or aqueous polymer dispersions. With organic polymer solutions, the drug is dissolved or dispersed in the organic ethyl cellulose solution, followed by spray-drying and removal of the organic solvent. The drug can be either dissolved or dispersed in a crystalline or amorphous state in the polymeric matrix. With aqueous polymer dispersions, the drug is dissolved or dispersed in the polymer dispersion; with plasticizer-free ethyl cellulose dispersions, a plasticizer has to be included to reduce the MFT of the dispersion, followed by spray-drying. The coalescence of the colloidal particles into microparticles has to be ensured.

Two microencapsulation methods that used the coalescence of colloidal particles into microparticles were recently developed. In the first method, the colloidal polymer particles were coalesced into microparticles by using the ionotropic gelation of polysaccharides with oppositely charged counterions as a process for the microparticle formation (87). In the second method, a drug-containing aqueous polymer dispersion was emulsified into a heated external oil phase to form a water-in-oil (W/O) emulsion. The colloidal polymer particles then coalesced into microparticles within the internal aqueous phase (88).

Naproxen microcapsules were prepared by a coacervation phase separation technique, and ibuprofen–ethyl cellulose microspheres were prepared by the solvent evaporation process (89). Both microparticles were compressed into tablets; the matrix-structure ibuprofen particles were intact after tabletting, whereas the coatings of the naproxen microcapsules were ruptured to some extend.

CELLULOSE ESTERS: CELLULOSE ACETATE, CELLULOSE ACETATE BUTYRATE, AND CELLULOSE ACETATE PROPIONATE

Cellulose acetate (CA), cellulose acetate butyrate, and cellulose acetate propionate are pharmaceutically used cellulose esters that are insoluble in physiological fluids. Their chemical structures are shown in Figure 1. Commercially available grades of the cellulose esters vary in their molecular weight, their degree of esterification, and

their type of alcohol substitution, resulting in a wide range of polymers with different physicochemical properties, such as melting temperature, glass-transition temperature, mechanical properties, permeability characteristics, and solubility (90). A major supplier of these polymers is the Eastman Chemical Company; detailed information about important properties of the different polymer grades is given in the product literature (91).

CA is obtained by the controlled esterification of purified cellulose with acetic acid and anhydride. The acetylation of CA is carried out to completion followed by hydrolysis to obtain CAs with lower acetyl contents. Cellulose triacetate has the highest acetate content and the highest melting point of the cellulose esters and is therefore soluble in fewer organic solvents. It has only limited compatibility with plasticizers. Decreasing the acetyl content increases the hydrophilicity of CAs. The water or moisture permeability can therefore be controlled through the acetyl content. Cellulose acetate butyrate is soluble in a variety of organic solvents; it has a low water permeability and good mechanical properties. It is compatible with a wide number of plasticizers.

Cellulose esters have been used as coating materials, particularly in osmotically driven coated drug-release systems, as carrier materials in matrix systems, and in the area of microencapsulation.

Coated Systems

CA coatings have been used for many years in osmotically controlled drug delivery systems. A review of the patent literature on osmotic drug delivery systems has been recently published (92). The Theeuwes elementary osmotic pump consists of an osmotically active drug-containing core surrounded by a semipermeable membrane, usually CA, having an orifice (93). The polymeric membrane is impermeable for the drug but permeable for aqueous fluids. Water is osmotically attracted through the membrane into the core and dissolves the drug, which is then released through the orifice at a constant rate as long as solid excess drug and a constant osmotic pressure gradient are maintained. The CA coating is rigid and does not expand during the drug release. The drug release from the elementary osmotic pump depends on the surface area, the water permeability of the membrane, its wall thickness, and the osmotic pressure gradient.

CA coatings with a controlled porosity were formed by including water-soluble agents (e.g., sorbitol) in concentrations between 10 and 50% based on the polymer into the polymer solution (27,28,94). After contact with dissolution fluids, the water-soluble additives leached from the film, leaving a membrane with controlled porosity. The sponge-like porous membrane was substantially permeable to both water and the drug. The drug is not released through a prefabricated orifice, as with the elementary osmotic pump, but through a porous network. Zero-order drug release was obtained, with the drug release being dependent on the level of pore former, the wall thickness, the drug loading, the solubility of the core, and the osmotic pressure difference across the membrane but being independent of the agitation and the pH of the medium. A microporous CA coating was also prepared from CA pseudolatexes containing urea as the pore former (95). The tablets had to be cured to promote the coalescence of the polymer particles in a film.

Tablets were coated with an asymmetric CA membrane by first dip-coating the tablets in a solution of the polymer in acetone and a nonsolvent (formamide or glycerol), followed by air-drying the tablets 5 s and then immersing the coated tablets for 3 min in a water quench bath (96). The coatings have an asymmetric structure, similar to membranes used for reverse osmosis. The new membranes have several unique characteristics when compared with conventional osmotic tablets. Higher water fluxes can be obtained, allowing the release of low-solubility drugs or higher release rates. The permeability can be controlled by the membrane structure.

A multiparticulate delayed-release system consisting of an osmotically active core and a CA coating was developed (97,98). The membrane was initially semipermeable and then also became permeable for the drug after expansion of the osmotically active core and creation of pores in the coating induced by the osmotic pressure gradient and the water influx. The drug release could be controlled by the properties of the coating and the core.

CA is normally applied from organic solutions to the solid dosage forms. To avoid organic solvents, aqueous colloidal CA dispersions have been prepared and evaluated (99–101). The problems with aqueous CA dispersions are their high MFT, requiring high amounts of plasticizer, and the hydrolytic instability in aqueous media, requiring storage at low temperatures. Plasticizer levels between 160 and 320% based on the polymer were required to form adequate films. Volatile plasticizers, which evaporated to some extent during the coating process, gave stronger films when compared with films prepared with nonvolatile plasticizers. The water permeability of the membranes was strongly dependent on the type of plasticizer and the processing conditions. A high-performance liquid chromatography (HPLC) method was developed to determine the acidic degradation products, acetic, propionic, and butyric acid in aqueous pseudolatexes (102). The preparation of a redispersible polymer dispersion would overcome the stability and inconvenient storage problems.

With a CA pseudolatex, 150% triacetin and 120% triethyl citrate had to be used as plasticizers to obtain dense and homogeneous films after coating propranolol HCl tablets (103). The permeability of the coating was too low, and 40% sucrose and 10% polyethylene glycol (PEG) 8,000 were included as flux enhancers to provide macroporous membranes with adequate release characteristics. The thermal and mechanical properties of films cast from a CA latex were evaluated by thermal mechanical analysis by the FMC Corporation, the manufacturer of the dispersion. Various plasticizers in the range of 0–160% were evaluated, with glyceryl diacetate, glyceryl triacetate, and triethyl citrate being the most effective. The water permeability of CA decreased with increasing plasticizer concentration to a minimum and then increased at higher concentrations (104). An antiplasticization effect was responsible for the decreased water permeability. This effect disappeared at temperatures above the glass-transition temperature.

Matrix Tablets

Powdered cellulose esters have been evaluated as matrix materials for both immediate- and slow-release preparations (105,106). The tablets were prepared by direct compression, wet granulation with aqueous binders, and solvent wet-granulation processes. All three cellulose esters were directly compressible. Sustained release was especially obtained with the solvent granulation method, whereby the polymer partially dissolved in the organic solvent. Plasticized CA powder has been used as a direct compression vehicle to form sustained-release theophylline matrix delivery systems. The drug release decreased with increasing polymer/drug ratio and the inclusion of a plasticizer, triethyl citrate. The release was not strongly affected by the polymer molecular weight and the particle size distribution. In a related study, the plasticizer triacetin was incorporated into CA by film casting, particles were then prepared by grinding the film with dry ice. Blending the plasticizer with the polymer resulted in wet powders that had poor flow properties.

Microencapsulation

The water-insoluble cellulose esters have also been used as carrier materials for microparticles. A review of the different methods is given in the product literature of Eastman (107). The major methods used are organic phase separation and solvent evaporation techniques. Cellulose acetate butyrate microcapsules were formed by organic phase separation by the addition of heptane to a cellulose acetate butyrate solution in heptane/chloroform (108). Theophylline–cellulose acetate proprionate microspheres were formed by the solvent evaporation method, whereby a drug suspension in the acetonic polymer solution was emulsified into mineral oil followed by solvent evaporation and microsphere formation (109,110). The drug release from the microspheres depended on the type of polymer, its molecular weight, the particle size of the microspheres, and the drug loading. Cellulose acetate butyrate microspheres were prepared by a similar technique, whereby hexane was added to the oil to precipitate the polymer (111,112). The drug release could be accelerated through the inclusion of PEG. Drug-loaded ion-exchange resins were encapsulated from an acetonic cellulose acetate butyrate solution by the nonaqueous solvent evaporation method (113,114). Overcoating dried gelatin beads with cellulose acetate butyrate by the nonaqueous solvent evaporation reduced the drug release rate (115).

HPMC

The chemical structure of HPMC is given in Figure 1. The physicochemical properties of this substance strongly depend on the following parameters: (1) methoxyl content, (2) hydroxypropyl content, and (3) molecular weight. HPMC 2208 is a well-defined U.S. Pharmacoreial Convention (USP) type with a nominal methoxyl and hydroxypropyl content of 22 and 8%, respectively. Dahl et al. (116) found broad variations concerning important characteristics of seven batches of HPMC 2208 provided by two different manufacturers. As can be seen in Table 1, three batches violated the USP specification with respect to the required methoxyl content (19–24%). Although all products were within the specified hydroxypropyl content limits of 4–12%, Dahl and coworkers presented relevant differences concerning the naproxen release rates from HPMC 2208 matrix tablets within this range (116). The observed differences (up to more than 100%) are of significant practical importance for the application of potent drugs. In conclusion, the USP specification concerning the hydroxypropyl content is insufficient and should be reinforced.

Grafting and cross-linking HPMC are common methods to achieve desired properties of the resulting polymer. To study these modifications in more detail, the reader is referred to numerous reviews and publications (117–120). A good summary of the work that has been done to determine the glass-transition temperature (T_g) of HPMC has been written by Doelker (117). He compares the results of various researchers and lists values ranging from 154 to 184°C (Table 2). Various techniques have been used to determine the T_g: differential scanning calorimetry (DSC), differential thermal analysis (DTA), thermomechanical analysis (TMA), torsional braid analysis (TBA), and dynamic mechanical analysis (DMA). Different techniques often lead to different T_g values, and usually only the results achieved with one special method can be compared directly. In addition, the variation of the degree of substitution and of the molecular weight (as discussed earlier) play a role in the observed variance of the T_g. Furthermore, a 57°C value was reported by Conte et al. (129), which seems to correspond to a low-energy secondary transition. The relevance of this low-temperature transition is unknown but could be of significance in the diffusion of oxygen and water.

The swelling and solubility behavior of HPMC strongly depends on the molecular weight, degree of substitution, cross-linking, and grafting. Non-cross-linked polymers absorb water, swell, and dissolve (erode); cross-linked HPMC swells to some equilibrium state, at which the retractive force of the network balances the swelling force. Recently,

Table 1. Physicochemical Characteristics of Various Batches of HPMC 2208 15,000 mPa s

Batch number	Viscosity (mPa s)	Methoxyl content (%)	Hydroxypropyl content (%)
1[a]	15,200	23.7	8.7
2[a]	14,000	22.5	10.9
3[a]	14,200	25.9	11.1
4[a]	15,000	26.4	7.2
5[a]	15,000	25.5	5.3
6[b]	15,600	22.7	10.7
7[b]	12,491	23.4	9.5

Source: Adapted from Dahl et al. (116) with permission from Elsevier Science Publishers B. V.
[a]From manufacturer a.
[b]From manufacturer b.

Table 2. Reported T_g for HPMC

Material	Method	T_g (°C)	References
Type 2910			
Methocel® E15	TMA	172–175[a]	121
Pharmacoat® 606	DSC	177	122
Pharmacoat® 606	DSC	155	123
Pharmacoat® 606	DSC	180	124
Pharmacoat® 606	DTA	169–174	124
Pharmacoat® 606	TBA	153.5, 158.5	124
Pharmacoat® 606	DSC	155.8	125
Pharmacoat® 606	TMA	163.8, 174.4	125
Pharmacoat® 603	DMA	160	126
Pharmacoat® 606	DMA	170	126
Pharmacoat® 615	DMA	175	126
Pharmacoat® 606	DMA	154	127
Type 2208			
Methocel® K4M	DSC	184	128
Methocel® K4M	DSC	(57)	129

Source: Adapted from Doelker (117) with permission from Springer-Verlag.
[a]The values obtained by TMA in the penetration mode have been reported by the authors as softening temperatures.

an excellent review concerning the quantitative treatment of these swelling processes has been written by Narasimhan and Peppas (130).

Talukdar and coworkers (131) investigated the rheological properties of HPMC by oscillatory as well as by steady shear measurements. The dynamic moduli, that is, storage modulus (G′) and loss modulus (G″), have been determined.

The formation of a gel layer is of evident importance for the drug release from HPMC systems. Initially, the polymer is in a glassy state. Upon exposure to the respective biological fluid, water penetrates into the device and decreases the T_g of HPMC (acting as a plasticizer). With increasing water concentration, this reduction of the T_g also increases. At a critical concentration of water, the T_g equals the temperature of the system, and the polymer undergoes the transition from the glassy to the rubbery state. The increasing mobility of the macromolecular chains results in drug-diffusion coefficients orders of magnitude higher than those in the glassy state. The kinetics of water penetration, swelling, and drug release have been studied extensively by Colombo and Peppas (132–135). Figure 2 shows the experimental as well as the theoretical concentration profiles of KCl (as a model drug), water, and HPMC 2208 in the gel phase of compressed tablets, 5 h (a) and 6 h (b) after exposure to water. The thickness of the swollen polymer changed from 1.75 mm at 4 h to 3 mm at 5 h and 5.25 mm at 6 h. In case of relevant dissolution of the polymer, the kinetics of this process must also be taken into account (136). In 1987 Lee and Peppas presented an appropriate model (137). The equilibrium swelling behavior of porous and nonporous hydrogels as well as their characterization has been reviewed by Brannon-Peppas and Peppas (138,139).

Uncoated Matrix Systems

A newly developed antihistaminergic drug, TA-5707F, has been released from HPMC matrix tablets by Yamakita et

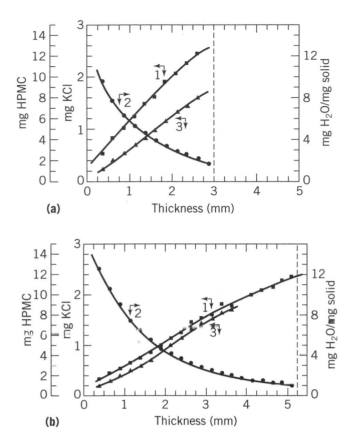

(a)

(b)

Figure 2. Concentration profiles of KCl (1), water (2), and HPMC 2208 (3) in the gel phase of compressed tablets after (**a**) 5 h and (**b**) 6 h. The dashed line corresponds to the swelling front. *Source:* Reprinted from Peppas et al. (132) with permission from Elsevier Scientific Publishing Company.

Figure 3. Schematic drawing of the matrix tablet (Case 0) and of the four coating designs investigated: Case 1, Case 2, Case 3 and Case 4. *Source:* Reprinted from Conte et al. (150) with permission from Elsevier Science Publishers B. V.

trix (Case 0), matrix with one base coated (Case 1), matrix with two bases coated (Case 2), matrix with lateral surface coated (Case 3), and matrix with one base plus lateral surface coated (Case 4). The applied coating modifies the relaxation rate of the polymer by affecting the dimension of the swelling of the plain matrix while leaving the diffusion characteristics of the active agent practically unchanged. The resulting drug release behavior is shown in Figure 4, for the case of diltiazem as active agent and Methocel® K100M as polymer. The release curves of cases 2–4 are nearly linear, except for a short period at the beginning of the experiment. These multilayer matrix systems for the controlled release of drugs have been patented by Colombo et al. (149) and are known as Geomatrix® systems. To facilitate the industrial production, the manual film-coating process can be avoided using press-coating techniques (150).

Polymer Blends

Perez-Marcos et al. (151) investigated the influence of the pH on the release of propranolol hydrochloride from matrices containing HPMC K4M and Carbopol® 974. At pH 1, the HPMC predominantly controlled the release of the drug, whereas at higher pH values, the Carbopol® became ionized and interacted with the active agent. In addition,

al. (140). They studied the in vitro as well as the (canine) in vivo kinetics. Liu and coworkers (141) presented the influence of the viscosity grade of HPMC on the release of diclofenac sodium in matrix tablets, performing in vitro and in vivo studies. The release mechanism of indomethacin containing HPMC matrix tablets in dependence on the initial drug loading and specific additives (e.g., starch) has been investigated by Xu and Sunada (142).

Pham and Lee (143) measured the transient dynamic swelling and dissolution behavior of HPMC matrices during drug release using a new flow-through cell (providing well-defined hydrodynamic conditions) and fluorescein as model drug. Studies of Ahlskog and Koller (144,145) deal with the treatment of Parkinson's disease, using a novel, potent, and selective dopamine D-2 agonist: MK-458 (PHNO; [+]-4-propyl-9-hydroxynaphthoxazine). The drug was administered in controlled-release devices (using HPMC matrices) as monotherapy in a double-blind, placebo-controlled, 12-week investigation.

Coated Matrix Systems

To achieve constant drug-release rates, Colombo and coworkers (146–148) covered different surface portions of an HPMC matrix tablet with an impermeable coating as can be seen in Figure 3. Systems prepared were uncoated ma-

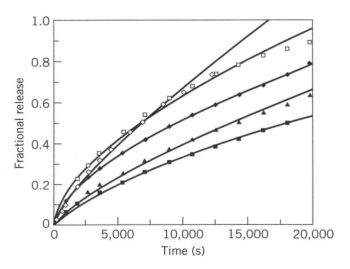

Figure 4. Fractional diltiazem release from five systems prepared by coating versus time. Case 0 (□), Case 1 (♦), Case 2 (▲), Case 3 (◇), and Case 4 (■). The straight lines have been calculated theoretically. *Source:* Reprinted from Colombo et al. (135) with permission from Elsevier Science Publishers B.V.

the interaction of the two polymers was significantly dependent on the pH. A controlled-release formulation for the α-MSH analog melanotan-I was developed by Bhardwaj and Blanchard (152) using HPMC and poloxamer 407. They characterized the release kinetics in vitro as well as in vivo (guinea pigs, intraperitoneal administration). Buccoadhesive morphine sulfate tablets have been developed and tested (in vitro and in vivo) by Anlar et al. (153). Carbomer (CP) served as the bioactive adhesive compound. The release behavior of systems containing 30 mg morphine sulfate and various amounts of HPMC and CP was found to be non-Fickian. The adhesion force was weakest at a ratio of 1:1 of the two polymers because of the formation of an interpolymer complex between HPMC and CP.

Poly(ethylene-vinyl acetate) (EVA) needle-shaped polymeric devices containing antitumor drugs may be applicable as drug carriers in cancer chemotherapy. Lin et al. (154) investigated the in vivo antitumor activity of adriamycin hydrochloride (ADH) in C3H mice bearing mammary carcinoma and nude mice bearing brain tumor. HPMC was used as a release rate regulator. Tumor growth was markedly inhibited by treatment with needle devices after being locally inserted into the solid tumor. Recent studies of Chowdary and Sankar (155) deal with solid dispersions of nifedipin in HPMC and microcrystalline cellulose (MCC). These systems gave a fast dissolution of the drug. However, when the dispersions were microencapsulated with Eudragit® RL PM, controlled, slow release was observed. The kinetics depended on the proportion of HPMC–MCC in the solid dispersion used as a core, on the coat/core ratio, and on the size of the microcapsules. The release was found to be independent of pH and ionic strength.

ACRYLIC POLYMERS

Besides cellulose derivatives, acrylic polymers are a popular choice for controlled-release dosage forms (156,157). Several derivatives of poly(methyl methacrylate) with different solubility properties were developed, predominantly for oral use. Enteric polymers were obtained by copolymerization of methyl methacrylate with methacrylic acid; polymers soluble at low pH by introducing dimethylaminoethyl methacrylate and water-insoluble but permeable polymers for diffusion-controlled drug delivery systems by the copolymerization of methyl methacrylate, ethyl acrylate, and small amounts of trimethylammonioethyl methacrylate chloride as monomers. The chemical composition of the commercially available poly(meth)acrylates, which are sold by Röhm under the trade name Eudragit®, is shown in Table 3. This review is limited to polymers insoluble in gastrointestinal fluids and used in controlled-release formulations and does not cover enteric polymers.

The poly(meth)acrylates were initially applied from organic solutions in alcohols, acetone, or solvent blends (156). Problems associated with the use of organic solvents led to the development of aqueous polymer dispersions. The water-insoluble methacrylate ester copolymers are neutral (Eudragit® NE 30D) or weekly cationic polymers

(Eudragit® RS or RL 30D), which are insoluble in gastrointestinal fluids. The aqueous dispersions have a solids content of 30%. The residual monomer content in the Eudragit® products for pharmaceutical applications is below 0.1%. The shelf-life specifications for aqueous polymer dispersions do usually not exceed 1 year.

Eudragit® NE 30D (a copolymer of ethyl acrylate and methyl methacrylate in a ratio of 2:1) is produced by emulsion polymerization. It has an MFT around 5°C and does not require plasticizers. The latex forms soft and highly flexible films upon drying. Eudragit® NE 30D could be blended with Eudragit® L 30D (an aqueous dispersion of an enteric polymer) to form enteric coatings without the use of additional plasticizer.

The cationic polymers, Eudragit® RL 100 or RS 100, are obtained by bulk polymerization of ethyl acrylate, methyl methacrylate, and trimethylammonioethyl methacrylate chloride. RL 100 contains twice as many quaternary ammonium groups than RS 100 and is therefore more hydrophilic and more permeable. The commercially available aqueous polymer dispersions are prepared by directly emulsifying the solid polymer into hot water at 80°C, which is above its T_g of 55°C. The dispersion process and the stability of the resulting polymer dispersion is positively affected by the positive charges of the polymer. No emulsifier is needed for the emulsification process. 0.25% sorbic acid is added as preservative. Eudragit® RL 30D and Eudragit® RS 30D require the addition of plasticizer to reduce the MFT below the coating temperature. The most frequently used plasticizers for the polymers are triethyl citrate, triacetin, and acetyltributyl citrate. The polymer dispersions are compatible with additives such as talc, titanium dioxide, and pigments. A colorimetric ion-pair complexation method has been developed to rapidly quantify RS and RL in pharmaceutical dosage forms (158).

RL and RS pseudolatexes were also prepared by a solvent change technique, whereby the polymer was dissolved in a water-miscible organic solvent (e.g., acetone) or solvent system followed by dispersion of this polymer solution in deionized water under mild agitation (159). The pseudolatex formed spontaneously after the diffusion of the organic solvent in the aqueous phase and solvent evaporation.

In Table 4, the mechanical and thermal properties of films from methacrylic ester copolymer latexes are summarized.

Coated Systems

Methacrylates have been used in the coating of pharmaceutical dosage forms for several decades. They can be applied either as an organic solution or as an aqueous colloidal dispersion.

The permeability of Eudragit® NE 30D films can be increased by adding water-soluble substances, such as sugars or water-soluble polymers: (PVP), poly(vinyl alcohol) (PVA), and PEGs (156). The addition of water-soluble cellulose ethers, such as HPMC, is not recommended because they can result in flocculation. Theophylline tablets have been coated with NE 30D latexes containing dispersed pore formers (160). Normally, microporous coatings are

Table 3. Methacrylic Acid and Methacrylic Ester Copolymers

Methacrylic acid copolymers

$$\left[-CH_2-\underset{\underset{OH}{\overset{\parallel}{C}=O}}{\overset{CH_3}{\underset{|}{\overset{|}{C}}}}-\right]_{n_1} -\;-\;-\;-\; \left[-CH_2-\underset{\underset{OR_2}{\overset{\parallel}{C}=O}}{\overset{R_1}{\underset{|}{\overset{|}{C}}}}-\right]_{n_2}$$

Scientific name	$n_1{:}n_2$	M_W	USP/NF type	R_1	R_2	Behavior in digestive juices	Eudragit® type	Marketed form
Poly (methacrylic acid, ethyl acrylate)	1:1	250,000	C	H	C_2H_5	Soluble, pH > 5.5	L 30D / L 100-55	30% aqueous dispersion powder
Poly(methacrylic acid, methyl methacrylate)	1:1	135,000	A	CH_3	CH_3	Soluble, pH > 6.0	L 100	Powder
Poly(methacrylic acid, methyl methacrylate)	1:2	135,000	B	CH_3	CH_3	Soluble, pH > 7.0	S 100	Powder

Methacrylate ester copolymers

$$\left[-CH_2-\underset{\underset{OC_2H_5}{\overset{\parallel}{C}=O}}{\overset{H}{\underset{|}{\overset{|}{C}}}}-\right]_{n_1} -\;-\;- \left[-CH_2-\underset{\underset{OCH_3}{\overset{\parallel}{C}=O}}{\overset{CH_3}{\underset{|}{\overset{|}{C}}}}-\right]_{n_2} -\;-\;- \left[-CH_2-\underset{\underset{OR}{\overset{\parallel}{C}=O}}{\overset{CH_3}{\underset{|}{\overset{|}{C}}}}-\right]_{n_3}$$

Scientific name	$n_1{:}n_2{:}n_3$	M_W	Behavior in digestive juices	Eudragit® type	Marketed form
Poly(ethyl acrylate,methyl methacrylate)	2:1	800,000	Insoluble films of medium permeability	NE 30D	30% aqueous dispersion
Poly(ethyl acrylate, methyl methacrylate) trimethylammonioethyl methacrylate chloride R: $CH_2\text{-}CH_2\text{-}N^+(CH_3)_3Cl^-$	1:2:0.2	150,000	Insoluble films of high permeability	RL 30D / RL 100	30% aqueous dispersion / Granules
Poly(ethyl acryate, methyl methacrylate)trimethylammonioethyl methacrylate chloride R: $CH_2\text{-}CH_2\text{-}N^+(CH_3)_3CL^-$	1:2:0.1	150,000	Insoluble films of low permeability	RS 30D / RS 100	30% aqueous dispersion Granules

Table 4. Mechanical and Thermal Properties of Films from Methacrylic Ester Copolymer Latexes

	Tensile stress at break (N/mm^2)	Elongation (%)	T_g (°C)
Eudragit® NE 30D			
	8	600	−8
Eudragit® RS 30D			
+10 % triacetine	5	40	–
+20% triethyl citrate	2	300	20
Eudragit® RL 30D			
+10% triacetine	5	22	35
+20% triethyl citrate	4	300	30

Source: Adapted from K. Lehmann (156) with permission from Marcel Dekker, Inc.

prepared by dispersing water-soluble pore formers in organic polymer solutions followed by the coating step. The pore formers then leach from the coating into aqueous fluids, forming a microporous coating. With this novel system, a microporous membrane could be prepared without organic solvents by using pore formers with pH-dependent solubility properties (e.g., calcium salts), which were insoluble at the pH of the latex but were soluble in gastric juice. The pore former was dispersed in the coating and leached in aqueous media to form a multiporous coating through which the drug was released in a zero-order fashion.

Although the release from RS or RL-coated systems has been described to be pH-independent, a "pH-dependent" drug release was observed (161–163). This was actually caused by the presence in the release media of different anionic buffers species, which acted as counterions for the quaternary ammonium groups and replaced the chloride ion. The drug release correlated well with the hydration of the polymer films in different buffers (161). In another study, the release of theophylline from pellets coated with RS also showed a great dependence on the composition of the buffer solution. In contrast, the drug release from pellets coated with NE and the swelling of NE films was not significantly affected by the buffer species (162). Although the influence of buffer species can be diminished by the addition of NaCl (163), anionic species in the gastrointestinal tract, such as bile salts, have also been shown to have a dramatic effect on the drug release (164).

RS and RL 30D dispersions can be mixed in any ratio, with the coatings showing intermediate permeability properties (165,166). The addition of silica or talcum increased the drug release (166). The permeability of the films can also be influenced by the choice of plasticizer (167). An overcoat with the enteric polymer, Eudragit® S 100, eliminated the agglomeration of RS-coated pellets (167,168). Otherwise, talc or glycerol monostearate are used as antitacking agents (157).

The lag time prior to the diltiazem HCl release from RS-coated pellets could be controlled by varying the thickness of the coating (169). The drug release had a pattern of a lag period followed by an instantaneous release phase. A linear relationship was reported between the lag time and the square of the amount of polymer coated. High drug solubility was required for the rapid drug release after the lag period, which was caused by the time necessary for the polymeric film to hydrate. A sigmoidal release system (time-controlled drug delivery system) was developed, which consisted of a prolonged lag time followed by a rapid release phase (170–172). Because of the low water permeability of the RS film, the lag time could be varied by varying the thickness of the film. The drug release phase after the lag period could be enhanced by electrostatic or other physicochemical interactions between the polymer and organic acids such as succinic acid. The organic acid affected the hydration of the polymeric film. The drug release from beads coated with NE 30D, which has no quaternary ammonium group in the polymer chain, was not affected by succinic acid. Ion-exchange experiments revealed that organic acids interacted with the quaternary ammonium groups of RS by an ion-exchange mechanism.

A wide range of release rates can be obtained by adding additives to a single polymer or by blending different polymers. The membrane permeability of film-coated theophylline pellets was controlled by using blends of different aqueous acrylic polymer dispersions (173). A film with pH-dependent permeability was obtained by blending the neutral acrylic polymer, NE, with the enteric polymer, L, showing higher release rates at intestinal pH values. A wide range of dissolution profiles was obtained by blending the more permeable RL with the less permeable RS to obtain pH-independent permeabilities. Heterogeneous film structures were obtained by blending RS 30D and ND 30D, as indicated by two individual glass-transition temperatures. Enteric polymers can be incorporated into the water-insoluble polymers to develop pH-dependent systems for the linearization of release profiles or to adjust the drug release with drugs with pH-dependent solubility.

A model was developed that permitted the quantitative correlation of the release kinetics from coated pellets with the permeation properties of free films (174). The film data allow the prediction of the drug release from coated pellets, under the condition that the manufacturing process was kept constant and the cores of the coated pellets were identical.

Coated particles or pellets have also been compressed into tablets. Various formulation and process parameters have to be optimized to obtain tabletted reservoir-type pellets having the same properties, and, in particular, release properties as the original, uncompacted pellets. The most important variable is the type of polymer selected for the coating of the pellets. The polymer coating must remain intact during compaction. When compared to ethyl cellulose films, films prepared from acrylic polymers are more flexible and therefore more suitable for the coating of pellets to be compressed into tablets (62). Films of Eudragit® NE 30D were very flexible. The elongation was in excess of the elongation limit of 365% achievable with the puncture test device. With plasticized Eudragit® RS and RL 30D, flexible films were obtained with elongation values in excess of 125%. Crystals, granules, and pellets were coated with various aqueous acrylic polymer dispersions (Eudragit® NE 30D, RS/RL 30D, and L 30D-55) and compressed into fast-disintegrating tablets (156,175). Multiparticulates coated with flexible polymers (Eudragit® NE 30D and plasticized Eudragit® RS/RL 30D) could be compressed without significant damage to the coating. No or only small changes in drug release were found with coatings with elongation values in excess of 75%. These films have enough elasticity to deform on coated pellets during compression without rupture. Very little difference in drug release was observed between the compressed granules and the noncompressed granules, which contained theophylline and were coated with an Eudragit® RL/RS dispersion. Enteric coatings based on Eudragit® L 30D-55, a methacrylic acid–ethylacrylate copolymer, were brittle, and the compression of the pellets resulted in film damage. This damage could be avoided by mixing the enteric polymer with the flexible Eudragit® NE 30D. Heterogeneous films, which retained their enteric properties, were obtained after the addition of Eudragit® NE 30D.

The effect of compression force on the dissolution from Eudragit® NE 30D–coated theophylline pellets was evaluated in a range of 6–20 kN (176). The compaction-induced pellet deformation was practically complete at 6 kN, and no change in dissolution rate was observed upon increasing the compression force to 20 kN. The increase in drug-release rate was not attributed to rupturing of the polymeric film but to a thinning of the flexible film because of stretching. A recent review provides an update on the tabletting of coated pellets and discusses important formulation and process parameters necessary to obtain pellet-containing tablets, which, ideally, have the same properties—in particular, drug-release properties—as the individual coated pellets (177).

Films

Various release, permeability, and mechanical properties of drug-containing or drug-free films have been determined to predict primarily the properties of film-coated dosage forms. The films can be prepared either from organic polymer solutions or from the aqueous polymer dispersions. The drug has to be compatible with the polymer dispersion; for example, the addition of anionic drugs to the cationic polymer dispersion, RS 30D, results in flocculation.

The choice of organic solvents affected the permeability of cast Eudragit® RL and RS films. Including ethanol in the acetonic casting solution resulted in a greater permeability, which was caused by a decrease in pore size but an increase in pore number. The microstructure of the film was therefore strongly affected by the composition of the solvent mixture (178). Differences in the solute diffusion were also observed between the lower and upper surface of polymeric films (179,180). The lower film surface, which was in contact with the mold during casting, was more permeable than the upper surface.

The partition coefficients and diffusion coefficients of progesterone and a synthetic progestin were determined with drug-loaded Eudragit® RL films. The partition coefficients showed that both steroids were dissolved in the polymer films, and the values of the diffusion coefficients revealed that the mechanism of diffusion was a solution-diffusion and not a pore-diffusion mechanism (181).

RL and RS films containing salicylic acid and chlorpheniramine maleate were prepared by organic solvent casting (182,183). The drugs were soluble in the polymers and acted as plasticizers for the polymers, as shown by a decreased T_g. The addition of hydrophilic adjuvants increased the release rate. Salicylic acid interacted with the cationic groups of the polymers via electrostatic interactions. Increasing the ionic strength of the dissolution media increased the drug release from the matrix films (184).

Drug-containing films have been prepared by casting the aqueous colloidal polymer dispersions followed by drying. The propranolol HCl release from RS films increased with increasing RS-RL ratio (185). The drug-release rate was high at low plasticizer concentrations because of incomplete coalescence of the colloidal particles and film formation and then was constant in a plasticizer range between 10 and 30% and then increased at higher plasticizer concentrations because of the leaching of the plasticizer. The drug release from latex-cast films was faster when compared with that from solvent-cast films of the same composition. Films cast from organic polymer solution were less porous and denser than the comparable latex-cast films, as observed with scanning electron microscopy.

Depending on the solubility of the drug, it could be either dissolved or dissolved/dispersed in the polymeric NE matrix (186). Depending on the drug loading, the drug release was a combination of diffusion through the polymer and diffusion through pores or channels. The drug release increased with increasing drug loading and increasing amount of HPMC in the NE film. Zero-order drug release could be achieved by laminating a second drug-free latex film onto the first reservoir layer (187).

The mechanical properties of RS 30D films were tested in the dry and in the wet state by a puncture test (188). The water-soluble plasticizer triethyl citrate leached into the dissolution medium, while the water-insoluble plasticizer acetyltributyl citrate remained in the film. While films were quite flexible with both plasticizers in the dry state (the elongation values at normally used plasticizer concentrations were in excess of 100%), the elongation values of wet triethyl citrate–containing films were significantly lower than the elongation values of wet acetyltributyl citrate–containing films. The choice of the plasticizer therefore strongly affects the mechanical properties of the resulting films in the wet and therefore in the gastrointestinal media. NE films were highly flexible in both the dry and wet state.

Eudragit® NE 30D and RL and Eudragit® RS 30D have also been used in dermal and transdermal systems. They form clear and transparent films that are insoluble in water but hydrate. Films for transdermal therapeutic systems have been prepared from organic polymer solutions, aqueous polymer dispersions, and by a hot-melt extrusion technique (156,157). Matrix films can be prepared by incorporating the drug in the polymer phase followed by casting/drying or extrusion. Forty to sixty percent plasticizer are used for the hot-melt extrusion of RS and RL at 80–120°C. Films of Eudragit® NE 30D have shown good skin tolerance; they are flexible and permeable to water vapor.

Matrix Tablets

Poly(meth)acrylate powders have also been used as retarding materials in matrix tablets (156,157). The polymer can be directly compressed or wet granulated. The necessary amount of polymer to obtain controlled release was in the range of 10 to 50% of the tablet weight. It is mainly affected by the solubility and dose of the drug. The polymer can also be incorporated by granulating the drug and excipients with the aqueous colloidal polymer dispersions. Eroding sustained-release tablets have been formulated by granulating Emcompress® and diprophylline with NE 40D. RS 100 and salicylic acid were directly compressed into tablet cores (189). The drug release was further retarded by a coating with aqueous RS–sucrose mixtures of varying ratios.

Microencapsulation

Micro- or nanoparticles based on the acrylic polymers as carriers have been prepared by various microencapsulation techniques including organic phase separation, solvent evaporation, and spray-drying techniques (see MICROENCAPSULATION).

Paracetamol was encapsulated with RS by an organic phase separation process. The nonsolvent, cyclohexane, was added to a chloroformic solution of the polymer. Polyisobutylene was used as an antiaggregating agent. The drug release increased with increasing proportion of the core material and with a reduced coating thickness (190). A gradation of the microcapsule wall porosity could be obtained by depositing polymer mixtures of RL and RS on drug particles by the organic phase separation process (191). The release rates increased with increasing polar group content (RL content). Salicylic acid has been encapsulated by a coacervation process whereby the nonsolvent, water, was added to an ethanolic solution of the drug and polymer. Both drug and polymer precipitated after the addition of water (192).

Various antiinflammatory agents were encapsulated within RS- and RL-microspheres by the solvent evaporation method, whereby an organic drug containing polymer solution was emulsified into an external aqueous phase (83). Nanoparticles in the colloidal size range were obtained after microfluidization of the oil-in-water (O/W) emulsion (86). Ketoprofen–RS microspheres were formed by a nonaqueous solvent evaporation method by emulsifying a drug–polymer solution in liquid paraffin (193). Aluminium tristearate was used as a stabilizing agent.

Multiple-unit hollow microspheres (microballoons) were prepared by an emulsion solvent-diffusion method (194). The drug and acrylic polymer were dissolved in an ethanol–methylene chloride mixture. This solution was poured into an aqueous PVA solution to form emulsion droplets followed by polymer precipitation. The volume of the internal cavity of the microballoons increased at higher polymer ratios. Floatable microballoons could be prepared. Ibuprofen–RS microspheres and microsponges with different intraparticle porosities were prepared by a similar method (195–197). The internal porosity of the microsponges could be controlled by changing the concentration of the drug and the polymer in the ethanolic emulsion droplet. The formation of the microspheres with ethanol, a water-miscible solvent, was possible because of the quaternary ammonium groups in polymer chain, which stabilized the emulsion.

Nanoparticles containing the water-insoluble drugs ibuprofen, indomethacin, or propranolol were formed spontaneously after the addition of solutions of the drugs and RS or RL 100 polymers in the water-miscible solvents acetone or ethanol to water without homogenization (198). The nanoparticle dispersion was stabilized by the quaternary ammonium groups of the polymer and did not require the addition of external stabilizers. Other water-insoluble polymers require the use of water-immiscible organic solvents (e.g., methylene chloride) and a homogenization step to form nanoparticles. The cationic acrylic polymers allowed the formation of nanoparticles without homogenization or toxic organic solvents. RS or RL nanoparticles could also be formed by the melt method. The drug containing acrylic nanoparticles could be transformed into films by including plasticizers. This could be useful for dermal applications of nanoparticle dispersions. The release from the resulting films could be controlled by the ratio of RS to RL or the inclusion of water-soluble polymers to the nanoparticle suspensions prior to casting.

Acetyl salicylic acid–RS microspheres were prepared by a falling-drop process (solvent-partition method) whereby a solution of the polymer in methylene chloride and acetone (9:1) was injected into a flowing mineral oil stream (199). The solvent was extracted, and drug–polymer microspheres were formed. This method is in principle very similar to a nonaqueous solvent evaporation method.

Microparticles containing diltiazem HCl were prepared by spray-drying RS and RL polymer solutions (200). The choice of the solvent affected the structure of the resulting microparticles; either microspheres or microcapsules could be obtained. When compared with other encapsulation methods, spray-drying has many attractive features. It is a rapid, single-operation procedure suitable for large-scale production. Most microencapsulation methods are based on two immiscible phases, and drug loss to the external phase resulting in low encapsulation efficiencies is often a problem. With spray-drying, the external phase is air, and drug loss is therefore not an issue. Alternatively to organic RS or RL solution, drug-containing aqueous polymer dispersions were used to form the microparticles by spray-drying (201–205). The drug was either dissolved (chlorpheniramine maleate) or suspended (ibuprofen, naproxen) in the aqueous phase of the polymeric dispersion (164). Under optimal spray-drying conditions, the colloidal polymer particles coalesced into microparticles within the atomized droplets. Spherical microparticles with drug loadings between 10 and 50% were obtained with an average particle size in the range of 5–20 μm. The yield decreased with increasing drug loading and plasticizer level because of sticking and agglomeration. Chlorpheniramine maleate and ibuprofen acted as plasticizers for the polymer. Although ibuprofen was suspended in the polymer disper-

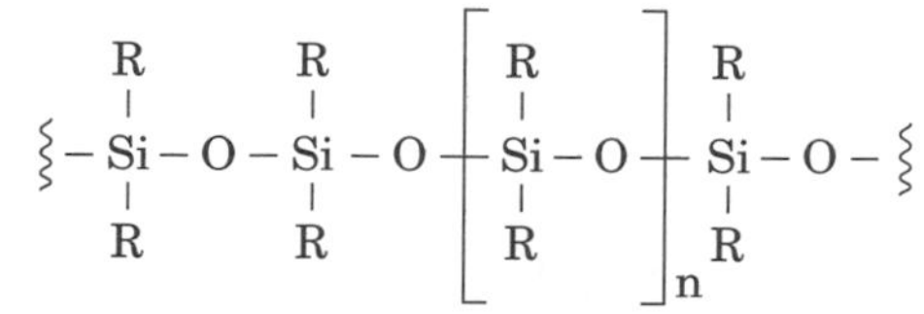

Figure 5. Structure of Si–O polymer chains; R is an organic substituent.

sion, it was dissolved in the microparticles, as indicated by X-ray diffraction studies.

Coprecipitates of ibuprofen and various acrylic polymers were prepared by adding a drug–polymer solution in acetone to water, followed by drying and milling of the precipitate (206). The coprecipitates had improved flow properties when compared with ibuprofen and are useful for the preparation of sustained-release tablets. Coevaporates of dipyridamole and the Eudragit® S, L, RL, or RS were prepared by dissolving the drug and polymer in an ethanol/methylene chloride (1:1) mixture, followed by removal of the solvent in a rotary evaporator and pulverization of the residue. Depending on the processing conditions, either a solid solution or dispersion was formed, as determined by X-ray and DSC. pH dependence and a variety of release profiles could be obtained by blending the different polymers (207).

SILICONES

Most silicones used in pharmaceutical applications consist of cross-linked Si–O polymer chains (shown in Fig. 5). R is an organic substituent, for example, CH$_3$ (in polydimethylsiloxane [PDMS]). There are several commonly used methods of synthesis, such as two-component condensation cures, one-component moisture cures, and two-component vinyl cures (208), resulting in different kinds of chemical cross-linking (Fig. 6a and b). Depending on the average chain length, type of substituent, and type and degree of cross-linking, the resulting polymers have significantly different properties (fluids, resins, elastomers). Generally, silicones are inert, poor conductors of electricity and hydrophobic.

The synthesis of drug-containing silicone systems is often very convenient. Before cross-linking, the adequate prepolymers are usually in a liquid state. The fluid components are mixed with the drug, and a cross-linking agent and/or a catalyst are/is added. This mixture is subsequently cast into a mold of the desired shape. After a few hours the formation of the polymer network (cross-linking reaction) hardens the device (209).

Owing to the ease of fabrication and high permeability for many drugs (e.g., steroids) silicones are often used for controlled drug delivery. The exceptionally high diffusion coefficients result from the high chain mobility of the Si–O backbones (210). The possibility of heat sterilization and remarkable biocompatibility make them favorable for parenteral systems.

As most silicones are physically weak, silica fillers are usually added to increase the mechanical stability of the resulting controlled-release system. The effective diffusion coefficient of the active agent is lowered by this addition of silica because the latter is usually not permeable for the drug and thus increases the diffusion pathways (211). Drug-release rates in these controlled-release systems are also significantly dependent on the amount and type of free polymer chains (that have not been cross-linked to the network during the synthesis of the device). Mazan et al. (211) used two different unreactive PDMS oils, MD$_{25}$M and MD$_{75}$M, to produce well-defined systems (M represents a terminal block with three methyl groups; D is an SiO group with two methyl groups). Not only the diffusion coefficient of the drug but also the swelling extent of the system is a function of these components. The dependencies of the progesterone diffusion coefficient (D) and swelling extent (Q) of the silicone network on the amount and type of free polymer chains is illustrated in Figure 7 (nomenclature: relative amount of free chains F = [mass of cross-linked sample − mass of dry sample after elution in hexane]/mass of cross-linked sample). Moreau et al. (212) studied the effect of grafting an organic pendent segment along the PDMS chains. They evaluated the impact of this modification on the drug solubility, diffusivity, and elastomer properties. Thermal analysis and measurements of the swelling ratio have been used to characterize the influence of vulcanization conditions and chemical modifications on the network mesh size and subsequently on the diffusion of an active agent (213). An excellent review has been written by Baker

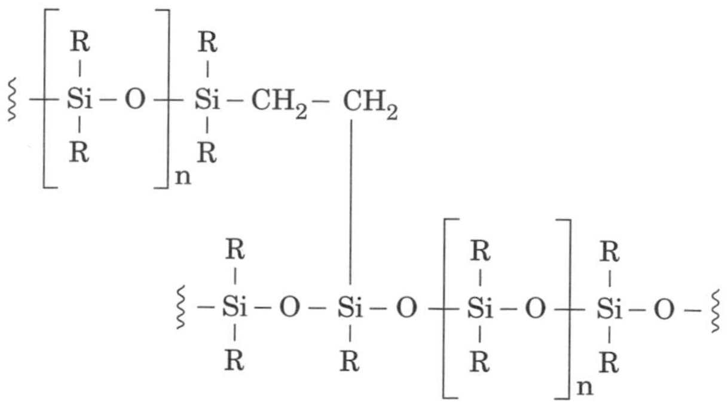

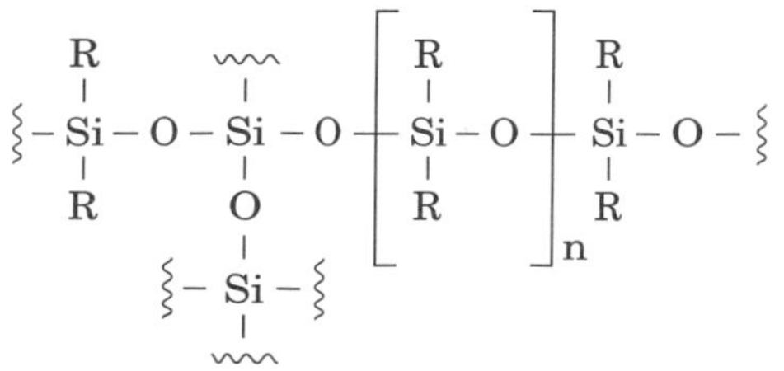

Figure 6. (a) and (b): Different types of cross-linkings in silicone networks.

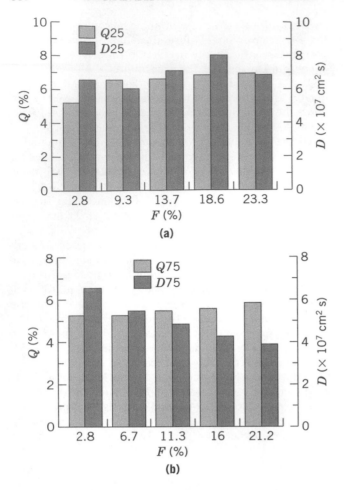

Figure 7. Variation of the swelling extend (Q) and the progesterone diffusion coefficient (D) as a function of the relative amount of free chains: (**a**) network loaded with $MD_{25}M$; (**b**) network loaded with $MD_{75}M$. *Source:* Reprinted from Mazan et al. (211) with permission from Pergamon Press.

(214) concerning the role of silicones in controlled drug delivery systems.

Implantable Systems

Norplant® (Leiras) is a contraceptive subdermal implant system consisting of six hollow PDMS cylinders filled with levonorgestrel crystals (215–217). Figure 8 shows schematically the design of this device, which is implanted in the inner aspect of the woman's upper arm. The drug-release rate is controlled by the total surface area and thickness of the silicone cylinders. Because of the excess of drug at the inner surface, approximately constant release rates are achieved over a period of 5 years (216). Compared to oral contraceptives, implantable long-term systems have two main advantages: (*1*) owing to the elimination of the hepatic first-pass effect, the applied doses can be reduced significantly; and (*2*) avoiding daily application, the compliance and safety of the system are markedly increased.

The utility of controlled-release norgestomet/silicone implants in synchronizing estrus and diagnosing preg-

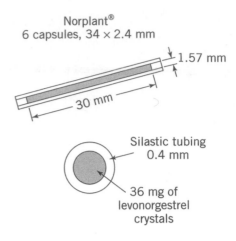

Figure 8. Design and dimensions of the contraceptive system Norplant®. *Source:* Reprinted from Sam (215) with permission from Elsevier Science Publishers B.V.

nancy in ewes has been investigated by Kesler and Favero (218). The overall estrus and lambing responses were 90 and 67%, respectively; the accuracy of the diagnosis of the pregnancy status was 100%. Refillable and implantable devices containing the anticancer drug 1,3-bis(2-chloroethyl)-1-nitrosourea (BCNU) were investigated by Ueno et al. (219). The release kinetics of various kinds of silicone and silicone–nylon-based systems were studied in dependence of the surface area and wall thickness of the device. Reversible chemical castration is one of the possible applications of RS-49947 ([D-Nal[6], aza-Gly[10]]-luteinizing hormone-releasing hormone)–silicone elastomer implants, investigated by Burns et al. (220,229). In vitro and in vivo studies have been performed, investigating the effect of drug loading, γ-irradiation, and particle and implant size. The sustained behavioral recovery from unilateral nigrostriatal damage produced by the controlled release of dopamine from a silicone polymer pellet placed into the denervated striatum of rats was studied by Becker et al. (222). Studies of Hirsch et al. (223) deal with the synergistic inhibition of the calcification of glutaraldehyde-pretreated bovine pericardium by $FeCl_3$ and calcium ethanehydroxydiphosphonate (CaEHDP) containing silicone–rubber matrices. Calcification is a frequent cause of the clinical failure of bioprosthetic heart valves fabricated from glutaraldehyde-pretreated porcine aortic valves or glutaraldehyde-pretreated bovine pericardium (GPBP). Twenty-one-day subdermal implants in 3-week-old male rats showed 1% $FeCl_3$–20% CaEHDP silicone–rubber matrices to be most effective for inhibiting GPBP mineralization.

Intravaginal Systems

Silicone-based intravaginal devices (diaphragms and discs) have been developed by Lee et al. (224,225). They optimized the loading dose of the spermicide Nonoxynol-9 and studied the effect of an additional cosolvent (optimizing drug release) and of storage time.

Ocular Systems

Ocular drug delivery systems based on silicones were developed and tested in vitro and in vivo by Urtti et al. (226–228). Timolol inserts were compared to conventional eyedrops and were found to give similar decreases in intraocular pressure in open-angle glaucoma patients but to produce lower drug concentrations in the blood. Thus, the unwanted absorption of timolol into the systemic circulation could be reduced significantly. Dissolving or dispersing various prodrugs of 5-fluorouracil in silicone oil for ocular drug delivery has been studied by Steffansen et al. (209). The effect of γ-irradiation and exposure to heat on the physicochemical properties of novel silicone-based gentamicin sulfate ocular drug delivery systems has been presented by Bawa and Nandu (230). The mechanical properties were found to be unchanged, whereas the drug-release rates were affected by γ-irradiation as well as exposure to heat. In addition, a certain degradation of the active agent was caused by long-term heat treatment.

Miscellaneous

Li et al. published various articles concerning the preparation and testing of silicone-based matrix tablets (e.g., 231–234). They investigated, for example, the effect of additives like PEG or colloidal silica as well as different shapes and methods of fabrication. Planar dimethylsiloxane matrix systems containing 10 different substituted pyridines at their solubility limit were presented by Chen and Matheson (235) with respect to the drug–polymer interactions. Hydrogen bonding between the pyridines and the polymer matrix was found to be one of the factors governing the release rate. Numerous studies were performed by Sutinen et al. concerning silicone reservoir systems (of various shapes) with different additives to manipulate the release kinetics (236–238). Osmotic (e.g., sodium chloride) and buffering (e.g., Tris buffer) additives are excellent tools to achieve a desired release profile (239,240). Zero-order release kinetics during a considerable time interval were observed for cinnamyl alcohol from spherical PDMS beads in pentane by Lee and Lum (241). In water, however, the corresponding release was completely Fickian. Veterinary controlled-release systems have been developed by Brochart et al. (242). Reservoir devices of different composition were tested and constant release rates were achieved over a period of 22 days.

The use of aqueous silicone latex for the coating of tablets and pellets as well as the impact of heat treatment and the addition of the pore former PEG 8,000 on the mass transport in these systems were presented by Dahl and Sue (56,243). pH-sensitive hydrogels, releasing the drug at enteric pH but not at gastric pH, have been synthesized by γ-irradiation of solutions of N-isopropylacrylamide (NIPAAm), acrylic acid (AAc), and bis-vinyl-terminated polydimethylsiloxane (VTPDMS) and tested by Dong and Hoffman (244,245). This property is especially interesting for stomach-irritating active agents like indomethacin. An in vitro study has shown that only a negligible amount of indomethacin is released at pH 1.4 within 24 h, while at pH 7.4 more than 90% of the total drug in the gel is gradually released over 5 h. The effect of propranolol on the

prevention of ventricular tachycardia/fibrillation due to acute coronary ischaemia using polyurethane–silicone copolymers was studied in dogs by Siden et al. (246). Loth and Euschen investigated liquid-crystalline side-chain silastomers (247). The type of polysiloxane main chain and the chain length of the PDMS cross-linker as well as the mesogenic group determine the structure and properties of the resulting silastomer. The relationship between the drug-release rate particle size, and swelling of PDMS matrices was studied by Golomb et al. (248). Controlled polymer cracking (osmotically induced) to promote macromolecular release (bovine serum albumin) was presented by Carelli et al. (249). Recent studies of Sheppard and coworkers (250) deal with a new class of controlled-release devices based on micromachined silicone structures. Processes developed for integrated circuit fabrication are used to produce three-dimensional networks that can be loaded with drugs. The advantage of this method is the possibility to gain well-defined pore structures instead of random pore size and shape distributions.

EVA

The general structure of the copolymer EVA is shown in Figure 9. EVA is chemically stable, nontoxic, and biocompatible. Owing to its thermoplasticity, it can be processed by extrusion and injection molding. Two other main advantages of this polymer are (1) its high flexibility (which allows avoiding plasticizers) and (2) its ability to be sterilized by radiation.

The physicochemical properties of EVA (and thus its permeability properties) are strongly dependent on the comonomer ratio. Not only the T_g but also the crystallinity of the resulting copolymer is determined by the relative vinyl acetate content. Generally, both the T_g as well as the crystallinity significantly influence the diffusion coefficient (D) of a drug (251). In crystalline regions, D is several orders of magnitude smaller than in amorphous regions (owing to the reduced chain mobility); in rubbery domains, D is higher than in glassy ones (for analogous reasons). Desired permeabilities can easily be achieved by varying the relative vinyl acetate content. Johnson and Nachtrab (252) investigated the influence of the vinyl acetate content on the crystallinity of the resulting copolymer. Pure polyethylene has a crystallinity of 70%. The addition of vinyl acetate into this structure destroys the regularity of the polymer chains, thus reducing crystallinity. Above 50 wt % vinyl acetate content, the copolymer is almost completely amorphous. On the other hand, the T_g of EVA varies sig-

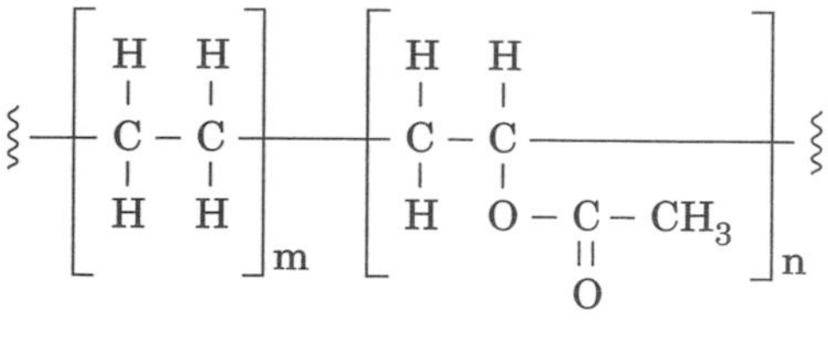

Figure 9. Chemical structure of the copolymer EVA [Poly-(ethylene-vinyl acetate)].

nificantly with increasing vinyl acetate content (Fig. 10). This dependence is biphasic: The Tg remains constant (approximately $-25°C$) for 0 wt % up to 50 wt % vinyl acetate and then linearly rises up to 38°C at 100 wt % vinyl acetate (253,254). There are two contrary influences on the diffusion coefficient of a drug with increasing vinyl acetate content: (1) a rising Tg generally lowers D, whereas (2) the decreasing crystallinity increases D. The resulting permeability properties for the model drug camphor have been studied by Gale and Spitze (255,256). As a result of the two competitive processes, the limiting flux of camphor through EVA goes through a maximum.

Recently, Shin and Byun (257) investigated the permeation of ethinylestradiol through EVA membranes as a function of the drug concentration, vinyl acetate content, membrane thickness, and temperature. Benzocaine was chosen as a model drug by Chen and Lostritto (258) to study the effect of ethanol in EVA membranes. As ethanol leads to significant swelling of the copolymer, the permeability of the drug was markedly increased. The release mechanism from drug containing EVA films was elucidated by Miller et al. (259). Considerable pore collapse was observed during the release process.

Implantable Systems

In 1976 Langer and Folkman opened the door for the controlled release of proteins and other macromolecules from polymeric systems (260). They presented a simple method for incorporating large molecules into noninflammatory polymers (like EVA) and demonstrated sustained release of biologically active agents for periods exceeding 100 days. In that study, pellets were prepared by casting a mixture of an EVA solution and the macromolecular drug into glass molds. No inflammation was observed after implantation into the eyes of rabbits. The in vitro and in vivo release of soybean trypsin inhibitor and tumor angiogenesis factor was investigated. Langer and coworkers studied the use of EVA in various different controlled drug delivery systems. For example, they developed a new fabrication technique (261), leading to more uniform drug distributions in the EVA matrices and higher reproducibilities of the release

kinetics. A mixture of powdered protein and polymer solution is cast at $-80°C$ and dried at $-20°C$ and subsequently 20°C. The effect of drug particle size, drug loading, and matrix coating has also been investigated. They observed three phases: (1) an initial burst, (2) a period of approximately $t^{1/2}$ release, and (3) a final period when release tapered off. The initial burst effect presumably is due to protein dissolution on the surface. As the macromolecules are too large to diffuse through a pure polymer film, it is possible that sustained release occurs via diffusion through channels in the matrix. The incorporation of the macromolecules during casting may introduce such channels through which the dissolved drug can diffuse. Thus, matrix characteristics (e.g., porosity and tortuosity) are very important for the resulting release rate. Figure 11 shows that the release rate increases with increasing drug particle size, probably due to the formation of larger channels or pores within the polymer matrix. Similarly, increased loadings may provide simple pathways (lower tortuosity) and greater porosity for diffusion, both of which facilitate the movement of water into and proteins out of the matrix (Fig. 12). The exposure to organic solvent can be avoided when mixing drug and EVA powders below the Tg of the polymer and compressing the mixture at a temperature above the glass-transition point (262). The mechanism of drug release (dissolution/diffusion) was studied in more detail 1989 by Saltzman and Langer (263). They developed predictive models using percolation concepts to describe pore topology and continuum models of diffusion/dissolution to describe protein movement at each single pore, and they measured pore size distributions. Up to 10-fold reversible increases in the release rate of incorporated molecules within EVA copolymers were observed when ap-

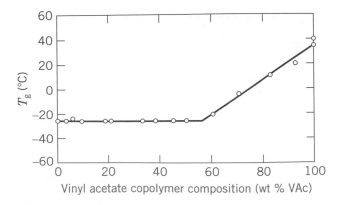

Figure 10. Glass-transition temperature of EVA, depending on the copolymer composition. *Source:* Reprinted from Baker (214) with permission from John Wiley & Sons.

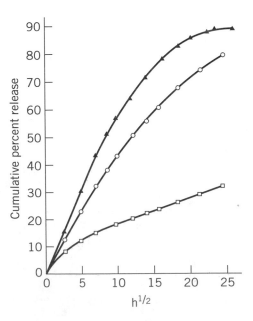

Figure 11. Particle size effect on cumulative release. Bovine serum albumin particles of three size ranges (<75 μm [empty squares], 75–250 μm [empty circles], and 250–425 μm [filled triangles]) were incorporated into EVA matrices. *Source:* Reprinted from Rhine et al. (261) with permission from APhA and ACS.

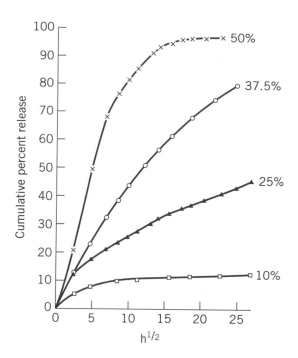

Figure 12. Loading effect on cumulative release. EVA matrices with four different loadings of bovine serum albumin (by weight) have been investigated. *Source:* Reprinted from Rhine et al. (261) with permission from ACS.

plying ultrasound, the increase being in proportion to the intensity of ultrasound (264). The treatment of Parkinson's disease is a potential application of a system releasing dopamine from EVA matrix discs for up to 65 days following stratial implantation. Drug release occurs through a single cavity present on one side of the disc, which is otherwise fully coated with an additional, impermeable layer of EVA (265). Langer and coworkers also embedded a drug and a small magnet into an EVA matrix and applied a magnetic field on this system (266). The presented drug release was increased up to 30 times above baseline levels. Using DSC and TMA, they studied the release of proteins from different types of EVA matrices over a wide range of temperatures. The observed effects could be related to the temperature-dependent diffusivity of the drug and elastic modulus of EVA (267). Another important system Langer et al. studied is an implantable, glucose-sensitive device releasing insulin. Feedback control is mediated by the glucose oxidase enzyme immobilized to Sepharose beads, which are incorporated along with insulin into an EVA matrix. When glucose in solution enters the device, gluconic acid is produced, causing a drop in the microenvironmental pH of the matrix. This fall in pH results in a rise in insulin solubility and consequently a rise in the insulin release rate from the matrix (268). Recently, they elucidated the role of the burst effect in an essentially zero-order controlled-release coated hemispherical EVA device (269). The macromolecular active agent bovine serum albumin (BSA) leaves the system through a single, small orifice.

The prevention of calcification of aortic walls using implants based on EVA and the calcium salt of ethanehydroxybisphosphonate (CaEHBP) and ferric chloride

($FeCl_3$) have been studied by Vyavahare et al. (270). They developed films releasing the drugs continuously over 60 days without any rapid burst phase. Calcification of the aortic walls was inhibited synergistically by the two active agents. Studies of Lesser et al. (271) investigate the in vitro and in vivo release of subcutaneous hydromorphone implants designed for the treatment of cancer pain. They developed and tested an implantable opioid delivery device capable of releasing the potent drug subcutaneously at a constant rate for 4 weeks. The treatment of Alzheimer's disease might be an application of the EVA discs prepared by Krewson et al. (272), releasing a protein (nerve growth factor [NGF]).

Intravaginal Systems

A very well known application of EVA in controlled-release devices is the intravaginal release of steroidal contraceptives, as in Progestasert® (marketed by ALZA Corporation). A liquid silicone oil serves as inert carrier medium for progesterone, surrounded by a controlling barrier of EVA (T-shaped reservoir device) (273–276). Barium sulfate is added to render the system radiopaque. Figure 13 shows a scheme of the device. The in utero release rate of the drug in humans remains approximately constant over a period of 400 days: 65 ± 10 μg/day (277). This is due to the constant progesterone concentration at the inner surface of the EVA copolymer membrane. Drug molecules leaving the reservoir are replaced due to the excess of progesterone in the silicone oil (initial concentration > solubility). Compared with conventional contraceptives, the decisive advantage of this system is the protection from pregnancy for more than 1 year without the need of daily self-medication or other regular patient action.

Ocular Systems

Another well-known system using EVA membranes is the Ocusert® (ALZA Corporation). It is placed in the conjunc-

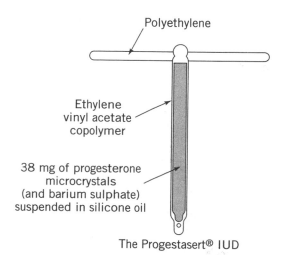

Figure 13. Scheme of Progestasert®, an intrauterine progesterone contraceptive system. *Source:* Reprinted from Sam (215) with permission from Elsevier Science Publishers B.V.

tival cul-de-sac to release pilocarpine during 1 week. The drug is dispersed in alginic acid and surrounded by two EVA membranes, controlling the release rate (278–281). As in Progestasert®, excess of drug (11.0 mg in Pilo-40, 5.0 mg in Pilo-20) leads to a constant drug concentration at the inner membrane surface of this reservoir system and subsequently to constant release rates, as shown in Table 5.

Miscellaneous

Miyazaki et al. (283) investigated the factors affecting the release patterns of 5-fluorouracil from EVA matrices. The influence of the surface area, temperature, pH, and an additional coating on the release characteristics of the devices has been studied. Blends of EVA and the bioerodable poly(D, L-lactic acid) (PLA) for controlled-release applications have been presented by Dollinger and Sawan (284). The PLA mass loss was evaluated as a function of blending technique employed, incubation media, and molecular weight of the polymer. Spherical devices composed of a core and a shell have been studied by David et al. (285). The core was made of a polymer able to absorb the agent to a large extent (more than 100%), while the shell exhibited both low diffusivity and low capacity. The release rate of an active agent was significantly influenced by the shell properties, such as thickness, nature of polymer, and capacity of absorption for the drug. A one-step preparation method of double-walled microspheres with layers made of PLA and EVA was described by Pekarek et al. (286). This technique takes advantage of the phenomenon of phase separation and can be used to produce spheres of diameters less than 20 μm and up to 1,000 μm. A completely different kind of release system containing EVA was developed by Amsden and Cheng (287). These devices consist of particles of intimately mixed sodium chloride and a protein dispersed in EVA. Protein and NaCl release results from osmotically induced membrane rupture subsequent to water inhibition.

POLY(ETHYLENE OXIDE)

PEG and poly(ethylene oxide) (PEO) are terms for materials containing a multiplicity of connected units of the structure [-CH$_2$CH$_2$-O-]. PEG is one subspecies of PEO that contains a hydroxyl group on each end of the chain: HO[-CH$_2$CH$_2$-O-]$_n$H.

The physicochemical properties of PEO have been described in detail by Graham (288). Depending on the mo-

lecular weight, PEO is a liquid, a waxy solid, or a solid. PEO has a very regular backbone structure, free of sidechains. In the absence of crystallinity, the amorphous material is a rubber with a low Tg, typically $-60°C$ and exhibiting a maximum of Tg at molecular weights in the region of 4,000 Da. Having no chiral centers in the structure and no sidegroups, the polymer is normally highly crystalline, with melting points up to 65–68°C. The crystalline structure of linear PEO has been determined by X-ray diffraction as a 7$_2$ helix (289). This is a coil containing 3.5 -[CH$_2$CH$_2$-O]- groups per turn and a repeat unit of seven such groups. The non-cross-linked polymer swells in water and subsequently dissolves, but it can also be made insoluble by cross-linking.

One major advantage of PEG is its low toxicity: It is approved by the U.S. Food and Drug Administration (FDA) for use in foodstuffs and in pharmaceutical products via injection, topical, or oral routes.

Matrix Systems

The drug-release mechanism from monolithic PEO devices depends strongly on the molecular weight (M_w) and the degree of cross-linking of the polymer. Low-M_w PEO dissolves fast, leading to an erosion (polymer dissolution) controlled process. On the contrary, high-M_w PEO swells owing to penetrant uptake and either dissolves (non-cross-linked polymer) or swells until an equilibrium state is reached. Depending on the diffusion characteristics of the incorporated drug, the entire release kinetics will be governed by diffusion, swelling, dissolution, or a combination of these. Apicella et al. (290) investigated the release of etofylline from compression-molded tablets of semicrystalline PEG with M_w of 600,000 and 4,000,000 Da, respectively. While the low-molecular-weight polymer dissolves at a constant rate (continuously delivering the practically immobilized drug), the release from the slowly dissolving high-molecular-weight polymer is exclusively driven by the drug diffusion. Similar results were found by Kim (291). He studied the release kinetics from compressed tablets manufactured with a powder mixture of PEO, a drug, and magnesium stearate. Several factors such as molecular weight, drug loading, drug solubility, the pH of the dissolution medium, and stirring rate were investigated. To provide a constant drug release over a long period of time (>20 h), Kim also produced tablets with a central hole (donut-shaped) (292). The release of theophylline was observed to be zero order for the first 80–90% of the drug. Semicrystalline, cross-linked PEG was used by McNeill and Graham (293) to prepare and study prostaglandin E$_2$ (PGE$_2$)–containing vaginal pessaries. To avoid drug degradation during the fabrication process of the device, the PEG hydrogel was swollen with a solution of PGE$_2$ in an organic solvent and not in water. Approximately zero-order release was achieved for the first 45% of drug from a dry slab in vitro. Laboratory pessaries have been stored at 4°C for more than a year with no significant change in the release profile or degradation of PGE$_2$.

Miscellaneous

Graham and McNeill (294) studied hydrogels based on PEG with a number average molecular weight of 3,000 to

Table 5. Average In Vitro Release Rates of Pilo-20 and Pilo-40

Time (h)	Release rate for Pilo-20 (μg/h)	Release rate for Pilo-40 (μg/h)
0–7	57.6 ± 2.2	108.0 ± 5.0
7–24	25.3 ± 0.6	54.4 ± 2.5
24–168	19.4 ± 0.3	40.4 ± 4.2

Source: Adapted from Ocusert® (Pilocarpine) Ocular Therapeutic System (282) with permission from ALZA Corporation.

8,000 Da. Drugs have been classified into five groups showing different release profiles. They also developed and tested morphine-loaded PEG suppositories, showing zero-order release. Urquhart and Theeuwes (ALZA Corporation) have a patent (295) on an orally administrable dispersing device for controlled delivery of drugs, comprising a matrix of nonhydrated PEO and a number of tiny pills dispersed through the polymer matrix. A cellulose-polymer coating controls the release rate. An oral capsule utilizing an aqueous polymer (like PEO) and an oil to control gastrointestinal transit time has been patented by Uemura et al. (Fujisawa Pharmaceutical Co.) (296). The capsule is filled with a substantially anhydrous mixture being in solid or semisolid form consisting of (1) a drug or a drug treated by a conventional manner, each of which is in solid form; and (2) a drug carrier that is a semisolid mixture comprising an aqueous polymer (e.g., PEO) and a liquid oil (e.g., arachis oil or medium-chain triglyceride). The ratio of the aqueous polymer to the liquid oil by weight is 2:1 to 1:40.

BIBLIOGRAPHY

1. G.S. Rekhi and S.S. Jambhekar, *Drug Dev. Ind. Pharm.* **21**(1), 61–77 (1995).

2. M.R. Harris and I. Ghebre-Sellassie, in J.W. McGinity, ed., *Aqueous Polymeric Coatings for Pharmaceutical Dosage Forms*, 2nd ed., Dekker, New York, 1996, p. 81.

3. Dow Chemical Product Information, *Ethocel® Premium Polymer*, Formular No. 198-1172-1095GW, Dow Chemical Company, Midland, Mich., 1995.

4. H. Arwidsson, *Acta Pharm. Nord.* **3**(1), 25–30 (1991).

5. H. Arwidsson and M. Nicklasson, *Int. J. Pharm.* **56**, 187–193 (1989).

6. R. Hyppölä, I. Husson, and F. Sundholm, *Int. J. Pharm.* **133**, 161–170 (1996).

7. R.C. Rowe, *Int. J. Pharm.* **29**, 37–41 (1986).

8. S. Narisawa, H. Yoshino, Y. Hirakawa, and K. Noda, *Chem. Pharm. Bull.* **41**(2), 329–334 (1993).

9. S. Narisawa, H. Yoshino, Y. Hirakawa, and K. Noda, *Int. J. Pharm.* **104**, 95–106 (1994).

10. S. Narisawa et al., *Chem. Pharm. Bull.* **42**(10), 2131–2134 (1994).

11. J.W. McGinity, ed., *Aqueous Polymeric Coatings for Pharmaceutical Dosage Forms*, 2nd ed., Dekker, New York, 1996.

12. *Aquacoat®—Aqueous Polymeric Dispersion*, technical literature, FMC Corp., Philadelphia, Pa., 1997.

13. *Surelease®—The Aqueous Sustained Release Coating System*, technical literature, Colorcon Ltd., West Point, Pa., 1997.

14. R.K. Chang, C.H. Hsiao, and J.R. Robinson, *Pharm. Technol.* **11**(3), 56–68 (1987).

15. F.W. Goodhart, M.R. Harris, K.S. Murthy, and R.U. Nesbitt, *Pharm. Technol.* **8**(4), 64–71 (1984).

16. B.H. Lippold, B.K. Sutter, and B.C. Lippold, *Int. J. Pharm.* **54**, 15–25 (1989).

17. B. Sutter, Ph.D. Dissertation, University of Düsseldorf, Germany, 1987.

18. R. Bodmeier and O. Paeratakul, *Int. J. Pharm.* **70**, 59–68 (1991).

19. G.M. Derbin, J.B. Dressman, D.C. Heldsinger, and T.A. Wheatley, *Proc. Int. Symp. Controlled Release Bioact. Mater.* **21**, 754–755 (1994).

20. J.B. Dressman et al., *J. Controlled Release* **36**, 251–260 (1995).

21. G.M. Derbin et al., *Pharm. Technol.*, **9**, 70–80 (1996).

22. B.C. Lippold, B.H. Lippold, B.K. Sutter, and W. Gunder, *Drug Dev. Ind. Pharm.* **16**, 1725–1747 (1990).

23. U. Kositprapa, J. Herrmann, and R. Bodmeier, *Pharm. Res.* **10**, S-153 (1993).

24. U. Kositprapa and R. Bodmeier, *Pharm. Res.* **11**, S-235 (1994).

25. U.S. Pat. 4,138,475 (February 6, 1979), J. McAinsh and R.C. Rowe (to idi, Ltd.).

26. M.R. Harris and I. Ghebre-Sellassie, in J.W. McGinity, ed., *Aqueous Polymeric Coatings for Pharmaceutical Dosage Forms*, Dekker, New York, 1989, pp. 63–79.

27. G. Källstrand and B. Ekman, *J. Pharm. Sci.* **72**, 772–775 (1983).

28. G.N. Zentner, G.S. Rork, and K.J. Himmelstein, *J. Controlled Release* **2**, 217–229 (1985).

29. G.S. Rekhi, R.W. Mendes, S.C. Porter, and S.S. Jambhekar, *Pharm. Technol.* **13**, 112–125 (1989).

30. S.P. Li et al., *Pharm. Technol.* **14**(3), 20–24 (1990).

31. R.U. Nesbitt, *Drug Dev. Ind. Pharm.* **20**(20), 3207–3236 (1994).

32. D. Wong and R. Bodmeier, *Eur. J. Pharm. Biopharm.* **42**(1), 12–15 (1996).

33. P. Sakellariou and R.C. Rowe, *Int. J. Pharm.* **125**, 289–296 (1995).

34. B. Lindstedt, M. Sjöberg, and J. Hjärtstam, *Int. J. Pharm.* **67**, 21–27 (1991).

35. B. Lindstedt, G. Ragnarsson, and J. Hjärtstam, *Int. J. Pharm.* **56**, 261–268 (1989).

36. J. Hjärtstam, K. Borg, and B. Lindstedt, *Int. J. Pharm.* **61**, 101–107 (1990).

37. W. Gunder, B.H. Lippold, and B.C. Lippold, *Eur. J. Pharm. Sci.* **3**, 203–214 (1995).

38. G.H. Zhang et al., *Proc. Int. Symp. Controlled Release Bioact. Mater.* **17**, 194–195 (1990).

39. D. Wong, Ph.D. Dissertation, University of Texas at Austin, 1994.

40. R. Bodmeier and D. Wong, *Eur. J. Pharm. Biopharm.* **42**, 12–15 (1996).

41. L.E. Appel and G.M. Zentner, *Pharm. Res.* **8**, 600–604 (1991).

42. E.M.G. van Bommel, J.G. Fokkens, and D.J.A. Crommelin, *J. Controlled Release* **10**, 283–292 (1989).

43. E.M.G. van Bommel, J.G. Fokkens, and D.J.A. Crommelin, *Acta Pharm. Technol.* **35**(4), 232–237 (1989).

44. S.C. Porter, *Controlled Release Symposium*, Colorcon Inc., West Point, Pa., 1990, p. I-1-54.

45. U. Iyer, W.H. Hong, N. Das, and I. Ghebre-Sellassie, *Pharm. Technol.* **14**(9), 68–87 (1990).

46. R. Bodmeier and O. Paeratakul, *J. Liq. Chromatogr.* **14**, 365–375 (1991).

47. R. Bodmeier and O. Paeratakul, *Int. J. Pharm.* **103**, 47–54 (1994).

48. R. Bodmeier and O. Paeratakul, *Int. J. Pharm.* **152**, 17–26 (1997).

49. G.S. Banker and G.E. Peck, *Pharm. Technol.* **5**, 55–61 (1981).

50. N.H. Parikh, S.C. Porter, and B.D. Rohera, *Pharm. Res.* **10**, 525–534 (1993).

51. S.T. Yang, G.V. Savag, J. Weiss, and I. Ghebre-Sellassie, *Int. J. Pharm.* **86**, 247–257 (1990).

52. Y. Fukumori et al., *Chem. Pharm. Bull.* **36**, 4927–4932 (1988).

53. S.T. Yang and I. Ghebre-Sellassie, *Int. J. Pharm.* **60**, 109–124 (1990).

54. M. Hossain and J.W. Ayres, *Pharm. Technol.* **14**, 72–82 (1990).

55. H. Nakagami, T. Keshikawa, M. Matsumura, and H. Tsukamoto, *Chem. Pharm. Bull.* **39**, 1837–1842 (1991).

56. T.C. Dahl and I.T. Sue, *Drug Dev. Ind. Pharm.* **16**, 2097–2107 (1990).

57. N.H. Shah et al., *Pharm. Technol.* **18**(10), 140–149 (1994).

58. C.A. Gilligan and A. Li Wan Po, *Int. J. Pharm.* **73**, 51–68 (1991).

59. M.R. Harris, I. Ghebre-Sellassie, and R.U. Nesbitt, *Pharm. Technol.* **10**(9), 102–107 (1986).

60. D. Hutchings, B. Kuzmak, and A. Sakr, *Pharm. Res.* **11**(10), 1474–1478 (1994).

61. R. Bodmeier and O. Paeratakul, *Drug Dev. Ind Pharm.* **20**, 1517–1533 (1994).

62. R. Bodmeier and O. Paeratakul, *Pharm. Res.* **11**(6), 882–888 (1994).

63. P. Bansal, S. Vasireddy, F. Plakogiannis, and D. Parikh, *J. Controlled Release* **27**, 157–163 (1993).

64. N. Sarisuta and K. Punpreuk, *J. Controlled Release* **31**, 215–222 (1994).

65. L. Maganti and M. Celik, *Int. J. Pharm.* **103**, 55–67 (1994).

66. L. Maganti and M. Celik, *Proc. 6th Int. Conf. Pharm. Technol.*, 1992, pp. 117–125.

67. R.-K. Chang and E.M. Rudnic, *Int. J. Pharm.* **70**, 261–270 (1991).

68. S.R. Béchard and J.C. Leroux, *Drug Dev. Ind. Pharm.* **18**(18), 1927–1944 (1992).

69. S.A. Altaf, S.W. Hoag, and J.W. Ayers, *Proc. Int. Symp. Controlled Release Bioact. Mater.* **22**, 290–291 (1995).

70. A.G. Ozturk et al., *J. Controlled Release* **14**, 203–213 (1990).

71. J.B. Dressman, B.O. Palsson, A.G. Ozturk, and S.S. Ozturk, in I. Ghebre-Sellassie, ed., *Multiparticulate Oral Drug Delivery*, Dekker, New York, 1994, pp. 285–306.

72. G. Zhang, J.B. Schwartz, and R.L. Schnaare, *Pharm. Res.* **8**(3), 331–335 (1991).

73. G. Ragnarsson et al., *Int. J. Pharm.* **79**, 223–232 (1992).

74. R.U. Nesbitt, M. Mahjour, N.L. Mills, and M.B. Fawzi, *J. Controlled Release* **32**, 71–77 (1994).

75. *Ethylcellulose*, technical information, Shin-Etsu Chem. Inc., Tokyo, Japan, 1991.

76. P.R. Katikaneni, S.M. Upadrashta, S.H. Neau, and A.K. Mitra, *Int. J. Pharm.* **123**, 119–125 (1995).

77. J.D. Bonny and H. Leuenberger, *Pharm. Acta Helv.* **68**, 25–33 (1993).

78. A. Stamm and J.C. Tritsch, *Drug Dev. Ind. Pharm.* **12**, 2337–2353 (1986).

79. S.M. Upadrashta, P.R. Katikaneni, G.A. Hileman, and P.R. Keshary, *Drug Dev. Ind. Pharm.* **19**, 449–460 (1993).

80. S.M. Upadrashta et al., *Int. J. Pharm.* **112**, 173–179 (1994).

81. G. Shlieout and G. Zessin, *Drug Dev. Ind. Pharm.* **22**(4), 313–319 (1996).

82. P.B. Deasy, *Microencapsulation and Related Drug Processes*, Dekker, New York, 1984, pp. 97–117.

83. R. Bodmeier and H. Chen, *J. Controlled Release* **10**, 167–175 (1989).

84. R. Bodmeier, H. Chen, P. Tyle, and P. Jarosz, *J. Controlled Release* **15**, 65–77 (1991).

85. H.-P. Huang and I. Ghebre-Sellassie, *J. Microencapsul.* **6**(2), 219–225 (1989).

86. R. Bodmeier and H. Chen, *J. Controlled Release* **12**, 223–233 (1990).

87. R. Bodmeier and J. Wang, *J. Pharm. Sci.* **82**(2), 191–194 (1993).

88. C.M. Chang and R. Bodmeier, *Int. J. Pharm.* **130**, 187–194 (1996).

89. S.J. Sveinsson, T. Kristmundsdóttir, and K. Ingvarsdóttir, *Int. J. Pharm.* **92**, 29–34 (1993).

90. J. Wallace, in J. Swarbrick and J.C. Boylan, eds., *Encyclopedia of Pharmaceutical Technology*, vol. 2, Dekker, New York, 1990, pp. 319–337.

91. Eastman Chemical Company, *Cellulose Esters for Pharmaceutical Drug Delivery*, Publ. EFC-223A, 2, Eastman Chemical Company, Kingsport, Tenn., 1995.

92. G. Santus and R.W. Baker, *J. Controlled Release* **35**, 1–21 (1995).

93. F. Theeuwes, *J. Pharm. Sci.* **64**, 1987–1991 (1975).

94. G.M. Zentner, G.S. Rork, and K.J. Himmelstein, *J. Controlled Release* **1**, 269–282 (1985).

95. L.E. Appel, J.H. Clair, and G.M. Zentner, *Pharm. Res.* **9**(12), 1664–1667 (1992).

96. M. Herbig, J.R. Cardinal, R.W. Korsmeyer, and K.L. Smith, *J. Controlled Release* **35**, 127–136 (1995).

97. P. Schultz, I. Tho, and P. Kleinebudde, *J. Controlled Release* **47**, 191–199 (1997).

98. P. Schultz and P. Kleinebudde, *J. Controlled Release* **47**, 181–189 (1997).

99. C. Bindschaedler, R. Gurny, E. Doelker, and N.A. Peppas, *J. Colloid Interface Sci.* **108**, 75–82, 83–94 (1985).

100. C. Bindschaedler, R. Gurny, and E. Doelker, *J. Pharm. Pharmacol.* **39**, 335–338 (1986).

101. C. Bindschaedler, R. Gurny, and E. Doelker, *J. Pharm. Sci.* **76**(6), 455–460 (1987).

102. R. Bodmeier and H. Chen, *Drug Dev. Ind. Pharm.* **17**(13), 1811–1822 (1991).

103. M. Kelbert and S.R. Béchard, *Drug Dev. Ind. Pharm.* **18**(5), 519–538 (1992).

104. J.-H. Guo, *Drug Dev. Ind. Pharm.* **19**(13), 1541–1555 (1993).

105. S.H. Wu, W. Hopkins, R. Fengl, and D. Wyatt, *Proc. Int. Symp. Controlled Release Bioact. Mater.* **23**, 53–54 (1996).

106. Eastman Chemical Company, *Cellulose Esters*, technical literature, Eastman Chemical Company, Kingsport, Tenn., 1993.

107. Eastman Chemical Company, *Cellulose Esters and Oxidized Cellulose*, Publ. No. EFC-216, Eastman Chemical Company, Kingsport, Tenn., 1991.

108. D.L. Gardner and D.J. Fink, *Polym. Prepr.* **21**(1), 102–103 (1980).

109. A.J. Shukla and J.C. Price, *Pharm. Res.* **6**(5), 418–421 (1989).

110. A.J. Shukla and J.C. Price, *Pharm. Res.* **8**(11), 1396–1400 (1991).

111. Y. Pongpaibul and C.W. Whitworth, *Int. J. Pharm.* **33**, 243–248 (1986).

112. Y. Pongpaibul and C.W. Whitworth, *Drug Dev. Ind. Pharm.* **12**, 2387–2402 (1986).

113. O.L. Sprockel et al., *Drug Dev. Ind. Pharm.* **15**, 1393–1404 (1989).

114. W. Prapaitrakul and C.W. Whitworth, *Drug Dev. Ind. Pharm.* **15**, 2049–2053 (1989).

115. C.S.L. Chiao and J.C. Price, *Pharm. Res.* **6**, 517–520 (1989).

116. T.C. Dahl et al., *J. Controlled Release* **14**, 1–10 (1990).

117. E. Doelker, *Polym. Sci.* **107**, 199–265 (1993).

118. K.D. Belfield and G. Garcia, *Proc. Am. Chem. Soc. Polym. Mater. Sci. Eng.* **76**, 383–384 (1997).

119. A. Hebeisch and J.T. Guthrie, *The Chemistry and Technology of Cellulosic Copolymers*, Springer-Berlin, New York, 1981.

120. Y. Tabata and Y. Ikada, *Biomaterials* **9**, 356–362 (1988).

121. F.C. Masilungan and N.G. Lordi, *Int. J. Pharm.* **20**, 295–305 (1984).

122. C.A. Entwistle and R.C. Rowe, *J. Pharm. Pharmacol.* **31**, 269–272 (1979).

123. A.O. Okhamafe and P. York, *Pharm. Res.* **2**, 19–22 (1985).

124. P. Sakellariou, R.C. Rowe, and E.F.T. White, *Int. J. Pharm.* **27**, 267–277 (1985).

125. A.O. Okhamafe and P. York, *J. Pharm. Sci.* **77**, 438–443 (1988).

126. T.T. Kararli, J.B. Hurlbut, and T.E. Needham, *J. Pharm. Sci.* **79**, 845–848 (1990).

127. K. Johnson, R. Hathaway, P. Leung, and R. Franz, *Int. J. Pharm.* **73**, 197–208 (1991).

128. E. Doelker, in L. Brannon-Peppas and R.S. Harland, eds., *Absorbent Polymer Technology*, Elsevier, Amsterdam, 1990, pp. 125–146.

129. U. Conte et al., *Biomaterials* **9**, 489–493 (1988).

130. B. Narasimhan and N.A. Peppas, in K. Park, ed., *Controlled Drug Delivery*, American Chemical Society, Washington, D.C. 1997, pp. 529–558.

131. M.M. Talukdar, I. Vinckier, P. Moldenaers, and R. Kinget, *J. Pharm. Sci.* **85**, 537–540 (1996).

132. N.A. Peppas, R. Gurny, E. Doelker, and P. Buri, *J. Membr. Sci.* **7**, 241–253 (1980).

133. P. Colombo, *Adv. Drug Delivery Rev.* **11**, 37–57 (1993).

134. P. Colombo et al., *J. Pharm. Sci.* **84**, 991–997 (1995).

135. P. Colombo et al., *Int. J. Pharm.* **88**, 99–109 (1992).

136. B. Narasimhan and N.A. Peppas, *Adv. Polym. Sci.* **128**, 157–207 (1997).

137. P.I. Lee and N.A. Peppas, *J. Controlled Release* **6**, 207–215 (1987).

138. L. Brannon-Peppas and N.A. Peppas, in L. Brannon-Peppas and R.S. Harland, eds., *Absorbent Polymer Technology*, Elsevier, Amsterdam, 1990, pp. 67–102.

139. L. Brannon-Peppas, in L. Brannon-Peppas and R.S. Harland, eds., *Absorbent Polymer Technology*, Elsevier, Amsterdam, 1990, pp. 45–66.

140. H. Yamakita, T. Maejima, and T. Osawa, *Biol. Pharm. Bull.* **18**, 1409–1416 (1995).

141. C.H. Liu et al., *J. Pharm. Pharmacol.* **47**, 360–364 (1995).

142. G. Xu and H. Sunada, *Chem. Pharm. Bull.* **43**, 483–487 (1995).

143. A.T. Pham and P.I. Lee, *Pharm. Res.* **11**, 1379–1384 (1994).

144. J.E. Ahlskog, M.D. Muenter, P.A. Bailey, and P.M. Miller, *Clin. Neuropharmacol.* **14**, 214–227 (1991).

145. W.C. Koller et al., *Clin. Neuropharmacol.* **14**, 322–329 (1991).

146. P. Colombo et al., *Acta Pharm. Technol.* **33**, 15–20 (1987).

147. P. Colombo et al., *Int. J. Pharm.* **63**, 43–48 (1990).

148. R. Bettini et al., *Eur. J. Pharm. Sci.* **2**, 213–219 (1994).

149. Eur. Pat. EP 598 309 A2 (June 25, 1994), P. Colombo et al. (to Inverni della Beffa S.p.A.).

150. U. Conte, L. Maggi, P. Colombo, and A. La Manna, *J. Controlled Release* **26**, 39–47 (1993).

151. B. Perez-Marcos et al., *J. Pharm. Sci.* **85**, 330–334 (1996).

152. R. Bhardwaj and J. Blanchard, *J. Pharm. Sci.* **85**, 915–919 (1996).

153. S. Anlar et al., *Pharm. Res.* **11**, 231–236 (1994).

154. S.Y. Lin et al., *Biomater. Artif. Cells Artif. Organs* **17**, 189–203 (1989).

155. K.P.R. Chowdary and G.G. Sankar, *Drug Dev. Ind. Pharm.* **23**, 325–330 (1997).

156. K. Lehmann, in J.W. McGinity, ed., *Aqueous Polymeric Coatings for Pharmaceutical Dosage Forms*, 2nd ed., Dekker, New York, 1996, pp. 101–176.

157. *Röhm Eudragit®*, Technical Literature Folder, Röhm, Darmstadt, Germany, 1996.

158. C.D. Melia, B.R. Hansraj, K.A. Khan, and I.R. Wilding, *Pharm. Res.* **8**(7), 899–902 (1991).

159. R.-K. Chang, J.C. Price, and C. Hsiao, *Drug Dev. Ind. Pharm.* **15**(3), 361–372 (1989).

160. R. Bodmeier and O. Paeratakul, *J. Pharm. Sci.* **79**(10), 925–928 (1990).

161. R. Bodmeier, X. Guo, R.S. Sarabia, and P.F. Skultety, *Pharm. Res.* **13**, 52–56 (1996).

162. K. Knop, *Eur. J. Pharm. Sci.* **4**, 293–300 (1996).

163. T.E. Beckert, E. Lynenskjold and H.-U. Petereit, *Proc. Int. Symp. Controlled Release Bioact. Mater.* **24**, 1031–1032 (1997).

164. X. Guo, Ph.D. Dissertation, University of Texas at Austin, 1996.

165. S.S. Jambhekar, P.J. Breen, and Y. Rojanasakul, *Drug Dev. Ind. Pharm.* **13**(15), 2789–2810 (1987).

166. R.-K. Chang and C. Hsiao, *Drug Dev. Ind. Pharm.* **15**(2), 187–196 (1989).

167. S.P. Li, K.M. Feld, and C.R. Kowarski, *Drug Dev. Ind. Pharm.* **17**(12), 1655–1683 (1991).

168. S.P. Li, K.M. Feld, and C.R. Kowarski, *Drug Dev. Ind. Pharm.* **23**(7), 623–631 (1997).

169. C.-C. Kao, S.-C. Chen, and M.-T. Sheu, *J. Controlled Release* **44**, 263–270 (1997).

170. S. Narisawa et al., *Pharm. Res.* **11**(1), 111–116 (1994).

171. S. Narisawa et al., *J. Pharm. Sci.* **85**(2), 184–188 (1996).

172. S. Narisawa et al., *J. Controlled Release* **33**, 253–260 (1995).

173. K. Amighi and A.J. Moes, *Drug Dev. Ind. Pharm.* **21**(20), 2355–2369 (1995).

174. I. Husson et al., *J. Controlled Release* **17**, 163–174 (1991).

175. K. Lehmann, H.-U. Petereit, and D. Dreher, *Drugs Made in Germany* **37**, 53–60 (1994).

176. M.-P. Flament et al., *Pharm. Technol. Eur.* **6**, 2–5 (1994).

177. R. Bodmeier, *Eur. J. Pharm. Biopharm.* **43**, 1–8 (1997).

178. S.A.M. Abdel-Aziz and W. Anderson, *J. Pharm. Pharmacol.* **28**, 801–805 (1976).

179. S.A.M. Abdel-Aziz, W. Anderson, and P.A.M. Armstrong, *J. Appl. Polym. Sci.* **19**, 1181–1192 (1975).

180. R.S. Okor, *J. Appl. Polym. Sci.* **39**, 43–48 (1990).

181. S. Blanchon et al., *Int. J. Pharm.* **72**, 1–10 (1991).

182. M.R. Jenquin, S.M. Liebowitz, R.E. Sarabia, and J.W. McGinity, *J. Pharm. Sci.* **79**(9), 811–816 (1990).

183. M.R. Jenquin, R.E. Sarabia, S.M. Liebowitz, and J.W. McGinity, *J. Pharm. Sci.* **81**(10), 983–989 (1992).

184. M.R. Jenquin and J.W. McGinity, *Int. J. Pharm.* **101**, 23–34 (1994).

185. R. Bodmeier and O. Paeratakul, *Int. J. Pharm.* **59**, 197–204 (1990).

186. R. Bodmeier and O. Paeratakul, *Pharm. Res.* **6**(8), 725–730 (1989).

187. R. Bodmeier and O. Paeratakul, *J. Pharm. Sci.* **79**(1), 32–36 (1990).

188. R. Bodmeier and O. Paeratakul, *Int. J. Pharm.* **96**, 129–138 (1993).

189. R.S. Okor, S. Otimenyin, and I. Ijeh, *J. Controlled Release* **16**, 349–354 (1991).

190. S. Benita, A. Hoffman and M. Donbrow, *J. Pharm. Pharmacol.* **37**, 391–395 (1985).

191. M. Donbrow, A. Hoffman, and S. Benita, *J. Microencapsul.* **12**(3), 273–285 (1995).

192. R.S. Okor, *J. Controlled Release* **12**, 195–200 (1990).

193. M. Kawata, M. Nakamura, S. Goto, and T. Aoyama, *Chem. Pharm. Bull.* **34**(6), 2618–2623 (1986).

194. Y. Kawashima et al., *J. Controlled Release* **16**, 279–290 (1991).

195. Y. Kawashima et al., *J. Pharm. Sci.* **78**(1), 68–72 (1989).

196. Y. Kawashima et al., *Chem. Pharm. Bull.* **40**(1), 196–201 (1992).

197. Y. Kawashima et al., *Chem. Pharm. Bull.* **41**(1), 191–195 (1993).

198. R. Bodmeier, H. Chen, P. Tyle, and P. Jarosz, *J. Microencapsul.* **8**(2), 161–170 (1991).

199. M.G. Vachon and J.G. Nairn, *J. Microencapsul.* **12**(3), 287–305 (1995).

200. T. Kristmundsdóttir, Ó.S. Gudmundsson, and K. Ingvarsdóttir, *Int. J. Pharm.* **137**, 159–165 (1996).

201. J. Traue and H. Kala, *Pharmazie* **39**, 233–237 (1984).

202. J. Traue and H. Kala, *Pharmazie* **39**, 331–333 (1984).

203. H. Takeuchi, T. Handa, and Y. Kawashima, *Drug Dev. Ind. Pharm.* **15**, 1999–2016 (1989).

204. S.Y. Lin and Y.H. Kao, *Pharm. Res.* **8**, 919–924 (1991).

205. G.F. Palmieri, P. Wehrle, and A. Stamm, *Drug Dev. Ind. Pharm.* **20**, 2859–2879 (1994).

206. M.S. Kislalioglu et al., *J. Pharm. Sci.* **80**(8), 799–804 (1991).

207. D.B. Beten and A.J. Moes, *Int. J. Pharm.* **103**, 243–251 (1994).

208. U.V. Banakar, in M.A. Kohudic, ed., *Advances in Controlled Delivery of Drugs*, Technomic Publishing, Lancaster, Pa., 1994, pp. 134–138.

209. A.G. Thombre and J.R. Cardinal, in J. Swarbrick and J.C. Boylan, eds., *Encyclopedia of Pharmaceutical Technology*, vol. 2, Dekker, New York, 1990, pp. 71–72.

210. J. Crank and G.S. Park, *Diffusion in Polymers*, Academic Press, London and New York, 1968, pp. 54–58.

211. J. Mazan et al., *Eur. Polym. J.* **28**, 1151–1154 (1992).

212. J.C. Moreau, B. Leclerc, J. Mazan, and G. Couarraze, *J. Mater. Sci.: Mater. Med.* **2**, 243–247 (1991).

213. J.C. Moreau et al., *J. Mater. Sci.: Mater. Med.* **5**, 177–180 (1995).

214. R. Baker, *Controlled Release of Biologically Active Agents*, Wiley, New York, 1986, pp. 156–161.

215. A.P. Sam, *J. Controlled Release* **22**, 35–46 (1992).

216. S. Diaz et al., *Contraception* **25**, 447–456 (1982).

217. S. Diaz et al., *Contraception* **35**, 551–567 (1987).

218. D.J. Kesler and R.J. Favero, *Drug Dev. Ind. Pharm.* **23**, 217–220 (1997).

219. N. Ueno, M.F. Refojo, and L.H. Liu, *J. Biomed. Mater. Res.* **16**, 669–677 (1982).

220. R. Burns, K. Peterson, and L. Sanders, *J. Controlled Release* **14**, 221–232 (1990).

221. R. Burns, G. McRae, and L. Sanders, *J. Controlled Release* **14**, 233–241 (1990).

222. J.B. Becker et al., *Brain Res.* **508**, 60–64 (1990).

223. D. Hirsch et al., *Biomaterials* **14**, 705–711 (1993).

224. C.-H. Lee, P.P. Bhatt, and Y.W. Chien, *J. Controlled Release* **43**, 283–290 (1997).

225. C.-H. Lee, R.E. Bagdon, P.P. Bhatt, and Y.W. Chien, *J. Controlled Release* **44**, 43–53 (1997).

226. A. Urtti, H. Rouhiainen, T. Kaila, and V. Saano, *Pharm. Res.* **11**, 1278–1282 (1994).

227. A. Urtti, J.D. Pipkin, G. Rork, and A.J. Repta, *Int. J. Pharm.* **61**, 235–240 (1990).

228. A. Urtti et al., *Int. J. Pharm.* **61**, 241–249 (1990).

229. B. Steffansen, P. Ashton, and A. Buur, *Int. J. Pharm.* **132**, 243–250 (1996).

230. R. Bawa and M. Nandu, *Biomaterials* **11**, 724–728 (1990).

231. L.C. Li and G.E. Peck, *Drug Dev. Ind. Pharm.* **17**, 27–39 (1991).

232. L.C. Li and Y.-H. Tu, *Drug Dev. Ind. Pharm.* **17**, 2197–2214 (1991).

233. L.C. Li and G.E. Peck, *Drug Dev. Ind. Pharm.* **18**, 333–343 (1992).

234. L.C. Li, *Int. J. Pharm.* **87**, 117–124 (1992).

235. Y. Chen and L.E. Matheson, *Int. J. Pharm.* **94**, 153–160 (1993).

236. R. Sutinen, A. Kovanen, A. Urtti, and P. Paronen, *Int. J. Pharm.* **57**, 149–154 (1989).

237. R. Sutinen, O. Bilbao-Revoredo, A. Urtti, and P. Paronen, *Int. J. Pharm.* **57**, 155–161 (1989).

238. R. Sutinen, A. Urtti, P. Raatikainen, and P. Paronen, *Int. J. Pharm.* **92**, 177–181 (1993).

239. R. Sutinen, A. Urtti, R. Miettunen, and P. Paronen, *Int. J. Pharm.* **62**, 113–118 (1990).

240. R. Sutinen, V. Laasanen, P. Paronen, and A. Urtti, *J. Controlled Release* **33**, 163–171 (1995).

241. P.I. Lee and S.K. Lum, *J. Controlled Release* **18**, 19–24 (1992).

242. H. Brochart, P. Ehret, P. Goldbach, and A. Stamm, *Int. J. Pharm.* **91**, 95–101 (1993).

243. T.C. Dahl and I.T. Sue, *Pharm. Res.* **9**, 398–405 (1992).

244. L.-C. Dong and A.S. Hoffman, *J. Controlled Release* **15**, 141–152 (1991).

245. L.-C. Dong and A.S. Hoffman, *J. Controlled Release* **13**, 21–31 (1990).

246. R. Siden, W.E. Flowers, and R.J. Levy, *Biomaterials* **13**, 764–770 (1992).

247. H. Loth and A. Euschen, *Drug Dev. Ind. Pharm.* **16**, 2077–2095 (1990).

248. G. Golomb, P. Fisher, and E. Rahamim, *J. Controlled Release* **12**, 121–132 (1990).

249. V. Carelli, G. Di Colo, C. Guerrini, and E. Nannipieri, *Int. J. Pharm.* **50**, 181–188 (1989).

250. N.F. Sheppard, Jr., D.J. Mears, and S.W. Straka, *J. Controlled Release* **42**, 15–24 (1996).

251. L.T. Fan and S.K. Singh, *Controlled Release*, Springer-Verlag, Berlin and New York, 1989, pp. 20–44.

252. U. Johnson and G. Nachtrab, *Angew. Makromol. Chem.* **7**, 134–146 (1969).

253. L.E. Nielsen, *J. Polym. Sci.* **42**, 357–366 (1960).

254. F.P. Reding, J.A. Faucher, and R.D. Whitman, *J. Polym. Sci.* **57**, 483–498 (1962).

255. R.M. Gale, M.Sc. Thesis, San Jose State University, San Jose, CA, 1973.

256. R. Gale and L.A. Spitze, *Proc. Int. Symp. Controlled Release Bioact. Mater.* **8**, 183–184 (1981).

257. S.C. Shin and S.Y. Byun, *Int. J. Pharm.* **137**, 95–102 (1996).

258. S.X. Chen and R.T. Lostritto, *J. Controlled Release* **38**, 185–191 (1996).

259. E.S. Miller, N.A. Peppas, and D.N. Winslow, *J. Membr. Sci.* **14**, 79–92 (1983).

260. R. Langer and J. Folkman, *Nature (London)* **263**, 797–800 (1976).

261. W.D. Rhine, D.S.T. Hsieh, and R. Langer, *J. Pharm. Sci.* **69**, 265–270 (1980).

262. J. Cohen, R.A. Siegel, and R. Langer, *J. Pharm. Sci.* **73**, 1034–1037 (1984).

263. W.M. Saltzman and R. Langer, *Biophys. J.* **55**, 163–171 (1989).

264. J. Kost, K. Leong, and R. Langer, *Proc. Natl. Acad. Sci. U.S.A.* **86**, 7663–7666 (1989).

265. M.J. During et al., *Ann. Neurol.* **25**, 351–356 (1989).

266. E.R. Edelman, A. Fiorino, A. Grodzinsky, and R. Langer, *J. Biomed. Mater. Res.* **26**, 1619–1631 (1992).

267. N.F. Sheppard, M.Y. Madrid, and R. Langer, *J. Appl. Polym. Sci.* **46**, 19–26 (1992).

268. L.R. Brown, E.R. Edelman, G.F. Fischel, and R. Langer, *J. Pharm. Sci.* **85**, 1341–1345 (1996).

269. B. Narasimhan and R. Langer, *J. Controlled Release* **47**, 13–20 (1997).

270. N.R. Vyavahare et al., *J. Controlled Release* **34**, 97–108 (1995).

271. G.J. Lesser et al., *Pain* **65**, 265–272 (1996).

272. C.E. Krewson, R. Dause, M. Mak, and W.M. Saltzman, *J. Biomater. Sci., Polym. Ed.* **8**, 103–117 (1996).

273. B.B. Pharriss et al., *Fertil. Steril.* **25**, 915–921 (1974).

274. G. Zador et al., *Contraception* **13**, 559–569 (1976).

275. M. Mall-Haefeli, *Gynaekol. Rundsch.* **18**, 253–262 (1978).

276. K.W. Schweppe, D. Tenhaeff, and D. Rache, *Fortschr. Med.* **96**, 1685–1690 (1978).

277. Alza Corporation, *The Progestasert® Intrauterine Progesterone Contraceptive System*, monograph, ALZA Corporation, Palo Alto, Ca., 1976, pp. 6–7.

278. R.L. Friederich, *Ann. Ophthalmol.* **6**, 1279–1284 (1974).

279. F. Ros, E. Greve, C. Dake, and W. Miller, *Ophthalmologica* **175**, 38–39 (1977).

280. K. Heilmann, *Klin. Monatsbl. Augenheilk.* **170**, 109–119 (1977).

281. K. Heilmann, *Fortschr. Med.* **96**, 1101–1106 (1978).

282. Alza Corporation, *Ocusert® (Pilocarpine) Ocular Therapeutic System*, Alza Corporation, 1984, pp. 1–6.

283. S. Miyazaki, S. Takeuchi, M. Takada, and K. Ishii, *Chem. Pharm. Bull.* **32**, 1633–166 (1984).

284. H.M. Dollinger and S.P. Sawan, *Polym. Prepr.* **31**, 429–430 (1989).

285. H. David, J. Bouzon, and J.M. Vergnaud, *Plast. Rubber Process. Appl.* **11**, 9–16 (1989).

286. K.J. Pekarek, J.S. Jacob, and E. Mathiowitz, *Adv. Mater.* **6**, 684–687 (1994).

287. B. Amsden and Y.-L. Cheng, *J. Controlled Release* **33**, 99–105 (1995).

288. N.B. Graham, in N.A. Peppas, ed., *Hydrogels in Medicine and Pharmacy*, vol. 2, CRC Press, Boca Raton, Fl., 1987, pp. 96–113.

289. J.L. Koenig and A.C. Angood, *J. Polym. Sci.* **8**, 1787–1796 (1970).

290. A. Apicella, M.A. Del Nobile, G. Mensitieri, and L. Nicolais, in R.M. Ottenbrite and E. Chiellini, eds., *Polymers in Medicine*, Technomic Publishing, Lancaster, Pa., 1992, pp. 23–37.

291. C.-J. Kim, *J. Pharm. Sci.* **84**, 303–306 (1995).

292. C.-J. Kim, *Pharm. Res.* **12**, 1045–1048 (1995).

293. M.E. McNeill and N.B. Graham, *J. Controlled Release* **1**, 99–117 (1984).

294. N.B. Graham and M.E. McNeill, *Biomaterials* **5**, 27–36 (1984).

295. U.S. Pat. 4,649,043 (March 10, 1987), J. Urquhart and F. Theeuwes (to Alza Corp.).

296. U.S. Pat. 4,690,822 (September 1, 1987), T. Uemura et al. (to Fujisawa Pharmaceutical Co.).

OLIGONUCLEOTIDE DELIVERY

C. Russell Middaugh
University of Kansas
Lawrence, Kansas

KEY WORDS

Antisense

Cationic lipids

Delivery

Liposomes

Membrane fusion

Microparticles

Oligonucleotide

Peptides

Polymers

Targeting

OUTLINE

Bibliography

One of the immediate consequences of the late twentieth century revolution in molecular biology was the availability of biological macromolecules and their analogues as potential drug substances. The first of these were the recombinant and synthetic proteins and peptides, which can be used as agonists and antagonists of their natural homologues. Recently, polynucleotides have moved to center stage in a similar manner. Thus, the coding regions of entire genes can be used to produce proteins or peptides of therapeutic consequence in situ. Furthermore, shorter oligonucleotides and oligonucleotide analogues can be employed to alter gene expression and, consequently, the in vivo levels of specific proteins. The utility of all four of these macromolecules, proteins, peptides, large polynucleotides, and oligonucleotides, is severely limited by delivery problems that include instability as a consequence of enzymatic, chemical, and conformational processes, as well as targeting, passage across the cytoplasmic membrane, and intracellular processing and targeting. A general consensus seems to be that delivery is in many if not most cases the limiting step in the ultimate therapeutic efficacy of these agents. Not surprisingly, work on the delivery of small molecules as well as proteins, peptides, and DNA plasmids has had a major influence on early attempts to deliver oligonucleotides. In this regard, the reader is referred to the article POLYMERIC SYSTEMS FOR GENE DELIVERY, CHITOSAN AND PINC™ SYSTEMS, in which many of the same problems are addressed with a molecule of related physical properties but of much greater size.

A discussion of oligonucleotide delivery presents several problems due to the embryonic state of the field. For example, a wide variety of different types of oligonucleotide analogues have already been synthesized and examined, with varying degrees of characterization. Besides the prototypic phosphodiester type, forms that have been modified in their backbone, termini, sugar base, and stereochemistry have all been produced (1,2). Because of their increased nuclease resistance (and therefore potentially longer half-life), the backbone-modified analogues have been most intensively studied. These include thiolated forms and the methylphosphonates, as well as the peptide nucleic acids, in which the phosphodiester linker is replaced by an amide moiety (3). For simplicity, here we will primarily consider the phosphodiester and phosphorothiolate forms because up to this point they have received the most extensive examination from a delivery perspective. Both have the property of being polyanions, which is the physical characteristic that might be expected to dominate their chemical and biological properties. These molecules are usually 15–25 nucleosides in length, although both larger and smaller chains are sometimes encountered.

Although not the subject of this review, the potential mechanisms of action of oligonucleotides need to be understood to rationally prepare them as pharmaceuticals (4). In fact, multiple mechanisms of action are recognized, and knowledge of the one (or more) involved in a specific case will usually be helpful. The one most often postulated to be involved in the reduction of expression of specific genes involves complementary binding to mRNA molecules (5). Changes in translation of these hybrids can be due to simple steric effects or result from activation of the enzyme RNase H, which specifically degrades the mRNA component of the complex (potentially releasing the pharmaceutical oligonucleotide for further activity). Alternatively, the oligonucleotide can bind directly to nuclear double-stranded DNA, forming a triple-helical structure that blocks transcription (6). It is a matter of semantics whether we consider such triple-helix-forming oligonucleotides as true "antisense" agents, but from a delivery perspective this is relatively unimportant with the exception of potential nuclear-targeting issues. A third class of oligonucleotides is the RNA-based ribozymes, which themselves manifest enzymatic activity (7,8). These molecules have primarily been used to target mRNA, but they also have the potential to attack nonnucleic acid targets (e.g., proteins) with therapeutic effects. Finally, a fourth type of oligonucleotide with potential therapeutic utility has recently been developed, the so-called aptamers (9,10). These are single- or double-stranded oligonucleotides that bind to sites on proteins that perturb their activity. These molecules are usually selected through combinational approaches and may contain specific tertiary structure that is involved in their biological activity. Extensive discussion of the mechanism of action of oligonucleotides can be found in the references already cited. Although the specific delivery method employed for a particular oligonucleotide will be dependent on the unique situation in which each will be employed, the basic principles of delivery will probably be similar among the various classes, at least in terms of organ and cellular targeting and entry.

It is convenient to begin our discussion of the oligonucleotide delivery process itself in the middle, at the cellular entry stage, and then consider earlier stages (e.g., pharmacokinetics and tissue targeting), followed by final elements of the delivery pathway (intracellular). It is perhaps somewhat surprising that highly negatively charged oligonucleotides are able to enter cells, but this is certainly the case. Without the assistance of transport facilitators this process is rather inefficient, but it is clear that incubation of cells in culture or administration to animals of phosphodiester or phosphorothiolate oligonucleotides at many sites will result in transport of these molecules into cells. It is fair to say, however, that the mechanism by which this is accomplished is currently unclear. Several non–mutually exclusive hypotheses can be advanced to explain such phenomena. Most postulate the existence of some type of receptor on the cell surface that can mediate entry. This is, of course, the mechanism used by viruses that are able to transfer very large oligonucleotides into cells with high efficiency. Attachment of oligonucleotides to such receptors could then facilitate entry by a number of well-recognized different processes including receptor-mediated endocytosis, pinocytosis, and phagocytosis. What is not known is the identity of the attachment size of oligonucleotides and oligonucleotide complexes on the outer surface of the plasma membrane (11).

Attractive candidates for this binding site are the cell surface proteoglycans. These molecules contain polyanionic polysaccharide side chains attached to proteins that are cycled into cells and back onto the cell surface at a rate commensurate with that seen for cellular entry of oligonucleotides (12). Thus, this can be viewed as one natural ingress pathway for polyanions. Oligonucleotide attachment to these similarly charged entities would presumably be mediated by a cross-linking mechanism through normally present cationic molecules (e.g., divalent metal cations, cationic peptides, proteins) or synthetically produced cationic sites on delivery vehicles (e.g., cationic lipids, polymers, peptides; see later). In support of this pathway, enzymatic removal of the heparan sulfate side chains of cell surface proteoglycans or inhibition of their sulfation produces a dramatic decrease in the passage of oligonucleotides into cells (13,14).

A second potential site of entry is the specialized structures known as caveolae, which have been implicated in transcytotic events. Studies of intramuscular delivery of polynucleotides have specifically identified these cell surface invaginations as potential sites of entry of "naked" polynucleotides (15). These membrane microdomains are enriched in cholesterol and various sphingolipids and are thus regions of positive charge concentration (16). It is therefore possible that they could be involved in direct electrostatic interactions with polynucleotides, although this has yet to be experimentally demonstrated. Certain proteins are also commonly found in these regions, including many involved in signal transduction events (17). These proteins could also provide potential polyanion binding sites and serve as vectors to "piggy-back" polynucleotides into cells. In this regard, it is still entirely possible that

one or more unknown proteins located elsewhere in the plasma membrane play a role in cellular entry (e.g., see Ref. 18), but no strong evidence in support of this idea as a general mechanism has yet been presented. Obviously if such proteins exist, efforts could be made to directly target these molecules. Because cell surface proteins are generally recycled from the cell surface into the interior, these molecules potentially provide a facile point of entry. Thus, as will be discussed later, by construction of artificial targeting vehicles, it is possible to attempt to target any cell surface molecule that eventually reenters the cell.

Once inside a cell, an oligonucleotide must be transported to an appropriate site of action. In the case of antisense or catalytic activity, this could be either the cytoplasm or the nucleus. If the target is DNA itself, then nuclear transport will be required. Aptamers, on the other hand, would need to be present at the specific intra- or extracellular location of the target protein. Most evidence suggests that oligonucleotides will initially be found in endosomal compartments (14), although this has been disputed (e.g., see Ref. 19). Thus it may be necessary to provide some active mechanism to release oligonucleotides from these membrane-bound vesicles. In general, the transport of oligonucleotides into the nucleus does not present the problem encountered with DNA plasmids because they are small enough to passively diffuse through nuclear pores. Nevertheless, it is at least possible in principle to either increase the efficiency of this process or enhance nuclear retention. In general, attempts to stimulate endosomal release or nuclear entry have been peptide or lipid based and will be considered below in that light.

By what routes might oligonucleotide-based pharmaceuticals be initially delivered? The major approach has been intravenous infusion, although numerous other routes such as direct injection into specific sites or oral, nasal, or bronchial administration have been examined with some limited success (20,21). Most pharmacokinetic information has been obtained from the intravenous route. In general, it is found that negatively charged oligonucleotides are rapidly distributed throughout the body, with most accumulation in organs such as the kidneys, liver, and spleen, with extensive secretion in the urine over a 24-h period (22–24). Extensive degradation of phosphodiester oligonucleotides is seen, but phosphorothiolate analogues are much more stable at all sites examined (22,23). Equilibration is slower upon intraperitoneal injection and much slower with subcutaneous administration. It should be noted that in many cases oligonucleotides rapidly become protein bound with serum albumin and immunoglobulins, the major binding proteins so far identified (25). Conjugation of oligonucleotides to cholesterol appears to retarget them to low-density lipoproteins and extend their circulation time (26). The exact role of oligonucleotide–protein complexes in oligonucleotide delivery is poorly understood but will be critical to the ultimate design and use of these pharmaceutical agents.

Informative comparative studies of the delivery of oligonucleotides by noninvasive methods have been performed (25). Somewhat surprisingly, direct introduction of 5'-^{32}P-labeled phosphodiester oligonucleotides into the nose, vagina, or rectum or onto the skin of mice resulted in significant levels of labeled compounds in the blood. Intranasal and oral administration resulted in serum levels 5–20% of those seen with intraperitoneal injection, and levels 5–10 times less than those seen with intravaginal and rectal application. The ocular route was also found to be about 10% as effective as i.p. administration. Interestingly, longer oligonucleotides seems to be more effective when introduced through the eye. The skin route was much less effective. The relative distribution of the oligonucleotide among the various organs examined was very similar.

Although oligonucleotides have some ability to pass through the circulation and enter cells, it is not clear that they will be able in most cases to do this with sufficient efficacy to be effective pharmaceuticals. Thus, efforts are actively underway to design vehicles that better target and more effectively enter and ultimately act at desired sites. Because the mechanisms by which oligonucleotides enter cells are still obscure, most efforts at designing novel vehicles have been semiempirical in nature. We therefore focus on a select number of approaches that currently appear most promising. In general, the design of oligonucleotide delivery vehicles is based on the following criteria. First, one wishes to protect the potentially labile oligonucleotide to the maximum extent possible from destructive processes; enzymatic digestion is probably the chief concern. Secondly, it is usually thought (although see earlier) that the polyanionic character of the oligonucleotide should be reduced or even eliminated. This is usually accomplished by some type of charge neutralization or shielding mechanism, although later-generation oligonucleotide analogues have this built directly into their intrinsic structure. Third, the surface characteristics of any resulting complex should be such that some degree of intrinsic targeting resides in the vehicle. Fourth, some type of endosomal release property might be incorporated. Fifth, nuclear targeting may or may not be included. In some cases, it is thought that creating a particle that could range from submicron to many microns in size might be advantageous. We consider here a number of examples in which one or, usually, more of these properties are included in oligonucleotide delivery vehicles. We discuss only representative examples in which more extensive citations to other examples are included, and the reader is referred to these for more extended considerations.

A potentially very powerful approach to the oligonucleotide delivery problem employs viral vectors. In this method, the nucleic acid sequence of interest is inserted into a viral genome where it can then be expressed as part of the normal viral infection and maturation process. This approach has the great advantage that it avails itself of the natural ability of certain viruses to infect specific cells with high efficiency. The virus particles may also possess intrinsic effective endosomal release mechanisms that further enhance their utility. The most common viruses usually considered for such use are the retro-, adeno-, and adeno-associated viruses. Unfortunately, this technology manifests several serious shortcomings. These include toxic effects often involving potential insertional mutagenesis, immunogenicity (especially upon repeat usage), and the complexity of the vehicle, which introduces major problems in analysis, reproducibility, and manufacturing. For these reasons, unlike the case in gene therapy, viral delivery systems are not generally pursued for oligonucleotide administration if a more classic chemical pharmacological approach seems possible.

By far, the area in which the most effort has been expended has involved the use of liposomes. Two somewhat different approaches have been undertaken. In the first, oligonucleotides are entrapped within anionic lipid vesicles of varied size, structure, and composition. In the second, the oligonucleotides are complexed to cationic lipids of various structural and assembly types. Most recently, the latter approach has received the most attention. We begin with the former.

Employing what is usually considered the "conventional" liposomal approach, several research groups have had some success in enhancing the uptake of oligonucleotides into cells. In an early report, Loke et al. (27) used phosphatidylserine-based liposomes to deliver oligonucleotides into cells in tissue culture. This required polyethylene glycol (PEG) to induce liposomal cell fusion, as well as calcium to enhance loading of the oligonucleotide. Using specially designed minimal volume entrapment approaches, Thierry et al. (28,29) have employed cardiolipin-based liposomes to enhance entry of oligonucleotides 10- to 20-fold into different types of cancer cells, resulting in measurable biological response. Biologically active ribozymes have been successfully delivered in a similar manner using a dipalmitoylphosphatidylglycerol-based system. Several important observations can be made from these and related studies. First, oligonucleotides are substantially protected by the anionic lipid barrier created. Secondly, uptake is enhanced, and activity is detectable. Thirdly, the oligonucleotides seem to be concentrated in the nucleus soon after administration. The efficiency of delivery, however, is not as high as desired for optimal therapeutic effects.

Although evidence exists that even unmodified anionic liposomes can enhance endosomal release to some extent, pH-sensitive liposomes have been designed with the intent of avoiding lysosomal destruction (30,31). The lipid most commonly used for the construction of pH-sensitive liposomes is dioleylphosphatidylethanolamine (DOPE). In bilayers, DOPE can be present in a lamellar form at neutral pH. Under certain conditions of temperature, salt concentration, and pH, however, an inverted hexagonal phase can be induced, which leads to fusogenic behavior. Most importantly from our perspective, low pH leads to protonation of DOPE headgroups, which removes their stabilizing repulsive interactions and induces hexagonal phases. Almost always, however, a second molecule (usually a fatty acid) is necessary to prevent premature formation of fusogenic hexagonal phases under physiological conditions. Examples of such agents include cholesterol hemisuccinate, palmitoylhomocysteine, and oleic acid. Alternatively, as described later, peptides or proteins that undergo pH-dependent conformational changes to structures that can insert into lipid bilayers or create pores can be employed; this latter approach more closely simulates the mechanism used by viruses to escape endosomal degradation, with actual viral proteins sometimes inserted

ways this is the "holy grail" of oligonucleotide as well as gene delivery because many of the potential problems of oligonucleotide therapy could be overcome if we could limit the delivery of oligonucleotides to specific sites (84,85). It will probably often be the case that the inherent selectivity of oligonucleotides will not be sufficient from either a toxicity, bioavailability, or efficacy perspective for optimum pharmaceutical use. The availability of numerous specific receptors on the surface of all cells seems to offer such an opportunity. Ligands can be attached to oligonucleotide delivery vehicles in any number of ways. This includes covalent attachment to a component of the vehicle, including the oligonucleotide itself, electrostatically through ionic complexes with the polyanionic component or through apolar interactions, perhaps by insertion into lipid bilayers. The choice of ligand is really limited only by the presence of an appropriate receptor and its intracellular pathway, the latter generally seeming to permit at least some limited release into the cytoplasmic compartment without the use of further mechanisms to stimulate endosomal membrane breakdown. Ligands that have so far been successfully employed to deliver oligonucleotides into cells with some degree of selectivity include carbohydrates (to the asialoglycoprotein and mannose scavenger receptors) (86–89), monoclonal antibodies and associated antigen-binding fragments (85,90), folic acid (91–93), and growth factors (94). The reader is referred to the article on gene therapy in this encyclopedia as well as reviews for further discussion of this topic (84).

We conclude by what is perhaps a statement of the obvious. Oligonucleotides will not be successfully developed as therapeutic agents unless they can be delivered to their site of action in a stable form and gain entry into the proper regions of a cell where they can exert their biological effects. An understanding of the biology necessary to accomplish this is still primitive, and current efforts at delivery thus remain semiempirical at best. Because current clinical studies of pure oligonucleotides hint at some activity (95–97), more complex delivery systems will be required to demonstrate a significant improvement on these simpler, more convenient formulations. Although much of the work described here would seem to offer some leads in this regard, much more extensive work including radically novel developments will probably be necessary to produce pharmaceutically acceptable delivery methods for oligonucleotide drugs.

BIBLIOGRAPHY

1. J.F. Milligan, M.D. Matteucci, and J.C. Martin, *J. Med. Chem.* **36**, 1923–1937 (1993).
2. D. Kregenow, M.Z. Ratajczak, and A.M. Gewirtz, in S. Akhtar, ed., *Delivery Strategies for Antisense Oligonucleotide Therapeutics*, CRC Press, Boca Raton, Fla., 1995, pp. 1–15.
3. D.R. Corey, *Trends Biotechnol.* **15**, 224–229 (1997).
4. M.D. Matteucci and R.W. Wagner, *Nature (London)* **384** (Suppl.), 20–22 (1996).
5. H. Lönnberg and E. Vuorio, *Ann. Med.* **28**, 511–522 (1996).
6. N. Chaudhary, J.S. Bishop, K. Jayaraman, and J.K. Guy-Caffey, in S. Akhtar, ed., *Delivery Strategies for Antisense Oli-*
7. D.A. Elkins and J.J. Rossi, in S. Akhtar, ed., *Delivery Strategies for Antisense Oligonucleotide Therapeutics*, CRC Press, Boca Raton, Fla., 1995, pp. 17–38.
8. H. Kijima et al., *Pharmacol. Ther.* **68**, 247–267 (1995).
9. L.C. Bock et al., *Nature (London)* **355**, 564–566 (1992).
10. J. Feigon, T. Dieckmann, and F.W. Smith, *Chem. Biol.* **3**, 611–617 (1996).
11. R.M. Bennett, *Antisense Res. Dev.* **3**, 235–241 (1993).
12. M. Yanagishita and V.C. Hascall, *J. Biol. Chem.* **267**, 9451–9454 (1992).
13. K.A. Mislick and J.D. Baldeschwieler, *Proc. Natl. Acad. Sci. U.S.A.* **93**, 12349–12354 (1996).
14. A.M. Gewirtz, C.A. Stein, and P.M. Glazer, *Proc. Natl. Acad. Sci. U.S.A.* **93**, 3161–3163 (1996).
15. J.A. Wolff et al., *J. Cell Sci.* **103**, 1249–1259 (1992).
16. K. Simons and E. Ikonen, *Nature (London)* **387**, 569–572 (1997).
17. J. Couet et al., *Trends Cardiovasc. Med.* **7**, 103–110 (1997).
18. P. Rockwell et al., *Proc. Natl. Acad. Sci. U.S.A.* **94**, 6523–6528 (1997).
19. P. Zamecnik et al., *Proc. Natl. Acad. Sci. U.S.A.* **91**, 3156–3160 (1994).
20. Y. Rojanasakul, *Adv. Drug Delivery Rev.* **18**, 115–131 (1996).
21. E. Wickstrom, *Trends Biotechnol.* **10**, 281–287 (1992).
22. R. Zhang et al., *Clin. Chem. (Winston-Salem, N.C.)* **41**, 836–843 (1995).
23. R. Zhang et al., *Biochem. Pharmacol.* **50**, 545–556 (1995).
24. R. Zhang et al., *Biochem. Pharmacol.* **49**, 929–939 (1995).
25. V.V. Vlassov et al., in S. Akhtar, ed., *Delivery Strategies for Antisense Oligonucleotide Therapeutics*, CRC Press, Boca Raton, Fla., 1995, pp. 71–83.
26. P.C. Shmidt, T.L. Doan, S. Falco, and T.J.C. van Berkel, *Nucleic Acids Res.* **19**, 4695–4702 (1991).
27. S.L. Loke et al., *Curr. Top. Microbiol. Immunol.* **141**, 282–289 (1988).
28. A.R. Thierry and A. Dritschilo, *Nucleic Acids Res.* **20**, 5691–5698 (1992).
29. A.R. Thierry, A. Rahmann, and A. Dritschilo, *Biochem. Biophys. Res. Commun.* **190**, 952–960 (1993).
30. C. Ropert, P. Couvreur, and C. Malvy, in S. Akhtar, ed., *Delivery Strategies for Antisense Oligonucleotide Therapeutics*, CRC Press, Boca Raton, Fla., 1995, pp. 233–245.
31. P. Couvreur, E. Fattal, C. Malvy, and C. Dubernet, *J. Liposome Res.* **7**, 1–18 (1997).
32. D. Collins and L. Huang, *Cancer Res.* **47**, 735–739 (1987).
33. C.J. Chu et al., *Pharm. Res.* **7**, 824–834 (1990).
34. C. Ropert et al., *Biochem. Biophys. Res. Commun.* **183**, 879–885 (1992).
35. A.R. Thierry and G.B. Takle, in S. Akhtar, ed., *Delivery Strategies for Antisense Oligonucleotide Therapeutics*, CRC Press, Boca Raton, Fla., 1995, pp. 199–211.
36. O. Zelphati and F.C. Szoka, Jr., *J. Controlled Release* **41**, 99–119 (1996).
37. C.F. Bennett, in S. Akhtar, ed., *Delivery Strategies for Antisense Oligonucleotide Therapeutics*, CRC Press, Boca Raton, Fla., 1995, pp. 223–232.

38. O. Zelphati and F.C. Szoka, Jr., *J. Liposome Res.* **7**, 31–49 (1997).

39. R.I. Mahato, A. Rolland, and E. Tomlinson, *Pharm. Res.* **14**, 853–859 (1997).

40. J.O. Radler, I. Koltover, T. Salditt, and C.R. Safinya, *Science* **275**, 810–814 (1997).

41. D.D. Lasic et al., *J. Am. Chem. Soc.* **119**, 832–833 (1997).

42. H. Gershon, R. Ghirlando, S.B. Guttman, and A. Minsky, *Biochemistry* **32**, 7143–7151 (1993).

43. J. Zabner et al., *J. Biol. Chem.* **270**, 18997–19007 (1995).

44. M.E. Dowty et al., *Proc. Natl. Acad. Sci. U.S.A.* **92**, 4572–4576 (1995).

45. F. Labat-Moleur et al., *Gene Ther.* **3**, 1010–1017 (1996).

46. Y. Xu and F.C. Szoka, Jr., *Biochemistry* **35**, 5616–5623 (1996).

47. O. Zelphati and F.C. Szoka, Jr., *Proc. Natl. Acad. Sci. U.S.A.* **93**, 11493–11498 (1996).

48. L. Perlaky et al., *Anti-Cancer Drug Des.* **8**, 3–14 (1993).

49. N. Meiri et al., *Proc. Natl. Acad. Sci. U.S.A.* **94**, 4430–4434 (1997).

50. N. Dean, *Proc. Natl. Acad. Sci. U.S.A.* **91**, 11762–11766 (1994).

51. D.C. Litzinger, *J. Liposome Res.* **7**, 51–61 (1997).

52. T. Boulikas, *Oncol. Rep.* **3**, 989–995 (1996).

53. O. Boussif et al., *Proc. Natl. Acad. Sci. U.S.A.* **92**, 7297–7301 (1995).

54. J.A. Hughes, A.I. Aronsohn, A.V. Avrutskaya, and R.L. Juliano, *Pharm. Res.* **13**, 404–410 (1996).

55. A. Bielinska et al., *Nucleic Acids Res.* **24**, 2176–2182 (1996).

56. S.W. Poxon, P.M. Mitchell, E. Liang, and J.A. Hughes, *Drug Delivery* **3**, 255–261 (1996).

57. M.X. Tang, C.T. Redemann, and F.C. Szoka, Jr., *Bioconjugate Chem.* **7**, 703–714 (1996).

58. L.C. Smith et al., in A.M. Gotto, Jr. et al., eds., *Drugs Affecting Lipid Metabolism*, Kluwer Academic Publishers, Dordrecht, The Netherlands, 1996, pp. 337–345.

59. B. Oberhauser, C. Plank, and E. Wagner, in S. Akhtar, ed. *Delivery Strategies for Antisense Oligonucleotide Therapeutics*, CRC Press, Boca Raton, Fla., 1995, pp. 247–266.

60. S. Soukchareun, G.W. Tregear, and J. Haralambidis, *Bioconjugate Chem.* **6**, 43–53 (1995).

61. J.-P. Bongartz, A.-M. Aubertin, P.G. Milhaud, and B. Lebleu, *Nucleic Acids Res.* **22**, 4681–4688 (1994).

62. M. Wilke et al., *Gene Ther.* **3**, 1133–1142 (1996).

63. E. Tomlinson and A.P. Rolland, *J. Controlled Release* **39**, 357–372 (1996).

64. V.J. Dzau, M.J. Mann, R. Morishita, and Y. Kaneda, *Proc. Natl. Acad. Sci. U.S.A.* **93**, 11421–11425 (1996).

65. M. Aoki et al., *Biochem. Biophys. Res. Commun.* **231**, 540–545 (1997).

66. I. Kitajima et al., *J. Biol. Chem.* **272**, 27099–27106 (1997).

67. R. Morishita et al., *Proc. Natl. Acad. Sci. U.S.A.* **90**, 8474–8478 (1993).

68. K. Yamada et al., *Am. J. Physiol.* **271**, R1212–R1220 (1996).

69. T. Boulikas, *Int. J. Oncol.* **10**, 301–309 (1997).

70. K. Kataoka et al., *Macromolecules* **29**, 8556–8557 (1996).

71. V.A. Kabanov, S.V. Vinogradov, Y.G. Suzdaltseva, and V.Y. Alakhov, *Bioconjugate Chem.* **6**, 639–647 (1995).

72. C. Emile et al., *Drug Delivery* **3**, 187–195 (1996).

73. M. Berton et al., *Biochim. Biophys. Acta* **1355**, 7–19 (1997).

74. P.Y.P. Kuo and W.M. Saltzman, *Crit. Rev. Eukaryotic Gene Expression* **6**, 59–73 (1996).

75. K.J. Lewis, W.J. Irwin, and S. Akhtar, *J. Controlled Release* **37**, 173–183 (1995).

76. A.J. Hudson, K.J. Lewis, M.V. Rao, and S. Akhtar, *Int. J. Pharm.* **136**, 23–29 (1996).

77. R.L. Cleek et al., *J. Biomed. Mater. Res.* **35**, 525–530 (1997).

78. I. Yamakawa et al., *Biol. Pharm. Bull.* **20**, 455–459 (1997).

79. E. Mathiowitz et al., *Nature (London)* **386**, 410–414 (1997).

80. S. Paillasson, M. Robert-Nicoud, and X. Ronot, *Cell Biol. Toxicol.* **12**, 359–361 (1996).

81. I. Habus, Q. Zhao, and S. Agrawal, *Bioconjugate Chem.* **6**, 327–331 (1995).

82. Q. Zhao, J. Temsamani, and S. Agrawal, *Antisense Res. Dev.* **5**, 185–192 (1995).

83. Q. Zhao, J. Temsamani, P.L. Iadarola, and S. Agrawal, *Biochem. Pharmacol.* **52**, 1537–1544 (1996).

84. C.R. Middaugh, M. Chastain, and C.T. Caskey, in N.R. Lemoine and D.N. Cooper, eds., *Gene Therapy*, Bios Sci. Publ., Oxford, 1996, pp. 11–32.

85. C.S.R. Gooden and A.A. Epenetos, in S. Akhtar, ed., *Delivery Strategies for Antisense Oligonucleotide Therapeutics*, CRC Press, Boca Raton, Fla., 1995, pp. 283–293.

86. Y. Rojanasakul et al., *J. Biol. Chem.* **272**, 3910–3914 (1997).

87. J.C. Perales et al., *J. Biol. Chem.* **272**, 7398–7407 (1997).

88. J. Madon and H.E. Blum, *Hepatology* **24**, 474–481 (1996).

89. E.P. Carmichael et al., in S. Akhtar, ed., *Delivery Strategies for Antisense Oligonucleotide Therapeutics*, CRC Press Boca Raton, Fla., 1995, pp. 267–282.

90. M.P. Selvam et al., *Antiviral Res.* **33**, 11–20 (1996).

91. S. Wang et al., *Proc. Natl. Acad. Sci. U.S.A.* **92**, 3318–3322 (1995).

92. P. Ginobbi, T.A. Geiser, D. Ombres, and G. Citro, *Anticancer Res.* **17**, 29–36 (1997).

93. S. Li and L. Huang, *J. Liposome Res.* **7**, 63–75 (1997).

94. B.A. Sosnowski et al., *J. Biol. Chem.* **271**, 33647–33653 (1996).

95. A.M. Gewirtz, *Mt. Sinai J. Med.* **63**, 372–380 (1996).

96. S. Akhtar and S. Agrawal, *Trends Pharmacol. Sci.* **18**, 12–18 (1997).

97. Antisense '97, *Nat. Biotechnol.* **15**, 519–524 (1997).

See also MICROENCAPSULATION FOR GENE DELIVERY; POLYMERIC SYSTEMS FOR GENE DELIVERY, CHITOSAN AND PINC SYSTEMS.

ORAL DRUG DELIVERY, SMALL INTESTINE & COLON

JOSEPH FIX
Yamanouchi Shaklee Pharmaceutical Research Center
Palo Alto, California

KEY WORDS

Absorption window

Bioadhesive

Enteric coating

Enzymatic activity

Gastrointestinal tract

Microspheres

Osmotic systems

pH

Pharmacokinetics

Prodrugs

Time-specific controlled release systems

Zero-order release

OUTLINE

Small Intestine
  Time Specificity
  Bioadhesives
  pH Sensitivity
  Prodrugs
Colon
  Time Specificity
  Enzymatic Control
Bibliography

Oral administration has been the traditionally preferred route of administration for most therapeutic agents and is, in general, the first avenue investigated in the discovery and development of new drug candidates and formulations. Owing to patient acceptance, convenience of administration, cost-effective manufacturing that does not require sterile processing, and a generally long product shelf-life that is often dictated more by the stability of the active drug itself rather than the formulation components, a continued emphasis on development of oral formulations will persist. For many drugs and therapeutic indications, conventional immediate-release formulations provide effective therapy. The required balance of pharmacokinetic and pharmacodynamic profiles with an acceptable level of safety to the patient can be achieved, and the often costly and complex development of specially designed controlled-release formulations is neither necessary or justified.

Oral controlled-release formulations for the small intestine and colon have, however, received considerable attention in the past 20–25 years for a variety of reasons, including pharmaceutical superiority and clinical benefits derived from the drug-release pattern that are not achieved with traditional immediate- or sustained-release products (1). The necessity for frequently repeated administration to maintain therapeutically effective plasma drug levels can present problems for both patient compliance and fluctuating pharmacodynamic responses. Obviously, drugs that are susceptible to acid hydrolysis or enzymatic degradation in the stomach require a delayed-release mechanism, most often accomplished with stable coatings that prevent drug release in the stomach and thereby postpone release until the formulation is in the more favorable environment of the small intestine. This technology, commonly referred to as enteric coating, is rather routinely employed and will not be discussed in any detail in this section. Some examples of oral formulations employing coating technology to delay drug release until the formulation exits the gastric environment are given in Table 1. Another relatively common problem requiring development of controlled-release formulations is peak-associated side effects that have the potential to be reduced or minimized if a formulation can provide lower, but effective, constant plasma levels of the active drug. The ultimate goal has been to develop true zero-order-release formulations that provide a constant rate of drug release that is independent of remaining drug content in the formulation. Although this approach has certainly proved effective for some drugs and has been utilized to prolong drug absorption or achieve a more stable pharmacodynamic response, the varying absorption rates and drug stability in different regions of the gastrointestinal (GI) tract has meant that a zero-order release pattern will not necessarily achieve constant plasma drug levels. Controlled-release systems that achieve pseudo-zero-order or first-order release can also achieve effective pharmacokinetic and pharmacodynamic results. Another factor that occasionally justifies the development of controlled-release formulations for the small intestine and colon is the apparent presence of drug absorption "windows" that can dictate the regions of the GI tract from which a potential drug candidate can be effectively absorbed (3–5). When an absorption window exists for a drug candidate, a time- or location-directed formulation may be required to achieve the necessary driving force in the proper region of the GI tract to effect adequate drug absorption. In some cases, particularly for drugs that are susceptible to enzymatic degradation in the small intestine, such as peptides and proteins, designed formulations that release the drug in the lower small intestine or colon are thought to present potential advantages by minimizing enzymatic degradation and achieving higher local concentrations of the drug at the absorptive surface (6,7). The relatively more quiescent state of the lower small intestine and colon, as well as reduced fluid content, have also been cited as rationales for developing controlled-

Table 1. Examples of Enteric-Coated Oral Products

Product Name	Drug	Company
Ery-Tab	Erythromycin	Abbott
Prilosec	Omeprazole	Astra Merck
Pancrease	Pancrelipase	McNeil Pharmaceutical
Easprin	Aspirin	Parke-Davis
Eryc	Erythromycin	Parke-Davis

Source: Ref. 2.

release formulations for the lower small intestine and colon. In addition to designing formulations to achieve specific release profiles, modifying the drug itself through complexes or conjugates, that is, prodrugs, can be utilized as a controlled-release technology to achieve specific delivery profiles. For the reasons previously cited as well as others specific to individual drug candidates, the interest in controlled-release formulations for the small intestine and colon remains high and is the target of major pharmaceutical research and development efforts.

By definition, oral controlled-release products refer to those formulations in which a "controlling technology or component" is incorporated that is critical to modulating the drug-release pattern in a predictable fashion or that controls the timing, and subsequently the location, of drug release within the GI tract. Also included in the category of controlled-release formulations are strategies that are conceived and design to improve the pharmacokinetic profile, often by improving the performance or stability of the oral formulation in the dynamic and often hostile environment of the GI tract, in other words, by utilizing bioadhesive technologies to localize the drug and formulation components in close spatial and temporal proximity at the epithelial barrier membrane of the GI tract and, hence, increase the driving force for drug absorption. Table 2 provides examples of some marketed products that have employed sustained- or controlled-release technologies to provide a product with therapeutic or marketing alternatives. To provide an organized discussion of various approaches to small intestine and colon controlled-release technology, the subject matter is divided into pharmaceutical approaches as indicated below:

- Small intestine
  1. Time specificity
  2. Bioadhesives
  3. pH sensitivity
  4. Prodrugs

- Colon
  1. Time specificity
  2. Enzymatic control

It is important to bear in mind that with the exception of the transition from the stomach to the duodenum, there are few, if any, dramatic changes in physiology. Rather, the changes that occur in the physiology of the GI tract are more truly characterized as a continuum or gradual change, with decreasing enzymatic activity, decreasing motility and fluid content, and increasing pH. The presence of specific bacterial populations in the colon and an apparent transient, small reversal in the otherwise increasing pH gradient (8) are exceptions that have been targets for pharmaceutical strategies. These gradually changing physiological parameters means that few "triggering" elements can be utilized to effect a sudden and dramatic change in the performance or release characteristics of an oral controlled-release formulation. As a result, many of the same principles have applied to developing technologies for the small intestine and colon, and in some cases, the duration or timing of the controlling factor has been modified to achieve the desired end result. As such, the performance of controlled-release formulations can often be precisely regulated only in an in vitro environment but becomes subject to the vagaries of GI physiology and its resultant impact on controlling elements in the formulation itself.

SMALL INTESTINE

Time Specificity

Time-specific controlled-release systems are engineered formulations that are designed to release the active drug(s) in a specific temporal pattern. The technology, which can be applied to both continuous and pulsatile release systems, is generally utilized to deliver the active drug to a specific region of the absorptive GI surface. In this section, a variety of time-specific controlled-release systems are reviewed to provide the reader an appreciation for the range of applications for which these technologies might be useful.

The performance of time-specific controlled-release systems for drug delivery to the small intestine can be dra-

Table 2. Examples of Marketed Oral Controlled-Release Products

Product Name	Drug	Form	Company
Tegetrol-XR	Carbamazepine	ER tablet	CibaGeneva
Procardia XL	Nifedipine	ER tablet (osmotic)	Pfizer
Glucotrol XL	Glipizide	ER tablet (osmotic)	Pfizer
Sinemet CR	Carbidopa-Levodopa	CR tablet	DuPont Pharmaceuticals
Indocin SR	Indomethacin	Pellets in capsule	Merck & Co.
Dilacor XR	Diltiazem	ER capsule	Rhone-Poulenc Rorer
Cardene SR	Nicardipine	SR capsule	Roche
Calan SR	Verapamil HCl	SR caplets	Searle
Covera-HS	Verapamil HCl	ER tablet (osmotic)	Searle
Theo-24	Theophylline	ER capsule	UCB Pharmaceuticals
Inderal AL	Propranolol HCl	ER capsule	Wyeth Ayerst
Toprol-XL	Metoprolol succinate	ER tablet	Astra USA
Isoptin SR	Verapamil HCl	SR tablet	Knoll Laboratories
Slow-K	KCl	ER tablet	CibaGeneva
Cardizem SR	Diltazem HCl	SR capsule	Hoechst Marion Roussel

Source: Ref. 2.

matically affected by residence time in the stomach. In the fasted state, the physiologic mechanisms responsible for emptying nondigestible solids from the stomach will generally ensure that a dosage form will exit the stomach within 15–120 min of administration as a result of the "housekeeper" wave of contractile activity (9). Drugs that are susceptible to acid hydrolysis or enzymatic degradation in the stomach will potentially, therefore, exhibit lower-than-desired absorption during residence of the formulation in the stomach environment. This can be overcome by applying specific coating technologies (as represented in Table 1) that prevent activation of the controlling mechanism until the dosage form exits the stomach. As a result, however, initiation of drug absorption will be delayed by a factor proportional to gastric residence time and may not be appropriate for therapeutic indications where an immediate pharmacological effect is necessary. The same issue of gastric residence times applies to time-specific bolus-release systems, that is, controlled-release systems where the drug is released in a manner similar to an immediate-release formulation except that the initiation of drug release is delayed by the controlling mechanism of the delivery system. These factors must be evaluated in the development of any oral controlled-release formulation designed for delivery of the therapeutic agent to the small intestine.

Of the variety of approaches that have been employed to incorporate a time-specific element to oral controlled-release systems, perhaps the most widely used approach has been designing technologies based on generation of osmotic pressure as the driving force. The rationale for this approach is that the presence of water in the GI tract is relatively constant, at least in terms of the amount required for activating and controlling osmotically-based technologies, and provides a more constant regulating parameter than does enzyme activity, pH, bacterial activity, or any other physiological or biochemical parameter. Not surprisingly, a rather incredible number of patent applications have been submitted and approved based on osmotic technologies. In a review published in 1995 (10), Santus and Baker identified 240 U.S. patents that have been approved in the past 20 years covering various applications of osmotic technology. Obviously, it is not possible to review and discuss all of the various osmotic technologies that have been evaluated and, in some cases, developed into commercialized products. The discussion here will deal with the basic concept of osmotically based time-specific drug delivery technologies and a presentation of representative examples that are in various stages of research and development.

In general, osmotic systems incorporate a drug core that contains an osmotically active drug and a semipermeable membrane coating that serves to regulate the influx of water into the device in response to the osmotic core (Fig. 1). In some cases, the drug core also contains an osmotically active salt, for example, NaCl, to assist in establishing the necessary osmotic driving force. Pressure developed as a result of the influx of water serves as a driving force to control the rate of drug release, which can be in either solution or suspension form. A port for drug release is normally created in the device through an orifice engineered

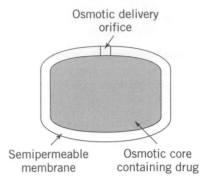

Figure 1. Osmotic pressure-controlled drug delivery system. *Source:* Reprinted from Ref. 11, with kind permission from Marcel Dekker, Inc., New York.

during manufacturing or created in the in situ environment of the GI tract. As long as the concentration of osmotically active agent(s) remains above saturation solubility, zero-order drug release can be achieved in which the rate of drug release $(Q/t)_z$ can be described as shown in the following equation (12):

$$(Q/t)_z = \frac{P_w A_m}{h_m(\Pi_s - \Pi_e)S_D} \tag{1}$$

where P_w, A_m, and h_m are water permeability, effective surface area, and thickness of the semipermeable membrane, respectively. S_D, Π_s, and Π_e are drug solubility, osmotic pressure of the saturated solution of osmotic drug and salt core, and osmotic pressure of the GI fluids, respectively. The mathematical description of the osmotically driven device permits calculation of a desired release rate based on such parameters as osmotic load (Fig. 2) and thickness of

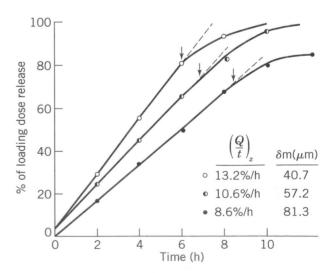

Figure 2. Effect of coating membrane thickness on the rate and duration of zero-order release of indomethacin from osmotic pressure-controlled gastrointestinal delivery system. *Source:* Reprinted from Ref. 11 with kind permission from Marcel Dekker, Inc., New York.

the rate-controlling membrane (Fig. 3) that modulates water influx (11). Several examples of employing osmotic technology to achieve time-controlled release of therapeutic agents are described in the following sections.

The absorption of metoprolol from conventional tablets, an osmotic OROS system (Ciba Geigy, lot No. L 001), and a multiple-unit coated pellet formulation (CR/ZOK) was evaluated in 18 healthy volunteers (13). The OROS design was a single-unit tablet coated with a semipermeable membrane according to principles of the elementary osmotic pump. The CR/ZOK formulation utilized metoprolol succinate as coated pellets in a disintegrating tablet. The CR formulations contained 95 mg metoprolol, while the conventional immediate-release formulation contained 100 mg. Both the OROS and CR/ZOK formulations afforded linear drug release for 2–3 h and continuous, nearly linear release for up to 6 h (Fig. 4). An analysis of the in vivo pharmacokinetics demonstrated that the CR and OROS formulations were essentially bioequivalent on the basis of C_{max} and AUC, and both resulted in a relatively constant maintenance of the plasma metoprolol profile (Fig. 5). The 24-h absorption profile for nifedipine was examined in 12 volunteers given a commercially available nifedipine GI therapeutic system (GITS, Adalat® XL, Miles Canada, Inc.) (14). The GITS system is a push–pull design that can be utilized for delivery of insoluble or poorly soluble drug suspensions and provides essentially zero-order release for 24 h following an initial 2-h hydration period, which is typical of these osmotically based systems (15,16). Measurable nifedipine levels were not observed in the first 2 h postadministration, which is expected based on the initial hydration period required for the GITS. Both 30-mg and 60-mg formulations were evaluated and showed that, as expected, the C_{max} and AUC were approximately doubled with the 60-mg dose compared with the 30-mg dose. The observed T_{max} value frequently occurred at 24 h in spite of the fact that a number of volunteers had total GI transit times considerably less than 24 h (6–32 h). The authors suggest that nifedipine chronopharmacokinetics

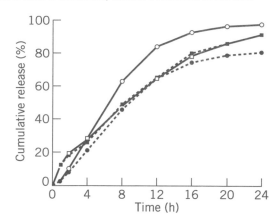

Figure 4. Cumulative in vitro dissolution profiles for metoprolol CR (95 mg metoprolol succinate; squares) and metoprolol OROS (95 mg metoprolol fumarate; circles). Mean of six tablets, determined at a paddle speed of 50 rpm in simulated gastric juice, pH 1.2 (open symbols), and in a phosphate buffer solution, pH 6.8 (filled symbols). *Source:* Reprinted from Ref. 13 with kind permission of Plenum Publishing Corporation, New York.

might account for this observation based on previously reported data that suggest a lower absorption of nifedipine when dosed in the evening versus the morning (17). Regardless of the underlying cause for the specific pharmacokinetic profile with nifedipine, this study points out a common concern with controlled- or sustained-release oral dosage forms, particularly those with release profiles approaching 24 h, in that total GI transit may occur in a significantly shorter time frame than the time required for total drug release from the formulation (i.e., the formulation is eliminated from the body prior to complete absorption). An obvious outcome is that less than the total dose is absorbed, which may have therapeutic implications.

Both OROS and GITS systems employ an engineered (i.e., laser-drilled) port for drug exit from the device. Other systems have been designed that do not require prefabrication of the exit port. Pore-forming agents can be employed in the coating process to effect in situ pore generation (18–20). Potassium chloride–core tablets were coated with a cellulose acetate–latex formulation containing a plasticizer (triacetin) and urea as a pore-forming agent (19). Coated tablets required high-temperature (60 or 80°C) curing to coalesce the latex beads into a film on the tablet surface. Urea content was found to be the most important variable in terms of the resultant release profile. Cure time did not affect performance. Excellent agreement was observed between in vitro release rates (14.6 ± 0.87%/h in U.S. Pharmacopeial Convention (USP) method 2) and in vivo release rates (12.04 ± 1.18%/h as determined after necropsy retrieval of devices from fasted dogs). The release profile, both in vitro and in vivo (Fig. 6), approximated linearity over 6–8 h. Controlled-porosity osmotic pumps (MODS) were also evaluated for their applicability to the sustained delivery of simvastatin, an HMG–CoA reductase inhibitor for controlling plasma cholesterol levels (20). Core tablets of 105 mg drug-free base, 25.4 mg trometham-monium II, 100 mg mannitol, 45 mg Dowex 50 × 8–100,

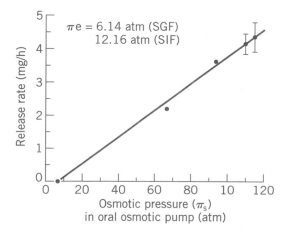

Figure 3. Effect of osmotic pressure Π_s in the osmotic pressure-controlled gastrointestinal delivery system on the rate of release of phenylpropanolamine. *Source:* Reprinted from Ref. 11 with kind permission from Marcel Dekker, Inc., New York.

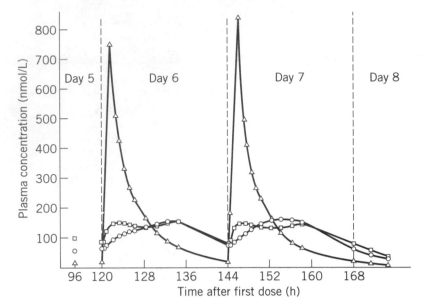

Figure 5. Mean plasma concentrations of metoprolol on treatment days 5 (predose) through 8 following once-daily dosing of (□) metoprolol CR (95 mg metoprolol succinate), (○) metoprolol OROS (95 mg metoprolol fumarate), and (△) conventional metoprolol tablets (100 mg metoprolol tartrate) in 18 healthy subjects. *Source:* Reprinted from Ref. 13 with kind permission of Plenum Publishing Corporation, New York.

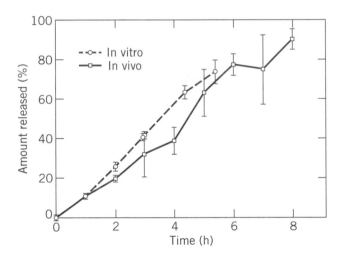

Figure 6. Comparison of in vitro (dashed lines) and in vivo (solid lines) release profiles. *Source:* Reprinted from Ref. 19 with kind permission of Plenum Publishing Corporation, New York.

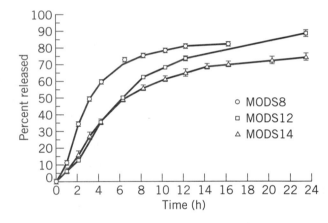

Figure 7. Mean ($\pm$ SD) in vitro release profiles from simvastatin MODS8 ($n = 6$), MODS12 ($n = 3$), and MODS14 ($n = 6$) devices. *Source:* Reprinted from Ref. 20, with kind permission of Plenum Publishing Corporation, New York.

25 mg Povidone 29–32 K, and 0.06 mg BHA were formulated by aqueous granulation. Magnesium stearate (1.5 mg per core tablet) was used as the lubricant, and 3/8-in.-round standard concave tablets were compressed. The controlled-porosity coat was applied to the core tablets by fluidized-bed spray-coating techniques with a coating solution of CA-398-30, CA-320S, sorbitol, and poly(ethylene glycol) (PEG) 400 dissolved in a water/methanol/methylene chloride (1:10:15) solvent blend. Simvastatin systems (8-, 12-, and 14-h release profiles) were prepared and evaluated in dogs and humans. The in vitro release profile for the 12-h system (Fig. 7) exhibited approximately zero-order release kinetics over the initial 6 h (55% release), with 74% release in 12 h and 90% released in 24 h. The 8- and 14-h MODS systems provided 76% release in 8 h and 70% release in 14 h, respectively. Comparing the MODS12 system with conventional tablets in a single-dose dog

study, 4-fold reduction in AUC and 13-fold reduction in C_{max} for MODS was observed compared with the conventional tablet. Similar results were observed in a phase I human study in which a 14-h 20-mg simvastatin MODS system afforded a 54% reduction in AUC and 73% reduction in C_{max} compared with conventional tablets. Given that the pharmacodynamic effects on cholesterol lowering were similar between MODS and conventional tablets in the dog study, the data indicate that the MODS controlled-porosity system could be utilized to afford lower but constant plasma simvastatin levels that provided the same therapeutic potential without wide fluctuations in plasma drug levels.

Other osmotically based systems have been reported that are designed to release drugs in a pulsed or bolus fashion rather than the continuous profile achieved by OROS or GITS. The PORT System (Fig. 8) comprises a gelatin capsule, a semipermeable membrane coating, an insoluble

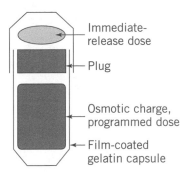

Figure 8. Design of PORT Systems. *Source:* Reprinted from Ref. 21, with kind permission of Elsevier Science–NL, Sara Burgerhartstraat 25, 1055 KV Amsterdam, The Netherlands.

plug, and an osmotic charge that can be balanced to achieve the desired drug-release time (21). A drug-osmotic core was placed in #-elongated hard gelatin capsules and overlayed with melted Gelucire 50/02 (Gattefosse). Following cooling, solidification of the Gelucire layer, and coating of the capsules with an acetone solution of 0.7% w/v triacetin and 2.1% w/v cellulose acetate, the release time was proportional to the number of coats applied. In vitro release times in simulated intestinal fluid (pH 7.5) of 0.23 ± 0.03 h, 1.68 ± 0.04 h, 2.96 ± 0.31 h, and 8.53 ± 0.28 h were observed for capsules with one, three, five, and seven coating layers. Combined with an understanding and estimate of GI transit times, one could envision utilizing these time-delayed systems to target relatively specific regions of the GI tract for drug release.

Not all controlled- or sustained-release technologies are based on underlying osmotic principles as the main driving force. A wide variety of other strategies have been employed and are being evaluated and developed with the goal of providing predictable, time-controlled oral drug delivery. The following sections, although not totally inclusive, describe a variety of technologies that may be appropriate for achieving time-controlled drug delivery.

TIME CLOCK, developed by Zambon Group SpA (Milano, Italy), is a pulsed-release system manufactured with conventional film-coating techniques and uses common pharmaceutical excipients (22). The principle behind TIME CLOCK involves applying a hydrophobic surfactant layer (as an aqueous dispersion) containing a water-soluble polymer onto a tablet or capsule core. The dried coating dispersion can then rehydrate and redisperse in an aqueous environment (e.g., GI tract fluids), and the time for rehydration/redispersion is proportional to the coating thickness (Fig. 9). A typical tablet core consisted of 74.5 mg lactose, 3 mg poly(vinylpyrrolidone), 13.5 mg corn

starch, and 1 mg magnesium stearate. The compression mixture is prepared by granulating lactose with an aqueous solution of poly(vinylpyrrolidone), drying and sieving, and adding additional components by blending. The mixture was compressed to a theoretical weight of 100 mg with convex, 5.5-mm-diameter punches. The dispersion coating consisted of 3.5% carnauba wax, 1.5% beeswax, 0.5% poly(oxyethylene) sorbitan monooleate, 1.0% hydroxypropylmethyl cellulose (HPMC), and 93.5% deionized water and was applied with fluid-bed techniques with inlet air at 75°C. Tablet weight increases due to the coating process were in the range of 45% (B45 batch) to 60% (B60 batch). Mean lag times for in vivo disintegration in human volunteers after a light breakfast for the two batches were 204 ± 18 min and 345 ± 54 min, reflecting the impact of the coating thickness on disintegration times. Uncoated tablets showed complete disintegration in less than 20 min. Lag and disintegration times were unaffected by pH. Scintigraphic evaluation indicated that the in vivo behavior of TIME CLOCK did not influence the absorption of a model drug, salbutamol.

Dry-coated wax matrix tablets comprised of a table core with disintegrator and an outer layer compressed from pentoxifylline and behenic acid provided sigmoidal drug-release profiles with the high rate of drug release occurring during core tablet disintegration (23). The disintegration time decreases with increasing tablet core weight due to the concomitant reduced outer layer. A linear relationship was shown for time for 50% dissolution versus disintegration time for tablet cores ranging from 31 to 63% drug content, indicating that drug-release rate was controlled by tablet disintegration. Tablets composed of 70% amylodextrin and 30% paracetamol exhibited constant in vitro drug release in pH 6.8 buffer for approximately 8 h and relatively constant plasma paracetamol levels for 14 h in human volunteers (24). The amylodextrin tablets were apparently not hydrolyzed in vivo by α-amylase. Plasma levels on repeated dosing tended to decrease, apparently due to excretion of tablets prior to complete drug release and absorption. Wax microspheres of ibuprofen were examined, and it was shown that modifiers such as stearyl alcohol and glyceryl monostearate significantly increased the in vitro dissolution rate (20% w/w optimal) (25). Drug concentrations of 17% could be achieved in these microsphere formulations. Approximately 80–90% of the drug load was released within 12 h, indicating the potential application of wax microspheres for drug candidates with physicochemical properties similar to ibuprofen. Multiparticulate sustained-release theophylline formulations (26) comprised of spherical pellets (ethylcellulose–methylcellulose) coated with rate-controlling membranes of two different thicknesses (4.1 and 2.3% weight gain) afforded in

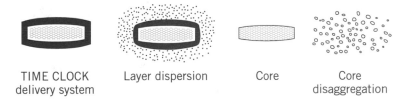

TIME CLOCK delivery system   Layer dispersion   Core   Core disaggregation

Figure 9. The working principle of the TIME CLOCK system. *Source:* Reprinted from Ref. 22, with kind permission of Elsevier Science–NL, Sara Burgerhartstraat 25, 1055 KV Amsterdam, The Netherlands.

vitro theophylline drug release that was independent of pH between pH 1 and pH 7. In vitro release was nearly complete within 5–8 h, while in vivo release was extended to 8–10 h. Although the rates of release varied with the two coating thickness, the extent of release was comparable and complete for both formulations, and the extent of theophylline absorption equated with that seen in solution dosing. Hydrophilic matrix tablets of felodipine, composed primarily of hydroxypropyl methylcellulose, were examined in human volunteers (27). In vitro disintegration and dissolution were linear over 8–10 h. In the human evaluation, felodipine absorption was related to tablet erosion as evinced by similarity between the in vivo erosion (as determined by γ-scintigraphy) and pharmacokinetic profiles.

Hydrophilic matrix tablets of zileuton, a 5-lipoxygenase inhibitor, were prepared by directly compressing hydroxypropyl methylcellulose and 50–60% zileuton (28). Wet granulations with water and low shear force were also used to compress tablets with magnesium stearate. In vitro release in USP I, II, and III methods was linear for 8 h. Sustained in vivo absorption in dogs was observed, which correlated with the in vitro release profiles although in vivo release was more rapid (release complete in approximately 4 h) than that noted in vitro. Prodan, a fluorescent marker, release from poly (D,L-lactic acid) (PLA) nanospheres coated with albumin or poly(vinyl alcohol) (PVA) was examined in vitro (29). In simulated gastric fluid where polymer degradation did not occur, release kinetics typified diffusion through the intact polymer matrix, with complete release within 120 min. In simulated intestinal fluid, release was dependent on the coating applied to the nanospheres. With PVA coating, the marker was released by diffusion through the PLA matrix, with only 44% released due to the marker's poor affinity for water. With an albumin coating, marker release was both matrix erosion and diffusion controlled with 100% release in 480 min.

A soluble oral controlled-release formulation regulated by both pulsatile and zero-order release kinetics has been described (30) that utilizes poly(ethylene oxide) and HPMC excipients with diclofenac in a three-layer matrix system (Fig. 10). In vitro dissolution studies suggested that both biphasic release and zero-order release kinetics up to 24 h could be achieved with this system. Dissolution and swelling/erosion are proposed to account for the linear portion of drug release, while disintegration and dissolution are

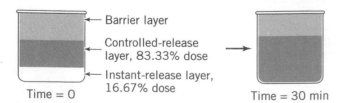

Figure 10. Schematics of diclofenac sodium asymmetric configuration delivery system. (**a**) Delivery system at time zero, (**b**) complete dissolution of one layer and gradual swelling of the system. *Source:* Reprinted from Ref. 30, with kind permission of Elsevier Science–NL, Sara Burgerhartstraat 25, 1055 KV Amsterdam, The Netherlands.

mechanistically suggested for the burst phase. Hydroxyethylcellulose (HEC) has been utilized as a gel-forming matrix to prepare delayed release tablets of diltiazem hydrochloride (31). The tablets are cores of diltiazem surrounded by an outer shell of HEC of different viscosity grades. Diltiazem was rapidly released from all tablets after an initial lag phase, which was a function of the HEC coating. Lag time increased as the HEC viscosity increased. The lag time was not greatly affected by pH between pH 1.2 and pH 6.8. In a human volunteer study, T_{max} and mean residence time increased with increasing HEC viscosity with small intersubject variability. In vitro and in vivo lag times appear to exhibit a reasonable correlation. The diltiazem AUC did, however, decrease as the lag time increased. This approach for time delaying could represent a useful approach for drug candidates where an initial delay is appropriate.

Although it has clearly not been possible to elucidate and discuss the tremendous number of approaches that have been, and continue to be, developed for oral time-controlled drug delivery, the examples presented here should at least provide a sampling of the varied approaches that can be considered. Inherent in the selection of any time-controlled release technology has to be the physicochemical properties of the drug candidate, as this can determine or modify drug release from a given formulation, depending on the release mechanism. The intended therapeutic regimen is also critical in the selection process because the duration of drug release is obviously dependent on residence in the GI tract, and the absorption profile of a given drug may be different depending on the location within the GI tract.

Bioadhesives

The use of mucoadhesive polymers to improve oral drug absorption or the performance of oral controlled-release drug delivery systems has received considerable attention in the past 10–15 years and has been the subject of previous review articles (32,33). This interest has been generated with several goals in mind, including increasing local drug concentrations to improve absorption, retarding the transit of controlled-release dosage forms to take advantage of upper-GI absorption windows, or targeting drugs or dosage forms to specific regions of the GI tract for specific applications, such as antigen sampling by the M-cells of the Peyer's patches in the lower small intestine and colon. In every case, the successful application of bioadhesive technology is a balancing act between the creativity and expertise of the pharmaceutical scientist and the physiologic mechanisms of the GI tract that function to dilute, mix, and propel food substances in a proximal to distal direction in the GI tract.

In one potential application for bioadhesive polymers, the intrinsic permeability of the drug candidate is too low or the drug is susceptible to hydrolytic or enzymatic degradation in the lumen of the GI tract, either of which results in insufficient absorption of the drug candidate. In both instances, it has been felt that the ability to localize high concentrations of the drug candidate at the absorptive epithelial surface would increase the driving force and thereby lead to increased levels of drug absorbed into the systemic circulation. The approach here has been attempting to link a mucoadhesive polymer to a drug candidate such that a selective attachment to the epithelial cells occurs and presents the drug candidate in high concentration and close proximity to the absorptive surface. To be therapeutically effective, the attached bioadhesive polymer must not interfere with the absorption or activity of the parent drug, or the linkage of the polymer to the active drug must be reversible such that the active parent drug is efficiently released, either at the epithelial surface or after absorption, and can exert its pharmacologic effect.

Another area of interest for bioadhesive polymers has been to retard the GI transit of controlled-release dosage forms for those drugs whose absorption is restricted to the upper regions of the GI tract, that is, absorption-window drug candidates. Some drugs have been clearly shown to be absorbed in specific regions of the upper GI tract, including chlorothiazide (33), riboflavin (34), and furosemide (35), and other drugs are likely to have specific preferred regions of absorption there. Additionally, for most drugs examined to date, it is generally felt that absorption in the colonic region is significantly lower than in the small intestine, probably because of differences in the lumenal contents of the colon that either impair the dissolution and diffusion of drugs from the lumen to the epithelial cell wall or impose additional degradative pathways, such as bacterial enzyme activity, that also decrease drug absorption. With this apparently common problem, controlled-release dosage forms whose release times exceed 5–6 h will likely exhibit a significant deviation in zero- or first-order kinetics owing to poor colonic absorption. To overcome this problem and extend the effective release time of controlled-release dosage forms, major interest has evolved in ways to prolong the upper GI residence time of controlled-release dosage forms such that a greater proportion of the drug load is released in an environment where reliable absorption can occur. Owing to the very high fluid content and mixing activity in the stomach, attempts to prolong gastric residence times via adhesive technologies have not been successful and will not be covered here. Rather, the focus will be on approaches that are being investigated to retard the small-intestine transit of small particulates where the balance of bioadhesion and physical forces in the GI tract offers some promise for success.

A final area of interest for bioadhesive technology has emerged from the advances in the biotechnology arena where biopharmaceuticals directed toward the gut-associated lymphoid tissues (M-cells in the Peyer's patches) are being developed for vaccination, immunization, and tolerance therapies. The M-cells are known as a preferred site for particulate uptake in the GI tract, and this mechanism has been proposed as a possible avenue for improving the absorption of particulate formulations, although it is not clear yet how effective this route will be for systemic delivery of drug candidates because the primary function of these cells is macromolecular sampling and degradation to feed the antigen-processing cells of the immune system. Regardless, bioadhesive polymers specific for M-cells, particularly lectins, have been evaluated as candidates for this approach.

A variety of bioadhesive molecules, particularly polymers, have been evaluated with varying results in terms of in vitro adhesive forces and in vivo efficacy. Polyanions with a high charge density, particularly those containing carboxylic acid groups, appear to exhibit the highest degree of bioadhesive properties. Mucoadhesive hydrogels have received the major share of attention and effort, from which polymers of poly(acrylic acid) derivatives (35), hyaluronic acid (36), and some chitosans (37) have demonstrated adhesive properties (Fig. 11). Linear cellulose polymers have not demonstrated effective in vivo bioadhesive properties, probably due to a lack of rigidity and structural integrity seen in hydrated, non-cross-linked polymers (38).

Akiyama and coauthors (39) reported on the preparation and evaluation of 177- to 500-μm-diameter polyglycerol ester fatty-acid microspheres composed of tetraglycerol pentastearate and tetraglycerol monostearate in which Carbopol 934P was either applied as a coating (CPC) or dispersed into the matrix of the microspheres (CPD). Carbopol 934P was chosen because of previously demonstrated bioadhesive properties (38,40). In an in vitro bioadhesion assay, more than 90% of the CPD microspheres adhered to gastric and small intestinal tissue, whereas only <10% of CPC and PGEF (similar composition without Carbopol 934P) microspheres showed adhesion. In an in vivo evaluation in conscious rats each receiving 100 PGEF and 100 CPD microspheres, the CPD microspheres showed significantly longer gastric retention time ($T_s 50 = 1.8$ h) and

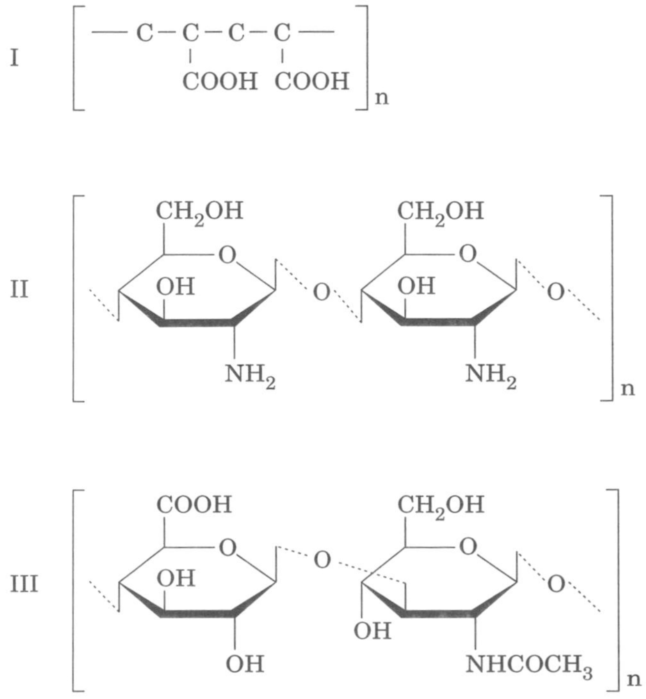

Figure 11. Polymers forming mucoadhesive hydrogels: I, poly(acrylic acid); II, chitosan (poly[D-glucosamine]); III, hyaluronic acid (poly[D-glucuronic acid-N-acetylglucosamine]). Source: Reprinted from Ref. 32, with kind permission of Begell House, Inc., New York.

these two polymers, in vivo evaluations were carried out in a rat model to determine whether the in vitro adhesive properties translated into an advantage that could be exploited in vivo in the development of oral drug delivery systems (52). Alginate microspheres were prepared by blending dissolved alginate and dicumarol or radioopaque marker and pumping droplets into a calcium chloride bath. Microsphere size range from 600 to 850 μm for radioopaque-loaded microspheres and <212 μm for dicumarol-containing microspheres. A phase inversion microencapsulation technique was used to prepare polyanhydride microspheres. Briefly, polymer and dicumarol were dissolved in an appropriate solvent (methylene chloride), and the solution was poured into a strong nonsolvent (petroleum ether) that was miscible with the solvent. Microspheres were spontaneously formed whose size ranged from 0.5 μm to 5 μm. The phase inversion microencapsulation techniques avoided the need to utilize a hot-melt procedure (with temperatures around 100°C), which can have significant limitations in terms of drug stability. Compatibility with an organic solvent, for example, methylene chloride, still has to be taken into consideration. The polyanhydride microspheres were at a fumaric acid/sebacic acid ratio of 20:80, P(FA:SA)20:80. The GI transit of barium-loaded microspheres was evaluated in a rat model in which fasted rats received approximately 200 mg of barium-loaded microspheres by stomach gavage in 0.9% sodium chloride. Transit of particles was quantitated by X-ray techniques, and the results (Fig. 16) indicated the P(FA:SA)20:80 microspheres had a significantly slower GI transit than the alginate microspheres. Pharmacokinetic analysis of dicumarol (6.5 dicumarol in 40-mg microspheres) plasma levels also demonstrated that improved absorption of dicumarol was achieved with the

P(FA:SA)20:80 microspheres relative to spray-dried dicumarol (Fig. 17). The plasma AUC for P(FA:SA)20:80 dicumarol microspheres was 363 $\pm$ 100.3 μg/h/mL compared to 232 $\pm$ 38.4 μg/h/mL and 211 $\pm$ 30.3 μg/h/mL for spray-dried dicumarol and alginate dicumarol microspheres, respectively. These data are highly encouraging with respect to potential utility for developing effective oral delivery technologies based on bioadhesive principles. However, it should be noted that the dose of microspheres employed in the GI transit studies, 200 mg per rat, is quite high and may or may not be reproducible in larger animal models or humans where the formulation mass relative to GI dimensional parameters may not favor such an intimate and highly concentrated contact of bioadhesive microspheres with the GI mucosal cell layer.

In addition to their potential utility in localizing drug or particulate formulations at the mucosal surface of the GI tract, several bioadhesive polymers have also been shown to possess activity with regard to inhibiting degradative enzyme activity and modifying the barrier function of the epithelial cell layer. This mixed function activity of the bioadhesive polymers offers an opportunity to coordinate both formulation localization and biological effects of a single formulation component.

Polycarbophil and carbomer have been shown to inhibit trypsin enzymatic activity in a calcium-dependent manner (53). Both poly(acrylic acid) derivatives are known to bind divalent cations in the undissociated state. Utilizing 0.35% (w/v) polycarbophil or 0.25% (w/v) carbomer in an in vitro incubation experiment, trypsin activity was inhibited approximately 93%, calcium was depleted to 10–15% of its original content, and free protein concentration was decreased approximately 30–40% (indicating the bioadhesive potential of polycarbophil and carbomer toward proteins).

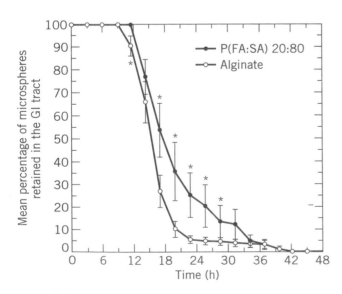

Figure 16. Percentage of microspheres retained over time. Paired, one-tailed t-tests were performed on the raw data, and those time points with percentages statistically different ($P \leq$ 0.05) from each other are represented by asterisks (*). Reprinted from Ref. 52, with kind permission of Elsevier Science–NL, Sara Burgerhartstraat 25, 1055 KV Amsterdam, The Netherlands.

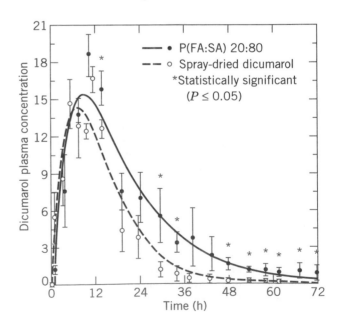

Figure 17. Dicumarol plasma concentration versus time (P[FA:SA] 20:80 versus spray dried). *Source:* Reprinted from Ref. 52, with kind permission of Elsevier Science–NL, Sara Burgerhartstraat 25, 1055 KV Amsterdam, The Netherlands

Carbomer, which has a higher binding affinity for calcium than polycarbophil, also was able to inhibit trypsin activity at lower concentration than polycarbophil, indicating a relationship between calcium-binding activity and enzyme inhibition. This is consistent, considering the important role of calcium in maintaining the thermodynamic stability of trypsin (54).

The enzyme inhibitory activity of polycarbophil and carbomer were also examined with a variety of peptide substrates (55). Employing brush-border membrane vesicles (BBMVs) obtained from the entire small intestine of rats, the capacity of polycarbophil (0.1–0.5%) and carbomer (0.1–0.5%) to inhibit the enzymatic degradation of buserelin, 8-arginine vasopressin (DGAVP), metkephamid, L-pyroglutamic acid p-nitroanilide (PGNA), hippuryl-L-arginine (Hipp-Arg), and insulin was determined. Because BBMVs were utilized as the biological system, only enzymes associated with brush-border membranes are evaluated by this method. Buserelin degradation was not affected by either carbomer or polycarbophil. Polycarbophil and carbomer were only weakly effective in inhibiting degradation of DGAVP and Hipp-Arg at the highest concentration (0.5%) tested. Insulin, which only exhibited an approximate 10% degradation by BBMV enzymes with 240 min, was slightly protected by 0.25% carbomer. Overall, the data indicate that carbomer and polycarbophil are only very weakly protective against brush-border enzyme activity isolated from rat GI tissue. Polymers with a stronger affinity for divalent cations could afford an advantage in terms of inhibiting BBMV enzyme activity.

In addition to the bioadhesive and enzyme inhibitory potential of some of the polymers utilized in the aforementioned studies, there are also data to indicate that these polymers may also be capable of modifying the barrier properties of epithelial cells in a manner that increases drug flux. Carbomer (0.5 and 1.5% w/v) and chitosan (0.5, 1.0, and 1.5% w/v) were evaluated for their effects on electrical resistance (TEER) and drug flux utilizing an in vitro Caco-2 cell monolayer derived from a human colon carcinoma cell line (56). TEER was significantly decreased to approximately 40–50% of the original resistance by both polymers but only at the highest concentration tested. If the polymer solutions were replaced with fresh buffer, TEER recovery was observed to occur (65% for carbomer and 88% for chitosan of original TEER), indicating that the change in resistance was not due to irreversible damage to the cell layer. Chitosan–glutamate at 1.5% did not increase mannitol flux over a 150-min incubation period, whereas 1.0% carbomer afforded a 2.7% flux of mannitol over a 120-min period. It should be noted that drug flux in this in vitro model is not directly proportional to what could be anticipated in vivo. In fact, an in vitro flux of 2.7% in 120 min would likely translate into a rather more significant in vivo absorption level. Carbomer was also found to significantly enhance the in vitro flux of FD-4 (FITC-dextran, M_W 4,000). Confocal fluorescence microscopy provided evidence that carbomer was loosening the tight junction structure of the epithelial cell layer and providing an aqueous pathway for molecule movement between cells of the monolayer. The affinity of carbomer for divalent calcium may account for its effect on tight junction structure be-

cause calcium depletion has been shown to open tight junctional pathways of epithelial cell monolayers.

Several polymers and polymer systems have been described that possess varying degrees of bioadhesive potential. Most of the data generated to date has involved in vitro evaluations and, in some instances, evaluation in small animal models, for example, rats. The practical utility of bioadhesive approaches for oral drug delivery will obviously depend on demonstrating a similar performance and efficacy in larger animal models and human clinical studies. The particular intriguing feature of some of the polymers employed, particularly the polyacrylate types as carbomer, is that they possess multiple functional capabilities, including a bioadhesive potential, enzyme inhibitory activity, and some membrane permeation–enhancing activity. These multiple effects may afford particular advantages to utilizing these systems for oral controlled drug delivery. Finally, the data and interpretations from several investigators would suggest that the potential for bioadhesive properties may be optimal in the lower GI tract where the epithelial mucus layer is thinner and there is at least a somewhat reduced state of fluid content and muscle contractility. It remains to be demonstrated that the mucoadhesive approaches evaluated here will have a practical utility in the upper GI tract.

pH Sensitivity

Controlled-release technologies based on pH-sensitive control mechanisms are designed to release acidic or basic drugs in the GI tract at a rate that is not dependent on the pH of the GI fluids, which can vary from pH 1.2–3.5 in the stomach to pH 6.0–7.5 in the lower small intestine. The general principle underlying this technology is the incorporation of an acidic (or basic) drug and appropriate buffering agents as a core granulation. These particles can then either be coated with a fluid-permeable membrane that allows influx of GI fluids, or the particles can be uniformly dispersed in a tablet core that serves a similar function. In either application, the influx of fluid from the GI tract dissolves the buffering agents and provides a microclimate pH within the formulation that regulates the rate of drug release. Ideally, the rate of drug release should be independent of the pH of the GI fluid being imbibed.

Sutinen et al. have reported on the development of pH-controlled silicone microspheres for controlled drug delivery (57). Silicone microspheres were prepared with an amine-resistant Dow Corning X7-3012 silicone elastomer. Monosodium phosphate, disodium phosphate, trisodium phosphate, and tris(hydroxymethylaminomethane) were used as potential buffering agents. Using timolol maleate as a model drug, spray-dried mixtures of timolol with and without varying compositions of buffering agents were prepared and mixed with the silicone elastomer. Spray-drying timolol and buffers together proved most effective, as opposed to mixing timolol and buffer that had been spray-dried separately, because the drug and buffer were localized in the same particle within the silicone elastomer microsphere. Spray-dried timolol particles were approximately 3 μm and incorporated into the silicone microspheres at a 30 wt % loading (loaded microsphere diameter, 143–301 μm). Without added buffering agents, timolol release was relatively slow, showing less than 20% release in 11 h. When trisodium phosphate was incorporated in the microsphere preparation, the timolol release rate was increased 3.3–8.2 times greater than nonbuffered microspheres. Release of timolol from the silicone microspheres followed square-root-of-time kinetics, which is typical of a matrix-controlled dissolution process (58). The rate of timolol release was directly proportional to timolol loading (wt %), basic nature of the added buffer, and the loading level of the buffer (10–25%). This reflected a higher proportion of timolol in the unionized state, which could more readily partition through the silicone matrix and be released in the dissolution medium. As the strength of the buffering agent increased, not only did the timolol release rate increase but the release rate also became independent of the pH of the dissolution medium (Fig. 18). These studies indicated the potential utility of silicone-type elastomers as components for developing pH-sensitive oral controlled-release systems.

Methacrylic acid copolymers (Eudragit, Rohm GmbH) have been utilized as pH-sensitive polymers in oral drug delivery. A peptide analog inhibitor of HIV-1 protease (CGP 57813) has shown increased bioavailability in mice when administered as a pH-sensitive polymeric nanoparticle formulation (59). Similar results have been recently reported in a dog oral bioavailability study (60). Nanoparticles (245–264 nm) were prepared from poly(methacrylic acid-co-ethylacrylate) with a 1:1 molar monomer ratio (Eudragit L100-55) or poly(methacrylic acid-co-methylmethacrylate) with a 1:2 molar monomer ratio (Eudragit S100). The Eudragit L100 nanoparticles were soluble above pH 5, and the Eudragit S100 nanoparticles were soluble above pH 7. Aqueous suspensions of CGP 57813 in an amorphous form were used as controls for oral dosing studies in dogs and showed no detectable plasma levels of the drug. Significant increases in CGP 57813 bioavailability were observed in the dog oral dosing study (Fig. 19) that were both polymer and food dependent. With both polymers, bioavailability

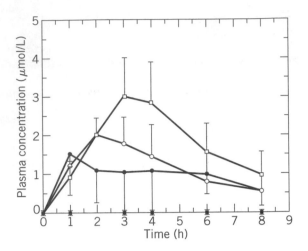

Figure 19. Plasma concentration profiles following oral administration of CGP 57813 from Eudragit L100-55 (● fasted dogs, ○ fed dogs) and S100 (■ fasted dogs, □ fed dogs) nanoparticles; mean ± SEM (n = 4). In vitro, the IC90 against HIV-1/LAV in MT-2 cells is 0.1 umol 1^{-1}. *Source:* Reprinted from Ref. 60, with kind permission of Plenum Publishing Corporation, New York.

was greater in the fed state than the fasted state, possibly reflecting a slowing of GI transit, allowing more efficient nanoparticle dissolution and drug absorption. S100 nanoparticles showed a greater effect on CGP 57813 bioavailability in dogs than did L100 nanoparticles, which is in contrast to results previously observed in mice. This discrepancy in results may be related to species-specific differences in GI pH and is a factor that requires further evaluation to predict the performance of these systems in a human clinical application. The results of this study do indicate, however, that pH-sensitive polymers that dissolve above pH 5.5 may be useful as controlled-release polymers for oral administration.

Narisawa et al. also employed Eudragit coatings in a pH-sensitive bead formulation to develop a sigmoidal release system (SRS) (61). Uncoated drug beads were prepared from a powder mixture of drug and sucrose or drug and succinic acid using a CF granulator. After applying the powder mixture to nonpareil seeds with continuous binder spray, the resultant beads were spray-coated with Eudragit RS 30D, talc, triethylcitrate, and water. The beads were approximately 1,100 μm in diameter, with a 90-μm coating film. Utilizing sucrose instead of succinic acid in the initial bead preparation led to beads from which the release of a model drug was dependent on the coating thickness and followed first-order (10% coating) or zero-order (15% or 20% coating) kinetics without a significant lag period. At 30% coating, there was little or no drug release. Conducting the dissolution studies in various organic acid media demonstrated that drug release was significantly increased in the presence of an acidic medium, with succinic acid providing the most dramatic increase in drug release. Incorporation of succinic acid into the bead formulation converted the release profiles to a sigmoid shape characterized by an initial lag phase that was followed by a rapid increase in drug release. The duration of the lag phase

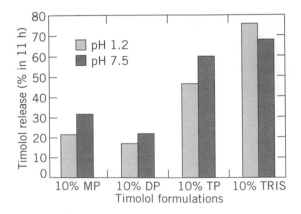

Figure 18. Effect of the pH of dissolution medium on the release of timolol from pH-controlled silicone microspheres (100 mg) at 37°C. Means ± SE of 3–5 experiments are presented. *Source:* with kind permission of Elsevier Science–NL, Sara Burgerhartstraat 25, 1055 KV Amsterdam, The Netherlands.

could be controlled by the thickness of the applied coating, but the release phase at a fixed succinic acid level was extremely constant after the lag delay. An evaluation of this bead formulation with acetaminophen as a model drug was evaluated in an oral dosing study in dogs (Fig. 20) and indicated that the lag and release phases observed in vitro were confirmed in vivo.

Polymer beads that are pH sensitive and thermally responsive have also been studied. The strategy employed with these systems is based on the fact that the polymer blends will not solubilize at gastric pH levels and the incorporated drug will be protected during residence time in the stomach. Linear terpolymers of (poly[N-isopropylacrylamide-co-butylmethacrylate-co-acrylic acid]) were fabricated into beads loaded with human calcitonin, an enzymatic labile peptide (62). The polymer becomes soluble in the vicinity of neutral pH and can thus release drug once in the small intestine. Higher loading of calcitonin was attained with increasing content of acrylic acid (hydrophilic polymer). Polymer beads with 7 and 10% acrylic acid achieved approximately 50% calcitonin loading with 85% drug release in 4 h at pH 4.5 (compared with 15% calcitonin loading and 15% drug release under similar conditions). The released calcitonin was apparently not aggregated into fibrillar structures because it could be isolated from the dissolution media and used in a rat intramuscular injection study to show the expected changes in plasma calcium levels. The ability to achieve high loading capacity and rapid release in a pH-responsive manner could provide a useful basis for developing this system into an effective oral controlled-release system. A somewhat similar system has been reported using theophylline as a model drug with polymeric nanobeads prepared from poly(N-isopropylacrylamide-co-methacrylic acid) with N,N'-methylenebisacrylamide as the cross-linking agent (63). Particle size ranged from 114 to 413 nm depending on polymer composition and experimental temperature (decreas-

ing size with increasing temperature at a fixed polymer composition). Volume-phase transitions of polymer lattices demonstrated clear dependence on polymer composition, temperature, and ionic strength. Regulation of volume changes and drug loading can be achieved by varying these parameters and can be envisioned to provide a rational basis for designing pH-sensitive controlled-release strategies for oral administration.

Gelling polymers have also been utilized with or without rate-controlling coatings to effect controlled release of active agents. Typically, water-soluble drugs are released by diffusion of dissolved drug across the gel layer, whereas poorly soluble drugs are primarily released via a surface erosion mechanism. Matrices incorporating alginate salt or a combination of salts have been utilized with several drugs (64–66). Sodium alginate is a high-molecular-weight linear random copolymer of D-mannuronic acid and L-guluronic acid residues. Below pH 3, alginic acid is insoluble but forms a swellable polymer. At or above neutral pH, sodium alginate is soluble and hydrates to form viscous solutions. Because of the pH dependence of alginate hydration and rheology, pH-dependent controlled-release formulations can be designed that afford varying release rates depending on the water solubility of the incorporated drug. Tablets prepared from 49% sodium alginate, 20% drug, 30% lactose, and 1% magnesium stearate can be manufactured by direct compression of the blend and have been shown to provide pH-dependent drug release (67). When chlorpheniramine maleate, a highly water-soluble drug, was prepared in this matrix, the release rate was significantly higher in simulated gastric fluid (pH 1.2) than in simulated intestinal fluid (pH 7.5). Incorporation of hydrochlorothiazide, a poorly soluble drug, afforded the opposite results, that is, release was faster at pH 7.5 than at pH 1.2. The differences in release rates for very soluble and poorly soluble drugs at different pH levels were attributed to differences in the internal microscopic structure of the

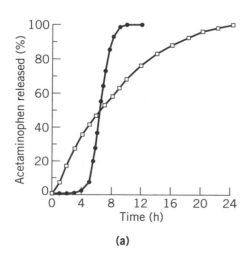
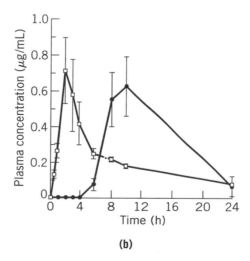

Figure 20. Release profiles in water (**a**) and plasma concentration-time profiles (**b**) of acetaminophen following oral administration to beagles of EC-coated beads or SRS with the same T_{50}. Preparations: (□) EC-coated beads (4% coating); (●) SRS (70% coating). *Source:* Reprinted from Ref. 61, with kind permission of Plenum Publishing Corporation, New York.

hydrated surface layer and the different hydration kinetics in the two pH conditions. At low pH, alginate matrices formed a particulate and porous gel medium, which could account for the very rapid release of highly water-soluble drugs through aqueous pathways. This same particulate hydrated layer observed at low pH, however, also exhibited strong mechanical properties that were much more resistant to surface erosion than the continuous gel that is formed at pH 7.5. The resistance to surface erosion at low pH can explain the slow release of poorly soluble drugs at low pH because the release of poorly water-soluble drugs from a hydrated gel matrix generally relies on surface erosion processes rather than diffusion.

pH-responsive gelatin microspheres have also been prepared by coating glutaraldehyde–cross-linked gelatin and applying either alginate or chitosan coatings (68). Chitosan is deacylated chitin and a linear, cationic polymer of 2-amino-2-deoxy-β-D-glucan that is soluble in dilute acid. Alginate is a linear, anionic polymer that is soluble at higher pH values. Cross-linked methotrexate gelatin microspheres of various particle sizes were prepared and coated with either alginate or chitosan. Nearly zero-order methotrexate release could be obtained that was inversely proportional to particle size and coating thickness. Alginate-coated microspheres afforded slower release rates in simulated gastric fluid than in simulated intestinal fluid, whereas chitosan coated microspheres gave the opposite result. As such, alginates coatings could be utilized to prolong drug release in acidic environments (for example, the stomach), whereas chitosan coatings could provide the same control in neutral or basic environments (for example, the intestine). The results from these studies, however, were of questionable utility because the release profiles generally extended over a period of days rather than hours. Although microsphere coatings that exhibited pH selectivity could be selected, the eventual practicality of the approach requires developing particles and coatings that provide release rates more consistent with the gastric and intestinal residence times that oral formulations normally experience.

The examples provided in the preceding paragraphs indicate the potential utility of pH-sensitive controlled-release systems. As indicated, the performance of these systems is determined by the effects of GI pH changes on the components of the dosage form and the incorporated active drug. Further optimization and development of this approach is required to lead to effective oral controlled-release systems that can be manufactured to perform in a reliable fashion.

Prodrugs

Many potential therapeutic candidates do not possess satisfactory physicochemical properties to be viable candidates for oral drug delivery, either as immediate-release formulations or through controlled-release technology. The limitations can be related to solubility, stability, aggregation tendency, and intrinsic membrane permeability. These factors, either alone or in combination for some drug candidates, can render the candidate ineffective as an orally administered drug. The general strategy of prodrug technology, which has been known and practiced for decades, is to synthesize a chemically modified version of the parent drug that overcomes the inherent problem in the ability of the drug to be adequately absorbed. For instance, a drug may be too hydrophilic to partition into biologic membranes. If a prodrug can be synthesized that modifies the parent drug partitioning behavior appropriately, then flux across a biologic membrane can be achieved. Inherent in this whole approach is the aspect that the prodrug must be readily reversible to the parent drug, either by hydrolytic or enzymatic mechanisms, and that the regenerated parent drug must retain its intrinsic pharmacologic activity. An additional item that has to receive careful attention is the potential pharmacologic or toxicological activity of the prodrug moiety. Because the prodrug moiety will be released in the in vivo setting after cleavage of the prodrug to the parent drug and prodrug moiety, the potential exists for either unwanted pharmacologic effects or undesired adverse effects due to the prodrug moiety itself. If the prodrug moiety is a chemical entity that has not been proven to be safe, then regulatory issues concerning additional required safety studies also become a factor. The prodrug itself, given that it will likely have to exist in the prodrug form for a discreet amount of time after administration, will also be subject to both pharmacologic and toxicological scrutiny in the development and regulatory cycles. Prodrug strategies have been frequently attempted to improve the absorption of poorly absorbed drug candidates. In some cases, such as sulindac sulfide, poor water solubility has limited absorption from oral formulations. Sulindac, which is a prodrug of sulindac sulfide with improved water solubility compared to sulindac sulfide, was developed to reduce GI toxic reactions but also demonstrated improved bioavailability (69,70). Improving aqueous solubility does not, however, ensure improved bioavailability of drug candidates. Absorption across biological membranes requires a certain degree of lipophilicity and the creation of very aqueous soluble prodrugs can, in fact, reduce membrane transport if a proper hydrophile/lipophile balance is not attained. In many cases, in fact, lipophilic prodrugs have been created to improve absorption of polar drug candidates including clindamycin (71), erythromycin (72), cefotiam (73), and ampicillin (74). The ester prodrugs of ampicillin, namely bacampicillin, pivampicillin, and talampicillin, show improved bioavailability compared to ampicillin and rapid reconversion via ester hydrolysis. Within the scope of this text, it is not practical to review all of the prodrug approaches that have been evaluated for a rather long list of potential drug candidates to which they have been applied. What will be attempted is a review of several approaches to provide a background for what may be achievable with prodrug approaches to oral controlled-release technology.

Phenytoin is an anticonvulsant with poor bioavailability that is most often attributed to poor water solubility. A number of investigators have evaluated various prodrugs of phenytoin, including fosphenytoin, which increased water solubility nearly 5,000-fold (75). A glyceride-derived prodrug of phenytoin has also been synthesized (76) and evaluated both in vitro (77) and in vivo (78) for its applicability as a phenytoin prodrug that can overcome the inherent poor oral bioavailability of phenytoin itself. Direct esterification of 3-hydroxy-2-hydroxymethylproprionic acid (bis-hydroxyisobutyric acid) with 3-hydroxymethyl-phenytoin yielded the test prodrug, phenytoin-bis-hydroxyisobutyrate as shown in Figure 21. The pharmacokinetic profile and pharmacologic activity of phenytoin-bis-hydroxyisobutyrate were evaluated in rat models. Both phenytoin and the phenytoin prodrug were orally administered to rats as oral suspensions in 0.5% methyl cellulose. Pharmacokinetic analysis based on plasma phenytoin levels indicated that the prodrug afforded an earlier T_{max} (0.74 ± 0.1 h versus 1.25 ± 0.5 h), a higher C_{max} (5.25 ± 0.99 μg/mL versus 1.90 ± 0.11 μg/mL), and a larger AUC (28.5 ± 4.2 μg.h/mL versus 10.0 ± 1.1 μg/h/mL) than that observed following administration of the parent drug, phenytoin. The plasma half-life of phenytoin was not significantly altered. Measurable quantities of the prodrug were not identified in the plasma samples. Phenytoin-bis-hydroxybutyrate was found to be equipotent with phenytoin following ip administration but more active than phenytoin following oral dosing in rats (based on the maximal electroshock test). Toxicity was not observed for the prodrug. The temporal profile of the anticonvulsant activity of phenytoin-bis-hydroxybutyrate was consistent with its pharmacokinetic profile, suggesting that the improved pharmacologic activity of the prodrug is due to its improved bioavailability relative to phenytoin itself.

Morpholinoalkyl esters (HCl) salts of naproxen and indomethacin (Fig. 22) were synthesized and evaluated with both in vitro and in vivo models (79). Both parent compounds are poorly water soluble (<5.9 × 10^{-5} M/L in simulated gastric fluid and <6.7 × 10^{-3} M/L in pH 7.4 phosphate buffer) and are known to present issues with regard

Phenytoin

Phenytoin-bis-hydroxyisobutyrate

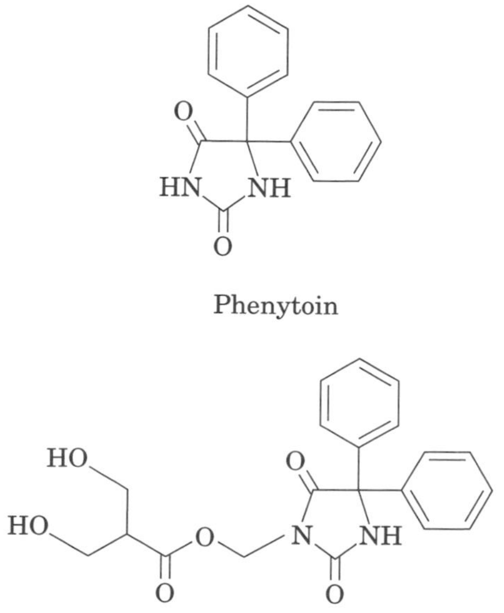

Figure 21. Structures of the compounds. *Source:* Reprinted from Ref. 78, with kind permission of Plenum Publishing Corporation, New York.

to a tendency to cause local tissue irritation. Aqueous solubility of prodrugs of both naproxen and indomethacin increased over 2,000-fold in both simulated gastric fluid and phosphate buffer. The pK_a values increased from a range of 4.2–4.5 for the parent drugs to 6.9–8.6 for the prodrugs. The prodrugs were more lipophilic at pH 7.4 but less lipophilic at pH 1.3 when compared with the parent drugs. As the carbon chain length was extended between the ester function and the morpholino function, stability in pH 7.4 buffer increased, while stability in pH 1.3 buffer decreased. The prodrugs of naproxen and indomethacin had half-lives in rat plasma of 1.1–4.1 min and 20.4–31.5 min, respectively. Based on an analysis of in vitro properties, naproxen and indomethacin prodrugs with a 4-carbon spacer were evaluated in a rat model for absorption kinetics and tissue irritation. When dosed to rats as an equimolar gavage solution, prodrugs of naproxen and indomethacin were 33.73 ± 8.4% and 34.3 ± 3.4% more bioavailable, respectively, than the corresponding parent drug. Using a ranked recording scale for tissue irritation or damage, both prodrugs were found to be less damaging than the parent drugs on both acute and chronic dosing regimens. These data indicated that the morpholino prodrugs of naproxen and indomethacin showed improved stability in gastric fluid, improved solubility at small-intestine pH, rapid in vivo conversion to the parent drug, and were more bioavailable and less irritating than the parent compounds. As such, this prodrug approach may be applicable to compounds similar to naproxen and indomethacin for oral delivery systems.

Another prodrug approach to indomethacin has utilized a triethylene glycol indomethacin ester (TIE) (80,81). The plasma half-life of TIE was 11.55 min in rat plasma with complete reversion to the parent drug, but it should be pointed out that this is significantly shorter than the half-life observed in human plasma, which was 3.8 h. Pharmacokinetic analysis of TIE prodrug indicated that in contrast to that observed with the morpholino ester prodrug (79), the relative bioavailability and time to C_{max} for TIE was less than that observed with indomethacin alone. The plasma profile was, however, significantly extended over that seen with indomethacin itself, which could indicate slower and more prolonged absorption or a partitioning into and slow release from a tissue compartment. Although the plasma profile of indomethacin was lower and more prolonged than indomethacin itself, the prodrug did not show an ulcerogenic potential, which could make this approach useful in spite of a lack of improvement in systemic bioavailability.

Phosphomonoester products of primary alcohols and unhindered phenols have shown good chemical stability and rapid enzymatic hydrolysis in vivo but exhibit a slow rate of conversion with sterically hindered secondary and tertiary alcohols (82,83). In an attempt to overcome this problem, an oxymethyloxycarbonyl spacer group has been utilized as a less sterically hindered spacer group between the hydroxyl group and phosphate functionality (84). Phosphoryloxymethyloxycarbonyl derivatives should be converted by phosphatase-mediated hydrolysis to an intermediate with subsequent rapid decomposition to the parent drug. The reconversion reaction scheme for these prodrugs is shown in Figure 23. Prodrugs of alcohols

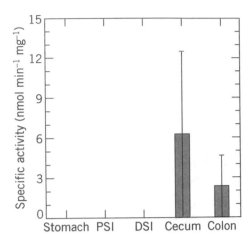

Figure 25. Hydrolysis of the prodrug menthol-β-D-glucuronide (nmoles of substrate hydrolyzed per min per mg of luminal contents) measured from various locations in the rat gastrointestinal tract. There was no menthol detected over the 1-h experiment in the luminal contents of the stomach, PSI, or DSI. Error bars are mean $\pm$ SD ($n = 6$). *Source:* Reprinted from Ref. 93, with kind permission of Plenum Publishing Corporation, New York.

Although most of the early prodrug efforts were directed toward traditional, organic drug candidates, the emergence of peptide and peptidelike drug candidates has spurred an interest in developing peptide prodrug strategies to improve their oral delivery. Unlike prodrug strategies for nonpeptidic drug candidates, where the goal is often to either modify solubility in the GI environment or alter the permeation properties of the parent drug in a favorable direction, prodrug strategies for peptides most often focus on providing increased protection against proteolytic enzymes in the GI tract because enzymatic degradation is generally a major barrier to effective oral formulation efforts. Several examples are provided to illustrate this approach.

A tripeptide prodrug of L-dopa was synthesized in an effort to develop a prodrug that overcame the decarboxylation of L-dopa in the gut wall and afforded acceptable oral bioavailability. Many prodrugs of L-dopa have been generated and evaluated, including esters, with varying degrees of success. In this study, the pGlu-L-Dopa-Pro prodrug was synthesized, and the proposed enzymatic pathway for reconversion to the parent drug in vivo is shown in Figure 26 (94). The prodrug structure effectively prevents L-dopa decarboxylation, which is the major intestinal degradative pathway for L-dopa. The conversion to parent drug involves two enzyme catalyzed steps, pyroglutamyl aminopeptidase I and prolidase. Evaluations with in vitro Ussing chambers with rat jejunal tissue and with an in situ single-pass intestinal perfusion model demonstrated that the prodrug was readily absorbed via an intestinal peptide transport that could be inhibited by captopril and various dipeptide competitors. The tripeptide was readily converted, both in vitro and in vivo, to the parent drug L-dopa, thereby demonstrating the potential utility of this approach.

Desmopressin (dDAVP), a synthetic analog of antidiuretic hormone, is normally administered nasally or orally,

although the oral availability is quite low ($<$1%). The poor oral bioavailability is generally attributed to low lipophilicity, but susceptibility to enzymatic degradation, particularly by α-chymotrypsin, probably also plays a role (95). In an attempt to address these issues with the oral bioavailability of dDAVP, a series of ester prodrugs were synthesized at the tyrosine phenolic group of dDAVP (96). Several aliphatic carboxylic acid esters and a carbonate ester were made as shown in Figure 27. The octanol/aqueous buffer pH 7.4 log P of dDAVP is < -3.5. The log P values for the various prodrugs ranges from < -3 for proprionyl to 0.41 for octanoyl. All prodrugs were essentially stable in pH 7.4 buffer (half-lives ranged from 66 to 4,460 h) but exhibited half-lives from $<$1 min (hexanoyl and octanoyl) to 40 min (pivaloyl) in the presence of α-chymotrypsin. In 80% human plasma, the prodrug half-lives were basically similar except for pivaloyl (5.9 h) and 2-ethylhexanoyl (14.1 h). Utilizing the Caco-2 cell culture model, all the prodrugs except isobutyloxycarbonyl showed increased permeability relative to the parent dDAVP. There was, however, no correlation between permeability and lipophilicity. Regardless, the data indicated that this prodrug approach led to ester prodrugs of dDAVP that were stable in a buffer environment but readily converted to the parent drug in the presence of enzyme or plasma and generally afforded improved permeability characteristics.

A final example of prodrug strategy for developing oral formulations for peptide drug candidates involves recent efforts to develop intramolecular cyclic prodrugs to provide prodrug candidates with improved absorption characteristics as well as reduced susceptibility to metabolic degradation via intestinal enzymes (97,98). A phenylproprionic acid prodrug of a model hexapeptide (H-Trp-Ala-Gly-Gly-Asp-Ala-OH) was prepared and evaluated. Previous work (99) had demonstrated that a cyclic acyloxyalkoxycarbamate prodrug of the same model hexapeptide gave enhanced membrane-permeation properties and increased stability to metabolic enzymes. The proposed scheme for metabolic breakdown of the phenylproprionic prodrug is shown in Figure 28 and involves a relative slow esterase-catalyzed step followed by a rapid chemical hydrolysis to regenerate the linear hexapeptide plus lactone. The permeability of the prodrug ($P_{app} = 1.21 \pm 0.12 \times 10^{-7}$ cm/s) across Caco-2 cell monolayers was approximately 70 times greater than that for the parent hexapeptide ($P_{app} = 0.17 \times 10^{-8}$ cm/s) and showed greater stability for the prodrug than the parent peptide. Enzymatic cleavage and hydrolysis of the prodrug to the parent compound was significantly faster in 90% human plasma, rat intestinal homogenate, or Caco-2 cell homogenate than in pH 7.4 aqueous buffer. The intramolecular cyclization prodrug strategy for peptides offers another novel approach to developing peptide drugs as oral formulation candidates that possess improved stability to enzymatic degradation (of the parent peptide) and improved absorption characteristics across epithelial cell layers.

In the scope of the text here, it has obviously not been possible to cover all the diverse prodrug strategies that have been evaluated in attempts to develop oral formulations for both traditional, organic drug candidates and peptide or peptidelike drug candidates. Hopefully, the exam-

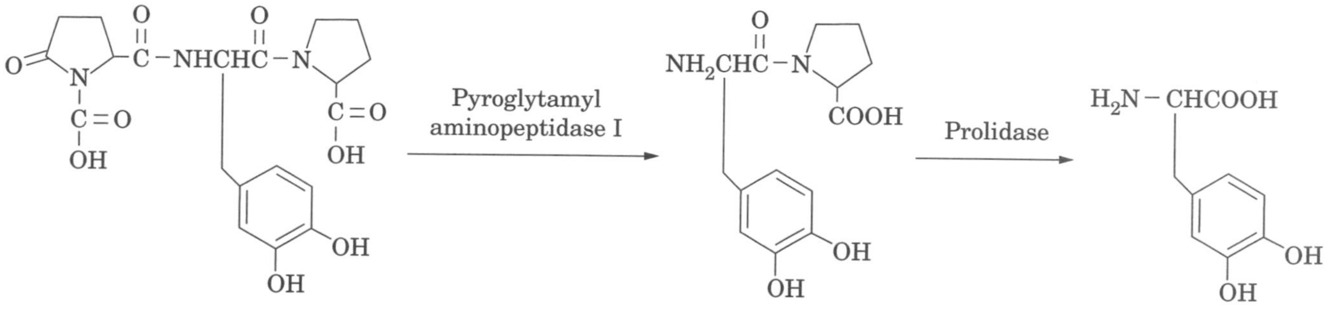

Figure 26. Release of L-dopa from pGlu-L-Dopa-Pro by successive actions of proteolytic enzymes. *Source:* Reprinted from Ref. 94, with kind permission of Plenum Publishing Corporation, New York.

ples given exemplify the varied approaches that can be considered and provide a basis for development and utilization of prodrug strategies toward drugs that would otherwise be unsuitable candidates for oral drug delivery systems.

COLON

Although it is generally felt that the small intestine is the primary site of drug absorption and therefore the preferred area of the GI tract to target with various controlled-release technologies, a major interest has developed in directing drugs and dosage forms to effect primary drug release in the colon region (100–102). The reasons for this interest are varied, but include (*1*) reduced proteolytic activity in the colon region, which may be helpful in effecting reasonable absorption of certain drugs that are enzymatically labile in the small intestine, particularly peptides and proteins; (*2*) reduced fluid and motility in the colon when compared with the small intestine, which could afford advantages in terms of incorporating multiple components in a formulation, such as permeation enhancers, that must reach the epithelial absorptive layer in a high concentration and in close spatial proximity to the each other; and (*3*) treatment of local pathologies of the colon such as carcinomas and inflammatory bowel disease.

Regardless of the therapeutic strategy justifying efforts to develop systems for drug release in the colon, some basic elements will apply from a therapeutic standpoint regarding drugs that are reasonable candidates for this approach. Because the arrival time of a drug or dosage form in the colon is subject to the vagaries of gastric emptying and small-intestine transit, drugs that require an immediate onset of action or a very specific time of onset after oral administration are not reasonable candidates. As an extension of this—and the fact that under normal conditions a patient is on a daily meal regimen—it can be assumed that the transit time to the colon will likely exceed 6–8 h on average. Therefore, twice-a-day dosing is the maximum frequency that can be expected from colon controlled-release systems, and, more likely, controlled-release systems for the colon will most commonly have to be once-a-day dosing therapies. This is particularly true if the

controlled-release system is a sustained-release formulation where a drug release profile of 6–8 h is superimposed on an average transit time of 6–8 h to the colonic region. In this case, the overall time from administration to completion of drug release will probably approach 12–16 h, thereby restricting applications to those where once-a-day dosing without a specific time of onset is an acceptable therapeutic regimen.

There have been three basic approaches to designing drugs or dosage forms for delivery of therapeutic agents specifically to the colon: (*1*) utilizing pH changes that occur in the upper colon (103); (*2*) timed-release capsules with sufficient delay to allow transit to the colon before activating significant drug release (104); and (*3*) polymeric carriers that are degraded by bacterial enzyme activity specific to the colon region (105). With all of these approaches, effectiveness will be limited by the capability of the dosage form to resist the hydrodynamic and enzymatic forces present during transit from the stomach to the colon and to protect the active drug from premature release or degradation prior to arriving in the colon. Another general concern, which will not be directly addressed here, is the viscous contents of the colon region. As food stuffs are digested and absorbed, nonabsorbed materials pass from the small intestine to the colon where water is gradually reabsorbed and the intestinal contents become more viscous, eventually reaching a semisolid state. The presence of this material in the colon can present significant problems to the effective performance of drugs or dosage forms in the colon. The viscosity of the contents can present a formidable barrier to release and diffusion of drugs from a controlling dosage form to the wall of the colon where absorption occurs. Additionally, a potential for significant nonspecific adsorption to colonic contents can reduce the effective amount of drug available for absorption. A third potential problem is that although bacterial contents can be utilized to effect drug release in the colon, these same bacteria may present a degradative pathway for the drug itself, again reducing the amount of drug available for absorption. This potential interference in drug release and absorption will not be evaluated here in any quantitative sense, but it is critical that the research and developer of colon controlled-release technologies be aware of this po-

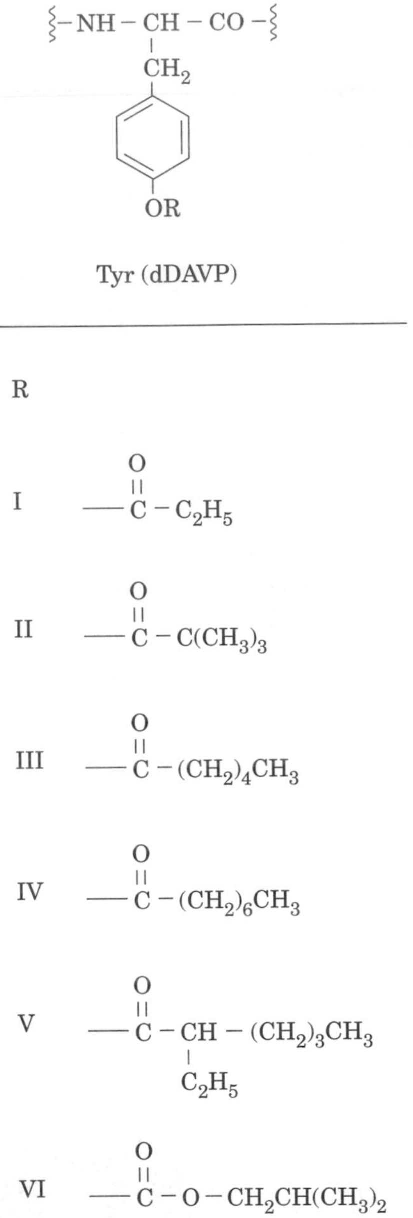

$$\{-NH-CH-CO-\}$$

$$CH_2$$

OR

Tyr (dDAVP)

R

I $-\overset{\displaystyle O}{\overset{\|}{C}}-C_2H_5$

II $-\overset{\displaystyle O}{\overset{\|}{C}}-C(CH_3)_3$

III $-\overset{\displaystyle O}{\overset{\|}{C}}-(CH_2)_4CH_3$

IV $-\overset{\displaystyle O}{\overset{\|}{C}}-(CH_2)_6CH_3$

V $-\overset{\displaystyle O}{\overset{\|}{C}}-CH-(CH_2)_3CH_3$

$$C_2H_5$$

VI $-\overset{\displaystyle O}{\overset{\|}{C}}-O-CH_2CH(CH_3)_2$

Figure 27. Scheme I. *Source:* Reprinted from Ref. 96, with kind permission of Plenum Publishing Corporation, New York.

tential and factor these parameters into any analysis of the effectiveness of a given drug or dosage form.

Time Specificity

Attempting to predict the time required for a dosage form to transit from the stomach to the colon has been tenuous at best. Some reasonably reproducible data have been generated indicating that, in humans, the small intestinal transit time generally falls in the range of 2–4 h (106). These data seem to be reasonably consistent, at least in the fasted dog model, regardless of the size or density of the formulation or the fed/fasted state of the volunteer (107). With multiparticulate dosage forms, data in dogs indicated that there is little spreading of multiparticulates

after exit from the stomach, (108) whereas in the fed state, considerable spreading and dilution of multiparticulate dosage forms might be expected due to mixing with food contents and variable gastric emptying (106). Although this 3- to 4-h time window of small intestinal transit can be argued as to its validity and reproducibility in humans, it is well accepted that the major variable in overall intestinal transit is residence time in the stomach and that this plays the predominant role in determining the average time it would take a dosage form of any size or geometry to traverse the stomach and small intestine en route to the colon. In humans with normal GI physiology, dosage forms exceeding approximately 2 mm in diameter are not readily emptied from the stomach during the fed state. Rather, these dosage forms are most typically emptied during the interdigestive phase, which is generally initiated somewhere in the range of 3–4 h after meal consumption, depending on the mass, volume, and caloric content of the meal. The interdigestive contractile activity, which is physiologically divided into several phases, has a repeating cycle of motility with each overall cycle lasting approximately 3–4 h. Therefore, it can be expected that a dosage form >2 mm in size might reasonably be expected to exit the stomach somewhere in the range of 4–8 h after ingestion with a meal. Obviously, the normal physiologic motility patterns of the stomach and small intestine can be affected by an individual's health, presence of GI pathologies, and any concomitant medications being taken. The net result of all these factors is that transit time from mouth to colon is very difficult to estimate in humans with any great deal of reliability. For the sake of discussion, it can be assumed that the overall transit time to the colon will be approximately 3–5 h in the fasted state and 6–10 h in the fed state. Given these rather wide ranges of overall transit times, it is apparent that predicting arrival of dosage forms in the colon, and targeting drug release to be dependent on a timing mechanism, is complicated at best. In spite of these normal variabilities that must be factored into any design of an oral controlled-release dosage form for delivery of drug to the colon, significant efforts have been directed toward achieving such goal.

The most well-studied and well-published time-based delivery system for targeting drug delivery to the colon has been the Pulsincap capsule of R.P. Scherer (109–111). The Pulsincap capsule consists of a water-insoluble body and a water-soluble cap. The drug formulation is contained and protected within the capsule body and separated, inside the water soluble cap, by a hydrogel polymer plug. After a predetermined lag due to dissolution of the cap, the hydrogel swelling rate controls the time of release. After reaching a critical swelling stage, the hydrogel plug is ejected, and the drug formulation is released. In theory, by designing the hydrogel plug with specific swelling and ejection times, the Pulsincap capsule can be made to deliver its contents to any site along the GI tract, including the colon. The additional apparent advantage is that the formulation itself is relatively protected from the GI environment prior to release, thereby affording advantages in terms of drug stability. Toxicologic evaluation of the polymeric hydrogel plug and components indicated no safety issues (R.P. Scherer data on file). The maximum size of the Pulsincap

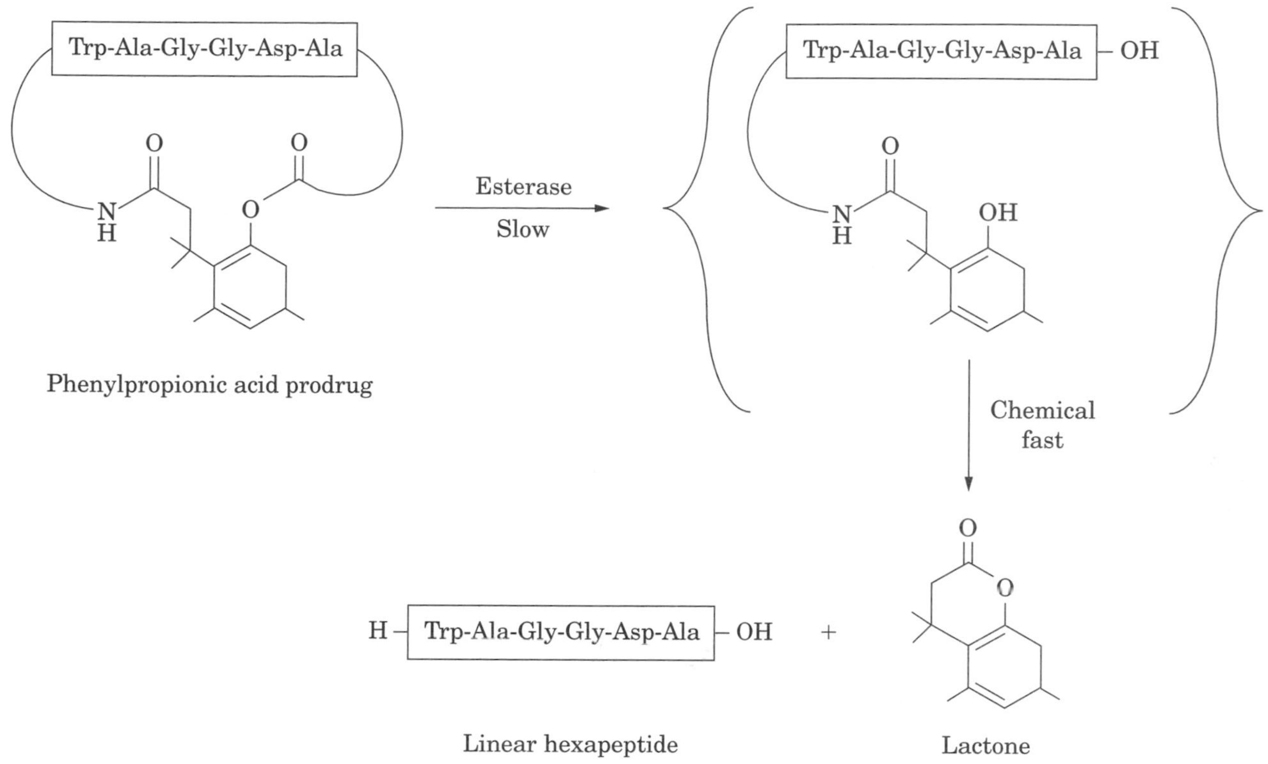

Figure 28. Proposed mechanism for the release of the linear hexapeptide from the cyclic phenylpropionic acid prodrug. *Source:* Reprinted from Ref. 98, with kind permission of Plenum Publishing Corporation, New York.

capsule approximates a size #0 standard gelatin capsule. In vitro studies indicated that the system maintained its integrity in pH 1.2 conditions for 5 h (simulating residence in the stomach) and exhibited a mean pulse-release time of 195 min after switching to pH 6.8 conditions. The mean 195-min lag time would represent the time interval over which the capsule must transit the small intestine to deliver formulation components to the colon. In an in vivo scintigraphic imaging confirmation study in humans (109), the Pulsincap capsule demonstrated integrity maintenance for 197–414 min in the stomach of fed volunteers with evidence of water-soluble cap dissolution within 29–70 min after exiting the stomach and entering the small intestine. A second phase of this study in fasted volunteers showed that the Pulsincap capsule hydrogel plug ejected at a mean time of 230 min postadministration, with a range from 208 to 275 mins. At the time of hydrogel plug ejection, all devices were shown to reside in the ascending colon. These data confirmed that, at least in the fasted state where gastric residence is not overly prolonged, the Pulsincap capsules successfully reached the colon prior to formulation release. The Pulsincap capsules were also evaluated in a double-blind placebo-controlled parallel group study evaluating the tolerability of a 28-day regimen of twice-daily dosing (no active drug agent). The incidence of reported adverse events was comparable between Pulsincap and placebo, with no indication of their being causally related to the formulation. This tolerability study indicated that this designed formulation for time-delayed

drug release to the colon holds promise as a technology that can be effective without significant tolerability issues.

Limited information has been presented on a somewhat similar time-delayed drug delivery system named Chronset from ALZA Corporation (112). This device contains the drug formulation within an impermeable capsule configuration in which the driving force is an osmotic engine contained in the base of the capsule. By controlling the rate of water imbibition with the osmotic load and a semipermeable membrane coating, a swelling polymer is utilized to expand the capsule over a preengineered time frame resulting in the release of active components at either 2 or 6 h. In the fasted state where residence time in the stomach could be expected to be less than 2 h, the 6-h systems hold promise for delivery of therapeutic agents specifically to the ascending colon region. Pharmacokinetic data, with acetaminophen as a model compound, demonstrated that the formulation was released in a bolus fashion (simulating an immediate-release profile) after the predetermined lag time designed into the system.

Niwa and coworkers have reported on the development and evaluation of a novel ethylcellulose (EC) capsule that releases drug in a time-controlled fashion (113). The capsule, shown in Figure 29, has four-components comprising a drug container, swellable polymer, capsule body, and cap. The cap, body, and drug container were made of EC. The capsule body was a #00 gelatin capsule coated internally with EC, with the gelatin capsule subsequently dissolved to yield an EC capsule body. Four micropores, each ap-

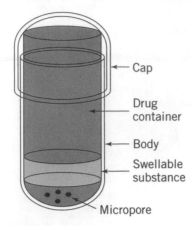

Figure 29. Schematic representation of the release time-controlled capsule used in this study. *Source:* Reprinted from Ref. 114, with kind permission of G + B Publishing Group, Lausanne.

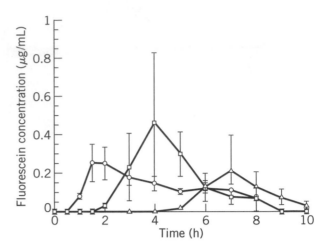

Figure 30. Plasma fluorescein concentrations versus time curves after oral administration of three kinds of EC capsules of which mean cap thicknesses are 39.1 ± 2.3 (SE) μm ($\bigcirc$), $63.1 \pm 5.0 \, \mu$m ($\square$), and $75.6 \pm 4.1 \, \mu$m ($\diamond$). Each point is the mean of three individual determinations and is expressed as the mean $\pm$SE. *Source:* Reprinted from Ref. 113, with kind permission of G + B Publishing Group, Lausanne.

proximately 400 μm in diameter, were mechanically drilled in the bottom of the body capsule. The drug container was made from an EC film. When assembled, the drug container is separated and placed above a swellable polymer (i.e., a low-substituted hydroxypropylcellulose) in the capsule body and sealed with the cap. The proposed mechanism controlling the timing of drug release is a balance between the swelling pressure of the polymeric material and the strength of the capsule cap. Utilizing the same swelling-polymer composition, it was shown that the time of in vitro drug release (or rupture of the EC cap) was dependent on the thickness of the cap. The mean times at which 50% of a model compound, fluorescein, was released were 2.4 ± 0.15 h, 3.39 ± 0.09 h, and 6.21 ± 0.15 h for caps with thickness of 44.1 μm, 65.7 μm, and 76.7 μm, respectively. In vivo, these same capsule designs performed comparably in fasted beagle dogs, with respective T_{max} values at 2.0 h, 4.0 h, and 7.0 h (Fig. 30). These data suggest the potential utility of this design, although lag times in excess of 7 h will most likely be required to ensure effective delivery to the colon, particularly in the fed condition. Additional studies examining the effects of food on these time-release capsules were conducted and suggested that in the postprandial study leg, the capsules actually disintegrated in the stomach rather than the colon (114). The mean residence time (MRT) of fluorescein in these capsules was not statistically different in the postprandial state (6.43 h) and fasted state (4.76 h). Simple enteric coating of capsules with either hydroxypropylmethylcellulose phthalate or Eudragit S afforded MRTs of 11.30 h and 12.83 h, respectively, in the fed state. These data suggested that the time-controlled capsule, which did not have an enteric coating, probably dissolved in the stomach. To effectively delivery a drug formulation to the colon with these time-controlled systems, an enteric coating is necessary to delay the initiation of the timing cycle until the capsule exits the stomach. Not only does this eliminate the variability due to gastric residence times but it also increases the likelihood that a 6- to 8-h time delay will be sufficient to deliver the formulation to the colon region prior to drug release.

In addition to the bolus or delayed-release systems just described for targeting drug delivery to the colon, more traditional or conventional sustained-release technology can also be considered as a means to provide continuous drug release in the colonic environment. Essentially any of the systems described in the section on time-controlled drug release for the small intestine could be extended to colonic applications. If a sustained- or continuous-release dosage form was enteric coated, then initiation of the release profile would not commence until the device empties from the stomach and the enteric coating dissolves. Given this circumstance and under normal GI physiological conditions, any sustained drug release beyond approximately 3 to 4 h will most likely occur in the colon. Therefore, an enteric-coated 12-h sustained-release system could be expected to release drug for approximately 8 h in the colon. Technical strategies for designing time-controlled, sustained-release formulations will not be repeated here (see "Time Specificity"). Obviously this approach is simply an attempt to utilize a general sustained-release delivery profile and time the release such that a significant portion of the dose is released after the formulation traverses the small intestine and enters the colon.

Enzymatic Control

A major share of the effort in designing and developing controlled-release technology for colon delivery has attempted to utilize the presence of colonic bacteria as a triggering element to initiate or control drug release on arrival of the drug or dosage form in the ascending colon. Although there is a significant population of bacteria in the lower small intestine (10^5–10^7 cfu/mL), there is a rather abrupt and dramatic increase in bacterial density (10^{11}–10^{12} cfu/mL) immediately distal to the ileocecal junction. The enzymes produced by these bacteria are the targets of controlled-release technology efforts. As with any other physiologic parameter, the specific strains and densities of bacteria resident in the ascending colon can be affected by numerous factors, including age, diet, pathological states, concomitant drug administration, general health, and normal interindividual variability. Although there is certainly variability in bacterial content, all individuals have very high resident populations of bacteria in the ascending colon, and this ubiquitous presence can justify efforts to target these bacterial enzymes as potential triggers for controlled-release technology. Additionally, the successful use of sulphasalazine and olsalazine, which depend on bacterial azoreductases for activity, strongly indicate that the bacterial enzymes of the colon are capable of providing the desired effect.

The vast majority of work in this field has been directed toward developing drugs or dosage-form technologies as substrates for bacterial enzymes and evaluating these approaches in either simulated in vitro environments or in small-animal studies. Simulated in vitro models are difficult to establish and validate, particularly because the colonic bacteria are primarily anaerobic, but they represent the first method of choice for comparing different substrates and strategies. Studies in small animals, while useful for verifying results observed in vitro, must be interpreted with a certain degree of caution because there may be considerable species-to-species variability in bacterial enzymes between selected animal models and humans. Enzymes produced by colonic bacteria can hydrolyze a wide variety of substrates, including glycosides, sulphates, nitrates, esters, amides, and sulphonates. They have also been shown to reduce double bonds, nitro groups, azo groups, aldehydes, sulphoxides, ketones, alcohols, N-oxides, and arsonic acids. Other metabolic processes affected by colonic bacterial enzymes include dealkylation, deamination, decarboxylation, ring fission, nitrosamine formation, acetylation, and esterification. Although obviously a very large number of metabolic process could be chosen as potential controlling elements in controlled-release drugs or dosage forms for colon delivery, the focus has been on azoreductases, which reduce azo bonds, and polysaccharides, which are represented by glycosidic enzymes.

Significant efforts have been directed toward utilizing the azoreductase capacity of colonic bacterial enzymes. Saffran and coworkers (115,116) synthesized various polymers that were cross-linked with aromatic azoaromatic groups. The polymer films developed in these studies were resistant to degradation or dissolution in the upper GI tract and could be utilized as tablet or capsule coatings that were substrates for bacterial azoreductase activity in the colon. Vasopressin and insulin were effectively delivered to the colon in animal studies utilizing this approach.

Van den Mooter et al. (117) investigated the release of a model compound, ibuprofen, from capsules coated with azopolymers. Gelatin capsules containing 20 mg of ibuprofen were dip coated in an ethanolic solution of azopolymers (20% w/w). PEG 400 (20% w/w) was utilized as a coating plasticizer, and the coating level on the capsules was 9.7% (w/w). The azopolymers employed in this study were co-

polymers of 2-hydroxyethyl methacrylate (HEMA) and methyl methacrylate (MMA) and terpolymers of HEMA, MMA, and methacrylic acid (MA). N,N'-bis-(methacryloyloxyethyloxycarbonylamino)azobenzene (B-[MOEOCA]AB) was used as the azoreductase substrate in the polymers. An in vitro dissolution medium was prepared from isolated rat cecal contents to which cofactors were added to create an electron-generating system capable of significant reducing activity that simulated the environment of the colonic milieu. Because ibuprofen has low water solubility, diffusion through the polymer coating prior to enzymatic degradation of the azopolymer coating is minimal. Copolymers of HEMA/MMA at ratios of 4:1 or 5:1 did not demonstrate in vitro drug release rates that were statistically different in buffer or reducing medium, indicating that the release most likely reflected diffusion of the drug through the polymer coating over extended time periods (34 h). Although a HEMA/MMA coating at a 6:1 ratio did demonstrate statistically faster drug release in the reducing medium compared to buffer, the lag phase exceeded 24 h, which is not practical for in vivo applications given the estimated residence time of dosage forms in the colon. The effectiveness of azopolymer coatings is based on a balance between the hydrophilic HEMA, which ensures good hydration and availability of azo bonds for enzymatic attack, and the hydrophobic MMA, which retards polymer swelling and prevents early drug release in the stomach and small intestine. Because neither of these components contains an ionizable group, swelling is pH independent. Incorporation of a small amount of methacrylic acid as a terpolymer with HEMA and MMA increases the degree of swelling when going from acidic to neutral or alkaline conditions owing to neutralization of the carboxylic acid group of MA while still retaining the generally water-insoluble nature of the polymer. As shown in Figure 31, a terpolymer of HEMA/MMA/MA 9:2:0.1 provided a coating that exhibited significant ibuprofen release beginning as early as 8–10 h after initiation of incubation

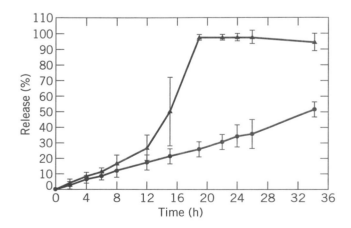

Figure 31. Release of ibuprofen from capsules coated with azopolymer P12 in RCCRM (▲) and phosphate buffer (●). $n = 6$; error bars indicate the standard deviation. *Source:* Reprinted from Ref. 117, with kind permission of Plenum Publishing Corporation, New York.

pared to incubation without rat cecal contents (Fig. 33). These results indicated that calcium pectinate, as well as pectin itself, can be degraded by bacterial enzyme activity. In addition, because indomethacin has very poor water solubility, it is unlikely that diffusion of indomethacin from the tablet could account for the observed release; more likely, an erosion process initiated by bacterial enzymes is responsible for initiating and controlling drug release.

The initial in vitro work with pectin and calcium pectinate tablets was subsequently confirmed in human clinical studies utilizing α-scintigraphy to visualize the performance of tablets in volunteers (138). Either CaP/P tablets (calcium pectinate and pectin) or CaP/GG tablets (calcium pectinate and guar gum) were evaluated in 10 fasted, healthy volunteers. Both tablet formulations were enteric coated with Eudragit L. Guar gum was added to CaP/GG tablets to slow the disintegration. External imaging of the physical state of the CaP/P and CaP/GG tablets indicated only slight disintegration of either formulation in the small intestine, with tablets reaching the cecum in a relatively intact condition. Both formulations reached the cecum in approximately the same time frame (CaP/P: 272 ± 48 min; CaP/GG: 223 ± 47 min). With the CaP/P tablets, complete disintegration was observed in the ascending colon for 7 of 10 tablets and in more distal colonic regions for 2 of 10; 1 did not totally disintegrate during colonic transit. With CaP/GG tablets, total disintegration was seen for 3 of 10 in the ascending colon and 3 of 10 in more distal colonic regions; 4 of 10 did not fully disintegrate during transit of the colon. The data from this human volunteer study indicate that CaP/GG tablets appear to disintegrate more slowly, as predicted, than CaP/P tablets, but that both may be potential candidates for controlled delivery of therapeutic agents to the colonic region.

Although compressed tablets as reported by Rubinstein et al. (137) indicated a potential utility for pectin and calcium pectinate to direct drug delivery to the colon, this approach may not be suitable for all applications. As with the azopolymers, the ability to develop a film-coating process that would protect the components of the formulation prior to arrival in the colon and then degrade to release the active drug in the colonic environment could be a significant advantage. Due to its high water solubility, pectin alone is not a good candidate for a film-coating process. Wakerly et al. investigated the potential utility of combining pectin with EC in a film coat intended for colon-specific drug delivery (139). Paracetamol tablets were compressed with a hardness of 8 KP and disintegration times of less than 15 min. The paracetamol tablets were film coated in a fluid-bed spray granulator with a coating solution of 2% w/v pectin in water blended with distilled water and Surelease S (EC). Three different film coats were prepared and evaluated: 60S:40P, 50S:50P, and 40S:60P. The amount of paracetamol release was significantly higher in pH 7.4 buffer than 0.1 N HCl for both compositions with the lower concentrations of EC (40S and 50S). Increasing levels of EC reduced drug release at both pH levels, and only marginal paracetamol release (≤5% in 6 h) was observed with the 60S coating under both pH conditions. The 50S:50P coating was tested in a system utilizing pectinolytic enzymes and shown to release paracetamol at a higher rate in the presence of enzymes than in the absence of enzymes. The difference (37% versus 23% in 400 min) was, however, not particularly dramatic, and the release curves did not begin to separate until after approximately 170 min of incubation in the presence of the pectinolytic enzymes. These data appear to suggest that although the pectin/EC coatings do provide some degree of control based on bacterial enzyme activity, the effect may not be rapid enough or the effect large enough to utilize in a practical sense. However, these studies do show a potential utility of pectin in film-coating processes if the solubility can be reduced by coformulation with other less soluble components. Additionally, it is not really possible to predict how these coatings would perform in an in vivo environment, particularly that encountered in the human colon.

Pectin-based multiparticulates have also been evaluated as potential formulations for specific delivery to the colon (140). Control of release from a multiparticulate systems requires tighter regulation because the large surface-to-volume ratio of beads relative to tablets increases the probability that a gel or swelling system will become diffusion controlled, particularly for very water-soluble compounds, rather than degradation controlled by enzymatic activity in the colon. Amidated pectin/indomethacin and amidated pectin/sulphamethoxazole beads (2 mm) were prepared either with or without a chitosan coating. Drug levels were 20, 33, and 50% w/w based on theoretical loadings of dry beads. Swelling increased as a function of increasing pH, and chitosan reduced the degree of drug release. In the presence of pectinolytic enzymes, complete bead degradation was observed with 135 min. Although significant drug release occurred in enzyme-free media, especially with the more water-soluble sulphamethoxazole, the presence of calcium and/or chitosan did reduce this release aspect. The results indicated that a particulate formulation for delivery to the colon may be feasible. The particularly attractive feature of the multiparticulate

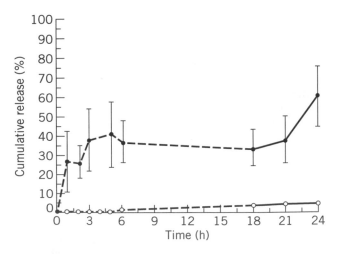

Figure 33. Percentage cumulative amounts of indomethacin released from CaP tablets in PBS medium, pH 7.0; (●) with rat cecal content, (○) without rat cecal content. Data are the mean of three experiments ± SD. *Source:* Reprinted from Ref. 137, with kind permission of Plenum Publishing Corporation, New York.

approach is that total degradation can occur in a much shorter time frame (i.e., 135 min) because of the large surface-to-volume ratio of multiparticulates compared to the much longer time (typically 15–24 h) required for total degradation of tablet formulations. If the early drug-release phase during transit through the stomach and small intestine can be adequately controlled with a particulate formulation, this approach offers promise for a delivery system that can effect more rapid and hopefully more complete drug release shortly after arrival of the dosage form in the colonic region.

Amylose is a linear α-D-glucan polymer composed of $\alpha(1{\rightarrow}4)$-linked D-glycosyl units and is comprised of approximately 20% starch. Films of amylose have been prepared that are resistant to pancreatic α-amylase (141) but are degraded by colonic bacterial enzymes (142,143). If used alone, amylose swelling in aqueous media is too rapid to be effective as a controlling coating because water-soluble drugs can diffuse through the coating membrane and would be released during transit through the stomach and small intestine. Milojevic et al. (144) have combined amylose with pharmaceutical polymers to decrease the swelling properties of amylose alone and provided a significant change in the resultant drug-release profile. Pellets (1.4–1.7 mm) containing 60% 5-ASA were prepared and coated in a fluidized bed coater with either a single coat comprised of mixed dispersions of amylose with acrylate polymer or with EC or as multiple coats with an inner amylose coat and an outer layer of either EC or acrylic polymer. During in vitro dissolution testing, uncoated pellets exhibited complete drug release in 2–3 h, while pellets coated with amylose alone showed complete release in 6 h. EC-coated pellets did not release drug over a 24-h period. Coatings comprised of amylose and EC showed a release rate that was dependent on the ratio of the two components. With low ratios of amylose to EC (e.g., 1:2.5 w/w), release was rapid and accompanied by cracking of the coating. An amylose/EC ratio of 1:4 appeared optimal for retarding drug release in simulated intestine fluid and was employed to further show a direct dependence of release rate on coating thickness. While release from the amylose/EC-coated pellets was significantly retarded in simulated intestinal fluid, dissolution studies conducted in a fermenter simulating bacterial flora (Fig. 34) showed a dramatic increase in 5-ASA release after approximately 2–5 h of incubation. A variety of other coating mixtures were evaluated, including Eudragit RS/RL30D and Aquacoat ECD30 in both mixed coatings and multilayer coatings. With Aquacoat ECD30, release was too rapid regardless of plasticizer or coating thickness. Eudragit RS/RL 30D was also ineffective in retarding amylose swelling and drug release, presumably because of pores formed by the dissolution of the soluble PEG plasticizer present in the coating formulation. The overall conclusion from this in vitro study was that an amylose/EC coating at a ratio of 1:4 provided the most promising formulation for coating tablets whose release rate could be initiated and controlled by colonic bacterial enzyme activity.

The potential utility of the amylose/EC coating technology was evaluated further in a human clinical setting (145). Pellets (1.4–1.7 mm) were prepared that contained

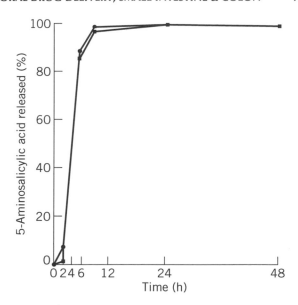

Figure 34. Release profile of 5-aminosalicylic acid in fermenter (simulated colon) system from pellets coated with (■) amylose-Ethocel (ratio 1:4 w/w) TWG 4.8% and (●) amylose TWG 4.8%. *Source:* Reprinted from Ref. 144, with kind permission of Elsevier Science–NL, Sara Burgerhartstraat 25, 1055 KV Amsterdam, The Netherlands.

50% [^{13}C]-glucose and coated with a 1:4 ratio of amylose:EC. Nine fasted subjects received a capsule containing 300 mg of the formulation and exhalation of $^{13}CO_2$ was monitored as a measure of pellet disintegration and release. A coadministered capsule of identical size and density containing a ^{99m}Tc marker was used to monitor GI transit and location by external scintigraphy techniques. The data obtained in this study (Fig. 35) indicated that less than 1% of the dose was recovered in the initial 6 h, followed by a steady increase in $^{13}CO_2$ recovery through 15 h, indicating degradation of the amylose/EC pellets over this time frame. The percent of dose recovered decreased from 15 to 24 h. External imaging of the second marker indicated that the pellets resided in the ascending, transverse, and descending colon during the rapid phase of $^{13}CO_2$ recover. These results in a human study confirmed the potential of the amylose/EC coatings as a colon-targeting technology that was previously demonstrated in the in vitro incubation studies.

A final approach to utilizing colon-specific bacteria as "triggering elements" for colon drug delivery involves the potential application of dextran-based hydrogels (146). Dextran-based prodrugs of naproxen have previously been shown to be specifically degraded in the presence of colon bacterial enzymes. In applying dextran to hydrogel technology, hydrogels were prepared that varied in dextran molecular weight (40,000 to 2,000,000), length of cross-linking agent (HDI: 1,6-hexamethylenediisocyanate; DDI: 1,12-dodecamethylenediisocyanate), cross-linking density from 2.9 to 17.5 mol %, and amount of DMSO (80–90% v/v) in the reaction mixture. The degree of hydrogel swelling in vitro was inversely related to dextran molecular weight and cross-linking density and directly related to the level

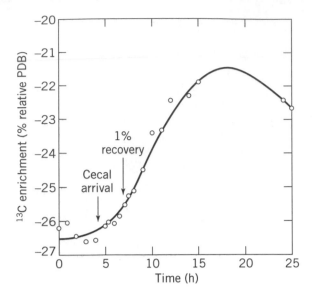

Figure 35. The time course of ^{13}C enrichment of breath CO_2 following the ingestion of pelleted ^{13}C-labeled glucose. The time at which >5% of the total observable activity was first recorded in the cecum and the time at which 1% of the dose given had been recovered in the breath are shown. *Source:* Reprinted from Ref. 145, with kind permission of Elsevier Science–NL, Sara Burgerhartstraat 25, 1055 KV Amsterdam, The Netherlands.

of DMSO in the reaction mixture. In general, both dextran molecular weight and cross-linking density were felt to increase the level of entanglement of dextran strands, thereby decreasing swelling. At the highest dextran molecular weight (2,000,000), however, hydrogel swelling actually increased, which may be related to interference with the cross-linking reaction. In vitro hydrocortisone release was determined with hydrogel discs (Dex-70, 85% DMSO, 11.6% cross-linking with HDI) in the absence and presence of dextranase. The observed release was approximately 32 and 100% in 120 min in the absence and presence, respectively, of dextranase. The in vitro performance of cross-linked dextran-based hydrogels appear promising as a potential technology for colon delivery of active agents.

Clearly, a variety of approaches have been evaluated with regard to identifying and optimizing a colon drug delivery system utilizing the endogenous bacterial enzyme activity as a site-specific triggering mechanism for drug release. Although considerable progress has been made at a research level, these approaches have not yet been commercialized. The primary advantage of utilizing colonic bacterial enzyme activity is that the relatively unique bacterial activity in the colon (both strain and density) represents a noncontinuous event that could serve as a mechanism relatively specific to the colon that has the potential of being independent of GI transit time. This potential benefit could be a major factor in practical utility because GI transit, which has to include the highly variable gastric residence time component, can be quite variable both between individuals and within the same individual depending on a variety of factors such as age, diet, pathology, and concomitant medications. The major drawback to the use

of bacterial enzyme activity would appear to be the kinetics of the degradation process. In general, degradation of polymer coatings or tablet matrices by pectinolytics, dextranases, amylases, and the like is relatively slow, generally necessitating 12–24 h for complete degradation. As such, this approach is unlikely to be useful in attempts to deliver therapeutic agents to the colon in a bolus or pulsed fashion. For similar reasons, the slow release of active agents in the colon over prolonged time periods may be less than optimal in effecting adequate systemic drug absorption. Attempts to increase the rate of degradation by utilizing thinner coats or particulates will have to balance changes in degradation rate with stability of the formulation in the upper GI tract. The most apparent application of these types of colon delivery formulations may be for local application of therapeutic agents to treat pathologies of the colon itself. In this case, a prolonged, slower release over a number of hours while the dosage form is traversing toward the distal colon may be an effective means to spread the therapeutic agent over the maximal colon surface area. Obviously, a great deal of additional work is needed to develop formulations based on these strategies, but the early data offer a hope for success and warrant further investigation.

BIBLIOGRAPHY

1. Y.C. Chien, *Med. Prog. Technol.* **15**, 21–46 (1989).
2. *Physicians' Desk Reference*, Medical Economics Data Production Company, Montvale, N.J., 1997.
3. M.A. Longer, H.S. Ch'ng, and J.R. Robinson, *J. Pharm. Sci.* **74**, 406–411 (1985).
4. G. Levy and W.J. Jusko, *J. Pharm. Sci.* **55**, 285–289 (1966).
5. L.L. Boles Ponto and R.D. Schoenwald, *Clin. Pharmacokinet.* **18**, 381–408 (1990).
6. V.H.L. Lee and A. Yamamoto, *Adv. Drug Delivery Rev.* **4**, 171–207 (1990).
7. J.F. Woodley, *Proc. Int. Symp. Controlled Release Bioact. Mater.* **18**, 337–338 (1991).
8. D.F. Evans et al., *Gut* **29**, 1035–1041 (1988).
9. J.N. Hunt and M.T. Knox, *Handbook of Physiology*, American Physiology Society, Washington, D. C., 1968.
10. G. Santus and R.W. Baker, *J. Controlled Release* **35**, 1–21 (1995).
11. Y.W. Chien, *Novel Drug Delivery Systems*, 2nd ed., Dekker, New York, 1992, pp. 139–196.
12. F. Theeuwes, *Drug Dev. Ind. Pharm.* **9**, 1331–1357 (1983).
13. A. Sandberg et al., *Pharm. Res.* **10**, 28–34 (1993).
14. J.S. Grundy, D.W. Grace, and R.T. Foster, *J. Controlled Release* **44**, 247–254 (1997).
15. J.S. Grundy and R.T. Foster, *Clin. Pharmacokinet.* **30**, 28–51 (1996).
16. D.R. Swanson, B.L. Barclay, P.S. Wong, and F. Theeuwes, *Am. J. Med.* **83** (1987).
17. B. Lemmer, G. Nold, S. Behne, and R. Kaiser, *Chronobiol. Int.* **8**, 485–494 (1991).
18. G.M. Zentner, G.S. Rork, and K.J. Himmelstein, *J. Controlled Release* **1**, 269–282 (1985).
19. L.E. Appel, J.H. Clair, and G.M. Zentner, *Pharm. Res.* **9**, 1001–1007 (1992).

20. H. Cheng et al., *Pharm. Res.* **10**, 1683–1687 (1993).

21. J.R. Crison, P.R. Siersma, M.D. Taylor, and G.L. Amidon, *Proc. Int. Symp. Controlled Release Bioact. Mater.* **22**, 278–279 (1995).

22. F. Pozzi et al., *J. Controlled Release* **31**, 99–108 (1994).

23. M. Otsuka and Y. Matsuda, *Pharm. Res.* **11**, 351–354 (1994).

24. J. Van der Veen, A.C. Eissens, and C.F. Lerk, *Pharm. Res.* **11**, 384–387 (1994).

25. C.M. Adeyeye and J.C. Price, *Pharm. Res.* **11**, 575–579 (1994).

26. K.H. Yuen, A.A. Desmukh, and J.M. Newton, *Pharm. Res.* **10**, 588–592 (1993).

27. B. Abrahamsson et al., *Pharm. Res.* **10**, 709–714 (1993).

28. Y. Qiu, H. Cheskin, J. Briskin, and K. Engh, *J. Controlled Release* **45**, 249–256 (1997).

29. F.B. Landry et al., *J. Controlled Release* **44**, 227–236 (1997).

30. L. Yang and R. Fassihi, *J. Controlled Release* **44**, 135–140 (1997).

31. K. Murata, H. Yamahara, and K. Noda, *Pharm. Res.* **10**, 1165–1168 (1993).

32. C.M. Lehr, *Crit. Rev. Ther. Drug Carrier Syst.* **11**, 119–160 (1994).

33. V.M. Lenaerts and R. Gurney, *Bioadhesive Drug Delivery Systems*, CRC Press, Cleveland, Ohio, 1990.

34. H.O. Alpar, W.N. Field, R. Hyde, and D.A. Lewis, *J. Pharm. Pharmacol.* **41**, 194–196 (1989).

35. J.M. Gu, J.R. Robinson, and H.S. Leung, *Crit. Rev. Ther. Drug Carrier Syst.* **5**, 21–67 (1988).

36. M.F. Saettone et al., *Int. Pharm.* **51**, 203–207 (1989).

37. C.M. Lehr, J.A. Bouwastra, E.H. Schacht, and H.E. Junginger, *Int. J. Pharm.* **78**, 43–48 (1992).

38. J.D. Smart, I.W. Kellaway, and H.E.C. Worthington, *J. Pharm. Pharmacol.* **36**, 295–299 (1984).

39. Y. Akiyama et al., *Pharm. Res.* **12**, 397–405 (1995).

40. K. Satoh et al., *Chem. Pharm. Bull.* **37**, 1366–1368 (1989).

41. E.A. Hosny, *Int. J. Pharm.* **133**, 149–153 (1996).

42. E.A. Hosny and M.A. Al-Meshal, *Pharm. Ind.* **56**, 71–73 (1994).

43. E.A. Hosny and M.A. Al-Meshal, *Drug Dev. Ind. Pharm.* **20**, 2715–2720 (1994).

44. B. Tirosh et al., *J. Controlled Release* **45**, 57–64 (1997).

45. D.C. Kilpatrick et al., *FEBS Lett.* **185**, 299–305 (1985).

46. T.P. King, A. Pusztai, and E.M.N. Clarke, *Histochem. J.* **12**, 201–208 (1980).

47. J.M. Irache, C. Durrer, D. Duchene, and G. Ponchel, *Pharm. Res.* **13**, 1716–1719 (1996).

48. N. Hussain, P.U. Jani, and A.T. Florence, *Pharm. Res.* **14**, 613–618 (1997).

49. M.A. Jepson et al., *J. Drug Target.* **3**, 75–77 (1995).

50. D.E. Chickering and E. Mathiowitz, *J. Controlled Release* **34**, 251–261 (1995).

51. D.E. Chickering, J.S. Jacob, and E. Mathiowitz, *Reac. Polym.* **25**, 189–206 (1995).

52. D.E. Chickering et al., *J. Controlled Release* **48**, 35–46 (1997).

53. H.L. Leussen et al., *Pharm. Res.* **12**, 1293–1298 (1995).

54. M.K. Delaage and M. Lazdunski, *Biochem. Biophys. Res. Commun.* **28**, 390–394 (1967).

55. H.L. Luessen et al., *Int. J. Pharm.* **141**, 39–52 (1996).

56. G. Borchard et al., **39**, 131–138 (1996).

57. R. Sutinen, V. Laasanen, P. Paronen, and A. Urtti, *J. Controlled Release* **33**, 163–171.

58. R.W. Baker and H.K. Lonsdale, in Tanquaray and R.E. Lacey, eds., *Controlled Release of Biologically Active Agents*, Plenum, New York, 1974, pp. 15–71.

59. J.C. Leroux et al., *J. Pharm. Sci.* **84**, 1387–1391 (1995).

60. J.C. Leroux et al., *Pharm. Res.* **13**, 485–487 (1996).

61. S. Narisawa et al., *Pharm. Res.* **11**, 111–116 (1994).

62. A. Serres, M. Baudys, and S.W. Kim, *Pharm. Res.* **13**, 196–201 (1996).

63. X.Y. Wu and P.I. Lee, *Pharm. Res.* **10**, 1544–1547 (1993).

64. M. Nakano and A. Ogata, *Chem. Pharm. Bull.* **32**, 782–785 (1984).

65. H.E. Huber, L.B. Dale, and G.L. Christenson, *J. Pharm. Sci.* **55**, 974–976 (1966).

66. M. Bamba, F. Puisieux, J.P. Marty, and J.T. Carstensen, *Int. J. Pharm.* **2**, 307–315 (1979).

67. A.C. Hodsdon, J.R. Mitchell, M.C. Davies, and C.D. Melia, *J. Controlled Release* **33**, 143–152 (1995).

68. R. Narayani and K.P. Rao, *J. Appl. Polym. Sci.* **58**, 1761–1769 (1995).

69. T.S. Shen and C.A. Winther, *Adv. Drug Res.* **12**, 89–246 (1977).

70. D.E. Duggan et al., *Clin. Pharmacol. Ther.* **21**, 326–335 (1977).

71. A. Sinkula, W. Morozowich, and E.L. Rowe, *J. Pharm. Sci.* **62**, 1106–1111 (1973).

72. A.A. Sinkula, *J. Pharm. Sci.* **63**, 842 (1974).

73. Y. Yoshimura, N. Hamaguchi, and T. Yashiki, *Int. J. Pharm.* **38**, 179–190 (1987).

74. P. Bolme et al., *Eur. J. Clin. Pharmacol.* **10**, 237–243 (1976).

75. S.A. Varia, S. Schuller, K.B. Sloan, and V.J. Stella, *J. Pharm. Sci.* **73**, 1068–1073 (1984).

76. G.K.E. Scriba, *Arch. Pharm. (Weinheim, Ger.)* **326**, 477–481 (1993).

77. G.K.E. Scriba, *Pharm. Res.* **10**, 1181–1186 (1993).

78. G.K.E. Scriba and D.M. Lambert, *Pharm. Res.* **14**, 251–253 (1997).

79. V.K. Tammara, M.M. Narurkar, M.M. Crider, and M.A. Khan, *Pharm. Res.* **10**, 1191–1199 (1993).

80. P. De Caprariis et al., *J. Pharm. Sci.* **83**, 1578–1581 (1994).

81. F.P. Donina et al., *J. Controlled Release* **41**, 187–193 (1996).

82. A. Williams and R.A. Naylor, *J. Chem. Soc. B*, pp. 1973–1979 (1971).

83. A.S. Kearney and V.J. Stella, *Pharm. Res.* **9**, 497–503 (1992).

84. M. Safadi, R. Oliyai, and V.J. Stella, *Pharm. Res.* **10**, 1350–1355 (1993).

85. J. Balzarini et al., *AIDS* **5**, 21–28 (1991).

86. J.E. Starrett et al., *J. Med. Chem.* **37**, 1857–1864 (1994).

87. P. Annaert et al., *Pharm. Res.* **14**, 492–496 (1997).

88. K.C. Cundy et al., *Pharm. Res.* **11**, 839–843 (1994).

89. P.J. Sinko, N.R. Patel, and P. Hu, *Int. J. Pharm.* **109**, 125–133 (1994).

90. B.D. Anderson et al., *J. Controlled Release* **19**, 219–230 (1992).

91. M.E. Morgan, S.C. Chi, K. Murakami, and B.D. Anderson, *Antimicrob. Agents Chemother.* **36**, 2156–2165 (1992).

92. B.D. Anderson, M.E. Morgan, and D. Singhal, *Pharm. Res.* **12**, 1126–1133 (1995).

93. H.W. Nolen and D.R. Friend, *Pharm. Res.* **11**, 1707–1711 (1994).

94. J.P.F. Bai, *Pharm. Res.* **12**, 1101–1104 (1995).

95. K. Morimoto et al., *Pharm. Res.* **8**, 1175–1179 (1991).

96. A.H. Kahns, A. Buur, and H. Bundgaard, *Pharm. Res.* **10**, 68–74 (1993).

97. D. Shan, M.G. Nicolaou, R.T. Borchardt, and B. Wang, *J. Pharm. Sci.* **86**, 765–767 (1977).

98. G.M. Pauletti, S. Gangwar, B. Wang, and R.T. Borchardt, *Pharm. Res.* **14**, 11–17 (1997).

99. G.M. Pauletti et al., *Pharm. Res.* **13**, 1615–1623 (1996).

100. M. Saffran, C. Bedra, G.S. Kumar, and D.C. Neckers, *J. Pharm. Sci.* **77**, 33–38 (1988).

101. T.N. Tozer et al., *Pharm. Res.* **8**, 445–454 (1991).

102. Friend, *Oral Colon-Specific Drug Delivery*, CRC Press, Boca Raton, Fla., 1992.

103. M. Ashford, J.T. Fell, D. Attwood, and P.J. Woodhead, *Int. J. Pharm.* **91**, 241–245.

104. S.S. Davis, J.G. Hardy, and J.W. Fara, *Gut* **27**, 886–892 (1986).

105. J.P. Brown et al., *J. Med. Chem.* **26**, 1300–1307 (1983).

106. P.K. Gupta and J.R. Robinson, in A. Kydoneius et al., eds., *Textbook on Controlled Release Technologies*, Dekker, New York, 1991, Chapter VI.

107. P. Gruber et al., *J. Pharm. Sci.*, 76–83 (1986).

108. G.A. Digenis, *Proc. Int. Symp. Biol. Mater.* **13**, 115 (1986).

109. J.S. Binns, H.N.E. Stevens, M. Bakhshaee, and C.G. Wilson, *Proc. Int. Symp. Controlled Release Bioact. Mater.* **21**, 260–261 (1994).

110. I.R. Wilding et al., *Pharm. Res.* **9**, 654–657 (1992).

111. J. Binns et al., *J. Controlled Release* **38**, 151–158 (1996).

112. J.A. Fix et al., *213th Natl. Meet. Am. Chem. Soc.*, 1997.

113. K. Niwa, T. Takaya, T. Morimoto, and K. Takada, *J. Drug Target.* **3**, 83–89 (1995).

114. K.I. Matsuda et al., *J. Drug Target.* **4**, 59–67 (1996).

115. M. Saffran et al., *Science* **233**, 1081–1084 (1986).

116. M. Saffran et al., *Pharm. Weekb. Sci. Ed.* **10**, 43–44 (1988).

117. G. Van den Mooter, C. Samyn, and R. Kinget, *Pharm. Res.* **11**, 1737–1741 (1994).

118. G. Van den Mooter, C. Samyn, and R. Kinget, *Pharm. Res.* **12**, 244–247 (1995).

119. C. Samyn, W. Kalala, G. Van den Mooter, and R. Kinget, *Int. J. Pharm.* **121**, 211–216 (1995).

120. K.L. Shantha, P. Ravichandran, and K.P. Rao, *Biomaterials* **16**, 1313–1318 (1995).

121. U. Klotz, K. Maier, C. Fischer, and K. Heinkal, *N. Engl. J. Med.* **303**, 1499–1502 (1980).

122. E. Schacht et al., *J. Controlled Release* **39**, 327–338 (1996).

123. M. Ashford and J.T. Fell, *J. Drug Target.* **2**, 241–258 (1994).

124. A.A. Salyers et al., *Appl. Environ. Microbiol.* **33**, 319–322 (1977).

125. H.N. Englyst, S. Hay, and G.T. MacFarlane, *FEMS Microbiol. Ecol.* **95**, 163–171 (1987).

126. J.H. Cummings, G.T. Macfarlane, and B.S. Drasar, in R. Whitehead, ed., *Gastrointestinal and Oesophageal Pathology*, Churchill-Livingstone, Edinburgh, 1989, pp. 201–219.

127. A.A. Salyers, S.E.H. West, J.R. Vercellotti, and T.D. Wilkins, *Appl. Environ. Microbiol.* **34**, 529–533 (1977).

128. D.A.T. Southgate and J.V.G.A. Durnin, *Br. J. Nutr.* **24**, 517–535 (1970).

129. J.L. Slavin, P.M. Braver, and J.A. Marlett, *J. Nutr.* **111**, 287–297 (1981).

130. J.H. Cummings, *Gut* **25**, 805–180 (1984).

131. J. Tomlin, N.W. Read, C.A. Edwards, and B.I. Duerden, *Br. J. Nutr.* **55**, 481–486 (1986).

132. C.M. Lancaster and M.A. Wheatley, *Polym. Prepr.* **30**, 480–481 (1989).

133. G.T. Macfarlane and H.N. Englyst, *J. Appl. Bacteriol.* **60**, 195–201 (1986).

134. U.S. Pat. 4,432,966 (1984).

135. EPO 460 921 A2 (1991), T. Suzuki, K. Hahiudo, T. Matumoto, and T. Fujii.

136. P. Zeitoun et al., *J. Controlled Release* **26**, 213–220 (1993).

137. A. Rubinstein et al., *Pharm. Res.* **10**, 258–263 (1993).

138. D.A. Adkin et al., *Pharm. Res.* **14**, 103–107 (1997).

139. Z. Wakerly, J.T. Fell, D. Attwood, and D. Parkins, *Pharm. Res.* **13**, 1210–1212 (1996).

140. O. Munjeri, J.H. Collett, and J.T. Fell, *J. Controlled Release* **46**, 273–278 (1997).

141. V.M. Leloup, P. Colonna, and S.G. Ring, *Biotechnol. Bioeng.* **38**, 127–135 (1991).

142. H.N. Englyst and G.T. Macfarlane, *J. Sci. Food Agric.* **37**, 699–706 (1986).

143. S.G. Ring et al., *Food Chem.* **28**, 97–109 (1988).

144. S. Milojevic et al., *J. Controlled Release* **38**, 75–84 (1996).

145. J.H. Cummings et al., *J. Controlled Release* **40**, 123–131 (1996).

146. L. Hovgaard and H. Brondsted, *J. Controlled Release* **36**, 159–166 (1995).

See also BIOADHESIVE DRUG DELIVERY SYSTEMS; CARRIER-MEDIATED TRANSPORT, ORAL DRUG DELIVERY; ORAL DRUG DELIVERY, TRADITIONAL.

ORAL DRUG DELIVERY, TRADITIONAL

KANJI TAKADA
Kyoto Pharmaceutical University
Kyoto, Japan

HIROSHI YOSHIKAWA
Toyama Medical and Pharmaceutical University
Toyama, Japan

KEY WORDS

Absorption enhancement

Beads

Capsules

Chemical modification

Emulsion

Liposome

Microgranules

Microparticles

Nanoparticles

Pellets

Spheroids

Stabilization of drugs

Tablets

OUTLINE

Before the advance of drug delivery systems (DDSs), tablets and capsules were the principal oral preparations for drugs. However, with the development of drug delivery technology, many novel oral DDSs have been invented in the last two decades. Although these oral DDSs are prepared in traditional dosage forms as tablets, capsules, suspensions, emulsions, and solutions, they are superior to the conventional oral preparations. Oral DDSs are divided into two categories: controlled-release preparations and targeting preparations. Targeting preparations such as colon delivery systems are described in the next section; oral DDSs having controlled-release characteristics as shown in Table 1 are described in this section.

TABLETS

Controlled-release technologies have been studied for a long time, and many preparations have been supplied on the market. The drug release-time is prolonged according to one of the following mechanisms (1) changing the physical properties such as solubility and stability of the drug molecules, (2) forming a complex of drug molecules with ion-exchanging resins, (3) incorporating drug molecules in slowly disintegrating or inert porous matrices, (4) coating drug molecules with pharmaceutical polymers that have a barrier function for the diffusion of drug molecules, and (5) osmotic pumps. In addition, new additives such as linear short-chain starches can be used to make sustained-release tablets (1). Delivery from this nonporous tablet is based on a swelling-controlled solvent-activated mechanism. In oral DDSs, this mechanism is used by itself or in combination with others (2).

Matrix-Type Tablets

Hydrophobic and Hydrophilic Matrices. To prepare a sustained-release tablet of water-soluble drugs, the drugs

Table 1. Traditional Oral DDS

1. Tablets
  1.1 Matrix type
    Hydrophobic and hydrophilic matrices
    Plastic matrices
    Ion-exchange resins
    Coprecipitates and solid dispersions
  1.2 Film-coating tablets
    Diffusion-controlled membranes
    Osmotic pumps
    Enteric coating
    Floating tablets
    Swellable tablets
    Mucoadhesive tablets
    Complexation
      Cyclodextrins
      Pharmaceutical additives
  1.3 Multiple-unit tablets
2. Capsules
  2.1 Hard capsules
  2.2 Soft elastic capsules
  2.3 Floating capsules
3. Microgranules/spheroids
4. Beads
5. Pellets
6. Stabilization of drug
  6.1 Stabilization in liquid preparation
  6.2 Factors affecting drug stability and method of stabilization
7. Control of absorption process
  7.1 Enhancement of absorption
    Absorption promoters
    Chemical modification
    Classical suspensions
    Emulsions
      Classification of emulsions
      Application of emulsions to gastrointestinal absorption
    Liposomes
    Employment of liposomes in gastrointestinal absorption
  7.2 Micro- and nanoparticles
    Particulates for gastrointestinal delivery
    Intestinal uptake of particulates

are mixed with hydrophobic matrices. With hydrophobic materials like fatty alcohols, acids, and esters, slow-release drug particles are prepared and are compressed into tablets. Voltaren SR is a commercial product of sodium diclofenac and is a hydrophobic matrix tablet consisting of a cetyl alcohol matrix. Ethylcellulose (EC), an inert and hydrophobic polymer that has been widely used in a number of dosage forms, was used as a matrix substance to prepare a sustained-release tablet of a water-soluble drug, pseudoephedrine HCl, by direct-compression technology (3). The lower-viscosity grades of EC are more compressible than the higher-viscosity grades, resulting in harder tablets and slower release rate. To prepare sustained-release tablets of a highly water-soluble drug, ABT-089, a cholinergic channel modulator for treatment of cognitive disorders, a hydrophobic matrix composed of carnauba wax and partially hydrogenated cottonseed oil were used as the rate-controlling materials (4).

Cellulose ether polymers such as hydroxypropylmethylcellulose (HPMC) in hydrophilic matrices are also used to prepare oral controlled-release tablets (5). In particular, high-viscosity grade of HPMC ($\approx$1,000–1,500 cps) is used to prepare matrix tablets by a dry-granulation method. The combination of high- and low-viscosity grades of HPMC was shown to be applicable as the matrix base to prepare diclofenac sodium (6) and zileuton (7) sustained-release tablets. A new ternary polymeric matrix system composed of pectin, HPMC, and highly water-soluble drugs such as diltiazem HCl was developed by direct-tablet compression (8). Further adjustments in the drug-release rate can be accomplished by two external layers (caps). This system, the Geomatrix trilayered tablet, was applied to develop a once-a-day formulation of diltiazem HCl (9). Diltiazem is contained in the hydrophilic polymer core, and two external layers serve to control the rate of hydration of the core, thereby restricting the surface area available for drug diffusion. Xanthan gum was also used as a hydrophilic matrix for sustained-release ibuprofen tablets (10). MSContin tablets, a controlled-release system for morphine, is a combination matrix consisting of a hydrophilic granular system inserted in a hydrophobic matrix. Theo-Dur is a controlled-release tablet of theophylline. As shown in Figure 1, it consists of 2 components: a matrix of compressed theophylline crystals and coated theophylline granules embedded in the matrix (11). One-third of the dose is in the matrix, and the remainder is in the pellets. In contact with fluid, the theophylline matrix disintegrates and dissolves. Next, theophylline diffuses slowly through the wall of the free granules. Finally, the granules dissolve completely. After oral administration of Theo-Dur 300-mg tablets to human subjects, serum theophylline concentrations over 1 mg/L were maintained over 24 h (12). A new melt-extrusion method for manufacturing matrix DDSs for theophylline was proposed (13). The powder mixture, drug, and polymerlike polyethylene and polycaprolactone were melted at 100–120°C for 30–45 s in a melt extruder. Thereafter, the mass was extruded into a disk mold (3 × 12 mm), and the polymer disk containing the drug was removed by cooling. Three-layer matrix tablets of diclofenac sodium have been reported in which poly(ethylene oxide) (PEO)

and HPMC together with diclofenac sodium were directly compressed into a three-layer matrix system (14).

Plastic Matrices. Sustained-release tablets can be also prepared by formulating an inert pharmaceutical polymer such as poly(vinyl chloride), poly(vinyl acetate), and methyl methacrylate. These polymers protect the tablet from disintegration due to the effects of peristalsis and turbulence and also reduce the dissolution rate of the drug inside the tablet. This technology was applied to theophylline (Theograd), sodium valproate, and iron. Theograd tablets consist of a matrix of a methylacrylate/methylmethacrylate copolymer that is mixed with theophylline and compressed into 250- and 350-mg tablets. In human studies, the extent of bioavailability increased about 1.4 times in fasting conditions (15,16). Therefore, it is recommended that Theograd sustained-release tablets be taken after a meal.

Owing to the shape of an average tablet (biconvex or disc), it is theoretically improbable for these tablets to release active drugs at a zero-order rate. Whether the matrix releases drug via swelling control or erosion (or both), it is almost impossible to attain a zero-order release. To solve this problem, core-in-cup tablets that release drug from a single, stable eroding surface of constant surface area were developed (17). As shown in Figure 2, the cup tablets were prepared by directly compressing the mixture of EC and carnauba wax, and the resultant cups were compressed with core tablets containing ibuprofen.

Ion-Exchange Resins. Drug molecules are formulated inside the tablets so as to be bound to ion-exchange resins and coated with a semipermeable water-insoluble polymer membrane made of EC or a similar substance. The merits of the ion-exchange resin–drug complex are (1) that sustained-release preparations can be made by formulating a gel-forming ion-exchange resin, (2) there is reduction of the degradation of drug molecules in the gastrointestinal tract by complexation, (3) the flavor is masked. Among the ion-exchange resins, divinylbenzenesulfonate is most commonly used because of its safety. This technology was applied to drugs with unpleasant flavors and strong effects on the stomach walls that, hence, need sustained-release characteristics. Phenylpropanolamine, codeine, dextromethorphan, acetaminophen, ephedrine, and chlorpheniramine are representative drugs to which cationic ion-exchange polymer matrices technology has been applied. For example, divinylbenzenesulfonate was used to prepare

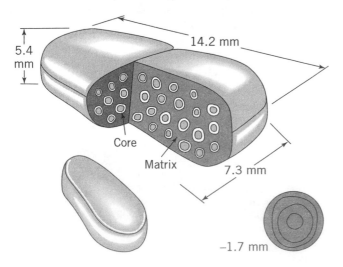

Figure 1. Structure of Theo-Dur.

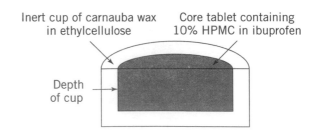

Figure 2. Schematic diagram of the core-in-cup tablet. *Source:* Ref. 17.

a sustained-release oral preparation of phenylpropanol-amine by coating the tablet with EC (18). A problem associated with this approach is that drug release can be very rapid in the presence of an excess of ions, and dose dumping can occur. This can be prevented by impregnating the ion-exchange resin with an agent to impart plasticity and then coating it with a permeable membrane such as EC so that diffusion through the coating becomes the rate-limiting step (19).

Coprecipitates and Solid Dispersions. To modify the dissolution characteristics of drugs, coprecipitation involving the dissolution of ibuprofen and Eudragit S 100 in alcohol followed by the addition of cold water under agitation was developed (20). The release of oxazepam, a poorly water-soluble drug, was enhanced from tablets containing dispersions with a carrier, Gelita collagel (molecular weight 18,300), an enzymatically produced collagen hydrolysate, where the solid dispersion was prepared by a spray-drying method using the mixture of oxazepam, carrier, and lactose in 70% ethanolic solution (21). The bioavailability of cyclosporin A, a water-insoluble drug, was improved by solid dispersion with enteric coating polymer and surfactant (22).

Film-Coating Tablets

The dissolution rate of drug molecules from the tablet can be controlled by coating the tablet with a polymer membrane. For this purpose, EC and enteric-coating polymers such as Eudragit L and S (methacrylic acid copolymer) and hydroxypropylmethylcellulose phthalate (HPMCP) have been used.

Diffusion-Controlled Membranes. The dissolution rate of drug molecules can be modified by selecting the coating materials. Cellulose derivatives are generally used for this purpose. When a water-insoluble polymer such as EC is homogeneously used, the dissolution rate is dependent on the membrane thickness. However, when both water-insoluble and soluble polymers are used for the coating, the drug-release rate is accelerated. The addition of large amount of plasticizers such as triethyl citrate and tripropyl citrate to the coating polymer solution also increases the release rate of drug molecules. For example, drugs such as captopril, diltiazem, or ranitidine are blended with HPMCP, microcrystalline cellulose, poly(vinylpyrrolidone) (PVP), and magnesium stearate, wetted with anhydrous ethanol, and then compressed into tablets after drying. When these tablets were coated with a semipermeable membrane made from a mixture of microcrystalline cellulose acetate, PVP, and tripropyl citrate, satisfactory sustained-release tablets were obtained.

A gastrointestinal diffusion system (GDS) is a typical example of a DDS and consists of a soluble core including drug and tablet excipients. The porous membrane composed from arabic gum, dextrin 40,000, sodium chloride, sucrose, and cellulose acetate covering the core controls the diffusion rate of the drug (23). GDS was applied to metoprolol, diltiazem, lithium acetate, and disopyramide. As a new coating material, cross-linked amylose was developed and gave a sustained drug delivery (24).

Osmotic Pumps. The osmotic pump consists of a drug contained in a rigid, semipermeable membrane in which an orifice of approximately 300 μm has been created by a laser beam. This system is applicable to a drug having a suitable aqueous solubility, such as indomethacin and metoprolol (25). These drugs are formulated within the system with hydrogel polymers. After water is drawn into the capsule by osmosis, osmotic pressure increases within the capsule, and as a result the saturated drug solution is forced out through the orifice. The factors affecting the drug-release rate from the system are (1) quality and quantity of the hydrogel polymer and (2) permeability of the membrane. As semipermeable membrane substances, cellulose acetate ethylcarbamate, polyamide, and polyurethane are used. When drug molecules are dispersed within the tablet in a hydrogel, controlled release is obtained. Among the hydrogel polymers, ionic materials such as carboxymethyl cellulose (CMC) were useful because the ionizable groups provide most of the osmotic pressure required to draw water through the semipermeable membrane. These polymers can be compressed into tablets with conventional machinery when dry. There are three representative products: (1) The generic osmotic pump, supplied as OSMET, in which antipyrine or theophylline was contained. These pumps were applied to human subjects as rectal delivery systems for antipyline and theophylline (26). (2) The elementary osmotic pump, which is called OROS, was applied to metoprolol. The merit of OROS is the capability of obtaining a zero-order release rate, and the release rate is independent of the gastrointestinal pH and food intake. (3) The push–pull osmotic pump, which was developed to overcome the shortcomings of the osmotic pump system, namely, to produce small tablets in large quantities with high reliability and low cost for clinic application.

The technology has been applied to nifedipine, phenylpropanolamine, prazosin, and salbutamol. The GITS (gastrointestinal therapeutic system) tablet is a representative one (27). This tablet consists of a push layer and a pull layer. After oral administration, drug molecules are suspended within the water owing to the gastrointestinal fluid, and the polymer in the push layer swells. Because of this pressure, nifedipine molecules stream through the micropores on the surface of the tablet.

The first drug to which the osmotic pump was applied was indomethacin, which is a representative nonsteroidal antiinflammatory drug. However, severe gastric irritation occurred because of the concentrated indomethacin solution liberated from the small hole. To overcome this problem, bilayered osmotic tablets were applied to atenolol (28).

These osmotic tablet formulations are well suited for soluble drugs and core excipients with high osmotic pressures. However, osmotic delivery of moderate- to low-solubility drugs is limited because the dense coatings have relatively low permeabilities. To improve this problem, asymmetric-membrane tablet coating was developed (29).

Enteric Coating. To protect the drug molecules from the gastric degradation, as can occur with digoxin or erythromycin, and to reduce the side effects by protecting the gastric mucosa from attack by drugs, such as can occur with indomethacin, enteric-coating tablets are used (30). The polymers used for enteric coating are acid-impermeable polymers. Commonly used enteric-coating materials and their threshold pH are as follows: cellulose acetate trimellitate (CAT), 4.8; HPMCP, 4.5–4.8; poly(vinyl acetate)phthalate (PVAP), 5.0; HPMCP 50, 5.2; HPMCP 55, 5.4; Eudragit L30D, 5.6; cellulose acetate phthalate (CAP), 6.0; Eudragit L, 6.0; and Eudragit S, 6.8. The use of CAP has been decreased because the phthalate ester group in CAP is known to be susceptible to hydrolysis during storage, with the gradual formation of phthalic acid and a reduction in acid resistance of the polymer film (30). Eudragit contains free carboxyl groups and is impermeable at low pH but disintegrates at a pH of about 7. According to the dissolution characteristics, several types of polymers are available. Eudragit S dissolves at pH 6.8, and two types of Eudragit L dissolve at pH 5.5 and 6.0 HPMCP dissolves at pH 5.5. These enteric-coating polymers were designed based on the assumption that the pH of the stomach is acidic, pH 1–3, while that of the intestine is neutral, pH 6–7. The reported ranges of the gastrointestinal pH values in healthy human subjects are 0.5–0.8 (stomach), 5.0–6.5 (jejunum), 6.0–7.5 (ileum), and 6.0–8.0 (colon). Although the normal gastric pH of human subjects is 1–3, the higher gastric pH was reported in the case of geriatric patients. Patients with achlorhydria also have higher gastric pH. In addition, the gastric acid is completely buffered by food in the case of postprandial administration. Therefore, considerable amounts of drug may be released into the stomach in these cases. The proximal jejunum usually lies within pH 5.0–6.5. The pH rises slowly along the length of the small intestine to reach only pH 6 to 7 in most subjects, although high values in the range 7 to 9 have occasionally been found. Therefore, the enteric coat should be soluble at a pH slightly lower than 7.

Enteric coating was applied to tablets using a solution of polymer dissolved with alcohol, acetone, methylene chloride, and similar substances. Usually, 6–8% of the tablets' weight is necessary to obtain acid resistance and impermeability. However, owing to environmental concerns, aqueous-based latex suspensions are used nowadays. In these cases, a much more precise coating technique is needed to eliminate the possibility of pinholes. Therefore, a higher quantity of coating material is required, approximately 10–12% of the tablet weight (30).

The evidence that enteric-coated drugs lessen or eliminate local side effects such as gastric irritation is conflicting. Enteric-coated aspirin is reported to be less likely to produce injury to the gastric or duodenal mucosa than plain or buffered aspirin. Enteric-coated potassium chloride tablets, however, are no longer used because of the risk of intestinal ulceration.

Erythromycin (EM) is rapidly degraded by gastric acid. Therefore, EM is administered as a stable ester prodrug or in enteric-coated tablets. However, the high pH (6.5–7.0) required for the dissolution of the enteric coating delayed the release of EM beyond its principle absorption site in the proximal small intestine. Therefore, choosing the right enteric-coating polymer is critical to produce efficacy. To obtain good reproducibility and less intersubject variation,

enteric-coated tablets with diameters of less than 5 mm or so are preferable.

Floating Tablets. A floating dosage unit is useful for drugs acting locally in the proximal gastrointestinal tract. These systems are also useful for drugs that are poorly soluble or unstable in intestinal fluids. The floating properties of these systems help to retain these systems in the stomach for a long time. Various attempts have been made to develop floating systems, which float on the gastric contents and release drug molecules for the desired time period. After the release of a drug, the remnants of the system are emptied from the stomach. As a floating tablet, the hydrodynamically balanced system (HBS) is representative (31). This system is based on the principle that an object of less specific gravity than the gastric fluid will float on the gastric fluid in the stomach and thus keep the tablet in the stomach for a long period. Consequently, gastrointestinal residence time will increase. This system is applicable to drugs that suffer degradation in the intestine, have a higher pH than the stomach, and are poorly absorbed from the lower part of the small intestine. Diazepam, captopril, and morphine are suitable drugs for this system. These drugs are mixed with gel-forming hydrocolloids such as HPMC and fillers of low density in a tablet. Therefore, the hydrocolloids also retain drug molecules inside the tablet by decreasing the diffusion rate of drug molecules in the gel matrix.

The developing theory of gastric floating systems is based on the assumption that the subject is always upright. However, if the subject lies on his or her left side, this assumption breaks down. This point is the shortcoming of the floating system.

Intragastric floating diltiazem HCl tablets were prepared from chitosan and its HCl salt, polyvinyl alcohol (PVA) and PVP (32). Chitosan, a natural polysaccharide, has mucoadhesive properties. Therefore, the residence time of the chitosan-based tablets in the stomach was thought to be increased.

Swellable Tablets. It is possible to retain tablets in the stomach by increasing their size. The stomach discharges its contents through the pylorus into the small intestine. If the tablets are larger than the pylorus, they can stay in the stomach for a long time. For the sake of ease of swallowing, the tablets must swell in the stomach and attain a large size quickly. If not, the tablets are emptied through the pylorus. In addition, the swelled tablet should not block the pylorus. The physical characteristics of tablets such as size, shape, and flexibility also affect gastric emptying. The cloverleaf-, disk-, string-, and pellet-shaped tablets shown in Figure 3 were prepared from a silastic elastomer, and their gastric retain was studied (33). The tetrahedron made with low-density polyethylene remained in the stomach for longer periods than other shapes of similar size. Gastric retention of rigid rings was affected by their size. Disk and cloverleaf shapes showed poor gastric retention. The stomach eliminated strings and pellets fairly rapidly. As swellable gel-forming polymer retain drug molecules within the tablet, sustained-release tablets can be prepared. A tablet composed of a pH-independent

Figure 3. Shapes tested in the in vivo size/shape study. *Source:* Ref. 33.

hydrocolloidal gelling agent, a pH-dependent polymer such as sodium alginate, and a binder showed a sustained-release pattern of incorporated basic drugs.

The effect of fasted and fed conditions on gastric retention of balloon dosage forms were studied by comparing the gastric emptying time of the balloon dosage forms and the uncoated nondisintegrating tablets. The balloon tablet was 3–6 times larger than the plain tablet (34). The balloon type and nondisintegrating types of tablets were emptied from stomach under fasted conditions quite quickly. However, the balloon tablets remained in the stomach for a longer time than the plain tablets under fed conditions. The balloon tablets remained in the stomach for about 6 h more than the plain tablets. The balloon tablets floated more quickly in fasted condition than in fed condition. This could be due to the presence of high-viscosity gastric contents during fed condition.

Mucoadhesive Tablets. Oral cavities such as the buccal and sublingual sites have advantages for drug administration, for example, rapid onset of action, high blood levels, avoidance of the first-pass effect, and no exposure of the drug to the gastrointestinal tract. Drugs are also applied, localized, and removed easily. Several synthetic polymers including cellulose derivatives, plant gums, and polyacrylic acid are bioadhesive. For the treatment of aptha and oral *Candida* infections, bioadhesive tablets containing steroids or miconazole have been studied (35). Mucoadhesive, erodible buccal tablets containing clotrimazole have also been reported (36). Alternatively, mucoadhesive films composed of the highly water-soluble drug lidocaine HCl, EC, and HPC were reported as controlled-release preparations (37). To achieve high bioavailability and extended absorption time for nitroglycerin and isosorbide dinitrate, a slowly disintegrating plain tablet and a film-covered tablet in which disintegration was controlled by a hole in the film coating were developed (38).

Complexation Cyclodextrins. Hydrophobic drugs must be dissolved in the gastrointestinal tract to cross the membrane of the enterocytes. To accelerate the dissolution of water-insoluble drugs, traditional formulation systems involved a combination of organic solvents, surfactants, and extreme pH conditions. However, these systems often

cause the irritation to the gastrointestinal tract. To solve this problem, cyclodextrins (CDs) have been included in tablets to improve the dissolution rate of drugs (39). CDs of pharmaceutical relevance are cyclic oligosaccharides composed of dextrose units joined through a $1 \rightarrow 4$ bond. CDs form complexes with hydrophobic drugs and increase the water solubility of drugs. Six types of CDs are now commercially available: α-, β-, and γ-CDs and three modified derivatives of β-CD-methyl, hydroxypropyl, and sulfobutylether (40). However, β-CD is the most popular pharmaceutical additive of these. The commercial pharmaceuticals with β-CD–based formulations are piroxicam as a plain tablet, prostaglandin (PG) F_2, and nitroglycerin as a sublingual tablet. CDs are capable of forming inclusion complexes with drugs. These noncovalent, inclusion complexes can have physical, chemical, and biological properties that are dramatically different from those of either the parent drug or CD. The safety evaluation of CDs have been reviewed (41). These complexes can be used to increase solubility (42,43) and dissolution rate, decrease volatility, alter release and dissolution rates, modify local irritation, and increase the stability of drugs. A complex formation of oxazepam and β-CD by the spray-drying method gave the most efficient dissolution characteristics (44). Solubility of ketoconazole was increased with β-CD complexation (45,46). In addition, sustained-release tablets were prepared by incorporating drug within the matrix in the form of a hydrophobic complex with β-CD. This technology was applied to diltiazem HCl using ethylated β-CD, and pH-dependent release of diltiazem was obtained. β-CD was also applied to salbutaine release preparations (47).

Pharmaceutical Additives. Polymeric complexes based on the interaction between Eudragit L and naltrexone HCl gave a significant reduction in the release rate of drug from the complex used as a naltrexone controlled-release system (48). New water-soluble polycations were synthesized and used as oral carriers (tablet) of diclofenac sodium and sulfathiazole sodium (49).

Multiple-Unit Tablets

The term *multiple-unit tablets* refers to tablets containing subunits that may be either the same (homogeneous) or different (heterogeneous). Multiple-unit tablets give much diversity in achieving dissolution profiles by combining various types of subunits in a tablet. Usually, by combining the immediate-release portion and controlled-release portion, sustained-release tablets are prepared. This system has been recently applied to nifedipine. The Adalat CR tablet is composed of two portions; the core is a immediate release, and the coat is a controlled release layer in which a gel-forming polymer is formulated with nifedipine. After oral administration, the coat tablet forms a gel by the permeation of gastrointestinal fluid. Thereafter, constant-rate drug release occurs according to the erosion of the matrix gel. In contrast to the finish of the drug release from the coat matrix gel, the core tablet releases drug at a comparatively fast rate. This nifedipine is a once-a-day tablet. After oral administration of an Adalat CR 40-mg tablet, plasma nifedipine concentration was maintained between 20 and 50 ng/mL for 24 h (50).

water-insoluble layer, and (3) drug release to the outside. By adjusting the thickness of the water-insoluble layer, beads having any release lag time can be prepared. By formulating several kinds of beads with different release lag times, sustained-release capsules have been prepared in which EC was used as a water-insoluble coating polymer. Granules were prepared by a centrifugal fluidizing (CF) granulator (83). As a variation of TES, a sigmoidal release system and pulsatile-release tablet were also designed (85,86). Flowable-bead cellulose (BC) coprecipitates consisting of spherical BC as carrier, the film former HPMC, the hydrophilic solubilizer PEG 6000, the plasticizers dimethyl phthalate and dioctyl phthalate, and the model drugs prednisolone and griseofulvin were prepared for controlled release (87). Chitosan was used to prepare controlled-release beads containing piroxicam by gelling the cationic polysaccharide with an anionic counterion, tripolyphosphate, solutions (88). Swellable porous hydrogel beads were loaded with diclofenac sodium, and sustained release was obtained (89).

PELLETS

Multiple-unit dosage forms are also known to have less variance in transit time through the gastrointestinal tract than single-unit dosage forms. Sustained-release diltiazem HCl pellets were prepared simply by coating inert diltiazem HCl pellets with soluble Eudragit L and S film-forming polymers (90). Alternatively, similar diltiazem pellets capable of controlling the drug release over 24 h were possible. Diltiazem HCl, fumeric acid, and talc were blended, mixed, and applied to Nonpareil using a coating solution of PVP to prepare the pellet core. The core was then coated by spraying solutions of Eudragit RS and Eudragit RL. The ratio of the two polymers could be optimized to get a controlled-release profile over 24 h. A comparative bioavailability study using two types of sustained-release oral isosorbide dinitrate (ISDN) showed that pellets had higher bioavailability than tablets (91). Two reasons are possible: One is the lower dissolution rate of ISDN from the tablet, as ISDN received high hepatic first-pass effect, and another is that ISDN was absorbed from the larger area of the gastrointestinal tract as pellets received wide distribution there. Moreover, to prevent the effect of gastric emptying or the change of the transit of the preparation through the gastrointestinal tract, pellets are preferred because the gastric emptying time for pellets is faster than that for tablets. For this purpose, sustained-release oral pellets of ISDN and propranolol have been developed. To prepare pellets, the mixture of drug, organic acid, and polymer was coated on the core substance. Organic acids like citric acid and tartaric acid have the role of accelerating the release rate of drug even in the high-pH environment of the gastrointestinal tract. As a polymer, HPMC, PVP, Eudragit RL and RS, methylcellulose, and EC are used. As a coating material that was used to control the release rate of drug molecules, EC, sometimes with a small amount of HPC, was used. In the case of sustained-release propranolol pellets, a mixture of 20% PVP in isopropanol/33% shellac in ethanol (19:1) was used

as a polymer solution. Sustained release from pellets is conventionally achieved by polymeric coating. However, versatile matrix pellet formulation based on the combination of a hydrophobic material and a starch derivative using a melt pelletization technique is possible (92).

Another method for the production of enteric beads using a purely aqueous system composed of HPMCP and riboflavin has been developed (93). Pellets containing enteric coprecipitates of nifedipine formed by nonaqueous spheronization have also been reported (57). Calcium pectinate was used as a coating material to prepare sustained-release theophylline pellets (94).

On the other hard, prolonged gastric residence was obtained by increasing the density of pellets. The critical density to achieve prolonged gastric residence was reported to lie between 2.4 and 2.8 g/cm^3 (95). For the manufacture of sustained-release pellets for highly dosed, freely soluble drugs such as diltiazem HCl, the hot-melt extrusion method was shown to be suitable (96). Figure 4 shows the extruder used in this study. The volume and viscosity of coadministered fluid also affect the gastrointestinal distribution of small particles (97). Recently, an extrusion–spheronization method was developed to prepare sustained-release indomethacin pellets whose shape and size are shown in Figure 5 (98).

STABILIZATION OF DRUG

Examinations of drug stability using chemical kinetics gives us clues to how to stabilize the drug and helpful suggestions for its preservation requirements as well as a determination of its validation date.

Stability in Liquid Preparation

In liquid preparations of drugs, hydrolysis, oxidation, racemization, decarboxylation, or ring-opening reactions are usually observed; however, the majority of drugs in liquid phase are disintegrated according to hydrolysis or oxidation (99). The most popular order of reaction observed in liquid preparation is first order due to a large excess of medium compared with drug, which is called pseudo-first-order reaction.

Factors Affecting Drug Stability and Method of Stabilization

Temperature, pH, and other factors such as kind of medium, concentration, ionic strength, or permittivity are major factors that affect stabilities of drugs in liquid phase (99). To investigate the effect of temperature, which is one of the strongest factors affecting the rate of drug degradation, an analysis using the Arrhenius equation should be performed. When this Arrhenius plot is linear, the reaction rate of the drug at normal temperature can be estimated by the results under a higher temperature; this relation is applicable when activation energy is 10–30 kcal/mol unless chemicals are separated or melted (99). In general, Arrhenius plotting is done at several temperatures. The statistical evaluation of accelerated stability can be determined for a single temperature, and by this method it was reported that a reasonable prediction of the expected

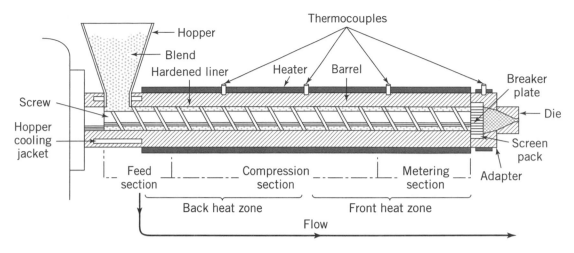

Figure 4. Cross-section of the single screw extruder. *Source:* Ref. 96.

shelf life as a function of activation energy may be possible (100). When we design a liquid preparation, the effect of pH on drug stability is also a frequently encountered problem. In pH analysis, the reaction rate of the pH profile can indicate the most stable pH range of the drug. There are three types of pH profiles: the so-called V type, the sigmoid type, and the bell type (101,102). Specific acid–base catalysis, an action of a single dissociation group, and that of two dissociation groups affecting reaction rate is a major cause of drug degradation according to the pH profile of the V type, sigmoid type, and bell type, respectively. From this information we can determine how to stabilize a drug in liquid preparation, that is, we can select a pH at which a drug is most stable, storage at lower temperature, blocking of oxygen in air, and preservation in a shaded container. In addition to these countermeasures, which sound like passive stabilization, various active stabilizations have also been attempted (Table 2). Stabilization of ampicillin in aqueous solution using a base formation with benzaldehyde and furfural has been reported (103). With an increase of added benzaldehyde and furfural, the degradation rate of ampicillin decreased, which is caused by binding of both chemicals to form a Schiff base, which is relatively insoluble in aqueous solution and thus leads to drugs being excluded from a degradation system. This stabilization by aldehyde is also observed in cephalexin, a β-lactam antibiotic that possesses an amino group at the α-

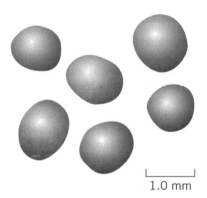

Figure 5. Shape and size of indomethacin pellets.

position (103). Inclusion compounds such as cyclodextrin can also stabilize drugs that are disintegrated by hydrolysis. In these attempts, bencyclane (104), prostacyclin (105), and a nonsteroidal antiinflammatory agent (106) were stabilized by an addition of cyclodextrin. In these chemicals' hydrolysis, sites are considered to be protected from reaction by means of cyclodextrin. Dissolved oxygen contributes to oxidative degradation that is accelerated by metal ions as catalysts, and an attempt to protect isoniazid in aqueous solution from oxidative degradation has been

Table 2. Factors Affecting Drug Stability in Solution and Methods for Stabilization

Major ways of degradation	Factors affecting degradation	Methods for stabilization	
		Passive methods	Active methods
Hydrolysis	Temperature pH Ionic strength Permittivity Polarity	Storage under suitable conditions	Formation of complex or base Chemical modification Addition of solvent or surfactant
Oxidation	Oxygen Metal ions Light	Protection from air and light	Addition of chelating agents and antioxidants

was shown in vivo using EC microspheres after oral administration in dogs (156). Encapsulated AZT showed significantly lower maximum concentration (C_{max}) values and longer times to C_{max} (t_{max}) values. And longer mean residence time (MRT) was also observed compared with AZT powder. In rats an oral delivery of γ-interferon was attempted in which it was encapsulated in polylacetate microspheres (157). In this report, a quite different distribution of interferon level was observed in vivo at 15 and 240 min after oral administration, in contrast to the control group, which received equivalent doses of unencapsulated interferon. These findings would suggest the tentative conclusion that microencapsulation of proteins markedly affects oral uptake and possibly postabsorption pharmacokinetic parameters as well. This experiment stands on the hypothesis that particulate material itself could be absorbed from the gastrointestinal tract.

Intestinal Uptake of Particulates.   Despite many findings in the past 20 years of the uptake of micro- or nanoparticles through the intestine after peroral administration, there is much difference of opinion as to the site of absorption and its mechanism. In 1977, so-called persorption of large starch microspheres (5–150 μm) via the intestinal villae tips was reported in animals including humans (158). It was pointed out that this persorption was an infrequent occurrence and also a rather pathological phenomenon (159). Several investigators examined cytosis of particulates by the intestinal epithelial cells. In these examinations, phagocytic transport of 1-μm polystyrene microspheres in the intestines of rats and dogs was found (160). The uptake of polystyrene nanospheres up to 100 nm with the aid of endocytosis was also reported histologically (161). However, it was insisted that 2-μm microspheres of polystyrene could be taken up through the epithelial cells of the intestine (162). In addition to these convenient routes of intestinal absorption, recent studies have revealed a predominant contribution of M cells on uptake of particulates at the Peyer's patch. Peyer's patch localizes in duodenum, jejunum, and ileum spottily and originally constructs a gut-associated lymphoid tissue in which there are M cells being specially compared with normal absorption cells (163). These M cells possess a high activity of endocytosis that is performed by specific receptors at the surface of its cell membrane. Macromolecules or particulates absorbed by M cells are released into extracellular space, being included by lymphocytes or macrophages, and thus appear in the intestinal lymph nodes (163). The effect of particulate size on their uptake through M cells has been argued by many investigators. In their research, various upper-limit sizes of particulates for uptake into Peyer's patch were reported: 15 μm (164), 10 μm (165), and 3 μm (161). It was also found that although particulates under 5 μm were transferred into the lymphatics, larger particles of 5–10 μm remained in the Peyer's patch (165). Recently, the usefulness of biologically erodable and adhesive particulates (0.1–10 mm) composed of a copolymer of fumaric acid with sebacic acid or lactide-*co*-glycotide was reported for potential oral drug delivery systems (166). These particulates were recognized microscopically to traverse both the intestinal absorptive cells as well as Peyer's patches

and to reach the spleen and liver tissues after lengthy contact with gastrointestinal mucosa. An enhanced exertion of pharmacological effects of three model chemicals (dicumarol, insulin, and plasmid DNA) with widely different molecular weights loaded in these particulates was observed inside the intestinal tissue, in the liver and in the blood. As just mentioned, despite the very limited area of Peyer's patch, microparticles or nanoparticles probably enable the absorption of loaded drugs through M cells. Thus, for drugs designed for lymphatic absorption, uptake through the Peyer's patch is surely significant; however, further examinations are necessary for drugs that require a transfer into systemic circulation. Additionally, the route as well as mechanism of particulate uptake in the intestine is not completely clear, and thus such examinations also should be continued for clinical usage of micro and nanoparticles.

BIBLIOGRAPHY

1. G.H.P. Te Wierik et al., *J. Controlled Release* **45**, 25–33 (1997).
2. L.F. Prescott and W.S. Nimmo, *Novel Drug Delivery and its Therapeutic Application*, Wiley, Chichester, England, 1989.
3. P.R. Katikaneni, S.M. Upadrashta, S.H. Neau, and A.K. Mitra, *Int. J. Pharm.* **123**, 119–125 (1995).
4. Y. Qiu et al., *Int. J. Pharm.* **157**, 43–52 (1997).
5. T. Salsa, F. Veiga, and M.E. Pina, *Drug Dev. Ind. Pharm.* **23**, 929–938 (1997).
6. C. Liu et al., *J. Pharm. Pharmacol.* **47**, 360–364 (1995).
7. Y. Qiu, H. Cheskin, J. Briskin, and K. Engh, *J. Controlled Release* **45**, 249–256 (1997).
8. H. Kim and R. Fassihi, *Pharm. Res.* **14**, 1415–1421 (1997).
9. I.R. Wilding et al., *J. Controlled Release* **33**, 89–97 (1995).
10. J.D. Ntawukulilyayo et al., *Int. J. Pharm.* **139**, 79–85 (1996).
11. A.L. Golub, R.W. Frost, C.J. Betlach, and M.A. Gonzalez, *J. Allergy. Clin. Immunol.* **78**, 689–694 (1986).
12. A.P. Sips et al., *Eur. J. Clin. Pharm.* **26**, 405–407 (1984).
13. O.L. Sprockel, M. Sen, P. Shivanand, and W. Prapaitrakul, *Int. J. Pharm.* **155**, 191–199 (1997).
14. L. Yang and R. Fassihi, *J. Controlled Release* **44**, 135–140 (1997).
15. M. Lagas and J.H.G. Jonkman, *Eur. J. Clin. Pharm.* **24**, 761–767 (1983).
16. M. Lagas and J.H.G. Jonkman, *Int. J. Clin. Pharm. Ther. Toxicol.* **23**, 424–426 (1985).
17. M.P. Danckwerts and J.G. van der Watt, *Int. J. Pharm.* **123**, 85–94 (1995).
18. Y. Raghunathan, L. Amsel, O. Hinsvark, and W. Bryant, *J. Pharm. Sci.* **70**, 379–384 (1981).
19. N.W. Read and K. Sugden, *Crit. Rev. Ther. Drug Carrier Syst.* **4**, 221–263 (1987).
20. M.A. Khan et al., *J. Controlled Release* **37**, 131–141 (1995).
21. R. Jachowicz and E. Nürnberg, *Int. J. Pharm.* **159**, 149–158 (1997).
22. K. Takada et al., *Chem. Pharm. Bull.* **37**, 471–474 (1989).
23. P. Arnaud, I. Guillard, D. Brossard, and J.C. Chaumeil, *Int. J. Pharm.* **129**, 279–282 (1996).
24. I.S. Moussa and L.H. Cartilier, *Int. J. Pharm.* **149**, 139–149 (1997).

25. G. Santus and R.W. Baker, *J. Controlled Release* **35**, 1–21 (1995).

26. L.G.J. de Leede, A.G. de Boer, and D.D. Breimer, *Biopharm. Drug Dispos.* **2**, 131–136 (1981).

27. J.S. Grundy, D.W. Grace, and R.T. Foster, *J. Controlled Release* **44**, 247–254 (1997).

28. S.V. Sastry, I.K. Reddy, and M.A. Khan, *J. Controlled Release* **45**, 121–130 (1997).

29. S.M. Herbig, J.R. Cardinal, R.W. Korsmeyer, and K.L. Smith, *J. Controlled Release* **35**, 127–136 (1995).

30. J.N.C. Healey, in J.G. Haedy, S.S. Davis, and C.G. Wilson, eds., *Drug Delivery to the GastroIntestinal Tract*, Ellis Horwood, Chichester, England, 1989, pp. 83–96.

31. A.A. Deshpande, C.T. Rhodes, N.H. Shah, and A.W. Malick, *Drug Dev. Ind. Pharm.* **22**, 539–547 (1996).

32. W. Hou, S. Miyazaki, and M. Takada, *Yakuzaigaku* **51**, 93 (1991).

33. R. Cargill et al., *Pharm. Res.* **5**, 533–536 (1998).

34. G.A. Agyilirah, M. Green, R. duCret, and G.S. Banker, *Int. J. Pharm.* **75**, 241–247 (1991).

35. S. Bouckaert, L. Vakaet, and J.P. Remon, *Int. J. Pharm.* **130**, 257–260 (1996).

36. R. Khanna, S.P. Agarwal, and A. Ahuja, *Int. J. Pharm.* **138**, 67–73 (1996).

37. Y. Kohda et al., *Int. J. Pharm.* **158**, 147–155 (1997).

38. K. Iga and Y. Ogawa, *J. Controlled Release* **49**, 105–113 (1997).

39. D.O. Thompson, *Crit. Rev. Ther. Drug Carrier Syst.* **14**, 1–104 (1997).

40. E. Albers and B.W. Müller, *Crit. Rev. Ther. Drug Carrier Syst.* **12**, 311–337 (1995).

41. T. Irie and K. Uekama, *J. Pharm. Sci.* **86**, 147–162 (1997).

42. R.A. Rajewski and V.J. Stella, *J. Pharm. Sci.* **85**, 1142–1169 (1996).

43. T. Loftsson and M.E. Brewster, *J. Pharm. Sci.* **85**(10), 1017–1025 (1996).

44. J.R. Moyano, J.M. Ginés, M.J. Arias, and A.M. Rabasco, *Int. J. Pharm.* **114**, 95–102 (1995).

45. M.T. Esclusa-Díaz et al., *Int. J. Pharm.* **142**, 183–187 (1996).

46. M.T. Esclusa-Díaz et al., *Int. J. Pharm.* **143**, 203–210 (1996).

47. V. Lemesle-Lamache, D. Wouessidjewe, M. Chéron, and D. Duchêne, *Int. J. Pharm.* **141**, 117–124 (1996).

48. J. Alvarez-Fuentes et al., *Int. J. Pharm.* **148**, 219–230 (1997).

49. N. Konar and C. Kim, *J. Pharm. Sci.* **86**, 1339–1344 (1997).

50. M. Ishii and T. Tanaka, *Clin. All-Round* **46**, 2336–2342 (1997).

51. C.J. Kenyon et al., *J. Controlled Release* **34**, 31–36 (1995).

52. M. Matsuo, K. Arimori, C. Nakamura, and M. Nakano, *Int. J. Pharm.* **138**, 225–235 (1996).

53. T. Yamamoto and S. Matsuura, *Pharm Tech Jpn* **8**, 1257–1260 (1992).

54. S.J. Burns et al., *Int. J. Pharm.* **134**, 223–230 (1996).

55. M.J. Arias et al., *Int. J. Pharm.* **123**, 25–31 (1995).

56. P. Sheen, V.K. Khetarpal, C.M. Cariola, and C.E. Rowlings, *Int. J. Pharm.* **118**, 221–227 (1995).

57. P.B. Deasy and M.P. Gouldson, *Int. J. Pharm.* **132**, 131–141 (1996).

58. V. Tantishaiyakul, N. Kaewnopparat, and S. Ingkataworn-wong, *Int. J. Pharm.* **143**, 59–66 (1996).

59. T. Ozeki, H. Yuasa, and Y. Kanaya, *Int. J. Pharm.* **155**, 209–217 (1997).

60. S.K. Dordunoo, J.L. Foad, and M.H. Rubinstein, *J. Pharm. Pharmacol.* **48**, 782–789 (1996).

61. M.E. Pina, A.T. Sousa, and A.P. Brojo, *Int. J. Pharm.* **133**, 139–148 (1996).

62. M.E. Pina, A.T. Sousa, and A.P. Brojo, *Int. J. Pharm.* **148**, 73–84 (1997).

63. T. Houjou et al., *J. Pharm. Pharmacol.* **48**, 474–478 (1996).

64. Y. Akiyama et al., *Int. J. Pharm.* **136**, 155–163 (1996).

65. Y. Akiyama et al., *Int. J. Pharm.* **138**, 13–23 (1996).

66. A. Kiriyama et al., *Biopharm. Drug Dispos.* **17**, 125–134 (1996).

67. J. Sujja-Areevath, D.L. Munday, P.J. Cox, and K.A. Khan, *Int. J. Pharm.* **139**, 53–62 (1996).

68. M. Takahashi, *Pharm Tech Jpn.* **8**, 1263–1268 (1992).

69. J.M. Sarciaux, L. Acar, and P.A. Sado, *Int. J. Pharm.* **120**, 127–136 (1995).

70. N.H. Shah et al., *Int. J. Pharm.* **106**, 15–23 (1994).

71. L. Halbaut, C. Barbé, and A. del Pozo, *Int. J. Pharm.* **130**, 203–212 (1996).

72. K.K.C. Tan, A.K. Trull, J.A. Uttridge, and J. Wallwork, *Eur. J. Clin. Pharm.* **48**, 285–289 (1995).

73. M.L. Shively and D.C. Thompson, *Int. J. Pharm.* **117**, 119–122 (1995).

74. L.A. Felton et al., *Int. J. Pharm.* **113**, 17–24 (1995).

75. P.P. Constantinides et al., *J. Controlled Release* **34**, 109–116 (1995).

76. A.J. Humberstone and W.N. Charman, *Adv. Drug Delivery Rev.* **25**, 103–128 (1997).

77. R.R.C. New and C.J. Kirby, *Adv. Drug Delivery Rev.* **25**, 59–69 (1997).

78. R. New et al., *Int. J. Pharm.* **156**, 1–8 (1997).

79. B.J. Aungst et al., *Int. J. Pharm.* **156**, 79–88 (1997).

80. S.G. Barnwell et al., *Int. J. Pharm.* **128**, 145–154 (1996).

81. S.J. Burns et al., *Int. J. Pharm.* **141**, 9–16 (1996).

82. S.J. Burns et al., *Int. J. Pharm.* **121**, 37–44 (1995).

83. P.B. Deasy, *Crit. Rev. Ther. Drug Carrier Syst.* **8**, 39–89 (1991).

84. T. Hata and S. Ueda, *Pharm Tech Jpn* **4**, 1415–1422 (1988).

85. S. Narisawa et al., *J. Controlled Release* **33**, 253–260 (1995).

86. S. Narisawa et al., *Int. J. Pharm.* **148**, 85–91 (1997).

87. B. Wolf, *Int. J. Pharm.* **156**, 97–107 (1997).

88. A.D. Sezer and J.A. Kbugǎ, *Int. J. Pharm.* **121**, 113–116 (1995).

89. Y. Sun, C. Chang, W. Huang, and H. Liang, *J. Controlled Release* **47**, 247–260 (1997).

90. K. Vasilevska, Z. Djurić, M. Jovanović, and A. Simov, *Drug Dev. Ind. Pharm.* **18**, 1649–1655 (1992).

91. V. Gladigau et al., *Arzneim-Forsch.* **31**, 835 (1981).

92. F. Zhou, C. Vervaet, and J.P. Remon, *Int. J. Pharm.* **133**, 155–160 (1996).

93. H.C. Zaniboni, J.T. Fell, and J.H. Collett, *Int. J. Pharm.* **125**, 151–155 (1995).

94. P. Sriamornsak, S. Prakongpan, S. Puttipipatkhachorn, and R.A. Kennedy, *J. Controlled Release* **47**, 221–232 (1997).

95. G.M. Clarke, J.M. Newton, and M.B. Short, *Int. J. Pharm.* **114**, 1–11 (1995).

96. N. Follonier, E. Doelker, and E.T. Cole, *J. Controlled Release* **36**, 243–250 (1995).

as drug delivery systems makes for interesting reading today. These early pioneering authors were apparently unaware that there are huge differences between making an ill-defined suspension of liposomes on a 5 mL scale in the laboratory and to manufacturing a 5,000 liter (or more) batch of a well-defined and well-characterized material suitable for administration to patients with efficacy, safety, and reproducibility. Moreover, these pioneers did not seem to be aware that before patients could receive these complex systems, the systems themselves had to have other basic requirements. Thus, knowledge of the reproducibility of the state of dispersion—not only the mean particle diameter itself but also the way in which the distribution of size was spread around the mean—were essential requirements for any product specification. In addition, because many of these laboratory-scale products were going to be injected directly into the patient, they had to be sterile and apyrogenic, requirements that were evidently of low priority to many of these early workers. Indeed, one early review on parenteral products failed to even mention sterility (10). Eventually, when it became necessary to scale-up these laboratory-scale experiments to make sufficient of a product for sale, issues such as particle size changes associated with chemical degradation of components on autoclaving or thermal effects produced on dispersions became evident and proved to be difficult to resolve for several years. These requirements resulted in significant delays in the development of some liposomal products, in some cases having profound economic consequences on their developers.

These issues have now become evident on hindsight for liposomal products; in fact, they are applicable to any controlled release product intended for parenteral delivery. A general review of issues associated with scale-up has recently appeared and can be strongly recommended as an introduction to the topic (11).

Essential Requirements of Parenteral Products

All parenteral products are designed to bypass the body's natural defenses against microorganism invasion associated with skin and mucosal tissues. Irrespective of the physical nature of the product, be it a simple solution of the drug in water or a complex insertable pump, all parenteral products have some basic requirements to which must be added the general requirements associated with all pharmaceutical products:

1. Sterility
2. Apyrogenicity
3. Reproducibility in performance
4. Safety
5. Efficacy

Methods of achieving *sterility* are reviewed in a later section, but it makes sense not to introduce a pathogenic microorganism into a body that is most likely already debilitated by disease and therefore has lower resistance to bacterial invasion. *Apyrogenicity* is closely associated with the need for sterility because, under some conditions, bacteria or products associated with dead bacteria can produce febrile reactions that are rarely fatal but can be unpleasant for the patient. Moreover, pyrogens can be measured with some precision and accuracy, and low levels of pyrogen infer a low bioburden in the product being tested. *Reproducibility* of the product implies that there is uniformity of drug content, not only in each item produced in a batch but also from batch to batch. The same implication applies to the rates of drug release from the device or system so that ultimately there is a reproducible effect produced on the target tissues over a sufficient and reproducible length of time. *Safety* is also clearly necessary, and even the Hippocratic Oath required that doctors (and their associated medications) do no harm. *Efficacy* is also implied—there would be little point in administering the system otherwise.

Over the past two decades or more, many elegant and ingenious methods for obtaining the controlled release of a wide variety of drugs have been described in the literature; few products based on these methods have actually achieved commercial success. Obviously, one could argue that much of this ingenuity was expended in what were, for the most part, academic exercises designed to train, learn, and stimulate. However, it could also be argued that the intellectual effort expended in this area may have been substantially dissipated by a failure to realize that parenteral products must have these five essential requirements before proceeding to test the devices or systems in humans. Nevertheless, some groups of workers still persist in making impressive claims for potential applications based on experiments involving laboratory experiments on a scale of 5–10 mL or less. Naturally, beginnings have to be made somewhere but one might suggest that these initial claims could have been somewhat muted.

The Importance of Scale-up and Reproducibility

Most of the five essential requirements have been covered by textbooks that are readily available. However, scale-up and reproducibility are generally not covered and the following section provides some pointers.

Parenteral sustained release products are usually dispersions of one phase, often a solid, or a liquid in another liquid phase, usually water. Exceptions are the implanted solid products, which are themselves macroscopic and therefore relatively easy to produce with precision and accuracy. In the same way, characterization in terms of dimensions and performance prior to administration is also straightforward. This is less true for dispersed systems, which are generally much more difficult to make reproducible and characterize with precision and accuracy. Although it is not appropriate to go into this area in more detail, it should be noted that regulatory authorities such as the U.S. FDA rightly demand that production and characterization methods used for human-use products must be validated. The scientific challenge is to prove (and validate) claims made for the product. If the specification calls for a product containing particles 200 nm in diameter, the key question to be answered by the validation process is just how true is that statement? How do different batches of the product compare; are they always 200 nm in diameter (as measured by an appropriate method itself validated as precise and accurate), and how does any batch-to-batch variation in the diameter, if detected, affect performance as measured by a suitable method, preferably in human patients? Scale-up and, to a large degree, reproducibility go hand in hand and should be considered together.

METHODS OF STERILIZATION OF PARENTERAL DRUG DELIVERY SYSTEMS

Introduction

Any material introduced into the body (human or animal) parenterally (that is, *para enteron* or "beyond the gut") should be sterile, because the body defenses have been bypassed. Philosophically, sterilization is quite absolute in concept and means (e.g., *The Concise Oxford Dictionary*) "rendered free of microorganisms"). Certainly it is important that any parenteral "should do no harm." The production of disease or even death by injection of contaminated product is not unknown, and it is certainly not acceptable. Even the production of abscesses following injection, which may ultimately heal, is not acceptable. Many patients receiving parenteral products are doing so because they have a disease or condition that impairs their natural defense mechanisms through the immune system. What would be easily dealt with by a healthy individual often cannot be tolerated by a sick person.

The absolute need for sterility is therefore easy to understand and one can appreciate why regulatory authorities insist on regarding sterility as an absolute concept. Nevertheless, there have been reasons to raise questions about this rigidity of definition because situations have arisen that ultimately lead to confusion. Sterility as such is easy to conceive but, in reality, microorganisms are ubiquitous in the environment and difficult to remove. In a closed system they can be killed by the application of heat or irradiation, but exposed to the environment once again, the product will become contaminated with more viable and therefore equally potentially dangerous microorganisms. The dictionary definition of sterilization, "rendering free of living microorganisms," can be carried out, but now we are becoming more aware of peripheral issues. For example, if we apply some environmental stress to a closed system containing living microorganisms (e.g., heat), how do we know just how much stress we need to apply to kill, or render nonviable, *all* of the microorganisms present? In practice a manufacturer uses a traditional overkill approach, such as autoclaving for 15 minutes at 121°C. These conditions are generally recognized as being sufficient to produce a "sterile" product. But what if the exposure time was only 14 minutes; does that mean the product is no longer sterile and therefore safe to use? How about only 10 minutes exposure to the stress or only 5 minutes?

The issue here is the rigidity of the thinking process and the attitude of regulatory authorities reviewing processing proposals. The absolute approach—15 minutes safe, 14 minutes unsafe—is safe from a regulatory standpoint but scientifically it is unlikely to be valid. A modern solution of a drug, filtered repeatedly through porous membranes down to 100 nm pore size, is "almost sterile," i.e., the bioburden is very low, before it is put into the autoclave, and a much lower heat insult is required to achieve "absolute sterility." To be fair, parametric release is now allowed by some regulatory authorities, and this process takes these considerations into account. There are additional issues if the drug itself is labile and is adversely affected by heat. In that situation it is likely that the solution would need to be "sterile filtered" and filled into a presterilized container in an "aseptic process." However, a filtration process is anything but absolute, and there are issues associated with running a truly satisfactory aseptic process. Here the absolute certainty associated with an overkill heating process is diminished considerably, and one has to start thinking in terms of an acceptable element of risk.

Some of the issues of this dilemma have recently been discussed by Gilbert and Allison (12) and their arguments expanded by Groves (13). The essential point of the argument is that a filtration process is certainly not an absolute process in the sense that, perhaps, a few microorganisms may not have been removed so the filtrate may not be truly sterile. Issues now arise, such as how can such small numbers of microorganisms per unit volume be measured or even detected. Gilbert and Allison pointed out that, in fact, not all microorganisms are pathogenic and are easily dealt with by the body's defense mechanisms or are simply not able to survive in a physiological environment. Moreover, even most pathogens require a sufficient number of organisms to produce some manifestation of disease. There are some interesting exceptions to this point but essentially their argument is that, if we remove most organisms from a product, that product can be regarded as aseptic and is therefore *safe* to use.

As already noted, in practice absolute sterility cannot be achieved in many situations because of the lability of the drug. In addition, because degrees of sterility of a product cannot be measured—it is either sterile or not—we have to start using statistical concepts to estimate the effectiveness of the sterilization process. Many of these concepts were proposed at the turn of the twentieth century with especial reference to foodstuffs, where levels of contamination were often very high and product lethality was a major concern. One must therefore question just how valid these earlier concepts are now when applied to modern pharmaceutical products that, by any standards, are exceptionally clean, so that the initial numbers/unit volume of contaminating microorganisms are very low. A real difficulty is that concepts or probabilities are not scientific *measurements* and many attempts to understand and explain modern ideas on the subject have simply become confused. Judgments are being made based on poor science, and one must suspect that nobody benefits, especially the patient who ultimately pays for all of this confusion.

It is also ironic that novel processes and ideas being used or explored in the food industry today are proving very difficult to translate into what is already a very conservative and economically driven pharmaceutical industry. It is also true that the death rate today due to microbiologically contaminated foodstuffs is finite although small, due to heavy regulation, the death rate in the pharmaceutical industry is infinitely small.

other words, if it works (i.e., if it can be validated to demonstrate effectiveness), that should be sufficient. The chapter actually states that with an article where extensive heat exposure may produce damage, the development of the sterilization process (Chapter ⟨1211⟩ uses the word *cycle*) depends heavily on the knowledge of the microbial burden over a suitable time period of a *substantial* number of lots of the presterilized product. The inference is there; the actuality is not. This means it is up to the manufacturer to present sufficient evidence to the regulatory authorities that any new process is satisfactory for its purpose.

Use (and Abuse) of the Sterility Assurance Level

The sterility assurance level (SAL) is defined (16) as the probability of the nonsterility of a unit from a batch of product in the final container. This author then goes on to explain that it is assumed throughout the parenterals industry and by regulatory authorities such as the FDA that where a process appears to have an SAL of 10^{-3}, approximately 1 vial per 1,000 could be contaminated with microbes.

There are two problems with this. The first is that SAL cannot be measured; it is a concept or probability. The second issue is that, as a concept, it applied to each and every vial in the batch—each vial, for example, has a *chance* of 1:1,000 of being contaminated. It is certainly not acceptable to produce a single contaminated vial in any batch of product, irrespective of the lot size. So where does this concept come from and how may it be used correctly?

It should be noted that D values for any microorganism are characteristics of the applied heat stress. A typically resistant endospore-forming organism such as *Bacillus stearothermophilus* has a D value of 1.5 minutes at 121°C, much longer at lower temperatures, and, typically, vegetative organisms have D values well below 1 minute at a temperature of 100°C. If we set the sterilization criteria at 6D and the actual, measured, D value is 4.5 minutes, and, if the initial solution contains 100 organisms mL, it will take $4.5 \times 6 = 27$ minutes at 121°C to reduce the count to one-millionth of the original count. The SAL is 100/1,000,000 or 10^{-4}. Under the same conditions, if the initial viable count in the product was 1 organism/mL, and, assuming a worst-case scenario, the SAL then drops to 1/1,000,000 or 10^{-6}. Sterility assurance is therefore a direct function of the number or organisms initially present in the product to be sterilized.

Again, SAL values cannot be measured directly, even in a heat sterilization process, and when talking about SALs for aseptic processes or other less dramatic sterilization processes, one is strictly speaking talking about a concept, not a precise entity. The concept has become abused, with "experts" speaking of the numbers of contaminated containers to be found in a production process. If there is a SAL of 10^{-6}, in principle one of the containers in a batch size of one million could be contaminated. Should the batch size be higher than a million, this implies that the lot has one or more contaminated units in it. The issue becomes more personal when considering that aseptically assembled products are required to have an SAL of 10^{-3} or better and are made in batch sizes that might suggest several

containers could be contaminated. This concept has encouraged regulatory authorities to insist on media fills to "validate" a particular aseptic process. If more than one "contaminated" sample appears in a run of 3,000, the process is considered to be unsatisfactory. One could argue that any contaminated sample in any run, irrespective of the size, is unacceptable and the fact that these guidelines have been written at all is an indication of just how far away the technology is from the older overkill situation of terminal heat sterilization. Application of the same concept to totally different and dissimilar processes would appear to be poor science and is certainly not justified.

Nevertheless, what the SAL is effectively doing is to suggest that there is a *chance* that every single vial in the batch has a *possibility* of being contaminated; it does not mean that there are going to be *x* vials in the batch that are contaminated. Nevertheless, the principle of a complete, validated process designed to reduce the presterilization bioburden to its lowest feasible level, together with a worst-case scenario in terms of the thermal resistance of any possible microbial contaminant is quite scientifically reasonable, but there must be emphasis on validation. Although the discussion here has tended to be concerned with a heat-stress situation, the same broad concepts apply to any other sterilization process.

Sterilization Using Gases

An attractive alternative to the application of heat stress is the use of reactant gases that are able to permeate a product and sterilize *surfaces*. The commonest gaseous sterilant at present is ethylene oxide, which is extremely effective, albeit a little slow compared with heat stress. The gas itself is highly flammable and must be mixed with suitable inert carrier gases such as nitrogen. Moreover, the mode of action depends on the humidity, concentration of sterilant, and time of exposure. The gas is also harmful to humans because of its mutagenic properties. The process, usually carried out in a sealed pressurized chamber, essentially similar to an autoclave, is designed to ensure that the product is exposed to the ethylene oxide without at the same time exposing the operators to even small residues of gas. After the sterilization process has been carried out in the presence of the required level of humidity for the requisite amount of time, often for 16 hours overnight at ambient room temperature, the residual gas must be removed by pulling a vacuum and passing sterile nitrogen through the system, again for the necessary amount of time. Sterilized product is often allowed to stand under atmospheric conditions to ensure that the last traces of gas have been removed, because even small amounts can be toxic or irritant. This is especially true for surgical dressing materials.

Again, the USP 23 emphasizes the need for adequate validation of the designed process, placing emphasis on using appropriate biological indicators such as *Bacillus subtilis* spores. Other gases have been evaluated, including β-propriolactone, but toxicity to equipment operators was unacceptably high and better alternatives are being sought.

Again, gases are useful for sterilizing surfaces, although the gas may permeate into some polymeric materials. In these cases this permeation through and below the surface only makes it even more difficult to remove gaseous residues.

Other Methods Used To Sterilize Surfaces

The surfaces of containers and the interior of barriers where sterilized components are aseptically assembled also need to be sterilized. Containers made of glass can be heat sterilized, often in hot air tunnels through which the containers pass on their way into the aseptic assembly area. Stoppers or seals, often made of natural rubber or suitable polymers, cannot be dry-heat sterilized but can be washed and autoclaved, often in smaller quantities enclosed in plastic bags to enable them to be more readily transported to the assembly area. An alternative is ethylene oxide gas, but this is more rarely used because of the associated difficulty of removing residual gas after exposure.

Barrier technology has been developed over the past decade for aseptic processes. It effectively places a barrier between the human operators, who are the main source of bacterial and particulate contamination, and the product being assembled by providing a blanket of sterile filtered air moving under laminar flow conditions. More and more computer-controlled robotic assembly processes are being employed inside the barrier but all of these surfaces need sterilization. Where robotic arms are moving this becomes more difficult because moving surfaces must have lubrication and the lubricants may react with some if not most of the chemically reactive materials used to sterilize the internal environment. Foremost amongst current sterilants are sprays or mists generated with steam of concentrated hydrogen peroxide, which is an extremely effective material but is equally a strong oxidizing agent. Surfaces under barriers are generally composed of stainless steel, poly(methyl methacrylate), or other transparent polymers. All materials used to construct barrier and isolates must be able to withstand hydrogen peroxide and, in the case of steam-generated mists, temperatures in excess of 100°C for at least the period required during the clean or sterilize in place cycle. Not only are moving surfaces of, for example, fans and pumps affected by the sterilants but sensors, and flexible materials such as rubber or latex gloves, may be affected. In addition, barrier systems require transfer ports. The evident complexity of an effective barrier system requires an integrative approach to its design and construction. Some of the issues involved are described by Melgaard and Haas (17), and this can be considered to be a rapidly developing subject.

Other sterilant gases are probably unsuitable for plastic and stainless steel constructions because chlorine and chlorides are known to attack stainless steel surfaces. Sprays of alcohols, phenols, and detergent bactericides, although less corrosive, are also less effective. The main advantage of steam or peroxide is that no residue is left, and the degradation products are environmentally acceptable water and oxygen.

Formaldehyde and glutaraldehyde are effective sterilants for surfaces but may leave residues. However, these materials are also used as cross-linking agents in the preparation of some particulate drug delivery systems such as those involving albumin, gelatin, or chitosan. It is tempting to suggest that bacterial bioburden during processing with these materials would most likely be reduced but this does not appear to have been demonstrated in practice.

The use and effectiveness of other chemical sterilant systems was recently reviewed by Olson (18).

Sterilization by Filtration

Because many drugs, especially those produced by the new biotechnology, are heat-labile, cold sterilization through appropriate filters has been widely employed. Many microorganisms can be physically removed from liquid products, and gases may also be filtered free of microorganisms. An assembly for filtration usually incorporates a porous matrix, sealed or clamped into a suitable nonporous holder, but the assembly needs to be considered as a whole. Groves (19) noted that the criteria for an ideal filter depends on the nature of the product to be filtered, but the following attributes are generally desirable:

1. A filter should be absolute in the sense that there should be a known limit to the size of the particles in the filtrate.
2. There should be an independent means of checking the efficiency of the filter.
3. The filtration process should not be materially affected by the pressure differential across it or pressure fluctuations produced by the pumping of fluids through it.
4. The filtration medium should not affect the product.
5. The filtration system as a whole should be capable of being sterilized by heat or gas.
6. It should be economical in use.

Unfortunately, there is no ideal filtration medium and, as described by Groves (19) and Olson (20), the whole area has been confused by overenthusiastic sales personnel for the various media, not by any means confined to one commercial source. The novice reader is therefore enjoined to use much caution when reviewing sales literature in this area.

Physically one can envision the passage of suspended particles through a porous matrix until the particles become trapped when the pore becomes smaller than the particle, a sieving mechanism. Although broadly true, some filters have a surface charge that also helps to trap particles carrying an opposite charge. Asbestos fiber filters, for example, carry a strong electropositive charge that helps to collect microorganisms, which often have an electronegative charge, depending to some degree on the pH of the continuum. Asbestos fiber filters are not used today because of concerns about possible toxicity, but the same type of charge–charge interaction may well help modern membrane filters to remove particles that are much smaller than the nominal size of the filter.

Membrane matrices are now available in a wide variety of materials, including cellulose derivatives and polymers, and have different porosities. Selection of a filter depends on the requirements of the process and compatibility with the product. Some membranes are claimed to be "absolute" in the sense already discussed, but this term is probably best avoided because the underlying science remains, even today, somewhat uncertain. Even very carefully regulated and controlled production processes result in filtration matrices with a range of pore sizes, although the range in some cases may be narrow. So-called anisotropic membranes, with coarser pores on the face of the filter decreasing in size to very small pores at the exit, are useful in effectively behaving like a staked pair of filters, one coarse and the other fine, but *all* filters have a range of pore sizes. To talk of a membrane filter with a pore size of 200 nm is misleading in an absolute sense because, in reality, the pores probably range in size from 100 to 300 nm diameter. One absolute sense would be to demonstrate that there was no pore larger than 200 nm present in the membrane, but it is not likely that a filter manufacturer would make that claim today. Instead, manufacturers have taken to claiming, again absolutely, that the filtrate will not contain particles larger than the 200 nm diameter, or whatever size is being claimed. This now becomes a performance issue that, in the case of 200-nm membranes, can be validated by challenging the sterilized filter with a suspension of 60 or fewer cm^2 filter area *Pseudomonas diminuta* organisms. This microorganism, when grown in unstirred saline–lactose broth, grows to a diameter of around 250–300 nm and is, as noted earlier, a worst-case scenario. Nevertheless, as discussed by Olson (20), if the filter is challenged with more than 60 organisms/cm^2 of filter, passage usually occurs. The use of filtration as an absolute sterilization procedure is therefore affected by the conditions of use. As noted by Olson (20), passage of particulate through a porous medium can almost certainly be considered as a probalitistic process, the higher the challenge the more likely particles are going to pass through. The success or otherwise of a terminal sterilization process therefore depends on the degree of the challenge, and this means that the bioburden prior to sterilization must be reduced to very low levels before the sterilization process is applied. This is a situation that will be familiar when considering heat sterilization, and the analogy is probably reasonably close.

These issues apart, some microorganisms are very likely to pass through filtration matrices, especially viruses. Although it may be true that many are removed by adsorption onto the medium surface as they pass across the charged surface of the matrix, this cannot be quantitated or relied on. Filtration is therefore anything but an absolute process and needs to be carefully designed into any cold sterilization process.

The Concept of "Size" Applied to the Filtration Process

Most bacteria have sizes somewhat larger than 1 μm, but spherical forms, with an unique dimension (diameter) defining size with precision, are generally only found in endospores which have diameters varying from 400 nm to 1 μm. Viruses are considerably smaller, with diameters of 50–100 nm, and fungi are often larger than 20 μm. The range of size to be removed from the system being filtered is therefore at least three orders of magnitude, varying from, say, 50 nm to 50 μm. This immediately suggests that the solid phase separation needs to be carried in stages, removing first the large particles with coarse screens, followed sequentially by smaller and smaller screens. Conventional wisdom suggests that final screens with pore sizes of 0.2 μm (200 nm) or even better 100 nm are required to remove most, if not all, of the biological particulate matter. When sterilizing a solution by this method, this size must be regarded as being a *maximum* size as determined by some externally applied physical test such as measurement by a mercury intrusion test or gaseous or liquid flow method. This consideration is important because in any filter surface a range of pore sizes is present, some large and some small, and obviously, it is the largest pore diameter that determines which is the smallest size of particle that will be retained on or in the surface. Very few membranes have uniformly sized pores, which may also vary in size as one passes from the front of the membrane to the rear. An exception to this may be found in the Nuclepore™ membranes made by weakening the structure of a polycarbonate film by etching the track left by exposure to neutron particles to remove damaged polymer. Another exception are glass membranes made by stacking bundles of acid-resistant and acid-soluble glass rods together. The acid-soluble glass is dissolved out to leave parallel and uniform pores in the sheets. In practical terms, although the maximum pore sizes represent a limit to the performance of the filter, in fact there are other considerations that affect the performance, including environmental factors such as pH and electrolyte concentration. These factors influence the electrical charge on the surface of the membrane or on the bacteria themselves, and electrostatic adsorption, quite apart from physical screening, is a mechanism by which particles much smaller than the nominal opening or pore size can be retained by the membrane.

Practical use of these types of membranes is substantially limited by the support equipment. Large filter surfaces can be wound onto cartridge-type filters that are connected to other filters or to other equipment. Flat filters made of cellulose or plastics need to be carefully supported by metal perforated screens, and a single hole in the entire system is a source of contamination because bacterial particles pass onto the product filtrate or are drawn in from the surrounding atmosphere. For this reason, performance tests designed to detect unusually large holes in a complete filtration system (filtration surfaces and supports) have been designed. These include bubble testing, in which gas is forced under pressure through the system wetted with product, the pressure at which bubbles are first detected being a measure of the largest hole.

Some microorganisms are capable of growing through or insinuating themselves through the porous filtration medium. This is especially true of protoplasts, which lack the rigid walls of most bacteria. Currently, a recommended pore size of 200 nm for a sterilizing filter is being advocated because there are forms of *Pseudomonas diminuta* that grow under certain conditions to be around 250 nm in diameter, thereby providing a useful challenge for the system. Nevertheless, it is noticeable that newer filters of 100-nm nominal diameter are being employed for sterilization of biotechnological products, in part because virus removal at this level becomes more efficient. However, an important requirement is to use stacked or sequential filters, passing the solution through the coarsest first back down to the finest. Nevertheless, there must always be doubts that filtration is an absolute sterilization process. The best that can be said is that the process is aseptic, following the argument put forward by Gilbert and Allison (12).

Sterilization by Ionizing Radiation

Although it was rapidly realized that ionizing radiation reduced bacterial counts, there was some uncertainty about the dose needed to achieve sterility. Two types of ionizing radiation are in use, γ irradiation from radioisotope decay and electron beam radiation. γ radiation is usually carried out by exposing the product to a source of ionizing radiation such as cobalt 60 (^{60}Co) or cesium 137 (^{137}Cs). Electron beam sources are usually Van de Graaff generators in some form, and X-rays may also be used. The same amount of energy is delivered slowly by a ^{60}Co source but very rapidly as an electron beam, and it is important to validate the product for a specific type of radiation to be used. Reed and Fairand (21) noted that when ^{60}Co radiation was first introduced there was general agreement that high absorbed doses of at least 25 kGy were necessary, but these became associated with color and viscosity changes, and in some cases undesirable chemical changes were also observed. As experience developed, it became evident that much smaller doses could achieve sterility without degradation. Taken with current advances in aseptic processing and the reduction of bioburden before sterilization, smaller radiation doses are likely to be required, but validation on a case-by-case basis is still required.

Radiation has a large number of advantages over other methods of sterilization. It is operated in the cold and radiation penetrates both product and container, so sealed containers and their bulk packages can be treated as one. The process does require investment in significant capital equipment, but it has a long and effective life, it is quiet and environmentally acceptable, and minimal maintenance is required, unlike that required for steam autoclaves. The process is now accepted as being cost-effective and experience gained in the treatment of foodstuffs and cosmetics has been successfully applied to pharmaceutical products.

Pulsed Light Sterilization

As part of a technology developed during the Star Wars initiative, the use of very short pulses of high-intensity, broad-spectrum white light is a technology that may become more widespread. The light has approximately the same spectrum width as sunlight but is actually richer in ultraviolet light since same ultraviolet light is usually filtered out by the earth's atmosphere. However, the intensity is 20,000 times brighter than sunlight but the pulse may only last a few milliseconds. Produced by condenser discharge through appropriate lamps, the light is a form of nonionizing radiation and appears to be very effective at rapidly sterilizing surfaces contaminated with vegetative and spore-forming organisms. One advantage of light

is that the intensity may be increased by focusing with mirrors to a point or target of the application. This means that individual containers in a production line may be sterilized as they pass through an appropriately designed tunnel, which is readily incorporated into a production line. The cost of incorporation of this type of device would therefore be minimal.

If the container is translucent to the ultraviolet radiation, the technique can be used to sterilize the contents. For example, plastic ampoules are transparent, and the method is being applied to automated filling lines associated with blow, fill, and seal methods. However, it may not work with glass ampoules because the appropriate ultraviolet wavelengths are filtered out, but development work in this area is ongoing. The Pure Bright® technique was reviewed in more detail by Dunn (22) and may be a valuable technique for sterilization of some types of packaging materials on a continuous basis.

Aseptic Processing

Aseptic processing is the assembly of a product using components sterilized by different methods in a suitable aseptic environment designed to minimize or totally eliminate contamination of the product. There is no final sterilization of the sealed container; it is assumed that sterility has been designed into the product. Now very widely used in the pharmaceutical industry, Groves and Murty (23) suggested that as many as 87% of parenteral products were being aseptically assembled. The likelihood is that, as more and more thermolabile products enter the marketplace, this number will increase. Regulatory agencies went on record a decade ago, requiring terminal sterilization unless the product was demonstrated to be labile. This was not a particularly timely move although the FDA still does not allow a large volume parenteral (100 mL or more in volume) to be assembled aseptically.

An aseptic process usually consists of filling a thoroughly filtered solution of a drug, the final filtration being regarded as a sterilization process, into glass or plastic vials sterilized by dry heat or gas and sealing these containers with rubber plugs sterilized batchwise using moist heat. A series of steps are required to bring the components to the assembly area, put them together in an aseptic environment, and remove the final product to the open environment. The success of an aseptic filling operation critically depends on the successful operation of the individual steps but must be considered as a whole. The entire operation needs careful and consistent planning and operation, with constant monitoring. Final and ongoing validation represents an essential stage that is often extremely difficult to carry out satisfactorily. The complete operation is operator-dependent, which means that the operators not only have to be properly trained but also have to know how to apply methodologies thoroughly documented in standard operating procedures that are such a critical element in GMP. It can be seen that an aseptic process is where all of these regulatory requirements come together. Nevertheless, some agencies, including the FDA, require validation to be carried out using media fills in which sterile growth media instead of actual product is passed through the system. In some ways it can be seen that this might be a proof of concept; to actually validate the process itself is an exercise in futility. First of all, the final product, with some exceptions, is unlikely to resemble a fluid culture medium. Secondly, the growth medium does not necessarily demonstrate a failure or breakdown in the system, because the level of contamination may be very low, and contaminating microorganisms may not grow rapidly enough to be visibly evident in the medium after only a few days incubation. Finally, it seems ludicrous to suggest that 1 contaminated vial in a media fill of 3,000 is satisfactory, because it indicates a SAL of less than 1 in 1,000. Surely *any* contamination is unsatisfactory, and SALs, being a statistical concept, are not measurable directly.

Improvements in system design, especially those involving the use of robotic and barrier technologies designed to eliminate human contact, have certainly increased confidence in the effectiveness of aseptic processing. Nevertheless, it is probably time to reexamine the concepts of Gilbert and Allison (12) and attempt to *measure* the risks involved in aseptic processing. Given the very low incidence of microbiological issues associated with the parenteral administration of millions of aseptically prepared products worldwide over 80 years or more, the issue may have become more remote.

STERILE IMPLANTS

Protein Compacts

One of the oldest drug delivery systems is the pellet or tablet produced by compaction or extrusion of powdered drug together with appropriate excipients. Tabletting technology is not confined to the pharmaceutical industry but the technology is exceptionally well developed and is both simple and inexpensive in its basic form. Generally applied to low molecular weight drugs for oral administration, tabletted proteins are also employed in a number of nonpharmaceutical industries. Compacted proteinaceous materials such as enzymes are used in dairying, fermentation, brewing, fruit processing, wine making, milling, baking, starch production, and detergent applications. All have been prepared as tablets as a convenient form for handling and ensuring accurate dosage as well as improved storage and transportation. With the advent of the newer highly biologically active proteinaceous drugs, this pharmaceutical presentation has assumed a major challenge. This is especially true for proteins or polypeptides for oral administration. For example, Saffran et al. (24,25) claimed that vasopressin or insulin in enteric-coated gelatin capsules were active orally, although these observations do not appear to have been confirmed. Nevertheless, compaction of dried proteins appears to allow them to retain much of their native conformation and, therefore, biological activity. They are readily protected from moisture when suitably packaged. Azain et al. (26) described prolonged release devices for parenteral administration of somatotropins and Oppenheim et al. (27) suggested that protein compacts could be used for subdermal administration. In both cases the final product must be sterilized using an appropriate procedure.

Effects Produced by Compaction of Proteins

During compaction the protein molecule is subjected to both pressure and shear (and possibly heat) that could result in reversible or irreversible denaturation. Most studies of denaturation have been carried out on protein solutions. Tirrel and Middleman (28), for example, showed that the jack bean urease-catalyzed urea hydrolysis reaction was both reversible and irreversible, depending entirely on the rate of shear and the presence or absence of additives such as glycerol or ethylene diamine tetra acetic acid. Similar results have been reported for lactic hydrogenase, peptidases, and rennet, and amongst the genetically engineered proteins, human growth hormone is known to be denatured by mild shearing conditions. These are all believed to be due to the hydrodynamic induction of conformational changes at the molecular level. There are relatively few published studies of dried protein compacts and the effects induced by the compaction process or the complex three-dimensional structure of a protein, especially as measured by the changes produced on subsequent biological activity. Graf and co-workers (29–31) studied the effect of compactional pressure on pancreatin and showed that a slight loss of activity occurred at 500 MPa, the minimum pressure needed to form a compact. However, this loss of activity was mitigated by incorporation of pharmaceutical adjuvants such as lubricants and diluents normally employed to make acceptable tablets. These observations would suggest, in retrospect, that solid-state shear caused loss of activity in an analogous fashion to that observed in the solution state. However, most authors agreed that compactional pressure produced some degree of adverse effects on biologically active proteins. Groves and Teng (32) reviewed earlier work and described their own investigations on the compaction of four enzymes with widely disparate molecular weights and functionalities. Working over a much wider range of compactional pressures, urease, lipase, α-amylase, and β-glucuronidase were all shown to be affected by pressure, although to different extents. More to the point, the mechanism of loss of biological activity was evidently different in each case. For example, α-amylase and β-glucuronidase both lost their α-helix structures, whereas the secondary structures of urease and lipase were unaffected. The molecular weight of urease showed an increase, suggesting effects on both tertiary and quaternary structures. The 30% loss of activity observed with lipase could not be correlated with any structural changes measured by sodium dodecyl sulfate-polyacrylamide gel electrophoresis (SDS-PAGE) or circular dichroism (CD) methods, indicating that, whatever structural changes had actually occurred were too subtle to be detected directly. In all cases limiting compactional densities were observed. This lead to the proposal that the mechanism of activity loss was due to a reduction of the space in between the molecules or particles, irrespective of the source of the protein. Compacting at different rates or holding pressures for different times had no measurable effect on activity loss, showing in these cases that thermal energy inactivation was not responsible for activity loss. Water adsorption onto dried proteins was also shown to be influential on the subsequent properties of compacts, especially the rate of release of the active component into an aqueous environment.

As noted, the range of pressures tested were in excess of pressures normally required to make serviceable compacts, and the additional of appropriate pharmaceutical adjuvants was not evaluated. Activity losses ranged from 50% (urease) at 190 MPa to 15% (β-glucuronidase) at 290 MPa, pressures well inside the approximately 500 MPa required to form a compact. Nevertheless, one can be optimistic about the issue because if a loss of activity of a biologically active protein is detected it would appear that the effect can be minimized by judicious selection of diluents and lubricants making up the rest of the tablet composition. However, it should be noted that if a compressed protein was required for parenteral use, the usual pharmaceutical diluents and formulation adjuvants used for orally administered tablets would be unlikely to be suitable. This may apply to fatty acid derivates, such as magnesium stearate, and certainly applies to the talc when used as a lubricant. Alternative adjuvants and diluents are available but should be selected with care. Indeed, in some cases, they may not be needed.

If a protein was to be compressed and a loss of biological activity was demonstrated, it would be necessary to totally evaluate the mechanism of degradation, to find methods of minimizing the effect, and to carry out a complete investigation of the influence of the presence of resultant degradation products on the biological behavior of the compact. Appropriate analytical methodologies are certainly more widely available today, and this type of investigation would be a normal part of providing a complete characterization of what is likely to be a complex drug entity.

Sterilization of Protein Compacts

The safest way of producing a sterile protein drug implant would be to operate the entire process aseptically, starting with sterile filtration of a solution of the drug and aseptic lyophilization to provide a sterile solid. If a diluent were needed, this could be added to the solution of the drug prior to the sterile filtration process. Suitable diluents such as lactose or mannitol are unlikely to be available as bulk sterile products so it would be necessary to go through the same process, especially if the diluent was required to be added as a separate entity. The compaction equipment would need to have metal surfaces cleaned and sterilized, which could be achieved with a gaseous sterilant such as ethylene oxide. The use of halogen oxides or hydrogen peroxide as gas or mist is likely to be corrosive to most metal surfaces and therefore unsuitable for sterilization of the compaction surfaces. Aseptic manipulation using barrier technology has certainly become more widely accepted in recent years, and providing the equipment was dedicated to this function, it should be an acceptable procedure. Shangraw (33) suggested that a dedicated single punch tablet machine was likely to be used but, more recently, extrusion of the material has been preferred, using poly(ethylene glycol) 6,000 as an external lubricant. Direct sterilization of the compact by heat is unlikely to be effective or acceptable but γ-radiation is a possibility, providing the drug itself is not damaged or the vehicle affected in terms of its performance such as release/time pattern.

Polymeric Implants

Polymeric implants are commonly prepared from hydrogels, silicone rubbers, or other biocompatible materials. Hydrogels generally have an advantage in that they are able to swell in an aqueous medium without necessarily dissolving. This capacity for water is useful in that it promotes or improves compatibility with body tissues but it has been suggested that incorporated low molecular weight drug substances are able to diffuse out of the device without necessarily being rate-controlled.

Implants are usually introduced subcutaneously using a surgical procedure. The need for surgery is an obvious disadvantage but, conversely, the device can also be removed when required or when exhausted of drug, which is an advantage. Numerous shapes have been explored, from plates, long rods, and short rods to spheres, and newer bioerodable matrixes are coming into use. For example, poly(lactide-co-glycolide) (PLGA) was originally developed as an absorbable suture so that it has obvious advantages as an implant containing a drug. The Norplant device has been introduced in which silicon rubber rods containing levonorsgestrel have been implanted under the skin with the aid of a local anesthetic. For additional information see the chapter FERTILITY CONTROL.

Subdermal injection of small rods or cylinders or even spheres through a cannula has some advantages, and these devices have also been evaluated clinically.

Sterilization of Polymeric Implants

Polymeric implants are readily made by extrusion of powdered components but application of heat would melt the polymer and affect the release properties of the device, assuming that the drug itself was stable enough for the purpose. γ-irradiation is effective and commonly used for this purpose because of the great deal of experience in the sterilization, for example, of PLGA suture threads. Oxidizing gases such as peroxides are not suitable for sterilization of surfaces because, with a bioerodable implant, there is a need to sterilize throughout the structure of the implant, not just its surface. Moreover, there is a real danger that these reactive chemicals produce chemical changes at the interface of both the biopolymer and its incorporated drug. One group has suggested that a volatile sterilant such as chlorbutanol be incorporated in the matrix, which is then removed by exposing the final product to a temperature of 80°C, preferably for a long time and under vacuum (34).

Implants, being introduced under the skin and exposed to a biological environment, must not irritate the tissues surrounding them or produce an infected or sterile abscess. Sometimes this may be due to the polymer alone. For example, PLGA hydrolyzes to lactic and glycolic acids, which in the high concentration immediately adjacent to the surface of the dissolving implant, may become irritating. However, one possibility here would be to insert the implant into muscle where the tissue environment is normally acidic due to lactic acid production.

lipid core surrounded by phospholipids, together with adsorbed protein. He envisaged an artificial chylomicron made of natural triglycerides, obtained from soybean oil, as an example, emulsified and stabilized with phospholipids purified from avian egg yolks. Wretlind went to a great deal of trouble to obtain and specific highly purified materials, and it was even rumored that he specified eggs from one particular source collected at the same time of the year to ensure that the natural and therefore variable constitution of the separated egg phospholipids were reproducible. The importance of storage conditions for the system was established and it was shown that these homogenized emulsions, with mean droplet diameters of 200–400 nm, were stable enough to be sterilized by autoclaving without the catastrophic destabilization that is characteristic of most other emulsions when heated. Indeed, it was later shown that the particle size of a heat-sterilized emulsion actually decreased, suggesting that structural changes were occurring in the emulsion or at the oil–water interface as a result of the application of heat (43). These considerations resulted in the realization that injectable emulsions can be terminally heat-sterilized, and this observation has contributed to confidence in their clinical application.

Phospholipid-stabilized emulsions have been used clinically for almost 40 years as nutritional supplements, for the most part without serious clinical problems. Their clinical usage is clearly understood, and limitations in their application are well recognized. Moreover, other manufacturers have marketed similar systems with artificial short-chain triglycerides, safflower or olive oils, and phospholipids obtained from soybean. The potential for the use of these emulsions as drug delivery systems is considerable, and a number of emulsion-based products are now in the marketplace.

For successful clinical application as a nutritional product or drug delivery system, an emulsion must be:

1. Miscible with blood and body tissues
2. Compatible with both blood and body tissues
3. Sterile
4. Nonpyrogenic
5. Prepared with droplets small enough not to pose a potential for forming embolisms
6. Fully metabolizable
7. Isotonic
8. Stable, both physically and chemically

For the most part, the aqueous phase does not provide a problem if it is Water for Injection (USP) or, more accurately, Water for Injections (BP). The tonicity is provided by adding a small amount of glycerol, and the initial pH is adjusted to around 8.0 with sodium hydroxide.

The oil phase, coming as it does from a natural source such as soybean oil, can vary in composition, and the Swedish workers associated with Wretlind (41) found that soybean oil could be fractionated and purified by cooling and filtration to remove the waxes, unsaponifiable matter, and higher-molecular weight entities usually found in the expressed oil. Oils with aliphatic unsaturated centers are prone to air oxidization so precautions have to be taken to avoid degradation. Natural oils usually contain antioxidants such as tocopherols, and either these are allowed to remain or are added after purification (44). Triglycerides are readily metabolizable and the differences between commercial products tend to lie on the distribution and degree of unsaturation of the various fatty acids. In Table 1, the Intralipid soy oil and Liposyn safflower and soy oil formulae are compared; the linolenic acid, deficient in the Liposyn II brand, was later determined to be an essential fatty acid. As noted, emulsions are intrinsically unstable, and a stabilizer, surfactant, or emulsifier is required to stabilize the dispersion. Most surfactants commercially available are unsuitable for parenteral administration because they have a potential to cause hemolysis and other direct manifestations of toxicity. Moreover, most stabilized emulsions break when heated, often due to significant movement of the interfacial material into one phase or another as the solubility characteristics change with temperature. Phospholipid stabilizers, on the other hand, are unusual in that the interface between the oil and water phases becomes more stable after heating. This effect was investigated by Groves and Herman (45,46). When freshly prepared, an emulsion system stabilized with an egg phospholipid containing phosphatidylcholine (PC), phosphatidylethanolamine (PE), and their respective lyso-derivatives had the phosphatides roughly equally distributed in the aqueous bulk phase and at the oil interface. On heating there was an irreversible movement of the PE and PC toward the oil phase and from the aqueous compartment. It was suggested that this could have been due to the heat-induced formation of an interfacial cubic liquid crystalline phase. There is some parallel evidence for this type of reaction in isolated systems although, in a true emulsion, this has proven difficult to investigate. Cubic phase material, forming a mesophase at the oil–water interface, would then revert to a semiviscous mesophase lamellar liquid crystal, and indeed the two may coexist as an equilibrium mesophasic composition. This organization of interfacial material was held to account for the unexpected enhanced stability of sterilized phospholipid stabilized emulsions during sterilization. When investigating the stability of freshly prepared emulsions to lysine, a known water structure-modifier, stability was markedly enhanced when the emulsion was heated even under relatively mild conditions for a sufficiently long period (47,48).

Emulsification. Direct emulsification involves application of shear energy to two separate immiscible liquids (for

Table 1. Distribution of Fatty Acids From the Triglycerides of Intralipid and Liposyn Intravenous Emulsions

Fatty acid	Intralipid (g/100 g)	Liposyn (g/100 g)
Linoleic acid (C18:2)	54	77
Oleic	26	13
Palmitic (C16)	9	7
Linoleic acid (C18:3)	8	—
Stearic (C18)	3	2.5

example, oil and water) in order to produce small droplets of one phase dispersed in the continuous phase. Inevitably a stabilizing agent is required to prevent (or at least minimize) coalescence of the dispersed drops back to their preferred condition for minimal energy (i.e., as a completely separated layer, one floating on top of the other). Properties of the stabilizing agents employed as systems used for parenteral administration vary widely although for the most part purified egg or soy phospholipids are considered suitable. Because phospholipids are not truly soluble in either oil or water, forming dispersions in both phases, they are often to be found at the oil–water interface. This interface is structurally complex, and these properties are essential for the stability of the dispersion, although at present knowledge and understanding of this arena is less than perfect. Application of shear forces to dispersed droplets often has the effect of decreasing the droplet size, probably down to the limiting surface coverage of the emulsifier. Below this monolayer (or even multilayer) coverage, the droplets are not stable and quickly coalesce to the minimum size of particle under the conditions of manufacture. Other factors are involved, in particular the interface surface tension between the disperse and continuous phases. In addition, relative viscosity of the two phases is most probably involved, as is the relative density.

Shear forces can be applied by a number of methods, including simple stirring, high speed stirring, and pumping through small orifices.

One factor that needs to be mentioned is the phase behavior of the dispersed droplets. Usually these are assumed to be liquids, capable of demonstrating internal fluidity or movement. In point of fact, as droplets get smaller internal circulation becomes limited, and the droplets start to behave as if they were solid. This behavior is facilitated by the properties of the external mesophasic stabilizing layers, which are often viscous to the point of being semisolid, and these properties also inhibit internal circulation inside the liquid droplet. For all practical purposes, therefore, dispersed droplets, especially in the submicrometer region, behave like solid spheres or particles. This has not prevented some authors from claiming special properties for systems made of waxes or high melting point oils. From a manufacturing perspective, at elevated temperatures these systems consist of molten waxes or liquid oil droplets dispersed in water, and these liquid droplets cool to solid particles at room temperature after dispersion. Known and widely used in the cosmetic industry for many years, these systems undoubtably have potential as drug delivery systems. A recent paper (44) has demonstrated that high melting point trilaurin nanoparticles formulated with phospholipids were effectively similar in composition to phospholipid-stabilized emulsions with phospholipid bilayers wrapped around the central lipid core. Like the liquid lipid emulsions, these solid lipid systems have the potential to trap hydrophobic guest molecules in the phospholipid bilayers, with hydrophilic materials being held in the aqueous spaces.

Surface-Modified Emulsions. The physiological compatibility, together with their optimal chemical and physical stability profiles, make phospholipid-stabilized emulsions

valuable parenteral drug delivery systems (49). It is inevitable that these systems should be compared with liposomes, and indeed the analogy is close when considered from the external surface view of the two systems. However, the interior structure differs, and it is the liquid triglyceride droplet that is the characteristic feature of the more stable emulsions systems. Some authors have claimed that solid lipid dispersions differ from liquid–liquid emulsions (44). This is not likely from a physical perspective because, as noted earlier, small liquid droplets behave physically as solid particles in the same size range. In addition, since the interfacial mesophase of phospholipid-stabilized systems is almost certainly very viscous if not solid in nature, the underlying liquid droplets would effectively behave like solid particles, and the similarities become quite evident.

Surface-modified systems have become available as modified liposomes or emulsions. One characteristic of both phospholipid-stabilized systems is the rapidity with which they are coated with apoproteins after coming in contact with blood as part of the opsonization process. Recently, liposomes surface-modified with poly(ethylene glycol) have appeared, sometimes referred to as Stealth® liposomes (36). These surface modifications, likened to disguising the surface with bound water, have effects on protein binding and, therefore, on physiological behavior and clearance. The net effect of surface modifications has been to extend the effects observed in the body produced by injected liposomes and, incidentally, to enhance the stability and commercial viability of these drug products (49).

Preparation of Sterile Product. Depending on the properties of the stabilizing entity used in the formulation, usually to be found at the interface of the dispersed droplets, it might be feasible to sterile-filter each of the components before processing under aseptic conditions. However, as noted earlier, most surfactants are too toxic to be employed as parenteral stabilizers and for the most part suitably purified egg or soy phospholipids are used. These have some curious properties in that phospholipid-stabilized emulsion systems can be terminally heat sterilized, thereby avoiding many of the issues associated with handling product under aseptic conditions. This, of course, presupposes that the drug entity itself is stable enough to be heat sterilized. If it is not, then presterilized emulsion would be aseptically manipulated to allow subsequent incorporation of the drug prior to packing. Nevertheless, it is extremely unlikely that any regulatory authority would approve an aseptically assembled large volume (>100 mL) parenteral and would insist on terminal sterilization of the product.

The Chemical Stability of Phospholipids. Phospholipids are heat-labile and hydrolyze in aqueous dispersion. Strictly speaking phospholipids are not truly soluble in water but readily form dispersions that could be recognized as liposomes. Groves et al. (50) reported the presence of liposomal-like material in phospholipid-stabilized emulsions, so aggregates of phospholipids readily form but a true solution of these materials, consisting of single molecular entities, does not.

Dispersions of pure PC or PE in water when heated, for example, in a sterilization process, hydrolyze to their cor-

once the capsule wall is broken. For injection, the system would be packed as an oil to which water or electrolytes would be added immediately prior to injection. Pouton (59) has found that 30% Tagat OT(poly(oxyethylene-(25)glyceryltrioleate) with 70% medium chain triglycerides (Miglyol 812) was a suitable system for oral administration but there appear to be no reports of similar systems being suitable for parenteral use.

Preparation of Sterile Product. Because both systems are effectively made by adding one liquid to another, it should be feasible to sterile-filter both components and operate under aseptic conditions for the rest of the process. Heat sterilization of liposomes has been attempted but this may cause considerable changes in the state of dispersion and generally redistribution of guest drug molecules (60). γ-irradiation has also been investigated for the sterilization of liposomes (60), but was found to be limited in application because of phospholipid degradation. Frozen liposomes in the presence of effective antioxidants may be an alternative application for sterilization by γ-irradiation, but this possibility requires further evaluation.

Polymer Emulsification. The production of polymer emulsions, especially nanoparticulate systems, is carried out by an emulsification process that is physically different from those processes used for the usual pharmaceutical processes. Polymers are usually derived from monomeric systems by providing an appropriate stimulus or catalyst. Some reaction initiators are heat or high-energy radiation and catalysts are often heavy metal salts or, in the case of methyl methacrylate, potassium peroxidisulfate. However, greater control over the polymerization process is exerted if the liquid monomer is emulsified in water and the catalysts added to the system. The polymerization process itself does not occur in the oily or dispersed droplets but rather to the monomer molecules that have dissolved in the aqueous continuous phase from the disperse phase. The polymerization or chain-growth process is maintained by more monomer molecules diffusing out of the dispersed phase. Because the polymerization process is always slower than the monomer diffusion process, polymerization continues in the continuous aqueous phase until the droplet reservoir is exhausted. The monomer droplets can be reasonably coarse by comparison with the dispersed polymer particles and, as noted by Kreuter (6), some systems do not require an interfacial stabilizer, although addition of casein (e.g., to a methyl methacrylate suspension) results in a finer, more monodispersed, polymer particles.

Preparation of Sterile Product. Although many of the monomeric compounds used are unfavorable for bacterial growth, this cannot be relied upon to sterilize the system prior to or during the polymerization process. In addition, the effect of a terminal heat-sterilization process on the polymer would be to change equilibrium conditions and, therefore, properties of the final product. Because the reactants are liquids, in a liquid medium, this would suggest that a process could be designed as an aseptic process in which components and reactants are sterile-filtered together into a sterile reaction vessel, and aseptic precautions maintained throughout.

Mixed Micelles

Mixed micelles, consisting of mixtures of phospholipids, especially PC, and bile salts have recently been advocated as solubilization systems for sparingly soluble drugs such as teniposide and paclitaxel (Taxol®) (61,62). Phospholipids are insoluble in both oil and water, forming swollen suspensions in both. In water these dispersions are better known as liposomes because they form spherical molecular aggregates with aqueous centers. Bile salts, on the other hand, are water-soluble and readily form micellar aggregates. When added together, bile salts and phospholipids form complex structures, most likely rod-like aggregates that have a significantly higher capacity for guest molecules (63). These structures are readily formed as transparent aqueous dispersions, and this transparency is maintained as the system is diluted (although the actual structure changes from rods to spheres, in other words to liposome-like structures). Both components are amphiphilic in nature and both can be used to solubilize water-insoluble (i.e., with aqueous solubilities of below 0.01%) drugs. Individually these materials can be employed to solubilize drugs although handling phospholipids on their own is not easy (see "Emulsions") and bile salts can manifest toxicities on administration principally due to their detergent properties. However, when mixed, the new structures vastly increased the solubilization capacity of the individual systems, and the incorporated "guest" molecules were not precipitated on further aqueous dilution. This was because the bile salt molecules were effectively disaggregated by dilution, but the phospholipids form curved bilayer structure-liposomes that retained the associated hydrophobic guest molecules.

These mixed micellar solutions therefore have a number of advantages:

1. Precipitation is eliminated when injected or diluted for injection.
2. The vehicle is aqueous throughout and can be adjusted for pH and osmolarity.
3. The solutions are clear, isotropic, and have low viscosities, which make them ideal for injection.
4. Mixed micelles form spontaneously by the internal energy of the system, which effectively means that they are thermodynamically stable and reproducible at defined compositions and temperature.
5. Technically these systems are readily made by solution in a mutual solvent such as isopropanol, which can then be removed.
6. These solutions can be easily sterilized by filtration. Terminal heat sterilization, often demanded by regulatory authorities, has not been evaluated but under carefully controlled conditions, may not represent a serious problem, depending critically on the properties of the incorporated drug.
7. Unlike liposomal formulations there is no problem with vesicle leakage and mixed micellar systems are readily lyophilized, spontaneously recovering their original properties on reconstitution with water.

8. In some cases pain on injection has been shown to be reduced.

9. The chemical stability of some labile molecules has been shown to be improved, hydrolysis being reduced or prevented altogether when the drug is incorporated into mixed micelles.

A number of other drugs have been explored in mixed micellar systems, including diazepam and steroids (63). A systematic evaluation of steroidal structures on solubilization by simple and mixed micelles has recently been published by Cai et al. (64) although here the emphasis was on oral absorption of these drugs. Ayd (65) demonstrated that linear increases in solubilized drug concentration with increased total lipid concentration were often observed. A critical lipid concentration was defined as a specific mixed micelle composition that existed over a limited range, showing a linear relationship between the phospholipid: bile salt molar ratio. Measurement of the particle size suggested that a molar ratio of $\approx$ 1.0 was optimal. Beyond this range the systems appear to react more until they restructured to form a gel-like state consisting of associated rods. Ayd (65) concluded that mixed micellar solubilization was a multifactorial event, with different types of aggregated structures contributing to the entire solubilization process.

Yet to be used in a commercial product, this approach to an old issue associated with poorly soluble drug substances would appear to be exceptionally promising and may well be investigated further.

Preparation of Sterile Product. The effect of terminal heat sterilization conditions on the final mixed micellar product remains to be explored. The use of filtration to sterilize components in an aseptic process may be necessary but the point of application may need careful selection because, often, the component solutions have high viscosities that renders any filtration process difficult to carry out.

Spraying Processes

Kwok et al. (66,67) were able to demonstrate that 5–15-μm diameter particles of alginate-poly(lysine) particles suitable for encapsulating microorganisms such as bacillus Calmette-Guérin (BCG) vaccine could be made by spraying solutions of the polymer system through a suitable atomizer. Later, this system was adapted to preparing gelatin or albumin microparticles (40). The process consisted of atomizing aqueous 1% gelatin or [human albumin] solutions through a Turbotak atomizer, Turbotak Ltd., Waterloo, Ontario, Canada) with a 1 mm orifice. Two sets of apparatus were used (Figs. 1 and 3). The gas inlet to a Turbotak was connected to a compressed carbon dioxide tank at an inlet pressure of 20 psi. The inlet solutions were sprayed into anhydrous ethanol (95% ethanol, 5% isopropanol) held at a temperature of −15°C. The droplets were then hardened by the addition of glutaraldehyde for 24 hours, followed by sodium metabisulfite to stop the cross-linking reaction. The particles were collected and washed before lyophilization in the presence of mannitol as a diluent. The process was improved by adding a second stage

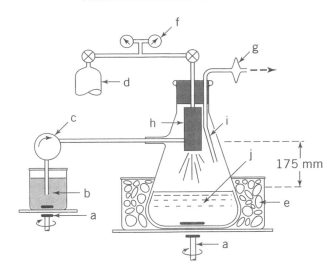

Figure 3. A closed system for making gelatin microparticles using a single-stage carbon dioxide-activated spray system. a, Magnetic stirrer; b, hot gelatin solution; c, peristaltic pump; d, carbon dioxide tank; e, solid carbon dioxide pellets; f, gas regulator; g, 0.45-μm membrane filter venting to atmosphere; h, Turbotak; i, vent tube; j, cold stirred anhydrous ethanol. *Source:* By permission of the editor, *Pharmaceutical Research*, from Ref. 40.

vessel designed to trap the larger droplets also produced by the Turbotak. This proved to be somewhat less effective and gave a much lower yield, most probably because it had already been shown that direct mixing of the aqueous gelatin and anhydrous ethanol was effective in producing gelatin particles (68). Nevertheless, the spraying technique did produce significantly smaller particles with an average size of 0.86 μm as opposed to an average of 1.18 μm made by the direct mixing process. Although relatively large volumes of flammable alcohol are required, one advantage of using the inexpensive carbon dioxide gas is that it is a flame retardant, suggesting that the process might have some potential for scale-up to an industrial process.

Preparation of Sterile Product. Refreshingly, Burgess and her co-workers (66,67,69) have continued work on sterile or axenic product (i.e., containing only one, predetermined microbiological species), and this has recently culminated in a detailed description of how sterile microparticles of alginate/poly(L-lysine) could be made (70). The process was described in detail, producing sterile particles from 3 to 16 μm diameter (volume weighted mean) according to the spraying conditions. The method involves using a Turbotak atomizer operating inside a bioreactor chamber and was shown to be robust enough for major changes in operating conditions to have insignificant effects on the product properties. Attention needs to be drawn to this important pioneering contribution to the subject of sterile microcapsules; it is likely that other processes could be designed in a similar fashion.

Preparation of Poly(L-lactide) Particles by Carbon Dioxide Precipitation Solutions. Müller and his colleagues (71) have recently described an aerosol solvent extraction system for

have an electropositive surface charge instead of the natural negative charge. Liposomes act as potent nontoxic immunological adjuvants and can be made to incorporate many antigens expressed at the surface. The versatility of the liposome as a drug delivery system is well recognized (76).

Adjuvants such as MDP and its analogues have been added to liposomes containing an antigen, and interleukin-2 has also been incorporated, confirming the versatility of the delivery system. Liposomes have another advantage in that the phospholipid bilayer is capable of fusing to cell walls. For this reason, they tend to get incorporated into elements of the reticuloendothelial system quite rapidly after administration. The recent introduction of surface-modified liposomes (sometimes called sterically stabilized or Stealth® liposomes) has produced a new generation of liposomes that are physiologically more stable. This has been achieved by covalently bonding poly(ethylene glycol) to the PE found in the lipid layer, producing a strongly hydrophilic surface that is not opsonized by proteins (36). This development appears to be exceptionally promising and may make the clinical application of liposomal products more realistic in the immediate future. Moreover, by attaching appropriate antibodies to the terminus of the liposome-attached poly(ethylene glycol) (77,78), the targeting of liposomes has been vastly improved.

Solid Particulate Systems. Biodegradable polymers, in particular PLGA, previously used as a surgical implant and suture material, have proved popular as particulate drug delivery systems. The polymer can be tailored to a specific purpose and has been explored as a matrix antigen delivery system. The polymer degrades by an aqueous hydrolytic process, producing acids and therefore low pH conditions close to the surface, which may be detrimental to any incorporated protein. In addition, as noted by Davis recently (79), storage of PLGA immunological systems can result in loss of immunogenicity, and "conventional" sterilization systems can cause damage, suggesting the need for aseptic processing. Davis also noted that scale-up of PLGA systems was proving to be difficult. According to Zhao and Leong (74), there have been vast differences between various workers in terms of vaccine preparation, immunization, and challenge protocols, as well as the assay methods. However, some general conclusions may be drawn. For example, the antigens need to be encapsulated in microspheres to elicit an enhanced antibody production and humoral protective immunity. The effect of particle size was evident, especially if the antigen dose was low. Because of the larger surface-to-mass ratio, release was faster from small particles compared with larger ones, and it seems that small (<10 μm) microspheres are capable of facilitating extracellular delivery of antigens to the phagocytic accessors cells that infiltrate the administration site, leading to enhanced antigen processing and processing.

Indeed, larger particles could not be phagocytosed by the macrophages until they had disintegrated into smaller debris. In principle it was suggested that a combination of large and small particles might produce a pulsatile pattern of antigen release, mimicking an immunization process that involved a primary dose followed by booster shots. Other particulate systems can be made from cross-linked albumin or gelatin, as noted earlier. Interestingly, empty gelatin microparticles produce only a mild inflammatory response at the injection site, suggesting that gelatin itself has only a minimal immunogenic activity.

However, gelatin on its own does have adjuvant activity and this probably arises from the ability of macrophages to phagocytose the microparticles. Poly(phosphazenes) are a class of polymers with a simple -P=N- backbone with physicochemical properties strongly influenced by side chain attachments to the phosphorus atom. Some can be rendered water-soluble, allowing the antigen to be encapsulated in the aqueous state at low temperature. Addition of ionic cross-linking agents such as calcium can then render the system insoluble, allowing sustained release from the precipitated solid. Further control is obtained by coating the solid surface with the cationic polymer, poly(lysine), and this approach has been used to control the release of antibacterial drugs in a controlled-release string made from calcium alginate, which was designed for impaction into dental periodontal cavities (80).

Other Current Formulation Issues

Pain on Injection. Injectable products are administered by various routes according to the physiological requirements of the product. The main routes are

1. *Intravenous* directly into the intravenous blood supply
2. *Subcutaneous* into the soft tissues just underneath the skin
3. *Intramuscular* directly into the muscles of the arm or gluteal region

Other routes include the *intrathecal* (subarachnoid space), *intraarticular* (directly into joints), *intracardial* (directly into the heart), *intraperitoneal* (used for kidney dialysis), and *intracutaneous* (just under the stratum corneum of the epidermis). However, all routes of parenteral administration require professional medical skills for successful delivery of the drug, and this can sometimes be stressful for the patient, contributing to pain. Nevertheless, although it is basically true that no parenteral administration is without pain, some drugs or their vehicles themselves produce pain. It is generally recognized that painful injections should be administered by intramuscular injection because there are few nervous receptors in these tissues. Nevertheless, this site is not always feasible and pain experienced by administration of a pain-causing drug can be difficult by the subcutaneous route or, due to drug residues along the needle-track, by the intravenous route. Some factors producing pain on injection, reviewed by Fransson and Espander-Jansson (81) include:

- Injection volume (the subcutaneous route should not exceed 1.0 mL and the intramuscular 2.0 mL)
- Speed of injection
- Injection site
- Size and quality of the hypodermic used (is it sharp or blunted?)

- Temperature of injection
- Presence of irritating substances (e.g., citrates)
- pH
- Osmolality

Fransson and Espander-Jansson (81) were concerned about severe pain experienced by patients receiving subcutaneous injections of human insulin-like growth factor. This protein is most stable at a pH of 6.0, which although not physiological, should have been acceptable. Morphine sulfate injections have a pH of 3.0, although these are administered into muscles where the ambient pH is often lower. These authors were able to demonstrate that the pain was not due to the drug itself but was caused by the concentration of the phosphate buffer used. Although lower concentrations of phosphate (10 mM compared with 50 mM) had lower buffer capacity, this was judged to be acceptable in view of the reduced pain experienced. In addition, it is probable that dilution to physiological pH occurred more rapidly around the administration site.

Pain is a subjective sensation and therefore difficult to measure. However, there are statistically valid methods of measuring it, and other sensations such as muscle damage, redness, paleness, and edema at the injection site can also be used to supplement the measurements (82,83).

Needleless or Jet Injectors. Alexander Wood invented the graduated glass syringe fitted with a hollow reed in Edinburgh around 1853, although syringes as such were widely employed in early Tudor times, to judge by artifacts found on the warship Mary Rose, which sank off Portsmouth in the early 1500s. After over a century of needle injections, the technology is well understood, although some issues have become evident, such as the associated dangers of needle sticks to health care personnel and cross-contamination during administration. A needleless injector, the Porton injector, was developed in the 1930s and used for routine mass inoculations in both military and veterinary applications. The principle was straightforward: a high-pressure liquid flow from a pressurized container penetrated the skin and deposited material in the dermis and subdermal layers. The equipment was heavy and required a compressor, which made it unsuitable for routine individual use. Various attempts to improve the technology have appeared in recent years and at least one of these, the Intraject® system, Weston Medical (United Kingdom), is one of several recently developed systems that have considerable promise as a technology for the immediate future. The Weston device uses a preloaded gas or coil spring-activated piston to force the liquid through an orifice that does not come into direct contact with the skin. The drug can be supplied in the type of filled cartridges already in wide use for dental syringes. The two are coupled together, and when activated, the spring-powered ram accelerates and strikes a piston with viscoelastic properties. This causes the formation of a liquid pulse in what is described as a "liquid nail," and this has sufficient energy to penetrate the skin, depositing a predetermined volume of fluid. The volume of liquid that can be deposited is limited to 0.2 to 1.0 mL, optimally 0.5 mL, but analysis of the hydrodynamics of the administration process has demonstrated that viscosity of the solution is relatively unimportant. In addition, if the orifice is very short, shear forces are minimized. This is relevant because many proteinaceous injections such as antigens are readily denatured by shearing. The advantages of the Intraject system is that it is light, readily portable, and allows individual patients to administer their own intradermal or subcutaneous injections. Intramuscular injections may also be possible, depending on the obesity of the patient. These may be more painful because of the speed with which liquid is introduced into the muscles, the individual fibers having insufficient time to displace and allow the injected fluid to penetrate into the tissues. In addition, because of the way the liquid pulse splays out on administration, some of the drug may be deposited into adipose tissue, potentially altering the pharmacokinetics. However, individual patients would be likely to adjust dosage according to their requirements, and this has been observed with diabetics using the system. The injector is automatically fired when the device is pressed lightly on the skin. This means that the amount of skill required for administration is minimal, and medical personnel are not required, thereby significantly reducing the associated costs. The device itself is also claimed to be inexpensive, below 20 cents (U.S.) in 1997 money. Obvious advantages of this system is the small size, speed of administration, and insignificant pain levels experienced on intradermal injection. It is therefore entirely possible that this type of device and others being commercially developed will provide a valuable means of administering sterile nanoparticulate systems subdermally for controlled drug delivery.

Albumin

Albumins are a group of proteins widely found in nearly all living body tissues. They are characterized by solubility in dilute salt solutions and precipitation at relatively low temperatures, heating at 55–65°C being sufficient to denature most albumins. Commercially they are obtained from egg white, bovine serum, and human serum, although significant quantities are also available from soybeans, milk, and some grains. Egg white albumins, for example, are usually called *albumins*, and the Latin for egg white is *albumen*. Pharmaceutical materials are generally from bovine or human serum and the remainder of the nonpharmaceutical albumins are widely used for baking although, as noted by Teng and colleagues (84), soy albumins are potentially valuable tablet excipients. Human serum albumin separated from whole human blood is employed as a plasma volume expander, and iodinated (^{131}I) albumin is used as a diagnostic in the measurement of blood volume. This protein has a relatively low molecular weight (~69 kDa) and comprises about 60% of the plasma proteins. Although it denatures and comes out of solution at temperatures below 65°C, the protein is carbohydrate-free and is stable at higher temperatures. The denaturation process in this case is reversible, and commercially available dried albumin, as an example, goes back into solution at lower temperatures, forming as much as a 40% solution at pH 7.4. Ovalbumin, on the other hand, is denatured at

Collagen

Collagen is widely used, especially in Europe, as a base material for a wide variety of drug carrier systems. In general, it is considered to be biocompatible and biodegradable, allowing, for example, its exploitation as lenses for ophthalmic delivery. Collagen sponges impregnated with antibiotics have been employed in surgery to improve wound healing and prevent diseases such as osteomyelitis (89). For the most part, parenteral collagen systems have been developed as matrices and are claimed to offer better alternatives to synthetic polyester of polyanhydride devices. However, most of the systems described to date are monomolecular collagen (atelocollagen) in which the non-helical telopeptides are removed enzymatically (see "Gelatin and Gelatin Vehicles" for a discussion of the structure of collagen and its degradation products). This soluble product requires chemical cross-linking to prevent or delay the devices from dissolving at body temperature, 37°C. Using glutaraldehyde increases the danger of side reactions that can occur on incorporated sensitive drugs, such as proteins, and reduces the biocompatibility. Friess and colleagues (90) suggested that an alternative method was to use the higher molecular weight soluble collagens as a drug carrier. This insoluble material comes about from the natural tendency of the collagen triple helix structure to aggregate, eventually forming fibers and bundles of fibers that were stabilized by inter- and intramolecular cross-links. Commercially, the insoluble collagen is available as a slurry after milling, purification, and enzyme treatment designed to remove the noncollagenous materials. Friess and Lee (89) lyophilized this slurry for storage but could rehydrate it by swelling in water followed by homogenization. Devices were easily prepared by casting films of hydrated suspensions and punching out discs after air-drying. Properties were modified by adding glutaraldehyde to induce cross-linking.

Differential scanning calorimetry demonstrated that denaturation occurred at relatively high temperatures, 80–103°C, higher than the 43°C recorded for aqueous solutions of the same material. Cross-linking caused some controlled slow release from the devices but, correspondingly, increasing amounts of drug were entrapped in the matrix. This entrapped material was shown to be released by enzymatic digestion (90). This observation suggests that implanted devices would release incorporated drugs, especially those of high molecular weight, under the influence of locally available enzymes such as collagenases.

Because chemical cross-linking is required to obtain controlled release, it was found to be important to load the devices after preparation and initial lyophilization by soaking and swelling in a solution of the drug, followed by a second lyophilization. Proteins were readily loaded by this method (90) as were polysaccharidic glycans (91). In this latter case the drug, PS1, as a known immunostimulant, stimulated the in vivo degradation of the devices, apparently by macrophage attack. The mechanism involved here was not clearly defined but any unexpected in vivo effect similar to that observed here would obviously negate the purpose of using this type of controlled release system.

Gelatin and Gelatin Vehicles

Constitution of Gelatin. Gelatin is a biopolymer obtained commercially by the controlled hydrolysis of collagens from a number of animal sources. Native collagen consists of rods formed from triple helices that are held together by covalent bonds. During the denaturation process, which usually consists of heating in the presence of acid or alkali, the covalent bonds are destroyed and the helical structure disrupted. Above 37°C solutions of gelatin in water are liquids, and the molecules behave effectively as random polymeric coils. However, when cooled to ambient room temperature in excess of 1% concentrations by weight, gelatin solutions change to gels and the random chains partially revert back to triple helix structures. The bulk of the gelatin chain is made up of glycine, proline, and hydroxyproline ($\cong 58\%$), which are weakly hydrophobic. Their periodicity along the chain, combined with the structural flexibility of the glycine molecule, provides a vehicle for the formation of helical structures (92).

At around neutral pH the gelatin chain is amphoteric and groups such as lysine and arginine ($\cong 7.5\%$ of residues) are positively charged, and others such as glutamic and aspartic acids ($\cong 11.8\%$) are negatively charged. These entities provide centers for electrostatic binding. Light, small angle neutron and x-ray scattering all provided evidence of the persistent length and stiffness of the chain as approximately 20 nm, with a radius of gyration R_G of $\cong 35$ nm. As the concentration was increased, two regions became evident by quasielastic light scattering. The fast mode was evidently due to cooperative movements of the entangled network of chains, and this appeared to persist over a range of concentrations and temperatures. The second mode was associated with the diffusion coefficient being inversely proportioned to the bulk Newtonian viscosity of the solution. This has been interpreted as being due to the self-diffusion of clusters of chains that have a constant hydrodynamic radius $R_C \cong 75$ nm. Contrary to the properties of the chains themselves, the clusters are affected by the molecular weight of the individual chains, the temperature and the presence of salts or surfactants such as sodium dodecyl sulfate. Herning et al. (93) concluded that clusters were stabilized by hydrophobic interactions between apolar lateral groups of the protein. Gelatin as such is not a single entity but behaves like a model protein. The bulk material is deficient in some amino acids, having only 18 constituent units, of which the principal constituents are glycine (32–35%), proline (11–13%), alanine (10–11%), hydroxyproline (9–19%), glutamic acid (7–8%), aspartic acid (4–5%), and arginine (5%). The parent collagen, for the most part, consists of three subunits of approximately equal molecular weight (95 kDa). When denatured to form gelatin, the collagen is broken down to a single chain α-fragment (M_w 95 kDa) and β-fragments (M_w 190 kDa), together with branched γ-chains of M_w 285 kDa which actually consist of three α-chains joined near the center point. As might be anticipated, there are also low molecular weight oligomeric degradation products (Table 2).

Using high-performance liquid chromatography and gel electrophoresis, Zavlin et al. (95) have examined the constitutional difference of gelatins from various sources al-

Table 2. Oligomers of Gelatin Showing the Relationship of the Basic α-chain to Other Components

Molecular weight class	Molecular weight range (kDa)	Possible composition (α-chains)	Approximate % w/w in B225 gelatin
Subalpha	<80	Low molecular weight fragments	20
Alpha (α)	80–125	1-α	14
Beta (β)	125–225	2-α	18
Gamma (γ)	225–340	3-α	8
Epsilon (ε)	340–700	6-α (or 2γ)	15
Zeta (ζ)	700–1,000	9-α (or 3γ)	5
Delta (δ)	1,000–1,800	12-α (or 4γ)	9
Microgel	>1,800	high molecular weight aggregates >12-α	11

Source: Ref. 94.

though with photographic film processing in mind. Skin or bone gelatins were basically similar one to another, β-chains being substantially missing from skin gelatins. Differences between acid and alkaline processed gelatin were noted, the former apparently containing more degradation products. The authors suggested that desired properties for any particular gelatin could be obtained by blending various samples to give the desired low molecular (α) or high molecular (γ) fractions according to the end product usage. What is certainly missing at the present point in time is evidence that the gelatin-producing industry is prepared to carry out this blending process for the pharmaceutical industry, in part because pharmaceuticals represent a relatively small section of the total economic requirement and in part because there have been relatively few pharmaceutical studies that have helped to define the essential requirements for pharmaceutical gelatins.

Phase Relationships. Although gelatin is proteinaceous, comprising linear assemblies of covalently bonded amino acids, in many ways it has atypical behavior because it shows no tertiary structure and is not denatured by heating up to temperatures of 100°C. Albumin, for example, is denatured at 55–60°C and is readily precipitated out of aqueous solution by the addition of ethanol or sodium or ammonium sulfate. Gelatin, on the other hand, is slowly precipitated by the addition of either of these desolvating components, resulting in a complex phase diagram that is influenced by the temperature of the system. Gelatin is a mildly hydrophobic protein, and the addition of solutes results in two-phase liquid systems, today called coacervates, and it is the creation of coacervate structures that is the key step in the production of many encapsulated gelatin products. Although this has been known for many years, it is only recently that attempts have been made to systematically, experimentally determine the effect of temperature and solutes on the transition between various constituent phases of what is an exceptionally complex system (96). Ternary phase diagrams are often used to depict the effect of a third component on the phase behavior of a particular compound in aqueous solution. More commonly used for inorganic systems, the ternary diagrams have proved to be invaluable for defining the phase behavior of surfactants and spontaneous emulsions. Effectively, defining points or boundaries between incompatible systems or

components, interpretation of ternary phase diagrams requires care and are rarely precise or exact. The first studies of the effects of salts on gelatin go back to the 1930s (97) but recently a systematic study of the effects of ammonium sulfate or ethanol on the solubility or constitution of Gelatin B (Bloom 225) has been published (96). These authors found after the inspection of several hundred gelatin–water combinations that a total of seven morphologies could be distinguished visually (Table 3) although only six were seen with the ethanolic systems. It must be assumed that the states described by these authors are stable and that the equilibrium phase boundaries are also stable, although these assumptions are not always justified. At least 33% water is needed to break apart and hydrate the gelatin in order to form a solution (Fig. 7). Interestingly, the addition of ethanol did not appear to change this situation, suggesting that the compact gelatin powder showed little preference for either water or ethanol and, as noted earlier, can therefore be defined as being relatively hydrophobic. It should be noticed that water-structure promoters such as sodium chloride destabilize gelatin structure, and almost 50% water is required to form a solution in the presence of 5% sodium chloride. This can be interpreted as indicating that both the gelatin and the salt compete for water of hydration. However, the question not answered by these authors is the nature of the structure of the opaque sols and gels described. It was pointed out that below 40°C, gelatin molecules began to interact with each other to form linkages stabilized by hydrogen bonds, which accounted for ethanol encouraging gel formation, as shown in morphology I, Figure 7. Herning et

Table 3. Gelatin Morphologies on Addition of Ethanol or Ammonium Sulfate

Morphology	Description
I	Transparent clear colorless liquid
II	Opaque liquid (small aggregates)
III	Coacervate region
IV	Transparent or opaque lower gel, upper liquid
V	Homogeneous transparent gel
VI	Powdery aggregates
VII	Transparent lower gel, upper, liquid phase with solid salt

Source: Adapted from Ref. 96.

tered as blood expanders proved to have unexpected toxicities. Accordingly, gelatin microparticles, although perhaps less likely to suffer from the same effects, should not be viewed as being entirely without potential harm. As discussed in the following section, gelatin (and collagen) bind to fibronectin with a high affinity (98–102). By specifically binding to fibronectin, gelatin could interfere with the cell binding interactions that are characteristic of cancers but are also required in the healthy body. Infusion of gelatin-based plasma substitutes produced severe side effects due to depletion of plasma fibronectin, and this obviously limits the widespread use of gelatin solutions. Nevertheless, side effects due to the injection of gelatin microparticles, for example, would not be anticipated to be so severe or widespread. However, in human use the investigator should at least be aware of the previously observed manifestations of toxicity and anticipate possible side effects associated with the therapy. Two other more problematic issues also need to be raised here. One is the slow release of aldehydic cross-linking agents, as the cross-linked polymer disassociates in vivo. Although obviously at low levels and probably over a prolonged time, the long-term effects of local administration of glutaraldehyde have not been evaluated. The second issues of contamination of bovine sources gelatins with BSE or mad cow disease, which appears to have originated in the United Kingdom and is therefore of more immediate concern to European regulators. Although some politicians have attempted to ban all products derived from cows, including leather, gelatin products have also been somewhat irrationally targeted. Although it is true that much needs to be learned about prions, the causative agents of BSE, it is difficult to imagine anything surviving the processes used to produce pharmaceutical gelatin. Other nonbovine sources of gelatin are available, although porcine sources are not acceptable in some cultures. Moreover, at the time of writing no pharmaceutical gelatin products have been found to contain prions, so the issue is obviously a remote one that can probably be ignored.

Sterilization of Gelatin Products. Gelatin as such does not have a precise chemical structure, and solutions of gelatin are readily heat sterilized. Obvious heat damage to the general structure occurs, in particular a loss of viscosity induced by hydrolytic destruction of covalent and hydrogen beads. But, as noted earlier, gelatin has a tendency to attempt to revert to its original collagen-type structure. The structures effectively heals or reforms, and the properties for which gelatin is so widely used can be restored. However, irreversible damage undoubtably occurs, suggesting that aseptic filtration is probably required for most, if not all, injectable gelatins.

Tissue Targeting With Gelatin Microparticles. As noted in the previous section, gelatin binds avidly to fibronectin and by analogy to fibronectin-enriched surfaces. This interaction has been studied extensively starting with Engvall and Ruoslahti in 1977 (103). Fibronectin is an ubiquitous asymmetric glycoprotein or, more accurately, a family of at least 100 glycoproteins with structural homology (104). They have two similar but not identical polypeptide chains joined near their c-termini that are held together with di-

sulfide bridges. The protein has a high molecular weight ($\sim$440 kDa) and is a normal constituent of blood plasma besides being widely deposited in connective tissues, blood vessel walls, and basement membranes. Excreted on the surface of a cell, fibronectin functions as a cell-to-cell or cell-to-basement membrane adhesive (Fig. 11). The free plasma fibronectin is considered to be the main opsonic protein modulating the functional capacity of the reticuloendothelial system. However, it is as a factor involved in the propensity of tumor cells to spread or metastasize from their site of origin to other body sites that fibronectin is of interest in the present context. As is well known, the high rate of death following diagnosis of cancer is due principally to the biological consequences of tumor cells disseminating from their original site. About half of all diagnosed cancer patients survive at least five years when treated by conventional means, involving surgery, chemotherapy, or radiotherapy alone or in combination. The failures are almost always due to metastases that removal of the primary tumor site has failed to eradicate.

The dissemination of malignant cells from a primary to a secondary site involves a complex sequence of biological events that are linked in both time and space, and although basically a very inefficient process in that thousands of cells may be detached from the tumor but only a few survive, malignancies can occur at sites well removed from the original tumor. The invasive process is assisted by the expression or recognition of a group of proteins called adhesins in the endothelial or subendothelial extracellular matrix; fibronectin is considered to have a key role in the metastatic process as an adhesion.

Because of the complexity of its function in a biological system, fibronectin has been shown to have areas or domains along its molecule that can be identified to specific binding functions. For example, as indicated in Figure 11, there are at lease two domains with direct cellular binding activity, another binds to DNA, and yet others to fibrin and to heparin. However, one domain has been specifically identified as being responsible for the binding to collagen or, in its degraded form, to gelatin.

A clear distinction need to be made between altered adhesive behavior that may come about because of a direct or indirect consequence of the neoplastic process and the exploitation by abnormal cells of the normal adhesion process. Tumor cells may need to adhere in order to proliferate or migrate through tissues but to do so may not necessarily require alternations to their normal adhesive machinery. Humphries (100) recognized this process and found that a simple peptide sequence, RGD (arginine-glycine-aspartic acid), actually in the form of a pentapeptide GRGDS, could interfere with the adhesion process. Although this peptide proved to be only effective with frequent administrations of high doses, because it had an exceptionally short half-life and it was not pharmaceutically stable, the work on RGD analogues and derivatives is still being developed a decade later. Nevertheless, the concept itself was of interest and has resulted in the development of the type of targeted drug delivery system implied in Gregordiadis's (1) definition.

Fibronectin-Targeted Gelatin Particles. In the treatment of human superficial bladder cancer with cellular suspen-

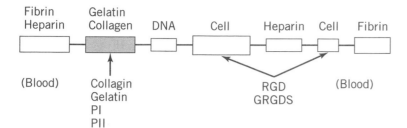

Figure 11. Schematic model of binding domains of the fibronectin molecule. *Source:* After Refs. 104–106.

sions of BCG vaccine, an attenuated living *Mycobacterium bovis*, it has become evident that the bacterial cells actually target and adhere to the tumor cells (99,100,102, 103,107). The mechanism of adhesion involves fibronection at or on the tumor cell surface and a specific fibronectin receptor on the bacterial wall thought to be cell wall proteins of the Antigen 85 homologous complex and other similar proteins of higher molecular weight. Because fibronectin has an affinity for collagen, Lou and her colleagues (99) hypothesized that gelatin would have much the same activity and measured the avidities of gelatin and gelatin microparticles for fibronectin-bearing surfaces as well as murine S180 sarcoma cells. This supposition was confirmed, and it was suggested that it might be feasible to load gelatin particles with suitable antineoplastics and substitute them for the viable microorganisms in the treatment of bladder cancer. It should be pointed out that although BCG treatment is clinically effective and the treatment of choice, most side effects associated with this treatment are due to the fact that a living organism is used and occasionally produces a form of septicemia and mild fever-like reactions as side effects. Lou later demonstrated that high molecular weight, highly water-soluble antineoplastics and thiotepa could be loaded onto gelatin microparticles and were effective in vivo (88). However, the clinical potential of this idea has not been evaluated.

Targeting of Macrophages Using Gelatin Microspheres. In a recent review by Tabata and Ikada (108) attention was drawn to the possibility of activating macrophages (Mφ) against neoplasms by incorporating biological response modifiers (BRMs). They suggested that the Mφ phagocytosed the biodegradable microspheres, in this case gelatin, digested them, and released any incorporated drug. In the case of BRMs these would be presented at the Mφ surface. These authors demonstrated that micrometer-range gelatin microparticles (mean ~1–5 μm) could be made by the water-in-oil method described for albumin. The drug, recombinant human α interferon (α-IFN), was incorporated in the initial aqueous gelatin solution so the subsequent glutaraldehyde treatment must have affected the α-IFN as well as the gelatin. Of interest was a figure in their paper showing spherical particles from approximately 200 nm to 2.0 μm diameter, suggesting a wide size distribution. The authors demonstrated the effect of glutaraldehyde on the solubility of the gelatin in the presence of collagenase. Using ^{125}I-labelled IFN demonstrated that the label was released slowly with time, although it is by no means clear if unmodified IFN was released at the same time, because it could be argued that this would be made available as the

gelatin was digested by the environmental collagenase. Later, in vivo experiments involving injection into the peritoneal cavity of mice demonstrated Mφ activation by gelatin microspheres containing IFN. The authors noted that IFN-loaded gelatin particles were not always effective in preventing or suppressing tumor growth in the mouse peritoneal cavity. One must therefore ask if the IFN incorporated into the cross-linked gelatin microparticles was also affected by the glutaraldehyde treatment. No evidence was offered either way but in vitro data based on a radiolabeled release in vivo data on antineoplastic activity are not necessarily the same thing. Indeed, these authors then went on to produce a covalently bonded IFN–gelatin conjugate that was water-soluble and superior in in vivo performance to the particulate forms of the drug. It would have been interesting to determine what would have happened if the α-IFN had been loaded into preformed gelatin microparticles, thus avoiding the likely glutaraldehyde-induced structural modification of the drug.

Chitosan

The availability of chitosan, its biocompatibility, and its unique chemical and biological properties make it an attractive biomaterial for a variety of pharmaceutical applications, especially in the areas of wound dressing and drug delivery. It has been used or tested in different forms, such as tablets, matrix, and microparticles for the purpose of sustained release, controlled drug delivery, mucosal formulations and, more recently, drug absorption enhancement protein and peptide drug delivery and vaccine development (109).

Chitosan is a biocompatible and biodegradable natural biopolymer consisting of β-1→4 linked 2-amino-2-deoxyglucopyranose (Fig. 12). It is currently manufactured commercially on the large scale by alkaline *N*-deacetylation of chitin, an abundant biopolymer isolated from the outer shells of crustaceans such as crabs and shrimps. Commercial chitosans have average molecular weights between 3.8 and 2,000 kDa and are from 66% up to 95% deacetylated (110). Chitosan has rather specific solution properties. It is only soluble at acidic pH when the free amino group (-NH$_2$) becomes protonated to form cationic amine group (-NH$_3^+$). At these pHs, chitosan has been identified as a linear polycation with an intrinsic pKa value of 6.5, independent of the degree of acetylation (111). The polycationic chitosan molecules have been found to readily adhere to negatively charged surfaces, such as skin, mucus, and proteins (112,113). Recent studies indicate that the binding of chitosan onto epithelial membranes resulted in cellular

38. M. Donbrow, in M. Donbrow, ed., *Microcapsules and Nanoparticles in Medicine and Pharmacy*, CRC Press, Boca Raton, Fla., 1991, pp. 17–45.

39. J.C. Boylan, A.L. Fites, and S.L. Nail, in G.S. Banker and C.T. Rhodes, eds., *Modern Pharmaceutics*, 3rd ed., Dekker, New York, 1998, p. 459.

40. L. Öner and M.J. Groves, *Pharm. Res.* **10**(4), 621–626 (1993).

41. A. Wretlind, *Acta Chir. Scand.* **325** (Suppl.), 31–42 (1964).

42. I. Håkansson, *Acta Chem. Scand.* **20**, 2267–2281 (1966).

43. P.K. Hansrani, S.S. Davis, and M.J. Groves, *J. Parenter. Sci. Technol.* **37**, 145–150 (1983).

44. H. Heiati, N.C. Phillips, and R. Tawashi, *Pharm. Res.* **13**(9), 1406–1410 (1996).

45. M.J. Groves and C.J. Herman, *J. Pharm. Pharmacol.* **45**, 592–596 (1993).

46. C.J. Herman and M.J. Groves, *Pharm. Res.* **10**(5), 774–776 (1993).

47. O. Lutz, M. Vrachopoulou, and M.J. Groves, *J. Pharm. Pharmacol.* **46**(9), 698–703 (1994).

48. O. Lutz and M.J. Groves, *J. Pharm. Pharmacol.* **47**, 566–570 (1995).

49. M. Rosoff, in H.A. Lieberman, M.M. Rieger, and G.S. Banker, eds., *Pharmaceutical Dosage Forms: Disperse Systems*, 2nd ed., vol. 3, Dekker, New York, 1998, pp. 1–42.

50. M.J. Groves, M. Wineberg, and A.P.R. Brain, *J. Dispersion Sci. Technol.* **6**(2), 237–243 (1985).

51. M. Grit, Ph.D. Thesis, University of Utrecht, The Netherlands, 1991.

52. M. Grit, J.H. de Smidt, A. Struijke, and D.J.A. Crommelin, *Int. J. Pharm.* **50**, 1–6 (1989).

53. H.V. Weltzien, *Biochim. Biophys. Acta* **559**, 259–287 (1979).

54. M. Grit and D.J.A. Crommelin, *Pharm. Res.* **7**, suppl., Abstr. 6060 (1990).

55. M. Blanko-Pieto et al., *Pharm. Res.* **13**(7), 1127–1129 (1996).

56. K. Ciftci et al., *Int. J. Pharm.* **131**, 73–82 (1996).

57. T. Yoshioka, M. Hashiba, S. Muranishi, and K. Sezaki, *Int. J. Pharm.* **8**, 131–135 (1981).

58. J.J. Marty, R.C. Openheim, and P. Speiser, *Pharm. Acta Helv.* **53**, 17–25 (1978).

59. M.G. Wakerly, C.W. Pouton, B.J. Meakin, and F.S. Morton, *ACS Symp. Ser.* **311**, 242–255 (1986).

60. M. Cherian and J.B. Portnoff, in H.A. Lieberman, M.M. Rieger, and G.S. Banker, eds., *Pharmaceutical Dosage Forms: Disperse System*, 2nd ed., vol. 3, Dekker, New York, 1998, pp. 395–422.

61. H. Alkan-Onyuksel and K. Son, *Pharm. Res.* **9**, 1556–1560 (1992).

62. H. Alkan-Onyuksel, S. Ramakrishnan, H.P. Chai, and J.M. Pezzuto, *Pharm. Res.* **11**, 206–210 (1994).

63. R.P. Hjelm, P. Thiyagarajan, and H. Alkan-Onyuksel, *J. Phys. Chem.* **96**, 8653–8661 (1992).

64. X. Cai, D.J.W. Grant, and T.S. Wiedmann, *J. Pharm. Sci.* **86**(3), 372–377 (1997).

65. S. Ayd, Ph.D. Thesis, University of Illinois at Chicago, 1998.

66. K.K. Kwok, M.J. Groves, and D.J. Burgess, *Pharm. Res.* **8**(3), 341–344 (1991).

67. K.K. Kwok, M.J. Groves, and D.J. Burgess, *Pharm. Res.* **9**, 410–413 (1992).

68. L. Öner and M.J. Groves, *J. Pharm. Pharmacol.* **45**, 866–870 (1993).

69. S.M. Abraham, R.F. Vieth, and D.J. Burgess, *Pharm. Res.* **11**(10), S-135 (1994).

70. S.M. Abraham, R.F. Vieth, and D.J. Burgess, *Pharm. Dev. Technol.* **1**(1), 63–68 (1996).

71. F. Ruchatz, P. Kleinbudde, and B.W. Müller, *J. Pharm. Sci.* **86**(1), 101–105 (1997).

72. M.F. Powell, *Pharm. Res.* **13**(12), 1777–1785 (1996).

73. M.J. Groves, *J. Pharm. Pharmacol.* **49**(Suppl. 1), 7–15 (1997).

74. Z. Zhao and K.W. Leong, *J. Pharm. Sci.* **85**(12), 1261–1270 (1996).

75. M.A. Selkirk, *Vaccine* **14**, 668–671 (1996).

76. L.B. Lachman et al., in M.F. Powell and M.J. Newman, eds., *Vaccine Design: The Subunit and Adjuvant Approach*, Plenum, New York, 1995, pp. 659–671.

77. T.M. Allen and E.H. Moase, *Adv. Drug Delivery Rev.* **21**, 117–133 (1996).

78. J.M.J. Marjan and T.M. Allen, *Biotechnol. Adv.* **14**(2), 151–175 (1996).

79. S.S. Davis, *Vaccine* **14**, 672–676 (1996).

80. U.S. Pat. 5,290,559 (March 1, 1994), M.J. Groves (to Illinois Board of Trustees).

81. J. Fransson and A. Espander-Jansson, *J. Pharm. Pharmacol.* **48**, 1012–1015 (1996).

82. S.C. Sutton, L.A.F. Evans, M.T.S. Rinaldi, and K.A. Norton, *Pharm. Res.* **15**, 1514–1518 (1998).

83. H. Park and K. Park, *Pharm. Res.* **13**(12), 1770–1776 (1996).

84. C.D. Teng, M.H. Alkan, and M.J. Groves, *Drug Dev. Ind. Pharm.* **12**(11–13), 2325–2336 (1986).

85. I. Zolle, F. Hosain, B.A. Rhodes, and H.N. Wagner, *J. Nucl. Med.* **11**, 379–382 (1970).

86. J.M. Gallo, C.T. Hung, and D.G. Perrier, *Int. J. Pharm.* **22**, 63–68 (1984).

87. Y. Lou and M.J. Groves, *Pharm. Sci.* **1**, 355–358 (1995).

88. Y. Lou and M.J. Groves, *J. Pharm. Pharmacol.* **47**, 97–102 (1995).

89. W. Friess and G. Lee, *Biomaterials* **17**, 2289–2294 (1996).

90. W. Friess, G. Lee, and M.J. Groves, *Pharm. Dev. Technol.* **1**(2), 185–193 (1996).

91. W. Friess, W. Zhou, and M.J. Groves, *Pharm. Sci.* **2**, 121–124 (1996).

92. D.J. Prockop and D.J.S. Hulmes, in: D. Yurchenco, D. Birk, and R. Mechan eds., *Extracellular Matrix Assembly and Structure*, 1994, pp. 95–104.

93. T. Herning, M. Djabourou, J. Leblond, and G. Takerkart, *Polymer* **32**(17), 3211–3217 (1991).

94. C.A. Farrugia, Ph.D. Thesis, University of Illinois, Chicago, 1998.

95. P.M. Zavlin et al., *Anal. Ind. Gelatins High-Perform. Liq. Chromatogr. Gel Electrophoresis*, 1993.

96. B. Elysée-Collen and R.W. Lencki, *J. Agric. Food Chem.* **44**, 1651–1657 (1996).

97. H.G. Bundenberg de Jong, in H.R. Kruyt, ed., *Colloid Science*, Elsevier, New York, 1949, pp. 250–258.

98. W.P. Olson, Ph.D. Thesis, University of Illinois at Chicago, 1992.

99. Y. Lou et al., *J. Pharm. Pharmacol.* **47**, 177–181 (1995).

100. M.J. Humphries, *J. Cell Biol.* **103**, 2637–2647 (1990).

101. K. Nakamura, S. Kashiwagi, and K. Takeo, *J. Chromatogr.* **597**, 351–356 (1992).

102. T.L. Ratliffe, L.R. Kavoussi, and W.J. Catalonia, *J. Urol.* **139**, 410–414 (1988).

103. R. Engvall and K. Ruoslahti, *Int. J. Cancer* **28**, 1–5 (1977).

104. S.E. Carsons, in S.E. Carsons, ed., *Fibronectin in Health and Disease*, CRC Press, Roca Baton, Fla., 1989, pp. 1–22.

105. M.J. Humphries et al., *J. Clin. Invest.* **81**, 782–790 (1988).

106. S. Akiyama et al., *Cancer Metast. Rev.* **14**, 173–189 (1995).

107. Y. Lou, M.J. Groves, and M.E. Klegerman, *J. Pharm. Pharmacol.* **46**, 863–866 (1994).

108. Y. Tabata and Y. Ikada, *J. Pharm. Pharmacol.* **39**, 698–704 (1987).

109. L. Illum, *Pharm. Res.* **15**(9), 1326–1331 (1998).

110. A. Berthold, K. Cremer, and J. Kreuter, *J. Controlled Release* **39**, 17–25 (1996).

111. A. Domard, *Int. J. Biol. Macromol. Mol.* **9**, 98–104 (1987).

112. C.M. Lehr, J.A. Bouwstra, E.H. Schacht, and H.E. Jüninger, *Int. J. Pharm.* **78**, 43–48 (1992).

113. P. Calvo, R. Remuñan-López, C.J.L. Vila-Jato, and M.J. Alonso, *Pharm. Res.* **14**, 1431–1436 (1997).

114. N.G.M. Schipper et al., *Pharm. Res.* **14**, 923–929 (1997).

115. R.A.A. Muzzarelli, *Cell. Mol. Life Sci.* **53**, 131–140 (1997).

116. G. Peluso et al., *Biomaterials* **15**, 1215–1220 (1994).

117. B.C. Thanoo, M.C. Sunny, and A. Jayakrishnan, *J. Pharm. Pharmacol.* **44**, 283–286 (1992).

118. J. Akbuga and G. Darmaz, *Int. J. Pharm.* **111**, 217–222 (1996).

119. X.X. Tian, Ph.D. Thesis, University of Illinois at Chicago, 1998.

120. R. Guy, M. Powell, J. Fix, and K. Park, *Pharm. Res.* **13**(12), 1759 (1996).

PATENTS AND OTHER INTELLECTUAL PROPERTY RIGHTS IN DRUG DELIVERY

PATREA PABST
Arnall Golden & Gregory, LLP
Atlanta, Georgia

KEY WORDS

Copyright

Enablement

Infringement

Intellectual property

Inventor

Nonobviousness

Novelty

Patent

Trademark

Trade secret

OUTLINE

Advancements in drug delivery technology often are achieved only through substantial investment of industrial, academic, and governmental resources. Patenting of these technological advancements is frequently employed to recoup that investment, to create profits that are used in part to develop new or improved products, and to enhance a competitive commercial edge. Other forms of intellectual property protection, such as trade secrets, copyrights, and trademarks, may also be used to further protect and exploit drug delivery processes, products, and services.

One of the most frequently asked questions is, why do we need to go to the trouble and expense of patenting a composition or method? The most common reason is that protecting a new composition or method of manufacture or use provides a means for obtaining the revenue required to develop a new drug or medical treatment. With the cost of developing and obtaining regulatory approval for a new drug approaching $200 million dollars in the United States, patent rights are essential to recovering expenses. For small companies that spend more time raising money then selling products, patents and patent applications represent the only tangible assets that they can show to potential investors. For universities and other nonprofit research institutions, patents and associated know-how and, in some limited cases, trade secrets, can be used to obtain royalties from license agreements, sponsored research funding in many cases, and equity in new companies started for the purpose of exploiting the technology.

Patents and other intellectual property are valued in many different ways. For example, a process for manufacture would typically be licensed for 2–3% of the gross selling price of a product of the process. This price would be decreased if multiple licenses had to be obtained to use the process. Patents claiming compositions tend to have a greater market value, for example, between 5 and 10% of the gross selling price, owing to the perception that these patents are easier to enforce than process patents.

Enforcement, however, is a risky business. A good patent strategy is to obtain patents that claim a product, methods of manufacture, and methods of use, broadly and specifically, so that a patentee is able to assert multiple patents against an alleged infringer. Patents with broad claims will generally be easier to invalidate than more specific patents. Faced with the prospect of fighting several patents, most parties will opt for settlement. The alternative, litigation, is extraordinarily expensive for both parties and can result in the patents being invalidated or the infringer being liable not only for damages for infringement but also attorney's fees and punitive damages.

Invention usually consists of two steps: conception and reduction to practice. There are two kinds of reduction to practice: actual and constructive. Constructive practice means that the applicant has described in the application for patent *how* to make and use that which is claimed but has not actually made and used what is claimed. This may be as simple as stating that although a biodegradable polymer such as poly(lactic acid-*co*-glycolic acid) is preferred for making a matrix for drug delivery, other biodegradable polymers such as poly(orthoesters)s or poly(anhydride)s could also be used. It may be less obvious that other drugs may be used when only one example showing reduction to practice of a type of drug is available. The rule of thumb in this case is the level of predictability. Therefore, in stating what kind of drugs one could deliver using the claimed technology, one might list a wide variety of drugs based on the data available with one type of drug. However, delivery of a peptide or a very hydrophobic compound, which usually are viewed as difficult to deliver, may or may not be possible to list based on data obtained with a drug that is relatively easy to delivery, such as a sugar or low-molecular-weight dye. Being too predictive (i.e., engaging in extensive constructive reduction to practice), which includes "nonenabling" or non-enabled technology, may in some cases be a detriment during prosecution of subsequently filed applications because the examiner may cite the earlier work as making obvious the applicant's subsequent work. Patent attorneys frequently must play a balancing game in determining how far to go with constructive reduction to practice to exclude competitors while not eliminating the applicant's own ability to obtain additional, subsequent patent protection.

In the United States, there is a requirement to disclose the best mode for practicing that which is claimed at the time of filing the application. No similar requirement exists outside of the United States. Because most applicants file the same application in the United States as outside of the United States, U.S. applicants frequently disclose their best mode in foreign-filed applications. Furthermore, U.S. applications are not published until they are issued as a patent, whereas applications filed in other countries are published 18 months after their earliest priority date. Thus, it may be desirable in some cases to omit the preferred embodiment as of the date of the foreign filing to prevent one's competitors from knowing the best mode for practicing the invention until the U.S. patent is issued, which may be many years after publication of the corresponding foreign application. However, this strategy may create a problem, as patent laws vary from country to country. In particular, Japan has, in the past, required one to provide examples of that which one intends to claim, thus limiting available protection.

Patent Term and Provisional Applications

A patent is awarded by individual government entities for a defined period of time. In most cases that period of time will run 20 years from the initial date of filing an application for patent. In some cases, the term can be shortened, for example, by disclaimers of patent term in view of earlier issued patents, or lengthened, owing to delays relating to appeals or regulatory approval. Provisional applications are useful for delaying the filing of a utility patent application while simultaneously serving to establish priority over subject matter disclosed within the provisional application.

Patent Term. Under the revised U.S. patent law that was enacted as a result of implementation of GATT, the term of a patent is 20 years from the original date of filing or the filing date of the earlier application to which priority is claimed. Applicants therefore have more incentive to prosecute all claims in a single application to minimize costs for prosecuting and maintaining the patent. Under the law in effect prior to June 8, 1995, the patent term was 17 years from the date of issue in the United States. Divisional applications were a commonly used method to extent patent protection to encompass different aspects of the technology over a period of time much greater than 17 years. For example, an application would be filed in 1990, and a single inventive concept (e.g., the composition) would be prosecuted in the first application. Three years later, when those claims were allowable and a patent was to issue, a divisional application would be filed with another set of the claims that had been restricted out of the original application. This divisional application would be prosecuted for another 2 to 3 years, the claims would be determined to be allowable, the second patent would issue with a 17-year term, and a third divisional application would be filed. The result is that patents on related technology would issue sequentially over several years, increasing the effective term of patent protection beyond 20 years. Under the new law, this mechanism to extend patent protection is not possible.

GATT was signed into law in the United States on December 7, 1994, and the initial provisions affecting U.S. patent practice were implemented June 8, 1995. The most significant changes arising from enactment of that agreement, now called the Uruguay Round Act, were changes in the patent term in the United States, the implementation of provisional patent applications, and the broadening of what constitutes infringement in the United States. The change in patent term has already been discussed. For those applications filed before June 8, 1995, the term of any issuing patent is 17 years from the date of issue or 20 years from the filing date, whichever is longer. The term of any patent issued on an application filed June 8, 1995 or later is 20 years from the earliest claimed priority date. Extensions of terms are available upon delays in issuance arising from appeals or interferences. Additional extensions of terms are available for delays in obtaining regulatory approval by the U.S. Food & Drug Administration (FDA) for a device or a drug. Legislation is currently pending that would further revise patent terms in the United States.

Because biotechnology is a complex field, especially in the areas of patentable subject matter and enablement, many of the general observations relating to patents may not be as directly applicable to more conventional patentable subject matter. For example, the U.S. Patent Office has consistently maintained that the change from a 17-year term from the date of issue to a 20-year term from the earliest priority date will not result in a significant loss of patent right. However, because the Patent Office applies such a stringent examination proceeding under §112 (enablement) in the biotechnology area, its assertion is likely untrue. Issue time in these cases typically has been considerably longer, not uncommonly taking as many as 5 to 7 years from the original priority date. The result is that these complex biotechnology patents will have a substantially shortened term as compared with many other types of patents. Because a patent extension can still be obtained for delays due to regulatory issues involving the FDA, as well as for appeals to the Board of Patent Appeals and Interferences, those in the United States who believe that their patent rights will be limited in term due to delays in prosecution should avail themselves of the Patent Extension Act if at all possible. One must bear in mind, however, that an extension for regulatory delays can only be obtained on *one* patent for any particular product or process; thus, the inventor or licensee with multiple, related patents clearly should choose the most important patent or the patent subject to the greatest increase in patent term when facing such a situation. The patent that is to be extended must be brought to the attention of the FDA. Following FDA approval of the claimed product or process, the extension must be applied for in a timely fashion.

Provisional Patent Applications. Provisional patent applications, while new to the United States, have been utilized for many years in other countries, such as the United Kingdom and Australia. These applications are a mechanism for obtaining a filing date at minimal cost and with fewer requirements for completeness of the application and determination of the inventive entity for a period of 1 year. The provisional application ceases to exist 12 months after the date of filing. If an application is filed as a provisional application, it can be converted to a standard utility application at any time during the 12-month period after filing. Alternatively, it can serve as a basis for a claim to priority in a subsequently filed utility application if the utility application is filed prior to the expiration of the 1-year life of the provisional application.

Although touted as a great benefit to the small entity or individual applicant, provisional applications have the same requirements for disclosure as a standard utility application. Failure in the provisional application to completely disclose and enable that which is subsequently claimed in an utility application can result in a loss of the claim to priority to the provisional application if that which is claimed is not enabled. Merely filing an article that will be published or presented to avoid loss of foreign rights usually will not comply with the enablement requirements and therefore will not serve as an adequate basis for priority. It is essential that applicants who file provisional applications based on an article amplify the description to encompass other embodiments and to provide the basis by which one of ordinary skill in the art can practice that which is claimed. Application sections that are not required for enablement but that are typically included in a utility application include the background of the invention, the problems that the claimed invention addresses, and the claims. These sections can be omitted from the provisional application, thus saving time and money in preparing the application. In many cases, fairly standard language can be used to expand or broaden the description in an article to meet the enablement requirements, providing a means for those with limited amounts of time or money to protect that which they are disclosing with minimum risk and expenditure.

The World Intellectual Property Organization (WIPO), which implements the provisions of the Patent Cooperative Treaty (PCT) and the European Patent Office, has confirmed that U.S. provisional applications serve as an adequate basis for a claim to priority in corresponding foreign file applications. However, under the Patent Convention, all foreign applications that claim priority from a previously filed application must still be filed within 1 year of the U.S. filing date or the filing date of the country in which the first application is originally filed.

Patent Procedure and its Implications to Inventors

An elaborate, detailed body of law and regulations has evolved to govern the granting of patents. These laws and regulations define, among other things, (1) the procedural steps that the Patent Office and applicant may undergo, (2) which individuals actually are the inventors of a particular claimed invention, and (3) the number of inventions or embodiments of an invention that properly can be claimed in a single patent. These laws and regulations also suggest certain beneficial habits, such as record keeping, that research scientists and other would-be inventors should undertake to facilitate issuance and enforcement of their patents.

Application Procedure. When a patent application is filed in the United States, it will be assigned to an examiner for review of the relevant prior art and for prosecution. The examiner may restrict the claims into more than one group, if, in his view, the claims are directed to patentably distinct inventions (see "Restriction Practice/Unity of Invention"). The nonelected claims can then be filed in divisional applications, which have the same effective filing date but issue as separate patents. The examiner likely will issue one or more office actions, objecting to the specification or rejecting the claims as lacking novelty, being obvious, not enabling the breadth of the claims, being indefinite, or a combination thereof. The applicant can amend the claims and present arguments and supporting data to overcome the rejections. The specification, or description, cannot be amended to add new matter once the application is filed. In many cases, an agreement will be reached as to what claims are allowable, and a patent will issue. In the event that the examiner finally rejects the claim and the applicant has exhausted her opportunities to respond to the rejections, an appeal to the Board of Patent Appeals and Interferences can be filed. A decision by the Board, which can be based not only on argument and data submitted during the prosecution of the application but also an oral hearing, typically will require 3 to 6 years. The applicant's only recourse following a negative decision by the Board is to file an appeal in the U.S. Court of Appeals for the Federal Circuit.

In the United States, patent applications are typically examined by a single examiner. In the European Patent Office, examination may be conducted by an examiner other than the one who conducted the initial search and issuance of a search report. If the applicant in the European Patent Office requests oral proceedings, at which oral arguments may be presented, the oral proceedings are held before a panel of three examiners, not just the original examiner. In contrast, the U.S. proceedings are between the applicant and the examiner, although the examiner's supervisor or a quality control specialist may be asked to attend if an in-person interview is held. In all cases, there are appeal procedures if an examiner maintains his rejection of the claims, asserting that the claims lack novelty, are obvious, or are insufficiently enabled.

Inventorship. The U.S. Constitution provides that inventors have the exclusive right to their discoveries (9). An application for patent must be made by the inventor, or under certain circumstances (such as when the inventor is dead) by persons on behalf of the inventor (10). When more than one person made the invention, the inventors are required to file jointly "even though they did not physically work together or at the same time, each did not make the same type or amount of contribution, or each did not make a contribution to the subject matter of every claim of the patent" (11). A patent may be invalidated if it names one who is not an inventor or if it fails to name an inventor, however, these errors may be corrected if they were not committed with an intention to deceive (12).

In a nutshell, an inventor is one who conceives and/or reduces to practice the claimed invention on his own and not at the direction of another. University settings are somewhat unique when it comes to determining what is prior art and what is the invention of another because it is often difficult to determine who is the inventor. When one attempts to remove prior art by demonstrating that one has conceived and reduced practice prior to the publication, one must first determine who the inventors are and whether the publication is in fact a publication by another entity. If the publication is the inventors' own, then it is easier to swear behind because they must have conceived and reduced to practice prior to that publication. Merely because a publication is coauthored by one of the inventors does not mean that the publication is the inventors' own work. There must be complete identity between the named authors and the inventors for the publication to be the inventors' own work. Publications typically will include coauthors who do not meet the legal definition of an inventor.

To determine who the inventors are, one must first ascertain that which is claimed. Second, one must determine what is already in the prior art; one is not an inventor if the claimed matter is already in the prior art. For example, if one is claiming a polymeric drug delivery device and the claim defines the matrix structure as formed from biodegradable polymer, then this particular element is probably already in the prior art, and that element alone would not be the invention of any named inventor upon the application for patent. However, if the polymeric matrix were defined as having a particular structure or shape or composition that has not previously been defined, then the

individual (or individuals) who determines that shape or structure or composition would be an inventor. In methods for manufacture, the person who is in the laboratory using the method may or may not be an inventor. If this person has been told by another to go and make composition X using steps A, B, and C, then the person who performs the method is not an inventor—even if there is some optimization of the concentration or selection of reagents or conditions under which they are combined. If, however, that person determines that it is essential to use a concentration 10 times greater than what she has been told to make it work, then she may be an inventor of the method of use. A patent may name multiple parties as inventors. They do not all have to be inventors of each and every claim that defines the invention. One person may be an inventor of composition claims, another the method of manufacture claims, and yet another the method of use claims. Inventorship may need to be corrected following a restriction requirement or after cancellation or amendment of the claims.

The definition of *inventor* elicits questions about the definitions of *conception* and *reduction to practice*. In a university research laboratory, has a graduate student participated in the conception of his professor's invention if he conducted the experiments under her direction that resulted in the reduction to practice, that is, the synthesis of the claimed protein? Did the professor conceive the invention if she thought of the general idea and desired result but left it to the graduate student to figure out how to synthesize the protein? Is the professor's conception of a protein and the detailed steps of producing it an invention if she has not yet actually reduced her idea to practice by synthesizing the protein? And in a different laboratory, is a technician an inventor if he added bearings to the design that the supervising engineer told him to build? In each case, who, if anyone, is an inventor?

Conception is "the formation in the mind of the inventor of a definite and permanent idea of the complete and operative invention as it is thereafter to be applied in practice," such that a person of ordinary skill in the art would be enabled to convert the idea to tangible form without extensive research or experimentation (13). Usually, one who conceives the inventive idea, or part of it, is an inventor, while those who perform the ordinary interim experimentation under the direction of the inventor in reducing the inventive concept to practice are not defined as inventors. Conception followed by reduction to practice is a common sequence during invention, but invention may result from other sequences of events. For example, conception and reduction to practice may occur together, or unexpected discovery coupled with recognition of the discovery as something new and useful may occur without previous conception. For invention to be complete, the inventor's conception must include a clear idea of how the new product, process, or machine can be reduced to practice, or put into a tangible form. Reduction to practice may be done by persons other than the inventor if they work under his or her direction. In both university and commercial laboratories, an invention may occur through discovery without any previous conception. This type of invention is not formulated by conception of the inventive idea followed by reduction to practice, as described earlier. Rather, the invention occurs through discovery coupled with recognition that the product, process, machine, or combination is new and useful. Experimentation involved in reduction to practice may also be part of conception.

Although coauthors may choose not to be named on a paper, the law requires that every person who contributes any part of what is claimed in a patent application must be named. If, in the course of prosecution of the patent application, all claims that reflect the contribution of one inventor are cancelled or rejected, that inventor's name must also be removed. There is an implicit lack of equality in coauthorship. Generally, the first or last listed author is considered to be the primary originator of the new ideas and data in the paper, and the others are assumed to be secondary collaborators. Joint inventors, however, are equal in the rights of patent that accrue to them, having a joint and undivided interest, unless they agree otherwise (14). Even though they did not conceive exactly the same idea together or each created a different part of the whole invention or the contribution of one was only a small but essential part of the invention, all are joint inventors and share an equal right to exclude others from making, using, or selling the claimed invention. In practice, university policy usually dictates that joint inventors assign ownership of the patent to the university, while the royalties that may accrue if the patent is licensed and the invention is marketed are allocated between the university and the inventors. The inventors' share of the royalties is distributed equally among them, unless they have contracted otherwise.

Ownership of the technology claimed in a patent is contractual. Unlike inventorship, ownership can be transferred by one or all of the inventors to one or more other entities merely by executing an agreement. Rights to use the technology can be granted by licensing of the patent to an entity by the owner of the technology. Once ownership is transferred from the inventors, they no longer have the right to allow a third party to make, use, sell, offer to sell, or impart that which is claimed. In fact, if a patent is exclusively licensed, or assigned, to another party, then the inventor and/or the assignee transferring the rights away will no longer be able to use the technology. In many cases, it may be important to retain the right to use the technology for noncommercial purposes (i.e., further research and development).

Provisional applications differ from standard utility applications in that there is no requirement to name all, or even the correct, inventors; neither do the inventors have to file a disclaimer of inventorship stating they believe they are the correct inventors of the claimed technology. This is in keeping with the absence of a requirement for having claims defining what applicants think constitutes their invention.

Outside of the United States, patent applications frequently are filed by the assignee rather than by the inventors. Inventorship is not usually a basis for challenging a foreign patent, and declarations of inventorship are not always required. A patent applicant may not even need an assignment to file and prosecute the foreign patent application.

Restriction Practice/Unity of Invention. A patent must have claims directed solely to a single invention (15). Guidelines for determining what constitutes a single invention in the United States are published in the *Manual of Patent Examining Procedures* (MPEP). For example, if the applicant has claims to a composition, a method of making that composition, and the method for using the composition, an examiner in the U.S. Patent Office may determine that multiple inventions are defined by the claims in the application as filed, and the examiner will require cancellation of the claims to all but the method of manufacture or use or composition from the application. The applicant would then be allowed to prosecute the elected claims in that application and file what are referred to as divisional applications with the nonelected claims, which may ultimately issue as a second or third patent. The effective priority date would still be the original filing date.

The standards for "unity of invention" are highly variable even within the United States, and U.S. standards are at wide variance with the standards of most foreign patent offices. One advantage of prosecuting PCT applications (discussed later) in the European Patent Office is the lower cost owing to far fewer restrictions being made.

Duty of Disclosure. Another unique requirement of the U.S. patent law is the duty of disclosure, described by Chapter 37 of the Code of Federal Regulations (C.F.R.), § 1.56. Applicants are required to submit to the examiner in the U.S. Patent Office copies of all publications or other materials that may be determined by an examiner to be material to examination of the claimed subject matter (16). Foreign publications must be accompanied by an English translation if they are not in English, although in some cases this may be limited to an abstract. Failure to cite relevant prior art to the Patent Office can result in a subsequent finding by an appropriate court of jurisdiction that the patent is invalid for fraud and violation of the duty of disclosure. Under the current standard, the applicant is not required to describe the relevance of the cited publication but may merely cite the publication and provide a copy to the examiner for the examiner's review. When many publications are being cited to the Patent Office, it may facilitate review to group the publications or even distinguish those that the applicant believes are most relevant. As discussed earlier, prior art includes oral or written publications made prior to applicant's filing date by applicant or any other entity. Relevance of material is more difficult to define. This requirement is in the process of again being revised and may soon change.

Record Keeping. It is extremely important in the intellectual property area that proper records be maintained. Laboratory notebooks should be completed and maintained in chronological order. Notebook pages should be consecutively numbered, entries should be recorded in ink, and each page should be signed and dated by the party making the entry. Furthermore, it is preferred that each page be witnessed at a time contemporaneous to the date the entries are made by one who is qualified to understand what is being entered on the page. The party does not have to completely understand every aspect of the entry; he or she merely must be qualified to say, with some degree of certainty, what the entries on that page were.

Laboratory notebooks are used to show the origin of an invention. This may be important if there is a dispute as to ownership, if there is a dispute as to inventorship, or to prove priority of inventorship where, in the United States, patent rights are awarded to the first party to invent as opposed to the first party to file a patent application. Proceedings conducted by the U.S. Patent Office to determine priority of inventorship are referred to as *interferences*. The laws and regulations governing interferences were changed following enactment of GATT to allow parties other than those residing and inventing in the United States to obtain a patent in a dispute with another party also claiming the same subject matter by demonstrating that they were the first to conceive and reduce to practice. Interference law is very complicated. In the biotechnology area, the dates of inventorship are frequently within weeks of each other. Moreover, the courts have increasingly altered the law regarding what is conception and reduction to practice as applied to the biotechnology field (17). As a result, it has become much more difficult to predict what acts ultimately will be critical in showing priority of inventorship. Accordingly, accurate record keeping by all members of a research group is extremely important.

Infringement

In addition to changes in patent term and creation of provisional patent applications, passage of GATT changed the definition of infringement in the United States. One who, without authority, makes, uses, offers to sell, or sells any patented invention within the United States or imports into the United States any patented invention during the term of the patent therefor infringes the patent (18). In the United States, a claim for infringement cannot be made until after issuance of the patent. In some other countries, including the European Patent Convention countries, translated claims can be filed prior to issuance of the patent, and damages can be backdated to the date of filing the translated claim once the patent issues. In the United States, a patent application is secret until it is issued as a patent, at which point it is published and can be asserted against parties whom the patent owner or exclusive licensee of the patent believes are infringing the claims, that is, against those they believe are making, using, selling, or importing subject matter falling within the scope of the issued patent's claims.

A party who believes that an issued U.S. patent is not valid may file a request for reexamination, citing art that was not made of record during the prosecution of the patent. If the patent is asserted against the party, that party may go into federal district court and ask for a declaratory judgment that the patent claims are invalid or that they are not infringed. In Europe, and in many other countries, there is a postgrant opposition proceeding available. In the European Patent Office, there is also a process whereby one may file observations during the prosecution of an application, which is public, unlike in the United States. Third-party observations can be used as a means to bring

relevant prior art, mischaracterized prior art, or problems relating to enablement to the attention of the European patent examiner and may result in revocation of the patent or narrowing of the claims.

TRADE SECRETS, COPYRIGHTS, AND TRADEMARKS

Other types of intellectual property that may have applicability to drug delivery technology include trade secrets and, to a lesser degree, copyrights and trademarks. Trade secret protection of an invention may be an appropriate alternative to patent protection for an invention or discovery in certain competitive circumstances. Copyrights and trademarks, which do not protect ideas or inventions, may have value in protecting other facets of a business related to the drug delivery technology. These three types of intellectual property are only briefly described in the following sections.

Trade Secrets

Trade secrets can be compositions or methods of manufacture or even uses that are maintained in secrecy. Most companies that have optimized methods for manufacture (e.g., methods for processing polymers to impart the most desirable physical and chemical properties) keep them secret. Trade secrets are unlimited in term but must be actively protected; they are lost if another party independently derives the same method or composition that is being maintained as a trade secret. Unlike patents, trade secrets are defined by and enforced pursuant to state laws. Trade secrets may be protected by asserting laws relating specifically to trade secrets as well as unfair competition and business practices.

To maintain the process or product as a secret, one must (*1*) not disclose the process or product in public and (*2*) take affirmative steps to protect the information from public disclosure. This duty includes informing parties who may accidentally become aware of the technology, as well as those who are intentionally informed regarding the technology, that the material is a trade secret and is to be maintained in confidence. Laboratory notebooks describing processes or products that are considered proprietary should be maintained in designated areas labeled "confidential" or "restricted access." Employees involved in the use of the trade secrets should be informed that the material is to be maintained as confidential and that breach of any agreement with the company by disclosing the trade secrets to a third party could result in irreparable harm and therefore be subject to injunctive relief. Trade secrets cease to be trade secrets upon public disclosure, as already discussed, or when they are independently developed by another party. If a third party independently develops the trade secret, the original holder of the trade secret has no recourse unless she can prove that the secret was acquired by theft, fraud, or other improper means. Unlike patents, which have a defined term during which the patentee can exclude others from competition, trade secrets are subject to no similar limitation. One of the most famous trade secrets is the formula for the original Coca-Cola®, which has been kept in secret for decades and is enormously valuable, demonstrating that it is not just patents that have value as an asset to a company.

Copyrights

Copyright protects original works of authorship fixed in any tangible medium of expression (19). Unlike patent and trade secret law, however, copyrights do not protect an idea but only the expression of that idea. Copyright protection may extend, for example, to visual depictions of products or to advertising material associated with the use and sale of products. Also, copyright may protect computer software programs, publications, protocols, or other materials. In many cases where the author is employed or engaged as a consultant, the copyrights will be owned by the party contracting with the author, the journal publishing the work, or the employer. Copyrights, which also can be extremely valuable, are transferable and enforceable under U.S. law and in many foreign jurisdictions as a result of international agreements relating to copyrights.

Trademarks

Trademarks are typically associated with the sale of goods or services and are used to denote the origin of the goods or services. Advantages of trademarks are that they are not limited in term, and rights arise upon use in either intra- or interstate commerce. One very well-known trademark is Coca-Cola®, which has been in continuous use since before the turn of the century. The company has used the trademark in combination with retaining the formula as a trade secret to create enormous value for itself. A company name, as well as a product name, can be a trademark. A trademark can be a name design or combination thereof. The trademark cannot be generic or totally descriptive of the product, and it must be distinct enough from other trademarks in a similar field of use or similar good or service to avoid any likelihood of confusion as to the origin of the good or service among the consumers of the trademark good or service. Trademarks can be protected under either state or federal law. An applicant for a trademark registration must show that the trademark has been used in *intra*state commerce for a state registration and *inter*state commerce for a federal registration. A federal "intent to use" application can be used to preserve the right to use a trademark prior to actual use in commerce. This provides for an initial determination of the registerability of the trademark, in other words, that the mark is not already in use by another in a way that would be confusingly similar to the applicant's use and that the mark is not generic or descriptive and not contrary to the public interest.

EXPLOITING INTELLECTUAL PROPERTY RIGHTS

As is now evident, intellectual property rights help increase the value of technology. This is easiest to place in perspective and understand in relation to patents. Patents give the patent owner the right to exclude competition. This is accomplished by asserting the patent against third parties who are marketing a product or service that falls within the scope of the claims. Referred to as *infringement*,

the criteria are totally different from the criteria for obtaining a patent, referred to as *patentability*. In simple terms, a patent claim consists of elements in a defined relationship. Certain phrases expand or limit the scope of the claim. For example, the term *comprising* can be translated as "including at least," whereas *consisting* means "including only." If a claim reads as follows: "Composition comprising: A, B, and C," then the claim would cover any composition including A, B, C, and any other component. Use of the term *consisting* would restrict the claim to a composition including *only* A, B, and C.

In determining infringement, one must look to the claims of the patent. Claims may be clear on their face or require reference to the specification, or description, of the patent. Claims may also be limited by agreements made during prosecution, a doctrine referred to as "file wrapper estoppel." For example, if the prosecuting attorney argues that the claims distinguish over the prior art on the basis that the prior art does not disclose a particular feature that the attorney argues is essential to the claims in the patent, then the claims will be construed to require that limitation, even if not explicitly recited in the claims as issued.

Asserting a patent allows the alleged infringer to file an action for declaratory judgment in a federal district court, asking the judge to declare the patent invalid or noninfringed. Litigation is very expensive and especially detrimental to small companies, thus providing a great deal of incentive to license the technology on terms favorable to both parties.

SUMMARY

Intellectual property rights provide a means for the owners of technology to recover their investment in the technology and, in some cases, to make a profit. More importantly, intellectual property rights provide a means for financing the incredibly expensive research and development and testing required for commercialization of new products and processes in the medical and biotechnology field. When the intellectual property rights have been lost or given away by publication, many times it is not possible to obtain the money required to see a product or process reach the clinic and benefit those for whom it is intended. It is only by protecting the technology that it can be used to help those who need it the most.

BIBLIOGRAPHY

1. U.S. Code, Title 35, Section 101, 1988.
2. See *Diamond v. Chakrabarty*, 447 U.S. 303,206 U.S. Patent Quarterly 193 (1980).
3. U.S. Code, Title 35, Section 102, 1988.
4. *Philips Elec. & Pharmaceutical Indus. Corp. v. Thermal & Elec. Indus., Inc.*, 450 F.2d 1164, 1169–1172, 171 U.S. Patent Quarterly 641 (3d Cir., 1971); *Gulliksen v. Halberg*, 75 U.S. Patent Quarterly 252 (Pat. Off. Bd. Int'f., 1937).
5. *Ciba-Geigy Corp. v. ALZA Corp.*, 864 F. Supp. 429, 33 U.S. Patent Quarterly 2d 1018 (D.N.J., 1994).
6. U.S. Code, Title 35, Section 103, 1998.
7. *Graham v. John Deere Co.*, 383 U.S. 1,148 U.S. Patent Quarterly 459 (1966).

fuse through the lysosomal membrane into the cytoplasm for cellular metabolism or removal. Macromolecules which are not degraded accumulate in the secondary lysosomes and can only be released slowly by exocytosis or upon cell death.

Lysosomotropic Delivery

De Duve and colleagues first suggested that macromolecules, particularly proteins, might be used to conjugate drugs and therefore restrict drug uptake by cells to the pinocytic route. This ensures that the secondary lysosomal compartment acts as a gateway for drug entry into the cell. They coined the term "lysosomotropic drugs" to describe compounds that exhibit pharmacological properties after internalization and delivery via this route (25).

Possessing the knowledge that macromolecular uptake by cells is limited to the pinocytic route (25,26), and that soluble synthetic polymers could be used as blood expanders (27,28), as prophylactics against radiation exposure (29), and as pharmacologically active agents (30–33), Ringsdorf proposed that polymers could also be systematically developed into targetable drug carriers (21,34,35), and that hydrophilic polymeric carriers could be used to solubilize poorly water-soluble drugs. His now famous model described how a polymer–drug linker might be used to allow controlled drug liberation at the target site. The model also proposed the coconjugation of targeting moieties capable of mediating cell-specific targeting.

The change in milieu during cellular internalization and the presence of specific lysosomal hydrolases provides the opportunity to design polymer–drug linkers from which drug is cleaved from the polymer only in the environment of the endosome or lysosome. This has allowed the design of polymeric anticancer conjugates that are essentially nontoxic in the extracellular environment (18). Ultimate antitumor activity is dependent on the efficient liberation of an active form of the drug from the polymer which can then permeate through the lysosome membrane into the cytoplasm to reach the pharmacological target. Structural characteristics of the released molecules including charge and hydrophobicity can influence the permeation rate of these molecules out of the lysosome; however, diffusion from the lysosome readily occurs at molecular weights below 200–220 Da (36–38).

Passive and Active Targeting of Polymer–Drug Conjugates

As conjugation of low molecular weight drugs to polymeric carriers restricts cellular uptake to the endocytic route, the biodistribution of conjugated drug is significantly changed. Increasingly, unequivocal evidence has shown that solid tumors exhibit enhanced or hyperpermeability of the tumor vasculature (39–44), and this, combined with the decreased lymphatic drainage of tumor tissue compared with healthy tissue (39,45), can produce significant tumor targeting of polymer–drug conjugates and particulate carriers that have a lengthy plasma residence time. Maeda and coworkers termed the passive targeting of polymer conjugates to solid tumor tissue the "enhanced permeability and retention" (EPR) effect (Fig. 4) (39,45).

Many macromolecules (39,46,47) passively accumulate within solid tumors, including albumin (48–55), antibodies (56,57), polymers (58,59), and polymer–drug conjugates (60,61). Tumor to blood ratios of the polymer–protein conjugate styrene maleic anhydride-neocarzinostatin (SMANCS) of up to 2,500 were measured in a rabbit tumor model (62,63) and N-(2-hydroxypropyl)methacrylamide (HPMA) copolymer–doxorubicin conjugates have shown tumor accumulation ranging from 2 to 20% dose/g in a B16F10 tumor model (64,65). Observations that tumor blood vessels are permeable to liposomes and particles in the size range 200 to 600 nm (44,66), and that neither the human colon xenograft LS174T (44), B16F10, or sarcoma 180 tumors (60) exhibited differences in tumor uptake of macromolecules in the 10,000 to 800,000 Da molecular weight range are indicative that passive tumor targeting by the EPR effect can be accomplished using polymeric and micellar carriers across a wide molecular weight and size range. Tumor accumulation of polymer–drug conjugates begins immediately after intravenous (i.v.) administration and the plasma concentration of polymer is the main driving force controlling the extent of tumor capture observed (47).

After i.v. administration polymers that do not bind to blood proteins display a plasma clearance that is primarily governed by the rate of kidney glomerular filtration and the rate of liver uptake. Macromolecules of molecular weight of 40,000–70,000 Da readily pass through the kidney glomerulus and are excreted. However, as the solution size of a molecule increases with molecular weight (or by forming supramolecular aggregates), extended blood clearance times result. Structural features including polymer flexibility, charge, and hydrophobicity affect the renal excretion threshold for macromolecules within this size range (67). Neutral, hydrophilic polymers including HPMA copolymers, poly(vinylpyrrolidone) (PVP) and PEG have flexible, loosely coiled solution structures, whereas proteins tend to be charged and exhibit more compact solution structures. For example, the molecular weight threshold limiting glomerular filtration of HPMA copolymer-tyrosinamide in the rat was approximately 45,000 Da (68) and the threshold for proteins is approximately 60,000 Da.

In addition to passive targeting, polymeric–drug conjugates can be targeted to specific cells by incorporation of targeting moieties into the polymer backbone (15,18). This process is termed *active targeting*. Although receptor-mediated endocytosis is highly efficient, particularly when cells display a high density of ligand-specific receptors, localization of a significant percentage of the dose of drug within the target in vivo by active targeting has not been very successful. Many candidate receptors proposed for tumor targeting have broad cellular distribution. For example, transferrin, low density lipoprotein, and growth factor receptors, which display elevated levels on tumor cells, have ubiquitous distribution. Many so-called tumor-specific receptors are actually only tumor-enhanced in terms of numbers of receptors per cell (69–74). Cell-specific receptors are present in the liver (75–78), and these have been used successfully to target polymer–drug conjugates after i.v. administration. For example, HPMA copolymer-doxorubicin containing additionally galactosamine (PK2,

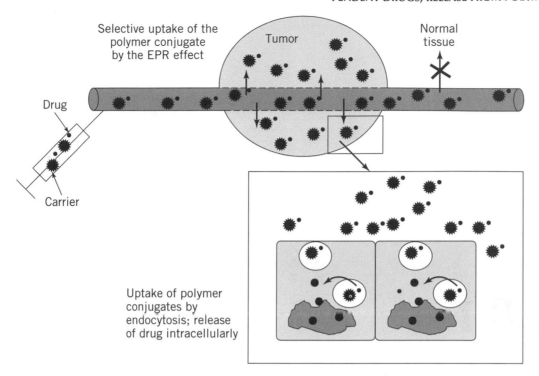

Figure 4. Passive tumor targeting by the EPR effect.

FCE 28069) localizes selectively in the liver due to uptake by the hepatocyte asialoglycoprotein receptor (79,80).

To be effective, it is important that polymer–drug conjugates are designed to improve drug localization in the target tissue, diminish drug exposure in potential sites of toxicity, and optimize drug release rate. Incorporation of a polymer–drug linker that only releases drug at the target site can reduce peak plasma concentrations, thus reducing drug-mediated toxicity. If the drug release rate is optimized, exposure at the target can be tailored to suit the mechanism of action of the pharmacophore being used (e.g., use of cell-cycle dependent antitumor agents) and to prevent the induction of resistance.

SOLUBLE POLYMERIC CARRIERS

An increasing number of soluble polymers have been used as macromolecular partners for pendent chain drug conjugation. Shown in Table 1 are representative examples of several polymers that have been used to prepare polymer–drug conjugates. Many of these polymers have been extensively studied and can be organized into two broad classes: (1) nondegradable synthetic polymers and (2) potentially degradable synthetic polymers and natural polymers. Although several polymers with intrinsic therapeutic activity (81) have been used to conjugate drugs, e.g., copolymers derived from divinylether and maleic anhydride (DIVEMA) and some polysaccharides (82,83), many polymers used for conjugation were selected because they were water-soluble and biocompatible (e.g., did not bind blood proteins and were nonimmunogenic).

Nondegradable Synthetic Polymers

The synthetic polymers PEG and HPMA copolymers have been extensively studied as polymeric drug carriers. They are hydrophilic and are well tolerated in man, but their main disadvantage is that the polymer backbone is not biodegradable in vivo. Only polymers of molecular weight lower than the renal threshold can be used for systemic administration.

Poly(ethylene glycol). PEG is generally recognized as safe and is used in a wide range of pharmaceutical and consumer products (7,84–86). Monodisperse PEG is commercially produced in a range of molecular weights from 200 to over 100,000 Da with various endgroup chemical functionality and morphology, i.e., linear, graft, and star. Although PEG has been widely used to prepare polymer–protein conjugates it is only now being used more widely to conjugate anticancer drugs such as doxorubicin (87), camptothecin (88–90), and paclitaxel (Fig. 5) (91,92). PEG–drug conjugates can be prepared by linking via one terminus or both termini of an end functionalized PEG (see Fig. 5). Usually the PEGs selected for protein conjugation have a molecular weight of 3,400 or 5,000 Da, but for preparation of drug conjugates a wider range of molecular weights has been explored (91,93). Many conjugation strategies have been described (3,4,86). One potential disadvantage is the extent of polymer drug loading, which is limited by the availability of only two reaction sites at the termini of the linear PEG molecule. However, branched PEG polymers (87), alternating PEG polymers [e.g., PEG-lysine (94,95)] and copolymers [e.g., PEG-oligopeptide-PEG (96,97)] with pendent chains capable of conjugating

Table 1. Polymers Used for Pendant Drug Conjugation

Polymer	Linker	Example polymer structures[a]
	Nondegradable synthetic polymers	
HPMA copolymers	Pendent chain; peptidic or acid labile for lysosomal release of covalently conjugated drugs. Pendent chains can be derivatized to chelate metals.	HPMA copolymer
PEG	Typically endgroup (terminal) drug conjugation. Both peptidic and acid labile linkers have been used, but PEG also directly conjugated to drug (i.e., via an ester bond).	PEG
DIVEMA	Metals (e.g., platinum) can be conjugated by chelation directly to the polymer side chains, which are carboxylates.	DIVEMA
	Potentially degradable polyers	
Polysaccharides Dextran Chitosan Carboxymethyl chitin Carboxymethyl pullulan Alginate	Most of these polymers are naturally occurring or can be synthesized from natural metabolites. Polymer usually derivatized to have caboxylate, amine, aldehyde, or reactive moiety on side chain, which is then conjugated with the drug. Can be conjugated with an appropriately derivatized drug to give either peptidic or acid labile pendent chain for lysosomal drug release. Pendent chains are also used to conjugate ligands for multivalent binding onto a cellular membrane surface.	Dextran

Poly[^{5}N-(2-hydroxyethyl)-L-glutamine]

Poly(α-malic acid)

Poly($\alpha\beta$-aspartic acid) block

PEG block

Poly(amino acids)
Poly[^{5}N-(2-hydroxyethyl)-L-glutamine) (PHEG)
β-Poly(2-hydroxyethyl aspartamide) (PHEA)
Poly(glutamic acid)
Poly(aspartic acid)
Polylysine

Polymer side chains tend to be derivatized analogous to polysaccharides to give pendent chain conjugation that can be either peptidic or acid labile. Pendent chains also used to conjugate ligands for multivalent ligand binding on the membrane surface.

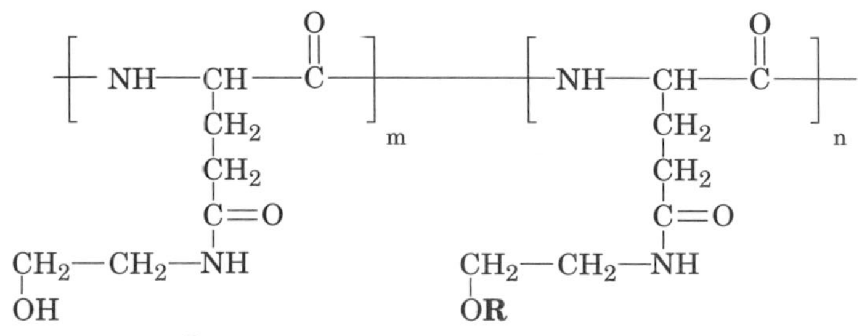

Polyesters
Poly(α or β-malic acid)

Pendent chain options are similar to poly(amino acids).

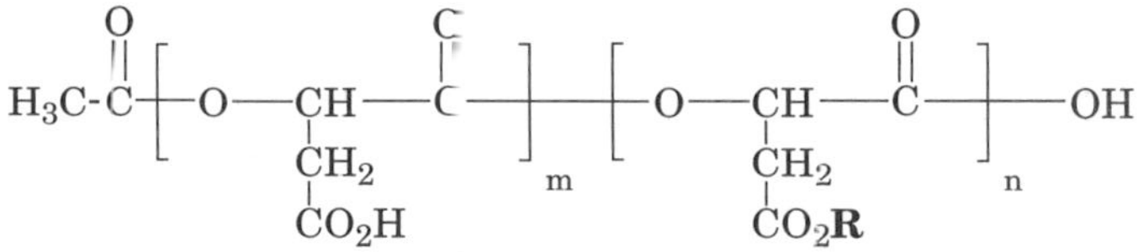

Alternating polymers
PEG-lysine

Provides practical means to incorporate pendent chains in a polymer which is predominantly PEG.

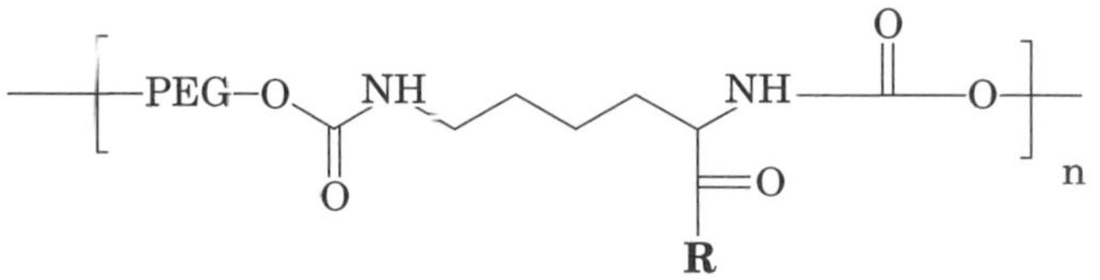

Block copolymers
Poly(ethylene glyco-aspartate)

Formation of polymeric micelles capable of both drug conjugation and entrapment. Linker potential similar to poly(amino acids).

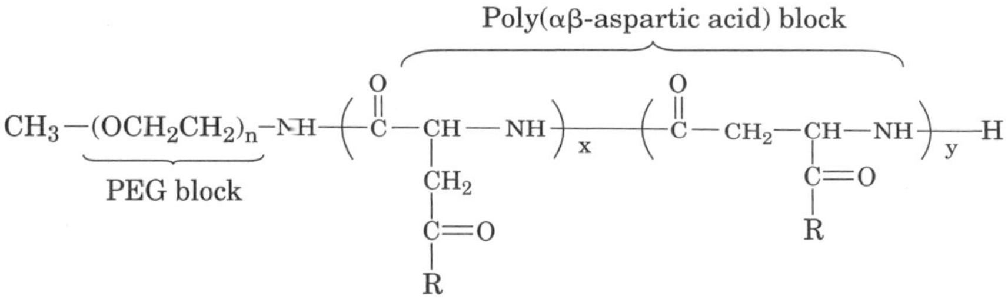

^{a}**R** denotes a pendent chain linker with a conjugated drug.

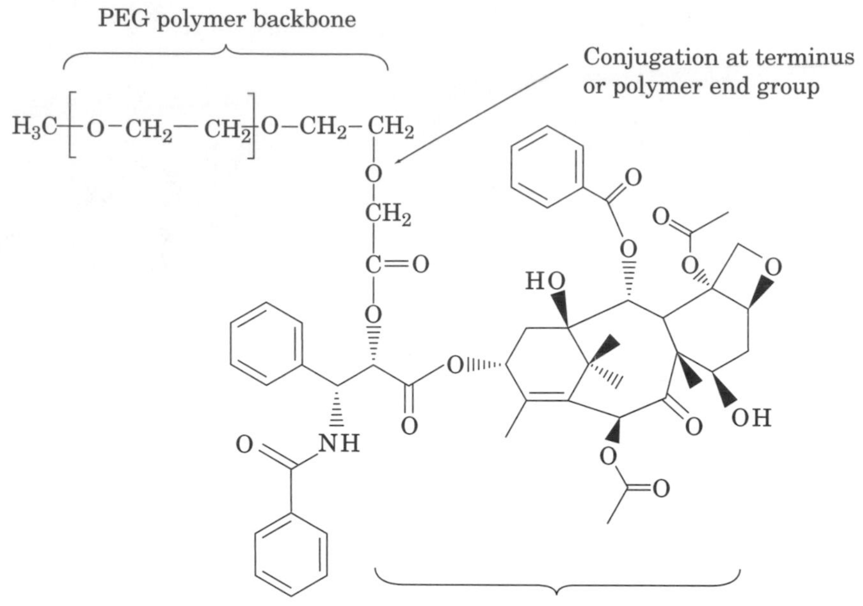

Figure 5. PEG–paclitaxel conjugate (91,92), an example of drug conjugation only at the polymer terminus.

a drug along the polymer backbone, and PEG block copolymers that can form polymeric micelles have recently been prepared (10,11,98–100).

N-(2-Hydroxypropyl)methacrylamide Copolymers. Many synthetic hydrophilic polymers used for drug conjugation are derived from methylacrylamides (e.g., HPMA copolymers). These polymers have generally been prepared by free radical polymerization. HPMA homopolymer is nontoxic up to 30 g/kg, does not bind blood proteins, and is not immunogenic. It was initially developed as a plasma expander (101,102), and copolymers derived from HPMA have been widely used for drug conjugation using pendent chain attachment (Fig. 6) (12,15,18). Early confirmation of low protein binding (103), low complement activation (104), and low immungencity (105–108) was instrumental in establishing the potential of HPMA homo- and copolymers to be used for drug conjugation. Although HPMA copolymers of molecular weight less than 40,000 Da are readily excreted, HPMA copolymers of molecular weight above the renal threshold remain in circulation for long periods and are retained in the body, typically exhibiting accumulation in the reticuloendothelial system (RES) and skin (68). It is imperative that the systemic use of nondegradable polymers such as HPMA copolymers, PEG, and PVP is limited to molecules of a molecular weight that is readily cleared, otherwise long-term deleterious accumulation in healthy tissue could result (68,109–112).

Potentially Biodegradable Polymers

Polysaccharides. Some polysaccharides have the advantage of being enzymatically biodegradable, e.g., dextran, and can therefore be administered over a wider molecular weight range without the fear of prolonged accumulation in the body. However, polysaccharides lack structural uniformity and exhibit the propensity upon chemical modification (i.e., drug conjugation) to become immunogenic or

nondegradable (113,114). Dextran is used safely as a blood plasma substitute (115) and has been investigated for use as polymeric carrier (14,116–123). The dextran backbone is composed of glucose repeat units. These hydroxylated, cyclohexyl units result in a more rigid polymer compared with many synthetic polymers (e.g., HPMA copolymers, PEG, and PVP), so dextran tends to exhibit a more compact solution structure than these polymers. Consequently, it has a higher renal threshold for excretion [55,000 Da (124) to 70,000 Da (46)]. Chemical modification of dextran by introduction of anionic moieties (carboxylates) reduces its rate of clearance (46), and addition of other substituents such as fluorescein isothiocyanate or sugar residues (113,125) promotes liver capture. Other polysaccharides that have been investigated include chitosan (126), alginate (127,128), hyaluronic acid (129), 6-O-carboxymethyl chitan (130) and 6-O-carboxymethyl pullulan (131). Typically, commercially available coupling agents have been routinely used to bind drugs to polysaccharides by direct conjugation to the polymer.

Polymers Derived From Natural Metabolites. Often hydrophilic polymers have been prepared from amino acids (e.g., poly(glutamic acid), poly[5N-(2-hydroxyethyl)-L-glutamine) (PHEG), β-poly(2-hydroxyethyl aspartamide) (PHEA), poly(L-glutamic acid), and polylysine. Other polymers and copolymers including pseudo-poly(amino acids) (132) and polyesters such as poly (α or β-malic acid) (133,134), and alternating polymers such as PEG-lysine (94,95) and poly(lysine citramide) (133) have also been investigated for drug conjugation. These polymers can be prepared by condensation or ring opening (135) polymerization reactions.

In principle, proteins can also be used to conjugate drugs, and albumin has been a popular candidate. Albumin with a molecular weight of approximately 66,000 Da is the most abundant protein in the circulatory system. It

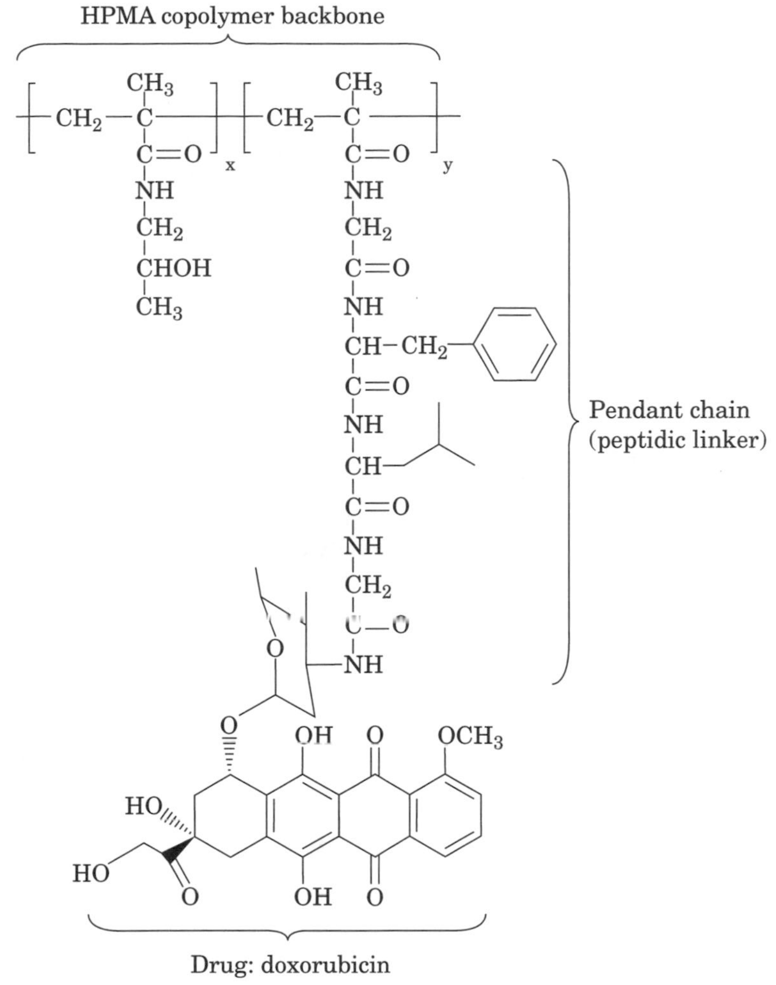

HPMA copolymer backbone

Figure 6. HPMA copolymer-doxorubicin conjugate (PK1, FCE 28068), an example of pendent chain drug conjugation using a peptidic linker (12,15). The conjugate has a M_W of approximately 30,000 Da and a doxorubicin content of approximately 8 wt %.

exhibits a circulation half-life of 19 days (only 2.2 days in the rat) and is found in every tissue and bodily secretion (136). Albumin continues to be actively investigated as a macromolecule candidate for drug conjugation (137–144), but the major limitations of proteins when compared with synthetic polymers as drug carriers are their increased propensity for inducing immunogenicity, denaturation, and nonspecific degradation. Other proteins such as transferrin [which binds to the transferrin receptor and thus have the potential to undergo receptor-mediated uptake (145,146)], and various immunoconjugates (57,147–158) have also been investigated. Narrow molecular weight distribution is often claimed to be a significant advantage for using proteins to conjugate drugs, but this can only be useful if a single species of the protein–drug conjugate can be created that is stable on storage. This has frequently been difficult to achieve in practice.

Polymer Micelles

Block copolymers, comprising hydrophilic and hydrophobic blocks, form polymeric micelles in solution (98,100,159–

162) and self-assembling micellar delivery systems are receiving increasing attention (10,163–165). A significant advantage of these systems is the ability to design higher molecular weight micellar aggregates that display prolonged circulation times that can maximize tumor capture by the EPR effect. Upon micelle disassociation, the individual block copolymer molecules are safely excreted, and as long as they are of low enough molecular weight these polymers can be nonbiodegradable. For example, poly(ethylene glycol-aspartate) block copolymer doxorubicin conjugates form micelles ranging in size from 20 to 60 nm that accumulate in solid tumors and exhibit antitumor activity (11,98,160,161,166). The doxorubicin is conjugated by its free amine directly to either the α- or β- pendent carboxylates in the poly-(aspartic acid) block. Details of this conjugate are further described in the section entitled "Other Linkers." Frequently physical entrapment of drug has accompanied conjugation (167), and with stable block copolymer micelles drug entrapment has become a viable strategy to deliver cytotoxic drugs to tumors (10,99,167–169). This aspect of block copolymer micelles is beyond the scope of this review (10).

PENDENT CHAIN LINKERS

Preparation and Characterization of Polymer–Drug Conjugates

Three distinct strategies have been employed to prepare polymer–drug conjugates incorporating pendent chain linkers.

1. Reaction of the linker or drug with functional groups already present in the polymer main chain. Generally, polymer side chains are activated using coupling reagents or by prior reaction. In this way, for example it is possible to derivatize -NH$_2$ groups in poly-L-lysine or -OH groups in polysaccharides.

2. Preparation of reactive polymeric intermediates by copolymerization using a monomer with a reactive pendent chain to which drugs or targeting groups can subsequently be bound (for example, conjugation of drugs to HPMA copolymers bearing pendent side chains containing reactive esters).

3. During polymerization use of a monomer containing the linker drug to produce the homopolymer or copolymer bearing linker and drug as pendent chains.

A significant amount of methodology for the conjugation of drugs to polysaccharides (170–172) has been developed using dextran as the model because this polysaccharide has been developed clinically as a blood plasma substitute (113,173) (for example, (1) partial periodate oxidation to give reactive aldehyde groups (113,174–177), (2) succinoylation (Fig. 7) or analogous derivatization (120,127) to give free carboxylates that can be conjugated, and (3) chloroformate (113,174) or cyanogen bromide (178) activation followed directly by reaction with a drug or drug derivative). Polymers derived from amino acids such as PHEG (179–181) and poly(L-glutamic acid) (182) have been directly conjugated to drugs using a commercial coupling agent (Fig. 8).

The majority of HPMA copolymer conjugates have been prepared by synthesis of polymeric precursors derived from free radical copolymerization of HPMA monomer and methacryolyated peptides terminating in *p*-nitrophenol. Subsequent aminolysis of the polymer precursor has been used to introduce covalently bound drug, drug analogue, or targeting ligand (183–192). This procedure for the preparation of polymer–drug conjugates is known as a polymer analogous reaction (101,102,108,184,193,194), and it has the significant advantage of allowing preparation of a common polymeric intermediate that can then be used to prepare different conjugates all having the same molecular weight characteristics (195). In the case of HPMA copolymers the polymeric precursor is prepared under very mild conditions by free radical precipitation polymerization (193). During aminolysis of the pendent chain terminal *p*-nitrophenol ester, the drug loading can be varied simply by using different drug stoichiometries (Fig. 9). The major limitations of the polymer analogous reaction are (1) incomplete removal of all free drug, which in the case of potent anticancer agents is essential to minimize potential toxicity associated with systemic administration, and

(2) the difficulty in fully characterizing a complex polymer–drug conjugate.

Polymer–drug conjugates can also be prepared by copolymerization of underivatized and drug derivatized monomers (Fig. 10) (15,20). Copolymerization of such comonomers often requires optimization of the polymerization chemistry to maintain molecular weight characteristics, comonomer incorporation, and conversion (yield) at different drug loadings.

Whatever the route of synthesis, it is essential that polymer–drug conjugates developed for clinical evaluation be carefully characterized. HPMA copolymer conjugates destined for clinical use have been characterised by detailed NMR (to confirm identity), gel permeation chromatography, and viscosimetry (to describe molecular weight averages and distribution) (195) and by high-performance liquid chromatography (HPLC) techniques to quantify total and free drug in the preparation (196,197). Typically an acceptable level of free drug in a polymeric conjugate produced on a commercial scale is approximately 1% of the total drug in the preparation, although laboratory synthesis can frequently yield compounds with ≤0.1% free drug.

In the case of conjugates containing potent anticancer agents it is important to note that such traces of free drug can contribute significantly to the observed in vitro cytotoxicity. This limits the opportunity to use a simple in vitro bioassay to confirm activity/toxicity of polymeric drugs. Whereas the free drug generally diffuses rapidly through the plasma membrane into the cell, the polymer conjugate is taken up slowly by endocytosis and, if a peptidyl linker is used, liberation of active agent is also a lengthy process. Thus in vitro cytotoxicity assays are frequently inappropriate for predicting the in vivo potential of candidate anticancer polymer conjugates; they often simply give an indication of the free drug content of a preparation or reflect a fast rate of release of drug from the conjugate during incubation in tissue culture medium. For example, the in vitro cytotoxicity testing of HPMA copolymer-doxorubicin conjugates showed that toxicity was caused by the unconjugated doxorubicin impurity (Fig. 11) (198). This was corroborated by HPLC analysis (196). If the biological reproducibility of commercial batches of a polymer conjugate are to be determined, carefully designed in vitro and in vivo tests are required depending on the therapeutic target of the bound drug.

The molecular weight distribution or polydispersity of a polymer is defined as a ratio of molecular weight averages, specifically, M_w/M_n (weight average molecular weight/number average molecular weight). If all molecules of a polymer sample have the same size (e.g., proteins), this ratio is 1. The higher this ratio (it is never less than 1), the broader the distribution of molecular weights. Polymer therapeutics must be rigorously characterized with respect to their molecular weight and polydispersity because biodistribution and pharmacological activity are known to be molecular-weight-dependent. For example, blood circulation half-life (199), renal clearance, deposition in organs (27), rates of endocytic uptake (200,201), and biological activity can depend on polymer molecular weight characteristics (81,202–206). If a polymer analogous reaction is used for drug conjugation, determination of polymer molecular

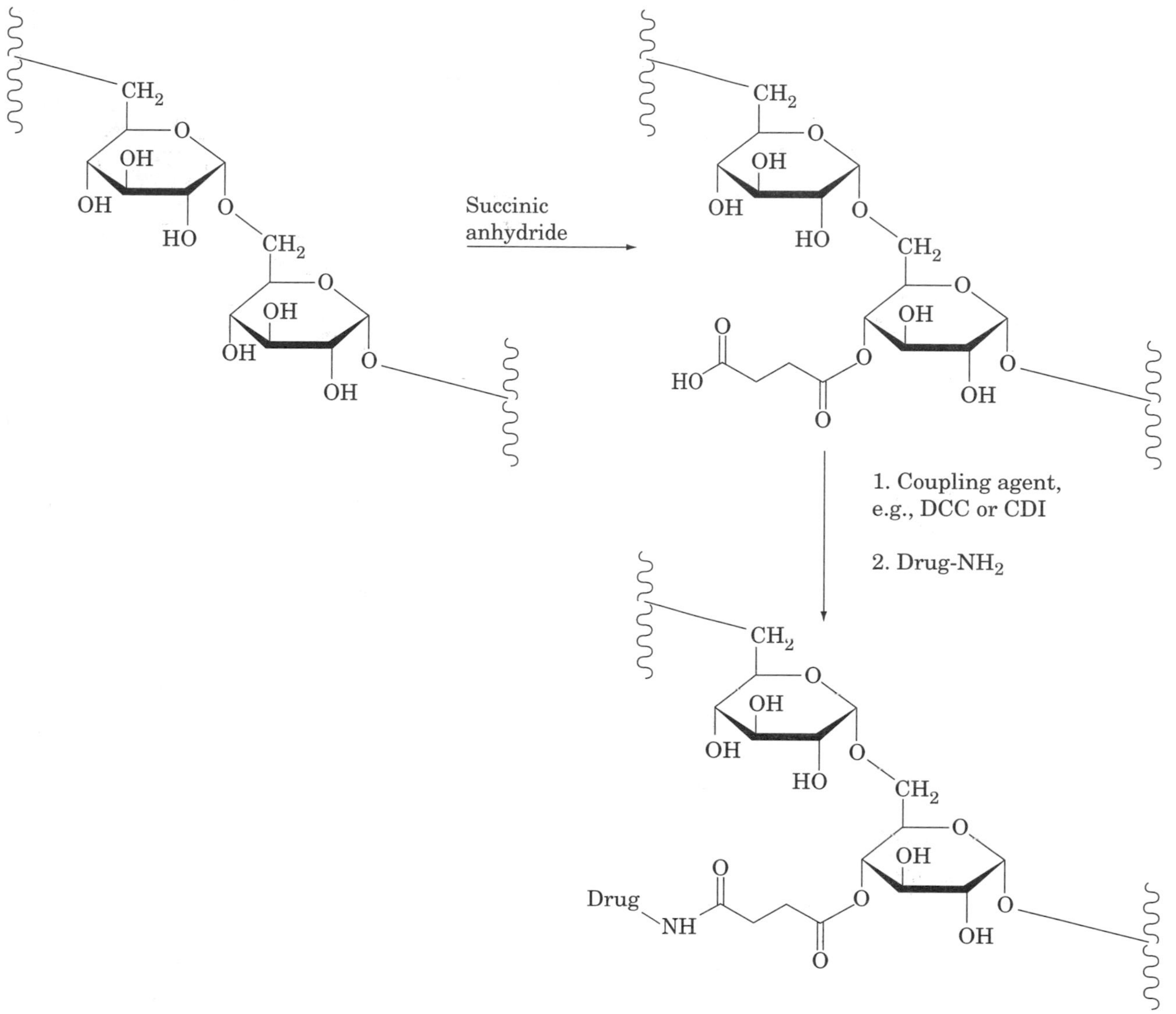

Figure 7. Succinylation of dextran, an example of polysaccharide derivatization often required prior to drug conjugation (113,173).

weight before and after the reaction ensures there has been no significant increase in molecular weight due to cross-linking.

Pendent Chain Linkers

A wide variety of linkages have been used to covalently bind a drug to the polymeric carrier (12,13,15,20). Several examples are illustrated in Table 2. Conjugation of metals to polymers by chelation has also been investigated (e.g., platinate anticancer conjugates (129,207–214; E. Gianas et al., unpublished data) and chelated conjugates for imaging (215–219)). Following the concept of lysosomotropic drug delivery (25,138) two broad classes of pendent chain linkers have emerged as the main focus of research over the last two decades.

1. Peptidyl linkers designed to be stable in the bloodstream but degradable by lysosomal enzymes and thus able to release the drug intracellularly (38,138,183,220–223).

2. Acid-labile, pH-dependent linkers designed to remain stable in plasma at neutral pH (7.4) but release drug intracellularly by hydrolysis in the more acidic environment of the endosome and lysosome (pH 5.5 to 6.5) (127,149,224).

Peptidyl Linkers

Early studies involving albumin-peptide-daunorubicin conjugates demonstrated that peptide linkers are able to mediate lysosomotropic drug delivery (138,225,226). It has become apparent that the best control of the rate and location of drug release from pendent chain polymers have occurred when a drug is bound to the polymer backbone via a peptidyl side chain, and the largest body of infor-

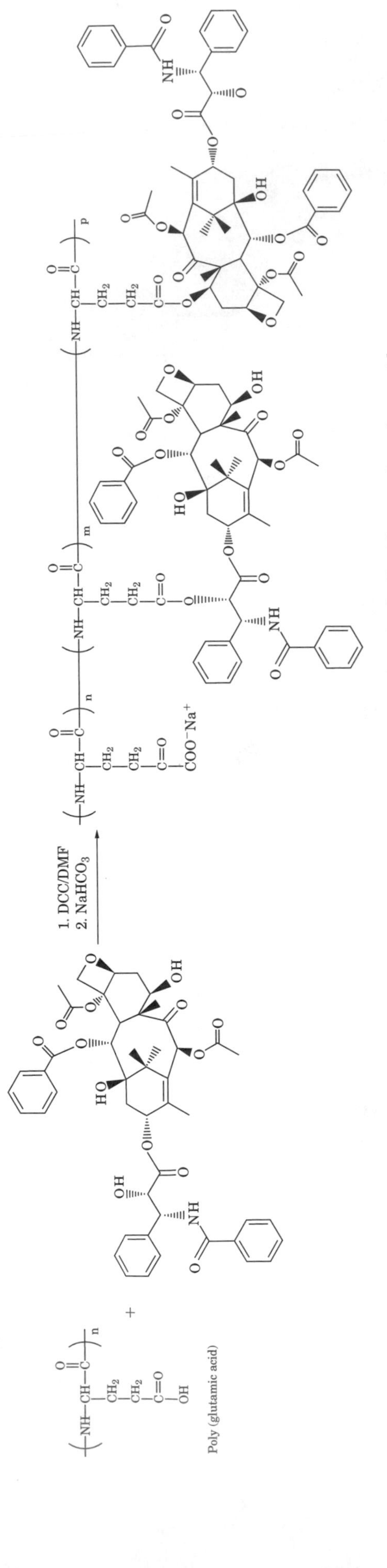

Figure 8. Direct conjugation of paclitaxel using dicyclohexylcarbodiimide onto the polymer side chains of poly(glutamic acid) (182).

mation has been collected thus far using HPMA copolymers synthesized to contain pendent peptide side chains for drug conjugation.

Since the discovery that peptidyl side chains in HPMA copolymers could be designed for cleavage by model enzymes such as chymotrypsin, trypsin, and papain (183,220,227–232), the last two decades have seen the systematic development of HPMA copolymer–anticancer conjugates containing peptidyl linkers tailored for cleavage by lysosomal proteases (15,18). Such linkers have now become more widely used in many different polymer conjugates (12,13,15). Initial studies using HPMA copolymers containing peptidyl pendent side chains terminating in p-nitroanilide (NAp) as a model compound found that mixtures of lysosomal enzymes (tritosomes) were not able to cleave many sequences in the absence of the reducing agent (reduced glutathione; GSH) (233), and indeed under these conditions the rate of NAp release was very slow (Table 3). In most cases, addition of GSH increased the rate of NAp release significantly (Table 3), and this, coupled with the observation that leupeptin inhibited degradation, indicated that the lysosomal thiol–dependent proteases (cathepsins B, H, and L) were particularly important for the degradation of such tri- and tetrapeptide sequences (220,222,230,231). It is preferable that a polymer–drug linker does not degrade in plasma and serum. Using similar HPMA copolymer conjugates, it was shown that release of NAp in rat serum was less than 5% in 5 h, varying to some extent depending on the exact structure of the peptide linker used (Table 4) (221).

Later studies sought to optimize the design of peptidyl linkers in HPMA copolymer conjugates as a means to control the site and rate of liberation of antitumor agents, particularly doxorubicin (223,227,228,232–234). As HPMA copolymer-Gly-Phe-Leu-Gly-doxorubicin (PK1, FCE 28068) (see Fig. 6) liberated doxorubicin over approximately 48 h when incubated with tritosomes (Fig. 12), this conjugate showed the ability to localize in solid tumors by the EPR effect (235–237) and demonstrated antitumor activity against a panel of solid tumor models including M5076 (237), Walker sarcoma (238), human colon xenograft LS174T (236,237), and established subcutaneous P388 (198) and B16 melanoma models (239). This compound was selected for clinical development.

HPMA copolymer-Gly-Phe-Leu-Gly-doxorubicin is stable in human serum, in vitro (223) and does not lead to liberation of drug in the circulation in vivo (240). The rate of anthracycline (doxorubicin and epirubicin) release from HPMA copolymers correlates with in vivo efficacy and toxicity (18,236,237). When doxorubicin conjugates with the slower releasing tripeptide linkers P-Gly-Phe-Gly-Dox and P-Gly-Leu-Gly-Dox were administered intraperitoneally (i.p.) to treat mice bearing an i.p. L1210 ascitic tumor model they proved more effective than conjugates with the faster-releasing tetrapeptide spacers. The slower release kinetics of the tripeptide linkers maintained a more sustained and relatively lower level of doxorubicin for a longer period of time in vivo. HPMA copolymer-doxorubicin conjugates containing a nondegradable linkers (e.g., P-Gly-Gly-Dox) did not display antitumor activity (241,242), confirming the need for lysosomotropic delivery with drug liberation.

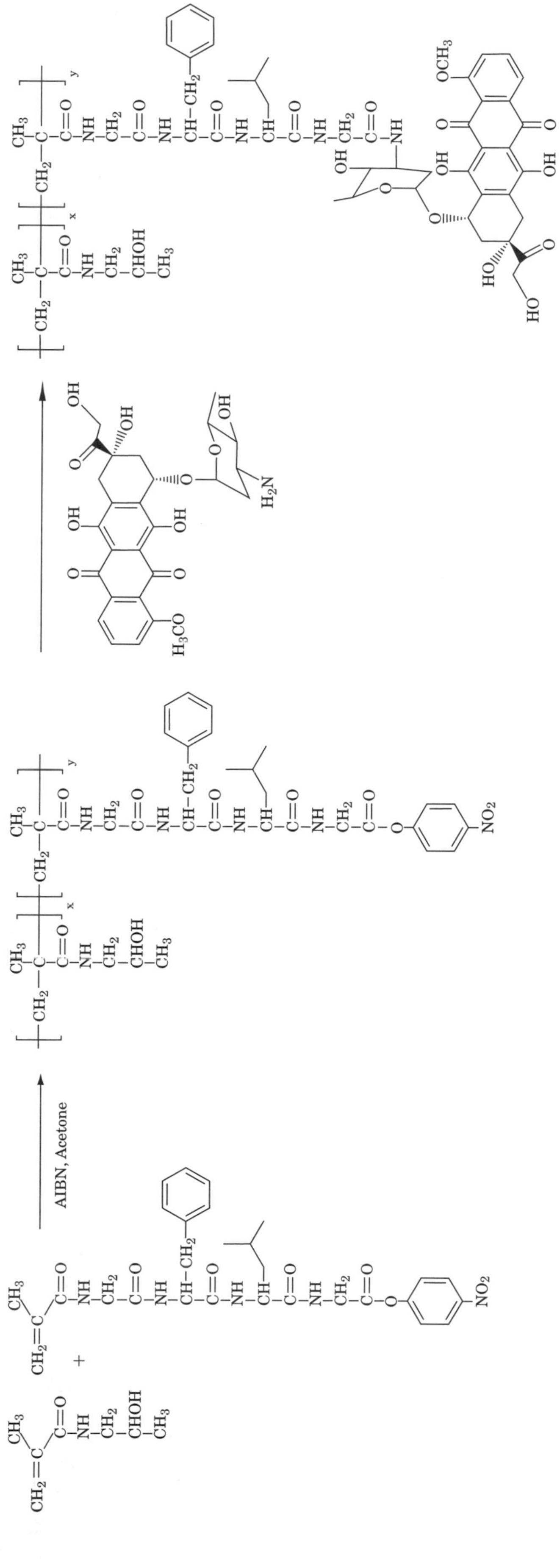

Figure 9. Aminolysis of a HPMA copolymer, an example of the polymer analogous reaction (184).

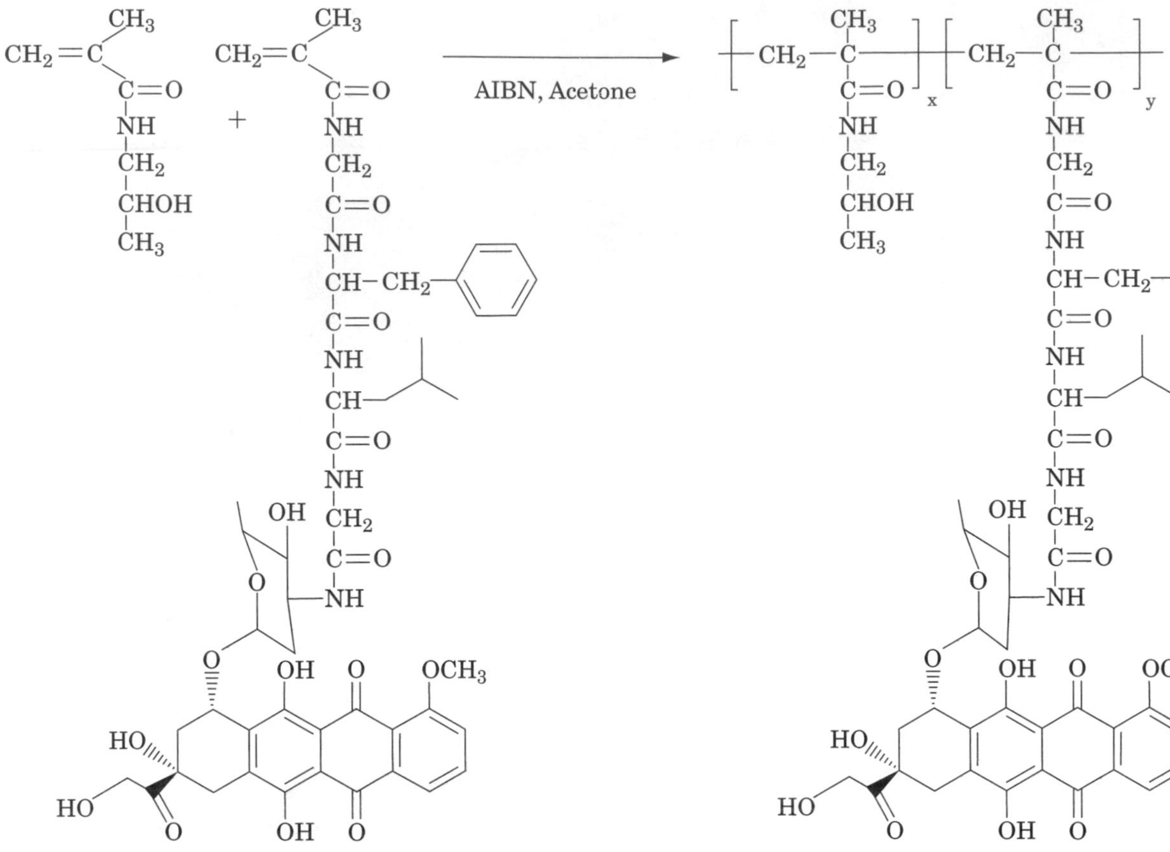

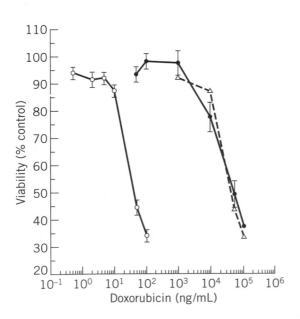

Figure 10. Preparation of HPMA copolymer-doxorubicin conjugate by the copolymerization of hydroxyproplymethacrylamide and a methacrylated doxorubicin tetrapeptide derivative (20).

Figure 11. In vitro cytotoxicity of HPMA copolymer doxorubicin (PK1) during incubation with L1210 cells. Cytotoxicity of doxorubicin (○), PK1 (●), and the free doxorubicin present in the PK1 preparation (△) as measured by the MTT assay (72h) are shown (198).

Alkylating agents have also been conjugated to HPMA copolymers using peptidyl linkers (234). For example, HPMA copolymer–melphalan conjugates prepared with a variety of peptidyl linkers were less toxic than free melphalan and exhibited improved antitumor activity against Walker sarcoma (subcutaneous). Again, the peptidyl linker structure influenced drug release in vitro and this release rate correlated with anticancer activity seen in vivo. No antitumor activity was observed when melphalan was conjugated to HPMA copolymers via a nondegradable linker (P-Gly-Mel), again confirming that drug liberation was required for antitumor activity to be observed.

The rate of drug release from the polymer chain can also vary according to the polymer molecular weight and the amount of drug conjugated to the polymer. As greater amounts of hydrophobic drug are conjugated onto a hydrophilic polymer, the possibility to form polymeric micelles increases (243). Micellar conjugate structures may hinder access of the lysosomal enzymes to degrade the linker and release the conjugated drug. Additionally, hydrophilic polymers conjugated to hydrophobic drugs can exhibit a lower critical solution temperature where phase separation occurs and the conjugate becomes insoluble. Simple turbidometric assays (244) have been used as a preliminary screen to determine the propensity for phase separation of various HPMA copolymer-doxorubicin conjugates of different molecular weight and drug loading (245). As a

Table 2. Bonds Used to Conjugate Drugs to Polymer Pendent Chains

Bond linking drug to pendent chain	Structure
Amide	
Ester	
Hydrazide	
Urethane (carbamate)	
Carbonate	
Imine (Schiff base)	

Table 2. Bonds Used to Conjugate Drugs to Polymer Pendent Chains (*continued*)

Bond linking drug to pendent chain	Structure
Thioether	⌇ S | Drug
Azo	⌇ N || N | Drug
Carbon-carbon	⌇ CH₂ | Drug

drug is released from a polymer conjugate, it would be expected that changes in polymer conformation will occur that might also lead to differences in drug release rate with time (246,247) and therefore pharmacological properties. The extent of drug loading and its influence on polymer solution properties is an important and yet poorly understood phenomenon and may well have a fundamental effect on the in vivo properties of therapeutic polymer conjugates.

A second HPMA copolymer conjugate containing the Gly-Phe-Leu-Gly-doxorubicin side chain has entered clinical testing, PK2 FCE 28069 (Fig. 13) (79,248–251). This conjugate benefits from the liver targeting mediated by introduction of galactosamine into the PK2 structure and demonstrated antitumor activity in two liver metastatic models: i.v. administered M5076 (237) and B16 melanoma (252).

A variety of anticancer agents have now been conjugated to other macromolecules using peptidyl linkers (12). For example, doxorubicin has been conjugated to poly(L-glutamic acid) (19,253,254), carboxymethylpullulan (131) and 6-O-carboxymethylchitin (130) via peptidyl linkers. Other anticancer agents including mitomycin (180) and paclitaxel (255–257) have also been conjugated to different polymers using peptidyl linkers (12,13,130,180,181). These cytotoxic compounds are potent and, when admin-

istered to patients, share similar problems as observed with doxorubicin, e.g., high toxicity and low solubility. The stability of mitomycin C (MMC) conjugated to PHEG (M_w~20,000 Da) (Fig. 14) (180,258) using peptidyl linkages has been systematically studied by measuring drug release in the presence of lysosomal enzymes (tritosomes, cathepsins B and D) and type IV collagenase in vitro. As expected, release characteristics were dependent on the structure of the peptide linker used (13,181).

The longer length spacers such as the hexapeptide (P-Gly-Phe-Leu-Gly-Phe-Leu-MMC) and the tetrapeptide (P-Gly-Phe-Ala-Leu-MMC) were readily degraded by tritosomes to release up to 80% of the conjugated MMC in 5 h, whereas tripeptide linkers released <10% MMC in the same time period (259). However, it was noted that the PHEG-hexa- and PHEG-tetrapeptide-MMC conjugates released Leu-MMC and Gly-MMC as well as free drug. These single amino acid–mitomycin derivatives were hydrolyzed (95%) in buffer (3 h) to give free MMC and were considerably less stable than the PHEG–MMC conjugates. This increased stability was attributed to the formation of polymeric intramolecular micelles with the MMC localized within the micellar core and thus making it less accessible for hydrolytic release (13,181). The in vivo antitumor activity of PHEG–MMC conjugates against P388 leukemia and C26 colorectal carcinoma solid tumors was highest for

Table 3. Stability of HPMA Copolymers Bearing Peptidyl Side Chains Terminating in NAp During Incubation with Lysosomal Enzymes

Peptidyl Side Chain	NAp release by Tritosomes (−GSH) Rate of degradation (nmol/h)	NAp release by Tritosomes (+GSH) Max. linear rate of release (%h)	NAp release by cathepsin B (%h)
	Dipeptides		
P[a]-Gly-Leu-NAp	0	0	—
P-Gly-Phe-NAp	0	0	—
P-Acap-Phe-NAp	15.6	0.6	—
P-Acap-Leu-NAp	0	0	0
	Tripeptides		
P-Gly-Ala-Phe-NAp	0	—	0.2
P-Gly-Ala-Tyr-NAp	0	0	—
P-Gly-Gly-Phe-NAp	0	0.4	0
P-Gly-Ileu-Ala-NAp	—	—	5.8
P-Gly-Ileu-Phe-NAp	0	1.4	—
P-Gly-Ileu-Tyr-NAp	0	6.0	—
P-Gly-Leu-Ala-NAp	—	—	7.8
P-Gly-Leu-Phe-NAp	7.8	3.0	—
P-Gly-Phe-Ala-NAp			10.6
P-Gly-Phe-Phe-NAp	0	3.0	—
P-Gly-D,Phe-Phe-NAp	0	3.6	—
P-Gly-Phe-Tyr-NAp	0	2.4	—
P-Gly-Val-Phe-NAp	0	3.7	2.2
	Tetrapeptides		
P-Ala-Gly-Val-Phe-NAp	0	12.6	2.4
P-Gly-Gly-Phe-Phe-NAp	4.3	1.8	—
P-Gly-Gly-Phe-Tyr-NAp	8.3	—	—
P-Gly-Gly-Val-Phe-NAp	0	3.1	—
P-Gly-Phe-Gly-Phe-NAp	—	—	0.2
P-Gly-Phe-Tyr-Ala-NAp	—	—	17.0
	Others		
P-Gly-Phe-Leu-Gly-Phe-NAp	—	NL[b]	0.2
P-Gly-Gly-Phe-Leu-Gly-Phe-NAp	—	NL	—

[a]HPMA copolymer backbone.
[b]NL, nonlinear.
Source: From Refs. 220, 228, 231, 233.

Table 4. Stability of HPMA Copolymers Bearing Peptidyl Side Chains Terminating in NAp During Incubation with Rat Plasma and Serum

Peptide linker	Percentage NAp released/5 h	
	Plasma	Serum
P[a]-Gly-Leu-Ala-NAp	0.9	0.9
P-Gly-Phe-Ala-NAp	0.0	0.9
P-Ala-Gly-Val-Phe-NAp	0.0	0.5
P-Gly-Phe-Phe-Ala-NAp	1.0	2.2
P-Gly-Phe-Phe-Leu-NAp	1.5	2.1
P-Gly-Phe-Leu-Gly-NAp	1.5	1.7
P-Gly-Phe-Tyr-Ala-NAp	1.3	1.3
P-Gly-Phe-Leu-Gly-Phe-NAp	3.3	3.8
P-Gly-Gly-Phe-Leu-Gly-Phe-NAp	3.5	5.1

[a]HPMA copolymer backbone.
Source: From Ref. 221.

the linkers with the best hydrolytic stability, e.g., P-Gly-Phe-Leu-Gly-Phe-Leu-MMC and P-Gly-Phe-Ala-Leu-MMC.

Peptidic linkers have also been used to bind the antimetabolite 5-fluorouracil (5-FU) to a variety of different polymers (259–263). The clinical dose of 5-FU is relatively high (often more than 500 mg/m²), thus, this anticancer agent may not be the best candidate for polymer conjugation unless high levels of polymer substitution can be achieved, or the tumor targeting mediated by the EPR effect results in significantly increased therapeutic benefit. 5-FU is, however, an interesting candidate, as unlike other commonly used anticancer agents such as doxorubicin and mitomycin, 5-FU is not polycyclic nor is lipophilic. These structural differences might allow the higher polymer loading of 5-FU needed while maintaining favorable physicochemical characteristics of such conjugates, e.g., plasma solubility, low blood protein binding, and the relatively open polymer conformation needed for enzymatic lysosomal degradation and drug liberation.

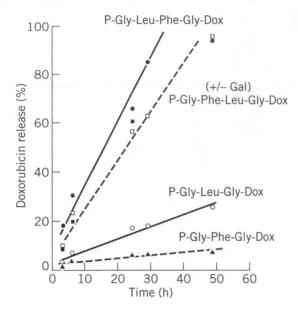

Figure 12. Release of doxorubicin from HPMA copolymer-peptide-doxorubicin conjugates during incubation with rat liver lysosomal enzymes (tritosomes). *Source:* Ref. 223.

PEG-, dextran- and PHEG-5-FU conjugates with about 1–4 wt % loading exhibited in vitro release of 5-FU that was dependent on the linker amino acid sequence (259,260). The peptide linkers chosen to bind 5-FU to these polymers had the structure P-Gly-Phe-X-Gly(5-FU)OEt (OEt is an ethyl moiety; on an acid denotes an ethyl ester) where P is the polymer backbone and X was Gly, Ala, Leu or Phe (Fig. 15). 5-FU was conjugated at the α-position of the glycine ethyl ester at the linker terminus. Initially cleavage by lysosomal enzymes gave X-Gly(5-FU)OEt (13), which then underwent further hydrolysis to produce free 5-FU. The release rate due to hydrolysis was slower in buffer at pH 5.5 (maximum drug release was 3% in 24 h) than at pH 7.4. (Maximum release ranged between 10 and 20% in 24 h depending on the structure of the peptide linker.) The degree of 5-FU liberation was greatest in the order PEG>PHEG>dextran and decreased with increased 5-FU content in the polymer.

Similar studies have been conducted using HPMA copolymers possessing peptidyl linkers terminated with an α-glycine derivative of 5-FU (2–3 mol %) (Fig. 16). These conjugates also exhibited release profiles that were a function of linker structure (261,262), and 5-FU was released as a dipeptide 5-FU derivative (261). The total length of the oligopeptide sequence (tetra- vs. hexapeptide), the stereochemistry of 5-FU substitution at the α-position of glycine (L or D) and the hydrophobicity of the penultimate

Figure 13. Structure of PK2. The conjugate has a molecular weight of approximately 28,000 Da, a doxorubicin content of approximately 7 wt %, and approximately 4 mol % galactosamine.

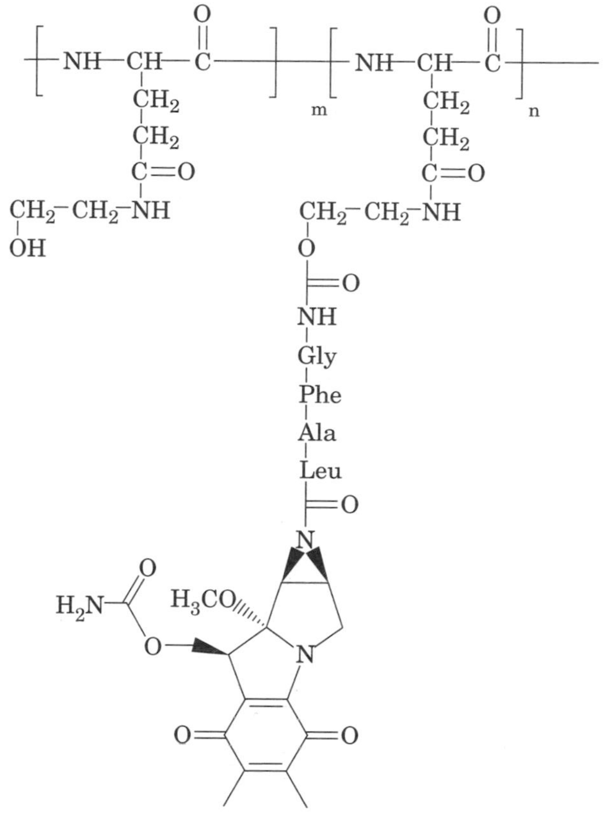

Figure 14. Structure of a PHEG conjugate of MMC using peptidic pendent chains (179,180,258).

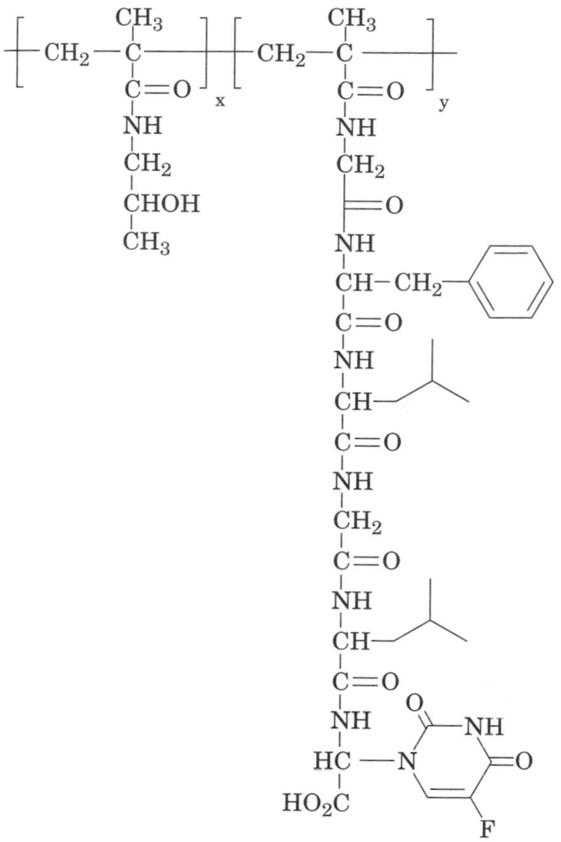

Figure 16. Structure of a HPMA copolymer–5-FU conjugate using peptidic pendent chains (261–263).

amino acid (Ala or Leu) all influenced the in vitro enzymatic release of 5-FU from HPMA copolymers, but in contrast with the studies mentioned already where tetrapeptide linkers in PEG, PHEG, and dextran resulted in 5-FU release, only the hexapeptide linkers in the HPMA copolymers underwent in vitro enzymatic cleavage to release 5-FU (261).

HPMA copolymers containing the -Gly-Phe-Leu-Gly linker used to prepare PK1 and PK2 have recently been used as a platform for conjugation of other antitumor agents. HPMA copolymer–paclitaxel conjugates (Fig. 17) contain an ester bond between a paclitaxel hydroxyl (C-2') and the amino acid carboxylate at the terminus of the pen-

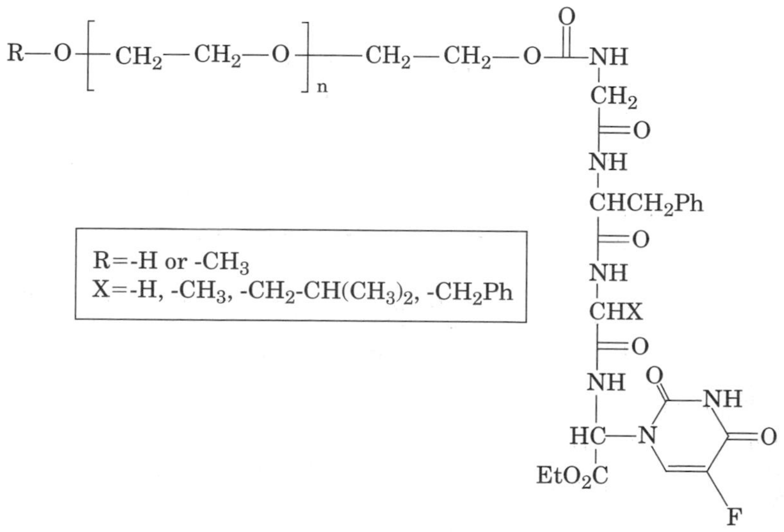

R=-H or -CH$_3$
X=-H, -CH$_3$, -CH$_2$-CH(CH$_3$)$_2$, -CH$_2$Ph

Figure 15. Structure of a PEG-5-FU conjugate. End-group conjugation (259,260).

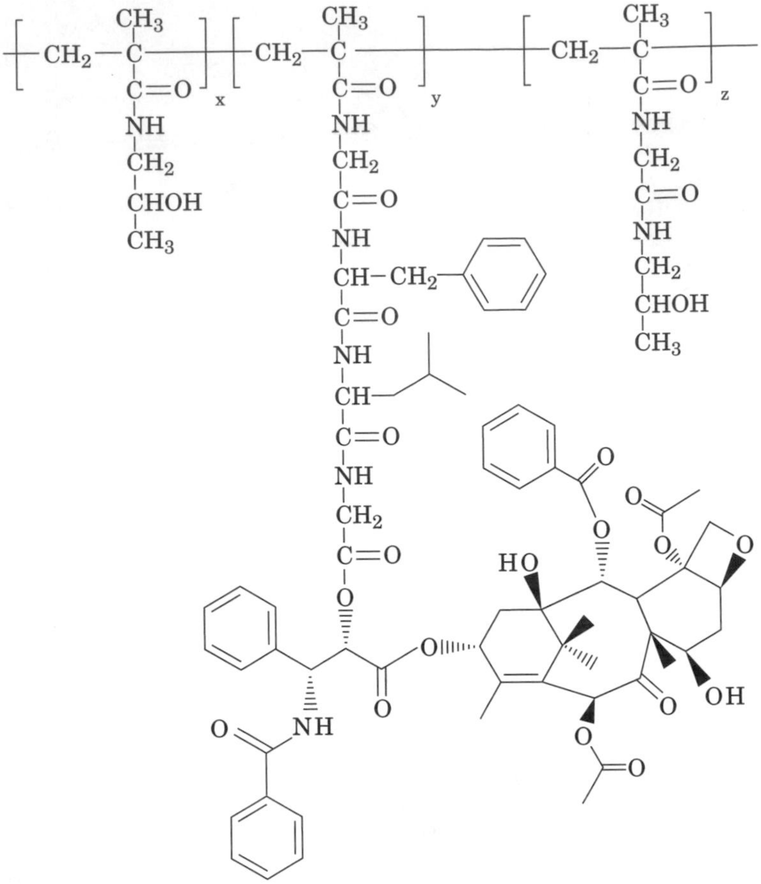

Figure 17. Structure of a HPMA copolymer–paclitaxel conjugate using peptidic pendent chains that are covalently bonded to the paclitaxel by an ester bond (255).

dent chain (255–257,264). In this case, the terminal bond linking the drug to the peptide pendent chain is not a hydrolytically stable amide bond (265,266). This may give rise to other possible hydrolytic mechanisms for drug liberation. These HPMA copolymer–paclitaxel conjugates were prepared to create a water-soluble paclitaxel conjugate that would slowly release free paclitaxel as the ester bond underwent hydrolysis, and in vivo studies (B16F10, M109, and M5076 murine models) showed that the conjugate exhibited greater efficacy of the conjugate compared to free paclitaxel.

Recently two types of HPMA copolymer–platinum chelates have been described. HPMA copolymers containing peptidyl side chains (Gly-Gly or Gly-Phe-Leu-Gly) terminating in carboxylate groups were allowed to react with cisplatin (E. Gianasi et al., unpublished data), or alternatively the same HPMA copolymers containing peptidyl sequences terminating in a diamine were allowed to react with potassium tetrachloroplatinate (Fig. 18) (E. Gianasi et al., unpublished data). The resultant HPMA copolymer platinates had a M_w of 25,000–31,000 Da with a platinum loading of 3–10 wt %. In vitro the HPMA copolymer platinates displayed a range of platinum release rates at pH 7.4 and 5.5; from <5%/24 h in the case of the diamino species, which requires lysosomal enzymatic degradation, up to >80%/24 h in the case of the carboxylate, which is a relatively poor hydrolytically labile ligand. Cisplatin and not surprisingly the fast-releasing carboxylate species displayed IC_{50} values of ~10 μg/mL Pt-equivalent against

B16F10 cells in vitro, whereas the slow-releasing conjugates were not cytotoxic over the dose range studied. When conjugates were administered i.p. to treat i.p. L1210 tumors, the antitumor activity seen was within the range for free cisplatin. However, when conjugates were administered i.v. to treat subcutaneous (s.c.) B16F10 tumors grown to palpable size, free cisplatin was not active, but the HPMA copolymer platinates bearing carboxylate and diamine platinates showed significant antitumor activity. Activity in the solid tumor model was attributed to the tumor targeting by the EPR effect; a ~60-fold increase in Pt AUC in B16F10 tumor tissue than was achieved after administration of cisplatin (E. Gianasi et al., unpublished data).

Hydrolytically Labile Pendent Chain Linkers

The relatively low pH within the endosomal and lysosomal compartments and the observation that the extracellular, interstitial environment in some tumors is also acidic (267,268) has inspired the development of pendent chain linkers that hydrolytically degrade more quickly at pH values less than 7.4. *Cis*-aconityl acid and Schiff base derivatives are the two predominant types of hydrolytically labile linkers that have been explored. An advantage of conjugating a drug via an acid-labile linker is that free drug alone can be released from the pendent chain rather than amino acid or peptide drug derivatives, which can occur with peptidyl linkers.

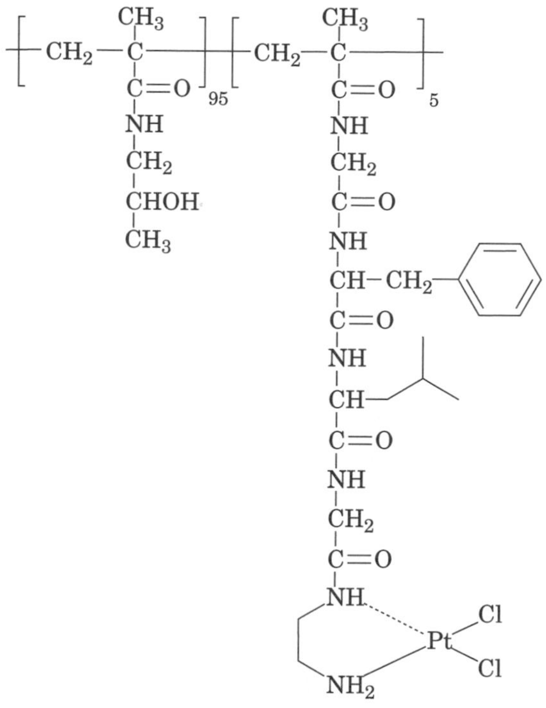

Figure 18. Structure of a HPMA copolymer-platinate (E. Gianasi et al., unpublished data).

The first example employing *cis*-aconityl linkers was the conjugation of daunomycin to poly(D-lysine) and Affi-Gel 701 (amionethyl polyacrylamide beads) (224). Poly(L-lysine) was not selected because it was thought in vivo degradation of this polymer would compete with release of daunomycin (269). When linked to Affi-Gel the *cis*-aconityl linker had a half-life for hydrolysis of 96 h at pH 6 but only 3 h at pH 4. The *cis*-aconityl linker has subsequently been used to conjugate anthracyclines to other synthetic poly(amino acids) (147,270), egg-white lysozyme (271), polysaccharides (127), lectins (272), alginates (synthesis shown in Figure 19) (127) and to monoclonal antibodies (Fig. 20) (149,158,273,274). Daunomycin release from alginate-*cis*-aconityl conjugates (127) incubated in buffers of different pH increased with lowering pH (Fig. 21). It has been pointed out that in some studies uncertainty exists as to which carboxylate is conjugated to the macromolecule (13). However, improved synthetic strategies have been developed so the *cis*-aconityl moiety can be unambiguously conjugated to the polymer at the requisite carboxylate to ensure pH-dependent drug release (272,273). Two possible mechanisms for *cis*-aconityl hydrolysis (275) are based on neighboring group interactions of the *cis*-carboxylic acid at lower pH values that accelerate the hydrolytic release of the conjugated drug (Fig. 22) (11,13).

Hydrazone-derived Schiff base bonds linking doxorubicin [and other drugs (276)] to polymers (277) have been prepared. These adducts may have slowly released doxorubicin while both in circulation and upon endocytosis (277). Analogous doxorubicin-immunoconjugates have also been studied (153,154,278). Doxorubicin conjugated via a Schiff base to oxidized dextran (176,177,279–281) has un-

dergone Phase I evaluation (282). The Schiff base was prepared first by the mild periodate oxidation of dextran to generate aldehyde functionality then by reaction of the amino moiety on doxorubicin.

Other Linkers

Linkers which are not lysosomally degradable peptides or pH-labile moieties have been used to prepare soluble polymer–drug conjugates. As with the aforementioned polymer–drug conjugates, circulation times tend to be increased compared to the free drug. Slow release of drug may occur resulting in prolonged drug action (21,34). Typically the drug can be conjugated directly to an existing pendent chain or endgroup as, for example, the conjugation of paclitaxel to the side chains of poly(L-glutamic acid) (182) or the endgroups of PEG (91–93,283). Drug can also be conjugated by chelation (Figs. 18 and 23) (129,207–214; E. Gianasi et al., unpublished data).

Sometimes an amino acid (e.g., ε-aminocapriotic acid or lysine) or an aliphatic spacer serves as a conjugating linker. Amide or ester bonds are generally the limiting degradable bonds in these linkers (i.e., the bond expected to be cleaved to release drug), but carbonate, iminocarbonate, urea, and dithiol moieties along with metal chelates have also been used (12,13,15,20). Pendent chain degradation to release the drug in these conjugates is probably a combination of both enzymatic and hydrolytic release mechanisms. For example, conjugation of *cis*-hydroxy proline to PEG–lysine copolymers (Fig. 24) (284–286) by an amide bond resulted in higher activity compared to conjugates bound by a more hydrolytically labile ester bond (285). Such observations may be due to a combination of release mechanisms or by multivalent interactions. This example also illustrates the possibility for direct conjugation of a drug to an existing polymer side chain.

Conjugates of 5-FU with poly(α-1,4-galactosamine) and N-acetyl-α-1,4-polygalactosamine linked with a hexamethlene spacer via urea bonds had drug loadings ranging from 17 to 58 mol % (126). Unfortunately these conjugates were poorly water soluble. Hydrolysis of the urea bonds was faster than the degradation of the glycosidic bonds of the polysaccharide backbone. Administration of the conjugates to animals bearing P388 lymphocytic leukemia resulted in life span increases greater than seen with free 5-FU. This prolongation in survival correlated with increased 5-FU loading and dose of the conjugate. To improve solubility, 5-FU was conjugated to another polysaccharide, 6-O-carboxymethyl chitin (287). Conjugation was via amide and ester bonds through pentamethylene linkers and produced 5-FU loading of up to 35.2 mol %. Release from the chitin was slower (6% over 20 h) compared to the chitosan conjugates (25% over 20 h). Again with the P388 lymphocytic leukaemia model (i.p. tumor and i.p. treatment), life span increased with increasing dose of the chitin conjugate. Conjugates of 5-FU via amide, ester, and carbamoyl bonds to poly(α-malic acid) have also been investigated (134).

As mentioned previously, the micelle-forming properties of macromolecules comprised of both hydrophobic and hydrophilic domains can influence the rate of drug release in the lysosome. This property can be exploited to carry

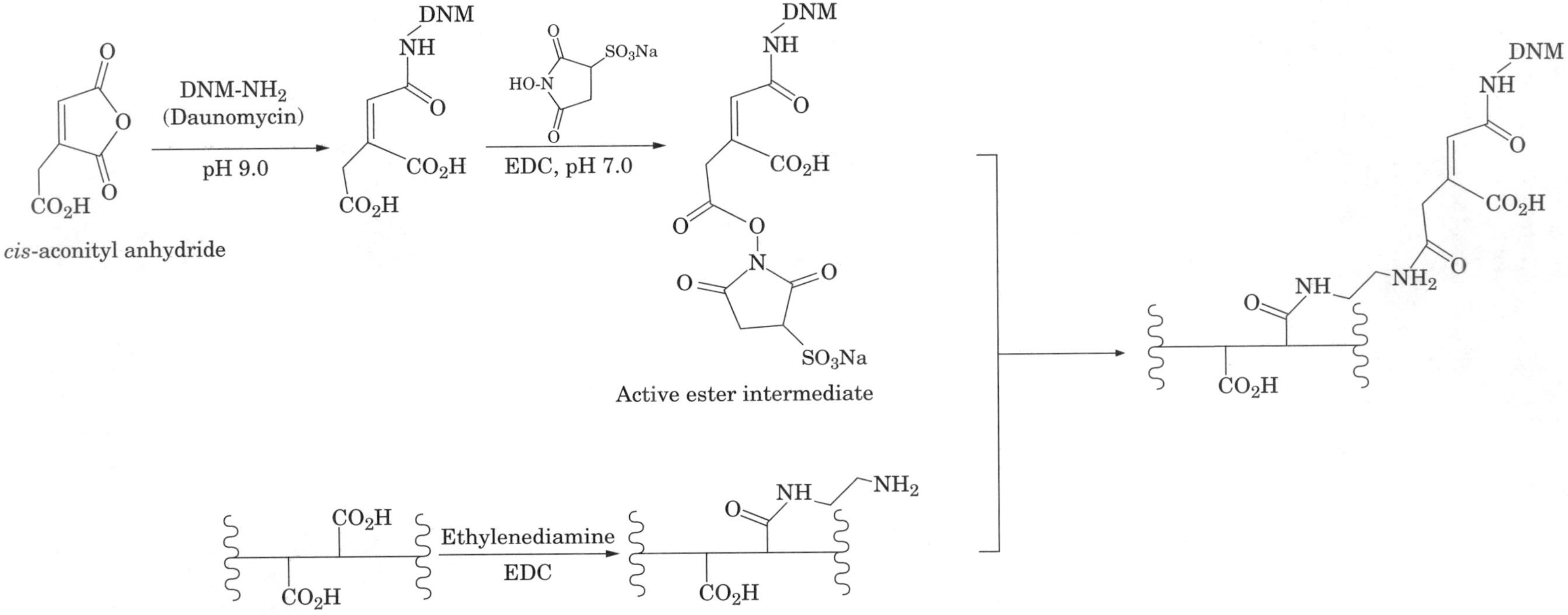

Figure 19. Preparation of alginate conjugates containing *cis*-aconityl-daunomycin (127).

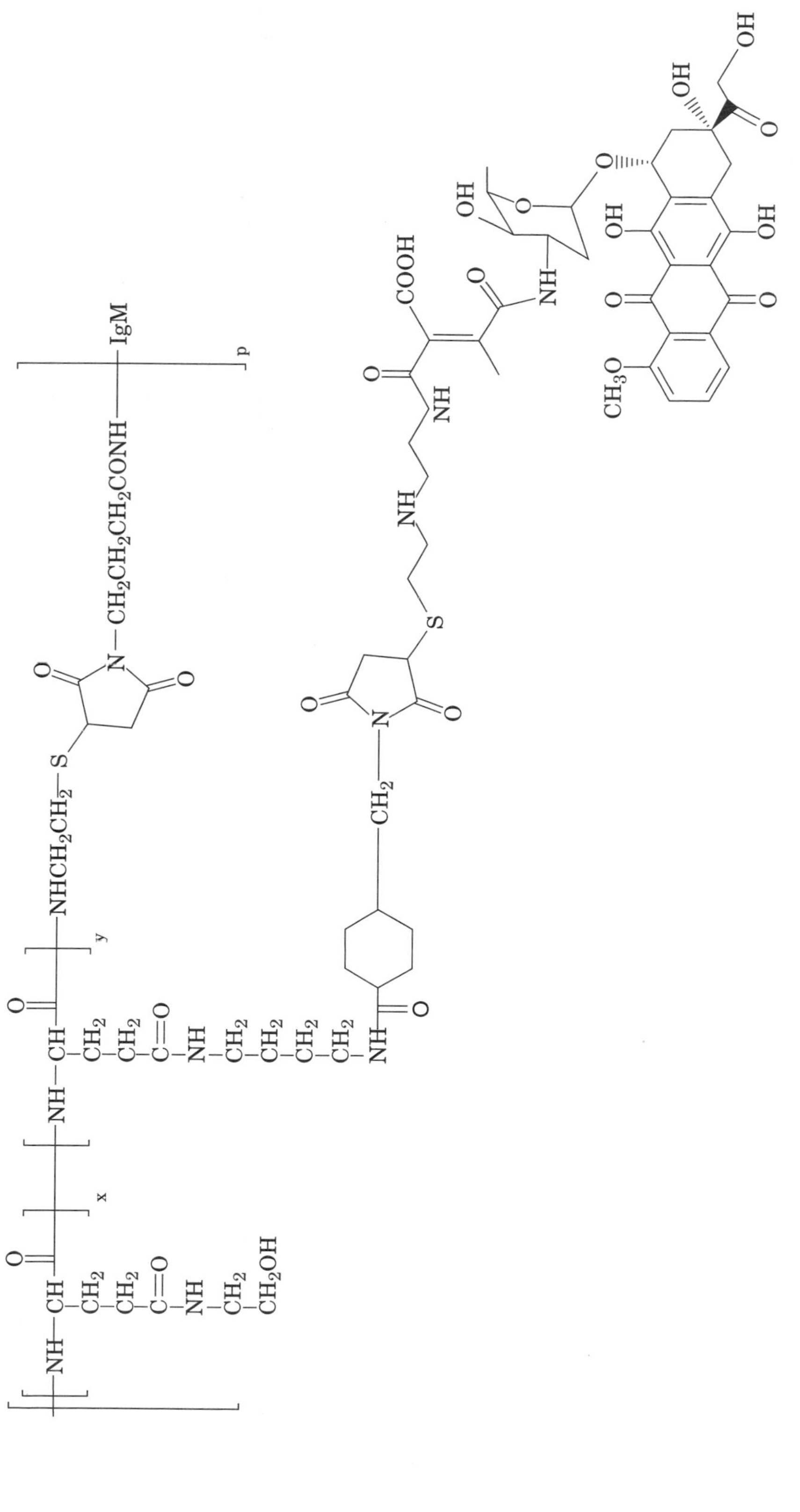

Figure 20. Structure of a PHEG-doxorubicin maleamic acid derived conjugate that is also conjugated to a human IgM (149).

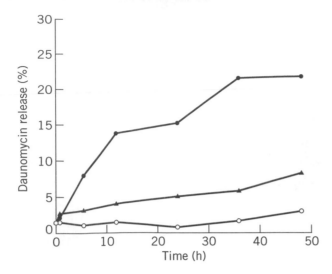

Figure 21. Release of daunomycin from alginate *cis*-acontinyl-daunomycin incubated in buffers of different pH. Release at pH 7 (○), pH 6 (▲) and pH 5 (●) is shown. *Source:* Ref. 127.

large amounts (up to 37 mol %) of doxorubicin within micelles which spontaneously form with PEG-poly(α,β-aspartic acid) AB-block copolymers (11,100,161,162,165,166, 289,290). Doxorubicin was conjugated by an amide bond directly to the pendent carboxyl moieties of the block copolymer (Fig. 25). Although the M_w of the block copolymer was approximately 14,000 Da and would have been expected to clear relatively quickly from circulation, these conjugates did exhibit increased tumor uptake. Micelle formation involved aggregation of several polymer chains to give constructs with an effective molecular weight exceeding 10^6 Da with a diameter of 50 nm. The hydrophilic PEG existed predominantly on the outer shell and the more hydrophobic poly(aspartic acid)-doxorubicin blocks existed within the micelle structure. The micelle remained stable in the presence of serum proteins (165) with low RES accumulation and prolonged circulation with 10% of the conjugate still in the blood after 24 h (160). These observations were attributed to minimal interaction of the PEG micellar surface with circulating proteins and with PEG-induced micellar stabilization. Biodistribution was dependent on micelle stability because with less stable micelles, free polymer was readily excreted. There was lowered toxicity (1/20 compared with free doxorubicin) and reduced nonspecific accumulation in major organs including heart, lung, and liver. In vivo studies with several murine and human solid tumor models (C 26, C 38, M 5076, and MX-1) resulted in higher antitumor activity compared with free doxorubicin.

It is increasingly evident that multivalent interactions (290) of polymeric molecules at cell surfaces can cause important biological effects (291,292); therefore, it is not necessary to rely on lysosomal delivery to exhibit pharmacological activity. Hence in this case, it is necessary to design linkers that do not degrade specifically in the lysosome. For example, the amino acid lysine has been used to link a carbohydrate, lysoganglioside GM$_3$ (a sialyl moiety), sphingosine, and a fluorescent probe to poly(glutamic acid)

(Fig. 26) (293). This conjugate was designed to act as a multivalent inhibitor of influenza hemagglutinin at receptors on the cell surface. Affinities for carbohydrate–receptor interactions may potentially be increased using polymers conjugated with monomeric carbohydrate ligands to act as multivalent ligands. In vitro studies indicated that this conjugate inhibited the influenza virus by a dual mechanism: (*1*) by the action of the sialyl moieties binding hemagglutinin proteins on the surface of the virus and (*2*) by hydrophobic interactions at the membrane caused by the conjugated sphingosine.

CLINICAL PROGRESS

Although the literature contains many examples of polymeric anticancer conjugates only dextran-doxorubicin (AD-70, DOX-OXD) (282) and three HPMA copolymer conjugates (of molecular weight approximately 30,000 Da) incorporating the peptidyl (Gly-Phe-Leu-Gly) side chain (PK1, PK2, and PNU 166945) have so far entered controlled Phase I/II clinical trials.

In Phase I studies HPMA copolymer-Gly-Phe-Leu-Gly-doxorubicin (PK1, FCE 28068) (see Fig. 6) given once every 3 weeks displayed greatly reduced toxicity compared with free doxorubicin and showed evidence of activity in chemotherapy refractory patients (240,294,295). The maximum tolerated dose (MTD) of PK1 was 320 mg/m^2 (doxorubicin equivalent), and this is 4–5 times higher than the usual clinical dose of free doxorubicin. There was no evidence of the PK1-related cardiotoxicity (despite individual cumulative doses of up to 1,680 mg/m^2 doxorubicin-equivalent), and the dose limiting toxicity was bone marrow suppression. No polymer-related toxicity was observed, and PK1 is currently undergoing Phase II trials. In contrast, the dextran-doxorubicin conjugate (AD-70, DOX-OXD) of molecular weight of approximately 70,000 Da also administered on a thrice-weekly schedule had an MTD of 40 mg/m^2 doxorubicin-equivalent (282), somewhat lower than that seen for doxorubicin alone (60–80 mg/m^2). The severe hepatotoxicity seen after administration of AD-70, DOX-OXD was attributed to uptake of the conjugate by the RES. This could have been simply caused by the choice of dextran as a carrier and/or the fact that doxorubicin was conjugated to dextran via a Schiff base. Although a structural study of a doxorubicin-oxidized dextran conjugate was published after the clinical trial (177), no details of the preparation or properties of the conjugate used in this Phase I study (e.g., loading of doxorubicin, amount of free unconjugated doxorubicin) are available. Further information relating to the formulation used and the kinetics of doxorubicin release might help establish exactly why the increased toxicity was observed. Observations from one study suggest that doxorubicin might be released from dextran prior to tumor cell uptake of the conjugate (176). Reduction of the Schiff base in the dextran–doxorubicin conjugates to give a nonhydrolytic (and presumably nondegradable) amine bond (296–298) did show increased therapeutic indices compared with free doxorubicin, but the antitumor activities were not high enough to warrant continued development (176).

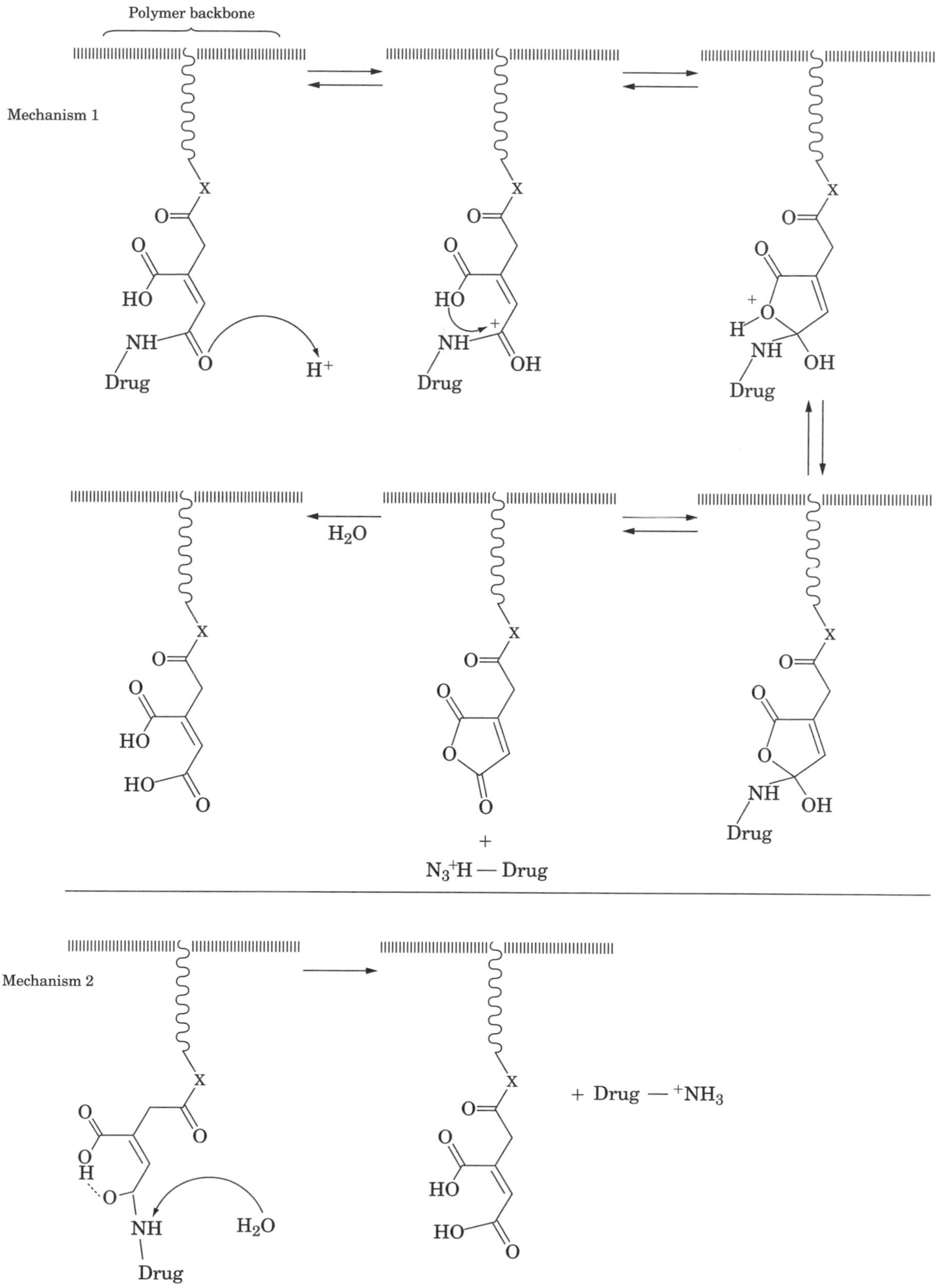

Figure 22. Possible mechanisms for acid-assisted hydrolysis of a *cis*-aconityl linker (11,13,275).

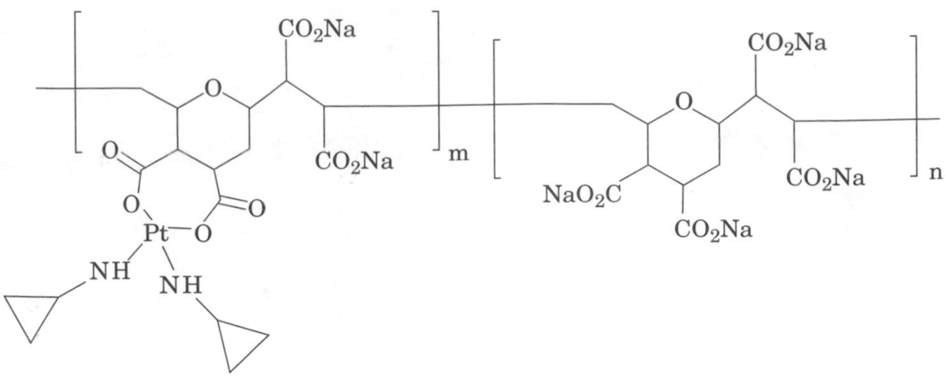

Figure 23. Chelation of platinum to the side chains of DIVEMA (129).

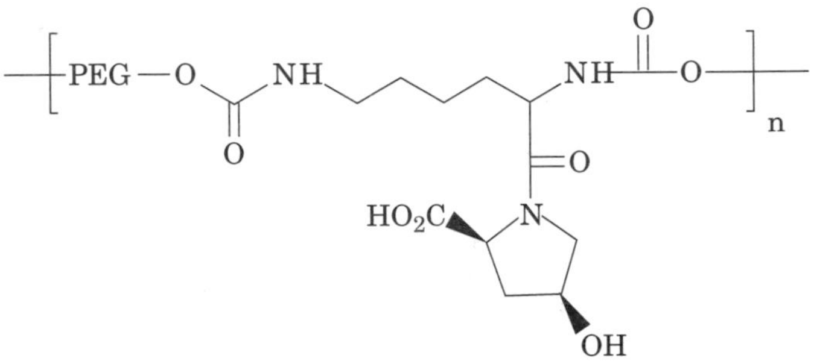

Figure 24. Structure of a PEG–lysine copolymer–hydroxyproline conjugate. Direct conjugation to a polymer side chain (284–286).

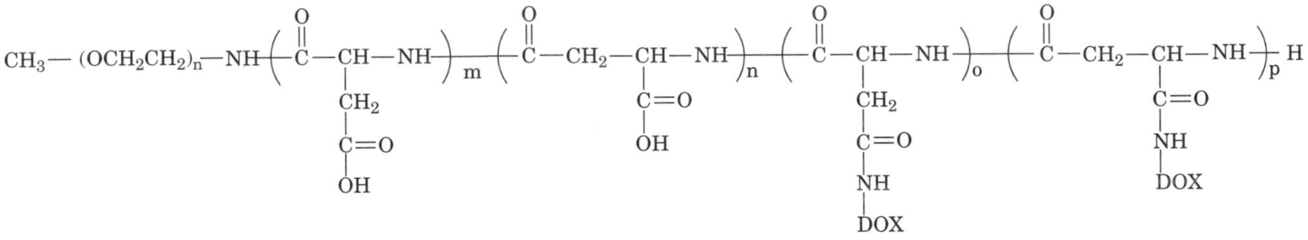

Figure 25. Structure of a PEG/poly(α,β-aspartic acid) AB-block copolymer–doxorubicin conjugate that can form polymeric micelles (11,98).

In Phase I/II trials of the HPMA copolymer doxorubicin–galactosamine conjugate, PK2 (see Fig. 13) (79,248–251), which is currently ongoing, the MTD for bolus (short infusion) administration of PK2 was found to be 160 mg/m^2 doxorubicin-equivalent with a dose limiting toxicity of neutropenia. Using an imaging analogue of PK2, γ camera imaging in humans verified that liver targeting of the conjugate occurred in patients having primary or secondary liver cancer. Liver targeting is now being maximized using a 24 h infusion rather than a rapid infusion.

During Phase I evaluation of an HPMA copolymer–paclitaxel conjugate (PNU 166945, see Fig. 17) (257) 13 patients were treated every 3 weeks with a 1 h infusion of conjugate at paclitaxel-equivalent doses of 80, 100, 140, and 196 mg/m^2. No significant myelosupression was observed up to the highest doses used, but grade 3 neurotoxicity was observed at 146 mg/m^2 paclitaxel-equivalents in one patient. Antitumor activity was observed (refractory breast cancer [1 patient] and disappearance of sigmoid cancer ascites [1 patient]), but the trial was interrupted due to concerns about neurotoxicity.

There are currently several other polymer–drug conjugates in preclinical development, and these compounds will soon to be evaluated clinically as anticancer compounds. They include an HPMA copolymer–camptothecin analogue, an HPMA copolymer platinate (see Fig. 18), poly(glutamic acid)-paclitaxel (see Fig. 8) (182), and a polymeric micelle containing noncovalently bound doxorubicin (168,169).

The two HPMA copolymer conjugates, like their previous relatives, contain the -Gly-Phe-Leu-Gly polymer–drug linkage. Although it is too early to draw definitive conclusions concerning the optimum means of polymer–drug conjugation, it is clear from the clinical experience emerging with PK1 and PK2 that drug conjugation via a peptidyl linker can only liberate anticancer agent after cleavage by lysosomal proteases is able to reduce the toxicity of the bound drug and may produce increased efficacy. Early

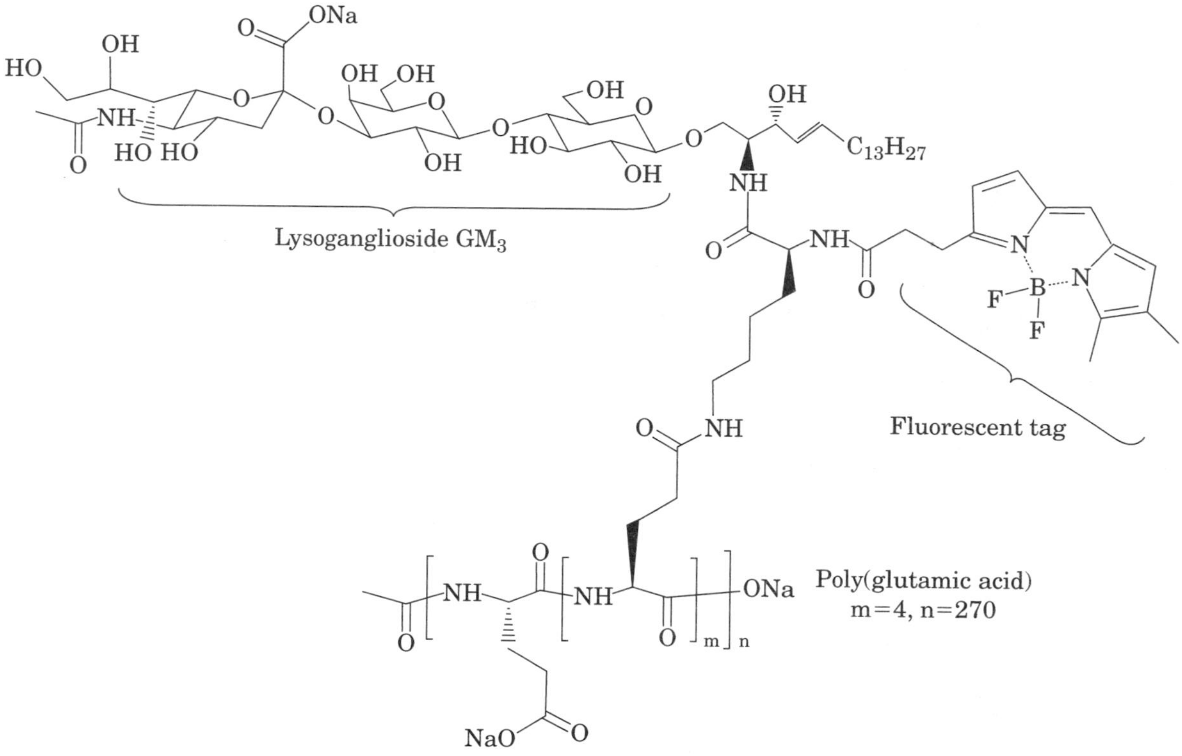

Figure 26. Structure of a multivalent poly(glutamic)–lysoganglioside conjugate designed for multivalent inhibition of influenza hemagglutinin at receptors on the cell surface (293).

clinical trials in oncology are designed to evaluate the safety of the therapy and determine the optimum dose (and schedule) for the later efficacy studies, not antitumor activity. However, the anticancer activity observed with PK1, PK2, and PNU 166945 is very encouraging, particularly as there is still an opportunity to maximize tumor targeting of such conjugates by the EPR effect with the aid of an optimal dosing schedule or polymer conjugate administration. There is also an opportunity to tailor further the rate of drug liberation from HPMA copolymer conjugates to suit the mechanism of action of the individual antitumor agent used in each case.

Most of the polymer–anticancer conjugates thus far described contain a relatively low drug payload (typically 5–10 wt % drug). Higher loading is often prohibited by loss of solubility. The clinical data emerging with the use of HPMA copolymer conjugates would advocate selection of more potent (than doxorubicin) anticancer agents for conjugation. Alternatively there is an obvious need for more hydrophilic carriers with greater solubilizing capacity.

CONCLUSIONS

It is evident from the early studies with anticancer compounds that polymer–drug conjugates have the potential to provide improved chemotherapy. The three basic components of a polymer–drug conjugate (i.e., polymer, linker, and drug) must be optimally matched to maximize therapeutic potential. Although the sophistication of synthetic chemistry can provide a plethora of structures, design based on the biological rationale and incorporating cost

and simplicity is imperative if compounds of real clinical value are to emerge. There is a need for continued basic research in chemistry to produce novel, preferentially biodegradable, polymers and to examine the effects of polymer architecture (e.g., dendrimers and hyperbranched polymers) on pharmacokinetics at the whole organism and cellular level. Further effort is needed to understand the details of the biological fate of polymer–drug conjugates. Although considerable progress has been made with peptidyl linkers, there is the possibility that research could fall into the "Me too" trap. New families of linkers designed with a clear rationale for bioactivation are required. Each polymer–drug conjugate is a unique molecule, so increased effort will be needed to prepare uniform conjugates. Systematic and improved analytical methods are required to correlate structure–property relationships required to optimize the biological profile of preclinical candidates.

Undoubtedly polymer–drug conjugates will progress from clinical trials in cancer patients to use in treatment of other diseases. These compounds will only succeed if designed to accommodate the pathophysiology of a chosen disease. Future success in developing polymer–drug conjugates will hinge upon the ability of people in the disciplines of pharmaceutical science (e.g., chemistry, biology, and medicine) to look at drug development with a new perspective focused on the properties of large molecules.

BIBLIOGRAPHY

1. R. Duncan, *Chem. Ind. (London)*, pp. 262–264 (1997).
2. P. Mason, *Pharm. J.* **260**, 382–385 (1998).

3. C. Monfardini and F. Veronese, *Bioconjugate Chem.* **9**, 418–450 (1998).

4. S. Zalipsky, *Adv. Drug Delivery Rev.* **16**, 157–182 (1995).

5. C. Delgado, G. Francis, and D. Fisher, *Crit. Rev. Ther. Drug Carrier Syst.* **9**, 249–304 (1992).

6. M.L. Nucci, D. Shorr, and A. Abuchowski, *Adv. Drug Delivery Rev.* **6**, 133–151 (1991).

7. G. Francis et al., *J. Drug Target.* **3**, 321–340 (1996).

8. S. Herman, G. Hooftman, and E. Schacht, *J. Bioact. Compat. Polym.* **10**(2), 145–187 (1995).

9. G. Hooftman, S. Herman, and E. Schacht, *J. Bioact. Compat. Polym.* **11**(2), 135–159 (1996).

10. V. Alakhov and A. Kabanov, *Expert Opin. Invest. Drugs* **7**(9), 1453–1473 (1998).

11. K. Kataoka, in K. Park, ed., *Controlled Drug Delivery: Challenges and Strategies*, American Chemical Society, Washington, D.C., 1997, pp. 49–71.

12. R. Duncan, S. Dimitrijevic, and E. Evagorou, *S.T.P. Pharma. Sci.* **6**, 237–263 (1996).

13. H. Soyez, E. Schacht, and S. Vanderkerken, *Adv. Drug Delivery Rev.* **21**, 81–106 (1996).

14. M. Nishikawa, Y. Takakura, and M. Hashida, *Adv. Drug Delivery Rev.* **21**, 135–155 (1996).

15. D. Putnam and J. Kopecek, *Adv. Polym. Sci.* **122**, 55–123 (1995).

16. H. Maeda, in A.J. Domb, ed., *Polymer Site-Specific Pharmacotherapy*, Wiley, New York, 1994, pp. 95–116.

17. R. Duncan and F. Spreafico, *Clin. Pharmacokinet.* **27**, 290–306 (1994).

18. R. Duncan, *Anti-Cancer Drugs* **3**, 175–210 (1992).

19. C. Hoes and J. Feijen, in F. Roerdink and A. Kroon, eds., *Drug-Carrier Systems*, Wiley, England, Chichester, 1989, pp. 57–109.

20. R. Duncan and J. Kopecek, *Adv. Polym. Sci.* **57**, 51–101 (1984).

21. H. Ringsdorf, *J. Polym. Sci. Polym. Symp.* **51**, 135–153 (1975).

22. I. Mellman, *Annu. Rev. Cell Dev. Biol.* **12**, 575–625 (1996).

23. R. Duncan and M. Pratten, in R. Dean and W. Jessup, eds., *Mononuclear Phagocytes: Physiology and Pathology*, Elsevier Biomedical Press, Amsterdam, 1985, pp. 27–51.

24. A. Barret and M. Heath, in J. Dingle, ed., *Lysosomes: A Laboratory Handbook*, 2nd ed., North-Holland, New York and Oxford, 1977, pp. 19–147.

25. C. deDuve et al., *Biochem. Pharmacol.* **23**, 2495–2531 (1974).

26. A. Trouet, D. Campeneere, and C. deDuve, *Nat. (London), New Biol.* **239**, 110–112 (1972).

27. L. Sprincl, J. Exner, O. Sterba, and J. Kopecek, *J. Biomed. Mater. Res.* **10**, 953–963 (1976).

28. L. Sprincl, J. Vacik, J. Kopecek, and D. Lim, *J. Biomed. Mater. Res.* **5**, 197–205 (1971).

29. H. Ringsdorf et al., in T. Sugahara and O. Hug, eds., Igaku Shoin, Tokyo, 1971, p. 138.

30. I. Iliev, M. Georgieva, and V. Kabaivanov, *Russ. Chem. Rev. (Engl. Transl.)* **43**(1), 69–75 (1974).

31. W. Regelson, *Adv. Chemother.* **3**, 303–371 (1968).

32. W. Regelson, in N. Bikales, ed., *Water Soluble Polymers II*, Plenum, New York, 1973, pp 161–177.

33. W. Regelson et al., in A. Rembaum and E. Seligny, eds., *Polyelectrolytes and their Application*, Reidel Publ., Dordrecht, The Netherlands, 1974, pp. 131–144.

34. H. Batz, H. Ringsdorf, and H. Ritter, *Makromol. Chem.* **175**(8), 2229–2239 (1974).

35. B. Weiner, M. Tahan, and A. Zilkha, *J. Med. Chem.* **15**(4), 410–413 (1972).

36. S. Foster and J. Lloyd, *Biochim. Biophys. Acta* **947**, 465–491 (1988).

37. P. Goddard and K. Petrak, *J. Bioact. Compat. Polym.* **4**, 372–402 (1989).

38. H. Chiu, P. Kopeckova, S. Deshmane, and J. Kopecek, *J. Biomed. Mater. Res.* **34**, 381–392 (1997).

39. Y. Matsumura and H. Maeda, *Cancer Res.* **6**, 6387–6392 (1986).

40. H. Maeda, L. Seymour, and Y. Miyamoto, *Bioconjugate Chem.* **3**, 351–362 (1992).

41. H. Maeda, *J. Controlled Release* **19**, 315–324 (1992).

42. R. Jain, *Cancer Res.* **48**, 2641–2658 (1988).

43. R. Jain, *J. Nat. Cancer Inst.* **81**, 570–576 (1989).

44. F. Yuan et al., *Cancer Res.* **55**, 3752–3756 (1995).

45. H. Maeda and Y. Matsumura, *CRC Crit. Rev. Ther. Drug Carrier Sys.* **6**(3), 193–210 (1989).

46. Y. Takakura, T. Fujita, M. Hashida, and H. Sezaki, *Pharm. Res.* **7**, 339–436 (1990).

47. Y. Noguchi et al., *Jpn. J. Cancer Res.* **89**, 307–314 (1998).

48. E. Day, J. Palnisek, and M. Pressman, *J. Natl. Cancer Inst. (U.S.)* **23**, 799–805 (1959).

49. H. Peterson and K. Appelgren, *Eur. J. Cancer* **9**, 543–548 (1973).

50. H. Dvorak, V. Harvey, and J. McDonagh, *Cancer Res.* **44**, 3348–3354 (1984).

51. A. Babson and T. Winnick, *Cancer Res.* **14**, 606–611 (1954).

52. J. Hradec, *Br. J. Cancer* **12**, 290–294 (1961).

53. C. Andersson, B. Iresjo, and K. Lundholm, *J. Surg. Res.* **50**, 156–162 (1991).

54. G. Stehle et al., *Crit. Rev. Oncol. Hematol.* **26**, 77–100 (1997).

55. A. Wunder et al., *Int. J. Oncol.* **11**, 497–507 (1997).

56. R. Jain and L. Baxter, *Cancer Res.* **48**, 7022–7032 (1988).

57. T. Shockley et al., *Cancer Res.* **52**, 357–366 (1992).

58. L. Nugent and R. Jain, *Am. J. Physiol.* **246**, H129–H137 (1984).

59. Y. Tabata, Y. Murakami, and Y. Ikada, *J. Controlled Release* **50**, 123–133 (1998).

60. L. Seymour et al., *Eur. J. Cancer* **31A**(5), 766–770 (1995).

61. P. Steyger et al., *J. Controlled Release* **39**, 35–46 (1996).

62. K. Iwai, H. Maeda, and T. Konno, *Cancer Res.* **44**, 2114–2121 (1984).

63. H. Maeda et al., *J. Med. Chem.* **28**, 455–461 (1985).

64. L. Seymour et al., *Br. J. Cancer* **70**, 636–641 (1994).

65. R. Duncan and Y. Sat, *Ann. Oncol.* **9**(S2), 149 (1998).

66. S. Hobbs et al., *Proc. Natl. Acad. Sci. U.S.A.* **95**, 4607–4612 (1998).

67. R. Duncan et al., *Biochim. Biophys. Acta* **840**, 291–293 (1985).

68. L. Seymour, R. Duncan, J. Strohalm, and J. Kopecek, *J. Biomed. Mater. Res.* **21**, 1341–1358 (1987).

69. C. Hopkins and I. Trowbridge, *J. Cell Biol.* **97**, 508–521 (1983).

70. I. Trowbridge and D. Domingo, *Nature (London)* **294**, 171–173 (1981).

71. P.D. Smidt and J.V. Berkel, *CRC Crit. Rev. Ther. Drug Carrier Syst.* **7**, 99–120 (1990).

72. C. King, *Cancer Biol.* **1**, 329–337 (1990).

73. C. Robinson, *Trends Biotechnol.* **9**, 147–148 (1991).

74. G. Ghanem *Int. J. Cancer* **41**, 248–255 (1988).

75. D. Vera, R. Stadalnick, and K. Krohn, *J. Nucl. Med.* **26**, 1157–1167 (1985).

76. R. Fallon and A. Schwartz, *Adv. Drug Delivery Rev.* **4**, 49–63 (1989).

77. P. Dragsten, D. Mitchell, G. Covert, and T. Baker, *Biochim. Biophys. Acta* **926**, 270–279 (1987).

78. F. Ceulemans et al., *Pathol. Biol.* **35**, 61–68 (1987).

79. R. Duncan et al., *Biochim. Biophys. Acta* **880**, 62–71 (1986).

80. L. Seymour et al., *Br. J. Cancer* **63**, 859–866 (1991).

81. L. Seymour, *J. Bioact. Compat. Polym.* **6**, 178–216 (1991).

82. M. Otterlei et al., *J. Immunother.* **10**, 286–291 (1991).

83. W. Regelson, *J. Natl. Cancer Inst.* **81**, 1920–1930 (1989).

84. N. Burnham, *Am. J. Hosp. Pharm.* **51**, 210–218 (1994).

85. N. Katre, *Adv. Drug Delivery Rev.* **10**, 91–114 (1993).

86. J. Harris, ed., *Poly(ethylene glycol) Biotechnical and Biomedical Applications*, Plenum, New York, 1992.

87. P. Denter et al., *Bioconjugate Chem.* **6**(4), 389–394 (1995).

88. R. Greenwald et al., *J. Med. Chem.* **39**, 1938–1940 (1996).

89. C. Conover et al., *Anticancer Res.* **17**(5A), 3361–3368 (1997).

90. R. Greenwald et al., *Bioorg. Med. Chem.* **6**(5), 551–562 (1998).

91. R. Greenwald et al., *J. Med. Chem.* **39**(2), 424–431 (1996).

92. C. Li et al., *Anticancer Drugs* **7**, 642–648 (1996).

93. R. Greenwald, *Expert Opin. Ther. Patents* **7**(6), 601–609 (1997).

94. A. Nathan et al., *Bioconjugate Chem.* **4**, 54–62 (1993).

95. A. Nathan, S. Zalipsky, and J. Kohn, *J. Bioact. Compat. Polym.* **9**(3), 239–251 (1994).

96. M. Pechar, J. Strohalm, K. Ulbrich, and E. Schacht, *Macromol. Chem. Phys.* **198**, 1009–1020 (1997).

97. M. Pechar, I. Strohalm, and K. Ulbrich, *Collect. Czech. Chem. Commun.* **60**, 1765–1780 (1995).

98. K. Kataoka et al., *J. Controlled Release* **24**, 119–132 (1993).

99. T. Inoue, G. Chen, K. Nakamae, and A. Hoffman, *J. Controlled Release* **51**, 221–229 (1998).

100. G. Kwon and T. Okano, *Adv. Drug Delivery Rev.* **21**, 107–116 (1996).

101. J. Kopecek and H. Bazilova, *Eur. Polym. J.* **9**, 7–14 (1973).

102. J. Kopecek, *Makromol. Chem.* **178**, 2169–2183 (1977).

103. V. Chytry et al., *Makromol. Chem., Rapid Commun.* **3**, 11–15 (1982).

104. J. Simeckova, D. Plocova, B. Rihova, and J. Kopecek, *J. Bioact. Compat. Polym.* **1**, 20–31 (1986).

105. B. Rihova, K. Ulbrich, J. Kopecek, and P. Mancal, *Folia Microbiol.* **28**, 217–297 (1983).

106. B. Rihova, J. Kopecek, K. Ulbrich, and V. Chytry, *Makromol. Chem., Suppl.* **9**, 13–24 (1985).

107. B. Rihova, I. Riha, *CRC Crit. Rev. Ther. Drug Carrier Syst.* **1**, 311–374 (1985).

108. B. Rihova et al., *Biomaterials* **10**, 335–342 (1989).

109. P. Schneider, T. Korolenko, and U. Busch, *Microsc. Res. Tech.* **36**, 253–275 (1997).

110. C. Hall and O. Hall, *Experientia* **17**, 544–545 (1961).

111. C. Hall and O. Hall, *Experientia* **18**, 38–40 (1962).

112. P. Goddard et al., *J. Bioact. Compat. Polym.* **6**, 4–24 (1991).

113. J. Vercauteren, D. Bruneel, E. Schacht, and R. Duncan, *J. Bioact. Compat. Polym.* **5**, 4–15 (1990).

114. W. Shalaby and K. Park, in S. Shalaby, ed., *Biomedical Polymers. Designed-to-Degrade Systems*, Hanser Publishers, New York, 1994, pp. 213–258.

115. P. Labrude and C. Vigneron, *Lyon Pharm.* **26**(6), 629–646 (1975).

116. L. Moteni, in G. Gregoriadis, ed., *Drug Carriers Biology and Medicine*, Academic Press, London, 1979, pp. 107–125.

117. T. Fujita et al., *J. Controlled Release* **11**, 149–156 (1990).

118. M. Hashida et al., *Proc. Int. Congr. Chemother.*, Kyoto, 1985.

119. H.S.Y. Imoto et al., *Cancer Res.* **52**, 4396–4401 (1992).

120. T. Nomura et al., *J. Controlled Release* **52**, 239–252 (1998).

121. H. Sezaki, Y. Takakura, and M. Hashida, *Adv. Drug Delivery Rev.* **3**, 247–266 (1989).

122. Y. Yasuda et al., *Chem. Pharm. Bull.* **38**(7), 2053–2056 (1990).

123. Y. Takakura, R. Atsumi, M. Hashida, and H. Sezaki, *Int. J. Pharm.* **37**, 147–154 (1987).

124. K. Granath and B. Kvist, *J. Chromatogr.* **28**, 69–81 (1967).

125. S. Vansteenkiste et al., *J. Controlled Release* **16**, 91–100 (1991).

126. Y. Ohya et al., *J. Controlled Release* **17**, 259–266 (1991).

127. A. Al-Shamkhani and R. Duncan, *Int. J. Pharm.* **122**, 107–119 (1995).

128. S. Morgan et al., *Int. J. Pharm.* **122**, 121–128 (1995).

129. B. Schechter, A. Neumann, M. Wilchek, and R. Arnon, *J. Controlled Release* **10**, 75–87 (1989).

130. Y. Ohya, K. Nonomura, and T. Ouchi, *J. Bioact. Compat. Polym.* **10**, 223–234 (1995).

131. H. Nogusa et al., *Chem. Pharm. Bull.* **43**, 1931–1936 (1995).

132. K. James and J. Kohn, in K. Park, ed., *Controlled Drug Delivery: Challenges and Strategies*, American Chemical Society, Washington, D.C., 1997, pp. 389–403.

133. K. Abdellaoui et al., *Eur. J. Pharm. Sci.* **6**, 61–73 (1998).

134. T. Ouchi, A. Fujino, K. Tanaka, and T. Banba, *J. Controlled Release* **12**, 143–153 (1990).

135. T. Deming, *Nature (London)* **390**, 386–389 (1997).

136. D. Carter and J. Ho, *Adv. Protein Chem.* **45**, 153–203 (1994).

137. P. Balboni et al., *Nature (London)* **264**, 181–183 (1976).

138. A. Trouet, M. Masquelier, R. Baurain, and D. Campaneere, *Proc. Natl. Acad. Sci. U.S.A.* **79**, 626–629 (1982).

139. Y. Kaneo, T. Tanaka, and S. Iguchi, *Chem. Pharm. Bull.* **38**, 2614–2626 (1990).

140. K. Ohkwada et al., *Cancer Res.* **53**, 4238–4242 (1993).

141. F. Dosio et al., *J. Controlled Release* **47**(3), 293–304 (1997).

142. T. Yasuzawa and K. Tomer, *Bioconjugate Chem.* **8**, 391–399 (1997).

143. A. Wunder et al., *Int. J. Cancer* **76**, 884–890 (1998).

144. T. Tanaka, Y. Kaneo, M. Miyashita, and S. Shiramoto, *Biol. Pharm. Bull.* **18**(2), 1724–1728 (1995).

145. T. Tanaka, Y. Kaneo, and M. Miyashita, *Biol. Pharm. Bull.* **21**(2), 147–152 (1998).

146. T. Tanaka, Y. Kaneo, and M. Miyashita, *Biol. Pharm. Bull.* **19**(5), 774–777 (1996).

147. D. Gaal and F. Hudecz, *Eur. J. Cancer* **34**(1), 155–161 (1998).

148. V. Omelyanenko et al., *J. Drug Target.* **3**, 357–374 (1996).

149. C. Hoes et al., *J. Controlled Release* **38**, 245–266 (1996).

150. E. Eno-Amooquaye et al., *Br. J. Cancer* **73**, 1323–1327 (1996).

151. R. Duncan, *Contrib. Oncol.* **48**, 170–180 (1995).

152. P. Trail, D. Willner, and K. Hellestrom, *Drug Dev. Res.* **34**, 196–209 (1995).

153. P. Trail et al., *Science* **261**, 212–215 (1993).

154. D. Willner et al., *Bioconjugate Chem.* **4**, 521–527 (1993).

155. P. Flanagan et al., *J. Controlled Release* **18**, 25–38 (1992).

156. C. Springer et al., *Eur. J. Cancer* **11**, 1362–1366 (1991).

157. M. Magerstadt, *Antibody Conjugates and Malignant Disease*, CRC Press, Boca Raton, Fl., 1990.

158. H. Yang and R. Reisfeld, *Proc. Natl. Acad. Sci. U.S.A.* **85**, 1189–1193 (1988).

159. L. Gros, H. Ringsdorf, and H. Schupp, *Angew. Chem., Int. Ed. Eng.* **20**, 301–323 (1981).

160. G. Kwon et al., *Pharm. Res.* **10**, 970–974 (1993).

161. G. Kwon and K. Kataoka, *Adv. Drug Delivery Rev.* **16**, 295–309 (1995).

162. M. Yokoyama, *Crit. Rev. Ther. Drug Carrier Syst.* **9**, 213–248 (1992).

163. P. Calibresi and B. Chabner, in J.G. Hardman and L.E. Limbird, eds., *The Pharmacological Basis of Therapeutics*, McGraw-Hill, New York, 1996, pp. 1225–1288.

164. A. Kabanov and V. Alakhov, *J. Controlled Release* **28**, 15–35 (1994).

165. M. Yokayama, T. Okano, Y. Sakurai, and K. Kataoka, *J. Controlled Release* **32**, 269–277 (1994).

166. M. Yokoyama et al., *Cancer Res.* **51**, 3229–3236 (1991).

167. M. Yokoyama et al., *J. Controlled Release* **50**, 79–92 (1998).

168. E. Batrakova et al., *Br. J. Cancer* **74**(10), 1545–1552 (1996).

169. A. Venne et al., *Cancer Res.* **56**(16), 3626–3629 (1996).

170. D. Bruneel and E. Schacht, *Polymer* **34**(12), 2628–2632 (1993).

171. D. Bruneel and E. Schacht, *Polymer* **34**(12), 2633–2637 (1993).

172. D. Bruneel and E. Schacht, *Polymer* **35**(12), 2656–2658 (1993).

173. R. Vercauteren, E. Schacht, and R. Duncan, *J. Bioact. Compact. Polym.* **7**, 346–357 (1992).

174. D. Bruneel and E. Schacht, *J. Bioact. Compat. Polym.* **10**(4), 299–312 (1995).

175. Z. Brich et al., *J. Controlled Release* **19**, 245–258 (1992).

176. K. Munechika et al., *Biol. Pharm. Bull.* **17**(9), 1193–1198 (1994).

177. Y. Ohe et al., *Drug Delivery Syst.* **9**(5), 351–356 (1994).

178. Y. Takakura, S. Mastsumoto, M. Hashida, and H. Sezaki, *Cancer Res.* **44**, 2505–2510 (1984).

179. A. deMarre and E. Schacht, *Makromol. Chem. Macromol. Chem. Phys.* **193**, 3023–3030 (1992).

180. A. deMarre et al., *J. Controlled Release* **36**, 87–97 (1995).

181. H. Soyez, E. Schacht, A. Demarre, and L. Seymour, *Macromol. Symp.* **103**, 163–176 (1996).

182. C. Li et al., *Cancer Res.* **58**, 2404–2409 (1998).

183. J. Drobnik et al., *Makromol. Chem.* **177**, 2833–2848 (1976).

184. P. Rejmanova, J. Labsky, and J. Kopecek, *Makromol. Chem.* **178**, 2159–2168 (1977).

185. H. Batz, G. Franzmann, and H. Ringsdorf, *Angew. Chem., Int. Ed. Engl.* **11**(12), 1103–1104 (1972).

186. P. Ferruti, A. Bettelli, and A. Fere, *Polymer* **13**, 462–464 (1972).

187. J. Labsky and J. Kalal, *Eur. Polym. J.* **15**, 603–605 (1979).

188. J. Labsky and J. Kalal, *Eur. Polym. J.* **15**, 167–171 (1979).

189. C. Su and H. Morawetz, *J. Polym. Sci., Polym. Chem. Ed.* **15**, 185–196 (1977).

190. C. Su and H. Morawetz, *J. Polym. Sci., Polym. Chem. Ed.* **16**, 1059–1062 (1978).

191. J. Frechet et al., *Makromol. Chem.* **178**(8), 2159–2168(1988).

192. C. Pitt and S. Shah, *J. Controlled Release* **39**, 221–229 (1996).

193. J. Strohalm and J. Kopecek, *Angew. Makromol. Chem.* **70**, 109–118 (1978).

194. J. Kopecek, *J. Controlled Release* **11**, 279–290 (1990).

195. R. Mendichi, V. Rizzo, M. Gigli, and A.G. Schieroni, *J. Liq. Chromatogr. Relat. Technol.* **19**(10), 1591–1605 (1996).

196. E. Configliacchi, G. Razzano, V. Rizzo, and A. Vigevani, *J. Pharm. Biomed. Anal.* **15**, 123–129 (1996).

197. V. Pinciroli et al., *Magn. Reson. Chem.* **35**(1), 2–8 (1997).

198. S. Wedge, Ph.D. Thesis, Keele University, England, 1990.

199. S. Cartlidge et al., *J Controlled Release* **4**, 253–264 (1986).

200. R. Duncan et al., *Biochem. J.* **196**, 49–55 (1981).

201. S. Cartlidge et al., *J. Controlled Release* **3**, 55–66 (1986).

202. A. Kaplan, in L. Donaruma, R. Ottenbrite, and O. Vogl, eds., *Anionic Polymeric Drugs*, Wiley, New York, 1980, pp. 227–254.

203. R. Ottenbrite et al., in L. Donaruma and O. Vogl, eds., *Polymeric Drugs*, Academic Press, New York, 1978, pp. 263–304.

204. G. Butler, in L. Donaruma, R. Ottenbrite, and O. Vogl, eds., *Anionic Polymeric Drugs*, Wiley, New York, 1980, pp. 49–142.

205. K. Mueck, H. Rolly, and K. Burg, *Makromol. Chem.* **178**, 2773–2784 (1977).

206. K. Mueck, O. Christ, and H. Keller, *Makromol. Chem.* **178**, 2785–2797 (1977).

207. B. Schechter, R. Pauzner, R. Arnon, and M. Wilchek, *Cancer Biochem. Biophys.* **8**, 277–287 (1986).

208. M. Filiova-Vopralova, J. Drobnik, B. Ramed, and J. Kvetina, *J. Controlled Release* **17**, 89–98 (1991).

209. E. Neuse, G. Caldwell, and A. Perlwitz, *J. Inorg. Organomet. Polym.* **5**, 195–207 (1995).

210. E. Neuse, *Macromol. Symp.* **80**, 11–128 (1994).

211. C. Mbonyana, E. Neuse, and A. Perlwitz, *Appl. Organomet. Chem.* **7**, 279–288 (1993).

212. M. Han et al., *J. Bioact. Compat. Polym.* **9**, 142–151 (1994).

213. Y. Sohn et al., *Preclinical Studies of a Water Soluble Polyphosphazene-Pt(DACH) Conjugate*, EORTC/NCI, Amsterdam, 1996.

214. A. Bogdanov et al., *Bioconjugate Chem.* **7**, 144–149 (1996).

215. A. Muhler, *Magma* **3**, 21–33 (1995).

216. A. Bogdanov, R. Weissleder, and T. Brady, *Adv. Drug Delivery Rev.* **16**, 335–348 (1995).

217. L. Harika et al., *Magn. Reson. Med.* **33**, 88–92 (1995).

218. A. Bogdanov et al., *J. Nucl. Med.* **35**, 1880–1886 (1994).

219. M. Wendland et al., *Magn. Reson. Med.* **32**, 319–329 (1994).

220. R. Duncan et al., *Biosci. Rep.* **2**, 1041–1046 (1983).

221. P. Rejmanova, J. Kopecek, R. Duncan, and J. Lloyd, *Biomaterials* **6**, 45–48 (1985).

222. V. Subr, J. Kopecek, and R. Duncan, *J. Bioact. Compat. Polym.* **1**, 133–146 (1986).

223. V. Subr et al., *J. Controlled Release* **18**, 123–132 (1992).

224. W. Shen and H. Ryser, *Biochem. Biophys. Res. Commun.* **102**, 1048–1054 (1981).

225. M. Masquelier, R. Baurain, and A. Trouet, *J. Med. Chem.* **23**, 1166–1170 (1980).

226. R. Baurain, M. Masquelier, D.D.-D. Campeneere, and A. Trouet, *J. Med. Chem.* **23**, 1171–1174 (1980).

227. J. Kopecek, *Biomaterials* **5**, 19–25 (1984).

228. P. Rejmanova et al., *Makromol. Chem.*, **184**, 2009–2020 (1983).

229. P. Rejmanova et al., *Makromol. Chem.* **182**, 1899–2010 (1989).

230. K. Ulbrich, E. Zacharieva, B. Obereigner, and J. Kopecek, *Biomaterials* **1**, 199–204 (1980).

231. R. Duncan et al., *Makromol. Chem.* **184**, 1997–2008 (1984).

232. V. Subr et al., *J. Controlled Release* **8**, 133–140 (1988).

233. R. Duncan, J. Lloyd, J. Kopecek, *Biochem. Biophys. Res. Commun.* **94**, 284–290 (1980).

234. R. Duncan et al., *J. Controlled Release* **16**, 121–136 (1991).

235. L. Seymour et al., *Biochem. Pharmacol.* **39**, 1125–1131 (1990).

236. R. Duncan et al., *Eur. J. Cancer* **27**(3), S52 (1991).

237. R. Duncan et al., *J. Controlled Release* **19**, 331–346 (1992).

238. J. Cassidy et al., *Biochem. Pharmacol.* **38**, 875–879 (1989).

239. K. O'Hare et al., *J. Drug Target.* **1**, 217–230 (1993).

240. P. Vasey et al., *Ann. Oncol.* **7**, 97 (1996).

241. R. Duncan et al., *Br. J. Cancer* **57**, 147–156 (1988).

242. R. Duncan et al., *J. Controlled Release* **10**, 51–63 (1989).

243. K. Ulbrich, C. Konak, Z. Tuzar, and J. Kopecek, *Makromol. Chem.* **188**, 1261–1272 (1987).

244. V. Chytry, M. Netopilik, M. Bohdanecky, and K. Ulbrich, *J. Biomater. Sci., Polym. Ed.* **8**(11), 817–824 (1997).

245. F. Uchegbu, H. Ringsdorf, and R. Duncan, *Proc. Int. Symp. Controlled Release Bioact. Mater.* **23**, 791–792 (1996).

246. C. Pitt, J. Wertheim, C. Wang, and S. Shah, *Macromol. Symp.* **123**, 225–234 (1997).

247. S. Shah, J. Werthim, C. Wang, and C. Pitt, *J. Controlled Release* **45**, 95–101 (1997).

248. K. O'Hare, I. Hume, L. Scarlett, and R. Duncan, *Hepatology* **10**, 207–214 (1989).

249. L. Seymour, K. Ulbrich, J. Strohalm, and R. Duncan, *Br. J. Cancer* **63**, 859–866 (1991).

250. L. Seymour et al., *Proc. Int. Symp. Recent Adv. Drug Delivery Syst.* **8**, 132–135 (1997).

251. D. Kerr, et al., *Proc. 3rd Int. Symp. Polym. Ther.*, London, January 7–9, 1998.

252. L. Seymour et al., *Br. J. Cancer* **63**, 859–866 (1991).

253. C. Hoes et al., *J. Controlled Release* **2**, 205–218 (1985).

254. C. Hoes et al., *J. Controlled Release* **23**, 37–53 (1993).

255. E. Pesenti et al., *Proc. Am. Assoc. Cancer Res.* **36**, 1824 (1995).

256. U.S. Pat. 5,362,831 (1994), N. Mongelli, E. Pesenti, A. Suarato, and G. Biasoli, (to Farmtalia Carlo Erba S.r.l.).

257. W.B. Huniunk et al., *Proc. 3rd Int. Symp. Polym. Ther.*, London, January 7–9, 1998.

258. A. deMarre, L. Seymour, and E. Schacht, *J. Controlled Release* **31**, 89–97 (1994).

259. M. Nichifor, V. Coessens, and E. Schacht, *J. Bioact. Compat. Polymer.* **10**, 199–222 (1995).

260. M. Nichifor, E. Schacht, and L. Seymour, *J. Controlled Release* **39**, 79–92 (1996).

261. D. Putnam and J. Kopecek, *Bioconjugate Chem.* **6**, 483–492 (1995).

262. D. Putnam, Ph.D. Thesis, University of Utah, Salt Lake City, 1996.

263. D. Putnam, J. Shiah, and J. Kopecek, *Biochem. Pharmacol.* **52**, 957–962 (1996).

264. R. Mendichi et al., *J. Liq. Chromatogr. Relat. Technol.* **21**(9), 1295–1309 (1998).

265. F. Angelucci, D. Ballinari, and M. Farao, *Proc. 13th Int. Symp. Med. Chem.*, Paris, September 1994.

266. M. Ripamonti et al., *Br. J. Cancer* **65**, 703–707 (1992).

267. I. Tannock and D. Rotin, *Cancer Res.* **49**, 4373–4384 (1989).

268. A. Kuin et al., *Cancer Res.* **54**, 3785–3792 (1994).

269. W. Shen and H. Ryser, *Proc. Natl. Acad. Sci. U.S.A.* **75**(4), 1872–1876 (1978).

270. F. Hudecz et al., *J. Controlled Release* **19**, 231–244 (1992).

271. E. Franssen et al., *J. Med. Chem.* **35**, 1246–1259 (1992).

272. M. Wirth et al., *Pharm. Res.* **15**(7), 1031–1037 (1998).

273. R. Dillman, D. Johnson, D. Shawler, and J. Koziol, *Cancer Res.* **48**, 6097–6102 (1988).

274. E. Diener et al., *Science* **231**, 148–150 (1986).

275. A. Kirby and P. Lancaster, *J. Chem. Soc. Perkin Trans. 2*, pp. 1206–1214 (1972).

276. M. Sato et al., *Biol. Pharm. Bull.* **19**(2), 241–245 (1996).

277. E. Hurwitz, M. Wilchek, and J. Pitha, *J. Appl. Biochem.* **2**, 25–35 (1980).

278. B. Mueller, W. Wrasidlo, and R. Reisfield, *Bioconjugate Chem.* **2**, 325–330 (1990).

279. Y. Ueda et al., *Proc. Int. Symp. Controlled Release Bioact. Mater.* **16**, 142–143.

280. Y. Ueda et al., *Chem. Pharm. Bull.* **37**, 1639–1641 (1989).

281. A. Kikukawa et al., *Drug Delivery Syst.* **5**, 255–260 (1990).

282. S. Danauser-Reidl et al., *Invest. New Drugs* **11**(2–3), 187–195 (1993).

283. Y. Ohya, H. Kuroda, K. Hirai, and T. Ouchi, *J. Bioact. Compat. Polym.* **10**(1), 51–66 (1995).

284. G. Poiani et al., *Am. J. Respir. Crit. Care Med.* **155**(4), 1384–1390 (1997).

285. G. Poiani et al., *Bioconjugate Chem.* **5**, 621–630 (1994).

286. M. Greco et al., *Am. J. Respir. Crit. Care Med.* **155**(4), 1391–1397 (1997).

287. Y. Ohya, K. Inosaka, and T. Ouchi, *Chem. Pharm. Bull.* **40**, 591–561 (1992).

288. N. Yokoyama et al., *Bioconjugate Chem.* **3**, 295–301 (1992).

289. M. Yokoyama et al., *Cancer Res.* **50**, 1693–1700 (1990).

290. M. Mammen, S. Choi, and G. Whitesides, *Angew. Chem., Int. Ed. Engl.* **37**, 2754–2794 (1998).

291. E. Gordon, L. Strong, and L. Kiessling, *Bioorg. Med. Chem.* **6**, 1293–1299 (1998).

292. D. Mann, M. Kanai, D.J. Maly, and L. Kiessling, *J. Am. Chem. Soc.* **120**(41), 10575–10582 (1998).

293. H. Kamitakahara et al., *Angew. Chem., Int. Ed. Engl.* **37**(11), 1524–1528 (1998).

294. P. Vasey et al., *Clin. Cancer Res.* **5**, 83–94 (1999).

295. P. Vasey, R. Duncan, S. Kaye, and J. Cassidy, *Eur. J. Cancer* **31A**, S193 (1995).

296. A. Bernstein, E. Hurwitz, and R. Arnon, *J. Natl. Cancer Inst. (U.S.)* **60**, 379–384 (1978).

297. E. Abound-Pirak et al., *Proc. Natl. Acad. Sci. U.S.A.* **86**, 3778–3781 (1989).

298. H. Onishi and T. Nagai, *Chem. Pharm. Bull.* **34**(6), 2561–2567 (1986).

See also CANCER, DRUG DELIVERY TO TREAT—PRODRUGS.

PEPTIDE AND PROTEIN DRUG DELIVERY

OluFunmi L. Johnson
Mark A. Tracy
Alkermes Incorporated
Cambridge, Massachusetts

KEY WORDS

Biodegradable polymers
Controlled delivery
Drug delivery
Microspheres
Particles
Peptide
Pharmaceutical development
Polymers
Process development
Process scale-up
Protein
Stability
Sustained delivery
Sustained release

OUTLINE

INTRODUCTION

Efficacious delivery of protein and peptide drugs is taking on increasing significance as biotechnology companies mature and begin commercializing their products. As a result, there has been increasing interest in the development of protein and peptide delivery systems. The high level of interest is attributable to several factors. As the pharmaceutical and biotechnology industries consolidate and mature, there is an interest in value-added technologies, which drug delivery systems can provide. There is also an impending stream of patent expirations, which is fueling the demand for the rapid development of new products that may be realized by drug delivery technologies.

Drug delivery systems provide a number of advantages, including one or more of the following:

- Improved patient convenience
- Improved patient compliance
- Cost reduction
- Reduced frequency of administration
- Reduced adverse effect profile
- Patent protection extension
- Potential to reduce product development time and costs
- Possible new and broader therapeutic applications

However, to realize these advantages, it is critical to define clearly why a drug delivery technology is being sought and understand thoroughly the advantages and disadvantages of each delivery system, the unique physicochemical and biological properties of the protein or peptide of interest, and the requirements of the therapeutic indication.

The production of proteins by recombinant technology was an important milestone in the development of this new class of therapeutic agents. Proteins and peptides are poorly suited to the standard oral delivery route for administering small-molecule drugs because of the enzymatic and absorption barriers posed by the gastrointestinal tract; therefore, virtually all protein and peptide drugs are administered parenterally by subcutaneous or intramuscular injection (the immunosuppressant cyclosporine, a cyclic polypeptide, is a rare exception). However, the half-life of these drugs injected parenterally is only a few hours in most cases, necessitating multiple injections per week (typically 3–7) for therapeutic effectiveness. As a result, parenterally administered drugs generally have lower compliance levels than orally administered drugs. One way of improving compliance and minimizing discomfort arising from frequent injections is to couple protein and peptide drugs with sophisticated parenteral delivery systems that reduce the frequency of injection by providing a sustained release of the drug over time. Alternatively, these advantages may be achieved by immediate or sustained delivery to the systemic circulation via nonoral or transmucosal routes such as the nasal, pulmonary, vaginal, rectal, and, in some cases, the transdermal routes (e.g., iontophoretic delivery of insulin). Thus, the availability of these new biopharmaceuticals has made their formulation and delivery an important part in the treatment of various disease states.

To address the challenges of protein and peptide delivery, a number of approaches are being pursued. One approach involves providing a controlled or sustained release of the drug by the parenteral route. Controlled delivery implies the incorporation of one or more elements of control on the release of an active ingredient from a dosage form to obtain a well-defined pharmacokinetic profile. A major advantage of controlled-release formulations over conventional dosage forms is the ability to manipulate the components of the dosage form to obtain a particular release profile. Sustained-release formulations are controlled-release dosage forms that have been engineered to release the active ingredient over an extended time period in a well-defined and reproducible fashion (1). As noted earlier, advantages include fewer injections and perhaps a therapeutic benefit for a sustained drug-release profile. For example, a short half-life may be increased either by chemically modifying the protein by coupling it to a moiety such as poly(ethylene glycol) (PEG) or by developing a degradable polymeric sustained-release formulation that would release therapeutic concentrations of the drug over an extended time period as the device degrades. A good example where a sustained drug serum concentration is actually required for therapeutic benefit is the sustained delivery of synthetic analogues of gonadotropin. It was demonstrated that the serum concentration of the drug needed to be above a certain threshold to produce a pharmacodynamic response, testosterone suppression in males and suppression of estrus in females.

Another delivery approach involves using nonparenteral routes for immediate or sustained release. A wide variety of dosage forms have been developed for the delivery of conventional small-molecule drugs for delivery via the oral, parenteral, buccal, transdermal, ocular, intravaginal, intrauterine, pulmonary, and nasal routes. Each of these routes of delivery has its own unique advantages and challenges that are a function of the physiology of the sites. The delivery of proteins via any of these routes requires special considerations that must be borne in mind in the development of protein formulations.

There are several sustained-release formulations of peptides on the market and, to our knowledge, there are no commercialized long-acting formulations containing a protein for humans; however, one long-acting protein-containing parenteral product is available for enhancing milk production in dairy cattle. Also, though there are a number of products for the delivery of proteins and peptides by nonparenteral routes in various stages of preclinical and clinical development, none (except cyclosporine), to our knowledge, have been commercialized for oral administration. One of the key reasons for the absence of novel protein formulations is their fragility and the need for suitable process and formulation approaches to maintain the protein structure while achieving desirable release characteristics. This article reviews the technical considerations in developing delivery products for proteins and peptides, focusing on injectable polymeric delivery systems as an example. Major stability, release, and manufacturing challenges in developing these products are discussed along with approaches to overcome them. Though we focus on polymeric delivery systems here, many of the principles presented are broadly applicable to a variety of peptide and protein drug delivery systems.

PROTEIN AND PEPTIDE STABILITY

Proteins differ from conventional small-molecule drugs in several respects, including size, but one of the most important differences affecting delivery and biological effectiveness is the complexity of protein structure. The full biological activity is dependent on preserving the integrity of this complex structure. The body has evolved ways of maintaining the specificity of action of proteins. This is controlled to a large extent by the different levels of organization within each molecule, that is, the primary, secondary, tertiary, and quaternary structure. Because of the close correlation between protein efficacy and the molecular three-dimensional structure, it is essential to maintain the structural integrity through all the formulation steps of a delivery system and while the drug is released from the dosage form at the site of delivery; otherwise, the activity of the protein or peptide drug may be reduced or lost entirely. Because of the fragile nature of proteins and peptides, the processes involved in the fabrication of the drug delivery systems may damage the protein and therefore, reduce its biological activity or render the protein immunogenic. For example, aggregated human growth hormone has less biological activity than the native monomeric form (2). The issues associated with ensuring the stability of a protein or peptide drug in various matrices have been discussed by several authors (3,4).

Strategies for stabilizing the protein in sustained-delivery systems are often more complex than those for proteins in solution for several reasons. First, the protein must survive the matrix fabrication process steps. It must also remain biologically active in the delivery system for an extended period in vivo where the protein may be subjected to pH, concentration, and temperature conditions conducive to degradation. In fact, overcoming the propensity for proteins to undergo degradation processes during incorporation into the delivery system or after injection into the body awaiting release is one of the key hurdles in bringing delivery systems for these drugs to market. It is therefore important to understand the degradation processes and the effects of protein stability on the biological response and release to devise formulation strategies to preserve protein stability. These approaches may include the addition of stabilizing excipients and the development of fabrication processes for delivery systems that are benign to proteins.

This section provides an overview of protein degradation pathways and discusses protein stability issues associated with the fabrication and delivery of protein drugs in sustained-release systems. Armed with this information, a variety of formulation approaches for developing stable formulations for delivery systems are presented.

Protein Degradation Pathways

The degradation mechanisms that proteins undergo can be divided into two classes, physical and chemical. Chemical degradation results in the modification of the protein's primary structure. In physical degradation, the native structure of the protein is modified by changes to its higher-order structure, that is, the secondary, tertiary, or quaternary structure. Degradation may be facilitated by environmental conditions such as pH, concentration, temperature, and the proximity of surfaces or chemically reactive groups. Examples of protein degradation pathways are shown in Table 1. Chemical degradation processes are usually preceded by a physical process such as unfolding, which then makes usually inaccessible amino acid residues available for chemical reactions.

Physical Instability. Proteins, because of their polymeric nature and ability to form higher-order structures, can undergo nonchemical changes (i.e., changes to the secondary, tertiary, or quaternary structure) that can alter their biological activity. The primary structure of a protein determines the native secondary and tertiary (and higher-order) conformation. In general, in globular proteins, hydrophobic residues are buried in the interior and hydrophilic residues are available near the surface for interaction with the aqueous solvent. Denaturation refers to the loss of the native globular structure and leads to protein unfolding. Once unfolded, newly exposed amino acid residues may interact with their surroundings by adsorbing to surfaces or aggregating with other protein molecules (5).

Denaturation may be reversible or irreversible and is caused by changes in the environment of the protein such as an increase or decrease in temperature, pH changes, the introduction of liquid interfaces by the addition of organic solvents, or the introduction of hydrophobic surfaces. In reversible denaturation, the protein refolds once the denaturing stimulus is removed, for example, unfolding when the temperature is increased and refolding correctly once the temperature is reduced. In irreversible denaturation, the native conformation is not regained by the removal of the stimulus (5). Precipitation often is the final result of self-association or aggregation of protein molecules. The aggregation of insulin has been well characterized and is thought to depend on unfolding of the insulin molecule (6).

Chemical Instability. Chemical degradation processes may occur at several points during the formulation and delivery of an encapsulated protein drug. It is important to be aware that the manifestation of a degradation process may occur sometime after the initial triggering step. For example, the pH of the buffer before freeze-drying can affect the stability of the lyophilized protein formulation (7).

Oxidation. Tryptophan, methionine, cysteine, histidine, and tyrosine amino acid side chains contain functionalities that are susceptible to oxidation. Methionine and cysteine can be oxidized by atmospheric oxygen and fluorescent light (2). Oxidation has been observed both in solution (8) and in the solid state (9). Oxidation of the methionine residues may cause a loss of bioactivity and, in the case of cysteine residues, the formation of nonnative disulphide bonds. Oxidation by atmospheric oxygen or auto-oxidation can be accelerated in the presence of certain metal ions such as copper and iron. Methionine residues under acidic conditions are especially prone to oxidation by reagents such as hydrogen peroxide, producing methionine sulphoxide. Oxidation by peroxide may be a concern if the protein is processed in a manufacturing area that is sterilized using hydrogen peroxide vapor or using equipment that is so treated (10). In this case, experiments must be performed and procedures put in place to ensure that the protein is not oxidized during manufacturing. A procedure for manufacturing sterile microspheres in an environment that was sterilized using vaporized hydrogen peroxide without oxidizing a protein has been described (11). Under conditions of higher pH, other groups, such as disulphide and phenol groups, may undergo oxidation reactions.

Deamidation. Deamidation is the hydrolysis of a side-chain amide on glutamine and asparagine residues to yield a carboxylic acid. The deamidation reaction has been extensively studied and is widely observed in therapeutic proteins and peptides (12). Some protein delivery system processing and formulation conditions that result in an increase in temperature or pH have been shown to facilitate deamidation. The deamidation process is important because of the potential loss in protein activity or function. Deamidation contributes to the reduction in catalytic activity of lysozyme (5) and ribonuclease at high temperatures (13).

Peptide Bond Hydrolysis. Aspartic acid residues have been implicated in the cleavage of peptide bonds, which have led to a decrease in biological activity. When lysozyme was heated to 90–100°C at pH 4, the loss in biological activity was attributed to hydrolysis of Asp-X bonds (5).

Disulphide Exchange. Many therapeutic proteins contain cysteine residues that form disulphide bonds. These bonds are important components of the structural integrity of proteins (14). Incorrect linkages of these disulphide bonds often lead to a change in the three-dimensional structure of the protein and therefore its biological activity. The reaction proceeds in both acidic and alkaline media, but the mechanisms are different. In neutral and alkaline media, the reaction is catalyzed by thiols. Thiols may be introduced during formulation (e.g., mercaptoethanol as an antioxidant) or by degradation of existing disulphide bonds via beta elimination of cysteine residues (15). The aggregation of lyophilized formulations of bovine serum albumin, ovalbumin, β-lactoglobulin, and glucose oxidase was attributed to disulphide interchange (16).

Table 1. Examples of Protein Degradation Pathways

Physical	Chemical
Noncovalent aggregation	Oxidation
	Deamidation
	Peptide bond hydrolysis
	Disulphide exchange
	Covalent aggregation

Protein Formulation Strategies

There is a large body of literature on protein-stabilizing excipients (especially for proteins in lyophilizates and solutions) including a number of excellent reviews on the subject (14,17,18). Some general approaches are reviewed in this section that are useful in developing stable protein formulations for incorporation in sustained-release systems (19,20).

Additives for Protein Stabilization.

Stabilizing additives used in the formulation of proteins are diverse and include proteins, sugars, polyols, amino acids, chelating agents, and inorganic salts. These additives can stabilize the protein in solution and also in the frozen and dried states, although not all the additives confer stability under all three conditions. The stabilization mechanism in the solution or frozen state is different from that which occurs in the dried state. For example, carbohydrates in particular have the ability to stabilize proteins in the dried state (18,21). Thus, for many delivery systems that involve a number of formulation and processing steps, multiple additives may be required to produce a stable formulation (18). For example, a stable liquid protein formulation is a usually prerequisite because it will often form the starting bulk material for processing. If subsequent processing steps involve the transformation of the protein from a liquid to a powder by, for example, lyophilization or spray-drying, additional stabilizers may be needed for the dry state (22). Also, additives may be required for maintaining protein stability in a powder upon hydration to ensure stability during release and perhaps long-term storage (16). Approaches have been described to stabilize protein powders during hydration to prevent aggregation in lyophilizates and in polymeric microspheres (7,23–25).

Many additives used in protein formulations (e.g., sugars, salts, amino acids, and polyols) stabilize proteins by a similar mechanism (26–28). Sugars such as trehalose, sucrose, maltose, and glucose have been used as protein stabilizers. Their addition causes an increase in the glass-transition temperature of a number of proteins including collagen, ribonuclease, and ovalbumin (29). Similarly, salts such as potassium phosphate, sodium citrate, and ammonium sulphate have also been shown to increase the glass-transition temperature of proteins, thereby imparting thermal stability. All these additives increase the self-association of protein molecules and reduce their solubility. It has been proposed that these cosolvent stabilizers are preferentially excluded from the surface of the protein, thereby imparting stability (29). On the other hand, stabilizers such as magnesium chloride bind to the protein surface. Cyclodextrins have also been used as stabilizing excipients in protein and peptide formulations (30,31). Hydroxypropyl cyclodextrin (HPCD) stabilized formulations of porcine growth hormone against thermal and interfacial denaturation (32). The mechanism is poorly understood but is thought to involve changes in the properties of the solvent. Cyclodextrins have been found to complex with peptides, resulting in enhanced solubility of the drug (30,31). The addition of heparin, a polyanion, stabilized acidic fibroblast growth factor by increasing the unfolding temperature by 15–30°C by a direct interaction between the polyanion and the protein (33).

Surfactants are frequently added as stabilizers to protein formulations (34). They serve various useful functions in sustained-release formulations. Several commercial preparations of proteins, for example, Nutropin® (recombinant human growth hormone, Genentech Inc.), contain surfactants such as the polysorbates (2). Because of the amphipathic nature of proteins, they have a tendency to adsorb and accumulate at interfaces. This interfacial adsorption may lead to unfolding and eventually loss of solubility, aggregation, and biological activity (35). The addition of surfactants may be an important step in stabilizing the three-dimensional structure of a protein during incorporation into a delivery device, for example, during emulsification processes (36). The surfactant, polysorbate 20, was found to be useful in stabilizing human growth hormone incorporated in a poly(lactide-co-glycolide) (PLG) polymer matrix (37). Sustained-delivery devices having relatively hydrophobic surfaces may induce unfolding of the protein by adsorption. In this instance, the addition of a surfactant with a high hydrophilic–lipophilic balance (HLB) would reduce protein adsorption because the surfactant itself would adsorb to the device surface via its hydrophobic moieties, leaving the hydrophilic moieties exposed to the surrounding milieu (34). The ability of a surfactant to stabilize a protein upon rehydration has also been demonstrated (38). Therefore, the addition of a surfactant can stabilize a protein against denaturation during several stages from incorporation to release at the site of delivery.

The addition of certain metals has been shown to confer stability on proteins (39). Cunningham et al. showed that certain transition metals stabilized human growth hormone (hGH) against urea induced denaturation (40). They hypothesized that the presence of zinc in the secretory granules of the anterior pituitary (where growth hormone is secreted) stabilizes the hormone during storage before it is released into the circulation. Johnson et al. showed that an hGH–Zn complex was a viable formulation for encapsulation into a sustained-release formulation of PLG microspheres (25). The hGH–Zn complex was more stable in PLG microspheres compared with hGH in the uncomplexed form. The authors demonstrated in primates (rhesus monkeys) that biologically active protein was released over a 1-month period as determined by measuring sustained serum hGH levels and elevated levels of insulinlike growth factor I (IGF-I), a pharmacodynamic marker for hGH. Although the addition of metals may stabilize some proteins, the presence of metals may also catalyze the oxidation of cysteine residues. To overcome this, chelating agents such as ethylenediaminetetraacetate (EDTA) were added to stabilize a formulation of acidic fibroblast growth factor (33). Under accelerated storage conditions at 45°C, it was shown that the addition of EDTA stabilized a freeze-dried formulation of ribonuclease A (41). Where there is evidence that the presence of trace amounts of metals accelerate protein degradation, the addition of chelating agents should be considered.

Protein Stabilization in the Solid State.

Changing the state of a protein or peptide from the liquid to the solid state by lyophilization or spray-drying increases the storage stability of proteins (17). However, in addition to this obvious advantage, incorporation of the protein into a delivery device in the form of a lyophilized powder may also significantly reduce the potentially damaging stresses to which a protein solution would be subjected. For example, proteins in the solid state would be less susceptible to shear forces that occur during emulsification or atomization steps or denaturation at oil-water interfaces because the protein would not be in solution. These processes are described more fully in the later in this article.

Special precautions should be taken during freeze-drying because the drying process itself will expose the protein to destabilizing stresses; therefore, suitable excipients are often included in formulations for stability during freeze-drying (36). Additives that are normally added to stabilize a formulation that will be lyophilized may include a bulking agent (sucrose, dextrose, mannitol) to prevent collapse of the freeze-dried cake (18). Cryoprotectants are also added to lyophilized formulations to stabilize the protein to freezing (37). Some of the salts, polyhydric alcohols, and sugars described earlier stabilize a protein to withstand the effects of freezing, but additional stabilizers may be required to impart stability during the drying and rehydration steps. Carbohydrates, disaccharides in particular, stabilize proteins during drying (21). Using infrared spectroscopy, it was shown that hydrogen bonding occurs between these dissacharides and the proteins (bovine serum albumin and lysozyme). As the protein becomes dehydrated during the lyophilization process, these disaccharides are thought to act as water substitutes and are able to hydrogen bond to the proteins, thereby maintaining the integrity of the protein. The physical state of the carbohydrate stabilizer is also thought to be important (9,42). A surfactant is often added to facilitate dispersion of the protein and reduce adsorption (and unfolding) of the protein to the walls of the dissolution vessel.

It should be borne in mind that a lyophilized formulation is not stable indefinitely. Over time the protein may become denatured and lose activity. The effect of excipients on moisture-induced aggregation of human serum albumin under conditions designed to simulate the environment within sustained-delivery devices has been investigated (7,19,23,43). The authors showed that the aggregation could be induced via both covalent and noncovalent routes and suggested some rational solutions based on an understanding of the underlying aggregation mechanisms. These approaches included the effect of the buffer pH before lyophilization, the addition of high-molecular-weight polymers such as dextran and carboxymethyl cellulose, the modification of the hydrophilic properties of the delivery matrix to reduce water uptake, and manipulation of the protein molecule itself to chemically alter the residues involved in the degradation pathway. The studies described underline the importance of understanding the underlying degradation process. The more information there is on these degradation pathways, the more likely a rational approach can be successfully applied. Finally, in developing products with commercial potential, the U.S. FDA *Inactive Ingredients Guide* serves as an invaluable resource in identifying additives that have a history of use in approved pharmaceutical products (44).

Protein Stability within a Delivery Matrix

In addition to the considerations given to protein stabilization during the formulation and incorporation processes, the environment that the protein encounters within the delivery device should be considered in the formulation development. For sustained-release or depot formulations, the objective is to have a reservoir of the protein or peptide drug that is released over a period of days to months. Potential interactions between the protein and its surroundings over this prolonged period of time should be investigated during protein formulation. In addition to interactions between protein molecules discussed earlier, important interactions to consider include those between the protein and the matrix such as adsorption and those due to the changing internal environment of the device as, for example, polymer degradation occurs. The nature of these interactions are described in the following section along with formulation approaches to minimize them.

Interactions between the Delivery Matrix and the Protein. The incorporation of protein pharmaceuticals into solid delivery matrices exposes them to a high surface-to-volume environment, creating ample opportunity for adsorption to the delivery device. One obvious drawback of adsorption is that it may severely limit the amount of free unadsorbed protein that is available for release. It has been shown that salmon calcitonin adsorbs to the surface of PLG matrices (45). Another consequence of adsorption may be surface-induced changes in the three-dimensional structure of the protein that could result in a loss of biological activity. A number of factors affect the adsorption of proteins to a solid interface. These include the charges on both the protein and the surface and the effect of the environment, that is the pH, ions present, specificity of adsorption, surface area, and temperature (46). The surface activity of a protein depends on its amino acid composition and three-dimensional structure. The primary structure determines which amino acid residues are exposed to the surface in the three-dimensional structure and are therefore available for interaction with its surroundings. Because proteins are ampholytes, the pH and ionic strength of the surrounding medium will determine the net surface charge and therefore affect the nature of the interaction with the surface. Consequently, there will be a stronger interaction between the matrix surface and the protein when both possess opposite charges.

In aqueous solution, the three-dimensional structure of a protein in its native conformation results in more hydrophobic residues being buried within the interior and more hydrophilic amino acid residues exposed to the aqueous solution. However, when the same protein comes into contact with a hydrophobic surface, there will be an entropic driving force for the hydrophobic residues that are normally buried within the three-dimensional structure to interact with the surface, perhaps causing unfolding or other structural rearrangements. Conformational changes in the protein at a surface may also be driven by electrostatics. The adsorption of a hard protein (characterized by a low adiabatic compressibility, greater hydrophilicity, and high thermal stability) often occurs owing to electrostatics and thus is less likely to adsorb to a similarly charged surface. A soft protein (characterized by a high adiabatic compressibility), however, can often adsorb to a similarly charged surface because it may experience greater conformational changes in the adsorption process (47,48). The extent and effect of adsorption on the biological activity of a protein is thus protein specific. The adsorption of antibodies on solid matrices in immunoassays suggests that interactions with solid matrices do not automatically result in a loss of activity.

The adsorption isotherms of proteins to solid surfaces display a saturation phenomenon. There is an initial rapid phase of adsorption in a particular medium that eventually reaches a plateau at a given protein concentration and temperature. The saturation point approximates a monolayer, suggesting that there is a fixed number of adsorption sites. The kinetics of adsorption may be controlled by either the transport of the protein to the surface (transport-limited adsorption) or by the intrinsic kinetics of adsorption at the surface (surface-limited adsorption). For example, bovine serum albumin (BSA) adsorption to PLG films was found to be surface-limited (S.M. Butler, M.A. Tracy, and R.D. Tilton, unpublished data).

Adsorption in a sustained-delivery system may be reduced by several formulation approaches. One of the most effective ways of formulating a protein to reduce adsorption to the delivery matrix or surface is the incorporation of a surface-active agent or the addition of another protein to compete for adsorption sites. Addition of albumin to insulin solution was found to reduce adsorption of the latter to solid surfaces. Addition of surfactants such as polysorbate or sodium dodecyl sulphate reduces the interfacial tension at the solid–liquid interface and therefore the driving force for the protein to adsorb (34).

Internal Environment of the Delivery Matrix. Many sustained delivery system matrices utilize biodegradable materials. Therefore, the protein is exposed to a changing environment as the delivery matrix degrades over time. For example, a number of implantable devices have been fabricated from polyesters made from lactide and glycolide monomer units that degrade ultimately to lactic acid and glycolic acid when exposed to water. It is feasible that the generation of acidic oligomers as these materials degrade could cause an increase in the acidity of the interior of the delivery device. The degree of isolation between the interior of the device and exterior will depend on the porosity and geometry of the device (49). There have been few studies to investigate the internal pH of PLG-based devices (50,51), but once implanted, it is unlikely that the interior of a porous device is totally isolated from the perfusion and buffering capacity of physiological fluids. It seems intuitive that if a large molecule such as a protein is able to exit the matrix (by diffusion through polymer networks or pores), then small molecules such as buffer salts or the soluble monomeric or oligomeric degradation products of biodegradable matrices should also be able to diffuse out of the matrix. If transport of acidic degradants out of a device is limited (due to perhaps a low porosity or a large size), it may be necessary to employ formulation approaches to overcome an acidic microclimate within the device. For ex-

ample, basic salts may be incorporated as a buffering system into the matrix to counteract the increase in acidity produced by the degradation of the polymer into lactic and glycolic acids (52,53).

PROTEIN RELEASE FROM POLYMERIC DELIVERY SYSTEMS

In addition to maintaining the drug stability during processing and release, another key obstacle in producing protein and peptide sustained delivery systems is developing processing and formulation approaches to achieve a target release profile and duration. Developing such approaches begins with an understanding of the microstructure of the delivery system and the mechanism of release of macromolecules from the device.

Sustained release of biologically active macromolecules from biocompatible polymer matrices was first described by Langer and Folkman in 1976 (54). Prior to this discovery, it had been shown that small molecules (<600 Da) could be released slowly from polymeric materials (3,55). However, it was thought that macromolecules such as proteins and peptides were too large to slowly diffuse through polymeric materials because of their low porosity even after swelling. Langer and Folkman (54) showed that by solvent casting normally impermeable hydrophobic polymers in volatile solvents containing powdered macromolecules, molecules of nearly any size could be released for periods of greater than 100 days. The encapsulation of macromolecules in this manner resulted in the formation of a series of interconnecting channels within the polymer matrix that were large enough to permit macromolecular release and sufficiently tortuous to allow release in a controlled, prolonged fashion. A variety of polymers have been used to demonstrate macromolecular sustained release including nondegradable ethylene-vinyl acetate copolymers, degradable lactide–glycolide copolymers, and even hydrogels such as poly(vinyl alcohol) (3,54,56,57). Hydrogels typically release proteins for shorter periods than more hydrophobic polymers (3,54).

It has been found from microscopy that matrices produced by the processes described here consist of two major phases distributed throughout the device, one consisting of the macromolecule drug and the other consisting of the polymer (58). The drug release from nondegradable polymers occurs by dissolution and diffusion through interconnecting pores formed by the macromolecules themselves (54,55,58–66). Thus, the size of the drug powder and loading are important factors affecting the release rate. Saltzman and Langer (61) presented a detailed model for macromolecule release from nondegradable systems in which release by diffusion was due to the following variables: drug physical properties such as the drug concentration in the pores, its solubility, its aqueous diffusion constant, and the effect of the pore geometry and connectivity, including the porosity and the size distribution and shapes of the pores. Release from biodegradable matrices is determined by the polymer degradation and erosion rates in addition to diffusion (Fig. 1). Drug stability also may influence release because the solubility of nonnative forms, such as protein or peptide aggregates, is often reduced.

Figure 1. Mechanism of release from PLG microspheres. The initial release phase is controlled by diffusion of drug molecules that are on the surface or have access to the surface via pores in the microsphere matrix. The sustained-release phase is determined by the erosion of the polymer. As the polymer erodes, entrapped drug molecules are released from the delivery matrix. *Source:* Ref. 25.

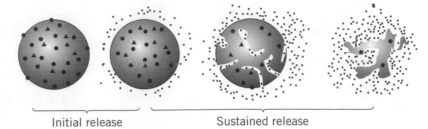

Initial release   Sustained release

Interactions between the drug and the polymer may also impact release whether or not there is an affect on drug stability. For example, the sustained release of leuprolide from biodegradable PLG microspheres (Lupron® Depot) is thought to be due, in part, to a charge interaction between the peptide and the carboxylic acid endgroup of the PLG used in the formulation (67,68).

Strategies for Obtaining a Desired Release Profile

The effects of various process and formulation variables on drug release and pharmacokinetics from biodegradable systems have been studied extensively by several authors (56,57,62,68). One of the most commonly used biodegradable polymers is PLG because of its biocompatibility and history of use in pharmaceutical products. The release profiles from PLG microspheres are usually described by two exponential curves attributed to drug diffusion and polymer erosion. After injection, there is an initial release phase, or "burst," that is thought to be dependent on dissolution and diffusion of drug at or near the surface of the microspheres. There may or may not be a lag period of little or no drug release depending on the characteristics of the polymer. The secondary release phase depends on erosion of the polymer, thereby exposing remaining encapsulated drug for dissolution and release (69). The onset and duration of the secondary release phase is modulated by polymer molecular weight, lactide glycolide ratio, and endgroup chemistry.

The initial release phase is affected by factors such as drug loading, drug particle size, drug solubility, microsphere diameter, and porosity. When the microsphere is hydrated after injection, for example, any entrapped drug that is present on the surface or that has unconstrained access to the surface via microscopic pores and channels will dissolve and diffuse out of the microspheres. This process usually occurs within 24–48 h after hydration. The proportion of encapsulated drug that is released during the initial phase is important for a number of reasons. Firstly, a large burst may pose safety and clinical concerns for narrow-therapeutic-index drugs. Secondly, if a significant proportion of the entrapped drug is released in the initial phase, there may be insufficient drug available for release later to provide a therapeutic benefit. Finally, there is also an economic imperative to reduce the burst and therefore, minimize drug wastage. Thus, formulation and processing approaches have been developed to minimize the initial burst. Formulation approaches for proteins and peptides include reducing drug solubility by complexing the drug for example with metal ions such as zinc (25). Alternatively,

processing approaches may be used, for example, utilizing additional processing steps such as sonication or homogenization to reduce the encapsulated drug particle size (11,70). Finally, particles may be coated to reduce the fraction of drug immediately soluble.

The sustained-release phase is controlled by polymer erosion, and this phase is therefore controlled by the factors that affect polymer degradation (53,71–76). PLG polymers degrade by hydrolytic chain scission. This degradation process is affected by factors such as water sorption and solubility, the polymer morphology (crystalline or amorphous), device geometry (monolithic implants or microspheres), glass-transition temperature, molecular weight, chemistry (e.g., lactide glycolide monomer ratio, presence of residual monomer, and endgroup chemistry), the nature of encapsulated drug (acidic, basic), additives to the polymer phase, and the site of implantation (77). If polymer degradation and therefore erosion is delayed significantly (for example, for a high-molecular-weight, high-lactide-content polymer) so that the diffusion and erosion phases do not coincide, there is a lag phase with little or no drug release. Okada (67) showed that the addition of a hydrophilic surfactant, monoleic acid, had no impact on the lag phase but reducing the molecular weight of the PLG from 22 to 14 kDa eliminated the lag phase. Pulsatile release may be desirable for vaccine formulations but for most protein applications, a continuous-release profile is preferred. Vert et al. (78) demonstrated that in microspheres, degradation proceeds via a homogeneous hydrolytic process in which the degradation rate is the same throughout the microspheres. In monolithic implants, however, there is a heterogeneous process where the polymer degradation rate is faster within the core than it is on the outside (49). It has been suggested that the difference in degradation rate may be due to a buildup of self-catalyzing acidic monomers or oligomers within the core of the device. Also, certain additives have been found to affect the degradation rate of some PLGs (79). For example, the incorporation of slightly soluble basic salts such as zinc carbonate decreased the degradation rate of PLG microspheres in vitro and in vivo, probably because of the neutralization of acidic oligomers (52,53).

Characterization of Release from Delivery Systems

In addition to understanding the in vitro physical and chemical characteristics of the protein and the delivery system, it is important to understand and characterize drug release from a delivery system in vivo as part of the development of a sustained-delivery product for proteins and peptides. This is invaluable in the development and selection of formulations with desirable release kinetics. It has been reported that in vivo release in small animal models such as rats was more predictive of release in primates and humans than in vitro release tests for proteins (11). As a result, microsphere formulations of rhGH were evaluated with respect to release in vivo. Once formulations with desirable release kinetics were identified, an in vitro release method was developed that correlated with in vivo release for quality control purposes. Kamijo et al. (80) also used in vivo models to confirm release of leuprolide from PLG microspheres and developed an in vitro release test to mimic in vivo release data as a quality control method for clinical samples. Variables that they investigated to develop a suitable in vitro test included the buffer pH, buffer salt concentration, the addition of additives such as mannitol or sodium chloride, and the mass of microspheres.

Drug release in vivo is affected by the physiology of the site of delivery because for systemic delivery, the drug, after being released from the delivery system, must be transported through the tissue at the site of administration before being absorbed into the bloodstream. Thus, before evaluating release from the delivery system, it is important to first characterize the drug absorption from the administration site and systemic clearance as a function of concentration and time by administering the drug as a solution bolus injection. Because the process of drug absorption from the administration site may depend on the kinetics of drug release, evaluating the pharmacokinetics of sustained delivery of the drug via osmotic pumps implanted in animals is useful in interpreting results from a new formulation of a delivery system.

In interpreting in vivo release data from sustained-delivery systems, it is important to characterize the expected biological responses. Parenteral introduction of any dosage form will induce a tissue response in vivo as a natural consequence of injection and the body's recognition of the presence of a foreign body (77,81,82). Release from the device may be affected by this response, so it is important to characterize its time course to aid in interpretation of release data (53,75). Also, a human protein or peptide is a foreign one to animals. Thus, they are expected to elicit an antibody response to the drug. The presence of antibodies (which reach measurable levels as soon as a couple of days after administration for IgM and about 7–10 days for IgG antibodies) may limit or prevent the ability to measure human protein levels. Antibodies may either impact the circulating levels of the drug or interfere with the assay (such as radioimmunoassays or ELISAs) used to quantify the drug in serum. Procedures have been developed to suppress antibody formation allowing the study of release from animal models beyond 7 days (83). Transgenic animal models may also be used to assess release and formulation immunogenicity in an animal producing circulating levels of a human protein (83).

PROCESSES FOR MAKING POLYMERIC DELIVERY SYSTEMS

A variety of processes have been developed to encapsulate drugs to produce biocompatible drug-containing polymeric matrices for sustained release that are capable of being implanted or injected. These processes most often involve the preparation of a drug solution, suspension, or emulsion with the polymer in solution followed by an extrusion or compression molding step for implants or a droplet formation step for microspheres. Processing solvents are removed by extraction and/or drying to produce the final microsphere or implant product. The fabrication steps must be performed under carefully controlled conditions of temperature, pH, and mixing to preserve the integrity of fragile proteins and peptides (84). Emulsion, coacervation, and extrusion/spray methods are described in the following sections with an emphasis on the protein stability implications of processing via these approaches.

Emulsification

Most microsphere fabrication processes are based on emulsification. Briefly, the water-soluble drug is dissolved in an aqueous solution (or water), and the polymer is dissolved in an organic solvent such as ethyl acetate or methylene chloride. A key characteristic is that the protein is processed in solution. The two solutions are mixed in the appropriate ratio to create a water-in-oil (w/o) emulsion. This primary emulsion is then again emulsified into a second aqueous solution containing an emulsifier such as poly(vinyl alcohol). The final product is a water-in-oil-in-water (w/o/w) emulsion (85). The organic solvent is then removed from the emulsion by evaporation under reduced pressure, filtration, or a moderate increase in temperature. The microspheres are then harvested and dried. There are variations on this basic approach where a range of aqueous and organic solvents and a range of aqueous phase emulsifiers are used. Alternatively, a single emulsion may be used for drugs that are dissolved or suspended in the polymer solution by forming an oil (containing dissolved polymer with dissolved or suspended drug) in water emulsion to create the microsphere droplet that is hardened as just described.

A commercial microsphere formulation of the peptide leuprolide acetate called Lupron® Depot is manufactured using a w/o/w double-emulsion method (56,68). Briefly, as depicted in Figure 2, the leuprolide acetate (Luprorelin) and gelatin are dissolved in water and added to a solution of the PLG polymer (in methylene chloride). The mixture is emulsified to produce a water-in-oil emulsion. This primary emulsion is then emulsified in an aqueous solution of poly(vinyl alcohol). The resulting w/o/w emulsion is stirred gently until the methylene chloride solvent evaporates and the wet microspheres are washed, collected, and freeze-dried. During the washing process, mannitol is added as an anticaking agent to prevent microsphere aggregation during drying and storage of the vialed commercial product.

The formation of an emulsion and its associated interfaces can create the potential for denaturation of fragile proteins and some peptides resulting from the use of mechanical agitation to facilitate formation of the droplets, exposure to organic solvent interfaces, and significant fluctuations in temperature, concentration and pH. There are a number of reports on the damaging effects on proteins of emulsification and exposure to organic solvent/aqueous in-

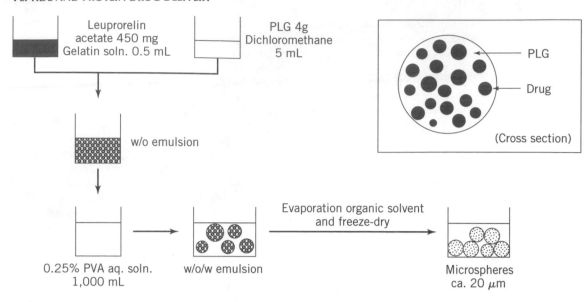

Figure 2. Schematic diagram of the double-emulsion process used to manufacture Lupron Depot®. The primary emulsion consists of leuprorelin acetate in an aqueous solution containing gelatin dispersed in a solution of PLG in methylene chloride. The water-in-oil emulsion is then emulsified in a solution of poly(vinyl alcohol) (surfactant and stabilizer). The microspheres are formed by evaporation of the methylene chloride, which is the continuous phase of the primary emulsion.

terfaces (86–88). In some cases, though, proteins have retained most of their biological activity after incorporation by an emulsion process (66,89). Emulsification is achieved by disrupting a mixture of the aqueous solution that contains the protein drug with other water soluble excipients and the organic water-immiscible phase that contains the polymer or matrix material. Emulsion droplets are formed by the input of energy, which may be mechanical, as with a homogenizer, or ultrasonic, with the use of an ultrasonic probe.

Formation of emulsion droplets is an energy-intensive process. It is initiated by film formation, generation of surface waves, deformation of the aqueous/organic solvent interface, and cavitation. Turbulence created by high-speed homogenization can cause the disruption of the interface and droplet formation. Cavitation is the main process by which ultrasonic waves form emulsion droplets, and it is the sudden formation and collapse of bubbles containing vapor that results in the generation of high pressures on the order of 10^{10} Pa and shock waves. It is the combination of high pressures, intense shock waves, and the dissipation of both over a short period that causes the formation of droplets. The energy that is generated is accompanied by an increase in temperature. Although these conditions may be short-lived, damage can still be done to the protein (90). Loss of protein activity or potency is often observed after encapsulation using these steps. The high shear rates that are generated during emulsification may be enough to cause foaming (adsorption of the protein at the air–water interface or at the aqueous–nonaqueous interface of the emulsion droplets) (9). As a result, emulsion processes are best suited for peptides and proteins that are sufficiently stable to these conditions. One advantage of an o/w versus a w/o/w emulsion process is that the protein

may be encapsulated starting with a suspension rather than a solution of the drug in the polymer solution. Proteins in the solid state are less sensitive than proteins in solution to many mechanisms of degradation that may occur during emulsion, such as shear-induced denaturation.

Also, owing to the high cost of protein and peptide drugs, a high efficiency of incorporation of the protein or peptide into microspheres during processing is an important objective. This is particularly a concern for emulsion processes utilizing solvents for the protein or peptide during the last emulsion step. For example, proteins are soluble in water, which is the solvent used in the second emulsion of the w/o/w process. Thus, the process must be optimized to minimize loss of the protein during this process step.

Coacervation

Microparticles containing a protein may also be formed by coacervation. In simple coacervation, a hydrocolloid containing the protein is desolvated by the addition of another substance (such as a salt or an alcohol) that competes for the solvent by virtue of its higher hydrophilicity, solubility, or concentration. In complex coacervation, the charge of the hydrocolloid is opposite to that of the competing substance so that on addition of the latter, a complex of the two is formed, and the mixed coacervate is separated by dilution (91). The microcapsules formed are then "cured" by the addition of a cross-linking agent such as glutaraldehyde. Hydrocolloids that are used in pharmaceutical formulations include gelatin, acacia, and chondroitin sulphate (92). For example, cytokines have been encapsulated in gelatin–chondroitin sulphate microspheres. The cytokine IL-2 (interleukin 2) was dissolved in chondroitin sulphate solution, and a solution of gelatin was added to form microspheres. The microspheres were then cross-linked using glutaraldehyde. In addition to the stresses that the protein molecules undergo as a result of pH changes during the coacervation process, the cross-linking step with glutaraldehyde is indiscriminate and cross-links the microsphere matrix as well as the encapsulated protein or peptide drug. This lack of selectivity accounts for some of the loss in bioactivity of protein drugs encapsulated in microspheres that utilize a chemical cross-linking process.

Another coacervation method for preparing PLG microspheres was described by Cleland and is shown in Figure 3 (93). In this process, the PLG polymer is dissolved in an organic solvent, and the drug is either dissolved in an aqueous medium and added to the polymer solvent or dispersed as a solid in the polymer solvent. The emulsion or dispersion is then added to a nonsolvent for both phases

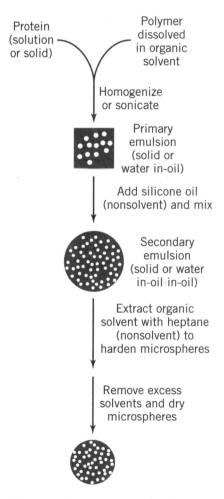

Figure 3. Schematic diagram of a coacervation process for the production of PLG microspheres. Silicone oil is a nonsolvent for methylene chloride; therefore, the primary emulsion can be emulsified in silicone oil to form a water-in-oil(methylene chloride)-in oil (silicone oil) emulsion. The microspheres are formed by extracting the methylene chloride from the primary emulsion droplets. This is achieved by the addition of heptane, which is a solvent for methylene chloride but a nonsolvent for silicone oil. *Source:* Reproduced from Ref. 93.

(e.g., silicone oil) and emulsified to give a water-in-oil-in-oil emulsion or a solid dispersion-in-oil-in-oil. A second nonsolvent for the outer oil phase (e.g., heptane) is then added to the double emulsion to extract the organic polymer solvent (e.g., methylene chloride) to harden the microspheres, and the silicone oil is then removed and the microspheres are dried. As discussed in the section on emulsions, steps in which immiscible phases are mixed must be carefully evaluated for their effects on the stability of the drug being encapsulated. In general, higher efficiencies of drug incorporation compared to w/o/w or w/o emulsions are expected from this coacervation approach because the last water phase is replaced with silicone oil and heptane, both nonsolvents for proteins and peptides.

Extrusion and Spraying Methods

Extrusion or spraying methods may be used in the fabrication of drug delivery systems to form droplets or in the formation of monolithic injectable delivery devices (85). In the former case, where extrusion or spraying is employed to form microspheres, the core material or matrix containing the protein drug, incorporated as a solution or particulate, is ejected from the orifice of a fine tube, syringe, or nozzle to form microdroplets. For example, in spray-drying, microspheres are produced by atomizing the polymer solution containing the drug at an elevated temperature to evaporate the solvent. The size of the droplets and, therefore, the final dosage form depends on the properties of the liquid (melt, solution, or suspension) to be sprayed and on the operating conditions of the extruder such as orifice diameter and jet velocities (94). The main considerations as far as the stability or integrity of protein is concerned are the processing conditions such as the melting temperature if a melt extrusion method is employed (84), the temperature for spray-drying processes, and the effect of the high shear forces that may be generated from the orifice at high jet velocities. Processes for producing sustained-release implants that maintain peptide and protein activity have been described in the literature. For example, Fujioka et al. (95,96) describe a low-temperature process for preparing an injectable rod implant containing α-interferon.

The ProLease® process, a spray method of producing microparticles containing proteins using a cryogenic process, has also been described (70). In this method, as depicted in Figure 4a and 4b, the protein drug is incorporated as a lyophilized powder, and all manipulations involving the matrix polymer (PLG) and the protein are performed at low temperatures (≤ −80°C). The fabrication process may be divided into two distinct processes. In the first process, the protein is formulated to form a stable, lyophilized product. During the protein-formulation process, stabilizing excipients such as surfactants or sugars may be incorporated. In the case of Nutropin Depot, hGH is complexed to zinc to form a Zn–hGH complex with reduced solubility. The encapsulation of this complexed form was demonstrated to stabilize hGH against aggregation postencapsulation (25). In the second part of the fabrication process, the protein powder is dispersed in a solution of the polymer in a solvent such as ethyl acetate, acetone, or methylene

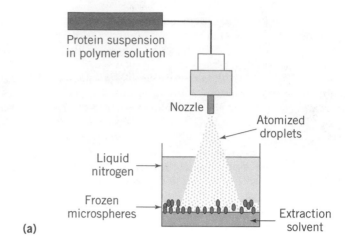

(a)

Figure 4. (**a**) Schematic diagram of the ProLease® encapsulation process (laboratory scale). The lyophilized protein formulation is dispersed in a solution of the PLG polymer and then atomized into a vessel containing frozen ethanol overlaid with liquid nitrogen. The droplets freeze as they travel through the cold nitrogen gas and liquid nitrogen and settle on top of the bed of frozen ethanol. As the ethanol melts, it extracts the methylene chloride (which is miscible with ethanol), and the microspheres harden. (**b**) Process steps in the production of ProLease® microspheres. The bulk protein may be formulated by the addition of stabilizing excipients or release modifiers or exchanged into a compatible buffer, spray-frozen, and lyophilized. The spray-freezing is performed with liquid nitrogen, and freezing occurs very rapidly. This rapid freezing may arrest degradation processes. The lyophilized drug is encapsulated as described in (**a**), and the dried microspheres are collected as a white or off-white, free-flowing powder and vialed. *Source:* Ref. 25.

(b)

chloride. The polymer and protein powder dispersion is homogenized to give a uniform suspension and then atomized over a bed of frozen ethanol overlaid with liquid nitrogen. The suspension droplets freeze as they travel through the liquid nitrogen and settle on the bed of frozen ethanol. The temperature of the frozen ethanol is increased, and the ethanol melts. Ethanol is miscible with the polymer solvents, so the polymer precipitates as the ethanol extracts the polymer solvent from the droplets. This solvent extraction process causes the microspheres to set and harden, and the microspheres are harvested by filtration. The wet microspheres are vacuum dried and vialed as a white or off-white free-flowing powder.

This fabrication process has several important benefits; first, the protein is in the more stable dry form, and any degradation processes that it is liable to undergo even in the dry state are hindered by the very cold temperatures. Additionally, stabilizing excipients may be included in the formulation during the lyophilization process. Because there are no aqueous phases, the protein is not subjected to freeze–thaw stresses or organic–aqueous solvent interfaces (which are present in emulsion-based processes) where some proteins may denature. This process effectively solves the issue of protein denaturation during incorporation or fabrication, provided a stable lyophilized formulation is available. It has been used to produce a stable microsphere formulation for hGH (25).

PROCESS SCALE-UP, MANUFACTURING, AND REGULATORY CONSIDERATIONS

The previous sections discuss approaches for stabilizing proteins, making polymeric sustained-delivery systems, and obtaining desirable release kinetics. Another major hurdle in developing a product is establishing the capability to produce the product in sufficient quantities for clinical testing and commercialization. This section reviews scale-up, manufacturing, and regulatory considerations in developing delivery systems for proteins and peptides, with a focus on polymeric microsphere systems for parenteral administration.

Scale-Up Considerations

The processes described in the previous sections are scalable. As noted in earlier sections, commercial products for peptides produced by emulsion and extrusion processes are on the market. Herbert et al. (97) described the scale-up of a cryogenic spray process for making microspheres. An effective scale-up effort begins with a detailed understanding at the laboratory scale of the effects of process unit operations on product characteristics and performance. Based on this knowledge and an estimate of the commercial scale batch size, suitable scalable unit operations can be selected and the operation conditions optimized to achieve the desired product characteristics. The equipment used at the small scale may not be suitable at larger scales owing to, for example, higher throughput requirements. For example, sonicating probes often used to produce microspheres are not easily scalable to the batch sizes usually required; therefore, it is prudent to select equipment scalable to commercial scale at the initial process scale-up stage (98). Table 2 compares unit operations used for the ProLease® process at the small, laboratory scales and at the large scale (11). In scaling up the process from the lab scale, unit operations that were scalable to commercial scale were selected and combined to produce a sterilizable, enclosed process suitable for producing sterile microspheres with the characteristics of the lab scale batches. Selecting scalable unit operations as early as possible in development will help minimize unforeseen effects of processing variables on microsphere performance. For example, adding, removing, or changing a unit operation may cause a subtle change in the porosity or surface characteristics of microspheres affecting release.

One of the prerequisites of successful scale-up and process development is having a comprehensive microsphere characterization scheme in place. It is essential to understand the effects of various fabrication variables on the physicochemical properties of the microspheres and, if possible, to relate these physicochemical properties to a biological performance criterion. Some physical properties that should be characterized include particle composition (drug load, residual solvents), particle size (volume and number mean or median, polydispersity or other measure of diameter distribution), microsphere morphology (by, for example, microscopy), particle density, particle porosity, polymer glass-transition temperature, molecular weight, and encapsulated protein integrity. It is often valuable to relate one or more of these physical attributes to microsphere performance characteristics such as in vitro release kinetics or in vivo pharmacokinetic or pharmacodynamic criteria. For example, the effect of various process variables on C_{max} (the maximum serum protein concentration) may be evaluated. With leuprolide acetate microspheres, it was shown that a reduction in particle size had an effect on initial release although the effect was small and not directly proportional to the surface area of the microspheres (68).

The use of statistical experimental design during the scale-up of microsphere fabrication processes is useful in optimizing process operating parameters. One of the advantages of this approach is that key fabrication variables and relationships between them can be identified with a relatively small number of experiments (99). This approach is ideal for troubleshooting complex processes where there are a large number of variables to study with limited time and drug supply. For example, important process variables in emulsion processes include the polymer and drug concentrations, the emulsifying agent, processing temperature, volumes of the oil and water phases, the mixing rate and time, the extraction solution composition, filtration device, and drying method (100). Key variables for spray methods include the mixer speed, homogenization and atomization pressures, the atomization nozzle type, and the extraction solvent and drying temperature/time profiles. Figure 5 shows the results of optimizing processing parameters for two unit operations of the ProLease process using experimental design methods (11). C_{max} was a sensitive variable reflecting improvements in the amount of protein initially released from the microspheres as the process conditions were optimized.

Manufacturing Considerations

For commercial manufacture, the fabrication process for parenterally administered polymeric protein and peptide delivery systems must be performed under well-controlled aseptic conditions to produce a sterile product because the final product cannot be sterilized by autoclaving or γ-irradiation after manufacturing and vialing (called *terminal sterilization*). Either terminal sterilization process may degrade both the drug and the polymer. A common approach for aseptic manufacturing in the pharmaceutical industry is to produce the drug product in a Class 100 clean room. A concern with this approach is the challenge of ensuring sterility in an environment where personnel can come in direct contact with the product during manufacturing.

A new approach to resolving the issue of sterile microsphere production is to couple isolation (or barrier) technology to the microsphere fabrication process (11). Isolation technology has been used extensively in microbiological testing and it is an effective way of maintaining the sterility of a drug product while providing handling access. An isolator is a soft- or hard-walled enclosure in which the environment may be controlled for particulate count, sterility, temperature, and humidity. The enclosure provides a barrier between personnel handling the product and the product itself, providing increased sterility assurance compared to a traditional clean room. Asepsis is maintained within the isolator by the use of vapor-phase hydrogen peroxide (VHP). Filters and various air treatment devices are attached to control the particulate count, temperature, and humidity. Reaction vessels may be autoclaved and transferred aseptically to the isolator using transfer ports. So-

Table 2. Microsphere Process Development and Scale-Up

Unit operation	Laboratory-scale process	Large-scale process
Protein spray freeze-drying	Ultrasonic spray nozzle/lyophilizer	Air atomizer/lyophilizer
Protein particle size reduction	Probe sonicator	High-pressure homogenizer
Microsphere droplet formation	Ultrasonic spray nozzle	Air atomizer
Solvent extraction	Frozen ethanol bed at −80°C	Temperature-controlled stirred tank containing liquid ethanol
Residual solvent removal	Vacuum dryer	Vacuum dryer

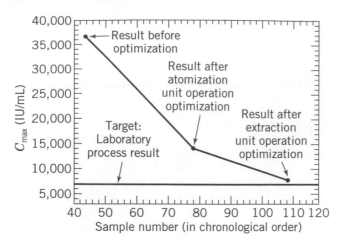

Figure 5. ProLease® process optimization. A target level of a critical performance characteristic (C_{max} in an animal model) was set based on the laboratory scale process. Samples 42–79 show the effect of varying atomization conditions on the C_{max}, and samples 80–110 show the effect of optimizing the extraction conditions combined with the optimized atomization settings. The optimization process was performed using a statistical design approach. *Source:* Ref. 11.

lutions may be sterile-filtered directly into the reaction vessels within the isolator.

Additionally, equipment such as lyophilizers, filter dryers, and filling machines may be coupled directly to the isolator, ensuring that the sterility of the microsphere product is maintained. The use of isolation technology enables the operation of complex, multistep microsphere production processes with a high degree of sterility assurance. Figure 6 shows a schematic of a manufacturing suite in which a microsphere production process is coupled to an isolator for aseptic manufacturing (11).

Regulatory Considerations

One of the considerations in manufacturing microspheres is minimizing the residual solvent and residual polymer monomer content in the microspheres. It has been suggested that bulk PLG polymers should be treated after manufacture to remove residual monomer or oligomers that may catalyze chain scission and, therefore, polymer erosion. Virtually all microsphere fabrication processes require the use of an organic solvent such as methylene chloride or ethyl acetate for polymer dissolution. Acceptable residual amounts of these solvents are determined by the regulatory agencies. For example, the International Conference on Harmonization (ICH) guideline for permissible methylene chloride content is 6 mg per day (101); unless it can be shown that the residual solvent is released in a sustained fashion over several days, the effective limit is <6 mg of methylene chloride per dose. Other solvents such as ethanol or other alcohols may not pose a direct safety hazard but may have a significant impact on the stability of the microsphere product. For example, high residual ethanol levels may reduce the glass-transition temperature of the polymer, which could impact the physical sta-

bility of the microspheres, causing them to agglomerate or clump either immediately or under long-term storage, and may result in poor injectability. Additionally, the presence of residual solvents at high levels may have a direct impact on encapsulated protein stability. Key regulatory issues in developing peptide products were reviewed by Niu and Chiu (102).

ADMINISTRATION OF MICROSPHERE DELIVERY SYSTEMS

The microspheres are vialed as a free-flowing powder and need to be resuspended in an aqueous medium before injection. To ensure that the microspheres do not sediment when dispersed in the injection vehicle, it is usually necessary to use a viscous medium. One of the most widely used suspending agents is a soluble, substituted cellulose, carboxymethyl cellulose. It is soluble in aqueous media at physiological pH. It is often necessary to add a wetting agent such as a hydrophilic surfactant to the vehicle to facilitate microsphere dispersion. Additionally, inclusion of a tonicifier and buffer are advisable to ensure that the microsphere suspension is isotonic and at (or close to) physiological pH upon injection. Successful injection of the microsphere dispersion is affected by factors such as microsphere diameter, microsphere concentration, and needle gauge. Large microspheres, or a high microsphere concentration, may cause clogging of the needle; therefore, it is important to conduct the appropriate studies to determine the optimum combination of microsphere diameter, concentration, vehicle, and needle gauge for successful injection.

SUSTAINED-RELEASE FORMULATIONS OF PEPTIDES AND PROTEINS

There are several sustained-release formulations of peptides (luteinizing hormone–releasing hormone [LH-RH] analogs) on the market. However, there is only one long-acting protein formulation, Posilac® (bovine somatropin), for increasing milk production in dairy cattle. Incorporating proteins into sustained-delivery systems has been a significant challenge compared to smaller peptide drugs because of the relative instability of proteins and the need to maintain their fragile three-dimensional structure for biological activity. Alkermes, Inc., in collaboration with Genentech, Inc., are in late-stage clinical trials with a protein sustained-release formulation for humans of rhGH (Nutropin Depot®). This section describes several products. More details on these and others can be found in the literature or directly from the companies producing them or their Web sites (103).

Lupron Depot®

One of the first peptide sustained-delivery products on the market was Lupron Depot®, a sustained-release formulation of leuprorelin acetate (Des-Gly-(d-Leu)–LH-RH ethylamide acetate) (56,67,68,103). Leuprorelin acetate is an LH-RH superagonist with a 10-fold higher biological activ-

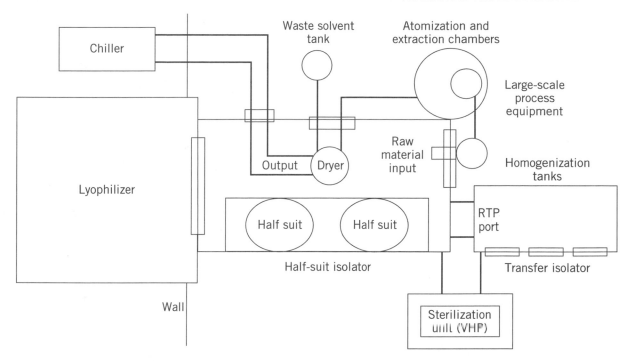

Figure 6. Isolator technology coupled with ProLease® microsphere production. Combining isolator technology with microsphere production enables the production of microspheres under controlled conditions (temperature, humidity, and Class 100 environment) and ensures the sterility of the product. The inside of the isolator is sterilized with vapor-phase hydrogen peroxide, and the non-autoclavable materials (protein and PLG polymer) are introduced into the isolator as sterile-filtered solutions. All subsequent processing, such as atomization, lyophilization, and extraction, occurs within the isolator or in equipment that is connected to the isolator and may be presterilized with VHP or steam. The operators are completely separated from the product being processed, but the half suits are comfortable and provide the dexterity required for the various manipulations. RTP = rapid transit port. *Source:* Ref. 11.

ity than native LH-RH. LH-RH and its analogs have a variety of effects on the gonads depending on the administered dose. At acute doses, the peptides stimulate gonadotropin production by the pituitary gland and production of the sex hormones in the genitals. Chronic administration at a higher dose causes "chemical castration," or an inhibition of testicular and ovarian production of the sex hormones. In this chronic administration regimen, LH-RH agonists are used in the treatment of endometriosis, uterine fibroids, and prostate and ovarian cancers. The chronic administration regimen required for these indications was an excellent opportunity to try and develop a long-acting formulation of the peptide. Okada (68) describes the problems associated with oral and transmucosal delivery (nasal, vaginal, rectal). The problem was poor absorption and, therefore, low bioavailabilities, which ranged from <0.1 to 1–5% for the transmucosal routes. In the presence of absorption enhancers, the bioavailability was increased to 5–10% for nasal and vaginal delivery. It was observed that sustained levels of the hormone produced a stronger castrating effect, suggesting that a sustained-release formulation might offer therapeutic benefits.

The microsphere formulations were based on the biodegradable polymers of lactic and glycolic acid, polylactic acid (PLA), and poly(lactic/glycolic acid). These polymers had long been used in biomedical applications such as su-

ture and orthopedic implants and were known to be biocompatible and nonimmunogenic and could be easily synthesized to give different physicochemical properties, so they seemed to be ideal candidates for the development of implantable drug delivery devices. The scientists at Takeda Industries in the early 1980s synthesized the polymers in their laboratories and evaluated the effect of various physicochemical properties of the PLA and PLG family of polymers on the encapsulated drug-release properties in vitro and in vivo. Figure 7 shows leuprolide release over time from the microsphere formulation.

Zoladex®

Zoladex is a long-acting formulation of a synthetic decapeptide analogue of LH-RH called goserelin acetate. Goserelin acetate is dispersed in a matrix of D, L-lactic and glycolic acid copolymers and is presented as a sterile, white- to cream-colored, 1-mm-diameter cylinder. The implantable device comes preloaded in a special single-use syringe with a 16-gauge needle and is administered by subcutaneous injection to give continuous release of goserelin over 1–3 months. The encapsulated drug is released by a combination of diffusion and erosion-controlled mechanisms (104). However, because the delivery device is a monolith, heterogeneous hydrolysis is thought to be the predominant erosion process.

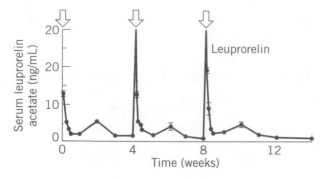

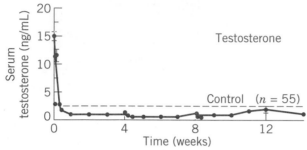

Figure 7. Serum levels of leuprorelin and testosterone following monthly im administration of Lupron Depot® in rats. The pharmacodynamic response, testosterone suppression, is achieved as long as the serum leuprorelin concentrations are above a threshold level. *Source:* Ref. 68.

De-Capeptyl® SR

De-capeptyl® SR is a long-acting formulation of triptorelin, another LH-RH agonist. Triptorelin is a decapeptide that functions in a manner similar to leuprorelin. The formulation contains microspheres made from a lactide–glycolide copolymer along with mannitol, polysorbate 80, and carboxymethyl cellulose sodium. For injection, the formulation is reconstituted using a vehicle containing mannitol in water. Injections are to be given every 4 weeks, usually in the buttocks.

Posilac®

Bovine somatotropin (bST), or bovine growth hormone, is secreted by the anterior pituitary gland and has growth-stimulating effects by direct stimulation of receptors or via mediators such as IGF-I. Posilac® is a sustained-release formulation of recombinant bST, sometribove, and is manufactured by Monsanto to increase milk production in dairy cattle. The formulation consists of the protein complexed to zinc and an oily base of aluminum stearate (5% w/w). The Zn–bST solid is dispersed in a hydrophobic gel matrix (semisolid at room temperature) of aluminum stearate and sesame oil. Oil-based formulations typically contain a vegetable-based oil such as sesame oil, a viscosity-imparting agent, and an antihydration substance. The increased viscosity is required for drug particle stability and injectability, and the antihydration agent is added to minimize moisture-induced degradation of the protein.

The development of oil-based injectable formulations for veterinary applications was appealing for several rea-

sons. Firstly, the oil-based formulations are easier and usually cheaper to manufacture aseptically than microsphere-based systems because there are fewer fabrication steps. Secondly, because the formulations can be prepackaged in a syringe and because of the low moisture content, the formulations are stable, and administration and storage on the dairy farm is convenient. For these reasons, oil-based formulation approaches are attractive for cost-sensitive veterinary applications. Several companies including Upjohn and Elanco have evaluated these formulations, although only Monsanto has a formulation, Posilac, that is commercially available. Posilac is administered subcutaneously to dairy cows in the tailhead or shoulder at a dose of 500 mg of bST (36 mg of bST per day). The dose is administered every 14 days and consists of 1.4 cc of injectate in a prepacked 2-mL syringe with a 16-gauge needle. The drug is administered to healthy cows from the ninth week after lactation begins, and the increase in milk production is rapid, with the maximum increase observed after three to four injections. Figure 8 shows the effect of Posilac on milk production.

Nutropin Depot®

Recombinant growth hormone is used to treat short stature in children resulting from growth hormone deficiency, and the current treatments are daily or thrice weekly injections. It is therefore a suitable candidate for a sustained-release formulation. Although the endogenous secretion of hGH follows a pulsatile pattern, clinical studies have shown that continuous infusion via pumps gives serum hGH and IGF-I comparable with that obtained by daily injections. The protein is stabilized and encapsulated in a PLG microsphere matrix (25). The microsphere fabrication process (ProLease®) involves formulation of the protein into a stable lyophilized powder; then the solid protein particles are dispersed in a solution of the polymer in methylene chloride and atomized over liquid nitrogen into cold or frozen ethanol. The ethanol acts as a curing solvent and removes the methylene chloride, and the microspheres harden. The wet microspheres are collected and dried under vacuum and vialed as a white, free-flowing powder. Immediately before subcutaneous administration, the microspheres are suspended in an aqueous vehicle and injected.

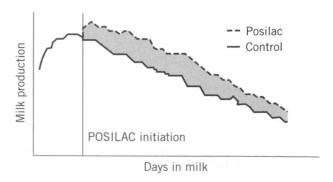

Figure 8. Effect of Posilac® on milk production in dairy cattle. Administration of Posilac to dairy cattle results in increased milk production compared with a control group of animals.

Preclinical studies in juvenile rhesus monkeys showed that a formulation that contained hGH in the complexed form, Zn–hGH, resulted in elevated serum hGH concentration for about 3 weeks, and serum IGF-I levels were elevated for 3–4 weeks. Four groups of animals each received 24 mg of hGH as a single, daily subcutaneous bolus injection for 28 days in a subcutaneously administered microsphere formulation or in a continuous-release osmotic pump. To mimic the expected release pattern from the microspheres, the pump group received 15% of the 24-mg dose as a single injection to mimic the initial, burst release phase, and the rest was delivered by the pump continuously. The serum hGH profiles for the microsphere formulation and the osmotic pump groups showed sustained hGH levels for 28–30 days (Fig. 9). The microsphere formulation group showed an initial release with a C_{max} of 260 ng/mL, and then the serum hGH concentration was maintained at about 10 ng/mL up to 30 days and then dropped to 4–5 ng/mL until 60 days. The animals that received the pump maintained serum hGH concentrations at ~16 ng/mL until day 28, when the pump was excised. A pharmacodynamic marker for hGH, IGF-I, was also measured. The serum IGF-I concentrations followed the serum hGH profile, with IGF-I levels above baseline for 1 month. The study demonstrated that it was possible to encapsulate a protein within a microsphere delivery system and obtain sustained release of the protein and biological activity of the released protein. This formulation is currently undergoing evaluation in phase III clinical trials.

CONCLUSIONS

Since it was first reported in the mid-1970s that sustained release of proteins and peptides from polymers was feasible, significant developments have occurred in the field to the point where there are now several peptide and protein

sustained-release products on or close to market. The purpose of this article is to review the key research results and considerations in developing delivery systems for proteins and peptides, with emphasis on polymeric injectable delivery approaches. Both the challenges in formulating products for the marketplace and the achievements to date are emphasized. Unfortunately, there is not a single, simple approach to ensure the successful formulation of protein or peptides for sustained delivery. Rather, successful formulation and product development result from a thorough understanding of protein and peptide degradation processes, the diverse environments that the drug will encounter during processing and release, the mechanism of release from the delivery system, and an understanding of scale-up, manufacturing, and regulatory issues in developing pharmaceutical products.

Key obstacles in developing protein and peptide delivery products include stabilizing the drug, obtaining desirable release kinetics, and scaling up the fabrication process to support clinical testing and commercialization. In general, though suitable for many peptides, incorporation processes, such as emulsion and coacervation processes, that involve interfaces may not be suitable for proteins that are susceptible to denaturation at aqueous–organic interfaces. Because proteins are generally more stable in the solid state than in solution, it is advantageous to incorporate proteins into delivery systems in a solid form, such as a lyophilized powder. If, as in the case of human growth hormone, the protein can be encapsulated in a stable form with reduced aqueous solubility, then the potential for degradation during release at the site of delivery is greatly reduced owing to decreased protein molecular mobility. Also, the mechanism of release must be well understood to develop formulation or processing approaches to achieve a target release profile. For polymeric delivery systems, the polymer chemistry and degradation characteristics are very important as is the ability to process the drug to achieve a desired particle size prior to encapsulation. In addition, approaches for scaling up and manufacturing sustained polymeric delivery systems were presented. Thus, with the examples presented here, we have demonstrated that sustained protein and peptide delivery is commercially feasible and offers significant therapeutic advantages. This reality, coupled with the development of an increasing number of injectable, macromolecular drugs (which require chronic administration), suggests that the future is indeed bright for improved delivery technologies.

ACKNOWLEDGMENTS

We would like to thank our colleagues at Alkermes for their insightful comments in the preparation of this manuscript.

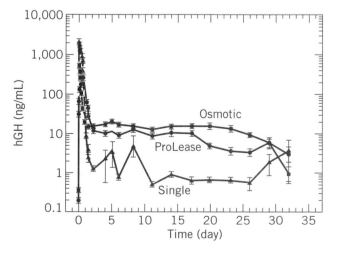

Figure 9. Serum hGH concentration from Nutropin Depot—juvenile rhesus monkeys. The ProLease® group show sustained serum hGH levels for about 28 days. The serum hGH profile was similar to the osmotic pump group that was preprogrammed to release hGH for 28 days.

BIBLIOGRAPHY

1. R. Langer, *Acc. Chem. Res.* **25**(10), 537–542 (1993).

2. R. Pearlman and T.A. Bewley, in Y.J. Wang and R. Pearlman, eds. *Stability and Characterization of Protein and Peptide Drugs: Case Histories*, Plenum, New York, 1993, pp. 1–57.

3. C.G. Pitt, *Int. J. Pharm.* **59**, 173–196 (1990).

4. W. Lu and T.G. Park, *J. Pharm. Sci. Technol.* **49**(1), 13–19 (1995).

5. M.C. Manning, K. Patel, and R. Borchardt, *Pharm. Res.* **6**(11), 903–918 (1989).

6. D.B. Volkin and C.R. Middaugh, in T.J. Ahern and M.C. Manning, eds., *Stability of Protein Pharmaceuticals. Part A: Chemical and Physical Pathways of Protein Degradation*, Plenum, New York, 1992, pp. 109–134.

7. H.R. Costantino, R. Langer, and A. Klibanov, *J. Pharm. Sci.* **83**(12), 1662–1669 (1994).

8. G.W. Becker et al., *Biotechnol. Appl. Biochem.* **10**, 326–337 (1988).

9. M.J. Pikal et al., *Pharm. Res.* **8**(4), 427–436 (1991).

10. A. Bardat, R. Schmitthaeusler, and E. Renzi, *J. Parent Pharm. Sci. Technol.* **50**(2), p. 83–88 (1996).

11. M. Tracy, *Biotechnol. Progr.* **14**(1), 108–115 (1998).

12. K. Patel and R. Borchardt, *Pharm. Res.* **7**(7), 703–711 (1990).

13. S.E. Zale and A.M. Klibanov, *Biochemistry* **25**(19), 5432–5443 (1986).

14. Y.-C.J. Wang and M.A. Hanson, *J. Parenter. Sci. Technol.* **42**(Suppl.), S3–S25 (1988).

15. D.B. Volkin and C.R. Middaugh, in T.J. Ahern and M.C. Manning, eds., *Stability of Protein Pharmaceuticals. Part A: Chemical and Physical Pathways of Protein Degradation*, Plenum, New York, 1992, pp. 215–248.

16. W.R. Liu, R. Langer, and A. Klibanov, *Biotechnol. Bioeng.* **37**, 177–184 (1991).

17. M.A. Hanson and S.K.E. Rouan, in T.J. Ahern and M.C. Manning, eds., *Stability of Protein Pharmaceuticals. Part B: In Vivo Pathways of Degradation and Strategies for Protein Stabilization*, Plenum, New York, 1992, pp. 209–233.

18. J.F. Carpenter, et al., *Pharm. Res.* **14**(8), 969–975 (1997).

19. S.P. Schwendeman et al., in S. Cohen and H. Bernstein, eds., *Microspheres/Microparticles: Characterization and Pharmaceutical Application*, Dekker, New York, 1996, pp. 1–49.

20. S.D. Putney and P.A. Burke, *Nat. Biotechnol.* **16**, 1–6 (1998).

21. J.F. Carpenter and J.H. Crowe, *Biochemistry* **28**, 3916–3922 (1989).

22. H.R. Costantino et al., *J. Pharm. Sci.* **87**(11), 1406–1411 (1998).

23. H.R. Costantino, R. Langer, and A.M. Klibanov, *Pharm. Res.* **11**(1), 21–29 (1994).

24. H.R. Costantino et al., *Int. J. Pharm.* **166**, 211–221 (1998).

25. O.L. Johnson et al., *Nat. Med.* **2**(7), 795–799 (1996).

26. T. Arakawa and S.N. Timasheff, *Biophys. J.*, **47**, 411–414 (1985).

27. T. Arakawa, *Biopolymers* **28**, 1397–1401 (1989).

28. K. Gekko and H. Ito, *J. Biochem. (Tokyo)* **107**, 572–577 (1990).

29. T. Arakawa, Y. Kita, and J.F. Carpenter, *Pharm. Res.* **8**(3), 285–291 (1991).

30. T. Loftsson and M.E. Brewster, *J. Pharm. Sci.* **85**(10), 1017–1025 (1996).

31. R.A. Rajewski and V.J. Stella, *J. Pharm. Sci.* **85**(11), 1142–1169 (1996).

32. S.A. Charman, K.L. Mason, and W.N. Charman, *Pharm. Res.* **10**(7), 954–962 (1993).

33. P.K. Tsai et al., *Pharm. Res.* **10**(3), 649–659 (1993).

34. H. Thurow and K. Geisen, *Diabetologia* **27**, 212–218 (1984).

35. T.A. Horbett, in T.J. Ahern and M.C. Manning, eds. *Stability of Protein Pharmaceuticals. Part A: Chemical and Physical Pathways of Protein Degradation*, Plenum, New York, 1992, pp. 195–214.

36. M.S. Hora, R.K. Rana, and F.W. Smith, *Pharm. Res.* **9**(1), 33–36 (1992).

37. J.L. Cleland and A.J.S. Jones, *Proc. Int. Symp. Controlled Release Bioact. Mater.* **21**, 514–515 (1995).

38. M. Mumenthaler, C.C. Hsu, and R. Pearlman, *Pharm. Res.* **11**(1), 12–20 (1994).

39. I. Gonda, *Adv. Drug Delivery Rev.* **19**(1), 37–46 (1996).

40. B.C. Cunningham, M.G. Mulkerrin, and J.A. Wells, *Science* **253**, 545–548 (1991).

41. M.W. Townsend, P.R. Byron, and P.P. Deluca, *Pharm. Res.* **7**(10), 1086–1091 (1990).

42. K-I. Izutsu, S. Yoshioka, and S. Kojima, *Pharm. Res.* **11**(7), 995–999 (1994).

43. S.P. Schwendeman et al., *Dev. Biol. Stand.* in press.

44. Food and Drug Administration, *Inactive Ingredients Guide*, Division of Drug Information Resources, Center for Drug Evaluation and Research, FDA, Washington, DC, 1996

45. S. Calis et al., *Pharm. Res.* **12**(7), 1072–1076 (1995).

46. W. Norde and J. Lyklema, *J. Colloid Interface Sci.* **71**(2), 350–366 (1979).

47. K. Gekko and Y. Hasegawa, *Biochemistry* **25**, 6563–6571 (1986).

48. T. Arai and W. Norde, *Colloids Surf.* **51**, 1–15 (1990).

49. I. Grizzi et al., *Biomaterials* **16**, 305–311 (1995).

50. P.A. Burke, *Proc. Int. Symp. Controlled Release Bioact. Mater.* **23**, 133–134 (1996).

51. K. Mäder, B. Gallez, K.J. Liu, H.M. Swartz, *Biomaterials* **17**, 457–461 (1996).

52. Y. Zhang, S. Zale, and H. Bernstein, *J. Biomed. Mater. Res.* **34**, 531–538 (1997).

53. M.A. Tracy et al., *Biomaterials*, in press.

54. R. Langer and J. Folkman, *Nature (London)* **263**, 797–800 (1976).

55. R. Langer, *Chem. Eng. Commun.* **6**, 1–48 (1980).

56. Y. Ogawa et al., *Chem. Pharm. Bull.* **36**, 2576–2581 (1988).

57. H. Okada et al., *J. Pharmacol. Exp. Ther.* **244**(2), 744–750 (1988).

58. R. Bawa et al., *J. Controlled Release* **1**, 259–267 (1985).

59. R. Langer, *Science*, **249**, 1527–1533 (1990).

60. T. Hsu and R. Langer, *J. Biomed. Mater. Res.* **19**, 445–460 (1985).

61. W.M. Saltzman and R. Langer, *Biophys. J.* **55**, 163–171 (1989).

62. S.S. Shah, Y. Cha, and C.G. Pitt, *J. Controlled Release* **18**, 261–270 (1992).

63. R.A. Siegel, *Pharm. Res.* **1**, 1–10 (1983).

64. M. Sefton, L. Brown, and R. Langer, *J. Pharm. Sci.* **73**, 1859–1869 (1984).

65. E.S. Miller, N.A. Peppas, and D.N. Winslow, *J. Membr. Sci.* **14**, 79–92 (1983).

66. S. Cohen et al., *Pharm. Res.* **8**(6), 713–720 (1991).

67. H. Okada et al., *J. Controlled Release* **28**, pp. 121–129 (1994).

68. H. Okada, *Adv. Drug Delivery Rev.* **28**(1), 43–70 (1997).

69. R.A. Batycky et al., *J. Pharm. Sci.* **86**(12), 1464–1477 (1997).

70. U.S. Pat. 5,019,400 (1991), W.R. Gombotz, M.S. Healy, and L.R. Brown (to Enzytech: United States).

71. A. Gopferich, *Macromolecules* **30**, 2598–2604 (1997).

72. R.A. Kenley et al., *Macromolecules* **20**, 2398–2403 (1987).

73. G. Spenlehauer et al., *Biomaterials* **13**, pp. 594–600 (1992).

74. N.S. Mason, C.S. Miles, and R.E. Sparks, in C.G. Gebelein and F.F. Koblitz, ed., *Biomedical and Dental Applications of Polymers*, Plenum, New York, 1981, pp. 279–291.

75. P. Flandroy et al., *J. Controlled Release* **47**, 153–170 (1997).

76. E.A. Schmitt, D.R. Flanagan, and R.J. Linhardt, *Macromolecules* **27**, 743–748 (1994).

77. G.E. Visscher et al., *J. Biomed. Mater. Res.* **19**, 349–365 (1985).

78. M. Vert, S.M. Li, and H. Garreau, *J. Biomater. Sci. Polym.* **6**, 639–649 (1994).

79. S. Li, S. Girod-Holland, and M. Vert, *J. Controlled Release* **40**, 41–53 (1996).

80. A. Kamijo et al., *J. Controlled Release* **40**, 269–276 (1996).

81. F.D. Anderson et al., *Pharm. Res.* **10**(3), 369–380 (1993).

82. J.M. Anderson and M.S. Shive, *Adv. Drug Delivery Rev.* **28**(1), 5–24 (1997).

83. H.J. Lee et al., *J. Pharmacol. Exp. Ther.* **281**, 1431–1439 (1997).

84. D.H. Lewis, in M. Chasin and R. Langer, eds. *Biodegradable Polymers as Drug Delivery Systems*, Dekker, New York, 1990, pp. 1–41.

85. H. Jeffrey, S.S. Davis, and D.T. O'Hagan, *Pharm. Res.* **10**(3), 362–368 (1993).

86. Y. Hayashi et al., *Pharm. Res.* **11**(2), 337–339 (1994).

87. Y. Tabata, S. Gutta, and R. Langer, *Pharm. Res.* **10**(4), 487–496 (1993).

88. M. Morlock et al., *Eur. J. Pharm. Biopharm.* **43**, 29–36 (1997).

89. M.S. Hora et al., *Pharm. Res.* **7**(11), 1190–1194 (1990).

90. Y. Tabata and R. Langer, *Pharm. Res.* **10**(3), 391–399 (1993).

91. M. Donbrow, ed., *Microparticles and Nanoparticles in Medicine and Pharmacy*, CRC Press, Boca Raton, Fl., 1992, pp. 1–14.

92. Z. Zhao et al., *Proc. Int. Symp. Controlled Release Bioact. Mater.* **21**, 51–52 (1995).

93. J.L. Cleland et al., *Adv. Drug Delivery Rev.* **28**(1), 71–84 (1997).

94. E. Mathiowitz and R. Langer, in *Microparticles and Nanoparticles in Medicine and Pharmacy*, CRC Press, Boca Raton, Fl., 1992, pp. 100–123.

95. K. Fujioka et al., *J. Controlled Release* **33**, 317–323 (1995).

96. K. Fujioka et al., *J. Controlled Release* **33**, 307–316 (1995).

97. P. Herbert et al., *Pharm. Res.* **15**(2), 357–361 (1998).

98. J.L. Cleland, in L.S. Sanders and W. Hendren, eds. *Protein Delivery: Physical Systems*, Plenum, New York, 1996, pp. 1–43.

99. R.G. Launsby and D.L. Weese, *Straight Talk on Designing Experiments*, 2nd ed., Launsby Consulting, Colorado Springs, Co., 1995.

100. J.L. Cleland, *Biotechnol. Progr.* **14**, 102–107 (1998).

101. International Conference on Harmonization, *Fed. Regist.*, **62**, 24302–24309 (1997).

102. C.H. Niu and Y.Y. Chiu, *J. Pharm. Sci.* **87**(11), pp. 1331–1334 (1998).

103. *Physician's Desk Reference*, Medical Economics Data Production Company, Montvale, N.J., 1998, pp. 2907–2918, 3194–3198.

104. F.G. Hutchinson and B.J.A. Furr, in *Drug Delivery Systems*: Fundamentals and Techniques, P. Johnson and J.G. Lloyd, eds., Ellis Horwood/VCH Verlag., Chichester, England, 1987, pp. 106–119.

PHARMACOKINETICS

PRAVIN R. CHATURVEDI
Vertex Pharmaceuticals
Cambridge, Massachusetts

KEY WORDS

Bioavailability

Biopharmaceutics

Clearance

Compartmental analysis

Deconvolution

Drug input rate

Half-life

Loo-Riegelman method

Noncompartmental analysis

Pharmacodynamics

Pharmacokinetics

Toxicokinetics

Volume of distribution

Wagner-Nelson method

OUTLINE

INTRODUCTION

The pharmacological response of drugs can be better correlated with the concentration of the drug (or its active metabolite) in blood or in some other biophase than with the dose administered. The concentration of the drug in blood or the biophase depends on disposition factors including distribution, metabolism, excretion, and on the efficiency and design of the drug delivery system. The drug delivery system is the sequence of events that provides the drug to the site of action. The pharmacological action of a drug is determined by its intrinsic activity, and drug delivery to the site of action is governed by physicochemical properties of the drugs.

The study of the relationship between the physicochemical properties of a drug in a dosage form and the pharmacologic, toxicologic, or clinical response of the drug after its administration is termed biopharmaceutics. Advancement in biopharmaceutics has primarily resulted from a better understanding of a descriptive discipline called pharmacokinetics (1).

Pharmacokinetics is a theoretical framework of the principles for determining the time course of drug absorption, distribution, metabolism, and excretion, as well as the study of the relationship of these processes to the intensity and time course of therapeutic and adverse effects of these drugs (2). Pharmacokinetics involves the application of mathematics and biochemistry in a physiologic and pharmacologic context. Two related disciplines have emerged from better understanding of pharmacokinetics. Clinical pharmacokinetics deals with the application of pharmacokinetics to safe and effective therapeutic management of patients. Toxicokinetics encompasses the study of the kinetics of absorption, distribution, metabolism, and elimination of large (toxic) doses of drug in the body, and the safety evaluation and assessment of adverse reactions caused by the excessive drug dose (3). The assessment of how drugs exert their therapeutic and toxic effects on the body by studying the relationship of drug concentration in a biophase to its therapeutic or toxic effect is called pharmacodynamics. Thus pharmacokinetics may be described as "what the body does to the drug," and pharmacodynamics can be described as "what the drug does to the body" (4).

Application of pharmacokinetics is critical to the development of various drug delivery technologies. The process of drug delivery includes the administration of the dosage form, the release of the drug from the dosage form, and transport of the drug across biological membranes to the site of action. Thus, increasing the rate and extent of drug delivery would improve the efficiency of the system leading to earlier onset of action and better intensity of pharmacological response. Administration of different formulations of the same drug does not necessarily produce the same response (5). The availability of the drug from different dosage forms may be affected. The term bioavailability is used to describe the rate and extent of drug absorption from a dosage form.

The goal of drug therapy is to produce therapeutic drug concentrations to produce the pharmacological effect without producing toxicity (6). This requires the maintenance of drug concentrations at effective levels while maintaining a reasonable dosing frequency such as once or twice daily. Conventional dosage forms are rapidly absorbed, producing rapid peak concentration and then declining as a function of the drug half-life. Drugs from such dosage forms usually require more frequent dosing due to half-life and duration of pharmacological effect requirements. A drug with a short half-life requires more frequent dosing than drugs with long half-life. The frequency of dosing is also affected by the therapeutic index of the drug. The therapeutic index of a drug is defined as the ratio of the concentration producing a toxic effect to that producing a safe and effective pharmacological effect. Thus, conventional dosage forms are significantly dependent on the pharmacokinetics of the drug (6). The rate and extent of drug absorption can be altered to produce controlled drug delivery via concepts such as sustained release, prolonged release, and delayed release. The discussion of various principles of controlled drug delivery is described in several other articles and is beyond the scope of this article. The goal of this article is to familiarize oneself with the fundamental principles of pharmacokinetics and its role in designing controlled drug delivery systems.

BACKGROUND

Currently four different approaches are used to describe the pharmacokinetics of drugs. The traditional approach is called compartmental analysis, which considers the rates of absorption, distribution, and elimination in terms of rate constants, usually of first-order. This approach is sometimes also called model-dependent approach to pharmacokinetic analysis. The main advantage of this traditional pharmacokinetic analysis is the ability to simulate and predict blood drug concentrations during altered physiological or pathological conditions and during chronic medication. The major disadvantage of the compartmental approach is the mathematical complexity of equations and the difficulty in obtaining reliable estimates of rate constants (2).

A second approach to describe pharmacokinetics is termed noncompartmental analysis. The parameters used to describe the pharmacokinetics of the drug are determined using statistical moments and are derived from relationships involving the area under the zero moment curve (AUC) and the area under the first moment curve (AUMC) of the blood drug concentration-time curve. The advantage of this approach is the ease of determination of these parameters and the lack of requirements of detailed description of the disposition of the drug (hence sometimes referred to as model-independent approach). However, knowledge of noncompartmental pharmacokinetic parameters is insufficient to predict or simulate blood drug concentration profiles in the body (2).

The third major approach to pharmacokinetic analysis focuses on the fundamental anatomical and physiological factors that influence drug uptake and disposition and is referred to as physiological pharmacokinetics. Individual organ systems are studied with respect to partitioning of drug between blood and the organ, the binding of drug in blood and tissues, and blood flow through the organ. Mass balance equations are developed to describe the rate of change in each organ system. The equations for all organs are solved simultaneously and change in drug concentration over time is predicted. The advantage of this approach is that the effects of changes in real physiological variables such as blood flow can be evaluated. This approach also provides reasonable predictions for human pharmacokinetics based upon preclinical animal data. However, the requirements of extensive computing power and unavailability of partitioning or tissue binding data for all species results in limited application of this approach for clinical studies (2).

Recently, with the availability of faster and better computers, a new approach termed population pharmacokinetics has been developed. The major advantage of this approach is the ability to collect sparse data from many subjects in clinical studies and predict the concentration-time profile in a population of patients. This approach allows one to understand inter- and intraindividual variability and is able to determine the role of different factors such as age, sex, and disease in the altered disposition of drugs. Thus, it is rapidly becoming more popular in the design and analysis of clinical studies. A major disadvantage of this approach is the requirement of a good understanding of statistics and mathematics and the need for powerful computers to perform the analysis of data.

Fundamental Pharmacokinetic Parameters

Although the pharmacokinetic approaches are different in the process, they are not mutually exclusive. Two fundamental parameters of pharmacokinetics are drug clearance and its volume of distribution (2). These two parameters can be estimated using any of these approaches and are invaluable to the understanding of pharmacokinetics. Furthermore, noncompartmental analysis can be used to determine some of the parameters for compartmental approaches, and the two approaches are often combined in pharmacokinetic analysis. Similarly, population pharmacokinetic analysis primarily provides an estimate of the drug clearance and its volume of distribution. A physiological pharmacokinetic approach requires the determination of organ clearance and volume of distribution, which can again be used to predict or simulate drug concentration-time profile in the body.

It has been suggested that for any pharmacokinetic analysis, 10 critical pharmacokinetic and pharmacodynamic parameters should be determined (7). These 10 parameters are (1) clearance, (2) effective drug concentrations, (3) extent of availability from a dosage form, (4) fraction of dose excreted unchanged, (5) blood/blood concentration ratio, (6) half-life, (7) toxic concentrations, (8) protein binding, (9) volume of distribution, and (10) rate of availability from a dosage form.

The estimates of clearance, effective drug concentration, and extent of availability are necessary to define the appropriate dosing rate (amount/day) of the drug by a particular route of administration (7). The knowledge of the fraction of the dose excreted unchanged in the urine allows one to estimate the nonrenal clearance of the drug (which may be assumed to represent the hepatic clearance). The ratio of blood to blood concentration ratio allows one to convert the more easily measured blood concentrations into blood concentrations. The ratio of hepatic blood clearance to hepatic blood flow subtracted from one allows an estimate of maximum oral bioavailability.

Half-life and toxic concentrations are very important in drug development. Half-life of the drug defines its dosing interval. Half-life is a derived parameter from clearance and volume of distribution of the drug. Hence, it should not be used as a tool to determine the disposition of the drug (7). The knowledge of toxic concentrations is important because the dosing frequency results in accumulation of drug, and the goal of drug therapy is to maintain effective and safe drug concentrations without entering the toxic concentration range. The knowledge of protein binding of the drug is important in the determination of drug clearance, and it is presumed that the unbound drug is responsible for pharmacological action of the drug because it is able to cross biological membranes.

The knowledge of volume of distribution is important in understanding drug distribution. The volume of distribution allows one to predict steady-state trough and maximum drug concentrations. Of most importance is the use of volume of distribution to determine whether disease states have affected the drug distribution rather than drug clearance (7). For this purpose, the estimation of the volume of distribution at steady-state, which relates the concentration of the drug in systemic circulation to the amount of drug in the body following multiple dosing of the drug. The rate of drug availability from a dosage form is considered a formulation parameter because it can be modified by a change in the formulation from a conventional dosage form to a controlled drug delivery system.

OVERVIEW OF THE THEORETICAL PRINCIPLES OF PHARMACOKINETICS

Several textbooks and review articles are available to provide a more detailed and thorough understanding of the fundamental concepts and mathematical principles of pharmacokinetics (8–10). This overview intends to provide the basis for the use of pharmacokinetics in the development of dosage forms. A brief description of different methods used in developing the mathematical basis for pharmacokinetics is provided in this section. These methods are generally applicable to the evaluation of pharmacokinetics regardless of whether compartmental, noncompartmental, physiological, or population pharmacokinetic methods are used in data analyses.

This review also intends to provide the reader with a general understanding of various methods available to allow the estimation of the fraction of the dose absorbed following extravascular administration for the assessment of in vivo absorption kinetics. For a more detailed understanding on assessment of drug input rate from a controlled drug delivery system, the reader is referred to reviews of this subject (11–14).

Laplace Transforms

Rate equations that describe apparent zero-order or first-order processes are termed linear equations. The Laplace transform is used for solving linear differential equations. Hence, the Laplace transform is applicable to the solution of many equations used in pharmacokinetic analysis. The basic idea of the Laplace transform is to replace the time domain of a rate expression by the complex domain of the Laplace operators. This is achieved by eliminating the independent variable (in pharmacokinetics that being time). The Laplace transform enables complex rate expressions to be manipulated easily by conventional algebraic techniques. The transformed expression can be rearranged into a form that is commonly found in tables of Laplace transforms (15–17). Upon transformation of the Laplace domain into time domain, the complete solution of the linear differential equation is obtained. A table of Laplace transforms of common pharmacokinetic functions is provided in *Pharmacokinetics* (8).

Linear Mammillary Models

A method has been developed using simple treatments to derive equations for any linear mammillary compartment model with any first- or zero-order, or bolus input process. This is accomplished by the use of general input and disposition functions, a method for solving partial fractions to obtain solutions to Laplace transforms, and a multiple dosing function. The input function and the disposition function are defined such that the product of these two functions yields the Laplace transform of the equation describing the time course of a drug in a model compartment. A disposition function defines the model necessary to describe the levels of the drug in the body or a compartment and includes all distribution and elimination processes. Input functions describe the processes needed to get the drug into the body. The following general equation has been empirically derived to describe the Laplace transform for the disposition function of the central compartment in a linear N-compartment mammillary model, where elimination of the drug from any compartment is allowed:

$$d_{s,c} = \frac{\displaystyle\prod_{i=2}^{N} (s + E_i)}{\displaystyle\prod_{i=1}^{N} (s + E_i) - \sum_{j=2}^{N} \left[(k_{lj}k_{jl}) \prod_{\substack{m=2 \\ m \neq j}}^{N} (s + E_m) \right]} \quad (1)$$

wherein $d_{s,c}$ is the disposition function for the central compartment (#1); it is a function of the Laplace operator, s, Π is the continued product where any term is defined as equal to 1 when the index takes a forbidden value, i.e., i = 1 in the numerator or m = j in the denominator, Σ is the continued summation where any term is defined as

equal to zero when the index takes a forbidden value, $k_{ij} \cdot k_{jl}$ are the first-order intercompartmental transfer rate constants, E_i, E_m are the sum of the exit rate constants out of compartments i or m; and N is the number of driving force compartments in the disposition model (i.e., compartments having exit rate constants).

Various input function rates for different processes of input such as instantaneous bolus input, continuous intravenous infusion, or first-order extravascular administration are described (18). The product of the input and disposition function yields the Laplace transform for the amount of drug in the central compartment, $a_{s,c}$.

$$a_{s,c} = in_s \cdot d_{s,c} \quad (2)$$

One can use either the anti-Laplace of the resulting transform or use the general partial fraction theorem (19) to solve for the amount of drug in the central compartment.

Method of Residuals

The method of residuals is a commonly used technique in pharmacokinetics for resolving a curve into its various exponential components (8). This method is sometimes also referred to as feathering, peeling, or stripping the curve. The residual method entails the logarithmic representation of the blood concentration-time curves, followed by the subtraction of the observed blood concentrations from the extrapolated log-linear curves, yielding a series of residual values. A log-linear plot of residual concentrations versus time allows one to estimate rates of absorption, distribution, etc.

Method of Estimating Areas Under the Curve

The estimation of areas under the curve are required for pharmacokinetic analysis by compartmental or noncompartmental analysis. These areas are usually determined by using an approximate integration formula. The trapezoidal rule is one such formula used for estimating the AUC. This particular method involves the description of a given blood concentration-time curve by a function that depicts the curve as a series of straight lines, thereby enabling the area under the curve to be divided into a number of trapezoids. The area of each trapezoid is determined, and the sum of all the areas of trapezoids yield an estimate of the true AUC. The area under each trapezoid for a given segment of a blood concentration-time curve is given by:

$$AUC(t_1, t_2) = (t_2 - t_1) \cdot (C_1 + C_2)/2 \quad (3)$$

The accuracy of the approximation of AUC by this method is dependent on the number of blood concentration-time points sampled within the time interval from 0 to t. Yeh and Kwan (20) have shown that the area under the curve is overestimated by linear interpolation between data points using the trapezoidal rule. In cases where there are long intervals between samples, or changes in curvature, the linear interpolation of the logarithmically transformed data has been suggested. In the log trapezoidal method, the area under a given segment is obtained as:

$$AUC(t_1, t_2) = (C_1 - C_2)(t_2 - t_1)/(\ln C_1 - \ln C_2) \quad (4)$$

Two alternative algorithms based on known interpolating functions have been described in the literature. These include the Lagrange interpolation, in which the linear interpolation is replaced by a cubic polynomial function, and the spline method, in which the cubic functions are modified so that the fitted curves are smooth. The advantages and disadvantages of these interpolation techniques, relative to trapezoidal or log-trapezoidal methods, are discussed in detail by Yeh and Kwan (20).

Principle of Superposition

Fitting the blood concentration-time data requires some assumptions regarding the absorption kinetics of the drug. An alternative approach that requires no assumptions regarding the pharmacokinetic model or absorption kinetics is based upon the principle of superposition, and it employs the overlay technique (21,22). This method requires the following assumptions:

1. Each dose of the drug acts independently of every other dose.
2. The rate and extent of absorption and average systemic clearance are the same for each dosing interval.
3. Linear pharmacokinetics apply so that a change in dose during the multiple dosing regimen can be accommodated.

The overlay technique requires that the concentration-time profile of the drug should be completely characterized following a single dose.

The in vivo performance of controlled drug delivery systems can be influenced by various factors, which may be physiological, biochemical, and/or pharmacological (6). Physiological factors influencing the performance of controlled drug delivery systems include prolonged gastrointestinal absorption, variability in gastrointestinal emptying and motility, gastrointestinal blood flow, and presence or absence of food. Biochemical (or pharmacokinetic) factors influencing controlled delivery systems include dose dumping, first-pass metabolism, variability in excretion organs, and enzyme induction or inhibition following multiple dosing of the drug. The pharmacological factors affecting controlled drug delivery systems include the changes in drug effect following multiple dosing and tolerance or sensitization to the drug following repeated dosing. In order to minimize the influence of such factors, one normally selects drugs with long half-lives to minimize the frequency of dosing and/or develops sustained or controlled release dosage forms. The ultimate purpose of the latter approach is to maintain uniform blood concentrations through reducing the ratio of maximum to minimum concentrations and improving the therapeutic management of patients.

General Principles of Pharmacokinetics

It is important to note that following drug administration (by any route) there are dynamic processes reflecting drug absorption, distribution, and elimination (1). The amount of drug at the absorption site decreases with time as the drug is absorbed into the systemic circulation and distributed throughout the body. As soon as the drug reaches the systemic circulation, various elimination processes are initiated and the excretion of the drug (as parent or metabolite) in urine and other excretory fluids occurs. Thus the amount of the drug in the body continually changes as a function of these absorption and elimination processes.

In case the drug is administered directly into the systemic circulation (such as with an intravenous bolus injection), there is no absorption process and the dynamics of the drug in the body are simply a function of the elimination processes. Hence, some basic concepts of pharmacokinetics are discussed here assuming intravenous bolus injection administration. For purposes of simplicity, the distribution of the drug following intravenous administration is assumed to be instantaneous (i.e., one-compartment kinetics), and only elimination processes are considered. The reader is referred to an excellent book on pharmacokinetics (8) for more details on any of the following concepts.

Elimination Rate Constant. A simple first-order elimination process usually describes the elimination of most drugs. Thus, the rate of elimination of a drug from the body following intravenous administration is described by

$$-dA/dt = dA_e/dt = k_e A \quad (5)$$

where A is the amount of drug in the body at time t, A_e is the amount of drug eliminated from the body (by all routes) at time t, k_e is the apparent first-order elimination rate constant, and $-dA/dt$ and dA_e/dt are the rates of change in the amount of drug in the body and the elimination rate, respectively, at time t. Integrating equation 5 describes the amount of the drug in the body at any time t as,

$$A = A_0 e^{-k_e t} \quad (6)$$

where A_0 is the intravenous dose and equal to the initial amount of drug in the body.

The elimination rate constant can be estimated from equation 6 by simple transformation of drug amounts to their natural logarithm values. Thus, equation 6 can be rewritten as

$$\ln A = \ln A_0 - k_e \cdot t \quad (7)$$

This equation assumes the properties of a straight line and the slope of the line is equal to the elimination rate constant of the drug. Because common logarithms are used more frequently, equation 7 can be described in common logarithms as

$$\log A = \log A_0 - k_e \cdot t/2.303 \quad (8)$$

Thus, the elimination rate constant can be obtained by multiplying the slope of the line obtained from a semilogarithmic plot of A versus time by 2.303.

Half-life. A more commonly used term in clinical studies to describe the rate of elimination of drug from the body is the half-life. The half-life of a drug ($t_{1/2}$) is the time required for the amount in the body to decline to one-half its initial amount. The half-life is related to the elimination rate constant and can be obtained as

$$t_{1/2} = 0.693/k_e \qquad (9)$$

Bioavailability. The fraction of an oral dose that reaches the systemic circulation is termed oral bioavailability (F). It is defined as the rate and extent of absorption of a drug. Bioavailability can be estimated as the ratio of the area under the blood concentration-time curve (AUC) following oral administration, to that obtained following an intravenous dose of the drug, corrected for the dose levels.

$$F = D_{iv}AUC_{oral}/D_{oral}AUC_{iv} \qquad (10)$$

When the intravenous AUC is used as the reference, the bioavailability is termed *absolute* bioavailability. However, other routes of administration can be used as the reference, and an estimate of "relative" bioavailability can be obtained for any drug.

Volume of Distribution. Because there is a relationship between the amount of drug in the body and the drug concentration in the blood, we can rewrite the differential equation describing the rate of change of drug in the body as

$$-d(VC)/dt = -VdC/dt = k_e \cdot (VC) \qquad (11)$$

or

$$-dC/dt = k_e \cdot C \qquad (12)$$

where V is the apparent volume of distribution of the drug and is the ratio of the amount of drug in the body to the concentration of drug in the blood (C_b) at time t, i.e.,

$$V = A/C_b \qquad (13)$$

The apparent volume of distribution is calculated by modifying equation 13 as

$$V = A_0/C_b^0 \qquad (14)$$

where A_0 is the intravenous dose and C_b^0 refers to the initial drug concentration in the blood obtained by back extrapolating the semilogarithmic plot of blood concentration versus time to obtain the y-intercept. It is important to note that the volume of distribution varies from extremely low to extremely high values and does not correspond to any anatomical or physiological space. Instead, the principal factors that govern the volume of distribution are the blood and tissue binding of the drug. This can be better understood from the following:

$$A = A_b + A_t \qquad (15)$$

where A is the amount of drug in the body, A_b is the amount of drug in the blood, and A_t is the amount of drug in the tissue compartment. By substituting the amount with the product of volume of distribution and concentration we get

$$V \cdot C_b = V_b \cdot C_b + V_t \cdot C_t \qquad (16)$$

where V, V_b, and V_t are the apparent volume of distribution, physiological volume occupied by blood, and physiological space occupied by the tissues, respectively, and C_b and C_t refer to the drug concentrations in blood and tissue, respectively. Dividing equation 16 by the blood concentration (C_b), we obtain

$$V = V_b + V_t \cdot (C_t/C_b) \qquad (17)$$

It should be noted that the total drug concentration in blood represents the sum of the bound and unbound fractions of the drug, and it is the free (unbound) fraction of drug that is able to freely diffuse out of blood into tissue spaces. Thus,

$$C_b^u = fu \cdot C_b \qquad (18)$$

$$C_t^u = fu_t \cdot C_t \qquad (19)$$

where C_b^u and C_t^u represent the unbound drug concentrations in blood and tissue compartments, respectively. Because the free concentration of drug is the same between blood and tissue, it is understood that

$$C_u^u = C_t^u \qquad (20)$$

By substituting the relationships for C_b^u and C_t^u in equation 20, we get

$$C_t/C_b = fu/fu_t \qquad (21)$$

Substituting this relationship in the relationship for volume of distribution in equation 21, we obtain

$$V = V_b + (fu/fu_t) \cdot V_t \qquad (22)$$

Equation 22 shows that the volume of distribution is determined by the physiological spaces into which the drug distributes and the relative affinity of binding of the drug to blood and tissue components (2). As seen from this relationship, drugs with a high binding affinity to blood and plasma components have low volumes of distribution, whereas drugs with high tissue binding have high volumes of distribution.

Systemic (Total Body) Clearance. The most important pharmacokinetic parameter of a drug is its systemic blood clearance (Cl_s). Clearance is defined as the volume of fluid from which the drug is completely removed in a given period of time (volume/time). The clearance of drugs can be obtained at a total body level (systemic) or for individual organs. By definition, the total body (systemic) clearance is the ratio of the overall rate of elimination (dA/dt) to the drug concentration in blood (C_b) (2,8)

$$Cl_s = (dA/dt)/C_b \qquad (23)$$

Integrating the right hand side of the equation from time $t = 0$ to $t = \infty$, yields

$$Cl_s = \int_0^\infty (dA/dt)dt \Big/ \int_0^\infty C_b \cdot dt \qquad (24)$$

It is seen that the term $\int_0^\infty (dA/dt)dt$ is equal to the total amount of drug that is ultimately eliminated, i.e., the intravenous dose administered (D_{iv}), whereas the term $\int_0^\infty C_b \cdot dt$ is equivalent to the total area under the curve of the drug concentration in blood versus time curve (AUC). Thus,

$$Cl_s = D_{iv}/AUC \qquad (25)$$

By analogy, we can also prove that the systemic clearance of a drug is equal to the rate of intravenous infusion of a drug (k_0) divided by its steady-state blood concentration (C_{ss}^b),

$$Cl_s = k_0/C_{ss}^b \qquad (26)$$

It can be also shown that systemic clearance can be estimated as the ratio of the dosing rate (in amount/time) to the average steady-state blood concentration of the drug

$$Cl_s = \text{Dosing rate/Avg } C_{ss}^b \qquad (27)$$

Renal Clearance. Following drug administration, polar drugs and metabolites are removed from the body by the kidney. The rate of drug excretion by the kidney can be estimated as

$$dA/dt = Cl_r \cdot C_b \qquad (28)$$

where Cl_r is the renal clearance of the drug, and C_b is the concentration of drug in the blood. Renal clearance is determined by three factors: glomerular renal filtration (Cl_{GFR}), active tubular secretion (Cl_{TS}), and passive tubular reabsorption (Cl_{TR}), of the drug. Thus, Cl_r can be represented as

$$Cl_r = Cl_{GFR} + Cl_{TS} - Cl_{TR} \qquad (29)$$

If the drug is not bound in the blood, its renal filtration rate is equivalent to the glomerular filtration rate (measured as inulin or creatinine clearance). Protein-bound drugs are unable to cross the glomerular membrane, and their renal filtration rate is expressed as fu $\cdot$ GFR (2). Thus, equation 29 becomes

$$Cl_r = \text{fu} \cdot \text{GFR} + Cl_{TS} - Cl_{TR} \qquad (30)$$

Renal clearance can be determined by dividing the total amount of the unchanged (unmetabolized) drug excreted in the urine (A_u^∞) with the area under the blood concentration versus time curve (AUC).

$$Cl_r = A_u^\infty/AUC \qquad (31)$$

Following administration of an intravenous dose, the systemic clearance can be determined as described in equation 31, and difference between the systemic and renal clearance is referred to as nonrenal clearance of the drug.

$$Cl_{nr} = Cl_s - Cl_r \qquad (32)$$

Hepatic Clearance. The difference between the systemic and renal clearance estimates is termed nonrenal clearance. For certain drugs, we can assume that the nonrenal clearance is the hepatic clearance, which is defined as the clearance of the drug from the body by the liver. For drugs that are completely metabolized (i.e., negligible renal clearance), the systemic clearance can be assume to be equal to the hepatic clearance. Under the latter assumption, hepatic clearance can be defined as the product of the hepatic blood flow (Q_h, about 1.5 L/min in humans) and the hepatic extraction ratio (E_h, ranging from 0 to 1). Thus,

$$Cl_h = Q_h \cdot E_h \qquad (33)$$

The extraction ratio is defined as fraction of the drug removed by any organ and can be estimated from the difference in the arteriovenous concentration of the drug as

$$E = (Ca - Cv)/Ca \qquad (34)$$

where Ca represents the concentration entering the organ (arterial blood) and Cv represents the concentration leaving the organ (venous blood). Because the extraction ratio is a fraction, it varies between 0 and 1 for all drugs. The extraction ratio is related to the fraction of drug escaping removal by the organ (F) by

$$F = 1 - E \qquad (35)$$

This relationship is very important for highly extracted drugs, because orally administered drugs must pass through the liver before entering the systemic circulation. For drugs that are highly extracted by the liver, a much smaller fraction of the orally administered dose reaches the systemic circulation. This phenomenon of removal of the drug prior to its entering the systemic circulation is termed a first-pass effect.

The extraction ratio of the drug is dependent on the fraction of the drug bound in the blood and the intrinsic clearance (Cl_{int}) of the drug by the liver. Intrinsic clearance is defined as the maximal ability of any organ to irreversibly remove the drug in the absence of any blood flow limitations to the organ (2). In case of the liver, intrinsic clearance is directly related to the ratio of Vmax to Km (Michaelis-Menten kinetic parameters for drug metabolism). An equation that relates the extraction ratio of any drug to its intrinsic clearance and binding in blood is

$$E_h = (\text{fu} \cdot Cl_{int})/(Q_h + \text{fu} \cdot Cl_{int}) \qquad (36)$$

Substituting this term for Eh in equation 36 for hepatic clearance, we obtain

$$Cl_h = Q_h \cdot [(\text{fu} \cdot Cl_{int})/(Q_h + \text{fu} \cdot Cl_{int})] \qquad (37)$$

Equation 37 has two limiting conditions. For highly extracted drugs, $Cl_{int} \gg Q_h$, which results in the elimination of the Q_h term in the denominator. Thus, equation 37 is reduced to

$$Cl_h = Q_h \qquad (38)$$

In case of drugs which are poorly extracted by the liver, $Q_h \gg Cl_{int}$, which results in the elimination of the Cl_{int} term in the denominator. For such drugs,

$$Cl_h = \text{fu} \cdot Cl_{int} \qquad (39)$$

As seen from the last two equations, highly extracted drugs are limited by blood flow to the liver, and poorly extracted drugs are limited by drug binding in blood and its intrinsic clearance.

First-Pass Effect. For some drugs with high extraction, a significant portion of an oral dose is removed by the liver and/or the gut, resulting in a reduced fraction of the oral dose reaching systemic circulation. This phenomenon is referred to as first-pass effect. The extraction phenomenon is sometimes called first-pass metabolism or presystemic elimination. Assuming complete gastrointestinal absorption, the fraction of an oral dose reaching the circulation (bioavailability, F) is given by

$$F = 1 - E \qquad (40)$$

where E is the extraction ratio of the drug. As defined earlier, bioavailability can be estimated as the ratio of AUC_{oral} to AUC_{iv} (assuming same intravenous and oral dose levels). Substituting the AUC ratio for F and expanding the relationship for E, we obtain

$$\text{AUC}_{oral}/\text{AUC}_{iv} = 1 - [(\text{fu} \cdot Cl_{int})/(Q_h + \text{fu} \cdot Cl_{int})] \qquad (41)$$

Rearranging equation 41 and multiplying both sides of the equation by the administered dose, we obtain

$$\text{D}(Q_h + \text{fu} \cdot Cl_{int})/Q_h\text{AUC}_{iv} = \text{D}/\text{AUC}_{oral} = Cl_{oral} \qquad (42)$$

Because D/AUC_{iv} is defined as the systemic clearance, and substituting for clearance as

$$Cl_h = Q_h \cdot [(\text{fu} \cdot Cl_{int})/Q_h + \text{fu} \cdot Cl_{int})] \qquad (43)$$

we obtain

$$Cl_{oral} = \{Q_h \cdot [(\text{fu} \cdot Cl_{int})(Q_h + \text{fu} \cdot Cl_{int})]\}$$
$$\div \{(Q_h)(Q_h + \text{fu} \cdot Cl_{int})\} \qquad (44)$$

Upon canceling terms, we find that

$$Cl_{oral} = \text{fu} \cdot Cl_{int} \qquad (45)$$

Thus, one can obtain an estimate of the intrinsic hepatic clearance of a drug of a drug from the area under the blood concentration-time curve following oral administration.

The extent to which a drug may be subject to first-pass effects can be estimated from either the oral or intravenous area under the blood concentration-time curve as follows:

$$F = 1 - E_h = 1 - (Q_h \cdot E_h)/Q_h = 1 - \text{D}/(Q_h \cdot \text{AUC}_{iv}) \qquad (46)$$

Multiplying equation 46 with AUC_{oral}, we obtain

$$F \cdot \text{AUC}_{oral} = \text{AUC}_{oral} - [(\text{D} \cdot \text{AUC}_{oral})/(Q_h \cdot \text{AUC}_{iv})] \qquad (47)$$

or

$$F \cdot \text{AUC}_{oral} = \text{AUC}_{oral} - \text{FD}/Q_h \qquad (48)$$

Rearranging equation 47, the bioavailability of highly extracted drugs can be determined as

$$F = Q_h/\{[Q_h + (\text{D}_{oral}/\text{AUC}_{oral})]\} = Q_h/(Q_h + Cl_{int}) \qquad (49)$$

Thus the systemic bioavailability of a drug (subject to first-pass metabolism) can be estimated by determining the AUC_{oral} and substituting an appropriate value for hepatic blood flow. As evident from equation 49, the higher the intrinsic hepatic clearance of any drug, the lower the anticipated oral bioavailability of the drug.

Gut Wall Clearance. The systemic availability of drugs subject to both first-pass hepatic and intestinal mucosa metabolism can be estimated as described by Gibaldi and Perrier (8). These authors have shown that the oral bioavailability (F) can be estimated as

$$F = (Q_h \cdot Q_{pv})/\{(Q_h + Cl_{hint})(Q_{pv} + Cl_{giint})\} \qquad (50)$$

where Q_h is the hepatic blood flow (sum of hepatic arterial blood flow and portal venous blood flow), Q_{pv} is the portal venous blood flow, Cl_{hint} is the hepatic intrinsic clearance, and Cl_{giint} is the intrinsic intestinal mucosal clearance.

Lung Clearance. The lung is an important extrahepatic route of elimination of drugs. As already described, in the absence of significant lung clearance, systemic clearance is estimated as the ratio of the intravenous dose and the AUC_{iv}. Because of the unique anatomical position of the lungs, the true systemic clearance should be estimated from the intraarterial area under the blood concentration-time curve (AUC_{ia}). The fraction of a dose escaping the lung can be estimated as the ratio of AUC_{iv} to AUC_{ia}. Because the gastrointestinal mucosa, the liver, and the lungs are anatomically presented in series, the oral bioavailability of any drug (F) is the product of the fractions escaping first-pass metabolism by each of these organs, i.e.,

$$F_{oral} = f_{gi} \cdot f_h \cdot f_l \qquad (51)$$

where f_{gi} is the fraction escaping first-pass metabolism by the gastrointestinal mucosa, f_h is the fraction escaping the first-pass metabolism by the liver, and f_l is the fraction escaping the first-pass metabolism by the lungs.

Multiple Dosing. Repeated administration of a drug results in accumulation in the body, particularly if the drug has a long half-life. When the drugs reach steady-state, the maximum and minimum concentrations of the drug fluctuate in a fixed manner. The peak concentration at steady-state should be (ideally) maintained below the toxic level, whereas the trough (minimum) concentration should be in an effective range. For drugs with narrow therapeutic index, this range has to be carefully maintained to avoid toxicity or therapeutic failure. It has been shown that the maximum and minimum concentrations (C_{max}^n and C_{min}^n) in the blood after n repeated doses are given by

$$C_{max}^n = (D/V)\{(1 - e_{-nke}{}^T)/(1 - e^{-keT})\} \qquad (52)$$

$$C_{min}^n = (D/V)\{(1 - e_{-nke}{}^T)/(1 - e^{-keT})\}e^{-keT} \qquad (53)$$

where T is the dosing interval of the drug.

Equations 52 and 53 also describe the peak and trough concentrations achieved at steady-state following repeated administration. Under steady-state conditions, the product of $n \cdot ke \cdot T$ becomes very large, resulting in e-$nkeT$ approaching zero. Thus,

$$C_{ss}^{max} = (D/V)\{1/(1 - e^{-keT})\} \qquad (54)$$

$$C_{ss}^{min} = (D/V)\{1/(1 - e^{-keT})\}e^{-keT} \qquad (55)$$

And the average concentration at steady-state is obtained as the ratio of the dosing rate to the drug clearance.

$$C_{ss}^{avg} = \{(Dose/T)\}/Cl \qquad (56)$$

It should be noted that the time taken to reach steady-state is usually at least four to five half-lives of the drug. About seven half-lives of the drug are required to reach 99% of the steady-state drug concentration in the blood.

As mentioned earlier, repeated dosing results in accumulation of the drug in the body (R). Accumulation can be estimated by dividing the minimum concentration in blood at steady-state by the minimum concentration of the drug following a single dose, i.e.,

$$R = (C_{ss}^{min})/(C_l^{min}) \qquad (57)$$

If one assumes that all the doses were administered in the postdistributive phase of the drug, or if the drug concentration profile can be described by one-compartment model, the accumulation factor (R) can be obtained from

$$R = 1/(1 - e^{-keT}) \qquad (58)$$

Thus accumulation of the drug can be predicted by knowing the half-life and dosing interval of the drug.

Compartmental Analysis Approach

The most common approach in pharmacokinetics is to represent the body as a system of compartments, although these compartments have no anatomical or physiological reality. Further, one assumes that the transfer between compartments and the rate of drug elimination from these compartments follow first-order or linear kinetics. Thus, the one-compartment model represents the body as a single, kinetically homogenous unit. This model is useful for drugs that rapidly distribute throughout the body, and the plasma is usually the anatomical reference to the compartment. The assumption is that the rate of change in the blood concentration quantitatively reflects the change in drug concentration throughout the body.

However, most drugs entering the systemic circulation require a finite amount of time to distribute throughout the body into various tissues. This is usually seen following intravenous bolus injection of drugs. During this distributive phase, the drug concentration in plasma declines more rapidly than that observed in the postdistributive phase. Assuming that drug distribution is blood flow–dependent, the highly perfused tissues such as liver and kidney achieve rapid equilibrium with blood. Hence, conventionally the blood and all accessible fluids and tissues are represented as a kinetically homogenous unit and are referred to as the central compartment. On the other hand, poorly perfused tissues show an increase, followed by a decrease during the distribution phase and achieve a pseudodistribution equilibrium with the central compartment. Because the rates of transfer to the poorly perfused tissues are different but cannot be distinguished from blood concentration-time data, the poorly perfused tissues are lumped into a single peripheral compartment. Such representation of the body as multiple, kinetically homogenous units is referred to as multicompartment analysis (e.g., two-compartment, three-compartment). Drug elimination from multicompartment models is assumed to occur in a first-order (linear) fashion. Transfer of drug between body compartments is also assumed to occur by first-order processes. The mathematical basis and details of compartmental analysis are reviewed in great detail in several books and chapters (1,2,8,10).

CLASSIC LINEAR COMPARTMENTAL MODELS

One-Compartment Open Models with Linear Elimination

The blood concentration-time data for a one-compartment open model following a bolus intravenous dose are described by:

$$C = (D_{iv}/V)e^{-ket} \qquad (59)$$

Similarly, the blood concentration-time data for a one-compartment model with zero-order input (such as continuous intravenous infusion) are described by

$$C = (k_0/Vk_e)(1 - e^{-ket}) \qquad (60)$$

The data for a one-compartment open model following first-order input (such as oral or other extravascular routes of administration) are described by:

844   PHARMACOKINETICS

all concentrations represent the free drug concentrations, and mass balance equations are written to describe drug in the extracellular and intracellular spaces and various tissues. These models are even more cumbersome than the blood flow-limited models because simple diffusion is usually not sufficient to describe membrane-limited uptake into certain tissues. However, membrane-limited models have been used to describe data for certain drugs including methotrexate and actinomycin D.

Because the correlation between simulated and real data is sparse in the literature, and because these models simulate an average concentration given that the models are based on average blood flows and average tissue partition coefficients, it is difficult to obtain any information on inter- or intrasubject variability using these models. However, these models are good tools to predict changes in disposition kinetics due to altered physiological or pathological conditions and provide a good mechanism to scale-up the data from preclinical studies to humans (28). The reader is referred to more detailed reviews of physiologically based pharmacokinetic models by Gibaldi and Perrier (8), Bischoff and Dedrick (29), and Bischoff (30).

Population Pharmacokinetics

The principles of population pharmacokinetics have been extensively studied, particularly by Sheiner, Beal, and others (31–35). Population pharmacokinetic parameters quantify population mean kinetics, interindividual variability, and residual variability including intraindividual variability and measurement error (35). An important issue in population kinetics is the identification of which pathophysiologic factor(s) influence the dose-concentration relationship and the degree to which they do so (34). Population kinetics are also popular because they require a fewer samples than traditional pharmacokinetic studies, thus making them amenable during the clinical use of the drug. Population pharmacokinetic studies are normally conducted during the clinical evaluation of a drug. They provide additional information regarding the drug but cannot be used to substitute the classic pharmacokinetic characterization of a drug.

NONMEM (Nonlinear Mixed Effects Model) is a software program developed for estimating population pharmacokinetic parameters from routine patient data (36). It is able to simultaneously determine all parameters including variance parameters, estimate intra- and interpatient variability, and using the extended least squares method, is able to take care of inadequate pharmacokinetic modeling, analytical error, and residual error. However, the use of NONMEM requires the specification of a model for the population being evaluated, and the individual data may be significantly different from the population mean. Although the use of NONMEM and population pharmacokinetics is increasing slowly, it is not yet used in the development of strategies for controlled drug delivery, although it has been used in the evaluation of data following administration of different dosage forms to patients.

ASSESSMENT OF DRUG INPUT RATE FROM CONTROLLED DRUG DELIVERY SYSTEMS

The measurement of the extent of absorption from a controlled drug delivery system provides useful but incomplete information of the absorption process. Additional information on the rate of absorption (i.e., rate of delivery to the systemic circulation) is needed to obtain a better understanding of the drug input (14). The pharmacokinetic principles described earlier provide simple measures such as maximum blood concentration (C_{max}) or time needed to reach the maximum blood concentration (t_{max}). Some more information can be obtained from statistical moments approach regarding the absorption rate. This is achieved via the estimation of mean absorption (input) time. However these single-parameter approaches are inadequate to provide an understanding of drug input rate. Hence more informative approaches involving the characterization of the full time course of the input process such as mass balance and deconvolution methods are used for assessment of drug input rate from controlled drug delivery systems. These methods require the assumption that the drug disposition should follow linear pharmacokinetics.

Mass Balance Methods for the Assessment of Input Rate

The estimation of the amount of the drug in the body at time t, $A(t)$, is determined via the measurement of blood concentrations of the drug following extravascular administration. The estimate of $A(t)$ requires the assumptions of one-compartment or two-compartment models for the disposition of the drug. The Wagner-Nelson method (37) assumes a one-compartment disposition of the drug, whereas the Loo-Riegelman method (38) is applicable to a drug following two-compartment disposition.

Wagner-Nelson Method. Assuming one-compartment disposition, the mass balance equation for the total amount absorbed up to time t is given by

$$A_{abs}(t) = V \cdot C(t) + Cl \int_0^t C(T)\mathrm{d}T \qquad (83)$$

where $\int_0^t C(T)\mathrm{d}T$ is the area under the blood concentration-time curve up to time t, i.e., (AUC_{0-t}), V is the volume of distribution and $C(t)$ is the concentration at time t. Thus equation 83 may also be written as

$$A_{abs}(t) = V \cdot C(t) + Cl \cdot \mathrm{AUC}_{0-t} \qquad (84)$$

The total amount of drug ultimately absorbed (at time infinity), noting that the drug concentration in the body at time infinity is zero, is given by

$$A_\infty = Cl \int_0^\infty C(T)\mathrm{d}T \qquad (85)$$

where $\int_0^\infty C(T)\mathrm{d}T$ at time infinity is the area under the blood concentration-time curve ($\mathrm{AUC}_{0-\infty}$). The fraction of drug absorbed up to time t can be estimated from the ratio

$$A_{abs}(t)/A_\infty = (V \cdot C(t) + Cl \cdot \text{AUC}_{0-t})/(Cl \cdot \text{AUC}_{0-\infty}) \tag{86}$$

It should be noted that the Wagner-Nelson method makes no assumptions for the absorption process. However, if a semilogarithmic plot of percent drug remaining to be absorbed (i.e., $100(1 - [A_{abs}(t)/A_\infty])$) versus time yields approximately a straight line, it suggests an apparent first-order absorption process and the apparent first-order rate of absorption, k_a, can be estimated from the slope of the line. Similarly, a straight line from the plot of percent remaining to be absorbed versus time on rectilinear coordinates suggests zero-order absorption of the drug.

In order to analyze data from microsphere systems used in sustained or prolonged release controlled drug delivery systems, one may not be able to sample the plasma samples until the entire dose has been released from the delivery system. Recognizing that the product of the systemic clearance and the area under the blood concentration-time curve at time infinity is equal to the total amount of dose administered, the amount absorbed at time t is given by

$$A_{abs}(t)/A_\infty = [V \cdot C(t) + Cl \cdot \text{AUC}_{0-t}]/\text{Dose} \tag{87}$$

The fraction of the drug absorbed at time t may also be estimated from the urinary excretion data as discussed by Gibaldi and Perrier (8). The blood concentration at time t, $C(t)$ may be estimated from the urinary excretion data as

$$C(t) = [dA_u/dt]/[k_e \cdot V] \tag{88}$$

where k_e is the apparent first-order excretion rate constant, and dA_u/dt is the rate of excretion of the drug. Following substitution and rearrangement of the resulting equation, the amount of the drug in the body at time t, is given by

$$A_{abs}(t) = [(dA_u/dt)_T]/k_e + (k/k_e)(A_u)_T \tag{89}$$

where k is the first-order elimination rate constant from the body, and $A_{u(T)}$ is the amount recovered unchanged in the urine following administration of the controlled drug delivery system. At time infinity, the amount of the drug excreted in the urine is given as

$$A_{abs\infty} = [k/k_e] \cdot A_{u\infty} \tag{90}$$

Multiplying both sides by $V \cdot k_e$ (i.e., renal clearance Cl_r) in equations 89 and 90, yields

$$Cl_r \cdot A_{abs}(t) = V \cdot [(dA_u/dt)_T] + Cl \cdot (A_u)_T \tag{91}$$

and

$$Cl_r \cdot A_{abs\infty} = Cl \cdot A_{u\infty} \tag{92}$$

The ratio of equations 91 and 92 yields the fraction of the drug absorbed at any time t as

$$A_{abs}(t)/A_{abs\infty} = \{V \cdot [(dA_u/dt)_T] + Cl \cdot (A_u)_T\}/(Cl \cdot A_{u\infty}) \tag{93}$$

In theory, the fraction of the dose absorbed following administration can be solely calculated from the urinary excretion data. However, the collection of urine over an adequate period to allow the estimation of the pharmacokinetic parameters may not be practical in case of some controlled drug delivery systems.

The most serious limitation of the Wagner-Nelson method is that it is applicable only to drugs displaying one-compartment disposition. In all other cases, it is shown to be an approximation. For drugs displaying multicompartment disposition, the Wagner-Nelson method results in an underestimation of the time at which absorption ceases, and an overestimation of the absorption rate (8). One approach to overcoming this problem is to use the Loo-Riegelman method (38), described later. However, the application of the latter method requires concentration-time data, following both intravenous and the intended route of administration of the drug, which may or may not be available at all times. For this reason, the Wagner-Nelson method serves as a valuable approximation method for the determination of the input rate following administration of pharmaceutical controlled drug delivery systems.

Cohen et al. (39) presented a modified version of the Wagner-Nelson method for the assessment of in vivo release rate from liposomal formulations intended for sustained release over a month, following subcutaneous (s.c.) administration. These investigators determined the input rate into the surrounding tissues (s.c. space) and in the plasma following drug absorption. Based upon the mass balance equation, the concentration of the drug in the plasma can be obtained from

$$dA_p/dt = F \cdot k_a \cdot V_s \cdot C_s - k_{el} \cdot V_d \cdot C_p \tag{94}$$

where F is the extent of absorption of the drug from a solution of the drug administered subcutaneously, k_a and k_{el} are the absorption and elimination rate constants, V_s and V_d are the volume of the subcutaneous space and the volume of distribution, respectively, and C_s and C_p are the concentrations of the drug in the subcutaneous space and plasma, respectively. Rearranging and integrating equation 94 yields the following relationship between the plasma and subcutaneous drug concentration:

$$F \cdot V_s \cdot k_a \cdot \int_0^t C_s(T)dT = V_dC_p(t) + k_{el}V_d \int_0^t C_p(T)dT \tag{95}$$

The amount of drug in the subcutaneous space can be estimated from

$$V_sdC_s/dt = R_0 - k_aV_sC_s \tag{96}$$

where R_0 is the instantaneous release rate of the drug from the controlled drug delivery system into the s.c. space. The rate of release from the controlled drug delivery system into the s.c. space can be obtained by rearrangement and integration of equation 96 to yield

$$\int_0^t R_0(T)\mathrm{d}T = V_s C_s + \mathrm{k}_a V_s \int_0^t C_s(T)\mathrm{d}T \qquad (97)$$

Dividing equation 97 by the total dose of the drug administered, the fraction of the dose released from the controlled drug delivery system can be estimated as

$$A_{abs}(t)/A_{abs\infty} = [V_d/F \cdot \text{Dose}] \cdot \{C_p \cdot (1 + \mathrm{k}_{el}/\mathrm{k}_a)$$
$$+ \mathrm{k}_{el} \int_0^t C_p(T)\mathrm{d}T + (1/\mathrm{k}_a)(\Delta C_p/\Delta t) \quad (98)$$

This method is again restricted to compounds with one-compartment disposition and assumes that the estimates for the rates of absorption and elimination remain constant among studies. Furthermore, depending upon the error in the estimation of the absorption rate constant, an error is introduced in the fraction of the dose absorbed, usually leading to an overestimation of the fraction of the dose absorbed. Nevertheless, this method allows a reasonable first approximation of the in vivo release rate of the drug from prolonged release microsphere controlled drug delivery systems.

Loo-Riegelman Method. The Loo-Riegelman method (38) is applicable to a drug following two- or multicompartment disposition. It requires the blood concentration-time data following intravenous administration to assess the fraction of the dose absorbed at time t. The mathematical basis for a drug with two-compartment disposition is based upon the mass balance equation

$$A_{abs}(t) = A_1(t) + A_2(t) + A_{el}(t) \qquad (99)$$

where $A_1(t)$ and $A_2(t)$ are the amounts of the drug in the central and peripheral compartments, and $A_{el}(t)$ is the total amount eliminated from the body by all pathways. Assuming elimination from the central compartment only, the amount in the central compartment is given by

$$A_1(t) = V_1 \cdot C_1(t) \qquad (100)$$

where V_1 and $C_1(t)$ are the volume of the central compartment and the measured blood or blood concentration, respectively. The differential equation for the rate of change of the amount of drug in the peripheral compartment is given by

$$\mathrm{d}A_2/\mathrm{d}t = \mathrm{k}_{1.2}A_1 - \mathrm{k}_{2.1}A_2 \qquad (101)$$

where $\mathrm{k}_{1.2}$ and $\mathrm{k}_{2.1}$ are the first-order intercompartmental transfer rate constants. Loo and Riegelman (38) used a linear approximation for $C_1(t)$ over each data interval, and the amount of the drug absorbed at time t was estimated as

$$A_{abs}(t) = V_1 C_1(t) + V_2 C_2(t) + Cl \int_0^t C(T)\mathrm{d}T \quad (102)$$

where

$$C_2(t) = C_2(t - 1)\mathrm{e}^{-\mathrm{k}_{2.1}\Delta t}$$
$$+ [\mathrm{k}_{1.2}/\mathrm{k}_{2.1}]\{C_1(t - 1)(1 - \mathrm{e}^{-\mathrm{k}_{2.1}\Delta t})\}$$
$$+ [\mathrm{k}_{1.2}/(\mathrm{k}_{2.1})^2]\{[C_1(t) - C_1(t - 1)]/\Delta t\}$$
$$\cdot (\mathrm{e}^{-\mathrm{k}_{2.1}\Delta t} - \mathrm{k}_{2.1}\Delta t - 1) \qquad (103)$$

Loo and Riegelman assumed that the sampling period was relatively short so that the term $\mathrm{k}_{2.1}\Delta t$ was less than or equal to 0.5; thus allowing the third term in the expression for $C_2(t)$ to be reduced using a Taylor expansion (i.e., $\mathrm{e}^{-x} = 1 - x + x^2/2$) to

$$\{\mathrm{k}_{1.2} \cdot [(C_1(t) - C_1(t - 1))/\Delta t] \cdot (\Delta t)^2\}/2 \qquad (104)$$

Boxenbaum and Kaplan (40) have shown that this approximation is a potential source of error and should be avoided. Although the Loo-Riegelman approach is limited due to the requirement of intravenous concentration-time data, it is a very useful approach for the evaluation of absorption kinetics. Furthermore, the method can be used for drugs that distribute in any number of compartments, provided elimination occurs from the central compartment. Wagner (41) has shown that the Loo-Riegelman method can also be applied when the elimination occurs from the peripheral compartment. Expressions analogous to that presented for the estimation of $C_2(t)$ must be written for each peripheral compartment and the amount of drug absorbed in the body at time t can be estimated from the mass balance equation. A modification of the Loo-Riegelman approach without the need for intravenous reference data is presented by Gerardin et al. (42). However, this approach requires the unrealistic condition that distribution occurs much more slowly than the input (13).

Cutler (43) has also shown that both the Wagner-Nelson and Loo-Riegelman methods are applicable to compounds showing a variable clearance and/or nonlinear disposition. Although the mass balance approaches provide a reasonable approximation of the input rate, they are still restricted by assumptions and are "model-dependent." These limitations may be overcome by "model-independent" methods termed deconvolution, which are described in the next section.

Assessment of Absorption Rate by Deconvolution Techniques

The process of determination of the drug input rate from a measured response (for example, blood concentration-time profile) is referred to as deconvolution. The prediction of a response from drug input is known as convolution. It is reported that the deconvolution process is very sensitive to noise in the output data, and the error is amplified in the estimation of the drug input rate. On the other hand, the variation in the drug input rate is dampened when estimating the output. The methods used for deconvolution of output data for microsphere systems is similar to the available methods for other traditional controlled drug delivery systems. Several methods have been proposed in the literature for estimating the drug input rate using deconvolution from pharmaceutical controlled drug delivery systems (13,43–45).

Deconvolution techniques are used to analyze the pharmacokinetics of drug input following administration of the controlled drug delivery system. These methods arise from considering the body as a linear system with respect to drug disposition. It is a model-independent approach and uses two fundamental properties of linear response systems. First is the property of superposition, i.e., the sum or superposition of any two inputs, $f_1(t) + f_2(t)$, results in a response that is the superposition, $c_1(t) + c_2(t)$, of the individual responses for their respective input rates. The second property of linear response systems used in analysis using deconvolution techniques is the convolution integral property. This convolution integral property defines the relationship between the input function and the observed response following the input and is given by the following equation:

$$G(t) = \int R(I)G_\partial(t - T)dT \qquad (105)$$

where $R(t)$ is the input rate of the drug into the body, and $G(t)$ is the resulting response from the input. $G_\partial(t)$ is the response following a unit dose impulse input (such as an intravenous bolus dose). Excellent reviews on the mathematical basis of deconvolution are available in the literature (43–45). The major assumptions underlying the convolution integral property are that the response is linearly related to the input, and the system is time-invariant, i.e., the unit impulse response, $G_\partial(t)$, is independent of the time of administration. The limitations of the deconvolution approaches include its applicability to noninteracting inputs only (14). Prior to applying deconvolution techniques to assess the input rate, the system should be evaluated for the principle of superposition and interaction.

The convolution integral defined in equation 105 can be evaluated either analytically or numerically, when $R(t)$ and $G_\partial(t)$ are known, to predict the response (such as drug concentration) following drug input. This operation is termed *convolution*. When $G(t)$ and $G_\partial(t)$ are known, equation 105 serves as the basis for the estimation of the input rate. This procedure of estimating $R(t)$ from the convolution integral is termed *deconvolution*. Many methods have been proposed for numerical deconvolution. These include the finite difference methods, the least-squares methods, and Fourier analysis (14). The objective of this section is to define some of the mathematical basis for these approaches.

Rationale for the Development of Methods for Numerical Deconvolution. Vaughan and Dennis (46) discuss the need for numerical evaluation of data to determine the input function. They have shown that even if $G(t)$ and $G_\partial(t)$ are known analytically in the convolution integral

$$G(t) = \int R(T)G_\partial(t - T)dT \qquad (106)$$

the integral function defined by equation 106 cannot be solved, except in certain cases, because the Laplace transform of the equation

$$g(s) = r(s)\,g_\partial(s) \qquad (107)$$

with solution

$$r(s) = g(s)/g_\partial(s) \qquad (108)$$

cannot be transformed back into time space by the convolution theorem, because $1/g_\partial(s)$ is not a Laplace transform (47). In general, numerical evaluation of $g(s)$ and $g_\partial(s)$, with subsequent numerical calculation of $r(s)$ and inversion, is unsuccessful because of instability (48,49). Although Coulam et al. (49), have shown that Fourier transform methods are reasonably accurate, these methods are cumbersome, and the use of simple numerical methods would be advantageous in the deconvolution of blood concentration-time data to assess the input rate (46).

Finite Difference Methods for Numerical Deconvolution. The application of the finite difference method for deconvolution was initially introduced by Rescigno and Segré (50) as the area-area method. The deconvolution method requires no assumptions regarding the number of compartments or the kinetics of absorption. However, this method needs data following intravenous administration in addition to that following the intended route of administration. Furthermore, the concentrations must be measured at the same times following both routes of administration. However, the concentrations do not need to be measured at equally spaced intervals.

The mathematical basis for the area-area method is somewhat ambiguous. It approximates the absorption rate by a constant over a time interval. Essentially this method approximates the absorption rate as an equal pulse length "staircase" function (14). Upon deconvolution, Vaughan and Dennis (46) have shown that this product of the pulse lengths and exact output is interpreted as the actual area of the output function itself. These investigators have also shown that via simulations that the area-area method results in large and unpredictable errors in the estimation of the 'staircase' input function.

Benet and Chiang (51) have suggested that the area-area method is only appropriate when the characteristic response is a single exponential function. Vaughan and Dennis (46) have shown that the response to a 'staircase' input function can be derived for both, equal and unequal pulse lengths, by the application of the Laplace transformation methods. If $Y(p_j)$ is the concentration (exact output) at time point p_j, then the response can be obtained from

$$Y(p_j) = \sum_{i=1}^{j} I_i \left\{ \int_0^{p_j - p_{i-1}} G_\partial(T)dT - \int_0^{p_j - p_i} G_\partial(T)dT \right\} \qquad (109)$$

where $j = 1, 2, 3 \ldots, p_0 = 0$, and $Y(0) = 0$, and $\int G_\partial(T)dT$ is the AUC following intravenous bolus administration over the defined time interval.

If all the staircase pulse lengths are equal, i.e., $p_j - p_{j-1} = a$ for all j, then the substitution of $p_j = ja$ and $p_i = ia$ into equation 110 yields:

$$Y(ja) = \sum_{i=1}^{j} I_i \int_{(j-i)a}^{(j-i+1)a} G_{\partial}(T)\mathrm{d}T \qquad (110)$$

where $j > 0$, $Y(0) = 0$, and $\int G_{\partial}(T)\mathrm{d}T$ is the AUC following intravenous bolus administration over the time interval.

Vaughan and Dennis (46) have shown that once the exact output, $Y(p_j)$ at time point p_j, or $Y(ja)$ at time point ja, and the response to a unit impulse dose are known, a particular staircase input function can be obtained from either equations 109 or 110, for unequal or equal pulse lengths, respectively.

Proost (52) proposed a general numerical deconvolution equation for drug concentration-time data with unequal lengths, applying model-independent methods. It was demonstrated that it is not necessary to know the response to a unit impulse input as an analytical function, i.e., curve fitting, and the drug concentration-time data from the unit impulse dose could be used directly. This method is an approximation of the method proposed by Vaughan and Dennis (46), with the exception that the integrals for $G_{\partial}(t)$ are obtained by the application of either linear or log-trapezoidal rule, and the concentration at time zero following an intravenous dose is estimated by logarithmic extrapolation. Proost (52) showed that the staircase approximation of the input rate, I_n, obtained by the trapezoidal approximation of the unit impulse data or an analytical solution for the integral of $G_{\partial}(t)$ yielded similar input rates. The cumulative fraction of the dose absorbed was estimated by the numerical integration of I_n as:

$$F_n = \sum_{i=1}^{j} [(I_{i-1 \text{ to } i})(T_i - T_{i-1})] \qquad (111)$$

where T_i is the ith sampling time point, and $I_{i-1 \text{ to } i}$ is analogous to the staircase input function of Vaughan and Dennis (46) in equation 111, with the exception that the integral of $G_{\partial}(t)$ is replaced by the trapezoidal approximation of the integral. The method of Proost (52) only assumes that the pharmacokinetics of the drug are linear.

A numerical deconvolution method has been derived for the determination of the in vivo input rates based upon the linear interpolation of the observed drug concentrations and deconvolution of the resulting trapezoidal function (53). The derived in vivo input functions are discontinuous and a general expression for the cumulative drug input is also derived. The expression for cumulative drug input was shown to be a generalization of the Loo-Riegelman equation, and it yielded similar results to the point-area method using the staircase approximation for input functions.

Wagner (54) has shown that the fraction of the drug remaining to be absorbed at the site of administration can be obtained from a similar expression. In terms of the sampling interval (Δt), the fraction unabsorbed (FR) can be obtained from:

$$FR_{n\Delta t} = [H_{(n+1)\Delta t}/H_{n\Delta t}] - \sum_{\substack{i=2 \text{ to } n+1}}^{j=1 \text{ to } n} \{[F_{i\Delta t}/F_{\Delta t}][FR]_{(j-1)\Delta t}\} \qquad (112)$$

where $n\Delta t$ is the time after n sampling intervals equal to Δt, H is a function describing the drug concentration-time curve following the intended route of administration, and F is a function describing the drug concentration-time curve following intravenous bolus administration. $F_{n\Delta t}$ may be expressed as the drug concentration at time $n\Delta t$, or as the area under the curve between $n\Delta t$ and $(n-1)\Delta t$. $H_{n\Delta t}$ can only be expressed in terms of drug concentration. When both, H and F are expressed in terms of drug concentrations, the method is referred to as the point–point method (8). Benet and Chiang (51) recommended the use of the point–area method, in which F should be expressed as the area under the drug concentration-time curve following intravenous administration, and H should be expressed in terms of drug concentration in equation 112. Vaughan and Dennis (46) also designate their method of deconvolution as the point–area method, because specific output data points, $Y(p_j)$, and the integral of $G_{\partial}(t)$, is used to derive the staircase input function.

Chiou (55) proposed a finite difference method for numerical deconvolution using an instantaneous midpoint-input principle. This assumes that all the drug absorbed during a given interval, regardless of the complexity of the absorption kinetics, is absorbed instantaneously at the midpoint of the interval. This assumption is based upon the finding that the blood concentration for a one-compartment model system following an intravenous infusion can be approximated by assuming that the entire dose was administered as a bolus at the midpoint of the infusion period (56). This approximation is valid when the infusion period is much shorter than the half-life of the drug. The deconvolution method proposed by Chiou (55) requires no assumptions regarding the pharmacokinetic models or the site of drug elimination. The fraction of the dose absorbed at time $t(F)$ can be calculated from:

$$F_1 = C_{t1}/C_{\text{i.v.}(0.5t1)} \qquad (113)$$

where C_{t1} is the blood drug concentration at time $t1$ after dosing, and $C_{\text{i.v.}(0.5t1)}$ is the blood drug concentration at time $0.5t1$, following an intravenous bolus dose. The amount of drug absorbed between times $t1$ and $t2$ can be estimated by a similar comparison, provided the drug concentration is corrected for the contribution from the drug absorbed prior to $t1$ (C_{p1}). To estimate C_{p1}, it is assumed that all drug prior to time $t1$ is instantaneously absorbed at time $0.5t1$, and the contribution is estimated as

$$C_{p1} = F_1 C_{\text{i.v.}(t2-0.5t1)} \qquad (114)$$

where $C_{\text{i.v.}(t-0.5t1)}$ is the theoretical blood concentration at time $(t2 - 0.5t1)$, when the same extravascular dose is administered as an intravenous bolus dose. This principle is used to estimate the fraction absorbed during other sampling intervals as follows:

$$F_n = \left[C_{tn} - \sum_{i=1}^{n-1} C_{pi} \right] \Big/ C_{\text{i.v.}0.5(tn-tn-1)} \qquad (115)$$

Vaughan (57) has shown that the method described by Chiou (55) is an approximation of the point–area method (53). Furthermore, the midpoint–input method is similar to the approximation of the area–area method (50), which uses rectangular functions to approximate the integrals of $G_\partial(t)$ centered about the midpoint of integration. Vaughan (57) cautions against the use of approximations of the point–area method for the estimation of staircase input, because it leads to large errors in the cumulative drug input functions.

The finite difference methods for numerical deconvolution provide a simple method to estimate the drug input rates without assumptions regarding the pharmacokinetic models or absorption kinetics. Their main drawback is the instability in presence of data noise, which may require smoothing procedures (58). Cutler (43) has pointed out that the smoothing procedures may yield errors in the estimates of the input functions. Because the finite difference methods are computationally simple, they can be used without the use of complex algorithms and computers, needed for the more complex, but stable, deconvolution methods such as the least-squares (11,12).

Least-Squares Method for Numerical Deconvolution. The least-squares method provides the determination of the best estimate of the true input rate. The criteria for determining the best estimate for the input function relies on the accuracy of the prediction of the response $G(t)$. Thus the proximity of the predicted $G(t)$ values with the observed $G(t)$ values determine the accuracy of the estimated input rate. The least-squares deconvolution method requires assumptions and specifications regarding the mathematical form of the input function. Once the function describing the input function is specified, it is introduced into the convolution integral and the observed response, $G(t)$, is compared with the predicted response, $G'(t)$.

When little or no information is available regarding the nature of the input function, Cutler (43) has proposed the use of polynomial functions to describe the input function. Cutler (11) has shown that an exponential input function and the cube-root dissolution law represent adequate approximations of the input rate with simulated data. Cutler (12) proposed the use of orthogonal functions to derive the polynomial functions for approximations of the input function. This approach was proposed based upon the difficulty in estimating the input function using a polynomial approximation by Gamel et al. (58), which was attributed to the ill-conditioned set of polynomial equations. The least-squares approach is more stable to data noise, but is computationally more complex and requires the use of fairly extensive and specialized programs to determine the drug input functions.

Veng-Pedersen (44,45,59) has also proposed a least-squares deconvolution method for estimating the drug input rate using both a polynomial and a polyexponential approximation of the input rate. This approach has led to the development of a method using an adaptive least-squares cubic spline function for the approximation of the input rate. Based upon simulated data, this method is reported to have significant advantages over the method proposed by Cutler (12). These include the superiority of fitting the bolus input response by a polyexponential expression which is a smoothing function and does not oscillate between the data points as a polynomial expression

does. Furthermore, the Veng-Pedersen (44) approach provided a simple and explicit mathematical function for the rate and extent of drug input rate, which alleviates the complexity of the back-transformation and summation of terms in the Cutler approach (12). Because the input function is calculated directly by linear regression in the Veng-Pedersen method, it is purported to be computationally simpler and does not require the extensive and specialized methods for deconvolution.

The least-squares method for deconvolution are considered model-independent even though they require the determination of the unit impulse response parameters by fitting the data to some function (e.g., polyexponential). The unit impulse response parameters require their determination by nonlinear regression. However, these estimated parameters do not require any uniqueness, and their actual values have no influence on the accuracy of the determination of the input function (60). The input function is approximated by a polynomial expression that uses these estimated parameters collective rather than individually. Hence, the least-squares method is not affected by the individual errors in the estimation of the parameters. Furthermore, because the input function is determined by linear rather than nonlinear regression, it is computationally simpler, and the problems of multiple minima are eliminated with this approach (60).

Despite the advantage of the stability of the least-squares deconvolution methods in presence of data noise, these methods require complex algorithms to determine the input functions. A simpler algorithm for easier implementation of this deconvolution technique has been provided (61). It is based upon a polyexponential approximation of the absorption response and the the response from intravenous bolus or infusion administration. The absorption response is represented by:

$$c(t) = \sum_{i=1}^{m} b_i e^{-\beta_i t_+} \tag{116}$$

where $t_+ = (t - t_{lag})_+$ and $c(0) = 0$; t_{lag} is the estimated lag time prior to appearance of the drug into systemic circulation following extravascular administration. The characteristic response from a unit impulse dose $c\partial(t)$ is obtained from the polyexponential approximation of the intravenous bolus response:

$$c_{iv}(t) = \sum_{i=1}^{n} a_i e^{-\alpha_i t} \tag{117}$$

where $\alpha_i > 0$. Thus, $c_\partial(t)$ can be obtained as:

$$c_\partial(t) = c_{iv}(t)/D_{iv} \tag{118}$$

where D_{iv} is the intravenous bolus dose.

The cumulative amount of drug absorbed, expressed as a percentage of the dose (PCT) has been shown to be:

$$\text{PCT}(t) = [100/\text{D}] \int_0^t f(t) dt \tag{119}$$

where $f(t)$ is the rate of direct input. This expression has been shown to be equivalent to:

$$\text{PCT}(t) = u_0 + \sum_{i=1}^{m+n-1} u_i e^{-v_i t_+} \qquad (120)$$

The absorption rate has been shown to be

$$f(t) = [D/100] \sum_{i=1}^{m+n-1} u_i(-v_i) e^{-v_i t_+} \qquad (121)$$

where $v_i = \beta_i$ for $i = 1, 2, 3 \ldots, m$; and $v_i = -\gamma_{i-m}$ for $i = (m+1), (m+2), \ldots, (m+n-1)$. u_i is defined as:

$$u_i = \text{K}_4 b_i \left[\text{K}_1 - (\text{K}_3/\beta_i) - \sum_{j=1}^{n-1} (g_j/\gamma_j(\gamma_j + \beta_i)) \right] \qquad (122)$$

for $i = 1, 2, 3, \ldots, m$; and

$$u_i = \text{K}_4(g_{i-m}/\gamma_{i-m}) \sum_{j=1}^{m} (b_j/(\gamma_{i-m} + \beta_j)) \qquad (123)$$

for $i = (m+1), (m+2), \ldots, (m+n-1)$. u_0 is obtained as:

$$u_0 = - \sum_{i=1}^{m+n-1} u_i \qquad (124)$$

The parameters $\{g_i, \gamma_i\}_1^{n-1}$ are obtained from the parameters $\{a_i, \alpha_i\}_1^n$. The γ parameters are $(n-1)$ roots of the $(n-1)$th polynomial and can be obtained by conventional numerical methods (61). The remaining parameters in the expression for PCT have been described by Veng-Pedersen (61).

This approach to deconvolution is purported to be computationally easier and Veng-Pedersen (61) has provided a computer subroutine for easy implementation of the algorithm. Although the use of least-squares deconvolution approach has been simplified by the use of more user-friendly algorithms, they still require the use of fairly extensive and specialized computer programs to estimate the input functions. These requirements, along with the a priori assumptions regarding the approximation of the input function, limit the routine use of this approach for deconvolution of data from extravascular administration of controlled drug delivery systems.

Miscellaneous Methods for Deconvolution of Extravascular Data. Berman (62) proposed a deconvolution scheme for the calculation of input function given a system and its response. It is based upon the conversion of the convolution integral equation to an initial value problem. This technique is particularly simple and advantageous when dealing with compartmental systems. Foster et al. (63) have illustrated the use of this deconvolution approach, using compartmental analysis, with commonly available numerical integration software. The scheme can be used to determine an unknown input over time, from the measured response and the impulse response of the system. These investigators report that this method requires the solution of two systems of differential equations; those specifying the compartmental systems for the response function and

the impulse response of the system. The input function can be calculated using simulations of these compartmental models. The accuracy of the simulations is determined from the goodness-of-fit of the function to the observed response data from the system.

A novel approach for deconvolution based upon the principle of maximum entropy has been introduced by Charter and Gull (64). The resulting input functions have been shown to be physiologically realistic and smooth, blood samples are not required to be taken at equally spaced intervals, and no preliminary smoothing or interpolation of data is required. The maximum entropy approach is conceptually complex, and it is proposed that the maximum entropy may offer the most reliable deconvolution for drugs exhibiting nonlinear kinetics (13).

CONCLUSIONS

This article has provided an overview of the mathematical basis and applications of pharmacokinetic principles in the design and analysis of drug from various dosage forms, with a particular emphasis toward controlled drug delivery systems. The choice of the appropriate pharmacokinetic models for the analysis of data depends on the availability of data from intravenous and extravascular routes of administration. The pharmacokinetic evaluation of any drug usually entails the determination of the pharmacokinetics of the drug following intravenous and/or the extravascular (intended) route of administration. Model-dependent and model-independent pharmacokinetic parameter estimates should be obtained from in vivo experiments to obtain a proper handle on the bioavailability (extent of absorption), systemic clearance, volume of distribution, and half-life of the drug.

In addition to the information on the extent of absorption from controlled drug delivery systems, mass balance and deconvolution techniques allow the estimation of in vivo input of drug into the biological system. Using the method of preference, one calculates the input rates from the controlled drug delivery system. The input rates allow the estimation of the fraction of the dose absorbed as a function of time. Cumulative amount of drug absorbed (in vivo) versus time plots are constructed, and are compared with in vitro dissolution rate plots to establish meaningful in vitro–in vivo correlation. Such correlation precludes the need for the conduct of expensive and time-consuming pharmacokinetic experiments during formulation development and/or optimization and provides a tool for quality control purposes. Thus, the appropriate understanding of pharmacokinetic principles leads to considerable advancement in the development of better controlled drug delivery systems for various drugs.

BIBLIOGRAPHY

1. M. Gibaldi, ed., *Biopharmaceutics and Clinical Pharmacokinetics*, 3rd ed., Lea & Febiger, Philadelphia, 1984, pp. 1–28.
2. P.R. Gwilt, in C.R. Craig and R.E. Stitzel, eds., *Modern Pharmacology*, 2nd ed., Little, Brown, Boston, 1986, pp. 75–95.

3. M. Leal, A. Yacobi, and V.K. Batra, in A. Yacobi, J.P. Skelly, V.P. Shah, and L.Z. Benet, eds., *Integration of Pharmacokinetics, Pharmacodynamics and Toxicokinetics in Rational Drug Development*, Plenum, New York, 1993, pp. 55–67.

4. G. Hochhaus and H. Derendorf, in H. Derendorf and G. Hochhaus, eds., *Handbook of Pharmacokinetic / Pharmacodynamic Correlation*, CRC Press, Boca Raton, Fla., 1995, pp. 79–120.

5. P.R. Gwilt, in C.R. Craig and R.E. Stitzel, eds., *Modern Pharmacology*, 2nd ed., Little, Brown, Boston, 1986, pp. 96–110.

6. B.M. Silber, M. Bialer, and A. Yacobi, in J.R. Robinson and V.H.L. Lee, eds., *Controlled Drug Delivery: Fundamentals and Applications*, 2nd ed., Dekker, New York, 1987, pp. 213–251.

7. L.Z. Benet, in A. Yacobi, J.P. Skelly, V.P. Shah, and L.Z. Benet, eds., *Integration of Pharmacokinetics, Pharmacodynamics and Toxicokinetics in Rational Drug Development*, Plenum, New York, 1993, pp. 115–123.

8. M. Gibaldi and D. Perrier, eds., *Pharmacokinetics*, Dekker, New York, 1982.

9. P.G. Welling and F.L.S. Tse, eds., *Pharmacokinetics: Regulatory, Industrial, Academic Perspectives*, Dekker, New York, 1988.

10. J.G. Wagner, in P.G. Welling and F.L.S. Tse, eds., *Pharmacokinetics: Regulatory, Industrial, Academic Perspectives*, Dekker, New York, 1988, pp. 1–56.

11. D.J. Cutler, *J. Pharmacokinet. Biopharm.* **6**, 227–242 (1978).

12. D.J. Cutler, *J. Pharmacokinet. Biopharm.* **6**, 243–263 (1978).

13. G.T. Tucker and P.R. Jackson, in L.F. Prescott and W.S. Nimmo, eds., *Novel Drug Delivery and Its Therapeutic Application*, Wiley, New York, 1989, pp. 113–120.

14. P.R. Chaturvedi, in S. Cohen and H. Bernstein, eds., *Microparticulate Systems for the Delivery of Proteins and Vaccines*, Dekker, New York, 1996, pp. 321–347.

15. N.F. Nixon, *Handbook of Laplace Transformation: Fundamentals, Application, Tables and Examples*, 2nd ed., Prentice-Hall, Englewood Cliffs, N.J., 1965.

16. N.F. Nixon, *Handbook of Laplace Transformation: Fundamentals, Application, Tables and Examples—Workbook (with answers)*, 2nd ed., Prentice-Hall, Englewood Cliffs, N.J., 1965.

17. H.S. Bear, Jr. *Differential Equations*, Addison-Wesley, Reading, MA, 1962.

18. L.Z. Benet, *J. Pharm. Sci.* **61**, 536–541 (1972).

19. L.Z. Benet and J.S. Turi, *J. Pharm. Sci.* **60**, 1593–1594 (1971).

20. K.C. Yeh and K.C. Kwan, *J. Pharmacokinet. Biopharm.* **6**, 79–98 (1978).

21. W.J. Westlake, *J. Pharm. Sci.* **60**, 883–885 (1971).

22. J.G. Wagner, (1974): *Med. Clin. North Am.* **58**, 479–492 (1974).

23. K. Yamaoka, T. Nakagawa, and T. Uno, *J. Pharmacokinet. Biopharm.* **6**, 547–558 (1978).

24. D.J. Cutler, *J. Pharm. Pharmacol.* **30**, 476–478 (1978).

25. D.M. Himmelblau and K.B. Bischoff, *Deterministic Systems*, Wiley, New York, 1968.

26. L.Z. Benet and R.R. Galeazzi, *J. Pharm. Sci.* **68**, 1071–1074 (1979).

27. J.J. Stefano, III, *Am. J. Physiol.* **243**, R1–R6 (1982).

28. R.L. Dedrick, *J. Pharmacokinet. Biopharm.* **1**, 435–461 (1973).

29. K.B. Bischoff and R.L. Dedrick, *J. Pharm. Sci.* **57**, 1347–1357 (1968).

30. K.B. Bischoff, *Cancer Chemother. Rep.* **59**, 777–793 (1975).

31. L.B. Sheiner, (1984): *Drug Metab. Rev.* **15**, 153–171 (1984).

32. L.B. Sheiner and S.L. Beal, *J. Pharmacokinet. Biopharm.* **8**, 553–571 (1980).

33. L.B. Sheiner and S.L. Beal, *J. Pharmacokinet. Biopharm.* **9**, 635–665 (1981).

34. L.B. Sheiner and L.Z. Benet, *Clin. Pharmacol. Ther.* **38**, 481–487 (1985).

35. L.B. Sheiner, B. Rosenberg, and V.V. Marathe, *J. Pharmacokinet. Biopharm.* **5**, 441–479 (1977).

36. S.L. Beal and L.B. Sheiner, *NONMEM Users Guide Part I. Users Basic Guide*, University of California, Division of Clinical Pharmacology, San Francisco, 1979.

37. J.G. Wagner and E. Nelson, *J. Pharm. Sci.* **52**, 610–611 (1963).

38. J. Loo and S. Riegelman, *J. Pharm. Sci.* **57**, 918–928 (1968).

39. S. Cohen et al., *Proc. Natl. Acad. Sci. U.S.A.* **88**, 10440–10444 (1991).

40. H. Boxenbaum and S. Kaplan, *J. Pharmacokinet. Biopharm.* **3**, 257–264 (1975).

41. J.G. Wagner, *J. Pharmacokinet. Biopharm.* **3**, 457–478 (1975).

42. A. Gerardin, D. Wantiez, and A. Jaouen, *J. Pharmacokinet. Biopharm.* **11**, 401–424 (1983).

43. D. Cutler, *Pharmacol. Ther.* **14**, 123–160 (1981).

44. P. Veng-Pedersen, *J. Pharm. Sci.* **69**, 298–305 (1980).

45. P. Veng-Pedersen, *J. Pharm. Sci.* **69**, 305–312 (1980).

46. D.P. Vaughan and M. Dennis, *J. Pharm. Sci.* **67**, 663–665 (1978).

47. G. Doetsch, *Guide to the Applications of Laplace Transforms*, Van Nostrand, New York, 1961, Chapter 7.

48. R.E. Bellman, B.E. Kalaba, and J. Lockett, *Numerical Inversion of the Laplace Transform*, Elsevier, New York, 1966.

49. C.M. Coulam, H.R. Warner, H.W. Marshall, and J.B. Bassingthwaighte, *Comp. Biomed. Res.* **1**, 124–138 (1967).

50. A. Rescigno and G. Segré, *Drug and Tracer Kinetics*, Blaisdell, Waltham, Mass., 1966.

51. L.Z. Benet and C.-W.N. Chiang, *Abstr. Pap., 13th Nat. Meet. Am. Acad. Pharma. Sci.*, 1972, vol. 2, p. 169.

52. J.H. Proost, *J. Pharm. Sci.* **74**, 1135–1136 (1985).

53. D.P. Vaughan and M. Dennis, *J. Pharmacokinet. Biopharm.* **8**, 83–98 (1980).

54. J.G. Wagner, *J. Pharmacokinet. Biopharm.* **3**, 51–57 (1975).

55. W.L. Chiou, *J. Pharm. Sci.* **69**, 57–62 (1980).

56. W.L. Chiou, G.W. Peng, and R.L. Nation, *J. Clin. Pharmacol.* **18**, 266–271 (1978).

57. D.P. Vaughan, *J. Pharm. Sci.* **70**, 831–832 (1981).

58. J. Gamel, W. Rousseau, C. Katholi, and E. Mesel, *Circ. Res.* **32**, 516–523 (1973).

59. P. Veng-Pedersen, *J. Pharm. Sci.* **69**, 312–318 (1980).

60. P. Veng-Pedersen, *J. Pharm. Sci.* **69**, 318–324 (1980).

61. P. Veng-Pedersen, *J. Pharmacokinet. Biopharm.* **8**, 463–481 (1980).

62. M. Berman, *Math. Biosci.* **40**, 319–323 (1978).

63. D.M. Foster, D.G. Covell, and M. Berman, *Comput. Biol. Med.*, **18**, 253–266 (1988).

64. M.K. Charter and S.F. Gull, *J. Pharmacokinet. Biopharm.* **15**, 645–655 (1987).

POLY(ORTHO ESTERS)

Jorge Heller
Advanced Polymer Systems
Redwood City, California

Robert Gurny
University of Geneva
Geneva, Switzerland

KEY WORDS

Biotolerance

Bovine serum albumin

Cancer treatment

Diabetes

5-Fluorouracil

Glaucoma

Insulin

Levonorgestrel

Malaria

Naltrexone

Ocular delivery

Periodontal disease

Poly(ortho ester)

Protein delivery

OUTLINE

The development of bioerodible drug delivery implants has now been an area of great importance for a number of years. A major driving force in developing such implants is the ability to deliver therapeutic agents directly to the systemic circulation, which is important with drugs that undergo significant inactivation by the liver. Two major areas of application deserve special mention. These are the development of bioerodible drug delivery devices for protein delivery and site-specific delivery for the improved treatment of cancer.

At the present time, there are three major classes of totally synthetic bioerodible polymers under active development. These are polyesters, polyanhydrides, and poly(ortho esters). Poly(ortho esters) have been under development since 1970, and three major families have been described. These are shown in Scheme 1.

Because the history of their development and applications prior to 1992 has been comprehensively reviewed (1,2), it is not the purpose of this article to again comprehensively review all past work. Rather, we concentrate on significant developments that have taken place since the last review, but for the sake of completeness, for each polymer system we present a brief, updated review with pertinent references and refer the reader to the original literature for additional details.

POLY(ORTHO ESTER) I

Poly(ortho ester) I, the first such polymer prepared, has been developed at the Alza Corporation and described in a series of patents by Choi and Heller (3–7). This polymer was originally designated as Chronomer™ but the name was later changed to Alzamer®. The polymer is prepared as shown in Scheme 2. However, the Alza Corporation has now discontinued all work with poly(ortho ester), and because the polymer is no longer available, collaborative efforts have also been discontinued.

Polymer Erosion

When placed in an aqueous environment, the polymer hydrolyzes as shown in Scheme 3. Because ortho ester linkages are acid sensitive and hydrolysis of this polymer produces γ-butyrolactone, which rapidly opens to γ-hydroxybutyric acid, the polymer must be stabilized with a base such as Na_2CO_3 to avoid an uncontrolled, autocatalytic hydrolysis reaction.

Drug Release

Even though a considerable amount of work with this polymer has been carried out at Alza, there is little detailed published information available, Alza publications do not specifically disclose the structure of the polymer, and only code names are used. However, it is now known that the code name of C111 represents a polymer prepared using 1,6-hexanediol, and C101ct is a polymer prepared using *cis/trans* cyclohexanedimethanol. The polymer has been used in the treatment of burns (8), in the delivery of the narcotic antagonist naltrexone (9), and in the delivery of the contraceptive steroid levonorgestrel (10). The polymer has also been investigated by Sudmann in a number of orthopedic applications (11–19).

Typical Synthetic Procedure

To 45 g (0.312 mole) of anhydrous *cis/trans*-1,4-cyclohexanedimethanol and 0.05 g polyphosphoric acid in a commercially available polymerization reactor is added with constant stirring under an inert nitrogen environment and normal atmospheric pressure 50 g (0.312 mole) of anhydrous 2,2-diethoxytetrahydrofuran. Next, the mixture is heated to 110–115°C and held at that temperature for 1.5 to 2 h with slow distillation of ethanol. Then, while main-

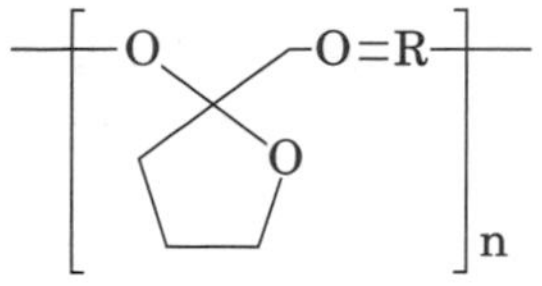

Poly (ortho ester) I 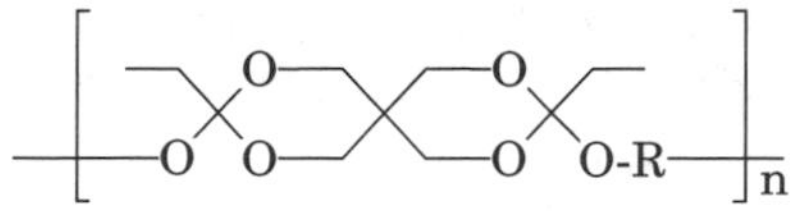   Poly (ortho ester) II

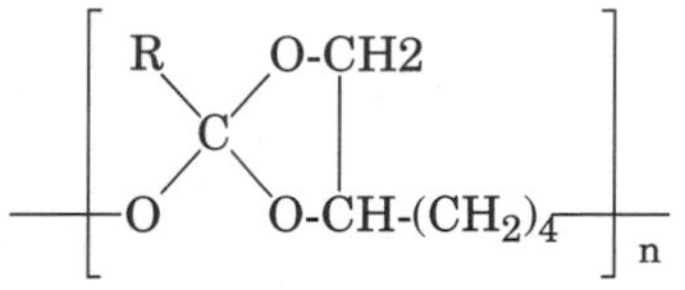

Poly (ortho ester) III   **Scheme 1.**

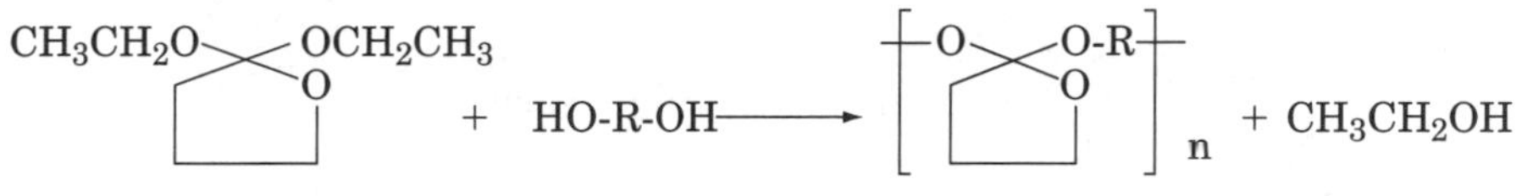

Scheme 2.

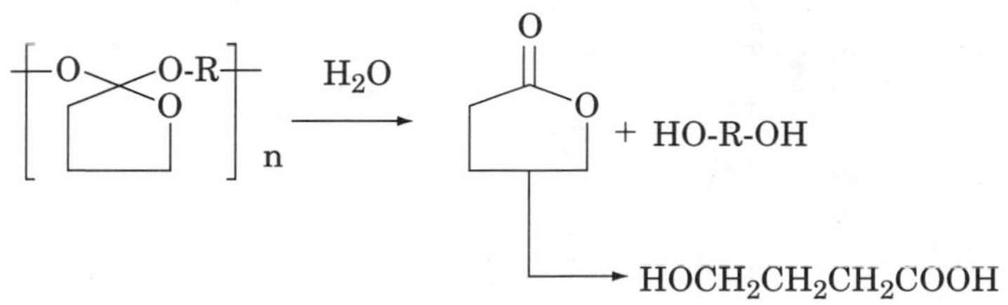

Scheme 3.

taining the temperature, the pressure is gradually reduced to 0.01 mm Hg, and at this reduced pressure the temperature is slowly increased to 180°C. The reaction is continued at this temperature for 24 h. The polymer is isolated by extrusion from the reactor.

POLY(ORTHO ESTER) II

Poly(ortho ester) II was developed at the Stanford Research Institute, now known as SRI International, under contract with the National Institute of Child Health and Human Development, and was prepared as shown in Scheme 4. A history of the development of this polymer has been published (1).

The diketene acetal, 3,9-diethylidene-2,4,8,10-tetraoxaspiro [5.5] undecane is not commercially available, but can be readily synthesized as shown in Scheme 5 (20).

Because a condensation between a diketene acetal and a diol, just like that between a diisocyanate and a diol, proceeds without the evolution of volatile by-products,

dense, cross-linked materials can be produced by using reagents having a functionality greater than two (21). To prepare cross-linked materials, a molar excess of the diketene acetal is used, and the resulting prepolymer with ketene acetal end-groups is reacted with a triol or a mixture of diols and triols. This synthesis is shown in Scheme 6.

Polymer Erosion

Use of Excipients. As shown in Scheme 7, this polymer hydrolyzes to initially neutral products so that it is not necessary to use bases to neutralize acidic hydrolysis products. Details of the hydrolysis mechanism have been published (22).

Even though ortho ester linkages are quite labile, polymers belonging to this family are extremely hydrophobic, and uncatalyzed poly(ortho esters), as shown in Figure 1, are very stable. Therefore, in order to achieve shortened erosion times, it is necessary to use small amounts of acidic excipients that are physically incorporated into the polymer (23,24). Then, rate of hydrolysis can be manipulated

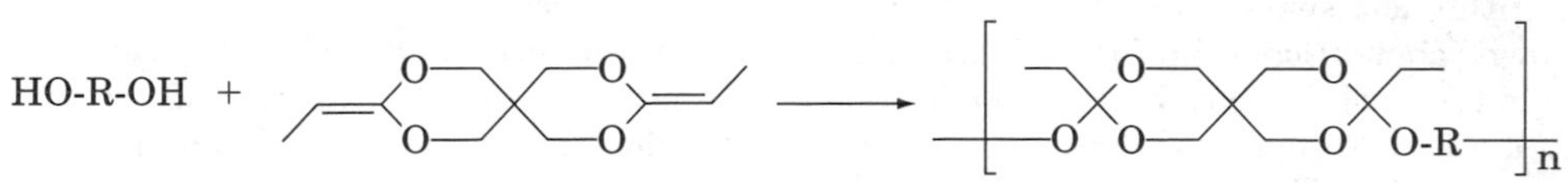

Scheme 4.

Scheme 5.

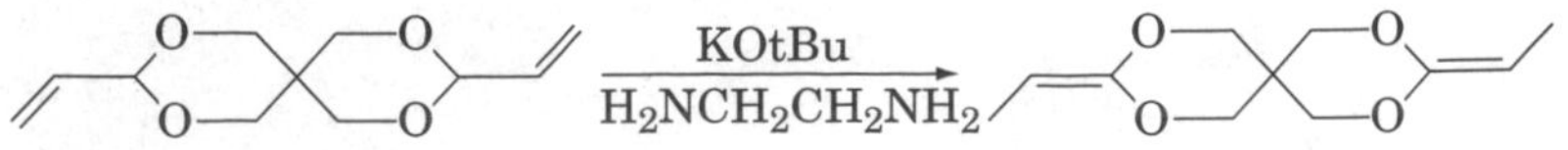

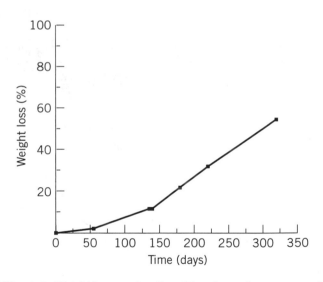

Scheme 6.

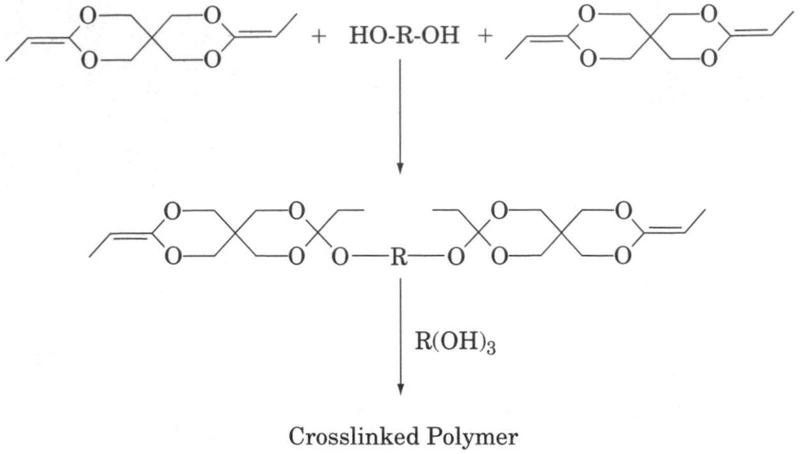

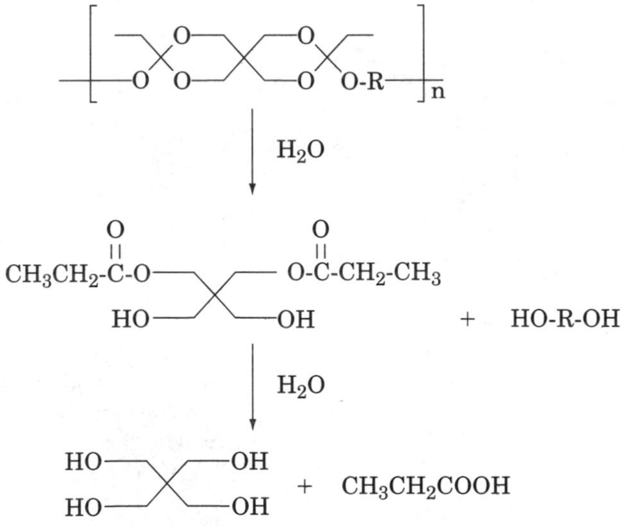

Crosslinked Polymer

Scheme 7.

Figure 1. Weight loss as a function of time for a polymer prepared from 3,9-dimethylene-2,4,8,10-tetraoxaspiro [5.5] undecane and 1,6-hexanediol. 0.05 M phosphate buffer, pH 7.4, 37°C.

by varying the pKa and/or concentration of the acidic excipient. Although a number of different acidic excipients have been used with poly(ortho esters) (25), good results can be achieved by using suberic acid. When long delivery rates are desired, bases such as Mg(OH)$_2$ have been used to retard polymer erosion (21).

When the hydrophobic polymer with a physically dispersed acidic excipient is placed into an aqueous environment, water diffuses into the polymer, dissolves the acidic excipient in the surface layers, and the lowered pH accelerates hydrolysis of the acid-sensitive ortho ester bonds. This process is shown schematically in Figure 2, where it has been analyzed in terms of the movement of two fronts, F_1, the movement of a hydrating front, and F_2, the movement of an erosion front (26). The ultimate behavior of a device is then determined by the relative movement of

these two fronts. If $F_1 > F_2$, the thickness of the reaction zone gradually increases, and at some time, the matrix is completely permeated by water. At that point, all ortho ester linkages hydrolyze at comparable rates and bulk hydrolysis takes place. However, if $F_1 = F_2$, then hydrolysis is confined to the surface layers and only surface hydrolysis takes place. In this latter case, rate of polymer erosion is completely determined by the rate at which water intrudes into the polymer.

Water sorption by poly(ortho esters) II has been found to be relatively small, about 0.30 to 0.75%, with a diffusion coefficient ranging from a high of 4.07×10^{-8} cm$^2 \cdot$ s^{-1} for a polymer based on 1,6-hexanediol (T_g 22°C) to a low of 2.11×10^{-8} cm$^2 \cdot$ s^{-1} for a polymer based on *trans-*

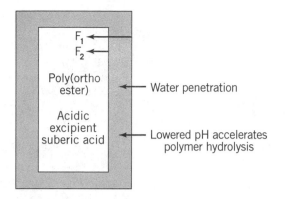

Figure 2. Erosion of a poly(ortho ester) containing dispersed suberic acid. F_1 is movement of eroding front, F_2 is movement of hydration front.

cyclohexanedimethanol (T_g 122°C) (27). Assuming a disk thickness of about 2 mm and using the lowest diffusion coefficient, the disk would be completely permeated by water in about 20 days if water penetrates only from one side of the disk and in about 10 days if water penetrates from both sides of the disk. Thus, the use of acidic excipients limits the design of surface-eroding devices to lifetimes that do not exceed 2–4 weeks, depending on the actual device size.

However, because ortho ester linkages are stable in base, very long time surface erosion is possible if the polymer is stabilized with a base that prevents hydrolysis even though the matrix is completely permeated by water. A plausible mechanism for erosion of devices that contain the base $Mg(OH)_2$ is shown in Figure 3. According to this mechanism, $Mg(OH)_2$ stabilizes the interior of the device, and erosion can only occur in the surface layers where the base has been eluted or neutralized. This is believed to occur by water intrusion into the matrix and diffusion of the slightly water-soluble $Mg(OH)_2$ out of the device where it is neutralized by the external buffer. Polymer erosion then occurs in the $Mg(OH)_2$-depleted layer (23).

Self-Catalyzed Polymers. Although the use of excipients represents a useful means of controlling rate of polymer erosion, when acidic excipients are used, diffusion of the excipient from the polymer is a serious problem that not only complicates kinetics of drug release, but more importantly, eventually leads to an excipient-depleted polymer

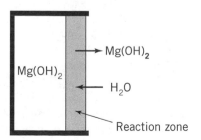

Figure 3. Water intrusion, $Mg(OH)_2$ diffusion, and erosion for one side of a bioerodible device containing dispersed $Mg(OH)_2$.

that remains in the tissues for a significant time. This residual polymer has been referred to as *ghosts*, and its formation has been mathematically modeled (28,29).

To eliminate complications inherent in using a low molecular weight excipient, the use of macromolecular excipients could be considered. However, a better approach is to incorporate into the polymer backbone a short segment that readily hydrolyzes to an acidic product that acts as the acidic excipient and catalyzes the hydrolysis of ortho ester linkages in the polymer. Then, by controlling the concentration of such a segments in the polymer, rate of erosion can be accurately controlled without complications arising from excipient diffusion (30).

We have found that a useful segment is one based on glycolic acid or lactic acid. Because the natural metabolite is L-lactic acid, this is the preferred segment. Lactic acid or glycolic acid segments can be readily incorporated into the polymer by first preparing a diol containing a hydroxyacid segment, as shown in Scheme 8, by reacting a diol with either a cyclic lactide or glycolide. By controlling stoichiometry, the diol contains either mono or dilactic acid, or mono or diglycolic acid segments.

A polymer is then prepared, as shown in Scheme 9, and by varying the relative amounts of the two diols, polymers containing varying amounts of mono or dilactic acid, or mono or diglycolic acid segments can be prepared.

Hydrolysis of a polymer containing a diglycolic acid segment proceeds, as shown in Scheme 10, where the most labile segment, the diglycolic acid segment, hydrolyzes first, liberating glycolic acid, which then catalyzes erosion of the acid-labile ortho ester linkages. A similar hydrolysis can also be written for a polymer containing dilactic acid segments.

Weight loss of a polymer prepared from *trans*-cyclohexanedimethanol and *trans*-cyclohexanedimethanol diglycolide, shown in Scheme 11, are presented in Figure 4 (30). Clearly, incorporation of diglycolic acid segments into the polymer not only results in excellent erosion control, which proceeds by close to zero-order kinetics to completion, but also allow an accurate control over erosion rates, which range from days to many months.

Figure 5 shows weight loss and changes in number average molecular weight as a function of time for a 50/50 copolymer of *trans*-cyclohexanedimethanol and *trans*-cyclohexanedimethanol diglycolide (30). The points represent weights of remaining polymer and molecular weights of the remaining polymer. There is a slight induction period of about 2 days where no weight loss nor molecular weight decrease is detected, after which the molecular weight decreases steadily until about day 20, after which it remains relatively constant at about one-half of the original value. Rate of weight loss remains relatively constant throughout the entire study carried out over 60 days.

In view of the relatively high concentration of glycolic acid dimer segments in the polymer backbone, it is clear that these segments hydrolyze gradually because rapid hydrolysis of all glycolic acid dimer segments in the polymer would result in a decrease of polymer molecular weight to a value of about 350. Thus, the linearity of weight loss and the slow changes in molecular weights are consistent with a process that occurs predominantly in the surface layers

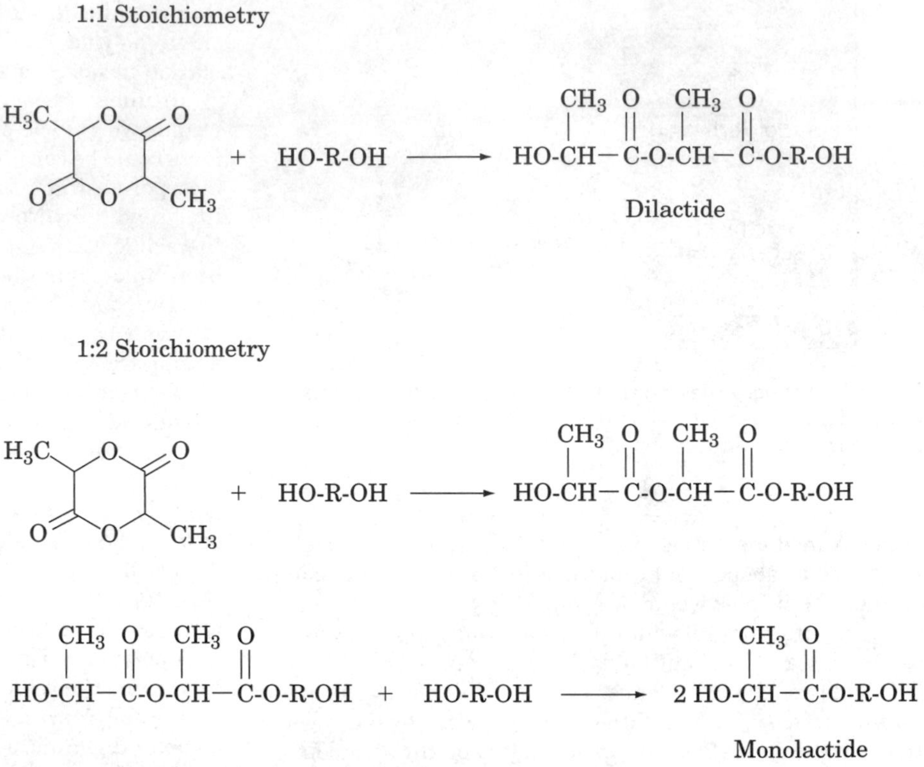

1:1 Stoichiometry

$$\text{Dilactide} + \text{HO-R-OH} \longrightarrow \underset{\text{Dilactide}}{\text{HO-CH}-\overset{O}{\underset{}{C}}\text{-O-CH}-\overset{O}{\underset{}{C}}\text{-O-R-OH}}$$

1:2 Stoichiometry

$$+ \text{HO-R-OH} \longrightarrow \text{HO-CH}-\overset{O}{\underset{}{C}}\text{-O-CH}-\overset{O}{\underset{}{C}}\text{-O-R-OH}$$

$$\text{HO-CH}-\overset{O}{\underset{}{C}}\text{-O-CH}-\overset{O}{\underset{}{C}}\text{-O-R-OH} + \text{HO-R-OH} \longrightarrow 2\ \underset{\text{Monolactide}}{\text{HO-CH}-\overset{O}{\underset{}{C}}\text{-O-R-OH}}$$

Scheme 8.

$$\text{HO-CH}-\overset{O}{\underset{}{C}}\text{-O-R-OH} + \text{HO-R-OH}$$

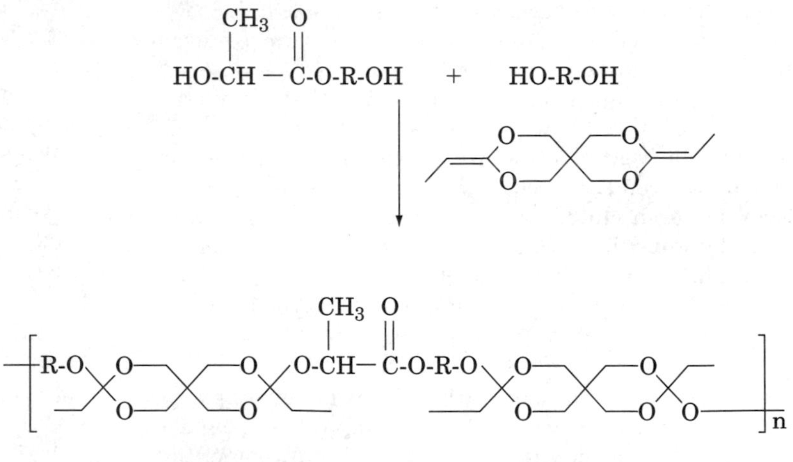

Scheme 9.

of the device with a gradual production of glycolic acid. At this point the discontinuity in the rate of molecular weight change that occurs at day 20, and details of the process are not yet fully understood. However, these preliminary results are encouraging and suggest that with this system, long-term surface erosion may perhaps be possible.

Polymer Physical Properties

The usefulness of a drug delivery system depends not only on an ability to control erosion rate and kinetics of drug release, but also depends on an ability to vary mechanical properties so that devices that have physical properties tailored to a specific application can be prepared. Poly(ortho esters) II are unique among all biodegradable polymers in that mechanical properties can be readily var-

ied by choosing appropriate diols, or mixtures of diols in their synthesis. Thus, materials can be prepared that are rigid, flexible, or low melting solids, or that at room temperature are semisolids. The semisolid materials can either be fluid enough so that they can be injected at room temperature, or at the body temperature of 37°C are so viscous that little deformation takes place, even when pressure is applied, but at temperatures below 45°C soften enough so that the warm polymer can be injected.

Polymers Without the α-Hydroxyacid Segment. Figure 6 shows glass-transition temperatures for materials prepared from 3,9-diethylidene-2,4,8,10-tetraoxaspirol[5.5]-undecane and a mixture of trans-cyclohexanedimethanol and 1,6-hexanediol (31). The data show an excellent cor-

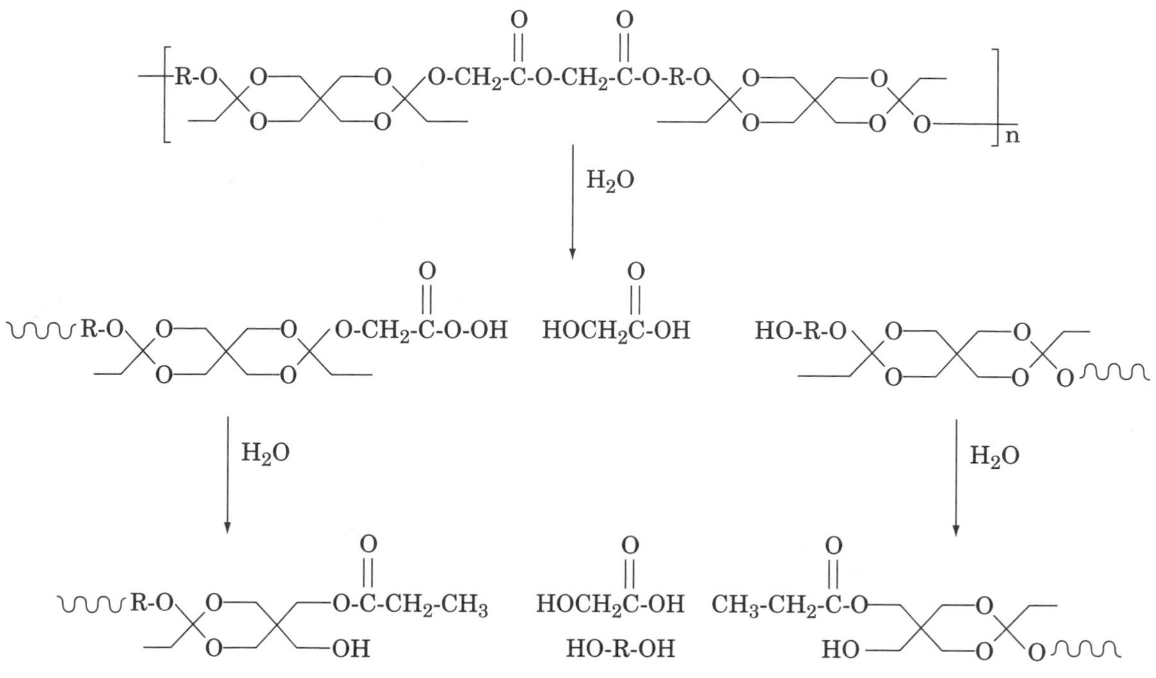

Scheme 10.

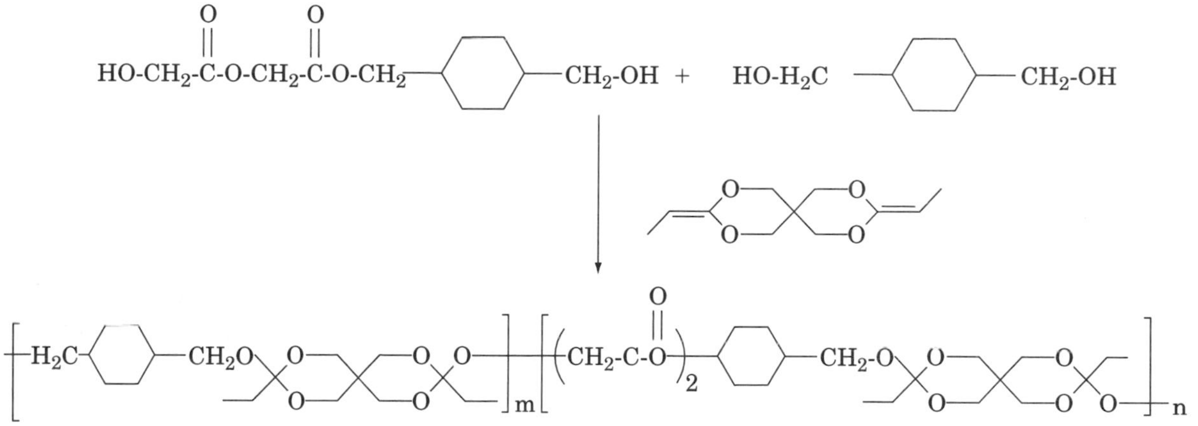

Scheme 11.

relation between mole ratios of the diols and glass-transition temperature and materials having glass-transition temperatures between 115 and 20°C can be readily prepared.

Materials having very low glass-transition temperatures can be prepared by using α,ω-diols. In Figure 7 is shown a correlation between the number of carbons in the diol and the glass-transition temperature (32).

Self-Catalyzed Polymers. The same variation in mechanical properties can also be achieved with polymers that incorporate an α-hydroxyacid segment. Depending on the desired mechanical properties, the α-hydroxyacid segment is incorporated into either the rigid or flexible diol.

Of particular interest are polymers that at room temperature are either fluid, ointment-like materials, or that

can be converted to such materials by gentle heating. Because therapeutic agents can be incorporated by a simple mixing procedure in the absence of solvents, at very low temperatures, and without an organic solvent–water interface, such materials offer significant benefits for the delivery of sensitive therapeutic agents such as peptides and proteins. Although not yet verified, such delivery devices should be able to deliver peptides and proteins without loss of activity.

Semisolid materials can be prepared by using the triethylene glycol glycolide/triethylene glycol monomer pair, shown in Scheme 12. By varying the ratio of the two components, it is possible to prepare materials that at the body temperature of 37°C are so viscous that they do not show significant flow even when moderate pressure is applied, but at temperatures no higher than about 45°C are suffi-

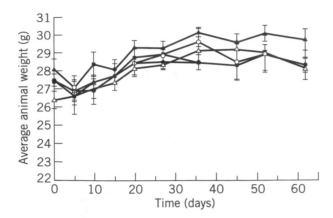

Figure 10. Effect of implantation of drug-free poly(ortho ester) matrices on animal weight. One (▲), two (○), three (△), or four (■) matrices were implanted i.p. in DBA₂ mice, and animal weights were compared with those of sham-operated control mice (●). Results are shown as mean ± S.E. *Source:* Reprinted from Ref. 36, p. 203, with permission of Elsevier Science.

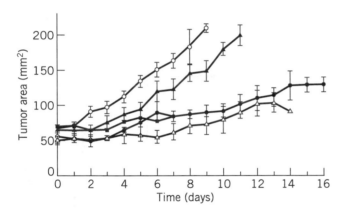

Figure 11. Effect of 5FU administration on the growth of LS174T xenografts in nude mice. Tumor size was measured as the product of two orthogonal diameters. One (▲), two (●), three (△), or four (■) matrices were implanted i.p. in DBA₂ mice, and tumor area was compared with that of sham-operated control mice (○). Results are shown as mean ± S.E. *Source:* Reprinted from Ref. 36, p. 204, with permission of Elsevier Science.

never exceeded 130 mm². In animals that received 3 implants, tumor growth was inhibited by more than 70%, and there were no overt signs of toxicity in the first days, but at day 6 they suffered substantial weight loss. Animals that received 4 implants showed very little tumor growth, but due to acute toxicity median survival was only 7 days.

These data suggest that a single dose intermediate between 260 and 580 mg/kg would be optimal for antitumor activity. However, this dose must be released at constant kinetics so as to avoid overdosing. Although the devices described here released 5-FU by excellent zero-order kinetics in vitro, we believe that in vivo 5-FU was not released at a constant rate. Additional work is in progress.

One of the current treatments of opiate addiction is to use narcotic antagonists, which generally have a chemical structure similar to those of opiates and which can pref-

erentially occupy the body's opiate receptors and thus block the opiate's euphoric effect. This makes opiate intake pleasureless and removes the addict's incentive for continuing use (37,38). A commonly used narcotic antagonist is naltrexone, but a single oral dose is only effective for about two days. Thus, long-term therapy depends on continuing oral naltrexone intake. Because discontinuing naltrexone therapy produces no withdrawal effects, significant patient motivation is required and a much improved therapy could be achieved if the decision to continue naltrexone treatment is removed from the patient. Clearly, development of an implant that could release naltrexone for at least one month is desirable.

Because naltrexone is a base with a pK_a of 8.13, a saturated aqueous solution has a pH of about 10. Thus naltrexone exerts a stabilizing effect on poly(ortho esters). For this reason, the neutral naltrexone pamoate was used. An additional benefit is that naltrexone pamoate has a water solubility of only 0.5 mg/mL, about eight times less than naltrexone, which has a water solubility of 4 mg/mL.

Although the exact therapeutically effective blood plasma concentration of naltrexone is not known with certainty, it has been estimated that it is in the range of 0.5 to 1 ng/mL (39). To achieve this blood plasma level, a minimum 3.0 mg/day delivery is required. Thus, a very high drug loading is necessary if reasonably sized devices are to be used. For this reason, a soft polymer prepared from 3,9-diethylidene-2,4,8,10-tetraoxaspiro[5.5]undecane and 1,6-hexanediol was used with a naltrexone pamoate loading of 50 wt % (40).

Figure 12 shows release of naltrexone pamoate from polymer slabs from an uncatalyzed polymer and as a function of suberic acid concentration. Good correlation between suberic acid concentration and release has been achieved. It is interesting that the uncatalyzed device released naltrexone pamoate at reasonably linear kinetics at about 1 mg/day for 50 days. The best device was one containing 1 wt % suberic acid because it released naltrexone

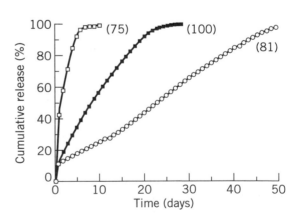

Figure 12. Cumulative release of naltrexone pamoate from polymer slabs (25 × 4 × 1.25 mm) prepared from 3,9-diethylidene-2,4,8,10-tetraoxaspiro [5.5] undecane and 1,6-hexanediol at pH 7.4 and 37°C. Numbers in parentheses indicate percent weight loss. Devices contain 50 wt % drug and varying amounts of suberic acid (SA). (□) 3 wt % SA, (■) 1 wt % SA, (○) no SA. *Source:* Reprinted from Ref. 40, p. 26, with permission of Elsevier Science.

pamoate at the desired 3 mg/day and because in this particular device drug depletion coincided with total polymer erosion.

Unfortunately, attempts to fabricate devices using a transfer molding procedures to produce rod-shaped devices for animal studies were not successful because at the temperatures and times necessary to produce devices, a naltrexone pamoate–induced polymer decomposition took place. Injection molding studies that could minimize heating times were not carried out because suitable small volume injection molding equipment was not available.

Malaria, dengue, yellow fever, and filiarisis are caused by stings of mosquitoes that introduce parasites into the body. Every year several hundred million people are infected (41). To this day, chemoprophylaxis remains the principal means of prevention, but because weekly administration of agents such as quinazoline, sulfadiazine, or pyrimethamine are necessary, poor compliance is responsible for one to two million deaths a year. Clearly, if an implant could be developed that would reduce the frequency of dosing, a significant improvement in prophylaxis could be achieved.

Pyrimethamine has been incorporated into a polymer prepared from 3,9-diethylidene-2,4,8,10-tetraoxaspiro-[5.5]undecane and a 40/60 mole ration of 1,6-hexanediol and *trans*-cyclohexanedimethanol. Disks containing 21 wt % pyrimethamine and varying amounts of suberic acid were then prepared and pyrimethamine release at pH 7.2 and 37°C investigated. Results are shown in Figure 13 (42). There is a very good correlation between amount of suberic acid, and good release kinetics have been achieved. Because pyrimethamine is a basic drug that stabilizes the polymer, fairly high amounts of suberic acid were needed.

Blood plasma levels of rabbits with implanted devices containing 5 wt % pyrimethamine are shown in Figure 14

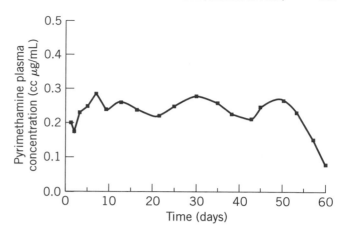

Figure 14. Plasma concentration of pyrimethamine in rabbits after administration of a disk, 25 × 3.0 mm containing 21 wt % pyrimethamine and 5 wt % suberic acid. *Source:* Reprinted from Ref. 42, p. 212, with permission of Elsevier Science.

(42). The values vary between 0.2 µg/mL and 0.3 µg/mL for 50 days after which they decline to zero, indicating that the implants have probably bioeroded, or at least have released their drug content. These results are highly encouraging because they demonstrate that constant blood plasma levels can be achieved for at least 50 days. Based on these results, development of delivery devices that could release pyrimethamine for 6 months at therapeutically useful levels should be possible.

The ability of the implants to protect mice injected with *P. berghei* is shown in Figure 15 (42). When pyrimethamine crystals were used, protection of the mice was limited to 3 weeks. However, when polymer implants with pyrimethamine and 5 wt % suberic acid were used, good chemoprophylaxis of malaria for 7–9 weeks was achieved, a very significant improvement.

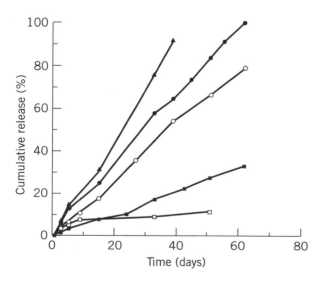

Figure 13. Release of pyrimethamine as a function of amount of incorporated suberic acid (SA). (□) no SA, (■) 1 wt % SA, (○) 3 wt % SA, (●) 5 wt % SA, (▲) 10 wt % SA. Disks, 25 × 3.0 mm. at pH 7.4 and 37°C. Pyrimethamine loading 21 wt %. *Source:* Reprinted from Ref. 42, p. 212, with permission of Elsevier Science.

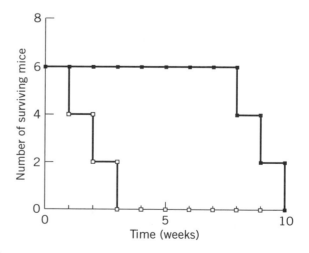

Figure 15. Mean survival time of *P. berghei* infected mice. (□) pyrimethamine base crystals, (■) disks, 25 × 3.0 mm containing 21 wt % pyrimethamine and 5 wt % suberic acid. *Source:* Reprinted from Ref. 42, p. 213, with permission of Elsevier Science.

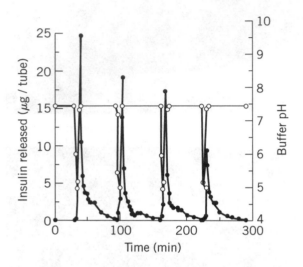

Scheme 14.

Figure 17. Release of insulin from a linear polymer prepared from 3,9-diethylidene-2,4,8,10-tetraoxaspiro [5.5] undecane and *N*-methyldiethanolamine as a function of external pH variations between pH 7.4 and 5.0 at 37°C. Buffer was continuosly perifused at a flow rate of 2 mL/min and total effluent collected at 1–10 min intervals. (○) buffer pH, (●) insulin release. *Source:* Reprinted from Ref. 46, with permission of Elsevier Science.

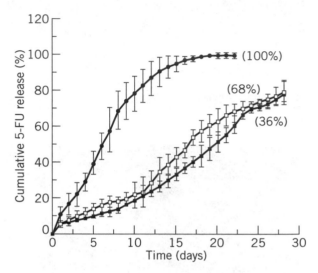

Figure 19. Cumulative release of 5-FU from a polymer prepared from 3,9-diethylidene 2,4,8,10-tetraoxaspiro [5.5] undecane and a C12 diol as a function of diol/lactide content. (■) 50 kDa, C12/5, (□) 41 kDa, C12/10, (●) 17 kDa, C12/20. Phosphate buffer, pH 7.4, 37°C. Drug loading 10 wt %. Percentage in parentheses indicate weight loss. *Source:* Reprinted from Ref. 48, with permission of Elsevier Science.

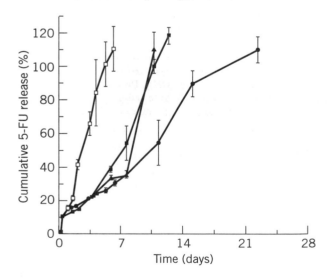

Figure 18. 5-FU release from a polymer prepared from 3,9-diethylidene-2,4,8,10-tetraoxaspiro [5.5] undecane, *trans*-cyclohexanedimethanol glycolide (tCDM/Gly), and *trans*-cyclohexanedimethanol (tCDM) as a function of diol ratios. (□) 75/25 tCDM-CDM/Gly, (■) 80/20 tCDM-tCDM/Gly, (▲) 85/15 tCDM-tCDM/Gly, (●) 90/10 tCDM-CDM/Gly. 0.05 M phosphate buffer, pH 7.4, 37°C. Drug loading 10 wt %. *Source:* Reprinted with permission from the New York Academy of Sciences.

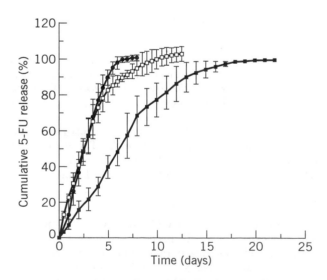

Figure 20. Cumulative release of 5-FU from a polymer prepared from 3,9-diethylidene 2,4,8,10-tetraoxaspiro [5.5] undecane and various diols as a function of diol chain length. (●) 21 kDa C8/20, (□) 31 kDa C10/20, (■) 17 kDa C12/20. Phosphate buffer, pH 7.4, 37°C. Drug loading 10 wt %. *Source:* Reprinted from Ref. 48, with permission of Elsevier Science.

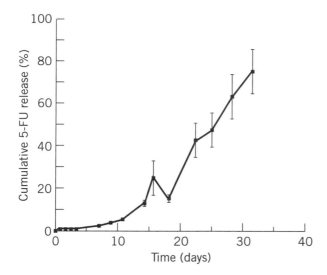

Figure 21. 5-FU release from a polymer prepared from 3,9-diethylidene 2,4,8,10-tetraoxaspiro [5.5] undecane, 50 mole % triethylene glycol, 49 mole % *n*-decanediol, and 1 mole % triethylene glycol DL-dilactide at pH 7.4 and 37°C. Drug loading 10 wt %.

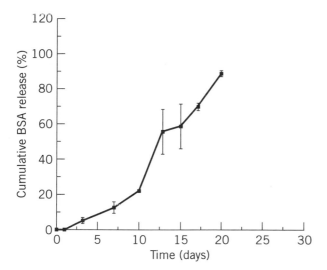

Figure 22. BSA release from a polymer prepared from 3,9-diethylidene 2,4,8,10-tetraoxaspiro [5.5] undecane, 99 mole % triethylene glycol, and 1 mole % triethylene glycol mono-DL, lactide at pH 7.4 and 37°C. Drug loading 10 wt %.

centrifugation at −5°C under an argon atmosphere. Distillation of the brownish product through a 12-inch vigreaux column at reduced pressure gives 313 g (61%) of 3,9-diethylidene 2,4,8,10-tetraoxaspiro [5.5] undecane as a colorless liquid, b.p. 82°C (0.1 torr), which crystallizes at room temperature, m.p. 30°C; characteristic IR band at 1700 cm^{-1}.

Preparation of Linear Polymers. Into a 5-L, three-necked flask equipped with an overhead stirrer, an argon inlet tube, and a condenser are placed 89.57 g (0.621 mole) of *trans*-cyclohexanedimethanol, 39.52 g (0.334 mole) of 1,6-hexanediol, and 1.8 L of distilled tetrahydrofuran. The

mixture is stirred until all solids have dissolved; then, 200 g (0.942 mole) of 3,9-diethylidene 2,4,8,10-tetraoxaspiro [5.5] undecane is added. The polymerization is initiated by the addition of 2 mL of a solution of *p*-toluenesulfonic acid (20 mg/mL) in tetrahydrofuran.

The polymerization temperature rapidly rises to the boiling point of tetrahydrofuran and then gradually decreases. Stirring is continued for about 2 h, 10 mL of triethylamine stabilizer added, and the reaction mixture then very slowly poured with vigorous stirring into about 15 gallons of methanol containing 100 mL of triethylamine. The precipitated polymer is collected by vacuum filtration and dried in a vacuum oven at 60°C for 24 h. The weight of the dried polymer is 325 g (98.8% yield).

Preparation of Cross-Linked Polymers. To a solution of 31.84 g (0.159 mole) of 3,9-diethylidene 2,4,8,10-tetraoxaspiro [5.5] undecane in 200 mL of distilled tetrahydrofuran is added 10.42 g (0.100 mole) of 2-methyl-1,4-butanediol. The solution is stirred under argon and 0.5 mL of *p*-toluenesulfonic acid solution in tetrahydrofuran (20 mg/mL) is added to initiate the reaction. After the heat of reaction has subsided, the solution is stirred until the temperature returns to ambient and then concentrated on a rotary evaporator followed by heating in a vacuum oven at 40°C to remove residual solvent.

Devices are then prepared by mixing into the prepolymer an excess of 1,2,6-hexanetriol and the desired excipients and curing the mixture in a mold at 75°C for 5 h. Best results are obtained when the mole ratio hydroxyl to ketene acetal is about 1:3.

Synthesis of Diols Containing a Glycolide Segment. The following represents a typical preparation. In a dry-box, 15.07 g (100 mmoles) of triethylene glycol and 11.06 g (100 mmoles) of glycolide were weighed into a 50 mL flask. The flask was sealed with a rubber septum and heated overnight at 180°C in an oil bath. Similar reactions were also conducted with *trans*-cyclohexanedimethanol and with 1,10-decanediol. The resulting oils were not purified and used directly in the polymerization reactions.

Polymerization. The following represents a typical preparation. Under anhydrous conditions 13.515 g (90 mmoles) of triethylene glycol and 2.663 g (10 mmoles) of the triethylene glycol monoglycolide described earlier were weighed into a 250 mL flask, and the mixture dissolved in 50 mL of tetrahydrofuran. Then 19.103 g (90 mmoles) of 3,9-diethylidene-2,4,8,10-tetraoxaspiro [5.5] undecane were added. After the exothermic reaction subsided, the solution was first concentrated on a roto-evaporator and the remaining solvent removed in a vacuum oven at 40°C.

POLY(ORTHO ESTER) III

The third family of such polymers was originally developed at SRI International (49) and is also under active development at the University of Geneva (50). It is prepared as shown in Scheme 15. The intermediate does not have to be isolated, and continuing reaction produces the final polymer.

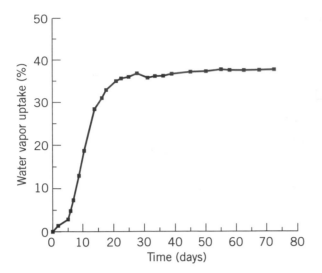

Figure 24. Water vapor uptake of a 21.5 kDa polymer prepared from a trimethyl orthoacetate and 1,2,6-hexanetriol at 80% relative humidity. *Source:* Reprinted from Ref. 53, p. 900, with permission of Elsevier Science.

Treatment of Periodontal Disease. Periodontitis is a group of dentoalveolar infections that are one of the major causes of teeth loss. These infections are caused by a pathogenic flora, established within the gingival sulcus, which later deepens to form a periodontal pocket. Treatments are based on strategies that shift the microflora within the periodontal pocket to that observed around healthy teeth and gingiva, and a widely used treatment is to mechanically remove plaque and calculus followed by local treatment with antimicrobial agents. Clearly, controlled release devices that would maintain a therapeutically effective concentration of an antimicrobial agent within the pocket

for the desired length of time would significantly improve treatment (57).

Ointment-like poly(ortho esters) III have been investigated as a tetracycline delivery device for the treatment of periodontal disease (58). In this application the ointment-like polymer with incorporated tetracycline was injected into the periodontal pocket using a blunt needle. Then if the polymer is dentoadhesive, it would reside in the periodontal pocket for 7 to 10 days, gradually releasing tetracycline. And because total erosion would take place, no removal of an expended polymer would be required.

Tetracycline Release. Figure 27 show release of tetracycline from a propionate polymer ($R = CH_3CH_2$) as a function of amount of $Mg(OH)_2$ dispersed in the polymer matrix (58). Release of tetracycline in the absence of $Mg(OH)_2$ was very rapid, but the addition of as little as 0.5 wt % $Mg(OH)_2$ resulted in a sustained release over about 10 days. Addition of 1 wt % Mg(OH)2 prolonged the release to about 25 days and addition of 2 wt % $Mg(OH)_2$ produced a release estimated to last about 75 days. In all cases drug depletion coincided with total polymer erosion so that satisfactory control over device lifetime and rate of tetracycline release should be possible.

Dentoadhesiveness. To test dentoadhesiveness, a microload cell was developed, and because the adhesiveness of human and bovine teeth are not significantly different (59,60), extracted bovine anterior teeth were used as adhesive substrates (56). It was found that for the pure polymer, the required force of detachment was 392 mN cm^{-2}. However, because the detachment occurred by cohesive failure of the polymer and not by failure of the bond between the polymer and the bovine tooth, this value was a minimal value, and the true value of the adhesive bond is very likely significantly higher.

However, this test was carried out with the neat polymer with no incorporated drug and excipient. Further, it

Scheme 18.

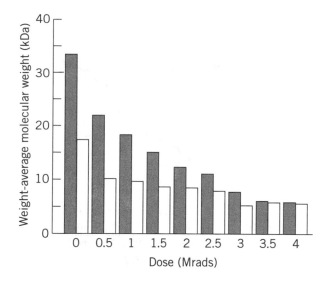

Figure 25. Influence of γ-radiation on the gel permeation chromatography average molecular weight of two different molecular weight polymers prepared from trimethyl orthoacetate and 1,2,6-hexanetriol as a function of radiation dose. (■) 33.3 kDa, (□) 17.4 kDa.

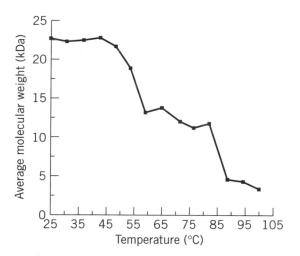

Figure 26. Gel permeation chromatography determination of the molecular weight of a polymer prepared from trimethyl orthoacetate and 1,2,6-hexanetriol after 24 hours of storage at different temperatures under anhydrous conditions ($n = 3$). *Source:* Reprinted from Ref. 53, p. 899, with permission of Elsevier Science.

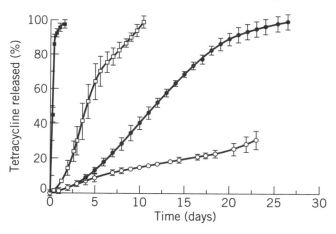

Figure 27. Cumulative release of tetracycline from a 27 kDa polymer prepared from trimethyl orthoacetate and 1,2,6-hexanetriol at pH 7.4 and 37°C as a function of $Mg(OH)_2$ content. 0.1 M phosphate buffer, flow rate 1 ml h^{-1}, drug loading 10 wt %. (○) 0%, (●) 0.5%, (□) 1.0%, (■) 2.0%. Error bars are standard deviation, $n = 3$. *Source:* Reprinted from Ref. 58, p. 316, with permission of Elsevier Science.

final formulation is also capable of strongly adhering to teeth. Thus, as judged from these in vitro studies, adequate residence time in the periodontal pocket should be possible.

Toxicology. Because there is the potential for ingestion of the polymer during treatment, acute and chronic feeding studies were carried out (61). Further, during bioerosion of the polymer, systemic absorption of hydrolysis products takes place so that acute intravenous toxicity studies using polymer hydrolysate were also carried out. All toxicological studies were carried out using adult Sprague Dawley rats using a doubly precipitated polymer that was then irradiated at 2.5 Mrad and stored in a dry-box at room temperature until use.

1. *Acute oral toxicity of intact polymer.* The intact polymer was emulsified in a vehicle consisting of 2 w/v % aqueous methyl cellulose solution with the aid of 1.6 w/v Tween 80 and administered to rats at a dose level of 3.3 g/kg. No deaths or adverse clinical signs were observed during the study, and no gross abnormalities were observed during necropsy. Thus, the polymer is nontoxic when administered as a single dose of 3.3 g/kg to rats.

2. *Chronic oral toxicity (28-day) of intact polymer.* The emulsified polymer prepared as already described was administered daily to rats at doses of 0.76, 1.64 or 3.27 g/kg for 28 days. At necropsy, no gross abnormalities were observed in the tissues or external features.

   Histopathologic examination revealed no significant microscopic findings and no target organs for poly(ortho esters) toxicity. All hematology and clinical chemistry parameters were in the normal range. Thus, the polymer is nontoxic when administered daily at a maximum oral dose of 3.3 g/kg for 4 weeks.

3. *Acute intravenous toxicity of polymer hydrolysate.* Sterile polymer was hydrolyzed by placing a known

was carried out on teeth surfaces that have not been exposed to proteins normally present in the oral environment. When the adhesion study was repeated using a formulation containing 10 wt % tetracycline and 1.0 wt % $Mg(OH)_2$ using teeth that had been exposed to dog serum (Sigma), rinsed with saline, and kept wet with saline, the detachment force decreased to 118 mN cm^{-2}. Again, as with the pure polymer, separation occurred by cohesive failure of the polymer and not between the bond between the specimen and polymer. The lower value indicates that polymer integrity has been weakened by the incorporation of tetracycline and $Mg(OH)_2$. However, it is clear that the

moles) in 500 mL of tetrahydrofuran was added dropwise over a 2-h period. The ice bath was removed and the reaction mixture stirred for 2 h at room temperature. It was then filtered to remove the pyridine HCl salt and evaporated to remove the tetrahydrofuran. The residue was dissolved in 2 L of ethyl acetate and the solution extracted with diluted aqueous HCl (2 × 300 mL), warm water (2 × 300 mL), and aqueous NaHCO₃ solution (2 × 300 mL). The ethyl acetate solution was dried over anhydrous MgSO₄, and the ethyl acetate removed on a rotoevaporator. Vacuum distillation of the residue yielded 335 g of product. Gel chromatographic analysis showed that the product contained 59% cyclohexanedimethanol monoacetate and 41% cyclohexanedimethanol diacetate. The overall yield of the monoacetate was 16.5%.

2. *4-Acetoxymethyl-1-cyclohexanecarboxaldehyde.* Under anhydrous conditions, oxalyl chloride (358 g, 2.82 moles) was dissolved in 2.5 L of methylene chloride and the solution cooled to −40°C. Dimethylsulfoxide (407 g, 5.2 moles) dissolved in 200 mL of methylene chloride was then added via a dropping funnel while the reaction mixture was vigorously stirred and the temperature maintained between −40°C and −20°C. Next, a solution of cyclohexanedimethanol monoacetate (600 g, 59% pure, 1.9 moles) in 200 mL of methylene chloride was added dropwise while the reaction temperature was kept below −20°C. After the addition of cyclohexanedimethanol monoacetate solution was completed, the reaction mixture was stirred for an additional 15 min and triethylamine (658 g, 6.5 moles) added. The cooling bath was removed and the reaction mixture stirred for 2 h. It was then extracted successively with diluted aqueous HCl, aqueous NaHCO₃, and aqueous NaCl. After drying over anhydrous MgSO₄, the methylene chloride solution was distilled under argon to remove the solvent. The residue was distilled at 80°C at 0.4 mm to give the aldehyde (248 g, 70.8% yield).

3. *4-Acetoxymethyl-1,1-cyclohexanedimethanol.* A mixture of 4-acetoxymethyl-1-cyclohexanecarboxaldehyde, (248 g, 1.46 moles), a 37 wt % formaldehyde solution (700 mL, 8.6 moles), and tetrahydrofuran (200 mL) was cooled in an ice water bath. Calcium oxide was then added in small portions while the mixture was vigorously stirred with an overhead mechanical stirrer. After the addition of CaO was completed, the ice bath was removed and the mixture stirred for 2 h. It was then evaporated to dryness and the product extracted into acetone. Evaporation of the acetone solution produced a viscous oil.

4. *1,1,4-cyclohexanetrimethanol.* The crude 4-acetoxymethyl-1,1-cyclohexanedimethanol was added 1 L of an aqueous 2N NaOH solution and the mixture heated at 100°C for 2 h. After cooling to room temperature, the reaction mixture was neutralized with aqueous HCl and extracted with methylene chloride. The aqueous solution was evaporated to dryness, and the residue extracted with acetone. After drying over anhydrous MgSO₄, the acetone solution was evaporated to dryness. Distillation of the crude product from the acetone solution at 175°C and 0.1 mm yielded a viscous liquid. Repeated trituration with methylene chloride produced a solid product (150 g, 59% yield, 98.8% purity by gel chromatography).

Polymerization. Under anhydrous conditions, 1,1,4-cyclohexanetrimethanol (3.524 g, 20 mmoles), trimethyl orthoacetate (2.403 g, 20 mmoles), *p*-toluenesulfonic acid (~3 mg), and distilled cyclohexane (80 mL) were added to a predried flask. The flask was fitted with a spinning band column and heated at 100°C under argon. Methanol was removed azeotropically at 56°C at a fast rate, and as the boiling point began to rise, the distillation rate was reduced to 4 drops/min and heating continued for 15 h. The polymer thus prepared precipitated out of cyclohexane. The powdery polymer is crystalline with a melting point (DSC) of 212°C. It is insoluble in the usual organic solvents such as methylene chloride, chloroform, ether, tetrahydrofuran, ethyl acetate, acetone, dimethylformamide, and dimethylsulfoxide.

In a similar manner, 1,1,4-cyclohexanetrimethanol (3.524 g, 20 mmoles) was allowed to react with triethyl orthopropionate (3.634 g, 20 mmoles). This reaction produced a polymer which remained in the cyclohexane solution. Precipitation into methanol yielded a polymer having a M_W of 51,000 (gel permeation chromatography using polystyrene standards) and a T_g of 67.8°C. The polymer was soluble in organic solvents with low or medium polarities such as methylene chloride, chloroform, ether, tetrahydrofuran, and ethyl acetate.

ACKNOWLEDGMENTS

This work was started in 1970, and a great number of individuals have contributed to the development of the three families of poly(ortho esters), both in the United States and in Switzerland. Although they all deserve coauthorship, their sheer number makes this impractical. The following individuals have made major contributions: Dr. Nam Suk Choi, Mr. Donald W. H. Penhale, Mr. Robert F. Helwing, Mr. Bruce K. Fritzinger, Mr. John E. Rose, Dr. Kenneth J. Himmelstein, Dr. Randall V. Sparer, Dr. Gaylen M. Zentner, Dr. Chung Shi, Dr. S. S. Bhosale, Dr. Andrea W. Chow, Dr. Kathleen V. Roskos, Dr. A. C. Chang, Dr. Yu Fu Maa, Dr. Patrick Wuthrich, Dr. Ann France Rime, Dr. Sue S. Rao, Dr. Michelle S. Taylor, Dr. Tierry Vandamme, Dr. Alain Merkli, Dr. Monica Zignani, Dr. Martina B. Sintzel Dr. S. F. Bernatches and Dr. Cyrus Tabatabay.

One of us (JH) wants to especially acknowledge the contributions of Mr. Steven Y. Ng without whose creativity and superb laboratory work this review would have been much shorter. And finally, one of the authors (JH) also wishes to thank Dr. Henry L. Gabelnick, then at the National Institutes of Health, for providing the initial funding for the development of poly(ortho ester) II. Without his patience and understanding of the difficulties in developing a useful monomer and polymer synthesis, this polymer would probably not exist today.

The following funding sources are gratefully acknowledged: NIH Contract N01-HD-7-2826, NIH Contract N01-HD-8-2905, NIH Grant DA 05726, NIH Grant GM 27164, NIH Grant DE 10461, FNSRS Grant 32.35925.92, and FNSRS Grant 32.46795.96. In addition to the government funding, funds were also provided by ComTech International and by the Finish funding agency TEKES.

BIBLIOGRAPHY

1. J. Heller, *Biomaterials* **11**, 659–665 (1990).
2. J. Heller, *Adv. Polym. Sci.* **107**, 41–92 (1993).
3. U.S. Pat. 4,079,038 (March 14, 1978), N. S. Choi and J. Heller (to ALZA Corporation).
4. U.S. Pat. 4,093,709 (June 6, 1978), N. S. Choi and J. Heller (to ALZA Corporation).
5. U.S. Pat. 4,131,648 (December 26, 1978), N.S. Choi and J. Heller (to ALZA Corporation).
6. U.S. Pat. 4,138,344 (February 6, 1979), N.S. Choi and J. Heller (to ALZA Corporation).
7. U.S. Pat. 4,180,646 (December 25, 1979), N.S. Choi and J. Heller (to ALZA Corporation).
8. L.M. Vistnes et al., *Surgery* **79**, 690–696 (1976).
9. R. C. Capozza, L. Sendelbeck, and W. J. Balkenhol, in R. J. Kostelnik, ed., *Polymeric Delivery Systems*, Gordon & Breach, New York, 1978, pp. 59–73.
10. B.B. Pharriss, V.A. Place, L. Sendelbeck, and E.E. Schmitt, *J. Reprod. Med.* **17**, 91–97 (1976).
11. E. Solheim, E.M. Pinholt, G. Bang, and E. Sudmann, *J. Neurosurg.* **76**, 275–279 (1992).
12. E. Solheim, E.M. Pinholt, G. Bang, and E. Sudmann, *J. Bone J. Surg. Am. Vol.* **74A**, 705–712 (1992).
13. E. Solheim, E.M. Pinholt, G. Bang, and E. Sudmann, *J. Biomed. Mater. Res.* **26**, 791–800 (1992).
14. E. Solheim et al., *J. Bone J. Surg. Am. Vol.* **74A**, 1456–1463 (1992).
15. E.M. Pinholt, E. Solheim, G. Bang, and E. Sudmann, *J. Oral Maxillofacial Surg.* **50**, 1300–1304 (1992).
16. B. Sudmann et al., *Acta Orthop. Scand.* **64**, 336–339 (1993).
17. M. Aaboe et al., *Clin. Oral Implant. Res.* **4**, 172–176 (1993).
18. E. Solheim et al., *J. Biomed. Mater. Res.* **29**, 1141–1146 (1995).
19. O. Bush, E. Solheim, G. Basng, and K. Tornes, *Int. J. Oral Maxillofacial Implants* **11**, 498–505 (1996).
20. S.Y. Ng, D.W.H. Penhale, and J. Heller, *Macromol. Synth.* **11**, 23–26 (1992).
21. J. Heller, B.K. Fritzinger, S.Y. Ng, and D.W.H. Penhale, *J. Controlled Release* **1**, 233–238 (1985).
22. J. Heller et al., *J. Controlled Release* **6**, 217 (1987).
23. J. Heller, in E. Chielini, P. Giusti, C. Migliaresi, and L. Nicolais, eds., *Polymers in Medicine II*, Plenum, New York, 1986, pp. 357–368.
24. R.V. Sparer, C. Shi, C.D. Ringeisen, and K.J. Himmelstein, *J. Controlled Release* **1**, 23–32 (1984).
25. C. Shi, S. Lucas, and G.M. Zentner, *J. Controlled Release* **15**, 55–63 (1991).
26. J. Heller, *J. Controlled Release* **2**, 167–177 (1985).
27. T.H. Nguyen, K.J. Himmelstein, and T. Higuchi, *Int. J. Pharm.* **25**, 1–12 (1985).
28. A.G. Thombre and K.J. Himmelstein, *AIChE J.* **31**, 759–766 (1985).
29. A. Joshi and K.J. Himmelstein, *J. Controlled Release* **15**, 95 (1991).
30. S.Y. Ng, T. Vandamme, M.S. Taylor, and J. Heller, *Macromolecules* **30**, 770–772 (1997).
31. J. Heller et al., *Contraception Delivery Syst.* **4**, 43–53 (1983).
32. J. Heller et al., in V.H.L. Lee, M. Hashida, and Y. Mizushima, eds., *Trends and Future Perspectives in Peptides and Protein Drug Delivery*, Harwood Academic Publishers, Chur, Switzerland, 1995, pp. 39–56.
33. M.B. Sintzel et al., *Biomaterials* **19**, 791–800 (1998).
34. Y.F. Maa and J. Heller, *J. Controlled Release* **13**, 11–19 (1990).
35. J. Heller et al., *J. Controlled Release* **16**, 3 (1991).
36. L.W. Seymour et al., *J. Controlled Release* **31**, 201–206 (1994).
37. G.M. Milne, Jr. and M.R. Johnson, *Annu. Rep. Med. Chem.* **11**, 23–32 (1976).
38. C.P. O'Brien, R. Greenstein, J. Ternes, and G.E. Woody, *Ann. N. Y. Acad. Sci.* **31**, 232–240 (1978).
39. C.N. Chiang, L.E. Holister, A. Kishimoto, and G. Barnett, *Clin. Pharmacol. Ther.* **36**, 704–708 (1984).
40. Y.F. Maa and J. Heller, *J. Controlled Release* **14**, 21–28 (1990).
41. J.M. Crampton, R. Galler, R.E. Sinden, and A. Crisanti, *Recherche* **259**, 1218–1227 (1993).
42. T.H. Vandamme and J. Heller, *J. Controlled Release* **36**, 209–213 (1995).
43. J. Du, B. Jasti, and R.C. Vasavada, *J. Controlled Release* **43**, 223–233 (1997).
44. J. Heller, R.V. Sparer, and G.M. Zentner, in M. Chasin and R. Langer, eds., *Biodegradable Polymers as Drug Delivery Systems*, Dekker, New York, 1990, pp. 121–160.
45. R.H. Unger, *Diabetes* **31**, 479–483 (1982).
46. J. Heller, A.C. Chang, G. Rodd, and G.M. Grodsky, *J. Controlled Release* **13**, 295–302 (1990).
47. S.Y. Ng, T. Vandamme, M.S. Taylor, and J. Heller, in A. Prokop, D. Hunkeler, and A. Cherrington, eds., *Bioartificial Organs: Science, Medicine and Technology*, New York Academy of Sciences, Vol. 831, 1997, pp. 168–178.
48. M.B. Sintzel et al., *J. Controlled Release* **55**, 213–218 (1998).
49. J. Heller, S.Y. Ng, B.K. Fritzinger, and K.V. Roskos, *Biomaterials* **11**, 235–237 (1990).
50. A. Merkli, J. Heller, C. Tabatabay, and R. Gurny, *J. Controlled Release* **29**, 105–112 (1994).
51. J. Heller, S.Y. Ng, and B.K. Fritzinger, *Macromolecules* **25**, 3362–3364 (1992).
52. P. Wuthrich et al., *J. Controlled Release* **21**, 191–200 (1992).
53. A. Merkli, J. Heller, C. Tabatabay, and R. Gurny, *Biomaterials* **17**, 897–902 (1996).
54. A.U. Daniels et al., *J. Appl. Biomater.* **5**, 51–64 (1994).
55. J. Hoborn, *J. Pharm. Technol.* **6**, 34–35 (1985).
56. A. Merkli, J. Heller, C. Tabatabay, and R. Gurny, *Pharm. Res.* **11**, 1485–1491 (1994).
57. J. Urquhart, *Drugs* **23**, 207–226 (1982).
58. K.V. Roskos et al., *Biomaterials* **16**, 313–317 (1995).
59. I. Nakamitchi, M. Iwaku, and T. Fusayama, *J. Dent. Res.* **62**, 1076–1081 (1983).
60. D.E. Caldwell and B. Johannessen, *J. Dent. Res.* **50**, 1517–1525 (1971).
61. J. Heller et al., in T. Okano, N. Ogata, J. Feijen, and S.W. Kim, eds., *Advances in Biomedical Engineering and Drug Delivery Systems*, Springer-Verlag, Tokyo, 1996, pp. 106–110.
62. A.R. Bellows and A. Johnson, *Ophthalmology* **90**, 807–813 (1983).
63. P.H. Madsen, *Acta Ophthalmol., Suppl.* **120**, 88–91 (1973).
64. D.K. Heuer, R.K. Parish, II, and M.G. Gressel, *Ophthalmology* **91**, 384–394 (1984).
65. M.M. Tahery and D.A. Lee, *J. Ocular Pharmacol.* **5**, 155–179 (1989).
66. K.S. Mallick, A.S. Hajek, and R.K. Parish, II, *Arch. Ophthalmol.* **103**, 1398–1402 (1985).

67. M.G. Gressel, R.K. Parish, II, and R. Folberg, *Ophthalmology* **91**, 378–383 (1984).

68. D.K. Heuer, R.K. Parish, II, and M.G. Gressel, *Ophthalmology* **93**, 1537–1546 (1984).

69. The Fluorouracil Filtering Surgery Group, *Am. J. Ophthalmol.* **108**, 625–635 (1989).

70. D.A. Lee, P. Hersh, D. Kersten, and S. Melamed, *Ophthalmic Surg.* **18**, 187–190 (1987).

71. S.F. Bernatchez et al., *J. Biomed. Mater. Res.* **27**, 677–681 (1993).

72. S.F. Bernatchez et al., *J. Biomed. Mater. Res.* **28**, 1037–1046 (1994).

73. C.M. Hutak and R.B. Jacaruso, in I.K. Reddy, ed., *Ocular Therapeutics and Drug Delivery*, Technomic Publishing, Basel, 1996, pp. 489–525.

74. M. Zignani et al., *J. Biomed. Mater. Res.* **39**, 277–285 (1998).

75. H.F. Smyth, Jr. et al., *Toxicol. Appl. Pharmacol.* **15**, 282–286 (1969).

See also BIODEGRADABLE POLYMERS: POLY(PHOSPHOESTER)S; BIODEGRADABLE POLYMERS: POLYANHYDRIDES; BIODEGRADABLE POLYMERS: POLYESTERS.

POLYMERIC SYSTEMS FOR GENE DELIVERY, CHITOSAN AND PINC SYSTEMS

FIONA C. MACLAUGHLIN
ALAIN P. ROLLAND
Valentis, Inc.
The Woodlands, Texas

KEY WORDS

Chitosan

Complexation

Condensation

Controlled gene delivery

DNA plasmid

Gene delivery

Gene therapy

Muscle

Nonviral gene therapy

PINCs™

Polymers

Poly(*N*-vinyl pyrrolidone)

OUTLINE

Protective Interacting Noncondensing Systems

Chitosan

Bibliography

The concept of using DNA as a predrug for the prevention, correction, or modulation of genetic and acquired diseases is becoming increasingly promising with the advent of the human genome project and the resulting greater understanding of diseases. By controlling gene expression, it is possible to act on diseases at their genetic origin, thus minimizing nonspecific side effects that conventional therapies often induce. In essence, gene therapy involves the replacement or correction of a defective gene in somatic cells and is not necessarily a permanent means of treatment. For a therapeutic gene to be effective, it must be carefully selected and cloned in a plasmid-based expression system, efficiently delivered to the target cells in sufficient copy numbers, produce sufficient amounts of the required protein over a reasonable time-frame, and furthermore, must not induce any undesirable side effects. The determinants of a gene delivery system can be described by the acronym DART: it must control distribution (D) of the plasmid, access (A) to the cell, or recognition by a cell-surface receptor (R) with intracellular trafficking, and final nuclear translocation (T). The essential components of a plasmid expression system are the gene to be expressed, coupled with necessary control sequences (ART). The protein must be produced in controlled amounts (A) and regulated in a cell- or disease-specific manner (R), with controlled timing (T). Delivery and expression elements have to be rationally designed and assembled together to address the key limiting steps in gaining access from the site of administration to the nucleus of the target cell. The question of delivery is challenging from the fact that a plasmid is a negatively charged hydrophilic macromolecule with a large hydrodynamic size (up to 200 nm); for it to be effective, it must cross a negatively charged surface, the cell membrane. Additionally, after systemic administration, other barriers include opsonization and clearance by the reticuloendothelial system (RES), and rapid degradation by extra- and intracellular nucleases. Because viruses possess sophisticated mechanisms that allow for their effective access to many cells, nonviral gene delivery systems and artificial viruslike structures have been developed using synthetic or semisynthetic materials to mimic some of the viral functions. Nonviral delivery systems have a number of advantages over viral systems. For instance, the plasmid in a nonviral delivery system rarely integrates into the host chromosome, persisting instead as an episome. Few limitations are also placed on the type and size of gene construct. The delivery systems are generally safe, effective in animal models, and can be repeatedly administered. However, it is not yet possible in most cases to meet the high transfection efficiencies demonstrated with viral vectors. Attractive targets for nonviral therapies include directly accessible tissues such as the lungs, skin, solid tumor, and muscle, as well as normal and proliferating endothelia by systemic administration.

Microinjection and calcium phosphate precipitation are well-established techniques for transferring DNA into cells in vitro but are not applicable for in vivo gene therapy. Recent methods shown to enhance transfection include electroporation (1,2), sonoporation (3), and needle-free jet injection (4). Suitable delivery systems include liposomes and cationic lipids (5,6), and cationic (7,8) and uncharged polymers (9), poly(peptides), or lipo(polypeptides) (10). A plasmid is not efficiently encapsulated within liposomes, nonetheless, detectable levels of human α-1 antitrypsin were measured in plasma after intravenous administration in mice (11). Cationic lipids and lipopolyamines were designed to overcome some of the problems associated with liposomal delivery and were shown to condense DNA into small particulates (12–14). Neutral lipids such as dioleoyl-phosphatidylethanolamine (DOPE) and cholesterol are often included in such complexes, either to stabilize the complex or affect plasmid intracellular trafficking. High levels of cellular uptake and subsequent expression have been measured in vitro (6,15) and in vivo, for example, after aerosol administration into the lung (16). The only non-viral delivery systems currently used in clinical settings are cationic lipids (17,18). Polymers that can be classified as either condensing or noncondensing polymers have been used recently with increasing success, resulting in positive gene expression in vivo (Table 1). Condensing polymers such as poly(vinyl pyridinium), hydroxylated nylons, poly-brene, polyethyleneimine, and linear and cascade poly-amidoamine dendrimers (Fig. 1) typically compact DNA via electrostatic interaction between the DNA phosphates and the positively charged groups present in the polymer. Polyamidoamine dendrimers are examples of cascade polymers that evolve from a central core by controlled chemical reaction to produce a molecule with a defined number of generations. They possess multiple terminal amine groups that have pK_a's of 6.9 and 3.9, so that at physiological pH these polymers are only partially protonated. The successful use of these polymers was first described by Haensler and Szoka who showed that in vitro transfection using a sixth-generation polymer was 1,000-fold and 100-fold higher than when using poly-L-lysine and a DOTMA-based system, respectively (7). Polyethyleneimine (PEI) was also selected on the basis that it had a large reservoir of cationic charge, because at physiological pH every sixth amine is protonated. PEI was shown to condense DNA into partic-ulates of 0.1–1 μm in size. Boussif et al. injected such complexes into the brains of newborn mice, and luciferase expression was observed in the brain fractions of the mice at 24 h (8). Transfection was also observed in adult brain; the highest expression was measured when formulations of charge ratios closest to neutral, using a 25-kDa molecular weight polymer, had been administered (19). Expression was observed up to 3 months after injection. Kabanov et al. have described the use of polyvinylpyridinium-based polymers for plasmid delivery, and proposed that, upon complexation with plasmid, hydrophobic interpolyelectro-lyte complexes form (20). Only complexes with an excess of positive charges were efficiently transfected in NIH3T3 cells. The correlation between complex charge and trans-fection efficiency was later described (21). One limitation in the use of these complexes is their instability under physiological conditions. Their use in vivo has not been described to date. Such cationic polymer-based systems can also provide the basis for introduction of other agents including endosomolytic molecules and ligands. Ligand-based systems have been synthesized in which transferrin (22–24) and asialoorosomucoid (25–26) have been chemically conjugated to DNA plasmid/poly-L-lysine complexes, and specific uptake in vitro and in vivo has been observed. Endosomolytic agents such as heat-inactivated adenoviruses or synthetic viral peptides have also been conjugated to the complexes and shown to enhance expression (27–29).

This article focuses on the noncondensing PINC℗ polymeric systems and the condensing polymer chitosan. The physical characteristics of both polymers are extremely different, and the use of these delivery systems has provided some promising results and an increased understanding of the properties required for enhanced in vivo gene transfer.

PROTECTIVE INTERACTING NONCONDENSING SYSTEMS

In skeletal muscle, the poor bioavailability of unformulated plasmid together with low and highly variable levels of expression are thought to be due to rapid degradation of plasmid by extracellular nucleases, which potentially occurs within minutes (30–33). Typically, less than 0.1% of the injected dose is taken up by muscle cells, and gene expression is limited to the myotubes located in the vicinity of the needle tract (30). By condensing the plasmid with cationic agents, such a stability problem might be overcome. However, in muscle, condensed plasmid does not diffuse easily through the extracellular matrix and gain access to the caveolae and T tubules (33). Protective interactive noncondensing polymers (PINCs), typically polyvinyl derivatives, were first reported for use as gene delivery agents in muscle by Mumper et al. (9,34). They have low toxicity, are biologically and chemically inert, and have the ability to stabilize proteins (35). PINCs are amphiphilic molecules that possess hydrophilic and hydrophobic regions (36–38). Among such PINC polymers, poly(vinylpyrrolidone) (PVP) is an example of a hydrogen-bond acceptor, and poly(vinyl alcohol) (PVA) is a hydrogen-bond donor. Potentially the hydrophilic portion interacts with DNA by Van der Waals or by hydrogen bonding, because DNA can function as either a hydrogen bond donor or acceptor. Such polymers have been shown by isothermal microtitration calorimetry, Fourier transform infrared spectroscopy, and dynamic dialysis to interact with DNA via hydrogen bonding, allowing the DNA to be maintained in a flexible form that can diffuse readily through muscle (39).

Molecular modeling showed that by placing PVP in a minimized conformation at pH 4 in the vicinity of DNA, PVP aligned itself in the major groove of the DNA model, permitting H bonds to form (Fig. 2). The vinyl portion of the PVP forms a hydrophobic shield around the DNA helix that may protect the plasmid from nuclease degradation and render the plasmid surface more hydrophobic (40). Similar hydrophobic regions were proposed by Kabanov et al. to form upon complexing pyridinium-containing polymers with plasmid (20,41). It was suggested that this enhanced hydrophobicity enabled adsorption to the cell membrane and hence facilitated uptake and gene expression. Zeta potential measurements showed that changes in the surface charge properties of the plasmid occurred upon complexation (40). In water, the zeta potential of PVP only decreased from $+8.7$ mV at pH 4 down to -5.8 mV at pH 7, indicating a small positive charge at lower pH due to the protonation and resonance between carbonyl groups of adjacent pyrrolidone monomers. Despite this slight positive charge, there was no evidence by laser light scattering that PVP condensed plasmid into particulates. The zeta potential of PVP only did not change over the pH range 4.5–7.5 in the presence of salt, supporting the fact that in a

Table 1. Polymers for Nonviral Gene Delivery

Polymer	Gene	In vitro	In vivo	Route	Species	References
Polyethyleneimine (PEI)	pCMV-*Luc*		Brain	Intracerebral	Adult rat	Abdallah et al. (19)
	Luciferase		Brain	Intracerebral	Newborn rat	Boussi et al. (8)
	Luciferase	3T3, HepG2, Cos-7, HeLa, MRC5, K562				Boussif et al. (8)
PEI/transferrin/antiCD3	Luciferase	Neuro 2A neuroblastoma, K562, Jurkat E6.1				Kircheis et al. (119)
pHPMA-pTMAEM	pCMV-β-*gal*	A2780, 293				Wolfert and Seymour (86)
pDMAEMA	pCMV-*lacZ*	Cos-7 cells				Cherng et al. (120)
pDMAEMA	pCMV-*lacZ*	Cos-7, OVCAR-3				van de Wetering et al. (121)
PEVP/PEVP-C	pBC16	*Bacillus subtilis*				Kabanov et al. (20)
	pCAT-*4XB*	NIH3T3, MDCK, Jurkat				Kabanov et al. (21)
	pRSV-CAT	NIH3T3, MDCK, Jurkat				Astafieva et al. (122)
PEVP/Pluronic P85	Luciferase	CV-1				Haensler and Szoka (7)
Dendrimers	Luciferase	Rat2				Kukowska-Latello et al. (123)
	pCAT		SCCVII tumor	Intratumoral	Mice	R. J. Mumper et al. (unpublished)
						Tang et al. (124)
Fractured dendrimers	Luciferase	CV-1				Goldman et al. (125)
Hydroxylated nylons/PolyCAT57	Luciferase	Human sarcoma HT-1080				MacLaughlin et al. (84)
Chitosan	pGFP	Cos-1				Roy et al. (91)
	pSA306 CFTR	HEK293				Walsh et al. (126)
Gelatin	pSA306 CFTR	3THE	Lungs	Bronchoscopy	New Zealand rabbits	Walsh et al. (126)
	pRSVLuc	HEK 293				Truong-Le et al. (127)
PINCs (PVP)	hIGF-I		Muscle	Intramuscular	Rats	Alila et al. (45)
	hGH, hFIX		Muscle	Intramuscular	Rats	Anwer et al. (44)
	INF-α		SCCVII tumor	Intratumoral	Mice	Coleman et al. (46)
Polybrene	β-*gal*	HUVEC				Sipehia and Martucci (128)

Note: Polyethyleneimine (PEI), poly-*N*-(-2-hydroxypropyl)methacrylamide-co-poly(trimethylammonioethyl methacrylate chloride) (pHPMA-pTMAEM); poly(2-dimethylamino)ethyl methacrylate (pDMAEMA); poly(*N*-ethyl-4-pyridinium) bromide (PEVP); poly(*N*-ethyl-4-pyridinium)-co-vinyl(*N*-cetyl-4-pyridinium) bromide (PEVP-C), protective interactive noncondensing (PINCs) polymers; polyvinyl pyrrolidone (PVP).

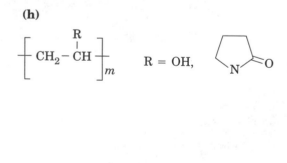

Figure 1. Structure of polymeric gene delivery systems: (**a**) poly(*N*-ethyl-4-vinylpyridinium)-covinyl(*N*-cetyl-4 pyridinium) bromide (PEVP-C); (**b**) chitosan; (**c**) hydroxylated nylons where R is linear alkylenediamines, branched alkylenediamines, arylalkylenediamines, or diamines with oxygen or nitrogen atoms in the alkylene chain; (**d**) polyethyleneimine; (**e**) polyamidoamine dendrimers; (**f**) poly(2-dimethylamino)ethyl methacrylate (pDMAEMA); (**g**) poly-*N*-(2-hydroxypropyl)methacrylamine-co-poly(trimethylammonio ethyl methacrylate chloride) (pHPMA-pTMAEM); (**h**) polyvinyl-based polymers where R is OH (polyvinyl alcohol [PVA]) or pyrrolidone (polyvinyl pyrrolidone [PVP]).

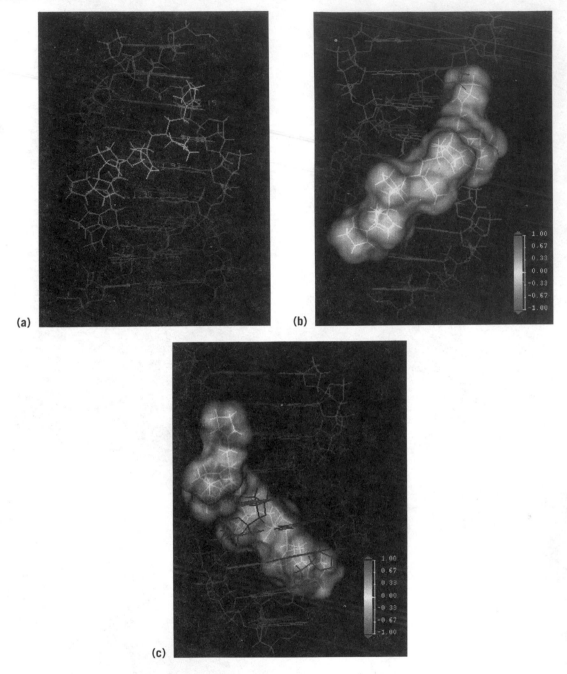

Figure 2. Molecular modeling of PVP–DNA interactions. (**a**) An oligomer of PVP (white) was minimized in the major groove of a plasmid at pH 4.0. The conformation of DNA was fixed, and the PVP was allowed to adopt a low energy conformation at pH 4.0. A number of hydrogen-bonding interactions can occur (hydrogen-bonding distances shown). (**b**) Connelly surface of PVP looking at a PVP coating of DNA. (**c**) Connelly surface of PVP looking through DNA with a coating of PVP. The surface has been colored to approximate the hydrophobic nature of the atoms, with dark gray being hydrophilic and white being more hydrophobic.

salt-containing medium, hydrophobic bonds potentially contribute to the complexation with plasmid. As increasing quantities of PVP were added to the plasmid in water, the zeta potential became increasingly neutral, indicating that the anionic phosphates were shielded. An ethidium bromide assay also indicated that PVP did not tightly condense plasmid. Upon adding increasing amounts of PVP to

preformed or postformed complexes in water, an exponential inhibition of fluorescence was observed, suggesting quenching of the fluorescence rather than inhibition of intercalation of ethidium bromide. The reduction in fluorescence was much less when the complexes were formed in water initially and then made isotonic (150–500 mM) by the addition of 5 M NaCl, and was completely abolished when the complexes were formed in HEPES buffer at pH 7.3.

As well as protecting the plasmid from nuclease degradation in vitro (39), PINCs have been shown to enhance the extent and levels of gene expression in a reproducible manner in muscle. Comparison of β-galactosidase expression in rat tibialis showed that upon administration of plasmid in saline (so-called naked DNA) (150 μg/50 μL), expression appeared to be low and localized around the needle tract, agreeing with previous studies (42,43). When plasmid was formulated with PVP in 150 mM saline (1:17 w/w), the number of fibers that expressed β-galactosidase was significantly higher (approximately 1 log), as was the distribution of expression. This could be due to increased protection against nuclease degradation as well as to hyperosmotic effects of the formulation. Variables shown to influence the extent of gene expression in muscle include PVP molecular weight and concentration, formulation pH and osmolality, and method of formulation. Maximal gene expression (typically 10-fold higher than with saline) was achieved using a 5% (w/v) polymer concentration (at 3 mg/ mL DNA). Expression levels decreased as the polymer concentration increased (39). Formulations containing 5% PVP (50 kDa) produced higher expression than those formulations containing 10-kDa PVP (39). This was thought to be due to the ability of higher molecular weight PVP to bind plasmid more efficiently, as also observed with other drugs. Higher expression was observed using formulations of pH 3.75 rather than pH 5.8 or higher, and similarly with formulations of 500 mM osmolality compared with formulations of 150 mM osmolality.

The use of poly(vinyl pyrrolidone) to deliver a muscle-specific gene medicine for long-term secretion of human growth hormone (hGH) from muscle into the systemic circulation has been reported (44). Skeletal muscle is a convenient and useful site of administration for gene therapy because some proteins expressed in muscle can be secreted into the systemic circulation. In addition, intramuscular administration of gene medicines also provides a useful approach for the treatment of local neuromuscular disorders or, alternatively, for the administration of a genetic vaccine. A plasmid with a muscle-specific promoter encoding human growth hormone was injected into the tibialis muscle of normal rats (150 μg/50 μL). In comparison with naked DNA in saline, the plasmid formulated with PVP (1:17 w/w) produced over a 10-fold increase in the levels of hGH protein detected in muscle. The plasmid expression system was shown to be muscle specific, with no detectable expression after administration in the lung or in the liver. The influence of the same formulation in hypophysectomized rats was also determined after intramuscular administration. In tibialis muscle, mRNA was detectable by RT-PCR 7 days postinjection. The levels of mRNA remained the same for 14 days and then decreased to lower levels at day 21. A statistically significant increase in growth rate was observed in those rats treated with the PVP-formulated plasmid. The inclusion of a chicken skeletal α-actin 3'-UTR in the plasmid further enhanced expression of hGH. The low levels of hGH in serum were difficult to detect, although it was evident that the expressed hGH was biologically active, because elevated levels of endogenous IGF-I and an increase in growth of the animals was observed. Difficulty in detecting levels of hGH protein may have been caused by the rapid clearance of the plasmid, its short half-life in blood, and/or the production of antibodies. For instance, it was evident that the administration of hGH plasmid resulted in production of serum hGH antibodies at day 14 that increased and plateaued at day 21 up to day 35 (Fig. 3a). Cyclosporin A was administered as an immunosuppressant once every other day for 10 days after plasmid administration (Fig. 3b). The antibody response was then totally inhibited, and increased levels of hGH mRNA were correspondingly detected. PINCs have also been used for delivering human

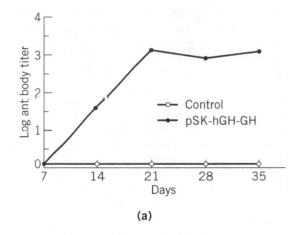

(a)

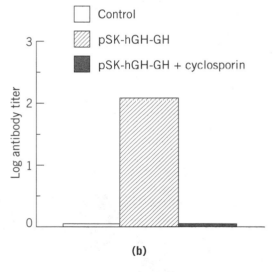

(b)

Figure 3. Production of serum anti-hGH antibodies after intramuscular administration of pSK-hGH-GH complexed with PVP. (a) Levels of anti–hGH antibodies 0, 7, 14, 21, 28, and 35 days after a single intramuscular injection of pSK-hGH-GH or control plasmid. Values are the average of two separate experiments; in each experiment the antibody titer was determined in pooled sera samples from five individual animals. (b) Effect of cyclosporin (5 mg/kg) on antibody response at day 35. Cyclosporin was given intramuscularly once every second day for 10 days (a total of five injections) after plasmid injection. The antibody titer was determined in pooled sera samples from five individual animals in each group.

factor IX gene, whose protein has a longer half-life than hGH. Detectable plasma levels of factor IX were measured at day 21 and increased up to day 29. Expression levels were 10- to 100-fold lower when this plasmid was injected in saline only (45).

An IGF-I gene medicine with reduced systemic toxicity was also developed based on a muscle-specific gene expression system formulated with a PINC polymer (45). The intent was to increase the therapeutic index of IGF-I by restricting local expression. When the human IGF-I plasmid was formulated with PVP, IGF-I protein and mRNA were measured in muscle for at least 28 days. The replacement of the skeletal α-actin 3'-UTR with an hGH 3'-UTR enhanced the secretion of IGF-I, thus improving biological activity. IGF-I plasmid, formulated with PVP, was administered to mice subjected to sciatic nerve crush injury. The formulations were administered intramuscularly every 7 days after nerve crush (E.D. Rabinovsky et al., unpublished data). Treated animals showed an increase and full recovery in gastrocnemius muscle mass, and the nerve conduction velocity in the muscle showed remarkable improvement. Expression of IGF-I plasmid peaked 7–14 days after injection and started to decrease at day 28.

Owing to the success achieved in muscle with PINC systems, such polymers have also been investigated for plasmid delivery to other solid tissues with a dense extracellular matrix, such as solid tumors (46). PINC polymers have been shown to enhance the extent and levels of expression in various mouse solid tumors as compared with naked DNA (Fig. 4).

Renca (murine renal cell carcinoma) and TS/A (differentiated mammary adenocarcinoma) tumors (10 mm^3) implanted in mice were treated using a plasmid encoding IFN-α. The tumors were harvested at 24 h, made into a single-cell suspension, and the supernatants were assayed. Tumors treated with the IFN-α/PVP formulation expressed active IFN-α; however, those that were treated with a control "empty" plasmid did not. The treatment regimen for measuring antitumor activity involved injecting the tumors eight times (four times per week), starting 7 days after challenging Balb/c mice with Renca or TS/A cells. The inhibition of tumor growth increased as the dose of administered plasmid increased (Fig. 5). In those animals implanted with Renca cells, inhibition of tumor growth was observed in 100% of the cases, with a 30% remission of tumors in those animals treated with the IFN-α/PVP formulation. When rechallenged 40–50 days later with the same cell line, all the mice that rejected the primary tumors were protected against this challenge, indicating a systemic immune response. Naïve mice were not protected. These results indicate that PINC systems can also be successfully applied to deliver expression plasmids to other target tissues such as solid tumors.

The uses of PVP as a gene delivery system have been well described, but it is necessary to determine if it is possible to improve its activity by replacing or substituting some of the polymer backbone. By substituting some of the vinyl pyrrolidone units with vinyl acetate groups, a decrease in hydrogen-bonding ability was accompanied by a decrease in gene expression. All formulations were formulated at the same pH and had similar viscosities. The structure–activity relationship (SAR) is shown in Figure 6 as the relationship between polymer structure and expression of β-galactosidase in the tibialis muscle of rats (47). Interestingly, when PVA, a hydrogen bond donor, was formulated with plasmid, higher levels of expression than with PVP were attained in skeletal muscle. A potential "interactive window of opportunity" was defined, such that by enhancing the interaction between the plasmid and the polymer, gene expression would be enhanced, but a point would be reached where the strength of interaction would

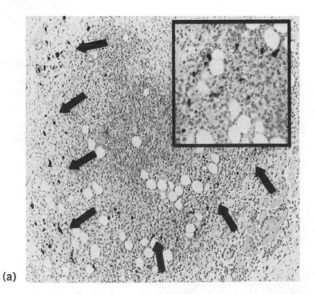
(a)

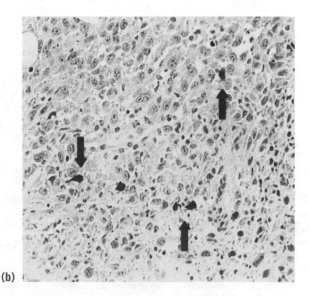
(b)

Figure 4. Immunohistochemical staining of paraffin cross sections (4 μm) for CAT in SCCVII tumors in C3HN mice, 24 h after intratumoral injection. (a) CMV-CAT (140 μg/50 μL) complexed with 3% PVA in 150 mM NaCl (4× magnification). Insert (40× magnification). (b) CMV-CAT (140 μg/50 μL) in saline (20× magnification).

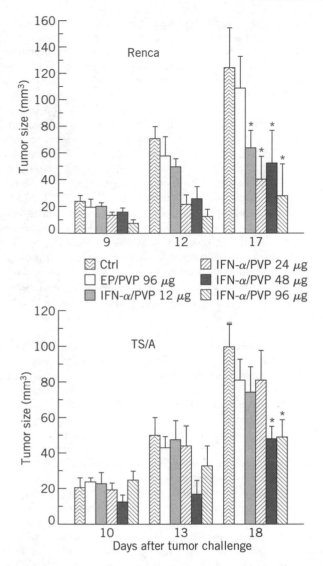

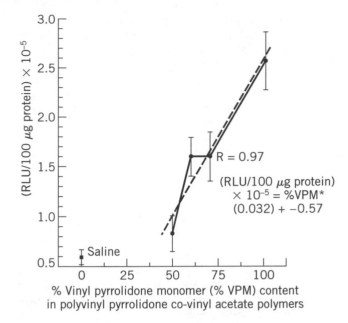

Figure 5. Induction of tumor growth inhibition following intra-tumoral injection of IFN-α/PVP. Renca and TS/A tumors were initiated by subcutaneous injection of 7×10^5 and 1×10^5, respectively, in BALB/c mice. Tumors were treated with scalar doses of IFN-α/PVP (from 12–96 μg) or empty plasmid (EP)/PVP (96 μg). Treatments started 7–8 days after tumor challenge when tumor size was approximately 10 mm^3, and repeated at 1-2-day intervals four times per week for 2 weeks (total of eight treatments). Representative experiments are shown (five mice per group). Each experiment has been reproduced twice. (*$p < 0.05$).

Figure 6. β-Galactosidase expression in rat tibialis muscle at 7 days after intramuscular injection of plasmid (150 μg/50 μL) complexed with copolymers (1:17 w/w) and formulated in 150 mM NaCl. β-Galactosidase expression is plotted as a function of the percentage vinyl pyrrolidone monomer (% VPM) content in the poly(vinyl pyrrolidone-covinyl acetate) polymers (●). The pH values (pH 3.7–4.0) of copolymer formulations and their viscosities were identical. These data are compared to β-galactosidase expression with a saline formulation at pH 6.5 (■). Results reported as mean ± S.E.M. ($n = 10$ rats).

inhibit gene expression (40,47). This SAR is being used at Valentis, Inc. (The Woodlands, Texas) to further design and synthesize novel PINCs that potentially will enhance gene expression. By enhancing the interaction between the plasmid and the polymer, it is envisaged that plasmid will remain protected from nuclease degradation but will promote more efficient gene transfer in vivo.

CHITOSAN

The concept of using chitosan and its derivatives as DNA delivery systems was introduced by Mumper et al. (9).

Chitosan is a polysaccharide composed of two subunits, D-glucosamine and N-acetyl-D-glucosamine, linked together by β(1,4) glycosidic bonds (Fig. 1). Chitosan is derived from chitin, a constituent of crustacean shells and the second most universally abundant biopolymer, next to cellulose. The potential availability of the raw material chitin therefore does not pose a problem, and over 1 billion tons of chitin is produced annually at low cost. The extraction process of chitin involves crushing the shells and removing proteins and minerals. Chitosan is formed upon deacetylation of chitin by treatment with sodium hydroxide at high temperature (48). Chitin and chitosan are copolymers: chitin is poly-N-acetylglucosamine with a small amount of deacetylation. Chitosan is the partially deacetylated derivative that is not polyglucosamine. Chitosan of 10,000–1 million Da can be readily made, with typical degrees of deacetylation in the 70–90% range. It is insoluble in water, alkalis, and organic solvents and requires the aid of select organic acids, such as acetic or formic acids, for solubilization. Other organic acids, for example, sulphuric and phosphoric acids, fail to dissolve chitosan. Due to its high molecular weight and integration of long unbranched chains, chitosan solutions are extremely viscous. Once in solution, chitosan behaves as a linear polyelectrolyte and a weak base; the amino groups present in the N-deacetylated subunits confer a highly positive charge density. A typical polyelectrolyte will exist in an extended conformation in the absence of salts due to the natural repulsion of like charged groups, in this case the amino groups. Once salt is introduced into the media, the ions neutralize the charged groups and thus reduce repulsion, which allows the polyelectrolyte to exist in a more random coil-type orientation. If too much salt is added, the polymer will precipitate out of solution by a salting-out mechanism.

Chitosan has been used as a drug delivery system (49–51), an excipient in controlled release systems (52–55), a biological membrane (56), and wound dressings (57), and for potential cell targeting (58). Chitosan microspheres have been formulated using different preparation techniques for the controlled release of drugs such as prednisolone sodium phosphate (53) and anticancer agents (52,54). Chitosan has been indicated in preventing and treating peptic ulceration while also acting as a demulcent (57). The gastric mucosa was protected by chitosan after oral administration of ethanol in rats. Also used as a thickening, suspending, and stabilizing agent (59), a chelating agent for removal of harmful metals in industrial and chemical wastes (60), and as a support for ion exchange and affinity chromatography (61), this agent appears to have extreme diversity. By coating liposomes with polymers such as chitosan, their stability can be improved (62–64). Potentially, such liposomes can be used topically for treating wounds and burns (63) and for cell targeting (62). Takeuchi et al. demonstrated that by increasing the presence of chitosan on the surface of liposomes, they became increasingly mucoadhesive in rat intestinal mucosa (62). The liposomes were loaded with insulin and administered orally in rats. Relative to uncoated liposomes, a prolonged reduction in the basal blood glucose levels was achieved (62).

Chitosan is an approved food additive in Japan and in the United States, and it is generally considered to be nontoxic (57,59,65). It is degraded by lysozymes (enzymes present in serum, saliva, and other body fluids) into oligomers, which are further hydrolyzed to N-acetyl glucosamine, a common amino acid sugar in the body used in glycoprotein synthesis or else excreted as CO_2 (66,67). Because other drug absorption enhancers have histologically damaged the nasal epithelia (68) it might be assumed that chitosan would induce similar problems. To the contrary, chitosan did not induce any damage when applied to the nasal epithelium of rats (49), and only slight toxicity was observed when administered orally to mice at doses of 18 g/kg for a 19-day period (48). Another study in mice showed a weight loss upon intraperitoneal administration of 5 mg chitosan for 12 weeks (69), but when dosed with 1 mg chitosan, a normal increase in body weight was observed. When orally treated, all mice suffered a weight loss. Richardson et al. administered radiolabeled chitosan systemically and showed accumulation within 5 min in lungs (<10 kDa) and in liver (>10 kDa), and at 60 min, both polymers were found in the liver (70). In the frog palate model, a transient decrease in the mucociliary transport velocity (MTV), measured as the time to clear graphite particles (71), and in human turbinates (51) ex vivo suggested no permanent damage to the nasal surface. Minimal epithelial damage, which may have occurred upon tissue preparation, was observed in turbinates removed from volunteers after treatment with chitosan (51). Aspden et al.

used a nasal perfusion technique in vivo to measure release of proteins that act as indicators of damage (50). Chitosan produced only minimal changes in comparison with laureth-9, a surfactant known to induce epithelial damage. In vitro toxicity of chitosan determined in erythrocytes and in a murine melanoma cell line (B16F10) displayed a concentration and salt dependency, the hydrochloride salt being most toxic (72). Chitosan was less toxic than poly-L-lysine but more toxic than DEAE-dextran. Red blood cell lysis was time and molecular weight dependent and occurred within 24 h, but not upon short-term exposure. Richardson et al. showed no toxicity of chitosan in rat red blood cells and L132 cells by the MTT (3-(4,5-dimethylthiazol 2-yl)-2,5-diphenyl tetrazolinium bromide) assay (70). Caco-2 cells were exposed to chitosan solution for 1 h, and discontinuities as well as a reduction in the number of microvilli were observed, but tight junctions appeared to be normal. Intracellular enzyme activity was not as greatly affected as with other absorption enhancers such as bile salts (65). Toxicity appears to be related to the degree of deacetylation and is higher with an increasingly positive charge density.

Chitosan has been used to enhance the absorption of poorly bioavailable drugs such as proteins and peptides across the nasal and intestinal epithelia in vivo (49,73) and in vitro (65,74). Enhanced plasma insulin levels and correspondingly reduced blood glucose levels after intranasal administration of insulin–chitosan solutions have been shown in sheep (49) and in rats (50). Chitosan is an example of a mucoadhesive agent, because at acidic pH, it becomes viscous and adhesive and binds sialic residues in mucus or on cell surfaces, due to its positive charge (49). Two explanations have been given to explain why chitosan works as an enhancing agent: the bioadhesive system is not cleared as efficiently by the mucociliary clearance system in the nose, permitting the drug to maintain a longer contact time with the nasal epithelium, and it is also thought to promote the opening of the tight junctions between cells, allowing larger molecules to pass through the membrane in a paracellular manner. A transient opening in the tight junctions between Caco-2 cells has actually been demonstrated using confocal laser scanning microscopy (75).

The amino groups on the glucosamine subunits have an intrinsic pK_a value of 6.5, and thus chitosan behaves as a polycation at acidic and neutral pH (65). It is these positively charged amino groups that make chitosan readily available for interaction with indomethacin (76), sodium hyaluronate (77), pectin and acacia polysaccharides (78), and polyacrylic acid (79). Such interactions have been well characterized in the literature. Variables shown to influence these electrostatic interactions include molecular weight, molecular size (particularly for controlled release), pH, weight and molecular ratios, and polymer concentration.

It also appears that chitosan possesses some of its own natural targeting ability. Structurally, chitosan resembles glycosaminoglycans, found in many tissues as cell membrane components (67), and is thought to mimic their behavior. It has also been shown to strongly associate with a number of mammalian and bacterial cells (80,81). Werner and Kissel have also described binding sites on ciliated cells in human nasal epithelium for *N*-acetyl-glucosamine (58). A mannose receptor (a 170-kDa glycoprotein) that has been indicated in receptor-mediated phagocytosis of certain bacteria mediated through a terminal sugar residue such as *N*-acetylglucosamine has reportedly been found on the surface of dendritic cells (82).

Chitosan is commercially available at low cost, is nontoxic, and possesses amino groups for interaction with polyanionic molecules such as plasmid. The concept of allowing DNA to interact with chitosan, in the form of either an oligonucleotide or a plasmid, was thus conceived (9,34). It was demonstrated that condensation occurred upon charge neutralization by electrostatic interaction between the positively charged amino groups present in chitosan and the negatively charged plasmid phosphates. Chitosan has been shown to stabilize calf thymus DNA to melting (83), and prevent nuclease degradation (70). Condensation of DNA plasmid by an 8-kDa chitosan was shown by transmission electron microscopy (TEM) to produce toroids and rod-shaped particles, the size and shape of which suggest a relatively tight interaction (84). Similarly shaped complexes have been observed previously upon interaction of plasmid with condensing peptides or polymers (85,86). The heat of interaction between chitosan and plasmid was measured using isothermal titration microcalorimetry, an extremely sensitive technique used to measure the heat of interaction between two species (84). Aliquots of a ligand are added to a macromolecule, and the heat changes are measured as a series of peaks. Initially, the heat flow is large, as are the number of available sites for binding, but as these sites become bound, heat flow reduces. The initial heat flow was exothermic, representing the electrostatic interaction between the plasmid and chitosan that decreased to an approximate 1:1 ($-/+$) charge ratio. An endothermic heat flow was then measured, indicating a conformational change in the complexation process, perhaps representative of the condensation phenomenon. No more heat flow changes occurred at higher charge ratios, indicating completion of the interaction. Unfortunately the shape of the heat flow profile is complex, so that information including the binding constant and enthalpy of interaction cannot readily be obtained. In terms of changes to the secondary structure of DNA, circular dichroism has shown that, upon binding chitosan oligomers, a transition from the highly hydrated B-form to the dehydrated A-form of DNA occurred (83).

A number of research groups have now prepared chitosan particulates using different methods for the delivery of DNA, such as plasmid, to endothelial (lung vasculature) or epithelial surfaces (intestine, vagina, nose, and lung) (87,88). Illum proposed that DNA could be adsorbed onto the surface of a chitosan microsphere; however, significant expression was not measured in vitro (87). Particles (10^6) formed by first condensing DNA with chitosan to an ideal size of less than 1 μm, then adsorbing the condensate onto a charged particle, were shown to be embedded deeply in the lungs only 3 h after i.v. administration to rabbits (87). Alternatively, Alexakis et al. have shown the successful encapsulation of calf thymus DNA within cross-linked chitosan membranes or within chitosan-coated alginate mi-

crospheres (89). Such microspheres were used for oral delivery in rats. Illum et al. have also described the preparation of chitosan particulates of size less than 1 μm by simple mixing of plasmid and chitosan (88), following the method previously described by Mumper et al. (9,34). The rate of mixing influenced the sizes of the complexes formed at a 1:5 (100–300 nm) or 1:10 (170–470 nm) w/w ratio. Equal in vitro transfection of the macrophage RAW 264 and rat glial tumor cell lines by such formulations (3-μg plasmid dose) was reported; however the error bars were large, and no positive control was included for comparison. Further, a 1:10 w/w complex (100 μg/100 μL) was administered into the nasal cavity of rats, and 72 h later, tissues were harvested and analyzed for chloramphenicol acetyl transferase (CAT) activity. A positive Lipofectin™ control (1:2 w/w) (61.4 μg/100 μL) produced little if any expression in the harvested tissues. In contrast, the chitosan-formulated plasmid was highly expressed in the mandibular lymph nodes, but less so in the nasal mucosa and esophageal and lung tissues.

The complex coacervation of plasmid and chitosan was demonstrated by Mao et al. (90). Complexes were formed upon mixing chitosan (0.2% w/v) with plasmid (100 μg/mL) in acetate buffer, and particulates in the size range 200–500 nm were observed by transmission electron microscopy (TEM). Such complexes demonstrated low toxicity in HEK 293 cells relative to poly-L-lysine and Lipofectin™ complexes, and they produced lower transfection than the positive Lipofectamine™ control in 293, IB3 (bronchial epithelial cells), and THE cells (human tracheal epithelial cells) (91). Such a trend in transfection was also shown in Cos-1 cells (84). In this study, complexes (10 μg/well) made with chitosan with a range of molecular weights at a 1:2 ($-/+$) charge ratio were formulated in saline and incubated with Cos-1 cells in the presence or absence of serum. Cells were harvested at 72 h. If the affinity of complexation was critical in the transfection procedure, then transfection efficiency would be influenced by complexing plasmid with different molecular weight chitosan oligomers and polymers. The results showed that chitosan molecular weight had little influence on the transfection efficiency. Maximum expression was obtained using the complex containing the 102-kDa chitosan, the level of which was 250-fold less than that achieved using the Lipofectamine™ control. In the presence of serum, the complex formulated with the 540-kDa chitosan was most readily expressed. In contrast, plasmid–chitosan "polyplexes" of charge ratios greater than 1:1.2 ($-/+$) were transfected in 293 cells with comparable efficiency to a positive control plasmid–PEI ($-/+1:5$) at 6 days (92). CAT expression was observed for 3 weeks. Interestingly, the presence of serum somewhat hindered expression of complexes bearing lower charge ratios compared with higher ratios or even PEI complexes. Köping-Höggård proposed that this occurred because the negatively charged proteins could not neutralize the highly positively charged complexes, which were also more stable to degradation by nucleases (92).

It was conceived that by altering the molecular weight of the chitosan, it might be possible to control the size of the complexes, hence formulating particles of a specific size for targeting. In a method developed by Peniston and Johnson, chitosan was chemically depolymerized by deaminative cleavage to produce chitosan oligomers of reduced chain length (93). The free aliphatic amino groups are deaminated by reaction with nitrous acid formed in situ by the presence of sodium nitrite and 6% acetic acid. A stoichiometric amount of nitrogen is produced, which can be used to measure the extent of reaction, and thus the extent of deamination. Treatment with concentrated acid at high temperature (94) or with dilute acid (95) yields oligomers with low degrees of polymerization. The former method was not particularly selective, but the oligomers made were very pure although difficult to separate and costly to process. Other methods for depolymerization employing enzymes, including chitosanase (96), wheat germ lipase (97), or papain (98), have been described. Dependent on the method of depolymerization, the level of deacetylation will vary, which subsequently influences physical, chemical, and biological properties of the oligomer. Deacetylation can be measured enzymatically (99) or chemically (100). MacLaughlin et al. (84) described the depolymerization of chitosan using the method of Peniston and Johnson (93). As the added amount of sodium nitrite increased, the molecular weight of each oligomer decreased, but the degree of deacetylation and nitrogen content did not change. These observations agreed with those previously made by Peniston and Johnson (93). To efficiently interact with DNA plasmid, it is essential that as many amino groups as possible be available, so that a high positive charge density and the ability to condense DNA can be retained. The amine content was determined using a modified ninhydrin assay (100) but showed differences between the theoretical and experimental amine content (84). This was explained by the fact that the experimental amine content of Seacure 143 (a commercially available medium-grade chitosan, Natural Biopolymer, Inc., Raymond, WA) did not match that stated by the supplier. Once depolymerized, the influence of reduced oligomer molecular weight on the size of the complexes formed with DNA was determined. A proportional decrease in the size of the complexes was observed as the molecular weight of the chitosan decreased (Fig. 7). Although it might be expected that a higher molecular weight chitosan can interact and condense plasmid more efficiently than lower molecular weight chitosan, this is outweighed by the fact that the high molecular weight chitosan has reduced solubility, which may produce an increase in particle diameter or even aggregation. Other factors such as plasmid concentration and charge ratio were also shown to influence complex size. In general, as the plasmid concentration increased, the diameter of the complex increased. Using a 32-kDa chitosan oligomer, the 1:6 (−/+) complexes were only slightly larger than the 1:2 (−/+) complexes at all plasmid concentrations; however, using a 102-kDa oligomer, the 1:6 (−/+) complexes were larger than the 1:2 (−/+) complexes, and this difference became more defined as the plasmid concentration increased.

The stability of complexes in the biological milieu is desired; however, the release of plasmid within the cell is also essential for expression to be achieved. A balance of these two characteristics needs to be maintained. Colloidal stability of the complex to salt and serum challenge was very

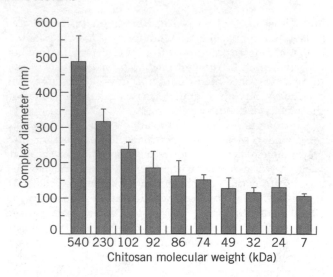

Figure 7. Factors influencing the size of chitosan–plasmid complexes. Complexes were made at 1:6 (−/+) with a plasmid concentration of 100 μg/mL.

much dependent upon the chitosan oligomer molecular weight and the charge ratio of the resultant complex (84). For example, when challenged with normal saline, the 1:0.5 (−/+) and 1:1 (−/+) complex prepared with a 7-kDa oligomer were stable, but the 1:2 (−/+) and 1:6 (−/+) complexes aggregated. The 1:2 (−/+) complex made with a 32-kDa oligomer was unstable, whereas the rest were stable. All complexes made with the 102- and 540-kDa oligomers were stable to salt challenge. The low molecular weight chitosan in positively charged complexes, which is only weakly associated with the plasmid, competes with the salt ions, but as the molecular weight of the oligomer increases, it will associate with plasmid more strongly. When challenged with a solution comprising 10% serum in normal saline, all complexes made with the 7-kDa chitosan dissociated over the 15-min challenge period. With the 32-kDa oligomer complexes, all complexes fell apart except the 1:6 (−/+) complex, which aggregated. Both the 102-kDa (Fig. 8) and the 540-kDa complexes behaved similarly to serum challenge. The 1:0.5 (−/+) and 1:1 (−/+) complexes fell apart, the 1:6 (−/+) complexes aggregated, but interestingly the 1:2 (−/+) complexes remained stable. It would appear that some component of the serum directly competes with the chitosan for association with the plasmid. Such 1:2 (−/+) complexes were also highly stable to challenge with sodium dodecyl sulfate and heparin. Other groups have observed high plasmid–chitosan complex stability. For instance, an insoluble polynucleotide–chitosan complex was formed that was highly stable in solution at 37°C for over 24 h (101). This very high stability may also become a rate-limiting step in the overall transfection process. Cos-1 cells were incubated with complexes containing fluorescently labeled plasmid, and by fluorescence microscopy, the 1:6 (−/+) complexes were observed to adhere to the cell surface in an aggregated manner, and the 1:2 (−/+) complexes adhered in a punctate manner. It was not possible to decipher the exact location of these complexes, and if they were intracellular.

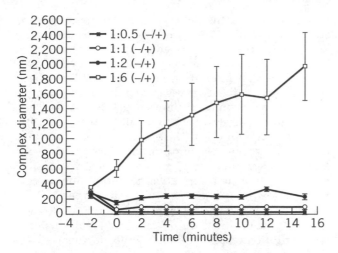

Figure 8. Stability of complexes made at a plasmid concentration of 200 μg/mL to serum challenge (10% v/v fetal bovine serum and 90% v/v normal saline). Complexes made with a 102-kDa chitosan were challenged. The complex diameter measured at −2 min is the diameter of the complex before challenge. The diameter at 0 min refers to the particle diameter measured upon immediate challenge. Where no error bands are shown, the particle distribution is considered to be broad.

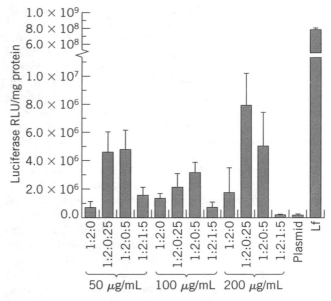

Figure 9. Transfection of Cos-1 cells with complexes containing the lipophilic endosomolytic peptide GM227.3 and chitosan (102 kDa). Complexes were made at a plasmid concentration of either 50, 100, or 200 μg/mL, with charge ratios (−/+/−) of 1:2:0, 1:2:0.25, 1:2:0.5, and 1:2:1.5. A 10-μg dose of plasmid was added to each well. The transfection levels obtained were compared with those obtained with 2.5-μg plasmid–Lipofectamine™ (Lf) (1:6 w/w).

One localization study using confocal microscopy has shown that, 1 h after transfection, particles made with fluorescently labeled plasmid and chitosan were localized in the vicinity of the cell membrane (91). In situ hybridization showed multiple copies of plasmid taken up into cells after 1 h, but after 4 h, some plasmid was observed in the cytoplasm and nucleus, while aggregates had formed outside the cells. At 24 h, most of the plasmid was observed in the nucleus. The researchers postulated that complete degradation or exocytosis of internalized plasmid may be one of the rate-limiting steps in the uptake process. In B16F10 cells, scanning electron microcopy showed that chitosan microspheres were taken into cells. The cell membrane was disrupted as the cell became laden with microspheres (72).

A reduction in the molecular weight of the chitosan did not influence expression, thus it was postulated that endosomal release might be a critical rate-limiting step (84). The influence of incorporating pH-sensitive lytic peptides in the plasmid–chitosan complex by electrostatic interactions was thus investigated. The lytic peptides GM225.1 (GLFEALLELLESLWELLLEA-OH) and GM227.3 (GLFEALEELWEAK(ε-G-dipalmitoyl)) were added to preformed plasmid–chitosan complexes and left to incubate at room temperature for 30 min. The presence of the lytic peptide was determined by zeta potential measurement and showed that, as more peptide was added, the zeta potential became electronegative. The presence of GM227.3 was shown to enhance the level of expression fourfold in Cos-1 cells for a 1:2:0.25 (−/+/−) complex formulated at a 200 μg/mL, compared with a complex containing no peptide (Fig. 9). Transfection efficiency was not improved by formulating complexes at different plasmid concentrations and thus different complex diameters. Some plasmid was taken into the cell and expressed, and the presence of the

pH-sensitive lytic peptide enhanced the levels of expression slightly. The authors postulated that a small number of DNA plasmid–chitosan complexes were endocytosed and subsequently expressed, whereas the remainder of the complexes stuck to the cell surface (as suggested by fluorescence microscopy), thus explaining the low levels of expression achieved.

A formulation containing GM225.1 in 10% lactose (1:6:0.5 −/+/−) (100 μg/mL) was subsequently administered in the upper small intestines or the colons of female New Zealand white rabbits, and higher levels of expression were measured at 72 h compared with naked DNA or a plasmid–DOTMA:DOPE (1:3 −/+) formulation (84). This is in contrast with the results obtained in vitro where the lipid formulation gave higher levels of expression than the chitosan–lytic peptide formulation. When treated in the upper small intestine with the chitosan–lytic peptide formulation, all animals showed expression in at least two of the four tissues examined (Peyer's patches, enterocytes, colon, and mesenteric lymph nodes). CAT expression in the colon was not observed. When dosed in the colon, only two of the four animals expressed CAT in the colon, but three out of four animals expressed CAT in the mesenteric lymph nodes. Naked DNA was not expressed after administration via either route. MacLaughlin et al. also reported no expression after dosing via the intranasal, intramuscular, or subcutaneous routes (84). Koping-Hoggard et al. administered 1:3 (−/+) complexes via the trachea and lungs (102). Gene expression of formulated plasmids descended in the following order: PEI > chitosan > naked plasmid. Interestingly, after nasal administration, unformulated plasmid produced the highest expression; however, orally administered plasmid–chitosan complexes were expressed more than unformulated plasmid. This data suggests that along with the fact that chitosan is an immunostimulant, it can be used as a potential carrier for oral nucleic acid–based vaccines. For example, upon rejection of chitosan a humoral response has been demonstrated in mice (103). Upon infection with Sendai virus, interferon levels were enhanced 1 day following infection, after treating with chitosan 1 day prior to infection (57). Chitosan was shown to activate a nonspecific immune response by stimulating the cell-killing abilities of peritoneal macrophages and NK cells. The mode of action for the stimulation of the immune response by chitosan was by enhancing production of lymphokines by NK and T helper cells, in response to stimulation by activated peritoneal macrophages but not spleen cells (57). Shibata et al. showed that intravenously injected chitin particles (1–10 μm) prime alveolar macrophages within 3 days, probably due to the production of interferon γ (IFN-γ), but neither soluble chitin nor chitosan induced an effect (104). Neither T nor B lymphocytes were involved. Chitosan was also shown to stimulate IgM production within 48 h in vitro in human lymphocytes, but did not promote the production of IgA or IgG (105). Deacetylated chitin (30% and 70%) was shown to induce antibody formation as well as cell-mediated immunity in guinea pigs and mice at 28 days (106). Roy et al. described how chitosan could be used as a delivery system for a DNA-based vaccine expressing a peanut antigen (107). The different dosing regimens were not described in detail. IgG (4 and 6 weeks) and IgA (3 and 4 weeks) responses were measured in those mice that were administered the formulations and then boosted. A weak antibody but no cellular immune responses were measured. When sensitized mice were challenged with the antigen, a delay in anaphylaxis and response was apparent. R.J. Mumper et al. (personal communication, 1998) measured the humoral response to expressed β-galactosidase following administration of plasmid/chitosan complexes in mice, 28 days after initial administration. Animals were boosted at day 14. Higher quantities of antigen-specific IgG were determined in sera with the plasmid–chitosan complex than with DNA plasmid alone. No cellular or mucosal effects were determined in this study.

The properties of the plasmid–chitosan complexes are intriguing thus far; however, they still have the potential for improvement. Fortunately, chitosan is an extremely versatile macromolecule possessing amino and hydroxy groups that can readily be modified to produce a molecule with improved properties, yet still retaining basic physical characteristics. For example, a new surface effective in reducing protein adsorption, platelet adherence, and activation was made by permanently immobilizing methoxy-poly(ethylene glycol) sulfonate on a chitosan surface by polyelectrolyte interaction (108). Esters of amino acids were conjugated to chitosan via an intermediate glyoxylic acid–substituted chitosan. The removal of heavy metal ions was enhanced independently of the amino acid sequence (109). Krysteva et al. covalently conjugated enzymes by oxidizing the amino group and treating with urea and formaldehyde (110). By derivatizing the amino group with a highly positively charged group, the potential of chitosan for anion exchange was demonstrated. Schatzlein et al. described an interesting new biocompatible delivery system where unilamellar vesicles formed upon mixing acylated glycol chitosan in the presence of cholesterol. These vesicles were loaded with a hydrophilic water-soluble drug such as bleomycin (111). These micelles remained stable for 28 days at room temperature, and over 24 h in plasma. Due to the low solubility of chitosan at neutral intestinal pH values, a soluble derivative, trimethylchitosan chloride, was synthesized and shown to enhance permeability of intestinal layers at neutral pH values relative to chitosan (112) and in vitro in Caco-2 cells (113). A higher degree of substitution results in higher levels of transport. Enhanced uptake of hydrophilic drugs was observed in rats after nasal or rectal administration of the N-trimethyl chitosan chloride formulation at pH 7.4 in comparison with chitosan. The chitosan backbone has also been grafted with pluronics (114). Hofmann et al. conjugated Pluronic L122 polyol to chitosan by activating the OH group of the polyol and interacting it with the amino groups of chitosan at different pH values (114). Not surprisingly, the interaction was more efficient at higher pH values, but chitosan is not soluble at pH >7. The reaction still occurred with somewhat reduced efficiency at pH 6. The polymer gelled on increasing the temperature from 4°C to 37°C, probably by physical cross-linking of the hydrophobic polypropylene oxide groups and the chitosan backbone. In the future, it might be possible to evaluate controlled release of plasmid from that type of gel, because plasmid can interact with cationically charged chitosan (115). Chitosan has also been modified with deoxycholic acid to increase its hydrophobicity (116), and the formation of stable complexes with plasmid was indicated by agarose gel electrophoresis. No evidence of colloidal stability was described.

As well as modifying chitosan to improve its properties, a ligand such as transferrin or asialoorosomucoid, or saccharide residues such as galactose can be conjugated to exploit receptor-mediated endocytosis. An N,N,N,-trimethyl-chitosan–galactose conjugate was synthesized (117), and the ability to form polyelectrolyte complexes with plasmid was determined. The aminochitosan functionality was protected with a trimethyl group; the CH_2OH group was derivatized with monochloroacetic acid and was mixed with a galactose residue overnight in vitro. Toxicity of the plasmid complexes was similar to DEAE-dextran. Chitosan nanospheres derivatized with transferrin or mannose-6-phosphate using succinimidyl chemistry have also been prepared (118). Interestingly, in HEK293 cells (2-μg plasmid dose) the presence of either targeting ligand did not significantly enhance transfection relative to plain nanospheres, although transfection was still at least 10-fold less than with the positive Lipofectamine® control. The transferrin conjugates were further derivatized with polyethylene glycol (PEG), and the excess hydrophilicity did not appear to inhibit transfection efficiency in any way. These PEGylated transferrin particles remained stable for 1 month in solution, as did the plain nanospheres and the PEGylated transferrin particles after lyophilization.

So far, the results using chitosan to produce gene medicines or gene-based vaccines appear promising. Many of the ideal characteristics of a gene delivery system are provided. Chitosan is readily available, cost-effective, and relatively nontoxic. Complexes of controllable sizes and high colloidal stability can be readily formulated, that have the potential for further modification for more specific cell targeting. The high stability and low expression achieved in vivo suggest that uptake and/or decomplexation, but to a lesser extent endosomal release, may be critical rate-limiting steps. These issues will have to be addressed to optimize that type of polymeric delivery system.

Potentially, gene therapy offers a useful and efficient option for preventing, correcting, or modulating diseases that typically have no other methods of treatment. In order to design and produce an ideal delivery system, the uptake and fate of the plasmid and barriers to expression need to be further understood. The ideal nonviral delivery system should produce controllable and reliable levels of protein upon in vivo administration and have minimal side effects. The polymers described here offer potential as gene delivery systems, but they still present some limitations. Future goals must involve identifying the location of the gene and controlling levels of expression upon delivery. It is understood that each disease and gene will require a rationally designed delivery and expression system enabling targeting of the gene, yet retaining plasmid functionality.

BIBLIOGRAPHY

1. T. Suzuki et al., *FEBS Lett.* **425**, 436–440 (1998).
2. M.-P. Rols et al., *Nat. Biotechnol.* **16**, 168–171 (1998).
3. J.A. Wyber, J. Andrews, and A. D'Emanuele, *Pharm. Res.* **14**(6), 750–756 (1997).
4. S.A. Johnston and D.C. Tang, *Methods Cell Biol.* **43**(A), 353–365 (1994).
5. P.L. Felgner et al., *Proc. Natl. Acad. Sci. U.S.A.* **84**, 7413–7417 (1987).
6. L. Vitiello, A. Chonn, J.D. Wasserman, and R.G. Whorton, *Transfus. Sci.* **17**(1), 63–69 (1996).
7. J. Haensler and F.C. Szoka, Jr., *Bioconjugate Chem.* **4**, 372–379 (1993).
8. O. Boussif et al., *Proc. Natl. Acad. Sci. U.S.A.* **92**, 7297–7301 (1995).
9. R.J. Mumper, J. Wang, J.M. Classpell, and A.P. Rolland, *Proc. Int. Symp. Controlled Release Bioact. Mater.* **22**, 178 (1995).
10. V. Escriou et al., *Biochim. Biophys. Acta* **1368**, 276–288 (1998).
11. S.F. Alino et al., *Biochem. Biophys. Res. Commun.* **204**, 1023–1030 (1994).
12. E. Tomlinson and A. Rolland, *J. Controlled Release* **39**, 357 (1996).
13. P.L. Felgner et al., *Ann. N. Y. Acad. Sci.* **772**, 126–139 (1995).
14. B. Sternberg, F.L. Sorgi, and L. Huang, *FEBS Lett.* **356**(2–3), 361–366 (1994).
15. P. Felgner, *Adv. Drug Delivery Rev.* **5**, 163–187 (1990).
16. R. Stribling et al., *Proc. Natl. Acad. Sci. U.S.A.* **89**, 11277–11281 (1992).
17. G.J. Nabel et al., *Proc. Natl. Acad. Sci. U.S.A.* **90**, 11307–11311 (1993).
18. N.J. Caplen et al., *Gene Ther.* **1**(2), 139–147 (1994).
19. B. Abdallah et al., *Hum. Gene Ther.* **7**, 1947–1954 (1996).
20. A.V. Kabanov et al., *Biopolymers* **31**, 1437–1443 (1991).
21. A.V. Kabanov et al., *Bioconjugate Chem.* **4**, 448–454 (1993).
22. E. Wagner et al., *Proc. Natl. Acad. Sci. U.S.A.* **87**, 3410–3414 (1990).
23. E. Wagner et al., *Bioconjugate Chem.* **2**, 226–231 (1991).
24. M. Zenke et al., *Proc. Natl. Acad. Sci. U.S.A.* **87**, 3655–3659 (1990).
25. C.H. Wu and G.Y. Wu, *J. Biol. Chem.* **262**(10), 4429–4432 (1987).
26. G.Y. Wu and C.H. Wu, *J. Biol. Chem.* **263**(29), 14621–14624 (1988).
27. E. Wagner et al., *Proc. Natl. Acad. Sci. U.S.A.* **89**, 7934–7938 (1992).
28. E. Wagner et al., *Proc. Natl. Acad. Sci. U.S.A.* **89**, 6099–6103 (1992).
29. D.T. Curiel, S. Agrawal, E. Wagner, and M. Cotton, *Proc. Natl. Acad. Sci. U.S.A.* **88**, 8850–8854 (1991).
30. M. Manthorpe et al., *Hum. Gene Ther.* **4**, 419–431 (1993).
31. S. Jiao et al., *Hum. Gene Ther.* **3**, 21–33 (1992).
32. M.Y. Levy, L.G. Barron, K.B. Meyer, and F.C. Szoka, *Gene Ther.* **3**, 201–211 (1996).
33. J.A. Wolff et al., *J. Cell Sci.* **103**, 1249–1259 (1992).
34. R.J. Mumper et al., *Pharm. Res.* **12**, 80 (1995).
35. U.K. Pat. WO 97 04122 (February 6, 1997) J.M. Lee, N.S. Magnuson, G. An, and R. Reeves (to Washington State University Research Foundation).
36. T. Hosono, S. Tsuchiya, and H. Matsumaru, *J. Pharm. Sci.* **69**(7), 824–826 (1980).
37. D. Horn and W. Ditter, *J. Pharm. Sci.* **71**(2), 1021–1026 (1982).
38. T.L. Lebedeva, V.E. Igonin, M.M. Feldstein, and N.A. Plate, *Proc. Int. Symp. Controlled Release Bioact. Mater.* **24**, 447 (1997).
39. R.J. Mumper et al., *Pharm. Res.* **13**, 701–709 (1996).
40. R.J. Mumper et al., *J. Controlled Release* **52**, 191–203 (1998).
41. A.V. Kabanov and V.A. Kabanov, *Bioconjugate Chem.* **6**, 7–20 (1995).
42. H.L. Davis et al., *Hum. Gene Ther.* **4**, 733–740 (1993).
43. R.A. Winegar et al., *Hum. Gene Ther.* **7**, 2185–2194 (1996).
44. K. Anwer et al., *Hum. Gene Ther.* **9**, 659–670 (1998).
45. H. Alila et al., *Hum. Gene Ther.* **8**, 1785–1795 (1997).
46. M. Coleman et al., *Hum. Gene Ther.* **9**, 2223–2230 (1998).
47. R.J. Mumper and A.P. Rolland, *Adv. Drug Delivery Rev.* **30**, 151–172 (1998).
48. R.A.A. Muzzarelli, *Natural Chelating Polymers: Alginic Acid, Chitin and Chitosan*, Pergamon, Oxford, 1973, pp. 144–176.
49. L. Illum, N.F. Farraj, and S.S. Davis, *Pharm. Res.* **11**, 1186–1189 (1994).
50. T.J. Aspden, L. Illum, and O. Skaugrud, *Eur. J. Pharm. Sci.* **4**, 23–31 (1996).
51. T.J. Aspden et al., *J. Pharm. Sci.* **86**(4), 509–513 (1997).
52. Y.M. Wang, H. Sato, I. Adachi, and I. Horikoshi, *J. Pharm. Sci.* **85**(11), 1204–1210 (1996).
53. A. Berthold, K. Cremer, and J. Kreuter, *J. Controlled Release* **39**, 17–25 (1996).
54. S.R. Jameela and A. Jayakrishnan, *Biomaterials* **16**, 769–775 (1995).
55. I. Henriksen, O. Skaugrud, and J. Karlsen, *Int. J. Pharm.* **98**, 181–188 (1993).

56. S. Hirano, K. Tobetto, M. Hasegawa, and N. Matsuda, *J. Biomed. Mater. Res.* **14**, 477–486 (1980).

57. R. Muzzarelli, in S. Dumitriu, ed., *Polymeric Biomaterials*, Dekker, New York, 1994, pp. 179–197.

58. U. Werner and T. Kissel, *Pharm. Res.* **13**, 978–988 (1996).

59. E.S. Lower, *Manuf. Chem.* **55**(10), 47–52 (1984).

60. DE Pat. 19544455, (June 5, 1997), P. Horlacher and J. Schad (to Henkel KGAA).

61. JP Pat. 62-288601 (December 15, 1987), A. Seiichi (to Japanese Agency of Industrial Science and Technology).

62. H. Takeuchi et al., *Pharm. Res.* **13**(6), 896–901 (1996).

63. I. Henriksen, G. Smistad, and J. Karlsen, *Int. J. Pharm.* **101**, 227–236 (1994).

64. I. Henriksen et al., *Int. J. Pharm.* **146**, 193–204 (1997).

65. N.G.M. Schipper, K.M. Vårum, and P. Artursson, *Pharm. Res.* **13**, 1686–1692 (1996).

66. K.M. Vårum, M.M. Myhr, R.J.N. Hjerde, and O. Smidsrød, *Carbohydr. Res.* **299**, 99–101 (1997).

67. T. Chandy and C.P. Sharma, *Biomater. Artif. Cells Artif. Organs* **18**(1), 1–24 (1990).

68. S.G. Chandler, L. Illum, and N.W. Thomas, *Int. J. Pharm.* **76**, 61–70 (1991).

69. Y. Tanaka et al., *Biomaterials* **18**, 591–595 (1997).

70. S. Richardson, H.V.J. Kolbe, and R. Duncan, *Proc. Int. Symp. Controlled Release Bioact. Mater.* **24**, 649 (1997).

71. T.J. Aspden et al., *Int. J. Pharm.* **122**, 69–78 (1995).

72. B. Carreño-Gómez and R. Duncan, *Int. J. Pharm.* **148**, 231–240 (1997).

73. H.L. Luessen et al., *Pharm. Res.* **13**(11), 1668–1672 (1996).

74. P. Artursson, T. Lindmark, S.S. Davis, and L. Illum, *Pharm. Res.* **11**, 1358–1361 (1994).

75. G. Borchard et al., *J. Controlled Release* **39**, 131–138 (1996).

76. T. Imai, S. Shiraishi, H. Saitô, and M. Otagiri, *Int. J. Pharm.* **67**, 11–20 (1991).

77. K. Takayama et al., *Chem. Pharm. Bull.* **38**(7), 1993–1997 (1990).

78. M.M. Meshali and K.E. Gabr, *Int. J. Pharm.* **89**, 177–181 (1993).

79. V. Chavasit and J.A. Torres, *Biotechnol. Prog.* **6**, 2–6 (1990).

80. K.D. Vorlop and J. Klein, *Methods Enzymol.* **135**, 259–268 (1987).

81. T. Ouchi and T. Banba, *Trans. Soc. Biomater.* **11**, 232 (1988).

82. Y. Shibata, W.J. Metzger, and Q.N. Myrvik, *J. Immunol.* **159**, 2462–2467 (1997).

83. T. Motomura and Y. Aoyama, *Bull. Chem. Soc. Jpn.* **65**, 1755–1760 (1992).

84. F.C. MacLaughlin et al., *J. Controlled Release* **56**, 259–272 (1998).

85. Y.Y. Vengerov and T.E. Semenov, *Electron Microsc. Rev.* **5**, 193–207 (1992).

86. M.A. Wolfert and L.W. Seymour, *Gene Ther.* **3**(3), 269–273 (1996).

87. U.K. Pat. WO 98/01161 (January 15, 1998), L. Illum (to Danbiosyst U.K. Ltd.).

88. U.K. Pat. WO 98/01160 (January 15, 1998), L. Illum (to Danbiosyst U.K. Ltd.).

89. T. Alexakis et al., *Appl. Biochem. Biotechnol.* **50**, 93–106 (1995).

90. H.-Q. Mao et al., *Proc. Int. Symp. Controlled Release Bioact. Mater.* **23**, 401 (1996).

91. K. Roy, H.-Q. Mao, and K.W. Leong, *Proc. Int. Symp. Controlled Release Bioact. Mater.* **25**, 673 (1997).

92. M. Köping-Höggård, M. Nilsson, K. Edwards, and P. Artursson, *Proc. Int. Symp. Controlled Release Bioact. Mater.,* **25**, 368 (1998).

93. U.S. Pat. 3,922,260 (November 25, 1975), Q.P. Peniston and E.L. Johnson.

94. A. Domard and N. Cartier, *Int. J. Biol. Macromol.* **11**, 297–302 (1989).

95. G.G. Allan and M. Peyron, *Carbohydr. Res.* **277**, 257–272 (1995).

96. RU Pat. 2073016 (February 10, 1997) V.P. Varlamov, K.O. Stoyachenko, and M.V. Budanov.

97. R.A.A. Muzzarelli, W. Xia, M. Tomasetti, and P. Ilari, *Enzyme Microb. Technol.* **17**, 541–545 (1995).

98. R.A.A. Muzzarelli, M. Tomasetti, and P. Ilari, *Enzyme Microb. Technol.* **16**(2), 110–114 (1994).

99. F. Nanjo, R. Katsumi, and K. Sakai, *Anal. Biochem.* **193**, 164–167 (1991).

100. E. Curotto and F. Aros, *Anal. Biochem.* **211**, 240–241 (1993).

101. H. Hayatsu, T. Kubo, Y. Tanaka, and K. Negeishi, *Chem. Pharm. Bull.* **45**(8), 1363–1368 (1997).

102. M. Köping-Höggård et al., *Am. Assoc. Pharm. Sci.* **1**, S278 (1998).

103. J. Knapczyk et al., *Archives Immunol. Ther. Exp.* (Warsz) **1–2**, 127–132 (1991).

104. Y. Shibata, L.A. Foster, W.J. Metzger, and Q.N. Myrvik, *Infect. Immun.* **65**(5), 1734–1751 (1997).

105. M. Maeda, H. Murakami, H. Ohta, and M. Tajima, *Biosci. Biotech. Biochem.* **56**(3), 427–431 (1992).

106. K. Nishimura et al., *Vaccine* **3**, 379–384 (1985).

107. K. Roy et al., *Proc. Int. Symp. Controlled Release Bioact. Mater.* **25**, 348 (1998).

108. M.M. Amiji, *Carbohydr. Polym.* **32**(3–4), 193–199 (1997).

109. H. Ishii, H. Minegishi, B. Lavitpichayawong, and T. Mitani, *Int. J. Biol. Macromol.* **17**(1), 21–23 (1995).

110. M. Krysteva, E. Naidenova, A. Andreeva, and N.D. Huyen, *Biotech. and Biotech. Eq.* **8**, 66–70 (1994).

111. A.G. Schatzlein et al., *Proc. Int. Symp. Controlled Release Bioact. Mater.* **25**, 435 (1998).

112. M. Thanou et al., *Proc. Int. Symp. Controlled Release Bioact. Mater.* **25**, 14 (1998).

113. A.F. Kotzé et al., *Pharm. Res.* **14**(9), 1197–1202 (1997).

114. A.S. Hoffman et al., *Proc. Int. Symp. Controlled Release Bioact. Mater.* **24**, 563 (1997).

115. R. Dagani, *Chem. Eng. News*, 26–37 (June 1997).

116. K.Y. Lee et al., *Proc. Int. Symp. Controlled Release Bioact. Mater.* **24**, 651 (1997).

117. J. Murata, Y. Ohya, and T. Ouchi, *Carbohydr. Polym.* **29**(1), 69–74 (1996).

118. H.-Q. Mao et al., *Proc. Int. Symp. Controlled Release Bioact. Mater.* **24**, 671 (1997).

119. R. Kircheis et al., *Gene Ther.* **4**, 409–418 (1997).

120. J.-Y. Cherng et al., *Pharm. Res.* **13**(7), 1038–1042 (1996).

121. P. van de Wetering, J.-Y. Cherng, H. Talsma, and W.E. Hennink, *J. Controlled Release* **49**, 59–69 (1997).

122. I. Astafieva et al., *FEBS Lett.* **389**, 278–280 (1996).

123. J.F. Kukowska-Latello et al., *Proc. Natl. Acad. Sci. U.S.A.* **93**, 4897–4902 (1996).

124. M.X. Tang, C.T. Redemenn, and F.C. Szoka, *Bioconjugate Chem.* **7**, 703–714 (1996).

125. C.K. Goldman et al., *Nat. Biotechnol.* **15**, 462–466 (1997).

126. S.M. Walsh et al., *Proc. Int. Symp. Controlled Release Bioact. Mater.*, **23**, 73 (1996).

127. V.L. Truong-Le, S.M. Walsh, J.T. August, and K.W. Leong, *Proc. Int. Symp. Controlled Release Bioact. Mater.* **22**, 466 (1995).

128. R. Sipehia and G. Martucci, *Biochem. Biophys. Res. Commun.* **214**(1), 206–211 (1995).

PROTEIN THERAPEUTICS FOR SKELETAL TISSUE REPAIR

Hyun D. Kim
Genetics Institute
Andover, Massachusetts

Robert F. Valentini
Brown University
Providence, Rhode Island

KEY WORDS

Bone
Bone morphogenetic protein
Carrier
Cartilage
Gene therapy
Growth factor
Matrix
Polymer drug delivery system

OUTLINE

INTRODUCTION

Defects in bone that result from trauma (e.g., fractures), malformation, or disease processes such as cancer or osteoarthritis can cause significant morbidity. Current therapies for bone replacement rely on the use of allograft transplants from bone banks or autologous bone grafts. Frozen or freeze-dried allografts from human cadavers have been used clinically but are problematic due to potential for disease transmission, rejection, and resorption (1). The autograft involves direct transfer of viable bone-derived cells, inductive factors, and growth factors from the transplanted bone matrix, usually taken from the corticocancellous bone of the anterior iliac crest. Al-

though trabecular autografts have ample osteogenic cells and good revascularization capabilities, it is often difficult to obtain a sufficient quantity of bone from the patient (2). Cortical autografts are more easily obtained and provide greater stability, but they often exhibit poor vascularity, a lower content of osteogenic cells, and a high rate of fatigue fractures occurring 6–8 months following operation (3). Autografts also subject the patient to surgery at a second site, which may lead to additional pain, risk of infection, nerve and vessel damage, and a prolonged hospital stay. Thus, the search for alternatives to autograft and allograft remains an important topic in medical research.

In recent years, considerable research has focused on improving bone repair through the use of various growth (e.g., platelet-derived growth factor [PDGF], transforming growth factor [TGF], fibroblast growth factor [FGF], epidermal growth factor [EGF], insulin-like growth factor [IGF]) and morphogenetic factors (e.g., bone morphogenetic proteins [BMP]). For example, initially isolated from demineralized bone matrix (DBM), partially purified BMP was found to be osteoinductive, inducing bone formation by causing host mesenchymal stem cells (MSCs) to migrate to the repair site and differentiate into bone-forming cells (4,5). The key difference between these two classes of molecules is that growth factors affect cell growth and function (e.g., proliferation and differentiation), whereas morphogenetic factors are involved in cell commitment and induction from an undifferentiated state to a specific cell type. Recombinant techniques are now used to isolate, identify, clone, and express different types of BMPs as well as other growth factors (PDGF, TGF, FGF, IGF) normally present in bone matrix, which may operate in complex synergy. At least two of these proteins, BMP-2 and BMP-7, induce significant bone formation in the absence of other BMPs when implanted into ectopic (nonbony) sites (6,7) as well as orthotopic (bony) sites (8–12), and will likely be the first available therapeutics for bone repair in the clinic. The exact role of other growth factors in the complex cascade of molecules involved in bone formation and maintainance is not well understood.

Many basic research and developmental challenges remain in protein- and gene-based therapeutics for skeletal tissue repair. Perhaps the most basic are the identification and understanding of the complex cascade of genes and proteins that regulate skeletal growth and repair, in both normal and diseased states. Significant progress is being made in this area. With regard to product development, one of the major challenges limiting clinical availability has been the issue of delivery. Traditional systemic delivery of these proteins has not been feasible for a variety of reasons, including short biological half-lives of proteins as well as lack of drug localization to the target injury site. Oral delivery of therapeutic proteins, on the other hand, has been limited by breakdown of proteins by digestive enzymes and challenges with proteins crossing the intestinal wall intact and active. Progress is being made to protect proteins in the digestive tract using encapsulation systems, and this route of drug delivery would be appropriate for certain proteins that have systemic effects. Delivery of proteins and genes for skeletal tissue repair are founded on local use, and various strategies are being developed to deliver these therapeutics to the local injury site. The emergence of polymeric drug delivery systems and biomaterials has contributed significantly to the challenges of local delivery of proteins and genes. These carriers of therapeutics serve to provide a reservoir that can maintain a local concentration of drugs as well as provide a controlled, sustained release of these drugs for extended therapeutic effect.

Three strategies exist when considering delivery of therapeutics for local skeletal tissue repair. Perhaps the simplest is protein delivery in which the recombinant protein itself is incorporated within a carrier system such as polymer microspheres or biomaterial matrices. Another method is direct gene therapy, whereby the goal is to deliver the naked genes themselves into the target site and have the genes incorporate into the host cells that can produce the gene products. A third option is cell-based delivery, in which the gene of interest is inserted into a specific cell line, usually autogenous or allogeneic, so that the cells become delivery systems for gene products. Active research is being carried out in all three areas with promising results that may become successful therapies in the clinic.

The ideal carrier for bone growth and morphogenetic factors and the genes encoding them is still under investigation. Various bioderived materials such as bone matrix collagen and DBM as well as synthetic materials including ceramics and degradable polymers (e.g., poly(lactic acid) (13), poly(lactide-*co*-glycolide) (PLGA) (10), poly(phosphazene) (14)) have been studied as suitable bone graft substitutes. Allogeneic DBM, which contains a cocktail of osteoinductive proteins, has been shown to form bone in vivo (15), but when the matrix proteins are extracted with guanidinium hydrochloride to yield insoluble collagenous bone matrix (ICBM), bone does not form. When ICBM is combined with this protein extract (containing various BMPs), the osteoinductive activity is restored. However, the use of ICBM or DBM in the clinical setting has serious drawbacks, including potential immunogenicity, potential pathogen transmission, sterility assurance, supply problems, and lack of structural integrity.

Consequently, growth and morphogenetic factors require a suitable matrix or carrier serving as an effective delivery system by localizing and creating a high concentration of protein at the injury site, preventing loss of protein into neighboring sites (i.e., when using scaffolds for local bone formation), providing a sustained release of protein for local or systemic delivery (i.e., when using polymer drug delivery systems), and maximizing the interaction between the protein and the target host cells. Ideally, the bone repair scaffolds should be biocompatible and biodegradable to minimize local tissue response and should resorb as new bone is formed. On the other hand, polymer drug delivery systems should provide a sustained, controlled release of therapeutics for either local or systemic action. Sustained, controlled delivery of growth and morphogenetic factors using polymer delivery systems, scaffolds, or other matrices are advantageous over conventional injection of these therapeutics in solution form due to the clearance or elimination of injected drug by the systemic circulation as well as the inconvenience and necessity for multiple or repeated injections for effective treatment. In this article, proteins and genes involved in skeletal tissue repair as well as novel strategies for delivering them are introduced.

GROWTH AND MORPHOGENETIC FACTORS FOR BONE REPAIR

Serious skeletal defects result from diverse causes including trauma, birth defects, oncologic resections, and disease pathosis (e.g., periodontitis, degenerative osteoarthritis, and osteomyelitis). To restore lost tissue or prevent fracture nonunion, orthopaedic, plastic, and oral surgeons perform more than 250,000 bone grafts annually in the U.S. (8). As currently practiced, bone grafting predominantly uses autogenous corticocancellous bone taken from a donor site such as the anterior iliac crest. Although highly effective, autologous bone grafting is limited by such issues as donor site morbidity and pain, donor site infection, blood loss, and limited supply of donor site material. Allogeneic human cadaver bone graft is the most common alternative to the bone graft, but allografts suffer from the potential for disease transmission, rejection, and resorption.

Urist first observed in 1965 that implanting DBM in extraskeletal sites generated osseous tissue in rats (4). This process has been termed osteoinduction, that is, bone formation from MSCs that have differentiated down the osteoblastic lineage. Osteoconduction, on the other hand, refers to the ability of a material to support bone ingrowth from surrounding bone and depends on the material itself, its biocompatibility, porosity, surface charge, surface texture, and biodegradability. Later studies demonstrated that extracting the DBM with aqueous guanidinium hydrochloride yielded ICBM that is not osteoinductive. Reconstituting ICBM with the aqueous extract, which Urist called BMP, restored the osteoinductive activity as in DBM. However, the use of ICBM or DBM in the clinical setting has serious drawbacks, including potential immunogenicity, potential pathogen transmission, sterility assurance, supply problems, and lack of structural integrity.

More recently, modern biotechnology techniques have been used to isolate, identify, clone, and express more than 15 individual BMPs, which are all members of the transforming growth factor-beta (TGF-β) superfamily. New molecules continue to be identified and cloned. These recombinant human BMPs (rhBMPs) are present in bone extracellular matrix in trace amounts and probably operate in complex synergies. However, at least two of the individual proteins, namely rhBMP-2 and rhOP-1 (osteogenic protein-1, also known as BMP-7), are potential candidates for clinical use because they induce bone formation in the absence of other BMPs when implanted into bony and nonbony sites (6,7). The rhBMP-2, which is expressed in Chinese hamster ovary cells, contains an aminoterminal propeptide of 40–45 kDa, a mature active 30 kDa homodimer consisting of 18 and 22 kDa subunits, and a small amount of uncleaved 60 kDa precursor protein (16).

In vitro, rhBMP-2 induces pluripotent MSCs to differentiate into bone, cartilage, and fat lineages in a dose- and time-dependent manner (17). When combined with ICBM fragments or polyester carriers (e.g., PLGA, PLLA), rhBMP-2 or rhOP-1 regenerates osseous tissue in various species and anatomic sites, including rat muscle (18), rat calvarium (8,11,12), rat subcutaneous tissue (6,7), rat femur (10,19), sheep femur (9), and canine maxillary cleft (20).

TGF-β (25 kD molecular weight) is another factor important in the regulation of cell proliferation and differentiation and has been implicated in bone and cartilage formation and maintenance (21). There are three isoforms (β1, β2, β3), which have the ability to influence the mesenchymal cell differentiation pathway to bone and cartilage in a dose-dependent manner (22). TGF-β is found in macrophages and other inflammatory cells, platelets during degranulation in hematoma formation, and bone matrix, where it is most abundant (23). TGF-β is converted to its active form under acidic conditions, such as those produced by macrophages or osteoclasts during bone resorption (24). There have been a number of studies that suggest that TGF-β is involved in cartilage differentiation and bone repair, although its exact role is not well understood. TGF-β has been shown to induce chondrocytic differentiation from micromass cultures of pluripotent C3H10T1/2 (T1/2) cells (25), chick limb bud mesenchymal cells (26), and periosteal cells (27). TGF-β has also been implicated in the process of endochondral ossification (22,27) (i.e., when TGF-β1 was injected subperiosteally into uninjured bone, it induced a cartilagenous mass that underwent endochondral ossification). Consequently, TGF-β has been shown to have both stimulatory and inhibitory effects on the differentiation of bone cells depending on the maturation stage of the cells used, cell density, and growth factor concentration (25,28).

PDGF is a polypeptide dimer of 30 kDa that is unrelated to the TGF-β superfamily but acts as a mitogen for a variety of cell types. PDGF was found to increase DNA synthesis in cultured rat calvariae and fibroblasts but did not stimulate collagen synthesis or organized bone formation (29). It exists as a homodimer or heterodimer comprising A or B subunits, although the BB homodimer is more effective than AA or AB in stimulating bioactivity in bone cells in vitro (29). Similar to TGF-β, the exact role of PDGF in bone repair is not clearly understood. Marden et al. (30) reported that PDGF inhibited bone regeneration in a rat cranial defect model, whereas Bolander (23) reported that PDGF subperiosteal injections resulted in stimulation of MSC proliferation and subsequent bone mass increase in rat femurs. Other proteins such as FGF and IGF have also been linked to bone cell function (23). In addition, many other types of factors have been identified to influence skeletal tissue development, repair, and maintenance (Fig. 1). Hormones (e.g., parathyroid hormone [PTH], estrogen, calcitonin), vitamins (e.g., vitamin A, C, D, etc.), and glucocorticoids (e.g., dexamethasone, cortisol, etc.) also have specific effects on mesenchymal stem cells, cartilage cells (chondrocytes), and bone cells (osteoblasts) as do growth and morphogenetic factors. The key difference between growth (e.g., PDGF, TGF-β) and morphogenetic

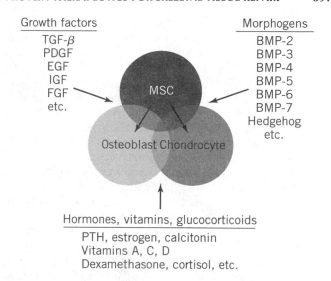

Figure 1. Skeletal tissue development, repair, and maintenance factors that affect MSC, osteoblasts, and chondrocytes.

(e.g., BMP) factors is that growth factors affect cell growth and function, whereas morphogenetic factors are involved in cell commitment and induction from an undifferentiated state to a specific cell type (Table 1). This will likely influence how they are used in the clinic and suggests that two or more proteins may be necessary for some treatments.

MESENCHYMAL STEM CELLS

MSCs are undifferentiated, pluripotent cells capable of differentiating into cells that form into various connective tissues such as bone, cartilage, tendon, ligament, muscle, and fat. During development, multipotential stem cells progressively become committed to specific paths. This process, called determination or commitment, irreversibly alters the cells so that the progeny inherits this more limited potential. Once committed or determined, the precursor cell may exist in this state until it differentiates. Differentiation is defined as the expression of one or more markers of the functionally mature cell and may be reversible or terminal. The environment of the progenitor cells (i.e., protein factors, extracellular matrix, cellular contact, and other unknown factors) may influence commitment and differentiation (31). Compared with hematopoietic stem

Table 1. Role of Growth and Morphogenetic Factors on MSCs, Cartilage Cells (Chondrocytes), and Bone Cells (Osteoblasts)

	MSCs	Chondrocyte	Osteoblast
PDGF	Proliferation	Proliferation	Proliferation
TGF-β	Proliferation	Proliferation Differentiation	Differentiation
BMP	Commitment Proliferation Differentiation	Differentiation	Differentiation

cells, much less is known about multipotential progenitor cells of mesodermal origin (also referred to as MSCs). Like hematopoietic factors, BMPs influence the commitment of MSCs.

Bone marrow is a complex tissue comprised of red and white blood cells, their precursors, and a connective tissue network or stroma. Bone marrow stromal cells have a close structural and functional relationship with bone cells, and it is generally believed that osteoblast precursors are derived from the mesenchymal stromal cell lineage. In vitro, typical bone phenotypic markers such as alkaline phosphatase activity, cAMP response to parathyroid hormone, osteocalcin synthesis, collagen I production and gene expression, osteonectin gene expression, and mineralized nodules are expressed by cultured human bone marrow stromal cells (32). The existence of cells in marrow that have osteochondrogenic potential has been demonstrated with whole marrow and cultured marrow stromal cells from a variety of animal species including humans (33). Additional evidence of in vivo osteochondrogenic potential of marrow stroma has been derived from experiments using grafts of whole marrow or cultured marrow stromal cells with calcium phosphate ceramics (34,35).

C3H10T1/2 cells are an established murine MSC line originally isolated as embryonic limb-derived fibroblasts, which differentiate into muscle, fat, and cartilage cells when treated with azacytidine. BMP-2 causes a dose-dependent differentiation of these cells into fat, cartilage, and bone cells; low concentrations favor adipocytes and high concentrations result in chondrocytes and osteoblasts (17). Osteogenic cell markers such as alkaline phosphatase activity have been used to demonstrate stem cell differentiation into osteoblastic cells by BMP-2 (36). Therefore, C3H10T1/2 cells serve as a simple in vitro cell culture system to characterize the osteogenic potential of BMPs and other proteins.

MECHANISMS OF BONE REPAIR

Ectopic bone formation refers to bone formation in a non-bony site, such as in subcutaneous or intramuscular sites. These sites have been mainly used to test the osteoinductive ability of bone morphogenetic proteins in an environment that is surrounded by tissue of mesodermal origin. On the other hand, because bone is a self-repairing tissue (limited by the defect size), a model to test bone formation in a bony site has also been established. A critical size defect is defined as the smallest intraosseous wound that does not heal by bone formation during the lifetime of the animal (37–39). A critical size defect heals by fibrous connective tissue formation and the actual critical size varies in different species, often increasing with animal size. For example, an 8-mm diameter skull defect has been characterized as a critical size defect in a rat, whereas a 4 mm heals eventually. The traditional bony sites involved in testing defects or nonunions (fractures that do not heal) have been the skull and the femur. Calvarial critical defects have been extensively characterized and established as a site to test bone repair materials (37). It is

important to note that the calvarium develops and heals by intramembranous ossification (direct formation of bone by osteoblasts) and is a non-weight-bearing bone. In contrast, femoral bone heals by endochondral ossification (bone formation through a cartilage intermediate), which is weight bearing (Fig. 2). BMP-2 has been shown to stimulate endochondral but not intramembranous bone formation.

CARRIERS FOR GROWTH AND MORPHOGENETIC FACTORS

Considerable effort has been dedicated to developing delivery systems for proteins targeted for bone repair. Oral administration presents difficulty for peptide-based drugs, which are rapidly digested by gastric and intestinal enzymes. Intravenous delivery results in alteration and clearance by the liver. Drug delivery vehicles facilitate the sustained, controlled delivery of growth factors and minimize the fluctuating levels achieved with single or multiple doses. A variety of delivery systems or carriers for peptides and proteins have been investigated (40–45) and are illustrated in Figure 3. For example, PDGF (40), basic FGF (46), EGF (47), and TGF-β (48) have been incorporated into various degradable (PLGA films, microspheres, rods, etc.) or nondegradable (mechanical pumps, diffusion

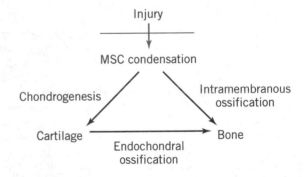

Figure 2. Bone and cartilage development and repair pathways.

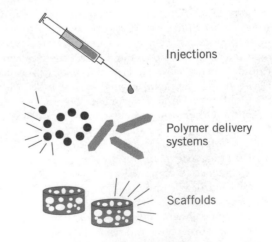

Figure 3. Strategies for delivering protein-, gene-, and cell-based therapeutics for local bone and cartilage repair.

based polymer matrices) delivery systems for controlled release. Ethylene vinyl acetate (EVA) copolymer is a nondegradable elastomer that has been used to deliver a host of small and large molecules (45). Bovine serum albumin (BSA) has been used extensively as carrier for EVA systems and EVA/BSA release has been shown to parallel growth factor release (45). Release kinetics for EVA systems can be controlled by varying drug loading, choice of carrier, device geometry, or by polymer surface coating (45). In one study, controlled, sustained release of bioactive PDGF and TGF-β was demonstrated from EVA polymer rods (40).

New tissue engineering approaches for bone and cartilage repair leverage the ability of growth and morphogenetic factors to control cell growth, differentiation, and new tissue formation at the site of injury or defect. Porous, degradable polymer scaffolds have been identified to be suitable bone or cartilage repair materials because they can be carriers for these tissue-inducing molecules and also allow the seeding of culture-expanded cells (i.e., chondrocytes, osteoblasts, MSCs) in vitro or host cell and tissue ingrowth in vivo. A wide variety of synthetic (e.g., PLGA) or natural polymers (e.g., collagen) have been explored as delivery vehicles for cells or growth/morphogenetic factors. These three-dimensional polymeric scaffolds have been fabricated using a variety of methods and used for a variety of applications such as cartilage repair, nonunion fracture defects, oral and maxillofacial defects, and spinal fusion. Various degradable polymer carriers or scaffolds containing BMPs have been used for local bone and cartilage formation (8,12,20,41,49–51).

Some semisynthetic polymers (e.g., chemically natural polymers) are also being explored. For example, derivatized hyaluronic acid is a class of semisynthetic biopolymer that can be fabricated into porous scaffolds for tissue reconstruction and repair. It is a benzyl ester derivative of the polysaccharide hyaluronic acid, which exists naturally in extracellular matrix and plays an important role in proteoglycan organization, cell hydration, cell differentiation, and wound healing (52). The benzyl esterification of the glucuronic acid residue of hyaluronic acid renders the polymer insoluble in aqueous conditions and significantly decreases the rate of degradation in vivo by hydrolysis and hyaluronidases (53). Hyaluronic acids are attractive choices for tissue repair scaffolds because biocompatibility has been well established (53). In addition, degradation can be controlled by altering the amount of esterification, and complex three-dimensional shapes with various porosities and pore sizes can be achieved (53).

Only a few formulations have been actively pursued for skeletal tissue repair. They include injectable formulations (such as microspheres, depots, and gels) and implantable matrices or scaffolds. Injectables can work as minimally invasive delivery systems by providing sustained release of a protein at the repair site. In open, surgical procedures, implantable scaffolds provide the opportunity for cells to migrate into the carrier, adhere, proliferate, and differentiate while also providing sustained release of protein. Scaffolds for tissue engineering should meet several design criteria: (1) the surface should permit cell adhesion and growth, (2) neither the polymer nor its degradation prod-

ucts should provoke inflammation or toxicity when implanted in vivo, (3) the material should be reproducibly processable into three-dimensional structures, (4) porosity should be high in order to provide a large surface area for cell migration, adhesion, and matrix regeneration, and (5) the scaffold should resorb in concert with new tissue formation.

Protein Delivery in Orthopedics

New advances are being made in the field of protein-, gene-, and cell-based therapeutics for skeletal tissue repair. Protein drug delivery is the direct delivery of already synthesized proteins using a specific carrier to the local tissue. Proteins are usually encapsulated or admixed within a polymer matrix and are released to the local site in a controlled, sustained fashion in the order of hours up to years (45). The simplicity of drug delivery systems and the ability to control dose and release rate remain the major advantages of this delivery strategy. However, drug stability and bioactivity must be carefully characterized within a particular carrier system.

Of all the growth and differentiation factors discovered to date, only a few have shown significant potential for skeletal tissue repair. These include human recombinant proteins of BMP-2, BMP-7 (or osteogenic protein-1, rhOP-1), basic FGF (bFGF), and TGF-β1. BMP-2 and rhOP-1 are currently in preclinical and clinical studies for a range of bone-specific indications such as fracture healing, oral and maxillofacial defects, spinal fusion, and cartilage repair. bFGF is also in clinical studies for accelerated fracture repair, whereas TGF-β1 is in preclinical studies for cartilage and bone repair. All of these proteins have been delivered in association with an appropriate drug delivery carrier (e.g., collagen), although simple injections of these proteins alone at high doses can still induce some level of efficacy (6). The presence of a matrix or carrier either enhances the volume of new repair tissue formed, decreases the amount of protein needed to induce efficacy, and prolongs residence of protein at the local repair site to allow sufficient time for responsive cells to migrate and react.

In the area of fracture and bone defect repair, BMP-2 and rhOP-1 have shown to be most effective when delivered in association with a carrier, which have mainly been collagen based to date. For example, BMP-2 loaded onto absorbable collagen sponges has shown good efficacy in accelerating healing in a fracture model (54). In another study, rhOP-1 incorporated with another type of implantable collagen matrix was shown to heal large segmental bone defects (55). Both of these devices performed equally or better than the traditional clinical standard of using autogenous bone graft for nonunion defects or immobilization for union fractures. Other carriers such as ceramic-based calcium phosphates containing BMP (56) have been shown to be effective for bone defect repair. More recently, injectable gels such as bFGF-containing hyaluronic acid have shown efficacy for accelerated fracture repair (57). Injectable gels that deliver the protein for the duration of the healing period and contribute to fracture callus formation would be ideal carriers. Polymer, ceramic, or composite matrices that can withstand soft tissue pressure or bear weight may represent the next generation of bone defect repair materials.

Other bone-specific indications for protein delivery include spinal fusion and oral and maxillofacial surgery. In one study, BMP-2 loaded onto absorbable collagen sponges has been shown to enhance fusion in nonhuman primate lumbar interbody spinal fusion models (58). In oral and maxillofacial surgery, collagen matrix/BMP-2 was shown to be successful in repairing mandibular defects in a canine model (59), alveolar ridge augmentation procedures in human clinical trials (60), osseointegration of titanium dental implants in nonhuman primates (61), and maxillary sinus floor augmentation procedures (62).

Cartilage, tendon, and ligament repair are also being using protein therapeutics. Recent studies using BMP-2 in combination with absorbable collagen sponges has shown success in repairing articular cartilage defects in a rabbit model (63). Injection of TGF-β1 encapsulated within liposomes was shown to accelerate the repair of articular cartilage defects in rabbits (64). New members of the TGF-β gene family, the growth and differentiation factors 5, 6, and 7 (GDF-5, 6, 7) have been shown to induce neotendon and ligament when implanted in association with a collagen matrix in rat models (65).

Direct Gene Therapy

An alternative to delivering proteins is to directly deliver the genes encoding these proteins to the host cells as naked plasmid DNA injections, or using nonviral transfection or viral transduction methods. Potential advantages of gene therapy over direct protein delivery include (1) no need for manufacturing or purification facilities, (2) constant production of fresh protein in bioactive form, and (3) lower dose requirements for achieving efficacy. Limits of gene therapy include poor long-term gene expression, inefficient transfection of genes to target cells, and the inability to control or cease expression as needed. Nevertheless, significant progress is being made in orthopedic preclinical studies. In one study, plasmid DNA encoding for either BMP-4 or a fragment of PTH (amino acids 1–34) alone resulted in new bone formation when implanted into segmental bone defects in the rat femur (66). When BMP-4 and the parathyroid fragment were implanted together, acceleration of bone formation was observed compared with either factor alone, suggesting synergy. Adenovirus containing the β-galactosidase reporter gene injected into the synovium of cartilage joints was able to infect the cells lining the synovium and express the marker gene for at least 8 weeks after injection (67). Expression of marker genes using an adenoviral vector injected into segmental defect sites for 6 weeks has also been reported (68).

Cell Based Gene Delivery

An alternative approach for delivering proteins is to use genetically engineered cells as carriers for genes encoding the proteins of interest. This strategy is a novel concept in orthopedic drug delivery and limited literature exists. The basic concept is to generate, in vitro, cells or tissues that are implantable protein factories. The cell-based factories are injected at the local tissue repair site and produce the protein of interest over time. Cells can be injected as a cell suspension or in association with a carrier such as a scaffold or gel. They can also be formed into organized tissue in vitro and subsequently implanted as a discrete structure (69). The advantages of this system are (1) the ability to control the dose of protein delivered (by controlling expression levels, cell numbers, etc.), (2) the ability to retrieve the cells as needed (if implanted in a defined scaffold such as a cell-occlusive membrane), (3) the ability to control transfection or transduction in only the desired cells, and (4) the ability to treat acute or chronic conditions. The cells that are transfected or transduced ex vivo can be autologous, allogeneic, or xenogeneic (if protected by a immunoisolatory membrane). Autologous cells are the currently preferred choice as they eliminate any immune response, but they must be harvested from the donor as a separate procedure. Preliminary studies for bone and cartilage repair are encouraging. In one study, a bone marrow stromal cell line infected with an adenovirus expressing recombinant human BMP-2 was able to form ectopic bone when injected into rat muscle (70). In another study, chondrocytes that were infected with adenovirus expressing a marker gene β galactosidase remained in the joint space and expressed the reporter gene for at least 45 days when injected into cartilage explants (71). Additionally, bone marrow cells transfected with a gene encoding for a new osteoinductive protein (LIM mineralization protein-1) and seeded onto a collagen matrix supported successful spinal fusion following implantation into rats (72). Despite promising results, further research is needed to develop cell-based approaches into viable therapies.

SUMMARY

Protein-, gene-, and cell-based systems offer powerful new approaches for skeletal tissue repair. Applications range from fracture healing, bone defect repair, spinal fusion, and oral and maxillofacial surgery to cartilage, tendon, and ligament repair. These approaches require the development of novel delivery systems. Delivery systems have several requirements and must (1) serve as effective carriers for therapeutic agents, (2) provide localization of the protein to the target repair site, (3) maintain bioactivity in vivo, (4) provide controlled, sustained release to the surrounding tissue, and (5) in some instances, concurrently serve as scaffolds for tissue ingrowth.

BIBLIOGRAPHY

1. G.D. Bos et al., *J. Bone J. Surg., Am. Vol.* **65-A**, 239–246 (1983).
2. D. Prolo and J. Rodrigo, *Clin. Orthop. Relat. Res.* **200**, 322–341 (1985).
3. W.F. Enneking, J.L. Eady, and H. Burchardt, *J. Bone J. Surg., Am. Vol.* **62-A**, 1039–1058 (1980).
4. M.R. Urist, *Science* **150**, 893–899 (1965).

5. M.R. Urist et al., *Clin. Orthop. Relat. Res.* **162**, 219–232 (1982).

6. E.A. Wang et al., *Proc. Natl. Acad. Sci. U.S.A.* **87**(6), 2220–2224 (1990).

7. T.K. Sampath et al., *J. Biol. Chem.* **267**(28), 20352–20362 (1992).

8. R. Kenley et al., *J. Biomed. Mater. Res.* **28**, 1139–1147 (1994).

9. T.N. Gerhart et al., *Clin. Orthop. Relat. Res.* **293**, 317–326 (1993).

10. S.C. Lee et al., *J. Biomed. Mater. Res.* **28**, 1149–1156 (1994).

11. L.J. Marden, N.C. Quigley, A.H. Reddi, and J.O. Hollinger, *Calcif. Tissue Int.* **53**, 262–268 (1993).

12. L.J. Marden et al., *J. Biomed. Mater. Res.* **28**, 1127–1138 (1994).

13. A.G. Mikos et al., *Polymer* **35**, 1068–1077 (1994).

14. C.T. Laurencin et al., *J. Biomed. Mater. Res.* **27**, 963–973 (1993).

15. T.A. Einhorn et al., *J. Bone J. Surg., Am. Vol.* **66-A**, 274–279 (1985).

16. D.I. Israel et al., *Growth Factors* **7**, 139–150 (1992).

17. E.A. Wang, D.I. Israel, S. Kelly, and D.P. Luxenberg, *Growth Factors* **9**, 57–71 (1993).

18. P.A. Lucas, G.T. Syftestad, V.M. Goldberg, and A.I. Caplan, *J. Biomed. Mater. Res.* **23**(A1), 23–29 (1989).

19. A.W. Yasko et al., *J. Bone J. Surg., Am. Vol.* **74-A**(5), 659–670 (1992).

20. M. Mayer, J. Hollinger, E. Ron, and J. Wozney, *Plast. Reconstr. Surg.* **98**, 247–259 (1996).

21. M. Centrella, M.C. Horowitz, J.M. Wozney, and T.L. McCarthy, *Endocr. Rev.* **15**, 27–39 (1994).

22. M.E. Joyce, S. Jingushi, and M.E. Bolander, *Orthop. Clin. North Am.* **21**, 199–209 (1990).

23. M.E. Bolander, *Proc. Soc. Exp. Biol. Med.* **200**, 165–170 (1992).

24. D.A. Lawrence, R. Pircher, and P. Jullien, *Biochem. Biophys. Res. Commun.* **133**, 1026–1034 (1985).

25. A.E. Denker, S.B. Nicoll, and R.S. Tuan, *Differentiation (Berlin)* **59**, 25–34 (1995).

26. E.F. Roark and K. Greer, *Dev. Dyn.* **200**, 103–116 (1994).

27. M.E. Joyce, A.B. Roberts, M.B. Sporn, and M.E. Bolanders, *J. Cell. Biol.* **110**, 2195–2207 (1990).

28. P.V. Hauschka, T.L. Chen, and A.E. Mavrakos, *Ciba Found. Symp.* **136**, 205–207 (1988).

29. J.M. Hock and E. Canalis, *Endocrinology (Baltimore)* **134**, 1423–1428 (1994).

30. L.J. Marden et al., *J. Clin. Invest.* **92**, 2897–2905 (1993).

31. A.I. Caplan, *J. Orthop. Res.* **9**(5), 641–650 (1991).

32. R.W. Zhang et al., *Calcif. Tissue Int.* **56**, 283–291 (1995).

33. S.P. Bruder, D.J. Fink, and A.I. Caplan, *J. Cell. Biochem.* **56**, 283–294 (1994).

34. J. Goshima, V.M. Goldberg, and A.I. Caplan, *Clin. Orthop. Relat. Res.* **262**, 298–311 (1991).

35. S.E. Haynesworth, J. Goshima, V.M. Goldberg, and A.I. Caplan, *Bone* **13**, 81–88 (1992).

36. T. Katagiri et al., *Biochem. Biophys. Res. Commun.* **172**(1), 295–299 (1990).

37. J.O. Hollinger and J.C. Kleinschmidt, *J. Craniofacial Surg.* **1**(1), 60–68 (1990).

38. J.P. Schmitz and J.O. Hollinger, *Clin. Orthop. Relat. Res.* **205**, 299–308 (1986).

39. J.P. Schmitz, Z. Schwartz, J.O. Hollinger, and B.D. Boyan, *Acta Anat.* **138**, 185–192 (1990).

40. H.D. Kim and R.F. Valentini, *Biomaterials* **18**, 1175–1184 (1997).

41. J.O. Hollinger and K. Leong, *Biomaterials* **17**, 187–194 (1996).

42. M. Isobe et al., *J. Biomed. Mater. Res.* **32**, 433–438 (1996).

43. J. Hollinger, *J. Craniofacial Surg.* **4**, 135–141 (1993).

44. J. Hollinger, *J. Craniofacial Surg.* **4**, 102–108 (1993).

45. R. Langer, *Science* **249**, 1527–1533 (1990).

46. E.R. Edelman, E. Mathiowitz, R. Langer, and M. Klagsburn, *Biomaterials* **12**, 619–626 (1991).

47. J.B. Murray, L. Brown, R. Langer, and M. Klagsburn, *In Vitro* **19**, 743–748 (1983).

48. W.R. Gombotz et al., *J. Biomater. Sci. Polym. Ed.* **5**, 49–63 (1993).

49. B.P. Robinson, J.O. Hollinger, E.H. Szachowicz, and J. Brekke, *Otolaryngol. Head Neck Surg.* **112**, 707–713 (1995).

50. J.H. Schimandle, S.D. Boden, and W.C. Hutton, *Spine* **20**, 1326–1337 (1995).

51. H.S. Sandhu et al., *Spine* **21**, 2115–2122 (1996).

52. B. Toole, *In* E. Hay, ed, *Cell Biology of Extracellular Matrix*, Plenum, New York, 1991, pp. 305–341.

53. L. Benedetti et al., *Biomaterials* **14**, 1154–1160 (1993).

54. R.D. Welch et al., *J. Bone Miner. Res.* **13**, 1483–1490 (1998).

55. S.D. Cook et al., *J. Orthop. Trauma* **12**, 407–412 (1998).

56. M.R. Urist et al., *Clin. Orthop.* **214**, 295–304 (1987).

57. M.L. Radomsky, A.Y. Thompson, R.C. Spiro, and J.W. Poser, *Clin. Orthop.* **355**, S283–S293 (1998).

58. S.D. Boden et al., *J. Spinal Disord.* **11**, 95–101 (1998).

59. D.M. Toriumi et al., (1991) *Arch. Otolaryngol. Head Neck Surg.* **117**, 1101–1112 (1991).

60. T.H. Howell et al., *Int. J. Periodont. Restorative Dent.* **17**, 124–139 (1997).

61. O. Hanisch et al., *Int. J. Oral Maxillofacial Implants* **12**, 785–792 (1997).

62. C.A. Kirker-Head et al., *Int. J. Oral Maxillofacial Implants* **12**, 403–411 (1997).

63. R.S. Sellers, D. Peluso, and E.A. Morris, *J. Bone J. Surg., Am. Vol.* **79-A**, 1452–1463 (1997).

64. T. Abe et al., *Proc. 44th Ann. Meet., Orthop. Res. Soc.*, 1998, p. 380.

65. N.M. Wolfman et al., *J. Clin. Invest.* **100**, 321–330 (1997).

66. J. Fang et al., *Proc. Natl. Acad. Sci. U.S.A.* **93**, 5753–5758 (1996).

67. B.J. Roessler et al., *J. Clin. Invest.* **92**, 1085–1092 (1993).

68. C. Niyibizi et al., *Clin. Orthop.* **355**, S148–S153 (1998).

69. H. Vandenburgh et al., *Hum. Gene Ther.* **7**, 2195–2200 (1996).

70. J.R. Lieberman et al., *J. Orthop. Res.* **16**, 330–339 (1998).

71. P.J. Doherty et al., *Osteoarthritis Cartilage* **6**, 153–159 (1998).

72. S.D. Boden et al., *Spine* **23**, 2486–2492 (1998).

PUMPS/OSMOTIC

Introduction

ALZET® System

VITS Veterinary Implant

DUROS™ Osmotic Implant for Humans

Ruminal Osmotic Bolus

PUMPS/OSMOTIC—INTRODUCTION

JEREMY C. WRIGHT
CYNTHIA L. STEVENSON
ALZA Corporation
Palo Alto, California

KEY WORDS

Diaphragm

Osmosis

Osmotic system theory

Semipermeable membrane

Sodium chloride

Zero-order

OUTLINE

Historically, pharmaceutically active agents have been chosen based on biological activity, with absorption, efficacy, and side effect profiles determined by metabolic processes. The effectiveness of the therapeutic agent can be enhanced by sophisticated drug delivery systems that actively control the delivery rate and site of drug action (1–8). Over the past 30 years, drug delivery systems based on the principles of osmosis have shown themselves to be reliable and adaptable to an impressive variety of uses, ranging from oral dosage forms that deliver for less than 24 hours to implantable systems that precisely deliver exquisitely small amounts of potent agents over periods of a year or more.

EARLY OSMOTIC SYSTEMS

The Rose–Nelson osmotic pump is generally recognized as the forerunner of most modern osmotic systems (9). This pump, developed in 1955 for pharmacologic research, consisted of a water compartment, an osmotic agent compartment, and a drug compartment (Fig. 1) (10). The water and osmotic agent compartments were separated by a semipermeable membrane, and the osmotic agent and drug compartments were separated by an elastic diaphragm. In operation, water was drawn into the osmotic agent compartment, resulting in volume displacement of the diaphragm and pumping of the drug solution from the drug compartment. If the osmotic agent compartment was filled with sufficient osmotic agent to maintain a saturated solution, zero-order delivery would be observed.

In 1971, Stolzenberg was issued the first patent for an osmotic pump, which incorporated pistons between the osmotic agent compartment and the drug compartment and between the water compartment and the exterior of the pump (11). Higuchi and Leeper proposed a variation of the Rose–Nelson pump in 1973 in which the internal water compartment was eliminated, placing the membrane in direct contact with the surrounding aqueous environment (12). In the mid-1970s, researchers at ALZA designed a capsular osmotic pump, in which the drug compartment was almost fully surrounded by an osmotic layer and a semipermeable membrane (this design was used in the ALZET® osmotic pump) (13). In 1975, Theeuwes developed the "elementary osmotic pump," which further simplified the design by combining the osmotic agent compartment and drug compartment into one (14). A subsequent variation on this design was the Push-Pull™ osmotic pump, which consisted of an osmotic layer and a separate drug layer (15,16). The development of these systems has been described in numerous articles (14,17–21). This article reviews the ALZET® osmotic pump and several newer applications of osmotic technology.

CHARACTERISTICS OF OSMOTIC SYSTEMS

Osmotic systems exhibit good correlation between in vitro and in vivo release; with proper system design, performance tends to be unaffected by in vivo variables. Therefore, these systems can be engineered to provide a variety of drug-release profiles such as increasing, decreasing, or zero order. The delivery rate can also be biochemically triggered (22) or patterned to mimic a periodic event, such as a circadian rhythm (23–25). Depending on the design, osmotic systems can deliver drug orally into the gastrointestinal tract or parenterally into the systemic circulation. Drug delivery also can be targeted via a catheter into the venous, arterial, or central nervous system or directly to an organ, such as the cerebrum, spleen, or liver. In general, bioavailability issues may be circumvented with osmotic pumps by selection of the optimum delivery site for drug delivery. Dosing is less frequent, and plasma drug concentrations are maintained within the therapeutic window, providing a dose-sparing effect, improved patient compliance, and minimized side effects for extended periods.

The osmotic systems described in this article release a therapeutic agent at a predetermined, typically zero-order, delivery rate based on the principle of osmosis. Osmosis is the natural movement of a solvent through a semiperme-

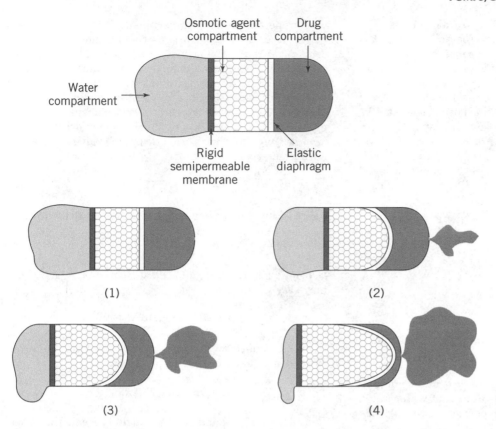

Figure 1. Principle of the Rose–Nelson osmotic pump. *Source:* Ref. 10.

able membrane into a solution of higher solute concentration, leading to equal concentrations of the solute on both sides of the membrane. Osmotic systems imbibe water from the body through a semipermeable membrane into an osmotic material, which swells, resulting in slow and even delivery of drug formulation.

In comparison with drug delivery systems based on diffusion and erosion, osmotic systems tend to be less volume efficient and more complex in design. However, osmotic systems also tend to provide better zero-order delivery and to deliver a greater percentage of the drug loading at a zero-order delivery rate.

OSMOTIC SYSTEM THEORY

Figure 2 illustrates the function of a semipermeable membrane (26). The semipermeable membrane (**a**) is permeable to water (compartment **c**) but impermeable to the solute (osmotic agent, e.g., NaCl) in compartment **b**. When the pressure is equal between compartments **b** and **c** ($P^0 = P$), water (solvent) will permeate through the semipermeable membrane from compartment **c** to compartment **b**, reflecting the gradient in chemical potential of the solvent between the two compartments. As the pressure is increased in compartment **b**, the chemical potential of the solvent increases in this compartment. When the pressure in compartment **b** reaches the osmotic pressure of the solution, the chemical potential of the solvent in the two compartments becomes equalized, and net transport of the solvent through the membrane stops.

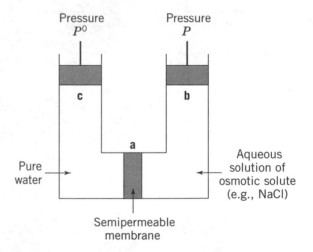

Figure 2. Diagram of a semipermeable membrane (**a**) separating an aqueous solution of an osmotic solute (**b**) from pure water (**c**). *Source:* Ref. 26.

The greater the gradient in chemical potential, the greater will be the rate of transport of solvent through the membrane. Considering the relationship between chemical potential and osmotic pressure, the rate of water transport through the membrane can be written as follows (14):

$$dV/dt = (A/h)L_P(\sigma\Delta\pi - \Delta p) \tag{1}$$

where dV/dt is the volume flow of solvent through the membrane, A is the cross-sectional area for transport, h is the membrane thickness, L_p is the hydraulic permeability of the membrane, σ is the reflection coefficient, $\Delta\pi$ is the osmotic pressure difference across the membrane, and Δp is the hydrostatic pressure difference across the membrane.

Table 1 presents the osmotic pressures of saturated aqueous solutions of common pharmaceutical solutes (27). Hydrostatic pressure inside most osmotic drug delivery systems is generally less than 1 atm, although some systems may attain pressures as high as several atmospheres. Hence, in comparison with the osmotic pressures reported in Table 1, the hydrostatic pressure differential is negligible:

$$\Delta\pi \gg \Delta p$$

Equation 1 can then be written as follows:

$$dV/dt = (A/h)k\Delta\pi \qquad (2)$$

where $k = L_p\,\sigma$. Therefore, k can be taken as the effective permeability of the membrane. (Reflection coefficients for membranes used in osmotic systems are generally quite close to 1.)

A cross-sectional diagram of a generic osmotic pump illustrates the semipermeable membrane and water influx into the pump (Fig. 3) (28). Water permeates through the

Table 1. Osmotic Pressures of Saturated Aqueous Solutions of Selected Pharmaceutical Solutes

Solute	Osmotic pressure (atm)
Sodium chloride	356
Fructose	355
Potassium chloride	245
Sucrose	150
Dextrose	82
Potassium sulfate	39
Mannitol	38
Sodium phosphate dibasic · 7 H_2O	31

Source: Ref. 27.

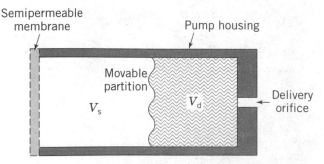

V_s = Volume of osmotic driving agent (e.g., NaCl) compartment

V_d = Volume of drug compartment

Figure 3. Schematic representation of a generic osmotic pump. *Source:* Ref. 28.

membrane and enters compartment V_s, causing it to expand; this expansion compresses compartment V_d, pushing drug out through the orifice. In equation 2, dV/dt represents the volume rate of change of the compartment indicated by V_s. If the compartment V_d is filled with a drug solution or suspension at concentration c and if the movable partition readily transmits displacement from compartment V_s to compartment V_d, the rate of drug delivery (dm/dt) from the generic osmotic pump is given by the following equation:

$$dm/dt = (dV/dt)c \qquad (3)$$

Substituting in equation 2 for dV/dt, we get the following:

$$dm/dt = (A/h)k\Delta\pi c \qquad (4)$$

Depending on the design of the system, A, h, k, $\Delta\pi$, and c may vary with time:

$$dm/dt = [A(t)/h(t)]k(t)\Delta\pi(t)c(t) \qquad (5)$$

For some applications, equation 5 can be written in terms of the degree of hydration of the system (H):

$$dm/dt = (A_H/h)k\Delta\pi_H c \qquad (6)$$

Consideration of equations 4 through 6 reveals that a variety of delivery rate profiles—increasing over time, decreasing over time, zero order, or some combination of these—are possible depending on the specific design of the osmotic system.

SYSTEM DESIGN CONSIDERATIONS

Osmotic drug delivery technology is based primarily on semipermeable membranes—membranes that are permeable to water but impermeable to ionic compounds and higher-molecular-weight compounds. For example, cellulosic ester membranes are permeable to water but reject sodium chloride. The water content of these membranes varies linearly with acetyl content (Fig. 4), and the hydraulic permeability varies exponentially with acetyl content (Fig. 5) (29). Typical membrane permeabilities range from 10^{-7} to 10^{-6} g/cm/s. Permeabilities can also be altered by incorporating additives into the membrane during processing (30).

For most pharmaceutical applications, the osmotic agent of choice is sodium chloride. Usually the system design provides for sufficient sodium chloride to maintain a saturated solution throughout the delivery period. In some applications, gellants are mixed with the osmotic agent; the resulting osmotic interactions can be complex and difficult to predict from theory.

CURRENT OSMOTIC PUMP APPLICATIONS

The following articles discuss four representative osmotic technologies: the ALZET® osmotic pump, an implant used in preclinical and basic research; the VITS veterinary im-

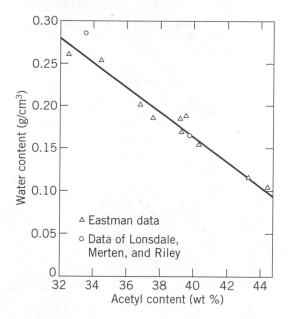

Figure 4. Water content of cellulose acetate at 100% relative humidity and 25°C versus acetyl content. *Source:* Adapted from Ref. 29, p. 112.

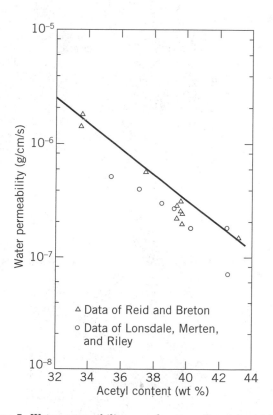

Figure 5. Water permeability as a function of acetyl content of normal cellulose acetate membranes. *Source:* Adapted from Ref. 29, p. 106.

plant, a tiny osmotic system for delivery of water-labile proteins and peptides; the DUROS™ implant, a miniature osmotic implant for use in humans; and the RUTS Push-Melt™ system, an osmotic ruminal bolus. Each article provides information on comparable technologies, design and function of the systems, and relevant applications of the technology.

BIBLIOGRAPHY

1. A. Zaffaroni, *Abstr. 31st Int. Cong. Pharma. Sci.*, Washington, D.C., 1971, pp. 19–20.
2. J.E. Shaw and F. Theeuwes, *Aust. J. Pharm. Sci.* **7**(2), 49–53 (1978).
3. A. Zaffaroni, *Drug Metab. Rev.* **8**(2), 191–221 (1978).
4. J. Urquhart, *Fed. Proc. Fed. Am. Soc. Exp. Biol.* **39**, 2460–2464 (1980).
5. J. Urquhart, in J. Urquhart, ed., *Controlled-Release Pharmaceuticals*, American Pharmaceutical Assoc., Washington, D.C., 1981, pp. 1–48.
6. F. Theeuwes, in F.G. McMahon, ed., *Principles and Techniques of Human Research and Therapeutics*, Futura, New York, 1985, pp. 63–85.
7. J. Urquhart, in L.F. Prescott and W.S. Nimmo, eds., *Rate Control in Drug Therapy*, Churchill-Livingstone, New York, 1985, pp. 19–29.
8. D. Edgren, H. Leeper, K. Nichols, and J. Wright, in *Kirk-Othmer Encyclopedia of Chemical Technology*, 4th ed., vol. 7, Wiley, New York, 1993, pp. 274–300.
9. S. Rose and J.F. Nelson, *Aust. J. Exp. Biol.* **33**, 415–420 (1955).
10. R. Baker, *Controlled Release of Biologically Active Agents*, Wiley, New York, 1987, pp. 132–155.
11. U.S. Pat. 3,604,417 (September 14, 1971), S.J. Stolzenberg (to American Cynamid Company).
12. U.S. Pat. 3,732,865 (May 15, 1973), T. Higuchi and H. Leeper (to ALZA Corp.).
13. F. Theeuwes and S.I. Yum, *Ann. Biomed. Eng.* **4**(4), 343–353 (1976).
14. F. Theeuwes, *J. Pharm. Sci.* **64**, 1987–1991 (1975).
15. D.R. Swanson, D.L. Barclay, T.S.L. Wong, and F. Theeuwes, *Am. J. Med.* **83**(6B), 3–9 (1987).
16. F. Theeuwes, in L.F. Prescott and W.S. Nimmo, eds., *Drug Absorption*, ADIS Press, New York, 1981, pp. 157–176.
17. F. Theeuwes, in A.F. Kydonieus, ed., *Controlled Release Technologies: Methods, Theory, and Applications*, CRC Press, Boca Raton, Fla., 1977, pp. 195–205.
18. F.E. Yates et al., *Adv. Biomed. Eng.* **5**, 1–34 (1975).
19. K. Chandrasekaran, F. Theeuwes, and S.I. Yum, in E.J. Ariëns, ed., *Drug Design*, Academic Press, New York, 1979, pp. 133–167.
20. F. Theeuwes, *Pharm. Ther.* **13**, 149–191 (1981).
21. F. Theeuwes, S.I. Yum, R. Haak, and P. Wong, *Ann. N.Y. Acad. Sci.* **168**, 428–440 (1991).
22. R.A. Siegel and B.A. Firestone, *J. Controlled Release* **11**, 181–192 (1990).
23. U.S. Pat. 4,723,958 (February 9, 1988), D.G. Pope and A.E. Royce (to Merck & Co., Inc.).
24. U.S. Pat. 5,017,381 (May 21, 1991), F. Maruyama and R. Cortese (to ALZA Corp.).
25. U.S. Pat. 4,957,494 (September 18, 1990), P.S.L. Wong, F. Theeuwes, and J.B. Eckenhoff (to ALZA Corp.).

26. K. Heilman, *Therapeutic Systems, Rate-Controlled Drug Delivery: Concept and Development*, 2nd ed., Thieme-Stratton, New York, 1984, p. 29.

27. U.S. Pat. 4,077,407 (March 7, 1978), F. Theeuwes and A.D. Ayer (to ALZA Corp.).

28. B. Eckenhoff, F. Theeuwes, and J. Urquhart, *Pharm. Technol.* **11**(6), 96–105 (1987).

29. H.K. Lonsdale, in U. Mertens, ed., *Desalination by Reverse Osmosis*, MIT Press, Cambridge, Mass., 1966, pp. 93–160, citing (1) C.E. Reid and E.J. Breton, *J. Appl. Polym. Sci.* **1**, 133 (1959); (2) Eastman Chemical Products, Inc., *Circular Cellulose Acetate*; and (3) H.K. Lonsdale, U. Merten, and R.L. Riley, *J. Appl. Polym. Sci.* **9**, 1341 (1965).

30. U.S. Pat. 4,160,020 (July 3, 1979), A.D. Ayer and F. Theeuwes (to ALZA Corp.).

See also Pumps/osmotic—ALZET® system; Pumps/osmotic—VITS veterinary implant; Pumps/osmotic—DUROS® osmotic implant for humans; Pumps/osmotic—ruminal osmotic bolus.

PUMPS/OSMOTIC—ALZET® SYSTEM

Lorri Perkins
Clarisa Peer
Virginia Fleming
ALZA Corporation
Palo Alto, California

KEY WORDS

Cellulose ester blend
Delivery rate
Drug reservoir
Osmotic sleeve
Semipermeable membrane
Therapeutic concentration range

OUTLINE

Background
System Design and Function
Applications
Conclusions
Bibliography
Additional Reading

ALZET® osmotic pumps are miniature, implantable research tools that deliver drug formulations at controlled rates in laboratory animals. Designed for preclinical and basic research, the ALZET® pump offers researchers enhanced control over drug levels in plasma and tissues. The capsule-shaped pumps (ranging from 1.5 to 5.1 cm in length and 0.6 to 1.4 cm in diameter) consist of a cylindrical, elastic reservoir for the drug solution surrounded by an osmotic layer, which is encased in a rigid, semipermeable membrane. Because of the osmotic gradient, water diffuses into the pump through the membrane and swells the osmotic layer, which collapses the reservoir and pushes the drug solution out of the pump at a controlled rate.

Although ALZET® pumps are most commonly implanted subcutaneously or intraperitoneally for systemic administration, they can be used with a catheter for intracerebral, intravenous, or intraarterial infusion. Specific regions can be targeted, such as the spinal cord, spleen, liver, gastrointestinal tract, and tissue transplantation or wound-healing sites. Table 1 lists the major routes of administration as reported in the literature.

Ten models of ALZET® osmotic pumps offer a range of delivery rates (from 0.25 to 10 μL/h) and durations (from 1 day to 4 weeks) (Fig. 1). The pumping rate is fixed at manufacture, but the dosage of drug delivered can be adjusted by varying the concentration of the drug solution placed in the pump. Multiple pumps can be implanted simultaneously to achieve higher delivery rates. For more prolonged delivery, pumps can be serially implanted.

Over 5,200 publications illustrate the use of osmotic pumps to deliver more than 1,600 compounds in 40 animal species, including rats, mice, cats, cattle, chickens, dogs, fish, frogs, guinea pigs, hamsters, iguanas, monkeys, pigs, sheep, and squirrels.

BACKGROUND

The ALZET® osmotic pump was originally developed by ALZA as an in-house research tool. In the mid-1970s, it became available for investigational use, and in 1977, the first commercial product was introduced. Alternatively, animals were connected to heavy infusion pumps, or homemade devices were implanted that were made from Silastic tubes in which a drug, typically a steroid, was packed. Other common administration schemes included dosing in food or water or repeated injection.

With ALZET® osmotic pumps, the typical peak and trough serum profile often seen with repeated injection dosing is replaced with a constant, continuous flat curve,

Table 1. Major Routes of Administration (As Reported in the Literature)

Subcutaneous	Intraruminal
Intraperitoneal	Local tissue microperfusion
Intracavity	Arterial wall
Articular cavity	Bone
Bladder	Brain
Cerebral ventricles	Eye
Intestine	Muscle
Spinal cord	Ovary
Stomach	Peripheral nerves
Uterus	Spleen
Intravenous	Testes
Intraarterial	

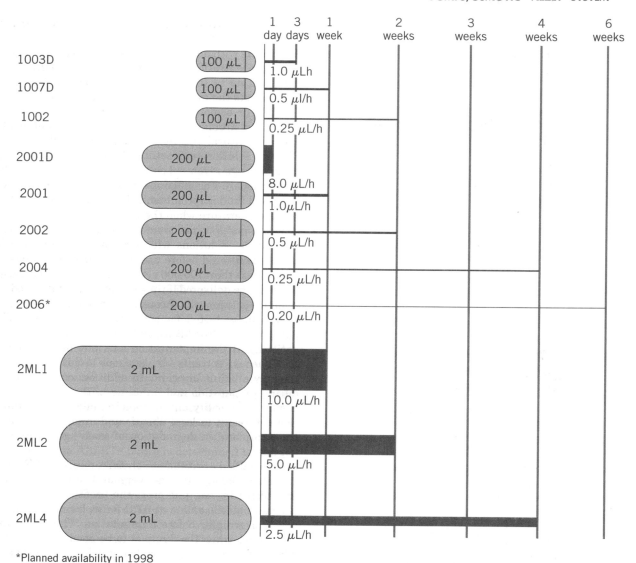

*Planned availability in 1998

Figure 1. Comparison of delivery rates, durations, and reservoir capacities of ALZET® osmotic pumps.

which can stay in the therapeutic concentration range. This avoids spike concentrations, when adverse effects are more likely, and troughs, when drug effects may dwindle (Fig. 2). ALZET® pump infusion is much more predictable than dosing in food or water. With Silastic tubes, rate control is imprecise because the diffusion rate across the tube wall is not constant and differs by compound (1), whereas with the ALZET® pump, the delivery rate is precise and is not dependent on the physical or chemical properties of the drug. With ALZET® pumps, animal handling and stress are minimized, and repeated nighttime and weekend dosing is not necessary. The ALZET® pump is tamperproof. It does not require any external connections, so animals need no restraint.

SYSTEM DESIGN AND FUNCTION

ALZET® osmotic pumps are composed of three concentric layers: the drug reservoir, the osmotic sleeve, and the rate-controlling, semipermeable membrane (Fig. 3). The drug reservoir is a cylindrical cavity molded from a synthetic elastomer. The reservoir walls are impermeable, blocking any exchange of material between the drug reservoir and the surrounding osmotic sleeve. Outside the reservoir wall is the osmotic sleeve, which contains a concentrated solution of sodium chloride. The difference in osmotic pressure between this solution and the surrounding fluid at the implantation site constitutes the osmotic gradient, which drives the delivery of the drug solution. The outermost layer of the system is a semipermeable membrane made of a cellulose ester blend. An additional component, the flow moderator, is a 21-gauge stainless steel tube that is inserted into the body of the osmotic pump after filling. It minimizes passive diffusion of the drug out of the reservoir, reduces the effect of air bubbles trapped in the drug solution, and prevents accidental spillage. It also provides a convenient attachment point for a catheter.

elapsed time to give the average pumping rate. The weight of an explanted pump cannot be used to determine the quantity of drug delivered because the pump imbibes water during operation.

The component materials of the ALZET® osmotic pump are highly compatible with tissue. When assembled units have been implanted in laboratory animals for the functional lifetime of the system, examination of the implantation site has shown minimal adverse tissue reaction.

ALZET® osmotic pumps are used most extensively in rats and mice. Animals that weigh at least 10 g tolerate subcutaneous implantation of the 100-μL-volume pumps. These pumps can be implanted intraperitoneally in animals weighing at least 20 to 25 g. Animals that weigh at least 20 to 25 g tolerate subcutaneous implantation of the 200-μL-volume pumps without deviation from their normal weight values. However, the same pumps are too large for intraperitoneal implantation in mice. Local tissue damage typically is not seen with subcutaneous, intraperitoneal, intravenous, or intraarterial administration and generally is not seen with local tissue microperfusion. For example, ALZET® osmotic pumps caused no noteworthy hydraulic damage or edema when used to perfuse the renal artery in rats at flow rates of 0.50 to 1.0 μL/h (4).

ALZET® osmotic pumps can be used for systemic or localized delivery. By use of a catheter, a drug can be targeted to discrete locations distant from the pump's implantation site, thereby maximizing local effects of the drug while limiting adverse systemic effects. For example, Ruers and colleagues (5) found that intrarenal infusion of prednisolone via the suprarenal or testicular artery prolonged graft survival time to a median of 26 days. In comparison, intraperitoneal injection, intravenous infusion, and intraperitoneal infusion sustained grafts for only 7, 8.5, and 9 days, respectively.

Direct access to the central nervous system (CNS) via a cannula implanted in the cranium is useful when a drug has effects in the CNS but does not cross the blood–brain barrier appreciably (6). Significant doses can be administered directly to the brain, eliminating the uncertainty of systemic pharmacokinetic variables. Drug can be infused into the cerebrospinal fluid via the cerebral ventricles for delivery to many brain regions or directly microperfused into specific regions of solid brain tissue to target discrete structures.

Although ALZET® pumps are designed to provide zero-order delivery, they can be adapted for pulsatile administration. This is accomplished by thermoforming a coil of polyethylene tubing around the pump (7) and filling the pump's reservoir with an appropriate solvent, such as Ringer's or saline solution. The drug solution is placed in the coiled external tubing in segments alternated with vehicle; each segment is separated with an immiscible barrier such as a small air bubble, mineral oil, or silicone oil. Once implanted, the constant flow of solvent from the pump into one end of the tubing forces the segments of the coil to flow out in sequence. For example, Lynch and colleagues (8) experimentally induced rhythms in plasma melatonin levels in pinealectomized rats using a 6-h-on, 18-h-off periodicity with an ALZET® pump. Additionally,

Cronan and colleagues (9) infused nicotine with an 8-h-on, 16-h-off periodicity in rats to mimic drug use in humans.

Detailed descriptions of various techniques for surgically implanting ALZET® osmotic pumps are available from ALZA Corporation (6,10).

APPLICATIONS

Thousands of publications document the use of ALZET® osmotic pumps in over 40 species with more than 1,600 compounds (see Table 3). Key disciplines include neuroscience, cancer and immunology, toxicology, biotechnology, endocrinology, pharmacology, physiology, and cardiology. For a complete bibliography, categorized by drug, route of administration, research discipline, and special interests, see the ALZET website at *http://www.alza.com/alzet*. A bibliography of review articles at the end of this article also provides a good perspective on the literature.

The ALZET® pump has enabled neuroscientists to manipulate the central and peripheral nervous systems of unrestrained animals, permitting simultaneous study of behavioral, motor, and sensory functions. Researchers have administered drugs directly to discrete brain structures, the ventricles, and the spinal cord to bypass the blood–brain barrier. Delivery to peripheral nerves has also been conducted. Using these techniques, ALZET® pumps have contributed to the study of learning and behavior, nerve regeneration, neuronal plasticity, neurodegenerative diseases, drug dependence and tolerance, and neural regulation.

In immunology/cancer research, the ALZET® pump has been used to administer cytokines, target chemotherapeutic agents to a specific organ, and evaluate dosing regimens. Toxicologists have used ALZET® pumps to achieve chronic drug exposure and to conduct teratology research.

Table 3. Classes of Drugs Delivered by ALZET® Osmotic Pumps (As Reported in the Literature)

Anesthetics	Heavy metals
Antibacterials	Hormones
Antibiotics	Immunologic agents
Antibodies	Indicator substances
Anticancer agents	Macromolecules
Anticoagulants	Metabolites
Antiepileptics	Nerve growth factors
Antihypertensives	Neurotransmitters and
Antiparkinson agents	neuromodulators
Antivirals	Oligonucleotides
Barbiturates	Opiates
Benzodiazepines	Peptides
Catecholamines	Prostaglandins
Chelators	Proteins
Cholinergics	Radioisotopes
Cytokines	Renin–angiotensin system
Drugs of abuse	components and inhibitors
Enzymes	Steroids
Gastrointestinal motility	Thyroid and thyroid-related
modulators	hormones
Growth factors	Toxic substances
Growth hormones	Vitamins and minerals

ALZET® pumps have proved useful in biotechnology for characterizing novel proteins and peptides, such as growth factors, while also facilitating exciting new research in which antisense oligonucleotides have selectively blocked expression of a specific protein product. In endocrinology, applications have included research on diabetes, growth and development, and hormone replacement. Targeted delivery using ALZET® pumps has proved helpful in pharmacokinetic studies, where it has allowed the characterization of local effects without the obfuscating effects of rapid drug metabolism and clearance. The pump has been used in pharmacologic studies investigating receptor modulation and animal models of human disease. In cardiology, the ALZET® pump has been used to evaluate novel antihypertensive agents and to stimulate angiogenesis in the arterial wall via adventitial delivery of growth factors.

Although ALZET® pumps are frequently used in preclinical research, they are also used in basic research or in other specialized studies. Some notable examples include studies in space, work with endangered species, and oceanographic measurements. ALZET® pumps have been used to dispense fresh medium in a prototype study of a cell cultivation instrument for Spacelab (11), to test the delivery of recombinant human growth hormone (rhGH) in rats on board the space shuttle *Discovery* (11), and to test the effects of rhGH on the atrophic response of the soleus muscle in space (12).

Endangered species have benefited from ALZET® pumps. The green iguana (*Iguana iguana*), native to Central and South America and once abundant in the rain forest, is now threatened throughout most of its natural habitat. Researchers at the Center for Reproduction of Endangered Species (CRES) have bred iguanas in captivity using infused gonadotrophin-releasing hormone (GnRH) to improve the survival potential of this species (13). CRES has also used the ALZET® pump to infuse GnRH in a previously infertile female cheetah at the San Diego Zoo, resulting in the birth of twins. Infertile for nearly 2 years, the cheetah received 10-min pulses of GnRH every 3 h, a regimen calculated to induce ovulation (14).

ALZET® osmotic pumps have also been adapted by oceanographers at the Monterey Bay Aquarium Research Institute and Moss Landing Marine Laboratories to create a self-contained, continuous flow analyzer that measures nitrate concentrations in seawater during long-term, deep-sea deployment (15).

CONCLUSIONS

For more than 20 years, the ALZET® osmotic pump has provided researchers from many scientific disciplines with continuous, zero-order delivery of drugs for basic and preclinical research. Currently these pumps can deliver drugs at volumes of 0.25–10 µL/h, systematically or targeted to specific tissues, for periods up to 1 month. Further work is planned to add additional volumes and durations and to offer a wider range of add-on delivery devices.

BIBLIOGRAPHY

1. J.W. Fara and N. Ray, in P. Tyle, ed., *Drug Delivery Devices, Fundamentals and Applications*, Dekker, New York, 1988, pp. 137–174.
2. K.T. Rodrigues and J.P. Sumpter, *J. Endocrinol.* **101**, 277–284 (1984).
3. T.F. Davison, B.M. Freeman, and J. Rea, *Gen. Comp. Endocrinol.* **59**, 416–423 (1985).
4. J.F.M. Smits et al., *Am. J. Physiol.* **244**, H304–H307 (1983).
5. T.J.M. Ruers et al., *Transplantation* **41**(2), 156–161 (1986).
6. ALZA Corporation, *ALZET® Osmotic Pumps, Technical Information Manual*, ALZA Corp., Palo Alto, Calif., 1996.
7. N. Ray and F. Theeuwes, in P. Johnson and J.G. Lloyd-Jones, eds., *Drug Delivery Systems: Fundamentals and Techniques*, Ellis Horwood, Chichester, England, 1988, pp. 120–138.
8. H.J. Lynch, R.W. Rivest, and R.J. Wurtman, *Neuroendocrinology* **31**, 106–111 (1980).
9. T. Cronan, J. Conrad, and R. Bryson, *Pharmacol., Biochem. Behav.* **22**(5), 897–899 (1985).
10. ALZA Corporation, *ALZET® Osmotic Pumps Surgical Implantation Techniques*, videotape, ALZA Corp., Palo Alto, Calif., 1986.
11. F.K. Gmünder et al., *J. Biotechnol.* **7**, 217–228 (1988).
12. M. Cronin et al., *Physiologist* **35**(1), S51–S52 (1992).
13. J.A. Phillips et al., *J. Exp. Zool.* **234**, 481–482 (1985).
14. ALZA Corporation, *Special Delivery*, March, p. 2. ALZA Corp., Palo Alto, Calif., 1986.
15. K.S. Johnson, K.H. Coale, and H.W. Jannasch, *Anal. Chem.* **64**(22), 1065A–1075A (1992).

ADDITIONAL READING

Amkraut A.A., Fara J.W., Nichols K.C., and Ray N.P., *The Pharmacology and Toxicology of Proteins*, UCLA Symp. Mol. Cell. Biol., New Ser., Liss, New York, 1987, pp. 131–148.
Amkraut A., Eckenhoff J.B., and Nichols K., *Adv. Drug Delivery Rev.* **4**, 255–276 (1990).
Chandrasekaran S.K., Capozza R., and Wong P.S.L., *J. Membr. Sci.* **3**(3), 271–286 (1978).
Chandrasekaran S.K., Theeuwes F., and Yum S.I., in E.J. Ariëns, ed., *Drug Design*, Academic Press, New York, 1979, Chapter 3, pp. 133–167.
Clarke D.O., *Toxicol. Methods* **3**(4), 223–251 (1993).
Collins J.M., Leyland-Jones B., and Grieshaber C.K., in F.M. Muggia, ed., *Concepts, Clinical Developments, and Therapeutic Advances in Cancer*, Martinus Nijhoff, Boston, 1987, pp. 129–140.
Daemen M.J.A.P., Thijssen H.H.W., and Struyker-Boudier H.A.J., *Adv. Drug Delivery Rev.* **6**, 1–18 (1991).
Eckenhoff B., in S.K. Chandrasekaran, ed., *Controlled Release Systems*, vol. 77, Am. Inst. Chem. Eng., New York, 1981, pp. 1–9.
Eckenhoff B., and Yum S.I., *Biomaterials* **2**, 89–97 (1981).
Eckenhoff B., Theeuwes F., and Urquhart J., *Pharm. Technol.* **5**(1), 35–44 (1981).
Fara J., *J. Parenter. Sci. Technol.* **37**(1), 20–25 (1983).
Fara J.W., *Methods Enzymol.* **112**, 470–484 (1985).
Fara J., and Mitchell C., in H.A.J. Struyker-Boudier, ed., *Rate-Controlled Drug Administration and Action*, CRC Press, Boca Raton, Fla., 1986, Chapter 5, pp. 115–142.

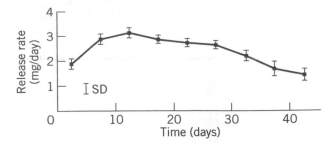

Figure 2. In vitro release profile of pST from a VITS system.

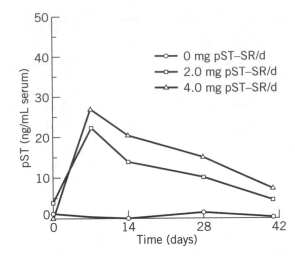

Figure 4. Comparison of serum concentrations of pST in lean gilts as a function of dosage. *Source:* Adapted from Ref. 24.

at 37°C). Pulsatile delivery can also be achieved through system design alteration.

In vivo data in finishing hogs show a good dose–response relationship, as demonstrated in Figure 3. For more than 40 days, pST plasma concentrations were maintained for the three dosages (1.2, 3.6, and 4.8 mg/day).

APPLICATIONS

One extensively studied application of VITS technology is the administration of bovine somatotropin (bST) to cattle and pST to pigs. For example, Baile and colleagues showed that administration of a 42-day VITS bST implant (17 mg/day) increased the growth rate by 16% for subcutaneous implantation and 25% for intraperitoneal implantation. Increases in growth rate were sustained with an 84-day VITS intraperitoneal implant when compared with two successive 42-day implants, suggesting that the formulation retains biological efficacy even when the delivery duration is extended to commercially significant time periods (21).

Another study by Kasser and colleagues compared a control group with a group that received bST from two consecutive 42-day intraperitoneal VITS implants at dosages of 6, 12, and 15 mg/day. Body weight and carcass weight were significantly ($P < .05$) higher in treated animals than in controls. Feed conversion was significantly ($P < .05$) better in treated animals than in controls (22).

Armstrong and colleagues found that multiparous beef cows receiving an 84-day subcutaneous VITS bST implant had significantly ($P < .05$) higher milk yields and calf weaning weights than did cows that received vehicle only (23).

Subcutaneous VITS implants containing pST were compared with controls in a 6-week study in genetically lean and obese barrows and gilts (24). Administration of pST by VITS implant significantly increased efficiency of gain and lean deposition while decreasing fat deposition. Serum pST levels, measured each week, remained significantly higher in treated pigs than in controls throughout the study (Fig. 4) (24).

CONCLUSIONS

VITS is an osmotic implant specifically tailored for subcutaneous or intraperitoneal administration of small amounts of potent substances to animals. The drug reservoir completely isolates drug formulations from the surrounding environment, thus protecting proteins and other water-labile compounds for long periods. VITS is typically designed for zero-order release of agents, but other delivery profiles can be obtained through system design alternatives. VITS has been studied extensively in the release of bovine and porcine somatotropins. Demonstration of its feasibility for zero-order delivery of small amounts of potent molecules in animals has led to its adaptation for use in humans—the DUROS™ technology.

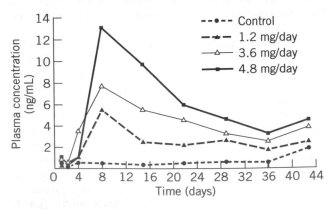

Figure 3. Comparison of plasma concentrations of VITS agent (pST) as a function of its dosage.

BIBLIOGRAPHY

1. P.R. Klink, T.H. Ferguson, and J.L. Magruder, in G.E. Hardee and J.D. Baggot, eds., *Development and Formulation of Veterinary Dosage Forms*, 2nd ed., Dekker, New York, 1998, pp. 145–229.

2. C. Shih, J. Fix, and R.L. Seward, *J. Controlled Release* **25**, 155–162 (1993).

3. S. Geerts et al., *Vet. Parasitol.* **50**, 15–21 (1993).

4. U.S. Pat. 4,959,218 (September 25, 1990), J.B. Eckenhoff et al. (to ALZA Corp.).
5. U.S. Pat. 5,034,229 (July 23, 1991), J.A. Magruder et al. (to ALZA Corp.).
6. U.S. Pat. 5,037,420 (August 6, 1991), J.A. Magruder et al. (to ALZA Corp.).
7. U.S. Pat. 5,057,318 (October 15, 1991), J.A. Magruder et al. (to ALZA Corp.).
8. U.S. Pat. 5,059,423 (October 22, 1991), J.A. Magruder et al. (to ALZA Corp.).
9. U.S. Pat. 5,110,596 (May 5, 1992), J.A. Magruder et al. (to ALZA Corp.).
10. U.S. Pat. 5,135,523 (August 4, 1992), J.A. Magruder et al. (to ALZA Corp.).
11. U.S. Pat. 5,137,727 (August 11, 1992), J.B. Eckenhoff (to ALZA Corp.).
12. U.S. Pat. 5,174,999 (December 29, 1992), J.A. Magruder et al. (to ALZA Corp.).
13. U.S. Pat. 5,180,591 (January 19, 1993), J.A. Magruder, J.R. Peery, and J.B. Eckenhoff (to ALZA Corp.).
14. U.S. Pat. 5,209,746 (May 11, 1993), S.M. Balaban, J.B. Pike, J.P. Smith, and C.A. Baile (to ALZA Corp.).
15. U.S. Pat. 5,234,692 (August 10, 1993), J.A. Magruder, J.R. Peery, and J.B. Eckenhoff (to ALZA Corp.).
16. U.S. Pat. 5,234,693 (August 10, 1993), J.A. Magruder, J.R. Peery, and J.B. Eckenhoff (to ALZA Corp.).
17. U.S. Pat. 5,234,694 (August 10, 1993), J.A. Magruder, J.R. Peery, and J.B. Eckenhoff (to ALZA Corp.).
18. U.S. Pat. 5,238,687 (August 24, 1993). J.A. Magruder, J.R. Peery, and J.B. Eckenhoff (to ALZA Corp.).
19. U.S. Pat. 5,320,616 (June 14, 1994), J.A. Magruder et al. (to ALZA Corp).
20. U.S. Pat. 5,443,461 (August 22, 1995), L.E. Atkinson, J.T. Dunn, R.M. Gale, and D.L. Rivera (to ALZA Corp.).
21. C.A. Baile et al., *J. Anim. Sci.* **71**(1), 131 (1993).
22. T.R. Kasser et al., *J. Anim. Sci.* **71**(1), 131 (1993).
23. J.D. Armstrong et al., *J. Anim. Sci.* **72**(1), 182 (1994).
24. J. Klindt, F.C. Buonomo, and J.T. Yen, *J. Anim. Sci.* **70**, 3721–3733 (1992).

See also PUMPS/OSMOTIC—INTRODUCTION; PUMPS/OSMOTIC—ALZET® SYSTEM; PUMPS/OSMOTIC—DUROS® OSMOTIC IMPLANT FOR HUMANS; PUMPS/OSMOTIC—RUMINAL OSMOTIC BOLUS.

PUMPS/OSMOTIC—DUROS® OSMOTIC IMPLANT FOR HUMANS

JEREMY C. WRIGHT
CYNTHIA L. STEVENSON
GREGORY R. STEWART
ALZA Corporation
Palo Alto, California

KEY WORDS

Biocompatibility
Osmosis
Recombinant technology
Semipermeable membrane
Site-specific delivery
Sodium chloride
Systemic delivery
Zero-order delivery

OUTLINE

Background
System Design
System Performance
Formulation Capabilities
DUROS® Leuprolide Implant
Disease State
Formulation Stability
In Vitro Performance
In Vivo Performance
In Vivo–In Vitro Release Rate and Stability Correlation
Implantation and Explanation
Clinical Experience
Conclusions
Acknowledgments
Bibliography

The DUROS® implant is a miniature, osmotically driven drug delivery system designed for the long-term, parenteral, zero-order delivery of potent therapeutic agents to humans. The DUROS® implant consists of an impermeable titanium alloy cylinder capped on one end by a rate-limiting, semipermeable membrane and on the other end by a plug with an orifice for drug delivery. The interior of the DUROS® implant contains a polymeric piston that separates the osmotic engine from the drug reservoir (Fig. 1). These single-use DUROS® implants are sterile, nonpyrogenic, and nonbiodegradable.

The DUROS® implant functions according to the same osmotic principles as described for other, similar pumps in

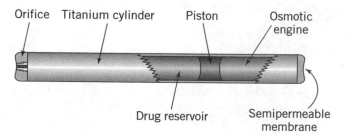

Approximate dimensions: 45 mm long × 4 mm wide

Figure 1. Cross section of a DUROS® Implant.

this encyclopedia. The osmotic engine, a concentrated salt mixture, establishes a very steep osmotic gradient between the interior of the DUROS™ implant and the surrounding interstitial fluid. In response to this osmotic gradient, water flows into the DUROS™ implant at a rate governed by the permeation characteristics of the semipermeable membrane. As water flows into the DUROS™ implant, drug is delivered from the reservoir via the orifice at the same rate and volume.

A unique feature of the DUROS™ implant, compared with other implantable pumps, is its small size (4 mm × 45 mm), allowing implantation virtually anywhere in the body; the resultant drug reservoir volume is less than 200 μL. (DUROS^SM implants with drug reservoir volumes of 50 to 500 μL have been designed.) For systemic administration, the DUROS™ system is implanted under the skin in an outpatient setting with local anesthesia. Explantation at the end of the delivery period is accomplished by a similar, simple surgical procedure. In addition to subcutaneous administration, intravenous, intrathecal, intratumoral, and other forms of targeted drug delivery can be accomplished with the attachment of a catheter.

BACKGROUND

As of 1997, more than 40 biotechnology drug products have been approved, and more than 270 new biotechnology drugs are currently in human clinical trials. Most of these agents are proteins produced by recombinant technology (1). Because of rapid degradation within the stomach and poor absorption from the gastrointestinal tract, proteins and other complex biomolecules cannot be given orally. Drug therapy must therefore rely on parenteral administration via acute injection or preferably through a continuous delivery system. In response to this growing need from the biotechnology sector, researchers designed the DUROS™ implant for the delivery of proteins and peptides.

More than 15 years of research, development, and widespread industry use of osmotic pump technology in animals (the ALZET® osmotic pump, the Push-Melt™ ruminal bolus, and the VITS veterinary implant technology) has demonstrated the potential clinical utility of an implantable osmotic pump suitable for use in humans. In particular, the ALZET® pump has been used in more than 5,200 studies to deliver proteins in nonclinical studies (see PUMPS/OSMOTIC—ALZET® SYSTEM). The widespread use of ALZET® pumps further highlights the need for a human implantable osmotic pump.

The use of a continuous drug delivery system such as the DUROS™ implant offers several pharmacokinetic, pharmacoeconomic, and quality-of-life benefits over traditional bolus dosing methods. Unlike dosing by injection, where blood levels (and clinical efficacy) of the drug vary widely with an initial peak and subsequent trough pattern, the DUROS™ implant delivers drug at a precisely controlled, constant rate within the therapeutic range for long periods. In some therapeutic indications or when using drugs with short half-lives, less drug may be required to achieve the desired effect than with conventional injec-

tions, providing substantial dose savings. The DUROS™ implant therapy may offer other pharmacoeconomic advantages in today's health care environment because it requires no maintenance after implantation. The type of "silent therapy" provided by the DUROS™ implant is not only convenient to the patient but also ensures compliance.

SYSTEM DESIGN

The most important design considerations for the DUROS™ implant were biocompatibility; delivery of stable, active drug molecules; and extended zero-order delivery. All tissue-contacting materials were chosen for their biocompatibility and history of use in human implants. Likewise, the components in contact with the drug formulation (e.g. reservoir, orifice, and piston) had to be compatible with a variety of solvents and excipients used to solubilize or suspend the drug. Additionally, the implant components could not adversely affect the drug stability. Design issues based on these considerations will now be discussed for each of the components of the DUROS™ implant.

The rugged titanium reservoir design possesses sufficient mechanical strength to maintain the system configuration despite possible mechanical stresses, such as impact at the implant site. Additionally, the titanium reservoir is impermeable to water, ensuring drug stability and continual zero-order release.

The DUROS™ implant has a polymeric, semipermeable membrane that is permeable to water but essentially impermeable to the osmotic solutes in the osmotic engine. The membrane may include cellulose esters, polyamides, and polyurethanes, depending on the desired characteristics of the membrane, such as system duration. Testing of polyurethane membranes has shown that the membrane material does not change permeability following implantation. Membrane function is not influenced by extracellular fluid, and the membrane remains chemically stable under physiological conditions.

The osmotic engine of the DUROS™ implant can utilize any number of osmotically active solutes but typically contains a combination of sodium chloride (more than 50% by weight) and other excipients, including gelling polymers such as poly(vinylpyrrolidone) (PVP) or sodium carboxymethyl cellulose. The osmotic engine is produced as one or more tablets.

The elastomeric piston seals the drug formulation from the osmotic engine, thus preventing leakage of osmotic solutes into the drug formulation, which could cause significant loss of drug formulation stability and deviations from zero-order delivery. In addition, the piston is compatible with the osmotic engine and moves with relatively little resistance.

The orifice was designed with a small inner diameter and a suitable length to minimize diffusion of drug from the system. Otherwise, diffusion could represent a significant and uncontrolled contribution to the overall rate of delivery at low pumping rates. The drug formulation is not exposed to the surrounding tissue environment until it is released through the orifice. These features also help to prevent back-diffusion of extracellular components when the system is implanted. Such design features are particularly important for the delivery of biotechnology drugs because proteins, peptides, and other macromolecules are easily rendered inactive by biological processes.

The DUROS® implant packaging maintains sterility and provides a moisture barrier to prevent premature system start-up. The assembled DUROS® implant is sterile and nonpyrogenic. Because most peptides and proteins will not withstand conventional sterilization methods (e.g., irradiation or autoclaving), a sterile DUROS® implant can be produced by irradiating a partially assembled system and performing the remaining filling and assembly steps under aseptic conditions.

SYSTEM PERFORMANCE

When the system is implanted, water is osmotically drawn from the body tissue surrounding the implant (osmotic pressure, π = ~7 atm) through the membrane into the sodium chloride–containing osmotic engine (π = 356 atm). The release rate of the DUROS® implant is given by equation 4 in PUMPS/OSMOTIC—INTRODUCTION, where A is the membrane cross-sectional area for water transport, h is the membrane thickness, k is the effective permeability of the membrane, and $\Delta\pi$ is the osmotic pressure difference across the membrane.

$$dm/dt = (A/h)k\Delta\pi c \qquad (1)$$

If A, h, k, and $\Delta\pi$ are held constant, then a constant rate of drug delivery will result. In the DUROS® implant, A and h are constant by design and manufacture, and k has been shown to remain constant over time, both in vitro and in vivo. The osmotic engine is manufactured with excess sodium chloride to maintain saturation, ensuring that $\Delta\pi$ will remain constant for the intended duration of drug delivery. Hence, a continuous zero-order release profile is expected for the DUROS® implant.

The release rate and duration of a DUROS® implant depend on the overall system size, membrane design, osmotic engine design, drug reservoir size, and concentration of the drug in the reservoir. Figure 2 shows the effect of changing the membrane permeability on release rate and duration while keeping the other parameters constant in the 4 mm × 45 mm device. For a particular reservoir size, the higher the release rate, the shorter the duration of drug delivery.

In vitro studies have demonstrated constant zero-order delivery from DUROS® implants. DUROS® implants were placed in test tubes containing phosphate-buffered saline (PBS) and held at 37°C. The implants were placed in fresh PBS weekly, and the remaining PBS was assayed for drug content. In one study with a target duration of 3 months, the delivery rate performance of five systems was measured by sampling at approximately weekly intervals. The systems exhibited zero-order delivery at 1.0 μL/day for 100 days, with coefficients of variation averaging 3% for days 7 to 104 (data not shown). In another study, 30 DUROS® implants maintained a target of 0.38 μL/day release of blue dye solution for 360 days with a coefficient of

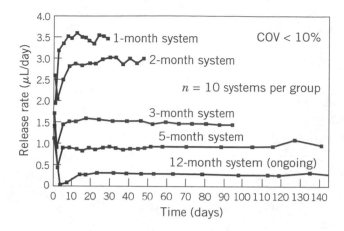

Figure 2. Comparison of release rates in DUROS® Implants as a function of system duration.

variation of less than 9% among the implants (Fig. 3). A zero-order release profile was obtained from the data when assaying on a weekly basis by reversed-phase high-performance liquid chromatography (RP-HPLC). Sampling of cumulative implant output by ultraviolet (UV) spectrophotometry with a flow cell at 6-min intervals for 24 h demonstrated a continuous zero-order release rate (Fig. 4).

FORMULATION CAPABILITIES

DUROS® implants with diameters up to 7 mm have been designed, resulting in drug formulation volumes of 50 to 500 mL. The reservoir volume of the 4 mm × 45 mm implant has a total volume of less than 200 μL. Given the limited formulation volume in a single implant, concentrated drug formulations are usually required. Formulation parameters such as saturation solubility and chemical and physical (aggregation) stability are important. For example, in a 150-mL drug reservoir, a 2-month system delivers 2.5 μL/day. Given a 400-mg/mL solution drug formulation, the implant delivers 1.0 mg/day (60 mg/implant). Similarly, a 500-mL drug reservoir (7 mm × 45 mm) lasting 12 months delivers 1.4 mL/day. In this system, a drug formulation at 400 mg/mL delivers 560 mg/day (200 mg/implant).

Important formulation considerations for the DUROS® implant include stability, solubility, and compatibility. For example, adequate drug stability and potency for a 2-year shelf life plus the implant life are desired. The formulated peptide or protein must be structurally stable and not unfold, gel, or precipitate with loss of activity or production of large particulates capable of clogging the orifice. The formulation must either chemically withstand terminal sterilization or possess sufficient physical stability for sterile filtration, if not aseptically processed. Generation of suspensions in an aseptic environment is often an important factor. The formulation must also be compatible with the pump components in terms of peptide adsorption characteristics and vehicle leachates.

Biotechnology drug moieties can be formulated in aqueous (up to 400 mg/mL) or nonaqueous (up to 500 mg/mL)

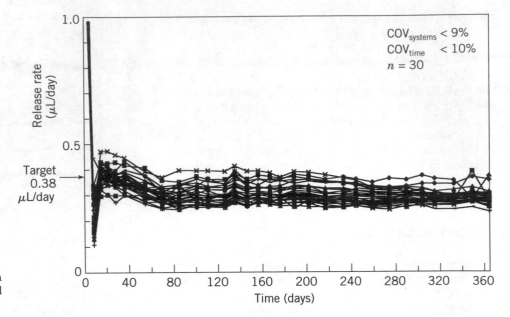

Figure 3. In vitro release rates in the DUROS® Implant as compared with the 0.38-μL/day target.

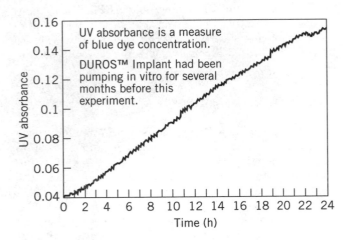

Figure 4. In vitro release rate in the DUROS® Implant, plotted in 6-min intervals.

solutions or in aqueous or nonaqueous suspensions (up to 500 mg/mL), depending on the solubility and stability of the specific molecule. Many times nonaqueous vehicles offer enhanced stability for biomolecules, such as proteins and peptides, by minimizing hydrolytic degradation pathways (2). For drug molecules with solubility or stability limitations, nonaqueous suspensions provide an alternative. For example, stable nonaqueous protein suspensions (e.g., α interferon) in excess of 30% weight in volume (w/v) for 3 to 6 months at 37°C have been reported (3).

DUROS® LEUPROLIDE IMPLANT

The DUROS® Leuprolide Implant is designed to deliver leuprolide continuously at a nominal rate of 125 μg/day over 1 year for the palliative treatment of prostate cancer. It is implanted subcutaneously in the upper arm and explanted after 1 year. The bioactive peptide for the

DUROS® Leuprolide Implant is formulated as a stable nonaqueous solution. This implant is designed to provide an alternative to periodic injections of leuprolide, with the goals of long-term patient compliance and improved quality of life.

DISEASE STATE

Because of the dependence of prostate cancer on circulating androgen levels, testicular androgen ablation (i.e., lowering of circulating testosterone levels) has been the standard for primary therapy of advanced prostate cancer for more than 50 years (4). Continuous administration of luteinizing hormone–releasing hormone (LH-RH) agonists, such as leuprolide acetate, results in the decrease of serum testosterone levels to castrate levels. Since the 1980s, LH-RH agonist therapy has been the primary treatment strategy for androgen ablation (5–7). LH-RH therapies are associated with 80% to 90% stabilization of the disease for 10 to 18 months on average, and 2-year survival is approximately 60% (8,9).

Uninterrupted drug administration is essential to the efficacy of LH-RH agonist therapy, so compliance is critical for prostate cancer patients. Unfortunately, compliance is often a problem, where 44% of patients failed to present for one or more monthly Lupron Depot® injections, and 24% of patients were more than 2 weeks late in obtaining a monthly injection in the U.S. Veterans Administration system (10).

FORMULATION STABILITY

Highly concentrated leuprolide solutions have demonstrated good chemical and physical stability when stored in sealed DUROS® implants at 37°C for the functional lifetime of the implant (2,11,12). Excipients used for the early screening of formulations included solution vehicles such

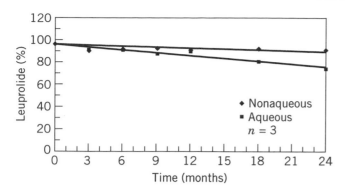

Figure 5. Comparison of the stability of aqueous and nonaqueous formulations in the DUROS® Leuprolide Implant (370 mg/mL at 370°C).

as propylene glycols, poly(ethylene glycols), ethanol, glycofurol, dimethyl sulfoxide, and water. Both aqueous and nonaqueous solution formulations demonstrated 80% to 95% leuprolide remaining after 12 months at 37°C (12). For example, a 370-mg/mL aqueous leuprolide formulation was stable for up to 6 months and then dropped off to slightly below 90% stability, whereas a nonaqueous formulation showed greater than 90% stability for more than 12 months (Fig. 5). The major degradation pathways for the nonaqueous formulation were hydrolysis, racemization, oxidation, and aggregation. Similar degradation pathways were observed for the aqueous formulation. However, in the nonaqueous formulation, the proportion of leuprolide degrading to hydrolytic products decreased while aggregation products increased, resulting in a more stable formulation. In general, no aggregates larger than a trimer were observed. The final formulation used for clinical trials was a 370-mg/mL nonaqueous formulation that provided 92% stability for 2 years at 37°C, which is

adequate for a 2-year shelf life (25°C) in addition to a 1-year implant life (37°C).

IN VITRO PERFORMANCE

When in vitro device release rates were measured ($n = 6$), a zero-order release rate was seen for up to 1 year (Fig. 6). In addition, RP-HPLC analysis revealed greater than 95% in vitro drug stability on average over the test duration.

IN VIVO PERFORMANCE

A 14-month canine study evaluated the DUROS® Leuprolide Implant for serum testosterone concentrations. In the control group, serum testosterone levels fluctuated widely up to 600 ng/dL through the year. Conversely, for every dog that received a DUROS® Leuprolide Implant, testosterone levels were suppressed to castrate levels (below 50 ng/dL) by day 25 and remained completely suppressed (Fig. 7). After 365 days, the first implant was replaced, and blood levels of testosterone remained suppressed to the end of the study (14 months). Histological evaluation of the implantation site did not reveal any unusual changes in the tissue, and neither was any systemic toxicity seen in the study.

Local tissue reactions to the DUROS® Leuprolide Implant were further investigated in rats and Hanford miniature swine. In rats, no unexpected local tissue reactions were observed with the implants over the 38-week study, and in general, tissue reaction scores were equal to or better than those of historical controls receiving control implant material (high-density polyethylene). In miniature swine, no infections or system expulsions occurred over the 12 weeks, and no macroscopic or microscopic evidence of untoward local tissue reactions was seen.

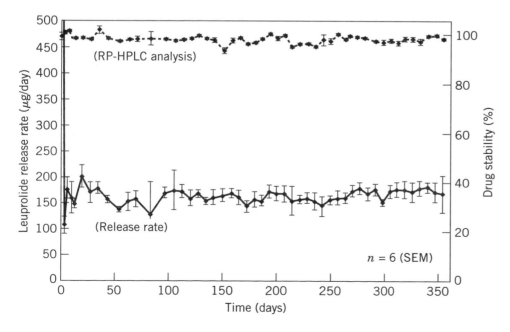

Figure 6. In vitro release rate and drug stability of the DUROS® Leuprolide Implant.

OUTLINE

The Ruminal Therapeutic System (RUTS) Push-Melt™ technology is designed to provide controlled delivery of a drug for up to 1 year in the rumen of cattle and sheep. After oral administration, each capsular system is retained in the rumen, delivering drug for an extended duration. Drug is absorbed through the ruminal or lower intestinal mucosa into the systemic circulation. For cattle, RUTS systems are generally 2 to 3 cm in diameter and up to 10 cm in length. Larger dimensions are possible, depending on the particular application. Up to 10 g of drug can be administered. The RUTS Push-Melt™ technology is applicable to the delivery of parasiticides, insecticides, nutritional supplements, antibiotics, growth promoters, repartitioning agents, and estrus suppressants.

BACKGROUND

In the mid-1980s, the RUTS Push-Melt™ technology was developed to meet the need for drug-dedicated osmotic systems for use in ruminant production animals (1,2). Ruminants such as cattle and sheep have a complex digestive system that includes a large four-chambered stomach; the chambers are the rumen, the reticulum, the omasum, and the abomasum (Fig. 1) (3). In the rumen, ingested cellulose is broken down by microorganisms into simple mono- and disaccharides suitable for digestion. Orally administered, sustained-release delivery systems are typically limited by the target animal's gastrointestinal transit time, but in ruminants (cattle, goats, and sheep) the transit time can be controlled by using a device with sufficient density or a geometrical configuration that keeps it in the rumen for an indefinite period. Objects are retained in the rumen if they are suitably dense (density greater than 2.0 g/cm³, preferably 2.7 to 3.0 g/cm³) or large enough to prevent passage to the lower portions of the gastrointestinal tract or upward through the esophagus in regurgitation. In addition to the RUTS system, density-based systems include a system with two semipermeable membranes attached to a stainless steel cylinder that delivers morantel tartrate (4), a system described by Conrad and Skinner that consists of a high-density cylinder containing monensin dispersed in a biodegradable matrix of polylactic acid (5), and a completely degradable corrosion-based Panacur SR bolus that releases 12 g of fenbendazole over 4 to 5 months (6). Geometry-based systems usually have a mechanism for unfolding to a larger size once in the rumen; before administration, the system is secured in a compact configuration by a degradable tape or closure. The Laby device has "wings" (polymeric strips held in place by a water-degradable tape) that expand in the rumen (7,8); this device has been used to deliver albendazole (Captec Proftril™, SmithKline Beecham) by dissolution from tablets in contact with ruminal fluids (9). Another system, consisting of a rolled trilaminate sheet, uncoils in the rumen and releases morantel tartrate (10).

SYSTEM DESIGN AND FUNCTION

The RUTS Push-Melt™ osmotic system consists of an injection-molded semipermeable membrane that encapsulates an osmotic tablet, a partition layer, drug formulation, and an iron densifier. An exit port screen can be included (Fig. 2). Systems can vary in size from 2 to 3 cm in diameter and up to 10 cm in length, with overall drug loading capacity of up to 10 g.

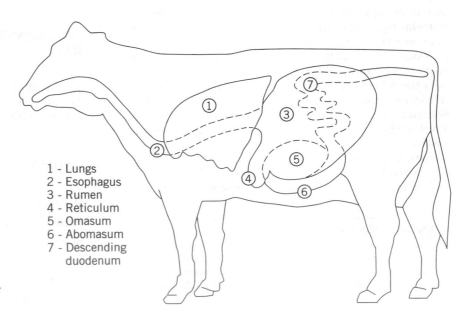

1 - Lungs
2 - Esophagus
3 - Rumen
4 - Reticulum
5 - Omasum
6 - Abomasum
7 - Descending duodenum

Figure 1. Bovine digestive system. *Source:* Ref. 3.

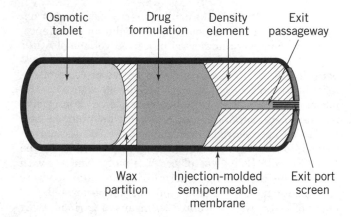

Figure 2. Cross section of the Push-Melt™ Ruminal Therapeutic System (RUTS).

In the aqueous environment of the rumen, water is imbibed through the semipermeable membrane into the osmotic tablet, which swells and pushes against the partition layer. The partition layer forces the thermoresponsive drug formulation through the orifice in the densifier and through the exit port screen if it is present.

The semipermeable membrane controls the rate of water imbibition and therefore the pumping rate of the system. This membrane, composed of cellulosic esters and plasticizers, must be rigid enough to ensure device integrity. The osmotic tablet consists of a swelling hydrogel (e.g., sodium carbomer) and an inorganic, osmotically active salt (e.g., sodium chloride), which provides a high osmotic gradient (more than 300 atm) across the membrane. Between the osmotic tablet and the drug formulation layer is the partition layer, which acts like a plunger in a syringe to ensure a smooth response to the swelling of the osmotic tablet. It consists of a compound with a higher melting point or a higher viscosity than the drug formulation layer. By altering the size of the partition layer, researchers can change the duration of the system while keeping the total dosage constant.

A RUTS Push-Melt™ system can deliver one or more drugs up to 50% by volume in a solution or a suspension. In the drug formulation, drug is suspended or dissolved in a thermoresponsive vehicle that is easily stored as a solid at room temperature. The drug formulation softens to form a viscous, flowable solution or semisolid in the 40°C ruminal environment. Microcrystalline waxes have proved useful as such vehicles (11); drugs can be suspended in these waxes at concentrations in excess of 30% by weight. Because many drugs are essentially insoluble in the wax, such formulations have minimal osmotic activity and high stability. Preparing the drug formulation as a solid improves the stability of compounds with limited solubility and increases the shelf life of the systems. Drugs can be hydrophobic or hydrophilic; if hydrophilic, they are prepared in a hydrophobic vehicle.

The densifier, made of sintered iron, adds sufficient weight to the system so that it will not be regurgitated; the amount of weight required varies with the species. At the end of the exit passageway, the optional exit port screen

provides the system with additional protection from ruminal debris.

Although ruminal boluses are typically removed by magnets during slaughter, all system components are designed to be fragmentable and compatible with rendering equipment in the event that they are not completely removed (12).

The basic mathematical expressions that describe drug release from osmotic systems are given in PUMPS/OSMOTIC—INTRODUCTION. The drug delivery rate equation is

$$dm/dt = (A/h)k\Delta\pi c$$

where $\Delta\pi$ is the osmotic pressure gradient between the osmotic engine and the ruminal environment.

For Push-Melt™ systems, the membrane surface area (A) and the osmotic pressure gradient ($\Delta\pi$) change over time as the degree of hydration (H) increases (2). The effective membrane surface area increases over time as the osmotic tablet swells, but the osmotic engine itself is diluted, decreasing the osmotic pressure gradient. To reflect these time dependencies, the equation is modified as follows:

$$dm/dt = (A_H/h)k\Delta\pi_H c$$

where the subscript H represents the dependence of A and $\Delta\pi$ on osmotic engine hydration. The osmotic pressures of the drug formulation and of the partition layer are assumed to be negligible.

The mechanism of RUTS Push-Melt™ drug delivery is independent of in vivo environmental conditions, mainly because of the low osmotic pressures in the in vivo environment. Because of this, in vivo and in vitro system performance are closely correlated, and in vitro assessment is predictive of in vivo performance and therapeutic outcome.

RUTS Push-Melt™ systems can be designed for a variety of drug delivery profiles such as zero-order, pulsatile, ascending, or descending. They are typically designed for zero-order drug delivery of up to 5 g/day for durations ranging from 1 day to 1 year. With zero-order drug delivery, the RUTS Push-Melt™ system prevents drug plasma concentrations from attaining toxic levels or declining to subtherapeutic levels. Drug can be delivered in pulses by alternating the drug and placebo layers in the formulation layer (13). Ascending and descending release profiles can be designed into the system: Creating an increase in the membrane surface area (through choice of appropriate membrane materials and osmotic agents) results in an ascending profile, whereas providing a subsaturated solution in the osmotic tablet gives a descending profile.

PRODUCTS

Two commercial products have been developed and marketed using the RUTS Push-Melt™ technology. Dura SE®, introduced in 1989, delivers sodium selenite to selenium-deficient cattle for up to 4 months. IVOMEC SR® (ivermectin), released in 1992, delivers the parasiticide ivermectin to cattle for 135 days, controlling parasitic bronchitis and parasitic gastroenteritis for the entire grazing season when used at turnout. It is also effective in the treatment and control of sucking lice, mange mites, and warbles for 135 days after administration.

IVOMEC SR® Bolus (Ivermectin)

Ivermectin is a unique chemical entity discovered and developed by scientists at Merck Research Laboratories. Its broad-spectrum efficacy and wide margin of safety make it an ideal anthelmintic agent (14). Ivermectin acts by paralyzing parasitic nematodes, arachnids, insects, and warbles; this result is attributed to ivermectin's effect on the central nervous system of these parasites, specifically its effect on the mediation of neurotransmission by γ-aminobutyric acid (GABA) (15). At therapeutic doses, ivermectin has no effect on cattle because it does not readily penetrate the bovine central nervous system. For a discussion of the pharmacokinetics of ivermectin, see Baggot and McKellar (16).

Ivermectin can be given orally, parenterally, or topically. Continuous release is advantageous because animals are susceptible to reinfection when grazed on infected pastures. When ivermectin is given as a continuous-release ruminal bolus, steady-state levels of ivermectin can be ensured with minimal stress to the animal and minimal handling by the producer.

When ivermectin was delivered ruminally by a weighted ALZET® osmotic pump, mean plasma levels of ivermectin were predictable over a 0- to 40-μg/kg/day dosage range; bioavailability was 40% (17). Using the same method of administration, Egerton and colleagues showed that ivermectin was effective in preventing the establishment of nine nematode parasite species in cattle (18). A daily dose of up to 40 μg/kg/day, delivered intraruminally, was effective in protecting grazing calves against these parasites. This work helped establish the target delivery rate for ivermectin in fully grown cattle (300 kg) at 12 mg/day (2).

The IVOMEC SR® Bolus for cattle contains 1.72 g ivermectin as a 22% (w/w) suspension dispersed in a white, microcrystalline wax. The system includes an exit port screen (Fig. 2), which prevents ingress of ruminal matter into the system and increases the internal operating pressure of the system. The IVOMEC SR® Bolus is 9 cm long and 2.5 cm in diameter. Delivering 12 mg/day of ivermectin for 135 days, it is effective for the treatment and season-long control of parasitic bronchitis (lungworm), gastrointestinal nematodes, sucking lice, mange mites, and warbles.

Administration of the IVOMEC SR® Bolus is accomplished by using a balling gun of appropriate size to deliver the bolus into the pharynx just beyond the back of the animal's tongue (Fig. 3) (19). Once administered, the IVOMEC SR® Bolus has sufficient density to be retained in the rumen for an extended duration. Biting or regurgitation of the system occurs infrequently. In the few reported cases of biting, system integrity was not compromised, and the system could be readministered.

Because of the homogeneous nature of the drug formulation (a hydrophobic suspension), ivermectin delivery in an IVOMEC SR® Bolus can be directly calculated from the weight of the pumped drug formulation (2). Hence, when systems were immersed in a fixed volume of water or phosphate-buffered saline maintained at ruminal temperature (40°C), in vitro system performance could be determined from assayed ivermectin delivery or gravimetric measurements of the formulation delivered. For in vivo measurement, ruminants were fistulated so that the system could be removed periodically for analysis, then returned to the ruminal environment. In this case, the IVOMEC SR® Bolus was placed in a metal canister with perforations on one end to permit ruminal fluid access to the osmotic tablet; the other end was not perforated, and entry of water was prevented by means of O-rings. Drug formulation was released into this latter end of the collection vessel and analyzed on periodic removal (2).

IVOMEC SR® Start-up and Shutdown Delivery Profiles. Rapid, reproducible, and predictable drug delivery start-up is important with ruminal boluses for immediate prophylaxis, especially in the spring when animals are sent to fresh pastures, where an increase of parasitic larvae is typical. With prototype IVOMEC SR® boluses, drug delivery was not instantaneous; a time lag was associated with water permeation into the osmotic tablet and pressurization of the drug formulation. To minimize this start-up time, the IVOMEC SR® Bolus is prehydrated by adding a fixed amount of water to the packaged system, causing an increase in the internal hydrostatic pressure as water is imbibed into the osmotic tablet. Once in the 40°C ruminal environment, the thermoresponsive drug formulation softens, with rapid onset of osmotic pumping. Zingerman and colleagues (2) have shown that the onset of drug delivery for hydrated (1.3 g of water added) IVOMEC SR® boluses is rapid (2–3 days). Steady-state delivery is reached in 7 to 10 days. Anhydrous systems took 2 to 3 weeks to reach steady-state delivery (Fig. 4) (2).

Reproducible and predictable delivery termination for the IVOMEC SR® bolus is critical to establish the optimum withdrawal period so that drug residues are minimized to safe levels before slaughter. For the IVOMEC SR® Bolus, the withdrawal period (period since last drug administration in which the animal cannot be slaughtered for human consumption) is 180 days. As shown in Figure 4 (2), termination occurred rapidly at approximately 135 days for both in vivo and in vitro systems; within 14 days, shutdown was complete (2).

IVOMEC SR® In Vivo–In Vitro Release-Rate Correlation. Good agreement has been shown between the in vitro and in vivo release profiles for the IVOMEC SR® Bolus (2). Figure 5 (2) demonstrates this agreement, which has also been verified with seven large, commercial-scale batches. The cumulative coefficient of variation at the time when all the drug formulation was expelled was 4% for in vivo systems and 4.2% for in vitro systems.

IVOMEC SR® Efficacy. In a study by Yazwinski and colleagues, calves treated with the IVOMEC SR® Bolus had significantly fewer fecal egg counts and significantly fewer nematodes at necropsy than did the untreated calves; both

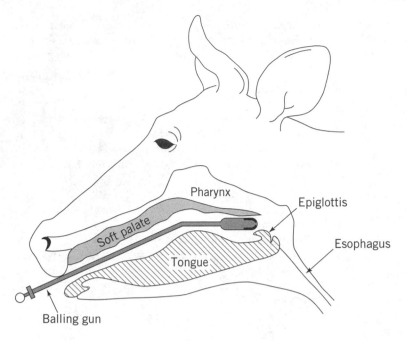

Figure **3.** Bolus administration technique for controlled-release boluses. *Source:* Ref. 19.

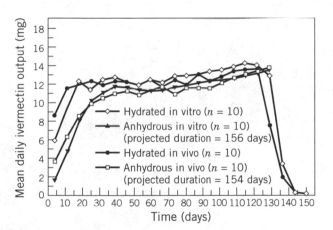

Figure 4. Comparison of anhydrous and hydrated (1.3 g) in vitro and in vivo ivermectin output profiles of IVOMEC SR® Bolus samples. *Source:* Ref. 2.

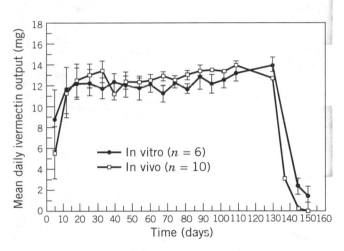

Figure 5. Comparison of in vitro and in vivo release profiles of ivermectin (bolus samples hydrated at 1.3 g). *Source:* Ref. 2.

groups were given infective larvae inoculum and grazed on an infected pasture. The ivermectin bolus prevented the establishment of not only actively developing parasitic nematodes but also arrested larvae (e.g., *Ostertagia* EL₄). No adverse reactions were seen, and all IVOMEC SR® boluses remained in the rumen throughout the study (20).

Dura SE® Bolus (selenium)

Selenium deficiency in cattle is a problem in many areas of the world, including parts of the United States. A Push-Melt system, the Dura SE® Bolus has been developed to deliver sodium selenite at the rate of 3 mg of selenium per day to cattle for 120 days. The system does not include the optional exit port screen; otherwise, the design is as shown in Figure 2. The drug formulation consists of sodium selenite dispersed in a microcrystalline wax. Figure 6 shows the in vitro, zero-order release profile obtained for

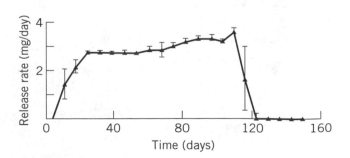

Figure 6. In vitro release profile of selenium delivered from a Dura-SE® bolus.

the Dura SE® Bolus. Adair and colleagues examined the in vivo behavior of Dura SE® Bolus and found that release reached a steady state within 4 weeks, continued at steady-state levels for 16 weeks, and dropped to less than 1% of steady-state levels in the final 2 weeks. Mean in vivo release was 3.1 mg/day, with a range of 2.4 to 4.1 mg/day. Excellent in vivo–in vitro correlation was obtained (21). Figure 7 shows selenium blood levels from selenium-deficient cattle treated with the Dura SE® Bolus. Selenium has a relatively long half-life, which is reflected in the slowly rising selenium levels. Nevertheless, selenium levels were in the normal range (more than 0.08 ppm) by day 35 (22).

In a 220-day study, Campbell and colleagues assigned 150 selenium-deficient, pregnant beef cattle to one of four treatment groups: one Dura SE® Bolus at day 0, two Dura SE® Boluses (one administered on day 0 and the second one on day 119), two selenium pellets at day 0, and control. The Dura SE® Bolus is designed to release 3 mg/day for 120 days; the 30-g pellets contain 10% elemental selenium and are designed to provide selenium supplementation for up to 18 months. At the end of the study, blood levels of selenium were significantly ($P < .01$) higher in the two-Dura SE® Bolus group than in any other group. Calves from cattle in the selenium-supplemented groups had significantly ($P < .001$) higher blood selenium levels, both before and after suckling, than did controls (23).

Maas and colleagues administered the Dura SE® Bolus to selenium-deficient beef heifer calves and found that mean blood selenium was maintained at more than 0.10 μg/mL for 188 days. No untoward effects were seen in the treatment group (24).

CONCLUSIONS

The RUTS Push-Melt™ osmotic system is an innovative adaptation of osmotic technology for the delivery of agents to ruminants. It extends the delivery duration beyond the 28-day lifetime of the ALZET® pump to 4 months or longer. Formulation options include suspensions as well as solutions. Commercialized applications of this technology have been developed for the delivery of ivermectin, a potent parasiticide, and sodium selenite, a nutritional supplement.

BIBLIOGRAPHY

1. U.S. Pat. 4,595,583 (June 17, 1986), B. Eckenhoff, R. Cortese, and F.A. Landrau (to ALZA Corp).
2. J.R. Zingerman et al., *J. Controlled Release* **47**(1), 6 (1997).
3. G.L. Zimmerman and E.P. Hoberg, *Parasitol. Today* **4**(2), 55 (1988).
4. R.M. Jones, *Vet. Parasitol.* **12**, 223–232 (1983).
5. J.M. Conrad and D.S. Skinner, *J. Controlled Release* **9**, 133–147 (1988).
6. P. Berghen et al., *Vet. Q.* **16**, 161–164 (1994).
7. U.S. Pat. 3,844,285 (October 29, 1974), R.H. Laby (to Commonwealth Scientific and Industrial Research Organization).
8. N. Anderson, R.H. Laby, R.K. Prichard, and D. Hennessey, *Res. Vet. Sci.* **29**, 331–341 (1980).
9. M.Y.K. Ho, D.W. Gottschall, and R. Wang, in D.H. Hutson, ed., *Xenobiotics and Food-Producing Animals: Metabolism and Residues*, American Chemical Society, New York, 1992, pp. 149–157.
10. W.A. Boettner et al., *J. Controlled Release* **8**, 23–30 (1988).
11. J.B. Tuttle, in A. Standen, ed., *Kirk-Othmer Encyclopedia of Chemical Technology*, 2nd ed., Interscience, New York, 1963–1970, pp. 92–112.
12. U.S. Pat. 5,206,024 (April 27, 1993), B. Eckenhoff (to ALZA Corporation).
13. U.S. Pat. 4,723,958 (February 9, 1988), D.G. Pope and A.E. Royce (to Merck & Co. Inc.).
14. W.C. Campbell, *Ivermectin and Abamectin*, Springer-Verlag, New York, 1989.
15. W.C. Campbell et al., *Science* **221**, 823–828 (1983).
16. J.D. Baggot and Q.A. McKellar, *J. Vet. Pharmacol. Ther.* **17**, 409–419 (1994).
17. D.G. Pope, P.K. Wilkinson, J.R. Egerton, and J. Conroy, *J. Pharm. Sci.* **74**(10), 1108–1110 (1985).
18. J.R. Edgerton, D. Suhayda, and C.H. Early, *Vet. Parasitol.* **22**, 67–75 (1986).
19. R.J. Gyurik, in P. Tyle ed., *Drug Delivery Devices, Fundamentals and Applications*, Dekker, New York, 1988, p. 569.
20. T.A. Yazwinski, H. Featherston, and C. Tucker, *Am. J. Vet. Res.* **56**(12), 1599–1602 (1995).
21. D. Adair et al., *J. Pharm. Sci.* **76**(11), S253 (1987).
22. G.J. Sumner, *Proc. Acad. Vet. Consult. Meet.*, August 11–12, Kansas City, Kans., 1988.
23. D.T. Campbell et al., *Am. J. Vet. Res.* **51**(5), 813–817 (1990).
24. J. Maas, J.R. Peauroi, D.W. Weber, and F.W. Adams, *Am. J. Vet. Res.* **55**(2), 247–250 (1994).

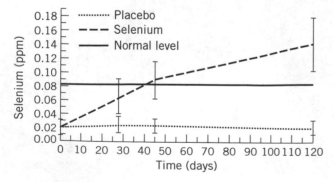

Figure 7. Selenium blood levels in cattle administered a Dura-SE® bolus. *Source:* Ref. 22.

See also PUMPS/OSMOTIC—INTRODUCTION; PUMPS/OSMOTIC—ALZET® SYSTEM; PUMPS/OSMOTIC—VITS VETERINARY IMPLANT; PUMPS/OSMOTIC—DUROS™ OSMOTIC IMPLANT FOR HUMANS.

R

RELEASE KINETICS, DATA INTERPRETATION

Balaji Narasimhan
Rutgers University
Piscataway, New Jersey

Surya K. Mallapragada
Iowa State University
Ames, Iowa

Nicholas A. Peppas
Purdue University
West Lafayette, Indiana

KEY WORDS

Drug release kinetics
Mathematical models
Polymer carriers
Release mechanisms

OUTLINE

Controlled release of drugs, proteins, and other bioactive agents can be achieved by incorporating them either in dissolved or dispersed form in polymers (1,2). During the design stage of these formulations or during experimental verification of their release behavior, it is desirable to develop and use simple and sophisticated mathematical models to describe the release kinetics (3). Although these models are clearly based on transport (diffusion) equations, they are commonly known in the pharmaceutical or drug delivery field as kinetic models or kinetic expressions, because they describe a time-dependent behavior of the drug release.

From a mathematical-modeling point of view, controlled-release systems may be classified according to the controlling physical mechanism(s) of release of the incorporated drug. We have proposed a convenient method (4) based on the mechanism of transport for categorizing them as diffusion-controlled, swelling-controlled, osmotically controlled, and chemically controlled systems.

Mathematical modeling of the release kinetics of specific classes of controlled-release systems may be used to

1. Predict drug release rates from and drug diffusion behavior through polymers, thus avoiding excessive number of experiments
2. Elucidate the physical mechanisms of drug transport by simply comparing the release data to mathematical models

Here we present a critical summary of important mathematical models for the description of drug release from controlled-release systems. In this article we have tried to incorporate only models that accurately depict the physical situation of the problems modeled. Unfortunately, the pharmaceutical literature includes a variety of inappropriately simplified, semiempirical or pseudo–steady-state models. The validity of these models is questionable, and their utility in analysis of drug diffusion data is doubtful. Most of these models have been ignored, except for one (the Higuchi equation), which has been included for historical reasons.

Mechanistic aspects of the diffusion phenomena observed in drug delivery systems are by necessity related to an accurate mathematical model and to the structural characteristics of the polymeric material under consideration. However, very few reviews address these two aspects of controlled-release systems (3–6). Here, we critically evaluate existing mathematical models for drug release from polymeric systems. Unfortunately, lack of a systematic analysis and classification is responsible for the use of inappropriate models, not necessarily describing the experimental conditions of the work of many investigators.

DIFFUSION IN DRUG DELIVERY SYSTEMS

With the exception of a number of swelling-controlled release systems, most polymeric formulations for drug release may be described by the two forms of Fick's law of diffusion, which can be written as equations (1) and (2) for one-dimensional diffusion:

$$j_i = D_{ip} \frac{dc_i}{dx} \tag{1}$$

$$\frac{\partial c_i}{\partial t} = D_{ip} \frac{\partial^2 c_i}{\partial x^2} \tag{2}$$

In these equations, c_i and j_i are the concentration and mass flux of drug I, respectively; x and t are position and time of release; and D_{ip} is the drug diffusion coefficient through the polymer.

Several assumptions have been made in describing drug diffusion through polymers by equations 1 and 2. First, as one-dimensional diffusion is appropriate for treatment of drug release from thin, planar systems, application of this analysis to thick slabs or short cylinders is incorrect. Then, the drug diffusion coefficient D_{ip} is usually assumed to be independent of drug concentration. Finally, j_i is the drug flux with respect to the mass average velocity v of the system.

Fickian diffusion equations can be solved by standard mathematical techniques (7), provided that sufficient information about initial and boundary conditions of the pharmaceutical experimental situation is provided.

Solution of equations 1 or 2 provides the following information about drug release through polymers:

1. Determination of concentration profiles from the normalized drug concentration, c/c_o, versus dimensionless position, x/δ, as a function of dimensionless Fourier time, $D_{ip}t/\delta^2$. Here, c_o is a reference drug concentration, and δ is the slab thickness.

2. Drug release rates, dM_t/Adt, can be determined by differentiating the previous expressions with respect to position and evaluating the derivative at the water– or dissolution–medium interface. Here, A is the diffusional cross-sectional area.

$$\frac{dM_t}{Adt} = \left[D_{ip} \frac{\partial c_i}{\partial x} \right]_{x=surf} \tag{3}$$

3. The total amount of drug released per cross-sectional area, M_t/A, can be determined by integrating the previous expression over release time.

$$\frac{M_t}{A} = \int_0^t \frac{dM_t}{Adt} \, dt = \int_0^t \left[D \frac{\partial c_i}{\partial x} \right]_{x=surf} dt \tag{4}$$

Application of these equations to experimental data of drug release is often conveniently achieved with the use of the semiempirical equations 5 and 6 describing the fractional release, M_t/M_∞, and release rate, dM_t/Adt, as functions of release time, t. Here M_∞ is the amount of drug released at long times, which may or may not be equal to the total drug incorporated in a device (8,9).

$$\frac{M_t}{M_\infty} = kt^n \tag{5}$$

$$\frac{dM_t}{Adt} = nkt^{n-1} \tag{6}$$

The importance of this analysis is easily understood (Fig. 1) because most mathematical solutions of equation 2 for Fickian drug diffusion give release kinetics described by equation 5 with $n = 0.5$. Consequently, the release rate is proportional to $t^{-1/2}$.

A special case of release kinetics with $n = 1$ can be obtained when describing drug release from membrane-type diffusion-controlled systems, some geometrical

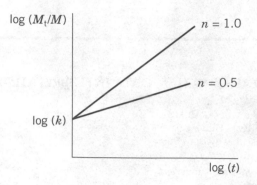

Figure 1. Schematic representation of log (normalized drug released) as a function of log (release time).

shapes of matrix systems (e.g., hemispheres), or swelling-controlled release systems. This type of release kinetics is commonly known as zero-order release kinetics because it is characterized by constant drug-release rates (10–13).

RELEASE KINETICS FROM DIFFUSION-CONTROLLED SYSTEMS

In diffusion-controlled release systems, drug diffusion through the polymer is achieved by molecular diffusion due to concentration gradients. Depending on the molecular structure of the polymer, these systems may be classified as porous or nonporous. Porous controlled-release systems contain pores that are large enough that diffusion of the drug is accomplished through water that has filled the pores of the polymer (14). These pores are usually of size greater than 200–500 Å.

Nonporous systems contain meshes of molecular (drug) dimensions. Molecular diffusion occurs effectively through the whole polymer, and the drug diffusion coefficient refers to the polymer phase (14). The macromolecular structure of the polymer affects drug diffusion according to theoretical analyses discussed elsewhere (15). Some of the polymer parameters controlling the drug diffusion coefficient are degree of crystallinity and size of crystallites, degree of cross-linking, degree of swelling, and molecular weight of the polymer. Many swollen, porous polymer systems retain the main characteristics of the porous structure so that drug diffusion occurs simultaneously through water-filled pores and through the swollen polymer per se.

The study of controlled release actually requires the study of diffusion, or transport through a particular medium. There are several types of transport mechanisms that can occur, with the most important being ordinary diffusion. The gradient that produces this diffusional behavior is due to a concentration gradient. It is only one of the forms of gradients that can be responsible for the drug release. In fact, it should be referred to as chemical potential gradient rather than concentration gradient. We are writing here for one dimension, but the actual system will be in three dimensions. The true type of release is a result of a gradient of activity, where the activity has incorporated in it the true nonideal behavior of the drug or solutes that is being released at the same time. The nonideal behavior is expressed in terms of the activity coefficient. By multiplying the activity coefficient by the mole fraction, we obtain the activity that leads to the gradient. In addition to this transport mechanism, one should expect to see convection when the pores of the carrier are large. In that case, there will be a flux of drug due to the drug being carried along with the solvent itself.

Another type of transport we may sometimes see is facilitated transport, otherwise known as carrier-mediated transport. It effectively involves one or more components being transported relatively quickly because they have reacted or formed a complex with another chemical agent that has a higher solubility in the phase through which it is diffusing. These are the three main mechanisms of transport, and within these there are unusual transport processes like osmotic transport. There is also relaxation-controlled mechanism, which is a significantly different mechanism. It happens in only one type of controlled-release device, which will be discussed separately. Many of the situations that will be discussed involve transport and reaction at the same time. This may be a reaction into the polymer or into the drug being released, so the equation will have this included in the expression.

The classical equation by which one expresses drug transport through a carrier is Fick's law. Fick's first law describes the flux of the drug, peptide, or protein that is diffusing as a function of a concentration gradient in one direction. This is the simplest form of the equation and can be written in three dimensions or in different coordinate systems. It is important to note that in the simplest possible form that is found in the literature (7), the equation is given in terms of a concentration gradient, not an activity or chemical potential gradient. The equation is modified somewhat if it is in terms of a chemical potential gradient. It must be noted that the concentration units are usually in moles/cm^3, and that gives a flux of moles/cm^2/s. This is the difference between a flux and a rate, where the rate of transport of a drug is expressed in units of mol/s. The flux is expressed per area of release, whereas a rate is expressed simply per time.

For release from a thin film or tablet, the flux per area includes two areas, the upper and lower surface, whereas the rate doesn't have an area at all. As the equation is written here, it is assumed that the diffusion coefficient is constant. Several assumptions are made. The first one is that whether it is a controlled-release device with a large or a small amount of drug in it, the drug exhibits a constant rate. This assumes that the diffusion coefficient does not depend on the concentration of drug, a major hypothesis that is unfortunately incorrect. However, traditionally in the field of controlled release, it has been difficult to express the diffusion coefficient in terms of more sophisticated theories. The diffusion coefficient does not remain constant with concentration. Typical values of the drug diffusion coefficients in polymers range from 10^{-6} to 10^{-7} cm^2/s for diffusion in rubbery polymers and from 10^{-10} to 10^{-12} cm^2/s for diffusion in glassy polymers.

In the Eyring analysis (16), the diffusion coefficient, which is the ease of transport through the polymer carrier system, can be easily calculated as

$$D = \lambda^2 v/6 \qquad (7)$$

Here λ is the diffusional jump through the polymer or the specific system being studied. This diffusional jump is related to the polymer and the drug studied. The second parameter, v, is the frequency of jumping. Thus, in the Eyring theory, diffusion is not a continuous process, and we can distinguish specific jumps. The parameter λ, which is the diffusional jump parameter, is a function of the diffusing species, v_i, the available volume space, V_p, and other characteristics of the system.

Mathematical modeling of such situations has been a major problem in physical chemistry and has been addressed over the last 40 years by many investigators. One of the earliest published studies is that of Ogston (17) involving transport of spheres in stochastic networks.

In 1961, Fujita (18) introduced the idea of free volume in diffusional problems. He defined the free volume, v_f, and came up with a free-volume theory with the drug diffusion coefficient having an exponential dependence on the free volume.

$$D = D_o \exp(-k/v_f) \qquad (8)$$

The Fujita theory was modified in the late 1960s by Yasuda and Lamaze (19). This was the first exact free-volume theory in which the diffusion coefficient of the diffusing species through a polymer structure is described in a rather accurate way. This approach is based on the molecular level and tries to explain how diffusion occurs in a controlled-release device. Unfortunately, our field has been marred with improper expressions and incorrect definitions.

Transport through these systems is the classical solute transport in porous media that one would find in any chemical engineering textbook (20). The classical way of describing the diffusion coefficient in such a system is as an effective diffusion coefficient related to the diffusion coefficient of the drug through the pores filled with a solution of drug, D_{iw}.

$$D_{eff} = D_{iw}\varepsilon/\tau \qquad (9)$$

In reality, it is not water that occupies these pores but a solution of the drug. As the release occurs, more of the drug is dissolved, and the solution becomes more and more dilute. The porosity is the fraction of pores in the system that are open ($0 < \varepsilon < 1$). The tortuosity, τ, indicates the tortuous path of transport of a drug through this particular porous network structure. For example, in the case of a straight cylindrical pore, the tortuosity is 1 because the diffusion path is straight. If, however, the pores are tilted at 45°, the tortuosity becomes $\sqrt{2}$, or 1.41. As the path becomes more tortuous, τ becomes 3–5. This is the simplest way to describe a situation in a controlled-release system with large pores.

Faxén (21) proposed the following equation for diffusion of spheres through porous media:

$$D/D_b = (1 - \lambda)^2(1 + \alpha\lambda + \beta\lambda^3 + \gamma\lambda^5) \qquad (10)$$

Here λ is the ratio of the drug radius, r_s, to the pore average radius, r_p. The diffusion coefficient of the sphere through the pore, D, relative to the diffusion coefficient in bulk solution, D_b, is equal to the semiempirical relation just shown that has been proven for a variety of systems. The diffusion in this porous system is very much dependent on the size of the drug and the size of the pore. We should expect the parameter D/D to attain a limit of one.

A swelling mechanism requires that the water come to the surface and start swelling the polymer itself. In such situations, the diffusion coefficient is very much dependent on the concentration of water that is incorporated into the system. It is interesting that this process takes effectively place in "layers," so that in the case of a controlled-release device in the form of a thin disk or tablet, we expect that the layers on the surface will have swollen first whereas the center will still be a solid. The diffusional behavior of water into the drug-containing system can be described by the following Fujita equation:

$$D_{drug} = D_{do} \exp\{-\alpha(\beta - c_w)\} \qquad (11)$$

The diffusion coefficient of the drug is equal to a preexponential term multiplied by an exponential relation, where α and β are two characteristic constants of the polymeric system and c_w is the water concentration of the system. Hence, the higher the concentration of water, the higher the diffusion coefficient of the drug. The terms α and β can be determined by the free-volume theory or the Duda–Ventas theory (22), where several terms appear that are known for specific polymer systems and can be evaluated to give α and β.

Reservoir (Membrane) Systems

In reservoir (membrane) systems, the bioactive agent is usually enclosed at relatively high concentrations between two semipermeable membranes and is placed in contact with a dissolution medium (water or other biological fluid). The bioactive agent may be solvent free or in the form of a concentrated solution.

Equation 1 may be used to describe drug release through reservoir systems. However, because the concentration c_i in this equation refers to drug concentration in the membrane and because this value is difficult to determine experimentally, it is customary to relate drug concentrations in the membrane through the partition (distribution) coefficient, K.

The partition coefficient describes thermodynamic rather than structural characteristics of the drug/polymer/solvent system. It is rather easy to determine experimentally, and it is a measure of drug solubility in a swollen polymer.

When the concentration of the released bioactive agent in the phase external to the system is maintained at a constant low level of concentration, for example, by good agitation and continuous removal of the released drug, equation 1 may be integrated over the thickness of the membrane (for plane sheet geometry) to give equations 12

and 13, where c_{i1}, c_{i2} are drug concentration in the two sides of a membrane:

$$\frac{dM_t}{Adt} = \frac{D_{ip}K}{\delta} (c_{i2} - c_{i1}) \qquad (12)$$

$$M_t = \frac{D_{ip}KA(c_{i2} - c_{i1})}{\delta} t \qquad (13)$$

Clearly drug release from these systems is zero order, that is, the release rate of drug does not depend on time. The amount of drug released from such a device for the case of two specific drugs as a function of time is shown in Figure 2.

Similarly, for cylindrical devices it is readily shown that

$$\frac{dM_t}{dt} = \frac{D_{ip}KA}{\ln(r_e/r_i)} (c_{i2} - c_{i1}) \qquad (14)$$

and

$$M_t = \frac{D_{ip}KA(c_{i2} - c_{i1})}{\ln(r_e/r_i)} t \qquad (15)$$

where r_e and r_i are the external and internal radii of the cylinder, respectively, and A is the length of the cylinder. In both situations of slabs and cylinders, one-dimensional diffusion is assumed. This assumption requires that these equations be applied only for analysis of release from thin membranes or long cylindrical systems. Corrections for edge effects due to violation of the one-dimensional diffusion assumption are available (23), if thick membranes are used. However, the preferable method of modeling would be numerical solution of the three-dimensional diffusion problem.

For spherical reservoir systems, the corresponding equations for drug release are

$$\frac{dM_t}{dt} = \frac{4\pi D_{ip}K}{(r_e - r_i)/r_e r_i} (c_{i2} - c_{i1}) \qquad (16)$$

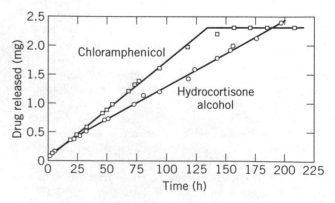

Figure 2. Zero-order release as obtained from a constant-activity reservoir source for chloramphenicol and hydrocortisone alcohol. *Source:* Reproduced with permission from Ref. 1. Copyright 1974 Plenum.

and

$$M_t = \frac{4\pi D_{ip}K(c_{i2} - c_{i1})}{(r_e - r_i)/r_e r_i} t \tag{17}$$

Therefore, drug-release rates from conventional reservoir systems are time independent. However, they depend on the concentration difference, geometry of the device, thermodynamic characteristics of the system (solubility, through the partition coefficient), and structure of the polymer (through the diffusion coefficient).

Situations of drug release from membrane systems at low initial drug concentration or to experimental vessels of finite volumes cannot be modeled with the equations given previously. Instead, equation 18 has been derived (23) for the drug release rate from these systems.

$$\frac{dM_t}{dt} = \frac{M_\infty D_{ip}KA}{V_1\delta} \exp\left[\frac{-D_{ip}KA(V_1 + V_2)}{\delta V_1 V_2} t\right] \tag{18}$$

Here V_1 and V_2 are the volumes of the device and the vessel, respectively, and M_∞ is the initial loading of the device. The release rate in this situation is an exponential function of release time.

Special release problems observed with reservoir devices include time lag and burst effects. These effects are related to the time history of the device, and they have been mathematically analyzed in previous reviews (1).

The time lag and burst effects alter the initial release kinetics of the expected steady-state release behavior of membrane systems due to accumulation of drug (burst effect) or due to the induction period for drug diffusion (time-lag effect).

It has been previously shown (1) that for membrane devices exhibiting time-lag effects, the steady-state expression (at long times) for fractional drug release is given by equation 19:

$$M_t = \frac{AD_{ip}c_{i1}}{\delta}\left[t - \frac{\delta^2}{6D_{ip}}\right] \tag{19}$$

Here c_{i1} is the initial drug concentration in the membrane.

In a similar manner, one can derive equation 20 for the fractional drug release of membrane devices exhibiting burst effects.

$$M_t = \frac{AD_{ip}c_{i1}}{\delta}\left[t + \frac{\delta^2}{3D_{ip}}\right] \tag{20}$$

The second terms in the parentheses of equations 19 and 20 are known as the characteristic time lag and burst time, θ_1 and θ_b, respectively, and they are useful in determining drug-diffusion coefficients in membranes by simple release experiments. More recently, the role of the burst effect in drug-release kinetics from matrix systems has been analyzed, and we discuss this in detail in the section on matrix systems.

Porous Reservoir Systems. Release from porous reservoir systems of hydrophobic polymers may be modeled by equations 9 to 11 where the diffusion coefficient is replaced by the effective diffusion coefficient, D'_{eff}. This parameter de-

scribes diffusion through water-filled pores (14,24) and incorporates the porosity (void fraction), ε, and tortuosity, τ, in the drug-diffusion coefficient through water, D_{iw}, according to equation 21:

$$D'_{eff} = D_{iw}\frac{\varepsilon}{\tau} \tag{21}$$

It is sometimes desirable to incorporate into this expression a partition coefficient, K_p, for possible adsorption of the drug on the walls of the pores, and a restriction coefficient, K_r, which accounts for hindered diffusion and is described according to equation 22, where λ is the ratio of the drug radius, r_s, to the pore average radius, r_p:

$$K_r = (1 - \lambda)^2 \text{ with } \lambda = r_s/r_p \tag{22}$$

Then, the effective diffusion coefficient of drug through the pores may be written as

$$D_{eff} = D_{iw}K_pK_r\frac{\varepsilon}{\tau} \tag{23}$$

The well-known theoretical analyses of Anderson and Quinn (25) and Colton et al. (23) are often used to predict the parameters K_p and K_r for drug-release systems with fine pores. Very often, diffusion through porous membranes is accompanied by osmotic effects as a result of which equations 9–11 and 21–23 do not fully describe phenomena occurring in porous reservoir systems.

Matrix (Monolithic) Systems

In matrix (monolithic) systems, the bioactive agent is incorporated in the polymer phase either in dissolved or in dispersed form. Therefore, the solubility of the drug in the polymer becomes a controlling factor in the mathematical modeling of these systems. When the initial drug loading is below the solubility limit, release is achieved by simple molecular diffusion through the polymer. However, when the drug loading is above the solubility limit, dissolution of the drug in the polymer becomes the limiting factor in the release process.

Solutions of the transient diffusion equation 2 can be obtained for a variety of initial and boundary conditions (7), which represent appropriate experimental situations. Some of these solutions are presented here. However, the reader is warned that unusual experimental conditions of release will require solution of equation 2 under the boundary conditions that best describe one's experimental situation.

It is also important to note that most mathematical models for controlled-release kinetics presented in the literature have been derived with the assumption of an experimentally rather unattainable boundary condition of zero (and constant) drug concentration at the interface of the device. This condition requires complete elimination of boundary layer effects, probably by high agitation during the release experiment.

In this section we include, in addition to the conventional solutions of the diffusion equation 2 widely used in controlled-release technology, new models and mathematical solutions with boundary conditions affected by drug mass transfer from the surface of the polymer to the liquid phase. These models do not require that the concentration at the polymer interface be constant or zero, although previous determination of the mass transfer coefficient is needed. The mass transfer coefficient can be determined by a variety of expressions or experimental techniques discussed in standard mass transfer monographs (26), if the flow characteristics of the release experiment are known.

Dissolved Drug, Nonporous Systems. In these systems the drug is loaded uniformly at initial concentration c_{io}. Several models may be readily developed for plane sheet matrix devices under different boundary conditions (27).

When the surface concentration of the drug in the dissolution medium is kept constant at c_i, we can derive

$$\frac{M_t}{M_\infty} = 1 - \sum_{n=0}^{\infty} \frac{8}{(2n+1)^2\pi^2} \exp\left[\frac{-D_{ip}(2n+1)^2\pi^2}{\delta^2} t\right]$$

(24)

Important simplifications of this equation may be used if one is interested in avoiding the lengthy calculations of this series solution. For example, for long release times ($M_t/M_\infty > 0.6$), this equation may be written as

$$\frac{M_t}{M_\infty} = 1 - \frac{8}{\pi^2} \exp\left[-\frac{D_{ip}\pi^2}{\delta^2} t\right]$$

(25)

For small release times ($M_t/M_\infty > 0.6$), equation 2 has an alternative solution in the form of equation 26:

$$\frac{M_t}{M_\infty} = 4\left[\frac{D_{ip}t}{\delta^2}\right]^{1/2}\left[\frac{1}{\sqrt{\pi}} + 2\sum_{n=1}^{\infty}(-1)^n \text{ierfc}\frac{n\delta}{\sqrt{D_{ip}t}}\right]$$

(26)

Equation 26 can be further simplified to give

$$\frac{M_t}{M_\infty} = 4\left[\frac{D_{ip}t}{\pi\delta^2}\right]^{1/2}$$

(27)

It is clear that when slabs of monolithic devices are kept at constant external drug concentration, the fractional release is proportional to the square root of release time. However, equation 27 is valid only for the early portion of a release experiment and only under the boundary conditions and assumptions discussed before. By differentiation, we can obtain

$$\frac{dM_t}{dt} = 2M_\infty\left[\frac{D_{ip}}{\pi\delta^2 t}\right]^{1/2}$$

(28)

This equation shows that the drug-release rate drops considerably during the release experiment and that it is dependent on $t^{-1/2}$. This observation is important for design of zero-order release systems because it shows that it is not possible to obtain constant drug release rates from "simple" matrix-type devices.

In many experimental studies, the drug concentration at the surface c_i cannot be kept constant. Instead a con-

stant drug concentration, c_o, can be obtained far enough from the surface (28). Therefore a boundary condition for equation 2 can be written as

$$\left[-D\frac{\partial c}{\partial x}\right]_{surf} = k(c_o - c_i)$$

(29)

where k is the mass transfer coefficient. Then equation 2 can be solved to give

$$\frac{M_t}{M_\infty} = 1 - \sum_{n=1}^{\infty} \frac{\frac{1}{2}\left[\frac{\delta k}{D_{ip}}\right]^2 \exp\left[-\frac{4\beta_n^2 D_{ip}}{\delta^2} t\right]}{\beta_n^2\left[\beta_n^2 + \left[\frac{\delta k}{2D_{ip}}\right]^2 + \frac{\delta k}{2D_{ip}}\right]}$$

(30)

where β_n are the positive roots of equation 31.

$$\beta \tan \beta = \delta k/2D_{ip}$$

(31)

Experiments can be also performed with surface concentration c_i of drug varying in a specific way. For example, when

$$c_i = k't$$

(32)

the corresponding expression of the released drug is

$$\frac{M_t}{A} = k'\delta t - \frac{k'\delta^3}{12D_{ip}} + \frac{8k'\delta^3}{\pi^4 D_{ip}} \sum_{n=0}^{\infty} \frac{\exp\left[-\frac{D_{ip}(2n+1)^2\pi^2}{\delta^2}\right]}{(2n+1)^4}$$

(33)

When the surface concentration increases according to equation 34,

$$c_i' = c_i[1 - \exp(-\gamma t)]$$

(34)

the corresponding expression for the released drug is

$$\frac{M_t}{A} = \delta c_i - \exp(-\gamma t)\left[\frac{4D_{ip}}{\gamma\delta^2}\right]^{1/2} \tan\left[\frac{\gamma\delta^2}{4D_{ip}}\right]^{1/2}$$
$$- \frac{8}{\pi^2}\sum_{n=0}^{\infty} \frac{\exp\left[\frac{-(2n+1)^2\pi^2 D_{ip}}{\delta^2} t\right]}{(2n+1)^2\left[1 - \frac{(2n+1)^2 D_{ip}\pi^2}{\gamma\delta^2}\right]}$$

(35)

Models for drug release from devices with other geometries can also be derived by appropriate solution of equation 2 in cylindrical or spherical coordinates (7).

For example, for cylindrical devices of radius r kept at constant surface concentration c_i, the amount released can be calculated by equation 36:

$$\frac{M_t}{M_\infty} = 1 - 4\sum_{n=1}^{\infty} \frac{\exp(-D_{ip}\alpha_n^2 t)}{r^2\alpha_n^2}$$

(36)

Here α_n are positive roots of a Bessel function of the first kind of zero order. For long times, only the first term of the summation of equation 36 is necessary. For short times, this equation can be approximated by equation 37:

$$\frac{M_t}{M_\infty} = 4\left[\frac{D_{ip}t}{\pi r^2}\right]^{1/2} - \left[\frac{D_{ip}t}{r^2}\right] - \frac{1}{3}\left[\frac{D_{ip}t}{\pi^{1/3}r^2}\right]^{3/2} \quad (37)$$

For spherical devices, the early term approximation is going to be again for $M_t/M < 0.4$ and is going to look something like that. Figure 3 shows a comparison of the fractional release and the release rate as a function of release time for slabs, cylinders, and spheres. This equation here is very useful because pharmacists often work with microparticulate systems. The only problem is that it is written for one-size particles. Basically, we have a dependency of $t^{1/2}$ and the first power at the same time. The rate is a function of $t^{-1/2}$. The rate drops with time, and this is why we need to have other particles to keep the rate constant.

Based on this idea, researchers started thinking that perhaps what they could create is a distribution of particle sizes. A design where one particle-size distribution working from the beginning is in contact with the physiological fluid, and a second particle-size distribution, which is much smaller, is brought into contact with the physiological fluid a little bit later, yields approximately zero-order release.

Solutions for other boundary conditions are available in standard references (7). For example, for cylindrical systems with boundary condition described by equation 29, the fractional drug release is

$$\frac{M_t}{M_\infty} = 1 - \sum_{n=1}^{\infty} \frac{4\left[\frac{kr}{D_{ip}}\right]^2 \exp\left[-\frac{\beta_n^2 D_{ip}}{r^2}t\right]}{\beta_n^2\left[\beta_n^2 + \left[\frac{kr}{D_{ip}}\right]^2\right]} \quad (38)$$

where β_n are the roots of equation 39:

$$\beta D_{ip} J_1(\beta) - krJ_0(\beta) = 0 \quad (39)$$

where $J_0(\beta)$ and $J_1(\beta)$ are Bessel functions of zero and first order, respectively.

An appropriate solution suitable for small times is

$$\frac{M_t}{M_\infty} = \left[\frac{2kt}{r}\right] - \left[\frac{8k^2t^{3/2}}{3D_{ip}^{1/2}\pi^{1/2}r}\right] - k^2\left[\frac{1}{2} - \frac{kr}{D_{ip}}\right]t^2 \quad (40)$$

For spherical matrix devices, equation 2 can be solved with spherical coordinates and constant surface concentration to give

$$\frac{M_t}{M_\infty} = 1 - \frac{6}{\pi^2}\sum_{n=1}^{\infty}\frac{1}{n^2}\exp\left[-\frac{D_{ip}n^2\pi^2}{r^2}t\right] \quad (41)$$

For long times, only the first term in the summation need be retained. For short times of release ($M_t/M_\infty < 0.6$) an approximate solution may be obtained in the form of equation 42:

$$\frac{M_t}{M_\infty} = 6\left[\frac{D_{ip}t}{\pi r^2}\right]^{1/2} - 3\frac{D_{ip}t}{r^2} + 12\left[\frac{D_{ip}t}{r^2}\right]^{1/2}\sum_{n=1}^{\infty}\text{ierfc}\frac{nr}{\sqrt{D_{ip}t}} \quad (42)$$

which may be further simplified for $M_t/M_\infty < 0.4$ by retaining only the first two terms of the right hand side (rhs) of this equation.

Solutions for other boundary conditions are available (27,28). For example, when using spherical devices in conjunction with the boundary condition of equation 29, the fractional drug release is given by equation 43:

$$\frac{M_t}{M_\infty} = 1 - \sum_{n=1}^{\infty}\frac{6\left[\frac{kr}{D_{ip}}\right]^2\exp\left[-\frac{\beta_n^2 D_{ip}}{r}t\right]}{\beta_n^2\left[\beta_n^2 + \frac{kr}{D_{ip}}\left[\frac{kr}{D_{ip}} - 1\right]\right]} \quad (43)$$

where β_n are the roots of equation 44:

$$\beta_n D_{ip}\cot\beta_n + kr - D_{ip} = 0 \quad (44)$$

In general, description of drug-release kinetics from matrix-type systems under different boundary conditions and different geometries can be achieved by selecting an appropriate model from the ones described by Crank (7). Consequently, unnecessary assumptions and gross simplifications, such as unfortunate use of equation 27 where it does not apply, can be avoided.

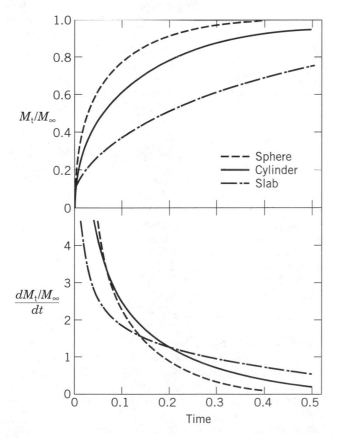

Figure 3. Fractional release and release rate as a function of time for slabs, cylinders, and spheres. *Source:* Reproduced with permission from Ref. 1. Copyright 1974 Plenum.

Dispersed Drug, Nonporous Systems. Monolithic devices may contain drug uniformly distributed at a loading, c_{io}, which is significantly higher than the drug solubility in the polymer, c_{is}. In these systems, dissolution of the drug may be the rate-limiting step of this release process. Therefore, several models have been proposed to describe this phenomenon.

A simple pseudo–steady-state model, the Higuchi model, has attained popularity among researchers working in this area (29). It is based on Fickian diffusion according to equation 1, with zero surface concentration, and it gives the amount of drug released and its release rate according to equations 45 and 46, respectively:

$$M_t = A[D_{ip}c_{is}(2C_{io} - c_{is})t]^{1/2} \qquad (45)$$

$$\frac{dM_t}{dt} = \frac{A}{2}[D_{ip}c_{is}(2c_{io} - c_{is})]^{1/2}t^{-1/2} \qquad (46)$$

Similar expressions have been developed for cylindrical and spherical devices (1,30). For cylindrical devices and for $c_{io} \gg c_{is}$, one obtains

$$\frac{M_t}{M_\infty} + \left[1 - \frac{M_t}{M_\infty}\right]\left[\ln\left[1 - \frac{M_t}{M_\infty}\right]\right] = \frac{4D_{ip}c_{is}}{r^2c_{io}}t \qquad (47)$$

For spherical devices, the corresponding expression for the fractional drug release is

$$\frac{3}{2}\left[1 - \left[1 - \frac{M_t}{M_\infty}\right]^{2/3}\right] - \frac{M_t}{M_\infty} = \frac{3D_{ip}c_{is}}{r^2c_{io}}t \qquad (48)$$

Solutions of the Higuchi model with finite external mass transfer resistance according to equation 44 have been presented by Paul and McSpadden (28) using pseudo–steady-state approximation and the boundary condition described by equation 29, with $c_i = 0$. For example, the amount of drug released as a function of release time is expressed by equation 49:

$$M_t = A\left[c_{io} - \frac{c_{is}}{2}\right]\left\{\left[\left[\frac{D_{ip}}{k}\right]^2 + \frac{2D_{ip}c_{is}t}{\left[c_{io} - \frac{c_{is}}{2}\right]}\right]^{1/2} - \frac{D_{ip}}{k}\right\}$$

$$+ \frac{Ac_{is}}{2}\left\{\frac{\left[\frac{D_{ip}}{k}\right]^2}{\left[\left[\frac{D_{ip}}{k}\right]^2 + \frac{2D_{im}c_{is}t}{\left[c_{io} - \frac{c_{is}}{2}\right]}\right]^{1/2}} - \frac{D_{ip}}{k}\right\} \qquad (49)$$

Clearly as the mass transfer coefficient increases to infinity (no mass transfer limitations), this equation reduces to the Higuchi model (equation 45). The pseudo–steady-state analysis is the only approximate modeling effort that is included in this contribution because of historical reasons and its wide acceptability by researchers working in this area.

However, exact solutions of this problem are available through the work of Paul and McSpadden (28). The total amount of drug released can be calculated by equation 50,

where x^* is the position of the dissolution front of the dissolving drug, which can be determined by solving equation 51 either numerically or using tabulated values from Crank's monograph (7):

$$\frac{M_t}{A} = \frac{2c_{is}}{\text{erf}\left[\frac{x^*}{2\sqrt{D_{ip}t}}\right]}\left[\frac{D_{ip}t}{\pi}\right]^{1/2} \qquad (50)$$

$$x^*\left[\frac{\pi}{D_{ip}t}\right]^{1/2}\exp\left[\frac{x^{*2}}{4D_{ip}t}\right]\text{erf}\left[\frac{x^*}{2\sqrt{D_{ip}t}}\right] = \frac{c_{is}}{c_{io} - c_{is}} \qquad (51)$$

Equation 50 corresponds to equation 45 for slabs under the boundary conditions of the Higuchi model. If in addition to this model, mass transfer limitations are taken into consideration (equation 29), an asymptotic solution may be obtained in the form of equation 52:

$$\frac{M_t}{A} = \frac{2c_{is}}{\text{erf}\left[\frac{x^*}{2\sqrt{D_{ip}t}}\right]}\left[\frac{D_{ip}t}{\pi}\right]^{1/2} - \frac{D_{ip}c_{io}}{k} \qquad (52)$$

Once again, x^* can be estimated from equation 51.

Mathematical problems of drug release from matrix systems initially loaded at concentrations above the solubility limit of the drug in the polymer are problems of moving boundaries, because the front of dissolved drug/undissolved drug clearly moves into the polymer as release proceeds. These problems are known as Stefan or Stefan–Neumann problems (31). Alternative solutions using moving coordinate systems may be obtained by analogy to mathematical solutions discussed by Danckwerts (32).

Certain problems require numerical or approximate solutions. For example, Lee (33) has recently discussed a variety of diffusional release problems for slabs, spheres, and cylinders using Stefan-type analysis, and he has offered some approximate solutions.

Narasimhan and Langer (34) have recently studied the role of the burst effect in an essentially zero-order, controlled-release, coated hemispherical polymeric device containing a single, small orifice in its center face. Asymptotic solutions of their model show that the burst effect is controlled by the solubility of the drug in the release medium and by the drug-diffusion coefficient. The rates of drug release during the burst effect (t → 0) and the steady state (t → ∞) are related by

$$\frac{[dM/dt]_{t\to 0}}{[dM/dt]_{t\to\infty}} = \frac{16}{B(6 + B)} \qquad (53)$$

Here B is given by c_s/c_0. The parameter c_0 is the initial drug loading, and c_s is the solubility of the drug in the release medium. From equation 53, it can be concluded that the burst effect is significant for systems where $B \sim O(1)$. It was shown that as drug solubility increased, the drug released faster, and the velocity of the interface between dissolved and dispersed drug is higher. The model solutions established that the burst behavior could be manipulated by using different initial drug distributions. Using the model, conditions under which the burst effect could be minimized/maximized were established. Figure 4 shows a plot of the fraction of bovine serum albumin released from an inwardly releasing ethylene-vinyl acetate (EVAc) hemisphere as a function of time, where the release as well as the burst period is zero order.

Porous Matrix Systems. Modeling of the drug-release kinetics of porous matrix systems is still at a rather primitive stage, despite significant developments in recent years. Before using existing models, one has to consider several aspects of the physics of this diffusion phenomenon.

1. If the polymer phase is hydrophobic, swelling is negligible, and the problem can be treated as a constant-volume diffusion problem. However, if the polymer phase is hydrophilic, two modeling routes may be considered.

2. If the pores are large enough to be thought of as "channels" for diffusion (pore diameter greater than 150 Å), diffusion occurs predominantly through these water-filled pores and the effective diffusion coefficient, D'_{eff}, of equation 21 must be used. However, if the pores are smaller than 100 Å, then the diffusion coefficient, D_{ip}, through the swollen polymer can be used without corrections for porosity and tortuosity.

3. Phenomena related to drug partition in the pore walls and hindered diffusion due to the relative size of the drug with respect to the pores can be addressed by including the parameters K_p and K_r in the diffusion coefficient through water and using the effective diffusion coefficient, D_{eff}, described by equation 23.

4. Phenomena related to elastically changing pore walls must be taken into consideration.

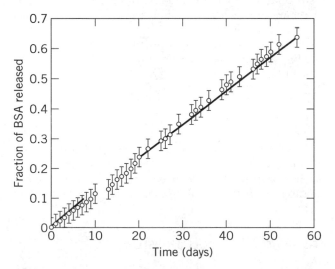

Figure 4. Fraction of bovine serum albumin released as a function of time from coated EVAc hemispheres. The open circles represent experimental data (37) while the line represents model predictions. *Source:* Reproduced with permission from Ref. 34. Copyright 1997 Elsevier.

Therefore, the models developed in "Reservoir (Membrane) Systems" and "Dissolved Drug, Nonporous Systems" may be used for porous systems, with D_{ip} for porous hydrophilic systems of pore size smaller than 100 Å or with D_{eff} for porous hydrophilic systems of pore size larger than 100 Å or with all types of porous hydrophobic systems. Release kinetics for porous systems containing drug at concentrations higher than the solubility limit are somewhat more difficult to model, and equations cannot be written by simple analogy to the models given in "Dispersed Drug, Nonporous Systems."

A traditional pseudo–steady-state model for these systems was developed by Higuchi (35) and predicts drug release according to equation 54, where D_{eff} is given by equations 21 or 23:

$$M_t = A[D_{eff}c_{is}(2c_{io} - \varepsilon c_{is})t]^{1/2} \qquad (54)$$

These models may be unable to describe many experimental results with porous systems loaded with drug above its solubility limit in water.

Two alternatives have been proposed to explain the experimental results. The first model (36) assumes that dissolution of the drug in the pores is the controlling mechanism of release and describes overall diffusion in terms of a modified diffusion equation where the term $k(c_{is} - c_i)$ is a dissolution-dependent contribution to diffusion:

$$\frac{\partial c_i}{\partial t} = D_{eff}\frac{\partial^2 c_i}{\partial x^2} + k(c_{is} - c_i) \qquad (55)$$

This model can be used under the assumptions of pseudohomogeneous dissolution and of initially unfilled pores in the matrix system, as is the case with tablets and other pharmaceutical systems produced by compression of solids. For finite slabs of thickness δ and zero surface concentration, the amount of drug released is expressed by equation 56, where α_n is defined as in equation 57:

$$\frac{M_t}{A} = \left[c_{is}\sqrt{D_{eff}k}\tanh\left[\frac{\delta}{2}\sqrt{\frac{k}{D_{eff}}}\right]\right]t$$
$$- \frac{c_{is}D_{eff}}{\delta}\sum_{n=0}^{\infty}\frac{1 - \exp[-D_{eff}\alpha_n^2 + k)t]}{(D_{eff}\alpha_n^2 + k)^2} \qquad (56)$$

$$\alpha_n = \frac{(2n + 1)}{\delta}\pi \qquad (57)$$

It is interesting to note that at long times, the last term of equation 56 is small, and zero-order release is predicted.

The second modeling effort assumes (11) that solid drug fills completely the pores and dissolution occurs. This phenomenon can be modeled as an unsteady-state, moving-boundary (Stefan-type) problem. For this case, it can be shown that the released drug can be determined by equation 58:

$$\frac{M_t}{A} = \frac{2\varepsilon^{2/3}c_{is}}{\mathrm{erf}\left[\dfrac{x^*}{2\sqrt{D'_{iw}t}}\right]}\left[\frac{D'_{iw}t}{\pi}\right]^{1/2} \qquad (58)$$

The position of the front x^* can be determined by equation 59:

$$x^* \left[\frac{\pi}{D'_{iw}t} \right]^{1/2} \exp\left[\frac{x^{*2}}{4D'_{iw}t} \right] \mathrm{erf}\left[\frac{x^*}{2\sqrt{D'_{iw}t}} \right] = \frac{c_{is}}{\rho_i M_i} \qquad (59)$$

The diffusion coefficient, D'_{iw}, is defined by equation 60; ϵ is the porosity upon complete dissolution, ρ_i is the density of the drug, and M_i is its molecular weight.

$$D'_{iw} = D_{iw}/\tau \qquad (60)$$

Because of the assumptions made, this model can be used to describe the unexpected release behavior of drugs from dense, hydrophobic matrix systems such as those studied by Langer and co-workers (10,37).

SWELLING-CONTROLLED SYSTEMS

Swelling-controlled release systems are rather difficult to model owing to complex macromolecular changes occurring in the polymer during release. These systems consist of water-soluble drugs that are initially dispersed in solvent-free glassy polymers. If a slab is placed in contact with water, diffusion of water into the polymer will be observed depending on the thermodynamic interactions between the polymer and the solvent. This dynamic swelling phenomenon may lead to considerable volume expansion of the original slab. Two fronts (interfaces) are characteristic of the swelling behavior:

1. The swelling interface that separates the rubbery (swollen) state from the glassy state and that moves inward with velocity v
2. The polymer interface that separates the rubbery state from water and moves outward

Swelling of glassy polymers is accompanied by macromolecular relaxation, which become important at the swelling interface (38). This relaxation, in turn, affects the drug diffusion through the polymer, so that Fickian or non-Fickian diffusion may be observed. In these systems, drug release is controlled by the velocity of the water penetration front, v, because drug diffusion through the glassy polymer is negligible.

Mathematical modeling of this type of diffusion behavior clearly belongs to a category of mathematical problems known as Stefan, Stefan–Neumann, or moving-boundary problems. The Fickian diffusion equation 2 is solved with concentration-dependent or concentration-independent drug-diffusion coefficients and moving-boundary conditions (at the two fronts). If, in addition, one imposes problems of non-Fickian diffusion due to macromolecular relaxation, then the mathematical analysis becomes rather complicated (39). Some attempts to describe this behavior have been discussed by Peppas et al. (40), and a more complete literature review is given elsewhere (31).

A common procedure for analyzing experimental data of drug release from swelling-controlled release systems is by fitting them to equation 5 and determining the exponent n. As discussed before (9), the value of this exponent is characteristic of the Fickian or non-Fickian diffusion behavior of swelling-controlled release systems. It is possible

to derive sufficient and necessary conditions for obtaining zero-order release from swelling-controlled release systems (41) by examining the dimensionless number, Sw, the so-called swelling interface number, defined according to equation 61:

$$Sw = \frac{v\delta(t)}{D_{ip}} \qquad (61)$$

When $Sw \ll 1$, zero-order release should be expected, whereas for values of $Sw \gg 1$, Fickian diffusion is observed.

Kou et al. (42) proposed a model for drug diffusion through swellable cylinders with Fickian equations and concentration-dependent diffusion coefficients. Cohen and Erneux (43,44) presented a treatment of free boundary problems that had fundamental ideas in solving drug delivery problems in swellable systems.

The first detailed model of drug transport with concentration-dependent diffusion coefficients and swelling was proposed by Korsmeyer et al. (45). Lustig and Peppas (46) proposed a free-volume–based model with three-dimensional swelling beyond the point where the fronts meet. Lustig et al. (47) proposed a mathematical model for drug release based on rational thermodynamics, containing a full viscoelastic description of the polymer and concentration-dependent transport of the drug, with three-dimensional swelling.

Drug release from environmentally responsive polymeric systems has also been studied in great detail. Peppas and Brannon-Peppas (48) studied the drug-release rates in a system that responded to changes in temperature. The time-dependent response of the drug was also studied by Brannon-Peppas and Peppas (49) and by Bell and Peppas (50). Models for drug delivery from polymeric systems that responded to changes in the pH and ionic strength of the surrounding medium were proposed by Hariharan and Peppas (51,52).

In addition to these important modeling efforts, researchers have sought to analyze non-Fickian transport with relatively simple equations. One such effort relating the fractional release of the drug to time uses the so-called swelling area number (53). The swelling area number was defined as

$$Sa = \frac{1}{D}\frac{dA}{dt} \qquad (62)$$

Here, A is the area available for drug release, and D is the drug-diffusion coefficient. The swelling area number, Sa, has been used to describe systems with varying area (see Fig. 5) due to swelling (specifically the Geomatrix® systems).

CHEMICALLY CONTROLLED SYSTEMS

Chemically controlled release systems include all polymeric formulations where drug diffusion is controlled by the dissolution of the polymer matrix. Modeling of these systems is similar to that followed for swelling-controlled release systems, because mass erosion replaces the phase

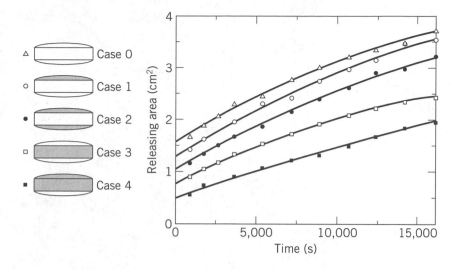

Figure 5. Releasing area as a function of time for the five systems shown. *Source:* Reproduced with permission from Ref. 53. Copyright 1988 Elsevier.

erosion (moving front) observed in swelling-controlled systems. Within this category, there are systems where a chemical reaction triggers the release. That reaction may be induced by hydrolysis, whether enzymatic or biochemical.

The difference between bioerosion and biodegradation is that the latter is the actual degradation, the breaking down of the polymer due to a chemical reaction that is taking place. The polymer will break down into small-molecular-weight materials. A matrix like that would be a polymeric material with the drug molecularly distributed throughout. In the case of biodegradable materials, the drug does not have to be molecularly dispersed; it can also be microscopically dispersed with large particles. The release process is controlled by a surface chemical reaction that will break down the polymer, giving oligomers and small-molecular-weight compounds. As time elapses, the geometry is unchanged but smaller, and the drug that was incorporated in the lost portion is free to dissolve and diffuse. That is why biodegradable systems, with a first-order biodegradation reaction with respect to the area, yield zero-order release for a planar device where the area remains constant.

Bioerosion is a process whereby a phase of the carrier is lost, not by chemical reaction but by dissolution. When bioerodible polymers are brought in contact with physiological fluids, the fluids simply dissolve the polymer rather than break it down. The definition is blurred, and people speak of bioerodible systems when they mean biodegradable systems.

In most chemically controlled systems, the geometric shape of the device controls drug release. The controlling mechanism may be either polymer dissolution or reaction and degradation at the polymer surface. Depending on the type of degradation reaction, these systems may be classified as chemically degradable (e.g., by hydrolysis) or biodegradable (e.g., by enzymatic reaction) controlled-release systems.

Shrinking-core models provide the most accurate description of this release. Cooney (54,55) developed simple expressions for drug release from cylindrical, spherical, and cylindrical devices.

Hopfenberg (56) derived expressions for drug release from erodible slabs, cylinders, and spheres. If one recognizes that the erosion rate is proportional to the continuously changing area of the device, A_e, one may write

$$\frac{dM_t}{dt} = k_e A_e \tag{63}$$

Solution of this equation for various geometries gives the following general expression

$$\frac{M_t}{M_\infty} = 1 - \left[1 - \frac{k_e t}{c_{io}l}\right]^n \tag{64}$$

Here $n = 1$ for a slab of thickness $\delta = 2l$, $n = 2$ for a cylinder of radius $r = l$, and $n = 3$ for a sphere of radius $r = l$.

Mathematical models of erodible systems where drug release from the surface is also important have been recently discussed by Lee (57) and further analyzed elsewhere (58). In order to obtain zero-order release from such erodible devices, the drug distribution was studied (57,58). It was found that a sigmoidal type of initial drug distribution gave almost zero-order release (58). This effect is represented in Figure 6.

Thombre and Himmelstein (59) developed models to describe drug release from poly(orthoester)s. The boundary condition used to solve the transport–reaction problem is given by equation 29, where k_i now represents the reaction constant of species i. The diffusion–reaction model was solved in terms of typical Thiele moduli, φ_i, to describe the reaction–diffusion ratio and Biot numbers, Bi_i, to describe the mass transfer–diffusion ratio. The solutions were reported as fractional amount of each species as a function of time as shown in Figure 7.

$$\varphi_i = a \sqrt{\frac{k_i c_i}{D_i}}$$
$$Bi_i = \frac{k_i a}{D_i} \tag{65}$$

where D_i is the diffusion coefficient of the ith species and a is the half thickness of the polymer film.

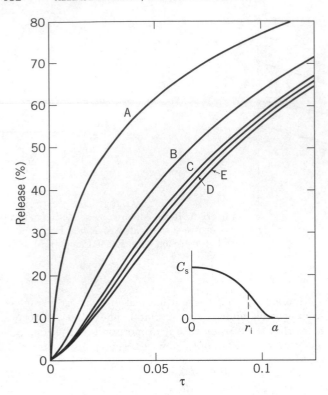

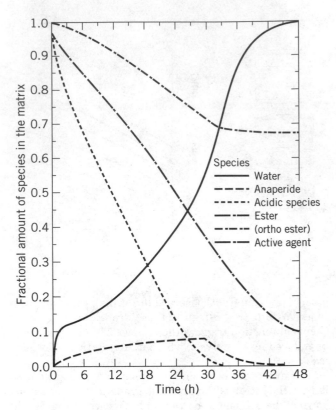

Figure 6. Effect of sigmoidal initial drug concentration distribution on the cumulative release from spherical matrices. Curves A through E represent different values of ξ_i. ξ_i is the initial position of the inflection point in the concentration profile. *Source:* Reproduced with permission from Ref. 58. Copyright 1986 Butterworth. The distribution function is

$$f(\xi) = \frac{1 - \exp\left[-0.5\left(\frac{1 - \xi}{1 - \xi_i}\right)^2\right]}{1 - \exp\left[-0.5\left(\frac{1}{1 - \xi_i}\right)^2\right]}$$

Computer-aided methods (60,61) have also been used to model bioerosion. In these approaches, the polymer matrix is represented as the sum of individual matrix parts, and the erosion of each part is regarded as a random event. Comparisons with experiment yielded good agreement. This analysis was later extended (62) to describe the release of a monomer from an eroding polymer. The model predicts parameters like the porosity of the eroding polymer, the matrix weight, and amount of monomer released. The analysis could be extended to model drug release from such systems (63,64).

Pendent Chain Systems

Models have been proposed by Anderson and his coworkers (65) to describe cortisol hydrolysis from bound PGA systems. The hydrolysis starts at the surface, giving hydrophilic polymer. The rate of water permeation, R_w, in the hydrophobic zone and the rate of hydrolysis, R_h, are important parameters in tuning the release kinetics.

Figure 7. Fractional amount of species in the matrix as a function of time. *Source:* Reproduced with permission from Ref. 59. Copyright 1985 AlChE.

OTHER ASPECTS OF RELEASE KINETICS MODELING

Osmotic Systems

Osmotic systems for drug delivery are designed by applying irreversible thermodynamics and the Kedem–Katchalsky (66) analysis. The total volume flow, J_u, and the total exchange flow, J_D, are respectively given by

$$J_u = L_p \Delta p + L_{pD} \Delta \pi_s$$
$$J_D = L_{Dp} \Delta p + L_D \Delta \pi_s \qquad (66)$$

Here, L_i ($i = p, pD, Dp, D$) represents Onsager coefficients, Δp is the hydrostatic pressure, and $\Delta \pi_s$ is the osmotic pressure of the solvent.

The systems under consideration may also be defined by the reflection coefficient, σ, and the permeability coefficient, L_p. The term σ is defined as

$$\sigma = -\frac{L_{pD}}{L_p} \qquad (67)$$

The osmotic pressure is given by

$$\Delta \pi_s = NRT/V = cRT \qquad (68)$$

where N is the number of moles of the solvent, V is the solvent volume, R is the universal gas constant, and T is the temperature.

The volume flux, dV/dt, for a membrane of thickness δ and cross-sectional area A is given by

$$\frac{dV}{dt} = \frac{A}{\delta} (\sigma \Delta\pi_s - \Delta p) \tag{69}$$

The value $\sigma = 0$ represents a coarse filter, and $\sigma = 1$ represents an impermeable drug. For large orifices,

$$\Delta\pi_s \gg \Delta p \tag{70}$$

Hence,

$$\frac{dV}{dt} = \frac{A}{\delta} L_p \sigma \Delta\pi_s = \frac{A}{\delta} k \Delta\pi_s \tag{71}$$

Using $dM/dt = c \, dV/dt$, we have

$$\frac{dM}{dt} = \frac{A}{\delta} k c \Delta\pi_s \tag{72}$$

Hence, the drug-release rate in osmotically controlled systems can be tuned to achieve zero-order kinetics.

Dissolution-Controlled Systems

Dissolution-controlled systems have the additional characteristic that in addition to polymer swelling and drug diffusion through the continuously changing phase, they are accompanied by slow disentanglement of the polymer chains, leading to complete dissolution of the carrier. Obviously, this mechanism will occur only in un-cross-linked polymer carriers.

Harland et al. (67) formulated for a model for drug release in a dissolving polymer–solvent system. The transport was assumed to be Fickian, and mass balances were written for the drug and the solvent at the glassy–rubbery interface and at the rubbery–solvent interface. The important parameters identified in the phenomenon were the polymer volume fraction c^* at the glassy–rubbery transition, the polymer volume fraction c_d for disentanglement of the chains, and the dissolution–mass transfer coefficient, k. The expression for drug release as a function of time was obtained as

$$\frac{M_d}{M_{d,\infty}} = \frac{c_b}{a c_{cd}}$$
$$\cdot \left(\sqrt{\frac{2[-D_s(c^* + c_s - c_d - c_b) + D_d(c_s - c_b) + D_d/c_b]^2 (1 - c^* - c_s)t}{D_s(2 - c^* - c_s)(c^* + c_s - c_d - c_b) + D_d(c^* + c_s)(c_s - c_b)}} + k c_b t \right) \tag{73}$$

Here, D_s is the diffusion coefficient of the solvent in the polymer, and D_d is the diffusion coefficient of the drug in the polymer. The parameter c_b is the volume fraction of the drug in the bulk. This model can predict both Fickian as well as non-Fickian behavior. It is to be noted that front synchronization leads to zero-order release in dissolution-controlled systems. The predicted normalized drug release as a function of time is shown in Figure 8.

The previous model was modified by Narasimhan and Peppas (68) by accounting for macromolecular chain disentanglement. An expression for the fraction of the drug released was derived as

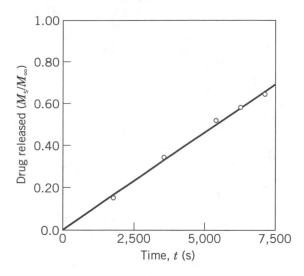

Figure 8. Normalized drug release as a function of time for drug–polymer tablet dissolution system. *Source:* Reproduced with permission from Ref. 67. Copyright 1985 Plenum.

$$\frac{M_u}{M_{d,\infty}} = \frac{v_{u,eq} + v_d^*}{2l} (\sqrt{2At} + Bt) \tag{74}$$

Here, A and B are given as

$$A = D(v_{1,eq} - v_1^*)\left(\frac{v_{1,eq}}{v_{1,eq} + v_{d,eq}} + \frac{1}{v_1^* + v_d^*} \right)$$
$$+ D_d(v_d^* - v_{d,eq})\left(\frac{v_{d,eq}}{v_{1,eq} + v_{d,eq}} + \frac{1}{v_1^* + v_d^*} \right) \tag{75}$$

$$B = \frac{k_d}{v_{1,eq} + v_{d,eq}} \tag{76}$$

Here, l is the half-thickness of the polymer, D is the diffusion coefficient of the solvent, and D_d is the diffusion coefficient of the drug. v_1^* and v_d^* are equilibrium concentrations of solvent and drug, respectively. The parameter k_d is the disentanglement rate of the polymer chains and is calculated using reptation theory (69–71). Figure 9 shows the fraction of drug released as a function of α ($\alpha = A/B$) and dimensionless time τ ($\tau = Bt/l$). It is observed that the model captures Fickian behavior, anomalous transport, as well as zero-order release.

For the drug-release rate to be zero order (see equation (74)), $B^2/A \gg 1$. Hence, choosing a polymer–drug–solvent system such that this inequality is satisfied would result in a zero-order drug release. This model also captures the transition between Fickian and non-Fickian type behavior.

When the polymer carrier is semicrystalline, the process of carrier dissolution is preceded by a process of phase erosion of the crystalline region to an amorphous region. Under certain conditions, this transition may lead to relaxation-controlled conditions of drug transport. Drug release from a new class of such systems—crystal dissolution–controlled-release systems—was modeled by Mallapragada and Peppas (72). In the presence of a thermodynamically compatible solvent, polymer crystals may start dissolving by crystal unfolding and disentanglement. In these dissolving phase-erosion systems, the drug-

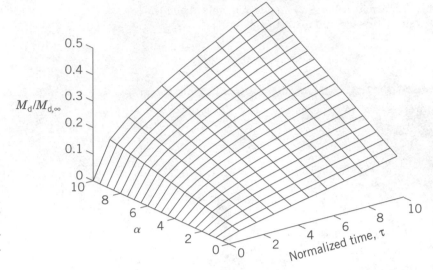

Figure 9. Predicted normalized drug released, M_d/M_d, as a function of normalized time, τ ($\tau = Bt/l$), for different values of α ($\alpha = A/B$). *Source:* Reproduced with permission from Ref. 68. Copyright 1997 ACS.

release rate is controlled by the transformation of the crystalline phase of the polymer to the amorphous phase. The crystalline regions are modeled as impermeable structures that do not permit drug diffusion. Therefore, as the polymer swells and drug is released, the concentration gradient for drug diffusion decreases, but simultaneously, disappearance of part of the crystalline phase causes an increase in the overall drug diffusion coefficient from the polymer. If these two effects compensate for each other, then zero-order drug release can be obtained.

A mathematical model was proposed by coupling crystal-unfolding theories with free-volume–based drug-diffusion theories (18) to predict conditions under which zero-order drug release can be obtained. Expressions were written for changes in the volume fractions of the crystalline polymer, amorphous polymer, and the drug as functions of time. The coupled partial differential equations were solved with the appropriate boundary conditions to yield drug-release profiles as functions of time under various conditions (Fig. 10). Factors affecting the drug-release rate were found to be the polymer degree of crystallinity, crystal size distribution, molecular weight of the polymer, the polymer–water interaction parameter, and the crystal-unfolding rate. The release from these systems was found to be non-Fickian.

CONCLUSIONS

Drug release through controlled-delivery polymeric systems has been modeled predominantly by steady-state and transient description of drug diffusion by use of Fick's law. The correct interpretation of release kinetics from such drug-release models depends on the mechanism of the release itself, the polymer microstructure, and the conditions of the experiment (in other words, the boundary conditions). More accurate mathematical descriptions are necessary in modeling drug release in swellable and porous polymeric systems. Consideration of aspects such as countercurrent solvent diffusion, chain disentanglement, polymer state transitions, degree of crystallinity, and porous

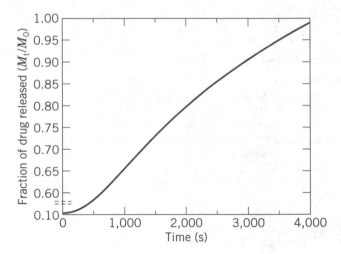

Figure 10. Predicted fraction of metronidazole released as a function of time from a poly(vinyl alcohol) sample with degree of crystallinity = 30% and drug loading of 2%. *Source:* Reproduced with permission from Ref. 72. Copyright 1997 Elsevier.

structure will enhance understanding and interpretation of release kinetics data from existing models. The advent of codelivery polymeric systems has necessitated the need for models incorporating interacting and noninteracting multicomponent diffusion through polymers.

BIBLIOGRAPHY

1. R.W. Baker and H.K. Lonsdale, in A.C. Tanquarry and R.E. Lacey, eds., *Controlled Release of Biologically Active Agents*, Plenum, New York, 1974, pp. 15–72.

2. R. Langer, *Chem. Eng. Commun.* **6**, 1–8 (1980).

3. B. Narasimhan and N.A. Peppas, in K. Park, ed., *Controlled Drug Delivery*, American Chemical Society, Washington, D.C., 1997, pp. 529–557.

4. R.S. Langer and N.A. Peppas, *J. Macromol. Sci., Rev. Macromol. Chem. Phys.* **C23**(1), 61–126 (1983).

5. C.E. Rogers, *ACS Symp. Ser.* **33**, 15 (1976).

6. N.A. Peppas, in V.H.L. Lee, M. Hashida, and Y. Mizushima, eds., in *Peptide and Protein Drug Delivery*, Harwood Academic Publishers, Chur, Switzerland, 1995, p. 23.

7. J. Crank, *The Mathematics of Diffusion*, 2nd ed., Oxford University Press, New York, 1975.

8. R.W. Korsmeyer and N.A. Peppas, in S.Z. Mansdorf and T.J. Roseman, eds., *Controlled Release Delivery Systems*, Dekker, New York, 1983, p. 77.

9. P.L. Ritger and N.A. Peppas, *J. Controlled Release* **5**, 23–36 (1987).

10. W.D. Rhine, V. Sukhatme, D.S.T. Hsieh, and R.S. Langer, in R. Baker, ed., *Controlled Release of Bioactive Materials*, Academic Press, New York, 1980, p. 177.

11. R. Gumy, E. Doelker, and N.A. Peppas, *Biomaterials* **3**, 27–32 (1982).

12. S.K. Chandrasekaran and D.R. Paul, *J. Pharm. Sci.* **71**, 1399–1402 (1982).

13. N.A. Peppas and R.W. Korsmeyer, in N.A. Peppas, ed., *Hydrogels in Medicine and Pharmacy*, vol. 3, CRC Press, Boca Raton, Fla., 1987, p. 109.

14. R.A. Siegel, in M. Rosoff, ed., *Controlled Release of Drugs*, VCH, New York, 1989, p. 1.

15. N.A. Peppas, in R.S. Langer and D. Wise, eds., *Medical Applications of Controlled Release Technology*, vol. 2, CRC Press, Boca Raton, Fla., 1984, p. 169.

16. H. Eyring, *J. Chem. Phys.* **4**, 283 (1936).

17. A.G. Ogston, *Trans. Faraday Soc.* **54**, 1754 (1958).

18. H. Fujita, *Fortschr. Hochpolym.-Forsch.* **3**, 1–47 (1961).

19. H. Yasuda and C.E. Lamaze, *J. Macromol. Sci., Phys.* **B5**, 111–120 (1971).

20. E.N. Lightfoot, *Transport Phenomena and Living Systems*, Wiley, New York, 1974.

21. H. Faxén, *Ark. Mat. Astron. Fys.* **17**, 27 (1923).

22. J.M. Vrentas and J.L. Duda, *J. Polym. Sci., Polym. Phys. Ed.* **17**, 1085–1092 (1979).

23. C.K. Colton, K.A. Smith, E.W. Merrill, and P.C. Farrell, *J. Biomed. Mater. Res.* **5**, 459–488 (1971).

24. R.S. Harland and N.A. Peppas, *Colloid Polym. Sci.* **267**, 218–225 (1989).

25. J.L. Anderson and J.A. Quinn, *Biophys. J.* **14**, 130 (1974).

26. T.K. Sherwood, R.L. Pigford, and C.R. Wilke, *Mass Transfer*, McGraw-Hill, New York, 1975.

27. J.C. Fu, C. Hagemeier, and D.L. Moyer, *J. Biomed. Mater. Res.* **10**, 743–758 (1976).

28. D.R. Paul and S.K. McSpadden, *J. Membr. Sci.* **1**, 33–48 (1976).

29. T. Higuchi, *J. Pharm. Sci.* **50**, 874–875 (1961).

30. T.J. Roseman and W.I. Higuchi, *J. Pharm. Sci.* **59**, 353–357 (1970).

31. J. Crank, *Free and Moving Boundary Problems*, 2nd ed., Oxford University Press, New York, 1975.

32. P.V. Danckwerts, *Trans. Faraday Soc.* **46**, 701 (1950).

33. P.I. Lee, *J. Membr. Sci.* **7**, 255–275 (1980).

34. B. Narasimhan and R. Langer, *J. Controlled Release* **47**, 13–20 (1997).

35. Higuchi, T., *J. Pharm. Sci.* **52**, 1145 (1963).

36. E.A. Swan and N.A. Peppas, *Proc. Symp. Controlled Release Bioact. Mater.* **8**, 18–19 (1981).

37. W. Rhine, D. Hsieh, and R. Langer, *J. Pharm. Sci.* **69**, 265–270 (1980).

38. N.A. Peppas and R. Korsmeyer, *Polym. News* **6**, 149 (1980).

39. J.C. Wu and N.A. Peppas, *J. Polym. Sci., Polym. Phys. Ed.* **31**, 1503 (1993).

40. N.A. Peppas, J.C. Wu, and E.D. von Meerwall, *Macromolecules* **27**, 5626 (1994).

41. N.A. Peppas and N.M. Franson, *J. Polym. Sci., Polym. Phys.* **21**, 983 (1983).

42. J.H. Kou, D. Fleisher, and G.L. Amidon, *J. Controlled Release* **12**, 241 (1990).

43. D.S. Cohen and T. Erneux, *SIAM J. Appl. Math.* **48**, 1451 (1988).

44. D.S. Cohen and T. Erneux, *SIAM J. Appl. Math.* **48**, 1466 (1988).

45. R.W. Korsmeyer, S.R. Lustig, and N.A. Peppas, *J. Polym. Sci., Polym. Phys.* **24**, 395 (1986).

46. S.R. Lustig and N.A. Peppas, *J. Appl. Polym. Sci.* **33**, 533 (1987).

47. S.R. Lustig, J.M. Caruthers, and N.A. Peppas, *Chem. Eng. Sci.* **47**, 3037 (1992).

48. N.A. Peppas and L. Brannon-Peppas, *J. Membr. Sci.* **48**, 281 (1990).

49. L. Brannon-Peppas and N.A. Peppas, *Int. J. Pharmacol.* **70**, 53 (1991).

50. C.L. Bell and N.A. Peppas, *Polym. Prepr.* **34**(1), 831–832 (1993).

51. D. Hariharan and N.A. Peppas, *J. Membr. Sci.* **78**, 1 (1993).

52. D. Hariharan and N.A. Peppas, *J. Controlled Release*, **23**, 123 (1993).

53. P. Colombo et al., *Int. J. Pharmacol.* **88**, 99 (1992).

54. D.O. Cooney, *AIChE J.* **17**, 754 (1971).

55. D.O. Cooney, *AIChE J.* **18**, 446 (1971).

56. H.B. Hopfenberg, *ACS Symp. Ser.* **33**, 222 (1976).

57. P.I. Lee, *Polymer* **25**, 973 (1984).

58. P.I. Lee, *J. Controlled Release* **4**, 1–6 (1986).

59. A.G. Thombre and K.J. Himmelstein, *AIChE J.* **31**, 759 (1985).

60. A. Gopferich and R. Langer, *Macromolecules* **26**, 4105–4112 (1993).

61. K. Zygourakis and P.A. Markenscoff, *Biomaterials* **17**, 125–135 (1996).

62. A. Gopferich and R. Langer, *J. Controlled Release* **33**, 55–69 (1995).

63. A. Gopferich, *Biomaterials* **17**, 103–114 (1996).

64. A. Gopferich, *Macromolecules* **30**, 2598–2604 (1997).

65. N. Tani, M. Van Dress, and J.M. Anderson, in D.H. Lewis, ed., *Controlled Release of Pesticides and Pharmaceuticals*, Plenum, New York, 1981, p. 79.

66. O. Kedem and A. Katchalsky, *Biochim. Biophys. Acta* **27**, 229 (1958).

67. R.S. Harland et al., *Pharm. Res.* **5**, 488 (1988).

68. B. Narasimhan and N.A. Peppas, *J. Pharm. Sci.* **86**(3), 297–304 (1997).

69. B. Narasimhan and N.A. Peppas, *J. Polym. Sci., Polym. Phys. Ed.* **34**, 947–961 (1996).

70. B. Narasimhan and N.A. Peppas, *Macromolecules* **29**, 3283–3291 (1996).

71. P.G. de Gennes, *Scaling Concepts in Polymer Physics*, Cornell University Press, Ithaca, N.Y., 1979.

72. S.K. Mallapragada and N.A. Peppas, *J. Controlled Release* **45**, 87–94 (1997).

RESPIRATORY SYSTEM DELIVERY

DAVID A. EDWARDS
Advanced Inhalation Research (AIR)
Cambridge, Massachusetts

KEY WORDS

Aerodynamic size

Asthma

Dry powder

Estradiol

Insulin

Lungs

Macrophage

Mass density

Porosity

Respiratory

OUTLINE

INTRODUCTION

Inhalation therapies have until now primarily provided fast-acting treatment for respiratory illnesses such as asthma and chronic obstructive pulmonary disease (COPD). Relative to oral delivery, inhalation of bronchodilators, corticosteroids, and other antiinflammatory agents to the airways often produces therapeutic levels in the respiratory tract while maintaining low systemic concentrations and thereby minimizing side effects (1–6). More recently, inhalation therapies for the systemic delivery of proteins and peptides to the body have made important advances in human clinical trials, notably owing to the success with which many macromolecules permeate the alveolar/blood barrier once inhaled (7). For these newer inhalation therapies, inhalation systems are often required that achieve high reproducibility and efficiency; this need has propelled active research and development in the inhalation drug delivery field (8).

The heightened scientific and industrial attention paid to inhaled drug delivery has exposed an unmet need for the controlled release of inhaled drugs (9). Controlled release of drugs in the respiratory system can benefit a variety of existing and future therapies whose success depends critically on multiple daily dosing. Examples include sustained release of bronchodilators and corticosteroids for asthma or drugs such as insulin for diabetes. A logical strategy to achieve sustained release of drugs in the respiratory tract involves encapsulating drugs in slowly degrading particles that can be inhaled. This strategy can, however, be foiled by the relatively rapid (less than a day) natural clearance of insoluble particles from the respiratory system. Efforts are therefore underway to create sustained-release particles that safely avoid respiratory clearance mechanisms, thereby permitting the development of practically useful controlled drug release in the lungs (10–15).

LUNG MORPHOLOGY AND PHYSIOLOGY

The human lung is often conceptually divided into conducting and respiratory zones. The conducting zone serves as the relatively long channel for inhaled air and consists of trachea, bronchus, bronchioles, and terminal bronchioles (Table 1). Insoluble particles deposited in this zone are propelled upward by means of cilia action within the mucus layer residing on the surfaces of the conducting zone. Eventually the insoluble particles reach the pharynx, where they are swallowed. The clearance of insoluble particles from the conducting airways by mucociliary activity is usually complete in 12–24 h (16–19). Respiratory bronchioles are located beyond the terminal bronchioles, followed by alveolar ducts and alveolar sacs; together they comprise the respiratory zone, where primary gas exchange occurs between the air spaces and the blood (Table 1). Insoluble particles deposited in this zone are quickly engulfed by alveolar macrophages, whose ability to chemically break down engulfed material makes them the nemesis of inhaled drugs.

The average alveolar surface area in human lungs (20) is 102 ± 21 m^2, corresponding to 95% of the total surface area in the lungs. The total surface area of alveoli in contact with blood capillaries is approximately 75 m^2 (roughly 40 times greater than the external body surface area) (21). This broad area facilitates the lung's function as the primary gas exchange organ (the lung receives all the blood circulated through each of the peripheral organs and tissues, whereas the abdominal organs receive about 24% of body blood [22]). The epithelial lining of the alveolar spaces, the most significant absorption barrier separating blood from the alveolar lumen (23), has an average thickness of only 0.2 μm—approximately 34 times smaller than the diameter of an average red blood cell (23). The thinness of this barrier and its extensive surface area permits a high accessibility of inhaled drugs to the blood stream. This makes the alveolar region a natural target for inhaled drugs destined for the systemic circulation.

AEROSOL DELIVERY TO THE RESPIRATORY TRACT

To possess a high likelihood of depositing in the alveolar zone of the lungs, inhaled particles must exhibit an aerodynamic diameter in the range of 1–3 μm (25–28). The aerodynamic diameter of a spherical particle (d_a) can be expressed as the product of the geometric diameter (d) and the square root of the particle mass density ρ (R. Vanbever et al., unpublished data) (appropriately normalized to give the proper units). It can be shown that a spherical particle

Table 1. Approximate Dimensions of the Human Lung.

Generation	Length (cm)	Diameter (cm)	Number	Cross-sectional area (cm³)
Trachea (0)	12.0	1.80	1	2.54
Bronchi (1)	4.8	1.22	2	2.33
Bronchi (2)	1.9	0.83	4	2.13
Bronchi (3)	0.8	0.56	8	2.00
Bronchioles (4–16)	1.3–0.12	0.45–0.06	16–60,000	2.48–180.0
Respiratory bronchioles (17–19)	0.12–0.10	0.06–0.05	60,000–500,000	180–1,000
Alveolar ducts (20–22)	0.10–0.05	0.05–0.04	5×10^5–8×10^6	10^3–10^4
Alveolar sacs (23)	0.05	0.04	8×10^6	10^4

Source: Ref. 24.

of any mass density, in flight, will settle with a velocity that depends only on its aerodynamic diameter (R. Vanbever et al., unpublished data). The concept can thus be used to predict a particle's expected lung deposition performance following inhalation. Numerous experimental (25–28) and theoretical (29–32) studies have shown that particles with aerodynamic diameters in the 1- to 3-μm-range deposit minimally in the mouth and throat and maximally in the lung's alveolar region. Tracheobronchial deposition, generally not desired for inhalation therapy, is maximized for mean d_a between approximately 8–10 μm owing to inertial impaction, whereas central airway deposition by gravity occurs maximally for $3\mu m < d_a < 5\mu m$. Particles possessing d_a less than 1 μm are mostly exhaled, and particles larger than about 10 μm have little chance of making it into the mouth.

For these reasons, inhalation therapies today rely on liquid or dry-powder aerosols comprised of particles with mean diameters in the range of 1–5 μm. Therapeutic particles in this size range are found to produce optimal therapeutic (whether systemic or local) effect.

However, aerosols formed of 1–5 μm particles, in addition to rapidly clearing from the lungs, can aggregate prior to delivery (33). This produces poor efficiency of delivery from standard inhaler devices; hence, devices on the market deliver only about 10% of an inhaled dose into the lungs (34,35). This inefficiency magnifies patient-to-patient variability and can lead to patient discomfort, as manifested in coughing or bronchospasm.

One way to address this problem involves adjusting inhalation procedures. An optimal inhalation maneuver appears to involve a slow, deep inhalation to reduce impaction losses in the orapharynx, with about 10 s of breath hold to allow particles that enter the lung to settle by gravity (36–41). Pulmonary deposition can also be greatly affected by patient inspiratory flow rate, as inertial impaction of particles in the mouth and throat increases sharply with increasing flow rate (42,43).

Greater progress has been achieved by modifications to the inhaler device. Inhalation devices broadly fall into three categories: pressurized metered-dose inhalers (MDIs), nebulizers, and dry-powder inhalers (DPIs). The most commonly used inhalers on the market are MDIs; they contain active ingredient as a solution or as a suspension of fine particles in a liquefied propellant (often a chlorofluorocarbon, CFC) held under high pressure. The drug is emitted through an orifice from a metering valve. Drop-

lets of a MDI tend to exit the orifice at a high velocity, potentially causing extensive orapharyngeal deposition. New breath-activated devices (44,45) now address this problem, and new non-CFC propellants address the CFC concern.

The typical maximum drug dose delivered by a single actuation of a MDI is around 1 mg (46). Nebulizers do not require propellants and can generate large quantities of small droplets capable of penetrating into the lung. As in the case of MDIs, new nebulizer systems avoid the problems of older generation nebulizers (bulk, excessive mouth–throat deposition) though they continue to be considered impractical for daily portable use. Given the concern about CFC's negative effects on the ozone layer, a great deal of work has been done to develop DPI systems. Although DPIs are sold widely in Europe, their use is still limited in other parts of the world, such as the United States. Current developments in the field may change this situation. DPIs have the attraction of storing the inhaled drug in a dry state, which often carries with it advantages of long-term stability and sterility. New generation DPIs modulate flow rate dependence and deaggregate powder, leading to significant improvements in device performance (8). Depending on the device, DPIs deliver either quantities of drug similar to MDIs (1–3 milligrams or less) or in certain cases considerably more.

DPIs may be most useful for controlled-release applications, as they can be maintained on the shelf in a dry state prior to delivery. On the other hand, MDIs might prove useful as well upon appropriate choice of propellant.

FAST-ACTING INHALATION THERAPIES

The mainstay of asthma treatment is the inhalation of a bronchodilator, such as albuterol, for fast-acting relief from bronchoconstriction and a corticosteroid, such as beclamethasone or fluticasone, for antiinflammation protection (1–6). Other bronchodilators and corticosteroids are commonly inhaled, as are anticholinergics. All these inhalation therapies involve fast action and delivery from either a MDI, DPI, or both. Nebulization is the preferred route of delivery in the clinic for a variety of substances, including lung surfactant for surfactant-replacement therapy and DNase for cystic fibrosis (46). DNase is the sole inhaled protein currently on the market, although other proteins are being tested in the clinic, including insulin, salmon calcitonin, parathyroid hormone, and LHRH (7). Each of these clinical therapies involves fast delivery of protein to the systemic circulation, with a delivery profile similar to intravenous injection.

SUSTAINED DRUG DELIVERY

Notwithstanding the rapid clearance of inhaled insoluble particles from the lungs, many efforts have been made to achieve sustained drug delivery from an inhalation aerosol. Primarily inhaled drugs have been encapsulated inside liposomes and biodegradable polymers (47,48), though the most successful long-acting inhaled drug (salmeterol, or Serevent) was developed by chemical modification of a fast-acting drug (salbutamol) (49).

Liposomal systems, delivered to the lungs by nebulization, are among the most commonly used methods for sustained pulmonary drug delivery. Liposome-encapsulated drugs have been released over many hours following inhalation in animals and humans; these drugs include, for local delivery, cytotoxic agents, bronchodilators, and antimicrobial agents (50–56); for systemic delivery, drugs such as insulin (57,58) have been released slowly from liposomes as well. Drawbacks to the inhalation of liposomes include (1) their relatively short action owing to clearance (they can be eliminated rapidly by alveolar macrophages [59–62]); (2) their poor stability during storage and use (63); and (3) their apparent need for delivery by nebulization.

Biodegradable polymer microspheres as drug carriers have also been extensively investigated. Albumin (59–62) and polylactide-co-glycolide (PLGA) microspheres (64–67) have repeatedly been used to achieve the sustained release of drugs in the lungs (9). Both biodegradable materials appear to be nontoxic and nonimmunogenic, although few if any chronic toxicity studies appear in the literature (9). Another approach to obtaining sustained release from inhaled drug particles involves incorporating macromolecules such as dextran (68,69) or poly(ethylene glycol) (70,71) to reduce particle hydrophilicity. One of the primary drawbacks to this approach for lung delivery is the possibility of accumulation of macromolecular materials within the lung over an extended administration period owing to the relatively slow removal of these materials from the lungs (9).

These techniques, among others, have achieved little success at maintaining therapeutic action following a single inhalation for more than several hours (9) (Fig. 1). To overcome this limitation posed by the lungs' natural clearance mechanisms, a new method to achieve sustained release in the lungs has involved preparing insoluble particles with aerodynamic diameter in the 1- to 5-μm range yet with very low mass density so that particles possess geometric diameters significantly greater than 5 μm (10). This permits the penetration of particles deep into the lungs (owing to small aerodynamic diameter) yet lowers the degree of clearance, because (geometrically) large particles tend to be cleared less by phagocytosis than particles in the size range of 1–5 μm (72–74).

Several studies have now appeared in the literature demonstrating the ability to achieve sustained release of

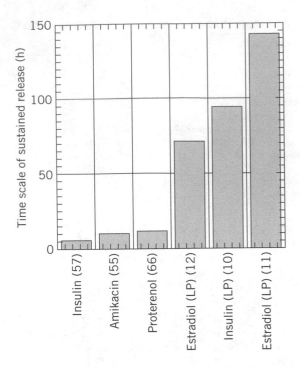

Figure 1. Approximate times of release in vivo from various controlled-release carriers following inhalation. The rightmost columns, indicated by the symbol LP, denote results from large porous particles in humans (12) and animals (10,11).

drugs from the lungs following a single inhalation of large porous particles for up to several days (10–15). In a first study, large, porous particles were prepared using PLGA biodegradable polymers and containing either insulin or testosterone for systemic delivery (10). For comparison purposes, small nonporous particles of similar composition and identical aerodynamic size were prepared. Both types of particles were aerosolized into the lungs of rats. In the case of the insulin aerosols, exogenous insulin appeared in the bloodstream for up to 96 h following inhalation of the porous particles, compared with 4 h for the nonporous particles. Given that the presence of insoluble particles in the lungs beyond 24 h indicates deep lung deposition and that bronchoalveolar lavage demonstrated that the large porous insulin particles were less avidly taken up by alveolar macrophages than the small nonporous insulin particles, the long release (>24 h) of insulin into the systemic circulation appears to owe to lower particle phagocytosis of large porous particles in the deep lungs. In another study, estradiol was formulated in large porous particles comprised of dipalmitoyl phosphatidyl choline (DPPC) as well as particles comprised of other soluble excipients (11). Particles were prepared with large size (approximately 10 μm) and low mass density (approximately 0.1 g/cc) as well as with small size (approximately 3 μm) and standard mass density. Both porous and nonporous powders were aerosolized into the lungs of rats. For two different formulations of the large porous estradiol particles, estradiol released into the systemic circulation following inhalation for 3 days or more. On the other hand, estradiol appeared in the systemic circulation following administration of two different small nonporous particle formulations for a day or less. As porous and nonporous subcutaneously injected estradiol formulations acted therapeutically for several days, the short action of the small nonporous inhaled estradiol formulation appears again to relate to the more rapid clearance of small nonporous particles from the lungs. Sustained release in the estradiol study (11) was achieved by the use of both a relatively water-insoluble drug (estradiol) and insoluble surfactant (DPPC) rather than by biodegradable polymers.

One of the DPPC/estradiol formulations (Fig. 2) that achieved several-day delivery in rats has recently been inhaled in a human subject study using a simple DPI system (Fig. 3) (12). Inhalation of the porous dry powder at 30 L/min led to systemic estradiol absorption for 72 h, with estimated absolute bioavailability of 47%. The systemic absorption profile obeyed a two-phase model, with an initial fast elimination of estradiol from the body consistent with rapid absorption of estradiol from the lungs and systemic clearance and a secondary slow elimination phase, reflecting slow release from inhaled particles (Fig. 4). This study confirms that inhalation of large porous particles can produce sustained (>24 h) release of drugs into the lungs of humans as previously demonstrated in animals.

An example of sustained release of drugs from large porous particles for the treatment of respiratory disease has recently been described involving albuterol sulfate for asthma therapy (13). Albuterol sulfate particles were prepared using DPPC, human serum albumin, and lactose. Large porous and small nonporous albuterol particles were delivered as inhalation aerosols to the lungs of guinea pigs. To induce bronchoconstriction, immediately prior to measuring airway resistance (at selected intervals following inhalation of albuterol particles), carbachol was intramuscularly delivered. The small nonporous particles provided significant bronchodilatory effect for approximately 5 h following inhalation at a dose of 200 μg. The large porous albuterol particles produced sustained bronchodilation for at least up to 15 h (13).

As the porous-particle and other new sustained-release technologies emerge in the inhalation drug delivery arena, the possibility of several-day, or even several-week, sustained-release inhalation therapies arises. Clearly the desire (and ability) to achieve long drug release times in the lungs will place demands on drug dosing by inhalation. The current limitation of most inhalation systems (other than nebulizers) to inhaled doses of a few milligrams or less will need to be removed so that several tens of milligrams of drug can be inhaled in a single breath, a feat that does not appear too difficult even given currently emerging technologies (75). Another challenge will be to design sustained-release inhalation formulations that comprise materials that are safe for inhalation. Given the slow absorption of very large macromolecules in the lungs, standard sustained-release additives used to achieve oral sustained release (for example, methyl cellulose) may not be

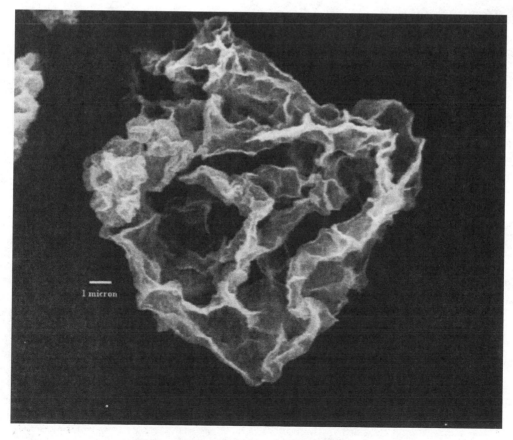

Figure 2. A large porous estradiol particle (12).

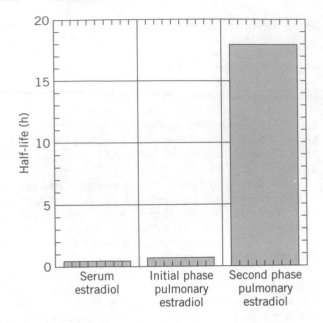

Figure 3. Approximate systemic half-lives of estradiol following intravenous injection and inhalation in humans. The second and third columns refer to clearance of estradiol following inhalation of a large porous particle formulation.

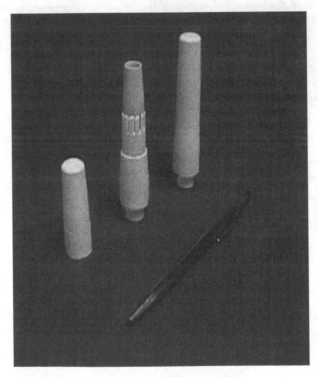

Figure 4. The AIR dry-powder inhaler.

appropriate for inhalation formulations. The search for excipients suitable for frequently dosed inhaled sustained-release formulations will play an important role in the practical success of sustained drug delivery in the respiratory tract.

SUMMARY

Efforts to achieve sustained drug delivery in the respiratory tract have been hindered in the past owing to the rapid clearance of insoluble drug particles in the lungs by mucociliary and phagocytic clearance processes, which remove or engulf particles within approximately 12–24 h after inhalation. Standard size and mass density liposomal and biodegradable polymer sustained-release systems have achieved drug release for modest periods, up to several hours. A new technique involving the production of large porous particles that display an ability to escape lung clearance has led to longer sustained release of drugs in the lungs, up to several days. One of the challenges of this technology will be to formulate sustained-release systems that do not lead to accumulation of materials in the lungs over time.

BIBLIOGRAPHY

1. T.J.H. Clark, *Lancet* **6**, 1361–1367 (1972).
2. S.D. Anderson et al., *Am. Rev. Respir. Dis.* **114**, 493–502 (1976).
3. A. Neville et al., *Br. Med. J.* **1**, 413–419 (1977).
4. S.P. Newman and S.W. Clarks, in F. Moren, M.T. Newhouse, and M.B. Dolovich, eds., *Aerosols in Medicine: Principles, Diagnosis and Therapy*, Elsevier, Amsterdam, 1985, pp. 289–301.
5. N. Svedmyr and G.-G. Lofdahl, in J.W. Jenne and S. Murphy, eds., *Drug Therapy for Asthma: Research and Clinical Practice*, Dekker, New York, 1987, pp. 177–185.
6. R.G. Taylor, in D. Ganderton and T. Jones, eds., *Drug Delivery to the Respiratory Tract*, Ellis Horwood, Chichester, England, 1987, pp. 27–32.
7. R.F. Service, *Science* **279**, 1631–1633 (1998).
8. C.A. Dunbar, A.J. Hickey, and P. Holzner, *KONA* **16**, 7–44 (1998).
9. X.-M. Zeng, G.P. Martin, and C. Marriott, *Int. J. Pharm.* **124**, 149–164 (1995).
10. D.A. Edwards et al., *Science* **276**, 1868–1871 (1997).
11. J. Wang, A. Ben-Jebria, and D.A. Edwards, *J. Aerosol. Med.* **12**, 27 (1999).
12. D.A. Edwards et al., *Int. Symp. Recent Adv. Drug Delivery Syst.*, Salt Lake City, Utah, February 22–25, 1999.
13. A. Ben-Jebria, D. Chen, R. Langer, and D.A. Edwards, *Pharm. Res.* **16**, 555–561 (1998).
14. D.A. Edwards, D. Chen, J. Wang, and A. Ben-Jebria, *6th Respir. Drug Delivery Conf.*, Hilton Head, S.C., 1998, p. 187.
15. D.A. Edwards, A. Ben-Jebria, and R. Langer, *J. Appl. Physiol.* **84**(2), 379 (1998).
16. D.J. Gore and G. Patrick, *Phys. Med. Biol.* **23**, 730–737 (1978).
17. G.C. Smaldone et al., *J. Aerosol Med.* **1**, 1–20 (1988).
18. W. Stahlhofen, J. Gebhart, G. Rudolf, and G. Scheuch, *J. Aerosol Sci.* **17**, 333–338 (1986).
19. P. Gehr et al., *Microsc. Res. Tech.* **26**, 423–436 (1993).
20. K.C. Stone et al., *Am. Respir. Cell Mol. Biol.* **6**, 235–243 (1992).
21. A.J. Vander, J.H. Sherman, and D.S. Luciano, *Human Physiology*, 6th ed., McGraw-Hill, New York, 1994, pp. 473–514.
22. A.J. Vander, J.H. Sherman, and D.S. Luciano, *Human Physiology*, 6th ed., McGraw-Hill, New York, 1994, pp. 393–472.
23. J. Patton, *Adv. Drug Delivery Rev.* **19**, 3–36 (1996).

24. E.R. Weibel, in H.K. Chang and M. Paiva, eds., *Respiratory Physiology: An Analytical Approach*, Decker, New York, 1989, pp. 1–56.

25. B. Altschuler, L. Yalmus, E. D. Palmes, and N. Nelson, *AMA Arch. Ind. Health* **15**, 293–303 (1957).

26. D.C.F. Muir and C.N. Davies, *Ann. Occup. Hyg.* **10**, 161–174 (1967).

27. C.N. Davies, J. Heyder, and M. C. Subba Ramu, *J. Appl. Physiol.* **32**, 591–600 (1972).

28. J. Heyder et al., *J. Aerosol Sci.* **6**, 311–328 (1975).

29. T.R. Gerrity et al., *J. Appl. Phys.* **47**, 867–873 (1979).

30. J. Heyder and R. Rudolf, *J. Aerosol Sci.* **13**, 697–707 (1984).

31. A.R. Clark and M. Egan, *J. Aerosol Sci.* **25**, 175–186 (1994).

32. I. Gonda, *J. Pharm. Pharmacol.* **33**, 692–696 (1981).

33. D. French, D.A. Edwards, and R.W. Niven, *J. Aerosol Sci.* **27**, 769–780 (1996).

34. I. Gonda, in A.J. Hickey, ed., *Pharmaceutical Inhalation Aerosol Technology*, Dekker, New York, 1992, pp. 61–82.

35. M.P. Timsina et al., *Int. J. Pharm.* **101**, 1–13 (1994).

36. J.D. Brain and R.A. Valberg, *Am. Rev. Respir. Dis.* **120**, 1325–1373 (1979).

37. J. Heyder, J. Gebliard, and W. Statilofen, in K. Willeke, ed., *Generation of Aerosols and Facilities for Exposure Experiments*, Ann Arbor Sci. Publ., Ann Arbor, Mich., 1980, pp. 135–152.

38. D. Pavia, J.R.M. Bateman, and S.W. Clarke, *Bull. Eur. Physiopathol.* **16**, 335–366 (1980).

39. T.T. Mercer, *Chest* **80**, 813–818 (1981).

40. G.C. Smaldone et al., *J. Aerosol* **2**, 81–87 (1989).

41. M. Dolovich, *J. Aerosol Med.* **2**, 171–186 (1989).

42. R.M. Auty, K. Brown, M.G. Neale, and P.D. Snashall, *Br. J. Dis. Chest* **88**, 371–378 (1987).

43. R. Richards, S.F. Simpson, A.G. Renwick, and S.T. Holgate, *Eur. Respir. J.* **1**, 896–901 (1988).

44. D. Genderton and N.M. Kassem, *Adv. Pharm. Sci.* **6**, 165–191 (1992).

45. K. Masters, *Spray Drying Handbook*, 5th ed., Lonmans, New York, 1991.

46. R. Langer, *Nature (London)* **392**, 5–11 (1998).

47. Int. Pat. Appl. No. PCT/WO96/09814 (1996), A.D. Sutton and R.A. Johnson.

48. S.S. Davis and L. Ilium, *Biomaterials* **9**, 111–115 (1983).

49. D.M. Hammerbeck et al., *J. Aerosp. Med.* **10**, 41–54 (1997).

50. R.L. Juliano and H.N. McCullough, *J. Pharmacol. Exp. Ther.* **214**, 381–387 (1980).

51. A. Kamarel, A. Wong, and T. McCalden, *Proc. West. Pharmacol. Soc.* **32**, 32–35 (1989).

52. R.M. Fielding, *Proc. West. Pharmacol. Soc.* **32**, 103–106 (1939).

53. K.M.G. Taylor, G. Taylor, I.W. Kellaway, and B. Stevens, *Pharm. Res.* **6**, 633–636 (1959).

54. I.W. Kellaway and F. Farr, *Adv. Drug Delivery Rev.* **5**, 149–161 (1990).

55. P. Couvreur, E. Fattal, and A. Andrernont, *Pharm. Res.* **8**, 1079–1086 (1991).

56. R.S. Gonzalez-Rothi, S. Cacace, L. Straub, and H.E. Schreier, *Lung Res.* **17**, 687–705 (1991).

57. P. Clothorpe et al., *Pharm. Res.* **9**, 764–768 (1992).

58. F.-Y. Liu, Z. Shao, D.O. Kildsig, and A.K. Mitra, *Pharm. Res.* **10**, 228–232 (1993).

59. P.K. Gupta and C.T. Hung, *J. Microencapsul.* **4**, 427–462 (1989).

60. M. Haghapanab, G.P. Martin, and C. Marriott, in J. Hadgraft, I.W. Kellaway, and G.D. Parr, eds., *Proceedings of the Second United Kingdom Association of Particle Scientists Annual Conference*, STS, Cardiff, Wales, 1993, p. 74.

61. X.-M. Zeng, G.P. Martin, and C. Marriott, *Int. J. Pharm.* **109**, 135–145 (1994).

62. X.-M. Zeng, C.P. Martin, and C. Marriott, *Eur. J. Pharm. Sci.* **3**, 87–93 (1995).

63. R.S. Langer, *Science* **249**, 1527–1533 (1990).

64. Int. Pat. Appl. No. PCT/GBS7/00566 (1988), R.N. Boyce, T.R. Tice, R.M. Gilley, and K.L. Pledger.

65. T.R. Tice, D.W. Mason, and R.M. Gilley, in L.F. Prescott and W.O. Nirruno, eds., *Novel Drug Delivery and its Therapeutic Application*, Wiley, New York, 1989, pp. 223–235.

66. L. Masinde and A.J. Hickey, *Pharm. Res.* **8**, 5–12 (1991).

67. Y.L. Lai et al., *Pharm. Res.* **10**, 119–125 (1993).

68. L. Molteni, *Methods Enzymol.* **112**, 285–299 (1985).

69. A.S. Williams and G. Taylor, *Int. J. Pharm.* **83**, 233–239 (1992).

70. E. Tomlinson, in L.F. Prescott and W.S. Nimino, eds., *Novel Drug Delivery and its Therapeutic Application*, Wiley, New York, 1989, pp. 257–259.

71. D.H.W. Ho ct al., *Drug Metab. Dispos.* **16**, 27–29 (1988).

72. H. Kawaguchi et al., *Biomaterials* **7**, 61–66 (1986).

73. Y. Tabata and Y. Ikada, *Biomaterials* **9**, 356–362 (1988).

74. S. Rudt and R.H. Muller, *J Controlled Release* **22**, 263–272 (1992).

75. D.A. Edwards et al., *ACS Symp. Drug Delivery 21st Century*, Annaheim, Calif, March 23, 1999.

SYNTHETIC VASCULAR GRAFTS AND CONTROLLED-RELEASE TECHNOLOGY

Mark R. Kreitz
Brown University
Providence, Rhode Island

KEY WORDS

Amikacin

Antibiotic

Controlled-release drug delivery

Expanded poly(tetrafluoroethylene) (ePTFE)

Heparin

Microsphere

Poly(ethylene terephthalate) (Dacron)

Polyurethane

Teflon

Vascular graft

OUTLINE

INTRODUCTION

The design of artificial organ systems typically incorporates those functions necessary for successful organ substitution and, if technology and circumstance permits, those of less critical value. Synthetic vascular grafts are replacements for organs of some chemical and physiologic complexity, but as a vessel substitute, their primary function is to provide a durable, relatively nonthrombogenic conduit for blood. Current larger-diameter vascular grafts accomplish this design goal remarkably well with simple synthetic materials. In smaller-diameter synthetic grafts, where the same synthetic materials perform less well, the absence of complex function may predispose them to fail-

ure. The abilities of controlled-release technologies may be able to compensate for the lack of some functions in smaller-diameter synthetic vascular grafts. This article will provide a limited review of the history of vascular grafts, the achievements of synthetic grafts of the past few decades, and some specific applications of controlled-release technology to synthetic grafts.

EARLY INVESTIGATIONS

In 1906 substitutive medicine made its debut into the emerging field of vascular surgery when, during a procedure to remedy a popliteal aneurysm, J. Goyanes replaced the degenerate vessel with a segment of autologous popliteal vein (1). The following year E. Lexer used this approach to repair an axillary artery gap defect with a saphenous vein (2). It could not have been known at the time but this seemingly intuitive resolution, the substitution of an autologous vein for a diseased or damaged artery, would become a preferred and commonplace solution in thousands of annually performed vascular surgeries many decades later. In part, such bold procedures owed their success to the endeavors in vessel repair of many surgeons of the prior three decades (3), but especially to Alexis Carrel, whose defining techniques on vascular anastomoses and philosophies concerning minimal trauma, meticulousness, and asepsis would illuminate the field and win him the Nobel Prize.

The following years witnessed radical and often disastrous attempts at vascular restitution. During World War I, desperate repairs of British soldiers' vascular injuries were sometimes attempted with silver tubes lined with paraffin while, across the battlefield, fresh cadaveric arterial and venous homografts were sutured into wanting German soldiers (2). Though patency of the silver tubes persisted in a few rare instances, the great majority of these and the homografts failed after thrombus formation. The use of paraffin-lined silver tubes as vascular substitutes was not as unconventional as would first appear because "foreign material" implant precedents, such as paraffined and gold-plated aluminum (4), glass (5), and even ivory (3) did exist.

During the following decades, novel vascular surgical concepts and practices were advanced but were concerned more with suture technique and repairing rather than replacing defects. It was not until the post–World War II era that as a result of many factors, vascular substitution again became a popular avenue of investigation. These factors—a growing need for an adequate vascular replacement, the proliferation of surgical research laboratories, the advent of arteriography, the expansion of blood banks, anticoagulant therapy, and the sudden abundance of military surgeons eager to return to career pursuits—invited vascular surgical discovery (3,6).

In 1947, Hufnagel reported on the use of methyl methacrylate (Lucite™) conduits in the "permanent intubation" of aortas of mongrel dogs, citing the material's strength, smoothness, ready availability, low cost, low tissue response, and its delaying of coagulation times as justifications for its selection (7). These arterial prostheses, 1–3 cm in length, remained patent until the scheduled dates of sacrifice and autopsy, this being from 6 h to 6 months. In 1948, homografts again emerged as though the reasons for past failures were no longer applicable. This time, however, experimental processing was performed on the harvested vessels in hopes of improving the results. After storage in a chilled, isotonic saline solution containing 10% human serum, Gross et al. implanted arterial homografts in humans and dogs in an attempt to correct cardiovascular defects (8,9). In 1952 and 1953, Dubost et al. (10) and Oudot (11), respectively, performed and reported on homograft replacements in human subjects, and others soon followed (12–14).

THE INTRODUCTION OF SYNTHETIC VASCULAR GRAFTS

The replacement of natural vessels with synthetic fabric conduits began somewhat serendipitously in 1947 after Voorhees noted the formation of a "glistening" coat on a silk suture that had remained in the ventricle of the heart of a dog for months (3). From this he reasoned that a fabric mesh formed into a tube and implanted as an arterial replacement would be similarly coated. Shortly thereafter, scraps of a parachute were fashioned into tubes on a home sewing machine and implanted. Following this, tubes fabricated from what was a more biologically preferred material, Vinyon N (vinyl chloride-acrylonitrile), were implanted into 15 mongrel dogs (15). In 1954 18 patients with aneurysms had defective vascular segments replaced with synthetic grafts (2). This experimentation, suggesting a new direction in vascular prosthesis exploration, came a few years prior to reports highlighting the less-than-adequate long-term performance of arterial homografts. Degeneration of the homograft, rather than progression of the patient's disease, was believed responsible for the 70% occlusion rate observed (2). In 1955, Szilagyi had reported on the treatment of arterial occlusion by resection and replacement with arterial homografts (14), but in 1957, after 2 years of experimentation in close to 400 dogs, his group had abandoned such homografts in favor of poly(ethylene terephthalate) (PET), or Dacron®, grafts (16). In a 1957 report on the fate of human arterial homografts, Szilagyi et al. predicted that degenerative changes and diminishing tensile strengths in aortic homografts would begin to endanger patients' lives after 5 years (17). In the following year, Linton noted a 40% failure rate in 38 patients during the first 2–3 postoperative years (2).

Now surgeons, harboring a growing dissatisfaction with long-term biologic graft performance and acknowledging the recent success of the implanted synthetic grafts, began viewing synthetic fabrics as a serious alternative for graft manufacture and implementation. This is not to say that biologic grafts were abandoned, but these factors, combined with the often unsuitable state of potential autograft vessels; advancements in surgical technique; and refinements in anticoagulation, antimicrobial therapy, and angiography, invited exploration.

The early explorations, not surprisingly, focused on the choice of material. However, even in the beginning, other graft characteristics were recognized to influence success or failure. After preliminary investigations, Harrison observed a correlation between graft diameter and occlusion and conducted a comparative study on smaller-diameter grafts (<9 mm) of nylon, Dacron, Orlon® (polyacrylonitrile, PAN), Ivalon® (formalized poly[vinyl alcohol], PVA), and Teflon® (poly[tetrafluoroethylene], PTFE), of varying porosities (18). Following implantation into the abdominal aorta and carotid and femoral artery positions of 133 dogs, he witnessed occlusion rates of up to 92% in periods of 6 weeks. He concluded that because none of the grafts satisfactorily maintained patency, these materials would not serve adequately as small-diameter replacements. However, the contributions of unrefined surgical techniques, crude graft constructions, and harsh preparations (e.g., concentrated acid and base washes, bleaching, and melting of cut ends to prevent unraveling) toward the failure rate should be acknowledged. Also, in retrospect, it is easy to recognize the difficulty of maintaining successful grafts in high-resistance/low-blood-flow positions. Even with modern sterilization techniques and surgical procedures, it is difficult to speculate on whether such poor results would be obtained today with similar graft materials.

In the same month and using the same materials, Harrison published results from a similar comparative study, this time on larger-diameter grafts (>9 mm, with 6–7 cm length) as replacements for thoracic aortas in 84 dogs (19). These results were remarkably different, with only 1 of the 84 grafts failing from occlusion. It was determined that Teflon, Orlon, and Dacron performed equally, well but nylon and Ivalon were not suitable graft materials, as some had extensively degraded during the study period. This study was extended to 2–3 years in 10 of these animals with patent nylon, Dacron, Orlon, and Teflon grafts (20). Of the four nylon grafts observed, only one remained patent at 36 months, though subsequent testing revealed an 80% loss of tensile strength in this graft. Again the Teflon, Orlon and Dacron grafts were viewed as superior, having lost no more than 25% of their tensile strength.

In a report the following year on the fate of human aorta replacements, knitted Dacron grafts were found to be superior to those of nylon and Orlon and to homografts as well (21). In 1964, this emerging trend of positive results was reinforced in an analysis by DeBakey et al. (22) of 67 Dacron grafts removed from 58 patients. After thorough visual, histological, and electron microscopy examinations and demonstrated sustained patency and function for many years, his group was convinced that Dacron could serve as an effective arterial substitute. However, it should be noted that many—if not most or all—of these grafts were in medium- to high-flow positions, primarily serving as aortoiliac and femoropopliteal bypasses. This doesn't lessen the significance of these findings concerning the suitability of Dacron, especially because DeBakey's investigations made this fabric an industry standard, but serves only to place them in perspective. The potential of Dacron as small-diameter replacements in humans was illustrated in a clinical note documenting the patency of a small-diameter Dacron graft (3 mm) as a coronary artery bypass graft at 17 months (23). But as exemplified in a report by Darling and Linton (24) that showed lower-extremity Dacron graft patency rates of less than 10% at 8 years compared with 65% for reversed saphenous vein, prolonged patency of synthetic grafts of this diameter are the exception, not the rule.

The other synthetic fabric that rose to the status of industry standard for vascular grafts, Teflon, was first used with some success in dogs in the early 1950s by Daniel (25). A few years later, Deterling and Bhonslay (26) obtained satisfactory function with a Teflon graft after some initial blood loss. In 1957 Harrison conducted a 6-month trial of Teflon grafts in the thoracic and abdominal aortas in dogs for which he witnessed an average occlusion rate of 8% (27). He noted that the inner surface layer was thinner and that the grafts healed faster than other grafts. Harrison's 1958 investigations with Teflon as material for larger-diameter grafts gave positive results (19,20), while the smaller-diameter Teflon grafts fared poorly (18).

While these results of Teflon grafts are near those of Dacron, there is one characteristic in the healing of Teflon grafts that sometimes lowers its success. Researchers have noted that the neointima formed on Teflon grafts does not always attach strongly and may be displaced with some ease, even after a year (28). This type of dissection would readily facilitate thrombus and emboli formation, originating not just from the loose intima but possibly from the newly exposed biomaterial surface as well.

In 1969, Robert Gore invented expanded poly(tetrafluoroethylene) (ePTFE) (29), a Teflon that when shaped is simultaneously stretched. The stretching, or expansion, produces a microscopic node–fibril–node pattern throughout the material, the lateral spaces between the fibrils forming the pores. This material, which was introduced in vascular grafts a few years later, can be stretched to varying degrees during fabrication, providing control over the degree of porosity in the graft (30).

The initial results with ePTFE were very favorable. Soyer et al. observed the presence of pannus ingrowth at the anastomoses but also noted its poor attachment (31). The following year Matsumoto et al. obtained extremely positive results of 100% patency in femoral artery replacements in dogs when using high-porosity ePTFE grafts in contrast to the 100% occlusion of ultralightweight woven Teflon grafts in the same study (32). These results were difficult to replicate, and as subsequent investigations indicated, the results were still good, though typically not as good as those of Matsumoto et al. The excitement about ePTFE was soon tempered however, as longer-term results began to be reported. Hobson et al. (33) published 30-month patency results of only 45%, compared with 54% for autogenous saphenous vein, in femoropopliteal, femorotibial, and femoroperoneal replacements. In 250 patients who had ePTFE grafts implanted as femoropopliteal artery reconstructions, a patency rate of 74% at 1 year dropped to 56% at 2 and 3 years (34,35).

The years of experimentation with different fabrics and modifications, by virtue of their poorer performance, reinforced these materials and made them the synthetic graft standards. But along the way, the characteristics to which success was attributed were noted, analyzed, and often integrated into general, but not necessarily universal, acceptance. This resulted in part from varying experimental results and in part from the poor results obtained from small-diameter grafts of fabrics that typically yielded good results when used in a larger-diameter graft. Today, the desired features of successful synthetic vascular grafts are, for the most part, standardized.

SMALL-DIAMETER SYNTHETIC GRAFT SUCCESS OR FAILURE

Synthetic vascular graft characteristics thought to be desirable haven't so much changed over the years as they have been refined. It was apparent early on that porosity, hemocompatibility, biocompatibility, sterility, flexibility, compliance, and durability were vital components of a successful graft (2). Today, little in the fundamental requirements has changed. Abbott et al. have recently published a list of preferable characteristics including optimal biomechanical properties, cosmetic acceptability, handling characteristics, sterility, reasonable cost, production consistency, durability, infection resistance, strength, and a thromboresistant flow surface (36). A comparison of preferred characteristics then and now are outlined and matched in Table 1. It is apparent that the major requirements have changed little and that the later additions reflect contemporary capabilities and realities.

Biology of Small-Diameter Vascular Graft Failure

Before exploring and enumerating the features of synthetic fabric grafts that contribute to success, it is appropriate to highlight and understand the mechanisms of graft failure. Beyond the obvious considerations of vascular graft failure attributable to infections, mechanical degradation, preexisting vascular disease progression, and technical errors are those related to the tissue and blood reactions to the implanted material, specifically the hyperproliferative cellular events occurring in and near the graft.

Upon exposure to a foreign material such as a polymer graft, specific blood components respond as if the integrity of a native vessel has been compromised and the endothelium denuded. These components recognize the material as foreign, become activated, and initiate a series of events

Table 1. Comparison of Preferred Synthetic Vascular Graft Characteristics of the 1950s and 1990s

1950s	1990s
Compliance	Biomechanical properties
Durability	Durability
Flexibility	Handling characteristics
Porosity	Porosity
Proper tissue reactivity	Flow surface, biocompatibility
Sterility	Cleanliness and sterility
	Consistency
	Cost
	Cosmetic attributes
	Infection resistance

in an attempt to repair the perceived damage. The first event is the immediate adsorption of multifarious plasma proteins to the entire graft surface, which may remain attached or desorb under the influence of other proteins or blood flow. It is thought that the graft surface can denature the proteins (37) and that these bound, altered protein configurations may bind platelets and initiate their activation. Additionally, direct contact with a foreign surface alone is sufficient to provoke platelet activation (38). Surface fibrin, platelet debris, and red blood cells (RBCs) comprising the newly formed layer, called *pseudointimal hyperplasia*, can lead to clot and thrombus formation, the progression of which could be the short-term failure of a vascular graft.

Subsequent to platelet coverage and activation upon the graft, specific substances are released from the platelets (e.g., platelet-derived growth factor [PDGF], transforming growth factor $\beta1$ [TGF-$\beta1$], and thrombin) that are chemoattractants and/or growth factors for smooth muscle cells (39). As a component of the vascular tunica media, the smooth muscle cells begin to migrate from the anastomotic vessel wall and progress into the synthetic graft via chemotaxis. On the graft lumen surface, the sustained proliferation of smooth muscle cells with attendant deposition of cellular matrix, collectively termed *intimal hyperplasia*, can develop substantially and narrow or eventually occlude the graft lumen (40). This mode of graft failure typically occurs more frequently at the anastomoses, reflected in the adjusted designation anastomotic hyperplasia.

In as much as synthetic vascular grafts are viewed as foreign surfaces and can effect compliance mismatches and therefore immediately approximate two components of Virchow's triad (endothelial injury, stasis, and hypercoagulability) (41) with the third not far behind, it would seem appropriate that modifications to the graft that eliminate one or more elements of the triad would improve its potential for success.

Materials

As was discovered very early, an unfortunate choice in graft material will doom the fate of the graft and probably the patient. Thus, in the quest for the best synthetic graft fabric, it was realized that not all implanted graft materials and constructs would behave equally. This opened the door to experimentation, and over the past few decades a variety of different synthetic fabrics (usually polymer derived), constructions, textures, and modifications have been evaluated.

Teflon and Dacron grafts remain the most durable ones available and are fabricated in a variety of sizes and constructions, including weaves and knits (42). Primarily because of their durability and stability and secondarily because of their ease of handling and relative lack of thrombogenicity, they are the only synthetic grafts in clinical use today. Their patency rates are fairly good, but they still suffer higher failure rates in low-flow, small-diameter situations.

Many synthetic graft materials have been investigated over the past few decades, and unfortunately, most either exhibited poorer performance than the available (and well

entrenched) grafts or demonstrated success based on difficult-to-reproduce fabrication or preparation techniques. Other synthetic grafts appear in the literature with limited claims of success, typically in small animals, and then disappear after failure in larger animals or after long-term studies reveal failures not foreseen in shorter-term studies.

In 1989, Chaikof et al. examined cross-linked poly(ethylene oxide) (PEO)/polysiloxane as a material for small-diameter vascular grafts (4 mm) based on PEO's low protein and cellular adsorption levels (43). Their results confirmed their predictions of low fibrinogen and platelet deposition, but unfortunately, no grafts were implanted. Subsequent research by this group, again without implantation into animals, alternately confirmed these results with similar-molecular-weight PEO (44) and contradicted the original expectations with low-molecular-weight PEO (45).

A few years later, Greisler et al. implanted 5-cm-long, 4-mm-diameter, woven polypropylene grafts in the aortoiliac position in dogs (46). The selection of polypropylene was based on its physical properties of high tensile strength, degradation resistance, and low platelet adhesion. Excellent results were demonstrated with a one-year patency of 92%, compared with 69% for Dacron and 20% for Teflon, but apparently no subsequent investigations were performed.

The genesis of grafts of bioresorbable materials began in the early 1960s when, as a means to control hemorrhaging at the time of implantation, degradable materials were incorporated into existing grafts (47). In subsequent investigations, significant reductions in hemorrhage with comparable patency rates were obtained for gelatin-treated Dacron and Teflon (48), bovine collagen–impregnated Dacron (49), and gelatin-impregnated Dacron (50). This method of preventing postsurgical graft hemorrhage was superseded by the preclotting of grafts with autogenous blood at the time of surgery.

The goal of bioresorbable grafts was, in principle, to provide a temporary scaffold for the ingrowth and permanent structural establishment of native tissues. In 1985, van der Lei et al. studied partially bioresorbable small-diameter grafts composed of mixtures of polyurethane (PU) and poly(L-lactic acid) (PLLA) in rats (51). Of the four PU/PLLA compositions investigated, the 19:1 PU/PLLA mixture yielded the best results, displaying regeneration of neointima and neomedia similar to the native and no aneurysm formation. However, this was virtually a polyurethane graft, which, if fabricated with porosity introduced by another method, would probably have yielded similar results and obviated the need for the degradable polymer.

Greisler et al. took the idea of bioresorption to the limit in 1985 when they constructed grafts solely of polyglycolic acid (PGA) and implanted these and Dacron controls into rabbit aortas for up to 12 months (52). Inflammatory reactions in each were equal, but the neointima that developed in the PGA grafts was three times thicker than that of the controls. Aneurysmal dilation was also observed in 15% of the PGA grafts, while none was seen in the controls. Two years later, as a means to prevent aneurysmal dilation, Greisler et al. (53) constructed woven grafts from yarns of bioresorbable polyglactin 910 (PG910) and non-resorbable polypropylene in a 69:31 ratio. Forty-two grafts were implanted into the infrarenal aorta position in rabbits and were explanted from 2 weeks to 12 months later. These grafts fared better than the completely bioresorbable grafts, showing 100% patency, no aneurysm formation, and stenosis in only one graft.

In 1988, Galletti et al. (54) experimented with fully bioresorbable Vicryl prostheses that were coated with either of two blends of bioresorbable polymers, which were included to retard the Vicryl fabric degradation time. Eighteen grafts were implanted in the infrarenal aorta position in dogs and were explanted from 3 days to 24 weeks later. Upon explanation, 14 of the 18 grafts were patent, though generally a neointimal thickness of 2–3 times that seen in similarly implanted Dacron grafts was observed. Resembling previous studies of Greisler et al. (52,55) and Bowald et al. (56,57), no elastin was found in the grafts, a consequence thought to be due to the graft rigidity inhibiting elastin expression (54). Aneurysm formation was observed in two of the animals.

Though a completely bioresorbable graft is an ideal, it was an optimistic assumption that the eventual tissue content and arrangement would resemble natural blood vessels in form and function. Unfortunately, these newly formed quasi vessels instead often possessed discordant tissue compositions and failed to maintain the necessary mechanical integrity. Frequent tissue degradation and aneurysm formation were commonly the reason for failure of these grafts.

In the search for an optimal small-diameter graft material, polyurethanes have generated tremendous excitement. These polymers can possess outstanding strength, flexibility, and fatigue resistance (58). Their consideration as a small-diameter graft material arose from concerns of compliance matching and investigations into polymers that preferentially bound albumin instead of fibrinogen, the binding of the latter correlating to thrombogenesis (47). In very early research, Dryer et al. implanted polyurethane foam grafts as aorta replacements in 16 dogs and obtained patency in 13 of the 16 for up to 6 months (59). Using the same polyurethane, Marinescu et al. implanted grafts in canine aortas that lasted for up to 10 years (60). Though minor, this inconsistency in patency results of different researchers could be attributable to surgical experience. In later earliest investigations, Lyman et al. (61) prepared porous, 4-mm-i.d. *co*-polyether-urethane-urea (PEUU) grafts that were implanted in the femoral artery position of 20 dogs. Upon removal, from 10 to 111 days later, 45% of the grafts were patent, comparing favorably with 6-mm-i.d. Dacron and solid-wall, noncompliant PEUU grafts that demonstrated almost zero patency in similar implant situations. These results are appreciably different from those of Dryer et al. and Marinescu et al. and could be due to polyurethane composition, which can vary tremendously between different polyurethanes. Alternately, the smaller graft diameter or the different surface morphology of the grafts could have been the determining factor.

Polyurethane grafts have been fabricated by a variety of unique methods other than the typical weaving or knitting. Annis et al. used an electrostatic spinning method to produce 10-mm-i.d. fibrous, porous poly(ether urethane) grafts, which were implanted in the thoracic aorta position in 42 minipigs (62). Of the 42 grafts, 4 failed due to "faults in the material," and the others remained patent for up to 12 months with no observed aneurysm formation. Hiratzka et al. (63) created polyurethane grafts with a replamineform process whereby machined, microporous, 6-mm-diameter sea urchin spines (tubes) of calcite acted as a templates into which polyurethane was injected. The calcite was dissolved away, leaving a microporous polyurethane tube as a form inversion of the template. These 3-cm-long grafts were implanted in the infrarenal position of dogs and explanted from 1 to 32 weeks later. At the time of removal, all grafts were patent with complete tissue ingrowth and no aneurysmal dilation, though complete endothelial coverage of the lumen was not observed in grafts explanted prior to 16 weeks.

It is believed by many that complete endothelial coverage would render synthetic vascular grafts nonthrombogenic and therefore greatly improve their chances for long-term patency. For unknown reasons, in humans the endothelial pannus ingrowth into the graft from the anastomoses almost always ceases after progressing a few centimeters. Because complete graft endothelialization usually occurs in nonhuman animals but not in humans, incomplete endothelialization of an experimental graft in animals *may* suggest potential failure for this graft in humans.

In 1983, Hess et al. published their results about implanted small-diameter, fibrous polyurethane prosthesis in the abdominal aorta of rats, focusing on the endothelialization process (64). Forty-seven of these 1.6-mm-i.d. grafts were implanted in place of abdominal aorta segments in rats and were explanted after 1 to 25 days and at 6 and 9 months with a patency rate of 91%. Endothelialization began at 5 days and progressed at 0.3 mm per day until day 21, when coverage was complete. In a similar investigation published the same year, Hess et al. (65) described the cells comprising the pannus ingrowth as a combination of layers of smooth muscle cells covered by a continuous endothelium.

The experimental successes of polyurethanes as small-diameter grafts has encouraged their commercial development. Physical and chemical comparisons of a novel microporous polyurethane graft (Vascugraft®) to another microporous polyurethane graft (Mitrathane® prosthesis) and to a microporous ePTFE graft (Gore-tex®) were made by Zhang et al. (66). The resulting favorable analyses and conclusions prompted larger-diameter graft (10 mm i.d.) implantations as thoracoabdominal bypasses in dogs, which yielded mostly positive results (67,68). With awareness of minor concerns raised in the canine studies, 15 femoropopliteal and femoroperoneal Vascugraft bypasses were performed in humans (69). Unfortunately, 8 of the 15 grafts failed during the first year, and the research program was ended by the manufacturer.

Porosity

Even in the first application of synthetic fabric grafts, Voorhees hypothesized on the benefit that porosity would contribute to healing. By 1964, vascular surgeons and researchers believed that the fate of a synthetic graft would be resolved, for better or worse, by its porosity (70). It was and is thought that anchoring of the neointima to the lumen surface would sustain the health of the neointima. Tissue and capillary ingrowth into the external graft surface are believed to stabilize the graft in situ and to supply the tissue ingrowth, and possibly the neointima, with oxygen and nutrients, respectively (71,72). Improved performance of porous synthetic grafts over nonporous grafts was observed early on (73).

In 1964 Fry et al. (74) reviewed case histories of patients who, after having received nonporous Teflon grafts in the aortoiliac position, suffered from complete occlusion of the grafts at 2 months to 3 years postimplantation. At reoperation it was discovered that the neointima of the Teflon grafts had separated from the prosthetic surface and caused thrombosis. Most of the patients then had woven, porous grafts implanted.

Hermansen et al. analyzed two types of Dacron grafts to assess the influence of their markedly different porosities on the viability of the neointima (71). Although dislodged neointima was attributed to the lower porosity in those grafts, no pronounced histological differences were seen. In a study on porosity and healing, White found minimal tissue ingrowth in grafts with pore sizes less than 15 μm, fibrohistiocytic tissue incorporation in grafts with pore sizes of 15–45 μm, and organized fibrous tissue incorporation in grafts with pore sizes greater than 50 μm (75).

Using the graft fabrication technique of Soldani et al. (76), which involves the phase inversion of polyurethane onto a rotating mandrel, Okoshi et al. (77) compared nonporous versus porous graft inner-surface morphologies. After explanation from rat abdominal aortas, the patency rates for the grafts with "skinned" and porous surfaces were 0 and 72% at 2 weeks, respectively, and 0 and 8% at 3 months, respectively. The lower-than-expected patency rate of the porous grafts prompted fabrication of grafts with highly porous inner surfaces, which showed a patency rate of 73% at 3 months.

An interesting and simple way of inducing custom pore sizes during the fabrication of polyurethane grafts was demonstrated by Fujimoto et al. in 1993 (78). Mixtures of polyurethane and monodisperse salt crystals were extruded as 3-mm-i.d. tubes, wrapped with Spandex yarn, and then coated with the same polyurethane/salt mixture. After evaporation of the solvent, the formed tubes were immersed in water to dissolve away the salt. Grafts with average pore sizes from 1.7 to 30 μm were fabricated and implanted into the common carotid arteries of dogs and explanted at 1, 2, and 6 months. All of the grafts with an average pore size of less than 5 μm were occluded by 1 month, while those with a 5- to 30-μm average pore size were patent at 2 months. All of the grafts with average pore size of 30 μm were patent at 6 months as well.

Compliance Matching and Blood Flow Patterns

When anastomotic hyperplasia was observed as a separate phenomenon from general neointimal hyperplasia, it was speculated that host artery/graft differences might have contributed to the failures (79). The difference in compliance between the artery and the graft was one factor thought to affect anastomotic blood flow patterns, which would induce higher shear stresses. This postulate, combined with animal data suggesting a relation between compliance and patency, led to experimentation with more elastic materials in the hope that similar compliances would avert the previously observed hyperplasia. Materials such as latex, Silastic, fluoroelastomers, and hydrocarbon rubbers were investigated, but any benefits derived from similarities in compliance were overshadowed by the thrombogenic effects of the materials, most of which failed (47). It was realized that one desired graft characteristic, however necessary it is thought to be, should not be sought at the expense of others.

Additionally, too often conclusions were drawn after comparisons between less compliant synthetic grafts and more compliant autografts (80). This was the case in a publication by Walden et al. that compared patency rates of various processed and unprocessed natural vessels with Dacron and ePTFE grafts (81). The attribution of an effect to one factor, in a comparison of grafts with multiple differences, is inappropriate. Regardless of the correlations, the conclusions derived from such flawed experimental schemata lack validity.

Lyman et al. examined the patency of otherwise similar small-diameter (4-mm-i.d.) copolyurethane compliant and noncompliant grafts in dogs (82). Although six of the nine compliant grafts were patent upon removal (at up to 77 days), most of the noncompliant grafts failed within 48 hours. In contrast to findings such as these, Annis et al. saw very little patency difference between polyurethane grafts with greater and lesser compliances (83). In this investigation it seems that the compliance of the less compliant grafts was sufficient for equal performance and was not low enough to effect a difference.

In consideration of compliance as a cause of vascular graft deficiency, as with any complex system, there is not always just one well-defined mode of failure. In a statistical investigation of reported vascular graft failures over a 30-year period, Pourdeyhimi et al. (84) concluded that the second leading cause of graft failure was compliance. However, the route to failure was not the expected compliance mismatch, inducing turbulent flow and leading to thrombosis path. Instead, suture line failure due to compliance mismatch, occurring mostly between 30 and 50 months, was the reason for the graft failures.

CELL SEEDING AND OTHER GRAFT MODIFICATIONS

With the incredible numbers of surface-modified vascular grafts and other experimental grafts studied and reported on every year, it may appear as though investigators have acknowledged the limitations of plain polymeric materials in their performance as synthetic vessels. This may be true, or there may be other reasons behind this growing direction in graft research. Possibly some biomaterials searches, now extending past those commonly available and inexpensive and in light of a looming biomaterials litigation crisis, are simply too costly in time and money to pursue. Also, potential elements of a synthetic graft that were once assumed relatively inconsequential may now be thought significantly influential. Or it simply may be that new ideas for grafts appear as technologies progress. Each of these reasons may be the motivation pushing researchers in different directions, or more likely, it is a combination of all of these reasons.

Speculation may have been expressed that because endothelial cells wouldn't completely cover the inner surface of a synthetic vascular graft in a human after implantation, an application of cells prior to graft implantation might improve long-term cell coverage. Cell seeding is the application of endothelial cells in a physiologic medium such as whole blood to a vascular graft and was first attempted on microfiber scaffolds in vitro by Burkel and Kahn in 1977 (85). The popularity of endothelial cell seeding arose from Herring's single-staged method, published in 1978 (86). In his procedure, he scraped endothelial cells from veins of dogs, mixed them with whole blood, and preclotted Dacron prostheses with the mixture before implanting them. In his 1978 report, 12 6-mm-i.d. Dacron grafts were implanted into the infrarenal aortas of dogs, half of which were seeded. Upon explantation at 2, 4, and 8 weeks, the seeded grafts displayed a higher percentage of clot-free surface (76% versus 31%), and Herring concluded that the formed lining was biologically superior to that which developed in the unseeded grafts. As an extension of this technique, Graham used cultured endothelial cells for seeding (87) and in 1982 performed this procedure with 25-cm-long (6- and 10-mm-i.d.) ePTFE grafts in dogs (88). The seeded grafts showed 64 and 91% endothelial cell surface coverage at 2 and 4 weeks, respectively, while the endothelial cell surface coverage of unseeded grafts never exceeded 10%.

In 1987 Emerick et al. determined that up to 90% of the endothelial cells seeded onto a graft are washed away in the first 24 hours (89). Consequently, additional modifications to the cell-seeding procedure, aimed at better endothelial cell retention, have been developed. A few of these are fibronectin (90), Transglutine (a biological glue) (91), and short peptide sequence (92) coatings of grafts prior to seeding. However, these techniques are more modifications of the graft than of the seeding procedure itself.

Other graft modifications focused on changing the graft surface so as to reduce thrombogenicity, prevent infection, induce endothelial cell coverage and retain the cells after coverage, and inhibit specific cell growth. Many of these techniques involve the bonding or application of specific materials or drugs to graft lumen surface to achieve the desired effect, while others employ somewhat unconventional techniques.

Greisler et al. fabricated an interesting small-diameter graft that harnessed the desirable surface properties of Teflon and the bulk properties of Dacron (93). In this study, gaseous tetrafluoroethylene (TFE) monomer was covalently bound to Dacron grafts by radio-frequency plasma discharge, creating a compound graft. Sixty-six grafts, including controls, were implanted into canine aortas (6-mm-i.d. grafts) and carotid arteries (4-mm-i.d. grafts). However, the TFE-coated PET grafts did not demonstrate significantly better performance than the similarly implanted controls.

For a long time it has been thought that capillary ingrowth into the graft wall might be a source of the endothelial coverage on the lumen surface (94). In an effort to induce this ingrowth, Noishiki et al. infiltrated the graft walls with autologous bone marrow cells and implanted these grafts into dogs (95). At all time points past 3 weeks, the marrow-infiltrated grafts showed complete endothelialization and patency, whereas noninfiltrated control grafts demonstrated endothelial coverage only at the anastomoses.

Heparin bonding to the inner surfaces of vascular grafts has been attempted by different researchers hoping to reduce the incidence of thrombogenesis. Esquivel et al. (96) ionically and covalently bonded heparin to polyurethane (PU) and ePTFE grafts (6 cm long and 4 mm i.d.) and implanted these into the carotid arteries of sheep. The results showed reduced early thrombogenicity in both types of grafts with covalently bound heparin and in ionically bound heparin PU grafts though not in ionically bound heparin ePTFE grafts. Unfortunately, this method has shown only sporadic success in humans

Synthetic graft infection carries far greater risk for the patient than focal infections in other areas of the body (97) and has resulted in limb amputation and patient death (98). The bacteria, which may be otherwise negligible in number at the beginning, can gain a foothold in the fabric interstices of grafts. There, protected from the reach of the immune system, the bacteria multiply virtually unchallenged. Today, infections of vascular grafts almost always necessitate their removal, an invasive procedure with unavoidable risks. Although some infections arise systemically, far past the date of implantation, others result from inadvertent contamination during implantation or the postoperative period. Short-term infection prevention would be welcome and may be possible.

Through methods similar to heparin bonding, antibiotics have been bonded to graft surfaces to prevent graft infections. Moore examined the effectiveness of amikacin bonded to 6-mm-i.d. Dacron grafts in preventing graft infection in dogs (99). After the grafts were implanted in the abdominal aorta, approximately 10^8 *Staphylococcus aureus* bacteria were administered intravenously. Infections were observed in only 8% of the experimental grafts versus 100% in the control grafts.

POLYMERIC CONTROLLED RELEASE

Conventional drug delivery methods are inherently inefficient. Typical bolus administrations often require repeated dosing to sustain drug levels within the therapeutic range, a waste of sometimes costly drugs. To ensure delivery of a sufficient quantity of drug to the intended organ(s), increased dosages can be required. Additionally, specific methods of administration (e.g., injections) can be painful. These combined factors can easily induce stress and avoidance behavior in patients, reducing their compliance and increasing their risk of prolonged illness or worse.

Through drug delivery systems, the controlled release of therapeutics offers significant advantages over conventional delivery methods of drug administration. Controlled-release devices can deliver drugs at a steady rate for extended periods of time, minimizing deviations from the therapeutic range and the need for repeated administrations. Localized controlled-release devices serve to reduce the amount of drug necessary. Oral and topical controlled-release formulations obviate the need for injections. The advantages of controlled-release devices increase patient compliance, reduce drug wasting, and save money for the manufacturer and the patient.

Vascular Grafts and Controlled Release

If synthetic materials are to succeed as small-diameter grafts, then closer approximation to a natural vessel is required. One function of a vessel that could be simulated in a synthetic graft is the controlled release of chemicals that influence the vessel's environment. Cell seeding may loosely be considered a form of controlled drug release from a synthetic graft because the seeded cells invariably secrete specific chemicals. However, the definition, as it is applied here, will include only the release of drugs from nonliving constructs.

Sometimes a sustained presence of antibiotics around an implanted graft is desired. With or without parallel prophylactic systemic administration, localized controlled release of antibiotics to or from the synthetic graft is one option. Ney et al. investigated this method of therapy with grafts that had been intentionally infected with solutions containing *Escherichia coli* and *S. aureus* and then implanted into the infrarenal aorta position in dogs (100). Prior to closure of the surgical wound, low-dose (100 mg antibiotic) or high-dose (300 mg antibiotic) amikacin-loaded biodegradable microspheres were applied topically to the vascular grafts. When the grafts were explanted and analyzed 14 days later, 88% of the control grafts (no administration of antibiotics) manifested clinical infections, while none of the treated grafts demonstrated clinical infection. However, two of the eight grafts treated with the low-dose microspheres did test positive for cultures of *S. aureus*.

Also, growth factors and other drugs have been openly and loosely incorporated into vascular grafts although not specifically engineered as controlled-release devices. In 1991 Soldani et al. fabricated small-diameter polyurethane grafts with an incorporated mixture of nonencapsulated albumin and basic Fibroblast Growth Factor (bFGF) particles (101). After an initial burst, the graft showed fairly constant release for 2 weeks, although the cumulative levels never exceeded 20% of the total amount incorporated.

In an effort to facilitate endothelialization and maintain patency, Lado et al. applied a biodegradable carrier polymer containing platelet-derived angiogenesis fraction (PDAF) to the inner surfaces of 2-mm-i.d. PTFE grafts (102). Twenty-four grafts, 12 experimental and 12 control, were implanted. After a 3-week initial implant period in the retroperitoneum of rats, the grafts were in situ anastomosed, end to side, into the abdominal aorta. Though capillary and tissue ingrowth differences were seen, no significant differences were observed between the treated and untreated grafts. A similar investigation by Greisler et al. (103), with fibrin glue containing fibroblast growth factor (FGF) applied to ePTFE grafts, demonstrated release of the FGF to 30 days. Capillary ingrowth and endothelial cell proliferation promoting endothelialization of the graft was observed. Similar techniques involving the controlled release of therapeutics from tubular structures such as vascular grafts have been patented (104).

Richey and Harris (105) examined the effect on in vitro platelet adherence of controlled-release indomethacin (IM) and aspirin (ASA) from PLA/PLGA-blend microspheres present in the pores of ePTFE discs (1.5 cm diameter). The samples were placed into tissue culture dishes with phosphate-buffered saline for periods of 2 h, 4 days, and 14 days. After these periods of drug release, the samples were exposed to a platelet preparation for 1 h and rinsed, at which time platelet adherence was measured. After 2 h the platelet adherence of the four experimental samples (10 and 20% loaded IM and ASA) was less than that of the controls, though only the two samples with 20% loaded microspheres demonstrated significant differences. The other time points showed similar, though not significant, differences.

Kreitz et al. describe the construction and characterization of controlled-release synthetic vascular grafts without and with incorporated biodegradable polyester microspheres, as shown in Figure 1. Using a modification of the spray–phase inversion technique of Soldani et al. (76), microporous polyurethane grafts were fabricated with heparin-loaded poly(lactic-*co*-glycolic acid) (PLGA) microspheres incorporated into the walls of the grafts (106,107). The controlled release of heparin is intended to inhibit smooth muscle cell (SMC) proliferation in the vascular grafts. Characterizations revealed PLGA degradation over 2–3 months, but with a very rapid heparin release. This was thought to be due to the use of water as a nonsolvent in the graft fabrication process, the extreme water solubility of heparin, and pores in the microsphere coatings of the heparin. Subsequently, an alternate nonbiodegradable controlled-release system was devised for the same graft fabrication technique. Heparin release from these grafts observed over 1–2 months was adequate to effect inhibition of SMC proliferation in vitro.

Therapeutics other than solids have been employed for controlled release to the vascular graft environment. Pulfer et al. (108) used cross-linked polyethyleneimine microspheres to release nitric oxide (NO), a reported inhibitor of thrombus formation, from Gore-tex grafts in vitro. Release from microspheres alone demonstrated nearly linear release of NO over 1 week, whereas the microspheres incorporated into the graft released substantially lower amounts of NO in less time. Because a mixture of microspheres was used, some with lower NO loadings, the results of NO release from the grafts were not unexpected.

TISSUE-ENGINEERED VASCULAR GRAFTS

It is ironic that after so many years of pursuing perfection of small-diameter synthetic vascular grafts, investigation should again turn to natural vessels, albeit in a different way. Researchers may have recognized evolution's power

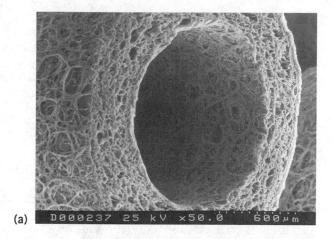
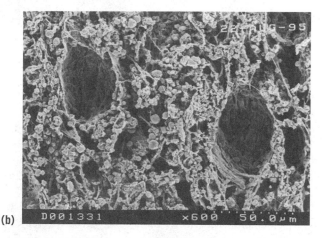

Figure 1. Scanning electron micrographs of vascular grafts produced by the spray–phase inversion process. (**a**) Micrograph shows the microfibrillar structure and porosity of the inner and outer surfaces (magnification 50×). (**b**) Micrograph of a cross section of a composite vascular graft fabricated with spray-dried polyester microspheres. The large quantity of spray-dried polyester microspheres are visible (magnification 150×).

to achieve what they yet cannot, and consequently have begun to focus on recreation instead of simulation. These new vessels are not harvested from animals or humans but rather engineered in the laboratory from human cells. L'Heureux et al. (109) produced tubular structures with three layers of cells, fibroblasts, smooth muscle cells, and endothelial cells, emulating in a natural vessel the adventitia, media, and intima, respectively. Positive indications of comparative function such as expression of von Willebrand factor, incorporation of acetylated low-density lipoprotein, and production of prostacyclin were observed in vitro. The burst strength capacity of this TEBV compared favorably with natural vessels, in contrast to a similar tissue-engineered blood vessel (TEBV) (110) previously constructed by others. In the L'Heureux TEBVs intended for implantation, the endothelial cell component was excluded to lessen the possibility of acute rejection. These human cell–derived TEBVs were implanted into the femoral artery position in dogs and when explanted 7 days later, they xenografts showed a 50% patency rate.

SUMMARY

With refinements in materials, surgical techniques, and related peripheral technologies, the performance of vascular grafts has improved since the initial trials in the 1950s. Though the currently used synthetic materials perform adequately as clinical larger-diameter vascular prostheses, their lack of sufficient antithrombogenicity becomes evident in smaller-diameter grafts. A variety of experimental materials and modifications to existing materials have resulted in limited successes, as have some novel biologically derived grafts. The application of controlled-release technology to smaller-diameter synthetic vascular grafts offers the possibility of emulating some of a natural vessel's functions, which may prove critical for maintaining patency.

BIBLIOGRAPHY

1. D.N. Ku and R.C. Allen, in J.D. Bronzino, ed., *The Biomedical Engineering Handbook*, CRC Press, Boca Raton, Fla., 1995, pp. 1871–1878.
2. A.D. Callow, in J.C. Stanley et al., eds., *Biologic and Synthetic Vascular Prostheses*, Grune & Stratton, New York, 1982, pp. 11–26.
3. A.B. Voorhees, Jr., *Arch Surg. (Chicago)* **120**(3), 289–295 (1985).
4. A. Carrel, *Surg Gynecol. Obstet.* **15**, 245–248 (1912).
5. R. Abbe, *N.Y. Med. J.* **59**, 33–40 (1894).
6. A.D. Callow, in A.D. Callow and C.B. Ernst, eds., *Introduction: Vascular Surgery: Theory and Practice*, Appleton & Lange, Stamford, Calif., 1995, pp. xxii–xxxv.
7. C.A. Hufnagel, *Arch. Surg. (Chicago)* **54**, 382–389 (1947).
8. R.E. Gross, E.S. Hurwitt, A.H. Bill, and E.C. Pierce, *N. Engl. J Med.* **239**, 578–579 (1948).
9. R.E. Gross, A.H. Bill, and E.C. Pierce, *Surg. Gynecol. Obstet.* **88**, 689–701 (1949).
10. C. Dubost, M. Allary, and N. Oeconomos, *Arch. Surg. (Chicago)* **64**, 405–408 (1952).
11. J. Oudot and P. Beaconsfield, *Arch. Surg. (Chicago)* **66**, 365–374 (1953).
12. M.E. DeBakey, O. Creech, and D.A. Cooley, *Ann. Surg.* **140**, 290–310 (1954).
13. O.C. Julian et al., *Ann. Surg.* **138**, 387–403 (1953).
14. D.E. Szilagyi, R.F. Smith, and P.R. Overhulse, *JAMA,* **157**, 426–433 (1955).
15. A.B. Voorhees, A. Jaretzki, and A.H. Blakemore, *Ann. Surg.* **135**(3), 332–336 (1952).
16. D.E. Szilagyi, *Ann. Vasc. Surg.* **1**(3), 357–363 (1986).
17. D.E. Szilagyi, R.T. McDonald, and R.F. Smith, *Arch. Surg. (Chicago)* **75**, 506–509 (1957).
18. J.H. Harrison, *Am. J. Surg.* **95**, 3–14 (1958).
19. J.H. Harrison, *Am. J. Surg.* **95**, 16–24 (1958).

20. J.H. Harrison, *Surg. Gynecol. Obstet.* **108**, 433–438 (1959).

21. B. Halpert, M.E. DeBakey, G.L. Jordan, and W.S. Henly, *Surg., Gynecol. Obstet.* **111**(6), 659–674 (1960).

22. M.E. DeBakey et al., *Arch Surg. (Chicago)* **89**, 757–782 (1964).

23. L.R. Sauvage, R. Schloemer, S.J. Wood, and G. Logan, *J. Thorac. Cardiovasc. Surg.* **72**(3), 418–421 (1976).

24. R.C. Darling and R.R. Linton, *Am. J. Surg.* **123**, 472–479 (1972).

25. W.W. Daniel, *Cancer (Philadelphia)* **5**, 1041–1048 (1952).

26. R.A. Deterling and S.B. Bhonslay, *Surgery* **38**(1), 71–91 (1955).

27. J.H. Harrison, *Surg. Gynecol. Obstet.* **104**, 81–87 (1957).

28. C.A. Kottmeier and M.W. Wheat, *Am. Surg.* **31**, 128–134 (1964).

29. B. Boyce, in J.C. Stanley et al., eds., *Biologic and Synthetic Vascular Prostheses*, Grune & Stratton, New York, 1982, pp. 553–561.

30. L.M. Graham and J.J. Bergan, in J.C. Stanley et al., eds., *Biologic and Synthetic Vascular Prostheses*, Grune & Stratton, New York, 1982, pp. 563–586.

31. T. Soyer, M. Lempinen, and P. Cooper, *Surgery* **72**, 864–872 (1972).

32. H. Matsumoto et al., *Surgery* **74**(4), 519–523 (1973).

33. R.W. Hobson, J.A. O'Donnell, and Z. Jamil, *Arch. Surg. (Chicago)* **115**, 833–837 (1980).

34. M. Haimov, F. Giron, and J.H. Jacobson, *Arch. Surg. (Chicago)* **114**, 673–677 (1979).

35. V. Echave, A.R. Koornick, and M.E.A. Haimov, *Surgery* **86**, 791–798 (1979).

36. W.M. Abbott et al., *J. Vasc. Surg.* **17**(4), 746–756 (1993).

37. J.D. Andrade and V. Hlady, in E.F. Leonard, V.T. Turitto, and L. Vroman, eds., *Blood in Contact with Natural and Artificial Surfaces*, N. Y. Acad. Sci., New York, 1987, pp. 158–172.

38. M.A. Gimbrone, in E.F. Leonard, V.T. Turitto, and L. Vroman, eds., *Blood in Contact with Natural and Artificial Surfaces*, N. Y. Acad. Sci., New York. 1987, pp. 5–11.

39. E.T. Choi and A.D. Callow, in A.D. Callow and C.B. Ernst, eds., *Vascular Surgery: Theory and Practice*, Appleton & Lange, Stamford, Calif., 1995, pp. 151–166.

40. A.W. Clowes, *Cardiovasc. Pathol.* **2**(3), 179S–186S (1993).

41. J.L. Halperin and P. Peterson, in V. Fuster and M. Verstraete, eds., *Thrombus in Cardiovascular Disorders*, Saunders, Philadelphia, 1992, pp. 215–236.

42. R. Guidon et al., in M. Szycher, ed., *High Performance Biomaterials: A Comprehensive Guide to Medical and Pharmaceutical Applications*, Technomic Publishing, Lancaster, Pa. 1991, pp. 449–474.

43. E.L. Chaikof et al., *J. Surg. Res.* **47**, 193–199 (1989).

44. S.L. Verdon et al., *Scanning Microsc.* **4**(2):341–349 (1990); discussion pp. 349–350.

45. E.L. Chaikof et al., *J. Biomed. Mater. Res.* **26**(9), 1163–1168 (1992).

46. H.P. Greisler, C.W. Tattersall, S.C. Henderson, and E.A. Cabusao, *J. Biomed. Mater. Res.* **26**, 1383–1394 (1992).

47. J.L. Cronenwett and G.B. Zelenock, in J.C. Stanley et al., eds., *Biologic and Synthetic Vascular Prostheses*, Grune & Stratton, New York, 1982, pp. 595–620.

48. J.U. Bascom, *Surgery* **50**, 504–512 (1961).

49. A.W. Humphries, W.A. Hawk, and A.M. Cuthbertson, *Surgery* **50**, 947–954 (1961).

50. G.L. Jordan, M.M. Stump, and J. Allen, *Surgery* **53**, 45–51 (1963).

51. B. van der Lei, H.L. Bartels, P. Nieuwenhuis, and C.R. Wildevuur, *Surgery* **98**(5), 955–963 (1985).

52. H.P. Greisler, D.U. Kim, J.B. Price, and A.B. Voorhees, Jr., *Arch. Surg. (Chicago)* **120**(3), 315–323 (1985).

53. H.P. Greisler et al., *J. Vasc. Surg.* **5**(4), 572–583 (1987).

54. P.M. Galletti et al., *Surgery* **103**(2), 231–241 (1988).

55. H.P. Greisler, *Arch. Surg. (Chicago)* **117**(11), 1425–1431 (1982).

56. S. Bowald, C. Busch, and I. Eriksson, *Surgery* **86**(5), 722–729 (1979).

57. S. Bowald, C. Busch, and I. Eriksson, *Acta Chir. Scand.* **146**, 391–395 (1980).

58. R.R. Kowligi and R.W. Calcotte, in M. Szycher, ed., *High Performance Biomaterials: A Comprehensive Guide to Medical and Pharmaceutical Applications*, Technomic Publishing, Lancaster, Pa., 1991, pp. 425–442.

59. B. Dryer, T. Akutsu, and W.J. Kolff, *J. Appl. Physiol.* **15**, 18–22 (1960).

60. V. Marinescu, E. Pausescu, and S. Carnaru, *Thorax* **26**(1), 108–111 (1971).

61. D.J. Lyman, D. Albo, R. Jackson, and K. Knutson, *Trans. Am. Soc. Artif. Intern. Organs* **23**, 253–261 (1977).

62. D. Annis et al., *Trans. Am. Soc. Artif. Intern. Organs* **24**, 209–214 (1978).

63. L.F. Hiratzka, J.A. Goeken, R.A. White, and C.B. Wright, *Arch. Surg. (Chicago)* **114**, 698–702 (1979).

64. F. Hess, C. Jerusalem, and B. Braun, *J. Cardiovasc. Surg.* **24**, 516–524 (1983).

65. F. Hess, C. Jerusalem, and B. Braun, *J. Cardiovasc. Surg.* **24**, 509–515 (1983).

66. Z. Zhang et al., *Biomaterials* **15**(7), 483–501 (1994).

67. Z. Zhang et al., *Biomaterials* **15**(13), 1099–1112 (1994).

68. Y. Marois et al., *Biomaterials* **17**(13), 1289–1300 (1996).

69. Z. Zhang et al., *Biomaterials* **18**(2), 113–124 (1997).

70. M. Krajicek, V. Zastava, and M. Chvapil, *Surg. Res.* **4**(7), 290–296 (1964).

71. C. Hermansen, K. Kraglund, E. Ludwigsen, and C. Mouritzen, *Eur. Surg. Res.* **12**(5), 349–362 (1980).

72. P. Misiuna, *Ann. Univ. Mariae Curie-Sklodowska, Sect. D* **19**, 1–12 (1964).

73. H. Lee and K. Neville, *Handbook of Biomedical Plastics*, Pasadena Technology Press, Pasadena, Calif., 1971, pp. 1–61.

74. W.J. Fry, M.S. DeWeese, R.O. Kraft, and C.B. Ernst, *Arch. Surg.* **88**, 836–842 (1964).

75. R.A. White, *Trans. Am. Soc. Artif. Intern. Organs* **34**, 95–100 (1988).

76. G. Soldani et al., *J. Mater. Sci. Mater. Med.* **31**, 106–113 (1992).

77. T. Okoshi, M. Goddard, P.M. Galletti, and G. Soldani, *Trans. Am. Soc. Artif. Intern. Organs* **37**(3), M480–M481 (1991).

78. K. Fujimoto et al., *J. Appl. Biomater.* **4**, 347–354 (1993).

79. D.E. Hokanson and D.E. Strandness, *Surg. Gynecol. Obstet.* **127**, 57–60 (1968).

80. W.M. Abbott and R.P. Cambria, in J.C. Stanley et al., eds., *Biologic and Synthetic Vascular Prostheses*, Grune & Stratton, New York, 1982, pp. 189–220.

81. R. Walden, G.J. L'Italien, J. Megerman, and W.M. Abbott, *Arch. Surg. (Chicago)* **115**, 1166–1169 (1980).

82. D.J. Lyman et al., *J. Biomed. Mater. Res.* **12**, 337–345 (1978).

83. D. Annis, A.C. Fisher, T.V. How, and L. deCossart, in E. Chiellini, P. Giusti, C. Migliaresi, and L. Nicolais, eds., *Polymers in Medicine II: Biomedical and Pharmaceutical Applications*, Plenum, New York, 1986, pp. 217–221.

84. B. Pourdeyhimi and D. Wagner, *J. Biomed. Mater. Res.* **20**, 375–409 (1986).

85. W.E. Burkel and R.H. Kahn, *Ann. N. Y. Acad. Sci.* **283**, 419 (1977).

86. M. Herring, A. Gardner, and J. Glover, *Surgery* **84**(4), 498–504 (1978).

87. S.P. Schmidt, W.V. Sharp, M.M. Evancho, and S.O. Meerbaum, in M. Szycher, ed., *High Performance Biomaterials*, Technomic Publishing, Lancaster, Pa., 1991, pp. 483–496.

88. L.M. Graham et al., *Surgery* **91**(5), 550–559 (1982).

89. S. Emerick et al., *J. Vasc. Surg.* **5**(2), 342–347 (1987).

90. J.M. Seeger and N. Klingman, *J. Surg. Res.* **38**(6), 641–647 (1985).

91. J.P. Mazzucotelli et al., *Int. J. Artif. Organs* **14**(8), 482–490 (1991).

92. S.K. Williams et al., *J. Biomed. Mater. Res.* **26**, 103–117 (1992).

93. H.P. Greisler et al., *Arch. Surg. (Chicago)* **124**(8), 967–972 (1989).

94. J.R. Mackenzie, M. Hackett, C. Topuzlu, and D.J. Tibbs, *Arch. Surg. (Chicago)* **97**, 879–885 (1968).

95. Y. Noishiki, Y. Tomizawa, Y. Yamane, and A. Matsumoto, *Nat. Med.* **2**(1), 90–93 (1996).

96. C.O. Esquivel et al., *Surgery* **95**, 102–107 (1984).

97. S.M. Lindenauer, W.J. Fry, G. Schaub, and D. Wild, *Surgery* **62**(3), 487–492 (1967).

98. R.B. Smith, K. Lowry, and G.D. Perdue, *Am. Surg.* **33**(9), 711–714 (1967).

99. W.S. Moore, in J.C. Stanley et al., eds., *Biologic and Synthetic Vascular Prostheses*, Grune & Stratton, New York, 1982, pp. 661–669.

100. A.L. Ney et al., *J. Surg. Res.* **57**, 698–705 (1994).

101. G. Soldani et al., *Clin. Mater.* **8**, 81–88 (1991).

102. M.D. Lado et al., *Int. J. Artif. Organs* **15**(12), 727–736 (1992).

103. H.P. Greisler et al., *Surgery* **112**(2), 244–255 (1992).

104. U.S. Pat. 5,290,271 (March 1, 1994), G.R. Jernberg (to Jernberg, G.R.).

105. T. Richey and F.W. Harris, *Proc. Int. Symp. Controlled Release Bioact. Mater.* **23**, 391–392 (1996).

106. M.R. Kreitz, W.L. Webber, P.M. Galletti, and E. Mathiowitz, *Biomaterials* **18**, 597–603 (1997).

107. M.R. Kreitz, J.A. Domm, and E. Mathiowitz, *Biomaterials* **18**, 1645–1651 (1997).

108. S.K. Pulfer, D. Ott, and D.J. Smith, *J. Biomed. Mater. Res.* **37**, 182–189 (1997).

109. N. L'Heureux et al., *FASEB J.* **12**, 47–56 (1998).

110. C.B. Weinberg and E. Bell, *Science* **231**, 397–400 (1986).

TISSUE–IMPLANT INTERFACE, BIOLOGICAL RESPONSE TO ARTIFICIAL MATERIALS WITH SURFACE-IMMOBILIZED SMALL PEPTIDES

Geoffrey Moodie
Robert F. Valentini
Brown University
Providence, Rhode Island

KEY WORDS

Biomaterial

Cell

Extracellular matrix

Peptide

Surface modification

OUTLINE

INTRODUCTION

The nature of the tissue–implant interface is a critical component in the success or failure of most medical implants. Investigators have sought to improve and control this interface by modifying surface chemistry, surface charge, and surface topography. This article focuses on a subset of approaches that immobilize bioactive peptides on a biomaterial surface to elicit a controlled tissue reaction, particularly for bone-contacting applications. Using small peptides has several practical and experimental advantages over the use of entire proteins:

1. Many extracellular matrix (ECM) proteins are not commercially available, are difficult to purify, and are difficult to work with chemically.
2. Synthetic peptides are widely available and pure, thus minimizing cost and the risk of infection.
3. Linear peptides do not require tertiary or quaternary structure.
4. Small peptides are more resistant than whole proteins to changes in pH and temperature (1) and are less susceptible to proteolysis and hydrolysis.
5. Bioactive peptides allow manipulation at the nuclear level. Specificity in cell stimulation can be gained through the use of sequences known to interact with certain receptors.

Peptides are referred to in this article by their single-letter amino acid sequences (Table 1). Peptides can be protected from proteolytic degradation by modifying the peptide bond, chemically blocking the termini, using NH_2 to COO-terminal cyclization, or using the D-forms of amino acids (which do not occur naturally in proteins) (2).

The Arg-Gly-Asp (RGD) sequence is the archetypal bioactive peptide, and many cells have receptors for it (2,3). Thus, RGD is an ideal model peptide and has been used widely to modify biomaterial surfaces. RGD and other peptides bind to a family of ECM receptors called *integrins* (described later). RGD is a promiscuous sequence that can bind to several integrin receptors. This tripeptide was first found in fibronectin (4). It has since been found to be in the integrin-binding sections of many proteins; of particular relevance to bones are bone sialoprotein (5) and osteopontin (6). Such a ubiquitous sequence may have the disadvantage of attracting undesirable cells such as fibroblasts to a bone implant. The presence of fibroblast-induced soft tissue versus hard tissue could, for example, lead to poor host–implant integration. Several types of bacteria also possess RGD receptors (7), which could lead to implant colonization, although this has not been studied in detail. For bone-contacting implants, the addition of flanking peptide sequences can increase receptor specificity. For example, the RGD-containing peptide CGGNGEPRGDTYRAY from bone sialoprotein has been used by Rezania et al. (5).

Ultimately, favorably controlling cell response is the goal of immobilizing bioactive peptides on biomaterial surfaces. In vitro properties such as cell adhesion, morphology, protein synthesis, and gene expression can be evaluated. In vivo cell and tissue response, cellular makeup, and degree of vascularization can be evaluated. Basic in vitro and in vivo approaches will be discussed, and specific immobilization schemes will be reviewed.

INTEGRINS

Integrins are heterodimeric cell surface receptors for extracellular proteins. The two subunits, designated α and β,

Table 1. Single-Letter Codes for Amino Acids

Amino Acid	Single Letter	Amino Acid	Single Letter	Amino Acid	Single Letter
Alanine (ala)	A	Isoleucine (ile)	I	Arginine (arg)	R
Cysteine (cys)	C	Lysine (lys)	K	Serine (ser)	S
Aspartate (asp)	D	Leucine (leu)	L	Threonine (thr)	T
Glutamate (glu)	E	Methionine (met)	M	Valine (val)	V
Phenylalanine (phe)	F	Asparagine (asn)	N	Tryptophan (trp)	W
Glycine (gly)	G	Proline (pro)	P	Tyrosine (tyr)	Y
Histidine (his)	H	Glutamine (gln)	Q		

are noncovalently associated. Both subunits are compact transmembrane glycoproteins with heavy disulfide binding and a single hydrophobic domain. Under electron microscopy, an integrin presents as a globular head with two stalks (one for each subunit) extending down into the lipid bilayer (8,9). Sixteen α- and nine β-chains have been identified, and they assemble to form the 24 distinct integrins currently identified (10). Each β-subunit can associate with multiple α subunits; however, of the α subunits only α_v can associate with multiple β-subunits (11).

Beyond simply adhering cells to the surrounding extracellular matrix, integrins are key components in many intracellular signaling pathways, and a number of functional changes occur when cells are in contact with ECM proteins. One example of this is mammary epithelial cells, which will not produce milk proteins until after they have attached to extracellular matrix proteins, even when milk-inducing hormones (prolactin and cortisone) are present (12). Synergies exist between integrins and growth factors. Vuori and Ruoslahti showed that insulin receptor substrate -1 (IRS-1) associates with the $\alpha_v\beta_3$-integrin in the presence of insulin. This association appears to increase DNA production in response to insulin, possibly by increasing the phosphorylation of IRS-1 and consequently enhancing intracellular signaling. When exposed to insulin, human pancreatic carcinoma (FG) cells transfected to overexpress $\alpha_v\beta_3$ showed a 250% increase in DNA synthesis versus nontransfected FG cells. When the transfected cells were plated on a non-$\alpha_v\beta_3$-binding substrate (collagen), DNA synthesis was similar to that seen in nontransfected cells (13). A similar association has been found between platelet-derived growth factor (PDGF) and α_v-integrins associating with a 190-kDa protein (14).

ECM–integrin binding can influence cell shape, migration, differentiation, and gene expression (9,15–19). Some integrins may, via cytoskeletal elements, connect directly with the nucleus and serve as mechanotransducers (20). Integrin expression can be regulated by external influences such as growth factors (most notably TGF-β), pharmacologic agents, mechanical stress, and infectious agents. Cells regulate integrin expression by transcriptional or posttranscriptional mechanisms, alternative splicing of mRNA, conformation control, and mobilizing intracellular stores (11).

Most immobilized peptides reviewed in this article target integrins (YIGSR-containing sequences are noted exceptions). Integrin receptors recognize specific amino acid sequences within their target proteins, such as the RGD sequence and its variants mentioned earlier. As another example, type I collagen, the major bone protein, contains the DGEA sequence that binds to the $\alpha_2\beta_1$-integrin (21).

APPLICATION TO BONE-CONTACTING PROSTHESES

Limitations of Total Joint Replacement

Total joint replacement is widely used to relieve pain, improve function, and enhance the quality of life for patients with medical conditions caused by osteoarthritis, rheumatoid arthritis, posttraumatic degeneration, avascular necrosis, and other aging-related conditions. Almost 600,000 total joint replacements are performed in the United States alone each year. Current techniques to stabilize the interface between bone and prostheses are physical or geometric in nature. Most orthopedic prostheses are composed of alloys of titanium (Ti6A14V) or cobalt (CoCrMo) and rely on poly(methyl methacrylate) cements for attachment and fixation to bone. Loosening due to cement failure has been implicated in revision of hip, knee, and elbow implants (22–28). Perioperative allergic, hypotensive, and embolic events, although currently unusual, have also been related to the use of cements (29–31). An unacceptably high number of implant failures occur. With cemented total hip arthroplasty, for example, long-term studies indicate a combined (aseptic and radiographic) loosening rate of 20–30% in the acetabulum and 5–10% in the femur, with about a 10% overall revision rate (32). In total knee arthroplasty, for which over 200,000 procedures were performed last year alone, cemented knees also exhibit a 0.5–1% per year loosening rate and approach a 10% revision rate (33–35).

Cementless prostheses are designed to encourage bone ingrowth through the use of porous or sintered coatings (36–38). These implants have the potential advantages of stable long-term fixation, circumventing the issues surrounding the use of cement, and are more easily retrieved should revision become necessary. Tissue ingrowth into porous materials is influenced by several factors, including pore size and implant stability (37,39–41). Experience thus far suggests that using "press-fit" prostheses is problematic for two major reasons (36,38): First, minimal or inadequate ingrowth is observed in a significant number of patients, resulting in loosening and failure, and second, the process of ingrowth occurs over a period of weeks to months, such that weight bearing is necessarily limited early on in an effort to prevent micromotion and allow stable osseointegration. This can potentially increase expense and complication and may become particularly problematic when addressing elderly patients, who comprise the greatest percentage of those needing arthroplasties performed today. Another approach is to coat prostheses with hydroxyapatite and tricalcium phosphate, but such implants have had difficulties with delamination and biodegradation and are still unable to demonstrate optimal bony ingrowth and biomechanical fixation (23,38,42).

Integrin-Mediated Control of Cell Function

The ability to enhance and accelerate ingrowth using biological factors with bone-promoting capabilities would be a significant advancement in implant technology. Bone-implant integration is regulated by numerous factors including extracellular matrix (ECM) elements and growth/morphogenic proteins. The development of orthopaedic devices incorporating bioactive surface molecules may improve our understanding of tissue repair mechanisms and enhance the design of bone-inducing substrates for clinical application. This may be done by stimulating integrin pathways (9,43,44).

Minimal peptide sequences that bind to integrins and mimic the action of much larger and insoluble ECM molecules have recently been identified (Table 2).

Small peptides can be used as agonist or antagonist drugs. In the latter case, soluble peptides can be used to occupy integrin receptors on migrating or blood-borne cells. Receptor occupancy blocks cell–ECM or cell–cell interactions. For example, metastatic melanoma and other tumor cell spreading can be decreased by injection of soluble RGD or laminin (e.g., YIGSR) peptides in animal models (59,74–77). Platelet aggregation has also been reduced by intravascular administration of soluble cyclic RGD peptides or RGD-containing analogs (51,78,79). Finally, osteoclastic resorption has been reduced by innoculation with RGD-containing peptides or analogs (80,81). Osteoclasts are known to express several integrin receptors (49,80). The fact that osteoclasts have RGD-binding integrins is relevant to the present work because activation of osteoclastic resorption at the bone interface is not favorable. Small peptides can be used as agonists to improve cell adhesion if they are immobilized on insoluble substrates (63,64,82,83). For example, endothelial cell and fibroblast adhesion to several biomaterials is enhanced by coatings of peptide ligands from fibronectin and laminin, RGD and YIGSR, respectively (52,63,64,84). YIGSR also supports nerve cell attachment, whereas a second laminin frag-

ment, SIKVAV, supports neurite outgrowth (85). Certain peptides can act synergistically to enhance binding affinity. For example, two nonadjacent peptide sequences from fibronectin, including RGD and PHSRN, a so-called synergy sequence, exhibit such behavior (74,86). The conformation of peptide is important because small chemical changes can have profound effects on cell adhesion (87). Peptides can also effect cell and tissue function beyond cell adhesion.

Osteoblast Adhesion and Integrins

Bone cells are known to attach to tissue culture substrates via fibronectin and vitronectin molecules (88), although the effect of cell attachment peptides has not been widely studied. Osteoblast adhesion, ECM synthesis, and mineralization are influenced by the chemical nature and electrical charge of tissue culture substrates such as modified polystyrene and bioglass (89–93). Osteoblast adhesion on some biomaterials results in the formation of focal adhesion contacts, which entail clustering of integrin receptors (94,95).

Recently, it has been shown that human and rat osteoblasts/osteocytes express a range of integrins (Table 3). There are, however, conflicting data regarding the expression of certain integrins. Most studies report the expression of integrins a5b1, avb3, and a1b1 in rat osteoblasts.

SPECIFIC IMMOBILIZATION CHEMISTRIES

These entries are arranged in roughly chronological order. The level of detail dedicated to each method is not intended to indicate the importance of any particular immobilization chemistry. Rather, it is simply a reflection of the amount of literature available on each technique.

Sepharose

Pierschbacher and Ruoslahti pioneered work in pursuit of active protein sequences and immobilized peptides to sepharose beads using a carbodiimide coupler. Rat kidney fibroblast attachment was assessed by staining the cells with toludine blue and examining with microscopy. They found that only those peptides containing RGD promoted cell attachment, and this sequence is still widely used by investigators today (4).

Further experiments pointed to the importance of immobilization chemistry. Normal rat kidney cells do not rec-

Table 2. Small Peptide Ligands

ECM protein	Peptide ligand	Integrin receptors
Collagen I	cRGD, RGDT, DGEA, GTPGPQGIAGQRGVV	a1b1, a2b1, a3b1
Bone sialoprotein	EPRGDNYR	avb3
Osteopontin	RGD	avb3
Fibronectin	RGDS, EILDV, REDV	a3b1, a4b1, a5b1, avb1, avb3, avb5, avb6, a4b7
Laminin	YIGSR, SIKVAV, RGD	a1b1, a2b1, a3b1, a6b1, a7b1, a6b4
Thrombospondin	RGD	avb3
Vitronectin	RGDV, HRNRKGV	avb1, avb3, avb5
Osteonectin (SPARC)	KKGHK	?

This table includes reported extracellular matrix proteins, their peptide ligands, and their integrin receptors. This table is not intended to be exhaustive and focuses on molecules relevant to bone research. *Source:* Refs. 3,8,9,21,44–73.

Table 3. Bone Cell Interins

Rat calvarial osteoblasts	a1b1, a5b1, avb1, avb3, avb5
Human osteoblasts	a3b1, a4b1, a5b1, avb3

Source: Refs. 3,57,70,96,97.

ognize RGDC when it is linked directly to cyanogen bromide–activated sepharose beads, but RGDS was recognized when tethered with a six-carbon spacer (98). Interestingly, RGDC has been found to be active when linked by a gold–thiol bond (see "Gold").

Polyacrylamide

Among the first to covalently link peptides to artificial surfaces were Brandley and Schnaar. The polymer used was a polyacrylamide gel surface to which cells do not adhere in the absence of serum proteins. The N-terminus of the peptide used (YAVTGRGDS) reacted with N-succinimidyl ester groups in the polymer. A linear correlation between the amount of peptide in solution to the amount of peptide immobilized was established, with about 80% of the peptide in solution being bound to the surface (99).

Balb/c 3T3 mouse fibroblasts were used to test these peptide-treated surfaces (5.6 ± 0.3 nmol peptide/cm^2 in the reaction fluid). Cells adhered to the RGD peptide-treated material but not to polyacrylamide with a non-RGD control peptide or plain activated acrylamide. Using a lactate dehydrogenase proliferation assay, they found that the proliferation of cells on the peptide-treated polyacrylamide was about the same as that on tissue culture plastic, but on control surfaces growth was not supported. These effects could be seen with as little as 2 nmol/cm^2 of peptide (99).

Silicone

Another group that first immobilized peptides to artificial substrates was Imanshi et al. Silicone rubber film was exposed to aminoalkylated polydimethylsiloxane followed by oxalic acid, water-soluble carbodiimide, and polyallylamine. This provided a surface amino group density of 0.713 μmol/cm^2. Water-soluble carbodiimide was used again to couple RGDS to these amino groups. Cell attachment increased in a linear manner with peptide surface concentration, from about 11,000 cells/cm^2 with no immobilized peptide to about 26,000 cells/cm^2 with 41 mmol/cm^2 of peptide (1).

Glass

Massia and Hubbell covalently linked the peptides GRGDY, GYIGSRY, GPDSGRY, and GREDVY to glycophase glass (63,100,101). Briefly, glycophase glass is prepared by reacting glass with sodium hydroxide followed by immersion in (3-glycidoxypropyl)-trimethoxysilane. Oxyrane moieties are converted to glycol groups by treatment with acid and heat. Tresyl chloride was used to couple peptides through their N-termini (63).

Peptide surface concentration was measured by radiolabeling the *C*-terminal tyrosine groups on the peptides prior to immobilization. They found that peptide surface concentrations rose linearly with available peptide up to 12.1 ± 0.1 pmol/cm^2. A maximum surface concentration of 12.1 pmol/cm^2 corresponds to a surface spacing of 3.3 nm between peptides (63). 10 fmol/cm^2 was required for complete spreading, focal contact formation, and f-actin cytoskeletal organization in human fibroblasts (102).

Cell proliferation studies were performed with human foreskin fibroblasts by counting cells in 10 fields under a phase-contrast microscope with a 100 × objective. The media used was DMEM + 10% fetal bovine serum. This data showed no differences between the growth rate on surfaces with immobilized RGD and that on nonglycophase glass (63).

Cell spreading was analyzed with image analysis; results are summarized in Table 4. For the sake of comparison, a well-spread cell area on tissue culture plastic in serum-containing media is 2,100 μm^2; a nonspread cell area is about 355 μm^2.

As can be seen from Table 4, cell spreading increased with time on the RGD substrates with and without serum but failed to do so on glycophase glass, especially in the absence of serum (63).

Cell spreading was also noted on YIGSR-treated surfaces with and without serum, but it was not as rapid as RGD, taking over 6 h to occur. At 9 h the median cell area with serum was 2,333 μm^2, without serum it was 1,400 μm^2. Glycophase glass without peptide did not show cell spreading greater than 600 μm^2 at any time point. The effects were due primarily to the immobilized peptide, as cells seeded on an immobilized control peptide, GRGESP, and preincubated with soluble forms of the active peptides did not spread. The fraction of cells that spread on YIGSR or RGD was not effected by the addition of cycloheximide to the media to prevent cellular protein synthesis. Spreading of quiescent or active platelets was absent on all surfaces. Data from several Massia and Hubbell experiments is summarized in Table 5.

As can be seen from Table 5, cell selectivity was demonstrated using this system. Whereas human endothelial cells (HUVECs) showed a high avidity for a GREDVY-treated surface, human foreskin fibroblasts, vascular smooth muscle cells, and platelets did not. In the absence of serum, small focal contacts were present on the RGD-treated surfaces around the outer margins of the cells and at discreet locations on the cell body. Serum promoted the formation of larger, well-defined focal contacts. The YIGSR-treated substrates did not form focal contacts without serum. When serum was added, elongated focal adhesions formed around the periphery of the cells.

Cells on RGD in serum-free conditions showed an extensive actin network. This thickened in the presence of serum. Very few microfilament bundles were seen on the YIGSR in the absence of serum, but in serum thick microfilaments formed (63).

Further in vitro spreading tests were done on this substrate with human umbilical vein endothelial cells (HUVEC). Table 6 summarizes the spreading data obtained. This experiment was done in serum containing medium.

Table 4. Fibroblast Spreading

Time (min)	RGD–glass + serum: median cell area (μm^2)	RGD–glass − serum: median cell area (μm^2)	Glycophase glass + serum: median cell area(μm^2)	Glycophase glass − serum: median cell area (μm^2)
15	265	248	385	377
30	906	950	397	325
60	1113	864	448	388
120	2130	1207	453	388

Table 5. Cell Spreading on Immobilized Peptides

Peptide grafted to surface	Serum in medium (10% v/v)	Peptide in medium (200 μg/mL)	Spread HFF cells (%)	Spread HVSMC cells (%)	Spread HUVEC Cells (%)
GRGEY	−	−	0	Not tested	Not tested
	+	−	0	Not tested	Not tested
GRGDY	+	−	87 ± 8	Not tested	Not tested
	−	−	91 ± 4	93 ± 3	90 ± 9
	−	+(RGDS)	0	Not tested	Not tested
GYIGSRY	+	−	78 ± 7	Not tested	Not tested
	−	−	81 ± 12	88 ± 9	84 ± 10
	−	+(GYIGSRY)	0	Not tested	Not tested
GPDSGRY	−	−	59 ± 6	62 ± 4	66 ± 8
GREDVY	−	−	9 ± 4	7 ± 2	89 ± 6
Glycophase Glass	−	−	9 ± 2	10 ± 4	8 ± 1

Source: Refs. 63,101.

Table 6. Cell Spreading Time Curve

Time (min)	RGD–glass mean cell area (μm^2)	YIGSR–glass mean cell area (μm^2)	Glycophase glass mean cell area (μm^2)
15	1196 ± 1548	1027 ± 606	249 ± 136
30	1064 ± 780	1389 ± 1076	343 ± 228
60	1812 ± 1429	1825 ± 1233	211 ± 132
120	2449 ± 2196	2370 ± 1587	372 ± 99
240	2679 ± 667	2373 ± 1904	456 ± 570

Source: Ref. 100.

As may be inferred from Table 6, there was no statistically significant difference in cell spreading between RGD and YIGSR treated surfaces with this cell type. Focal contacts and large close-contact regions formed on RGD-treated glycophase glass, but focal contacts with minimal close-contact regions were noted on the YIGSR-treated surface. More extensive actin networks formed in cells on the RGD surface than the YIGSR (100).

The type of peptide immobilized affected cell function. HUVECs showed proper antithrombogenic activity on GRGDY, GYIGSRY, GREDVY, and gelatin. However, when these cells were plated on GPDSGR, the antithrombogenic activity was lost even though their morphology was normal (101).

It was also of consequence whether or not the peptide was covalently immobilized or simply adsorbed. Adsorption was done with 20 μg/mL of protein or peptide for 1 h followed by bovine serum albumin for 30 min. Cells were incubated on surfaces in serum-free media for 6 h. Human foreskin fibroblasts incubated with antisera against laminin receptors failed to spread, indicating that these events are receptor specific.

A variety of cells showed consistently that although attachment occurred, cells failed to spread on adsorbed peptide. Two possible explanations for the improved spreading are that covalent immobilization (1) helps to stabilize the YIGSR in an active conformation and (2) may present the YIGSR to the receptor in a more favorable way (fixed end forward rather than adsorbed on its side) (103).

Polyurethanes

Polyurethanes are currently used as biomaterials in blood-contacting applications. It may be possible to improve the performance of polyurethane implants by developing an endothelial cell layer on the blood-contacting surface. Toward this end, Imanishi began work in 1988 to link a peptide substrate for thrombin, Val-Pro-Arg, to the surface of carboxylated polyurethaneurea (1,104). Three configurations were used. (1) immobilizing by the amine terminis of the peptide (P1), (2) immobilizing the carboxylic terminis at the end of a six-carbon spacer (P2), and (3) repeating P2 with a reversed amino acid sequence (Arg-Pro-Val) (P3).

When the polyurethaneurea samples were placed into solutions containing known amounts of thrombin, both the peptide P1–and nonpeptide-treated surfaces adsorbed the same amount of thrombin. However, the peptide-treated surface did so much more quickly (P1 required less than 30 min for 100% adsorption of 0.22 mg/mL thrombin, while plain polyurethaneurea needed more than 120 min). Thrombin was desorbed from the surfaces and tested for activity. The peptide P1 from the nonpeptide polyurethaneurea retained 73% of its original activity, while that from the peptide polyurethaneurea had only 12%, which would indicate a specific reaction between the thrombin and the immobilized peptide. In experiments using platelet-poor plasma from canine blood, it was found that increasing peptide P1 concentration yielded increasing time to clotting.

The other peptide attachment schemes (P2 and P3) failed to show as much antithrombogenic activity as P1 when incubated with canine platelet-poor plasma in a thromboplastin buffer solution activated with CaCl$_2$. Glass took 930 s; plain polyurethaneurea, 1,079 ± 10s; P1, 1,139 ± 7s; P2, 1,068 ± 11s; and P3, 1,077 ± 7s. It was theorized that the Arg side chain couldn't be blocked (1).

Lin et al. developed a method to carboxylate polyurethanes to facilitate peptide coupling. This was accomplished by grafting β-propiolactone to the polymer backbone using a bimolecular substitution reaction (105). Peptides were then coupled via their free N-termini to the carboxyl groups on the polymer using the coupling agent EDCI. Cold-stage and variable take-off–angle ESCA verified enhanced peptide presence at the surface of the polymer in aqueous environments, presumably due to its hydrophilicity and the ability of polyurethane surfaces to rearrange in response to their environment (106). In vitro tests for human umbilical vein endothelial cell (HUVEC) spreading and adhesion were performed with polyurethane grafted with GRGDSY, GRGDVY, and GRGESY. About 20,000 cells per cm^2 were plated onto glass coverslips coated with the experimental polymer. Four time points were taken for the adhesion experiments: 40 min, 80 min, 120 min, and 240 min. At each of these time points, nonadherent cells were rinsed away, and remaining cells were counted manually with the aid of a phase-contrast microscope. Cell spreading was measured using a combination of scanning electron microscopy and image analysis. These tests were done in both the presence and absence of serum (107). Cell growth on these surfaces was measured in serum with porcine pulmonary aortic endothelial cells. Twelve-millimeter-diameter glass coverslips coated with polymer were inserted into 24-well plates. Cells were seeded at 5,000 cells/well, and growth was quantified using an MTT (3-[4,5-dimethylthiazol-2-yl]-2,5-diphenyltetrazolium bromide; thiazolyl blue) assay (84).

The results of this experiment showed that after 4 h in serum-free conditions, the cell attachments on GRGDVY and GRGDSY were 50 and 23% of the original seeding density, respectively. On the control peptide GRGESY, plain polyurethane, and carboxylated polyurethane, the cell at-

tachment was only 5%. In serum, the cell attachment numbers were higher on all substrates and did not change significantly after the 40-min time point. This is most likely because of the fact that serum contains adhesive proteins that adsorbed onto substrates. The pattern was similar to serum free, however. 65 and 40% attachment was observed on GRGDVY and GRGDSY, respectively. Control peptide, carboxylated, and plain polyurethane all showed a 22% attachment (107).

Cell spreading was not supported in serum-free conditions on control peptide, carboxylated, or plain polymer. Rounded cells on these substrates had an area of 92 ± 15 μm^2. On GRGDVY, cells spread to an area of 532 ± 159 μm^2, and on GRGDSY their mean area was 281 ± 107 μm^2. In serum, spreading occurred on the GRGESP (330 ± 35 μm^2), carboxylated (315 ± 50 μm^2), and plain samples (320 ± 30 μm^2), but not to the degree found on GRGDVY (603 ± 119 μm^2) and GRGDSY (549 ± 138 μm^2) surfaces. It was proposed that the greater effect of the GRGDVY peptide might have been due to a greater affinity for the endothelial cell receptors (107).

Cell growth was relatively poor on noncarboxylated polyurethane, as it had less than half the number of cells on it at 72 h than any other substrate. Unlike the other experiments, the difference between the other controls and the active peptides were not large. This is probably due to the growth factors and adhesive proteins in the serum used in the media (84).

In vivo experiments were performed by Yanagi et al. using modified polyurethane sponges. The polyurethane was carboxylated by graft polymerization with acrylic acids. Proteins and GRGDSP were immobilized via the coupling agent CDI. These sponges were modified with immobilized collagen, fibronectin, GRGDSP, apatite, and a collagen coating. Fibronectin-, GRGDSP-, and apatite-treated rat subcutaneous implants showed lower inflammatory response at 3 days and high or vascularization at 7 days than plain polyurethane or collagen-treated sponges. When these sponges were implanted to fill partial defects in canine tracheas, epithelization on GRGDSP was about the same as that of untreated sponges, which was better than collagen-treated but inferior to fibronectin- and apatite-treated implants (108).

Breuers et al. used plasma polymerization to graft vinylacetate onto bulk polyurethane. After hydrolysing the acetate groups with sodium methoxide glycine and GRGDS, peptide was linked to the film via benzoquinone (109).

Poly(ethylene terephthalate)

Poly(ethylene terephthalate) (PET, commonly called Dacron) is used for vascular grafts and other medical implants. In one study, PET was surface modified with poly(ethylene glycol) (PEG) to make it nonadhesive to cells and proteins. Briefly, the PET surface is partially solubilized in dilute trifluoroacetic acid (TFA). PEG was introduced into this partially solvated surface and then was sterically "locked" into place by removing the PET from the TFA and putting it into water. Peptides were then linked to the hydroxyl groups on the PEG with essentially the same technique used for glycophase glass (101,110).

When compared with data obtained from glycophase glass, two important differences stand out. First, unlike glycophase glass, there is no attachment to the PET + GPDSGR, and second, the HVSMCs failed to adhere on PET. Both may be due to the much lower peptide surface concentrations of the peptide (<20 fmol/cm^2 on the PET, compared with 10 pmol/cm^2 on the glass) (101).

Telios Pharmaceuticals, Inc., developed PepTite (Ac-G(dR)GRSPASSKGGGGS(dR)LLLLLL(dR)-NH$_2$, which binds via a hydrophobic interaction between its polyleucine domain and the underlying material. This has been shown to attach to a number of materials and promote the integrin-specific attachment of varied cell types (79). Experiments with PET and poly(tetrafluoroethylene) (PTFE) vascular patches modified with PepTite were preformed. Two 2-by-0.5-cm elliptical patches of plain PTFE, plain PET, PTFE + PepTite, and PET + PepTite were implanted into the carotid and femoral arteries of mongrel dogs. The animals were sacrificed at 3 weeks, and the arteries were opened opposite the patches and photographed. Portions of the patch were sectioned for histological analysis, while other parts were used for scanning electron microscopy.

Three of the four PepTite-treated patches showed coverage by endotheliallike cells, and only one of the four plain polymer grafts showed such development, most displaying instead a platelet–fibrin mesh containing macrophages and leukocytes. Foreign-body giant cells were reduced on PET + PepTite fibers compared with plain PET fibers. The neointimal thickness on PET + PepTite was about half of that of on plain PET, while there was little difference between plain PTFE and PTFE + PepTite (both between plain PET and PET + PepTite).

PepTite was also evaluated on the PET sewing cuffs of artificial heart valves in juvenile sheep. After the native mitral valves were removed, artificial valves with plain PET or PepTite + PET sewing rings were implanted and left in place for 3 or 4 weeks. After gross and histologic evaluation, it was found that the tissue growth on the PepTite-treated valves was significantly greater in extent, maturity, and thickness (111).

Poly(ethylene acrylic acid)

RGDS, RGDV, and RGDT are derived from fibronectin, vitronectin, and collagen, respectively. Hirano et al. coupled these peptides plus RGD to the surface of poly(ethylene acrylic acid) (EAA) via carbodiimide-mediated activation of the EAA's carboxylic acid groups.

Adhesion of a mouse epithelial fibroblast cell line (L-929) was evaluated on plain EAA and peptide-treated EAA. Cells were plated at 100,000 cells/cm^2 in serum-free media and allowed to adhere for 1 or 3 h. The peptide-treated surfaces supported two to four times more cell adhesion than plain EAA.

Surprisingly, these investigators found that the peptides solubilized at 2 mg/mL inhibited the attachment of cells to plain polystyrene in serum-free media over 3 h. It is interesting that adhesion to polystyrene is blocked by soluble peptides, and more analysis is required (55).

Polyacrylonitrile

Beer et al. did some investigative work on peptides with varying spacer lengths on polyacrylonitrile and human blood platelets. After rinsing polyacrylonitrile beads in sodium acetate, RGDF peptides with spacers containing 1, 3, 5, 7, 9, 11, 13, 15, 17, and 19 glycine residues in length were reacted with N-hydroxysuccinimide groups. Unreacted groups were quenched with glycine ethyl ester. Calculations based on high-performance liquid chromatography (HPLC) data from pre- and postreaction solutions and the surface area of the beads gave a spacing of approximately 4.6 Å.

Platelets were introduced to these beads. When the platelets recognized the immobilized peptides, agglutination would occur. Minimal reaction occurred with a single glycine spacer, but nine-glycine spacers promoted maximal agglutination. Three glycine spacers were most sensitive to outside agents, with no appreciable agglutination occurring with prostaglandin E$_1$ platelet inhibitor, delayed and incomplete platelet agglutination normally, and extensive agglutination with platelets activated with ADP. Prostaglandin E$_1$ inhibited but did not eliminate agglutination of surfaces with peptides having nine or more glycine spacers.

Platelet preincubation with soluble forms of the peptides containing one to nine glycine spacers was done to test for inhibition of agglutination. Shorter peptides had a more potent effect than longer peptides, indicating that the glycine spacers were not increasing binding generally. It was hypothesized that a spacer putting the peptide 11 to 32 Å from the surface of the bead is optimal for interaction with its receptor. However, the possibility that this spacer was more important in allowing the peptide to "escape" from the complex molecular geometry of the polymer's surface was also mentioned. Antibody studies indicated that the GPIIb/IIIa receptor is the one targeted by the RGDF peptide (112).

Hydrogels

Hydrogels are hydrophilic cross-linked polymer networks that swell in an aqueous environment. Their mechanical properties are similar to that of some biological tissues and are permeable to tissue metabolites, which makes them potentially useful as scaffolds for cells to grow into during tissue repair. Peptides can be grafted onto these hydrogels to enhance this activity (113,114).

Moghaddam and Matsuda began work on a peptide-modified photocurable hydrogel in 1993. 7-hydroxy coumarin was reacted with potassium carbonate. The excess potassium carbonate is removed, and 2-bromoethyl methacrylate is added. The result is a methacrylic acid-(7-coumaroxy)ethyl ester (MACEE). N,N-dimethylacrylamide (DMAAm), MACEE, and N-acryloxy succinimide (NASI) were copolymerized and reacted with GGGRGDSP.

Moghaddam and Matsuda mixed 0.5 mL of the polymer solution in phosphate-buffered saline with 0.5 mL of Dulbeco's modified Eagle medium (DMEM) containing 25,000 bovine aortic smooth muscle cells/mL. This mixture was exposed to ultraviolet light, causing the polymer to cross-link and form a hydrogel matrix. Cells entrapped within this matrix took a few days to spread and proliferated slowly. It was suspected that either the 30 min of UV irradiation required to produce the gel damaged the cells, or the 3-D culture environment effected the proliferation rates (114).

Plant et al. created an N-(2-hydroxypropyl)methacrylamide (HPMA)–based hydrogel grafted with RGD. Incorporating glucosamine (NHGlc) or N-acetylglucosamine (AcNHGlc) into the polymer backbone enhances the biocompatibility of HPMA (115,116), and so RGD-modified HPMA was compared with these amino sugar–modified implants as well as unmodified HPMA. No control peptide was used.

Optic-tract lesions in 17- to 19-day-old PVG/c and Wistar rats were created and plugged with the experimental hydrogels. Nineteen-week-old PVG/c rats were given circular cortical lesions 500 μm in diameter that were again plugged with the hydrogels (all tested except AcNHGlc). Ten to 12 months after implantation, brains were excised and cryosectioned, and immunohistochemistry was performed. Positive staining for both glial fibrillary acidic protein and S100 marked astrocytes. Oligodendroglia could be identified with a stain against carbonic anhydrase II, and macrophages could be identified with a one against ED1. Antibodies against laminin (for evidence of neovascularization), neurofilaments, and myelin basic protein were also used.

Cortical Implant Results. Two unmodified HPMA plugs are implanted, but only one stayed in place for analysis. This showed no appreciable ingrowth. Macrophages were present outside the polymer, but not within it, and an astrocytic region surrounded the implant. Extensive integration was found around the two NHGlc-containing hydrogels, with 70% of the available hydrogel surface area attached to brain tissue. Laminin staining was evident throughout most of the hydrogel matrices. Astrocytes again surrounded the implant but the staining was only of low to moderate intensity, and unlike the unmodified HPMA a few astrocytes were present within the implant. There was evidence of a few ingrowing axons (average of 6 per section). Macrophage number and location were similar to unmodified HPMA, and here, too, no oligodendroglia could be seen in the implant.

One of the RGD-containing implants had become displaced, but of the remaining three, integration was very good, with about 90% of the available surface area attached to brain tissue. Laminin structures were evident throughout the hydrogels and were often associated with axonal ingrowth. The maximum number of axons found in one section was 78. An extensive matrix of astrocytes was also present within the implant, and there was little evidence of encapsulation by the surrounding tissue. Large numbers of macrophages were present, and no oligodendroglia could be located.

Optic Tract Implant Results. Four unmodified HPMA implants were used in these experiments. Only one of the four was found in the optic-tract lesion site after the brain was removed, and even this one was not attached to the host tissue. The surrounding tissue showed a low astrocytic response, and no astrocytes were found within the polymer matrix. There were no axons, oligodendroglia, or laminin in the polymer. Macrophages were present around the implant but not within.

The two NHGlc-modified implants showed attachment, with a good interface between host tissue and implant; however, a full bridge did not form across the lesion. Laminin staining indicated the presence of new blood vessels. A low number of astrocytes was found within the matrix. No oligodendroglia were present, and macrophages were present inside and outside the matrix. These appeared to be removing debris from the site, which would help explain these implants being a bit smaller than the unmodified HMPA. An average of six axons per section was found.

Three AcNHGlc implants were put into place. Only one of them was attached to host tissue. About 55% of available surface area on the implant was attached to tissue. Very little laminin and few astrocytes were seen in the matrix. No oligodendroglia and very few macrophages were seen in the implant. No axons had grown in.

Six of the seven RGD implants attached to host tissue, with about 75% of the available surface area attached. Laminin was present throughout the matrix and there were an extremely high number of astrocytes within the implant, with relatively little in the surrounding tissue. Many macrophages were present inside and outside of the implant and were in the same areas as astrocytes inside the implant. Five of the six implants showed axonal ingrowth, with an overall average of 36 axons per section. Once again axons were closely associated with laminin structures.

Poly(vinyl alcohol). GRGDSP were all immobilized to poly(vinyl alcohol) (PVA) by Matsuda et al. Hydroxyl groups on the surface of PVA films were activated with CDI, and the peptide in DMF was reacted with the surface. All unreacted active hydroxyl groups were reconverted to surface hydroxyls by treatment with a pH 8.1 solution.

Bovine aortic endothelial cells seeded on plain PVA surfaces in serum did not adhere, but cells seeded on peptide and fibronectin (covalently linked to the surface by the same method) did adhere and proliferate. In the absence of serum, cells on peptide-treated surfaces could be removed by soluble RGDS, indicating specificity for this reaction. The growth of cells at day 3 was greater on immobilized peptide than on fibronectin. Control over peptide density could be achieved by modifying the initial CDI reaction, and it was found that increasing the peptide density slightly enhanced cell growth (117).

Photocoupled Dimethacrylamide and PVA. Others have used coupling agents to covalently link peptides to polymers. Sugawara et al. immobilized an RGD-containing peptide (GGGRGDSP) to PVA and poly(N,N-dimethacrylamide-co-3-azidostyrene) (poly[DMAM]) using 4-azidobenzoyloxysuccimide. The succinimide reacted with the amine terminus of the RGD peptide and the azidobenzoyl bound to the polymer upon exposure to ultraviolet light. Photolysed phenyl-azido groups generate phenyl nitrenes, which are highly reactive (capable of addition to $C=C$ bonds, insertion of C—H bonds, and abstraction of protons from neighboring compounds). Even though the peptide was successfully immobilized to both polymers, the PVA also supported the nonspecific adsorption of the RGD peptide and was not used for most cell studies (118).

The poly(DMAM) alone did not support the adhesion and spreading of bovine aorta endothelial cells in serum-free medium, but once treated with photoimmobilized peptide, it did. These could be removed from the surface with soluble RGDS peptide, indicating a specific reaction between the cell and the immobilized peptide. A photomask was used to ensure peptide grafting to only specific areas of the polymer in a honeycomb or striped pattern. Cells were plated down in media without serum for a day and then switched to serum-containing media. Over the next few days, cells became confluent only in the peptide-grafted areas (118).

Silicon Dioxide

Rezania used this material to examine the morphology and attachment strength of cells to peptide-immobilized materials. Quartz surfaces were modified with an aminofunctional organosilane. A heterobifunctional cross-linker was used to link the terminal amines to the thiols of peptides with N-terminal cysteines. The experimental peptide was an RGD-containing sequence (CGGNGEPRGDTYRAY) derived from bone sialoprotein. A similar RGE-containing peptide was used as a control. Contact angle, ellipsometry, and ESCA were used to verify peptide attachment.

Cells used were isolated from neonate (6- to 12-day-old) rat calvaria and used at passage 2, 3, and 4. These were plated onto the test surfaces at 5,000 cells/cm^2 in DMEM with 1% bovine serum albumin (to block nonspecific binding).

To measure the strength of adhesion, a radial-flow apparatus (RFA) was used. This device is made of two parallel plates with a fluid jet in the center of one of the plates. The jet produces an axisymmetric flow pattern that in turn puts shear stresses on the surfaces of the plate. The shear stress at which 63.2% of attached cells would be expected to detach (Weibull characteristic strength) was significantly greater ($P < .05$) for RGD-grafted surfaces ($\approx 57 \pm 8$) than that of RGE-grafted surfaces ($\approx 37 \pm 4$).

Morphologically, cells were more spread ($P < .05$) on the RGD-grafted surfaces than on plain or RGE-grafted surfaces at 20 min and 2 h after plating. The spreading on the RGD was also significantly greater at 2 h than at 20 min (5). Fluorescent tagging of vinculin was also used to look at focal adhesion formation. RGE surfaces showed no focal adhesion formation even at 2 h. Though nothing was apparent at 20 min, at 2 h focal adhesions were present on the RGD-grafted surfaces. Focal adhesions were also present at 2 h when the substrate had been exposed to 15% serum-containing media. A major difference between RGD-grafted and serum-adsorbed surfaces was that the cells on the RGD showed many projections, while those on adsorbed serum were pancake shaped (5).

Fluorinated Ethylene Propylene

Vargo et al. developed a technique to immobilize peptides to the surface of a fluoropolymer without the use of cou-

pling agents. Fluorinated ethylene propylene (FEP) was hydroxylated using radio-frequency glow discharge, forming FEP-OH. This material was immersed in DMSO containing YIGSR peptide and K_2CO_3. This was heated to 50°C and allowed to react for 72 h, and the peptide was linked to the surface via its C-terminus. Covalent attachment was verified with attenuated total reflection–fourier transform infrared spectrometry, and fluorescent microscopy of rinse solutions indicated against the presence of physisorbed YIGSR. The integrity of the immobilized peptide was verified by time-of-flight secondary-ion mass spectrometry (119).

It was found that increasing the time in the RFGD chamber increased the surface hydroxylation but that the optimal peptide incorporation was achieved between 0.5 to 1 min of plasma treatment ($\approx 2\%$ oxygen at 12-Å sampling depth). This may be due to a decrease in electron density at the surface or surface degradation with longer treatments. As would be expected, Vargo et al. found this technique to be applicable to a number of peptides (119,120).

FEP films were thus modified with the laminin-derived YIGSR and IKVAV sequences (IKVAV in the form of the peptide CSRARKQAASIKVAVSADR). NG108-15 neuroblastoma cell and PC12 pheochromocytoma cell attachment was evaluated.

Cell attachment was performed in serum-free media. All surfaces were preadsorbed with albumin to prevent nonspecific attachment. Quantification was done by randomly selecting a minimum of 300 cells per well under a Zeiss microscope equipped with Hoffman optics at 200× and developing a cells/area plot. To test for the specificity of attachment, soluble IKVAV-containing peptide or CDPYIGSR was used at 1 mg/mL concentration to block cell surface receptors in solution, preventing them from interacting with the immobilized peptide. As a further step, soluble CDPYIGSK was used as a soluble control peptide to ensure that a nonspecific reaction between cell and soluble peptide was not to blame for any decrease in adhesion.

The attachment of the NG108-15 cells to the YIGSR-modified surfaces in the absence of soluble peptide was statistically greater than that with soluble CDPYIGSR ($P < .05$). There was no statistical difference between no peptide and control peptide attachment ($P > .1$). Attachment of PC12 cells to IKVAV-modified surfaces showed a similar pattern, with attachment inhibited by soluble IKVAV peptide ($P < .001$) (120).

FEP surfaces have also been used to immobilize peptides for bone cell applications (121–123). Our lab has shown increased osteocalcin and osteonectin mRNA expression on RGD and RGE surfaces and increased osteocalcin mRNA and protein expression on RGD surfaces and has found that the cells successfully mineralized on all substrates. RAD-treated FEP did not show the same levels of protein and mRNA expression that RGD and RGE treated samples did (123).

Gold

With the exception of silane coupling agents and PepTite, the techniques described earlier, while effective, cannot be directly applied to skeletal implant metals as they depend on covalent linkages with polymers. The gold–thiol bond has potential in this area.

Sulfur-containing molecules spontaneously form monolayers on gold surfaces. Gold interacts with ligands such as sulfur and phosphorous but remains inert to organic first-row elements (124). This makes this system especially useful for peptides, whose only non-first-row element is sulfur found in the amino acid cysteine.

The bond itself is not completely understood. Some call it covalent (125,126), while others refer to it as chemisorption (127). Basically, gold(I) (gold lacking one electron) thiolates (RS⁻ Au⁺) are formed from gold(0) (gold lacking no electrons) and organosulfur species and adsorbed onto the gold(0) surface. This reaction requires the loss of a proton, possibly leaving as water or H_2. The bond energy is high: 40–45 kcal/mol (127).

Monolayers formed by this reaction tend to be close packed, resist the pooling of like molecules in a mixed surface, and require hours or days to exchange with thiols in solution to a significant degree (127,128).

Moodie et al. used cysteine-terminated peptides to evaluate bone cell responses to modified surfaces. Peptides were all solubilized in 50% ethanol at a concentration of 0.22 mM. Gold-coated substrates were exposed to this solution overnight to allow the thiols to react with the surface and the peptides to reach a stable arrangement. The resultant surface is diagrammed in Figure 1.

Cell attachment doubled in the first 20 min on RGDC-treated surfaces, even in the presence of serum (129), and an increased rate of spreading has been recorded over a 2-h time span (130). Alkaline phosphatase, a marker for bone cell maturation, was up-regulated on RGDC-treated gold as shown in Figure 2 (129).

Changes in mRNA expression for integrin subunits were also observed, with increasing α_5 and maintained β_1 expression over 19 days (decreased on plain gold or CG-immobilized surfaces) (129). As mentioned earlier, $\alpha_5\beta_1$ is a known RGD receptor.

Focal adhesions formed on RGDC-treated surfaces, and even after storage for 4 weeks in aqueous media, the percentage of cells showing focal adhesions remained high. This contrasts with adsorbed fibronectin, which lost its ability encourage focal adhesion formations under identi-

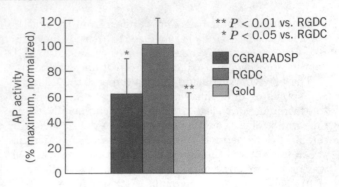

Figure 2. Alkaline phosphatase activity on peptide-modified gold surfaces.

cal storage conditions during this time, eventually falling to the same level as plain gold surfaces (G. Moodie et al., unpublished data). In vivo bone formation was also increased around RGDC-treated rat femur intramedullary rods as compared to plain gold-coated rods (D. Ferris et al., unpublished data).

BIBLIOGRAPHY

1. Y. Imanishi, Y. Ito, L. Liu, and M. Kajihara, *J. Macromol. Sci. Chem.* **A25**, 555–570 (1988).
2. M. Pierschbacher et al., *J. Cell. Biochem.* **56**, 150–154 (1994).
3. C. Brighton and S. Albelda, *J. Orthop. Res.* **10**, 766–773 (1992).
4. M. Pierschbacher and E. Ruoslahti, *Nature* **309**(3), 30–33 (1984).
5. A. Rezania et al., *Biomed. Mater. Res.* **37**, 9–19 (1997).
6. E. Ruoslahti, *J. Clin. Invest.* **87**, 1–5 (1991).
7. N. Sugano, H. Tanaka, K. Ito, and S. Murai, *J. Nihon Univ. Sch. Dent.* **39**(3), 154–155 (1997).
8. S. Vukicevic, F. Luyten, H. Kleinman, and A. Reddi, *Cell* **63**, 437–445 (1990).
9. R. Hynes, *Cell* **69**, 11–25 (1992).
10. G. Hannigan and S. Dedhar, *J. Mol. Med.* **75**, 34–44 (1997).
11. L. Kim and K. Yamada, *Proc. Soc. Exp. Biol. Med.* **214**, 123–131 (1997).
12. R. Juliano, *BioEssays* **18**, 911–916 (1996).
13. K. Vuori and E. Ruoslahti, *Science* **266**, 1576–1578 (1994).
14. N. Bartfeld, E. Pasquale, J. Geltosky, and L. Languino, *J. Biol. Chem.* **268**, 17270–17276 (1993).
15. N. Boudreau, C. Sympson, Z. Werb, and M. Bissell, *Science* **267**, 891–893 (1995).
16. R. Juliano and S. Haskill, *J. Cell Biol.* **120**(3), 577–585 (1993).
17. J. Meredith et al., *Endocr. Rev.* **17**(3), 207–213 (1996).
18. C. Roskelley, P. Desprez, and M. Bissell, *Proc. Nat. Acad. Sci. USA.* **91**(26), 12378–12382 (1994).
19. M. Schaller, *J. Endocrinol.* **150**, 1–7 (1996).
20. N. Wang, J. Butler, and D. Ingber, *Science* **260**, 1124–1127 (1993).
21. W. Staatz et al., *J. Biol. Chem.* **266**(12), 7363–7367 (1991).

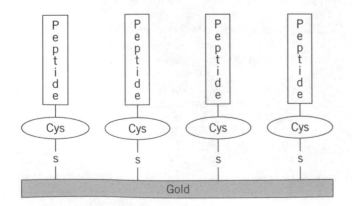

Figure 1. Peptide immobilized on gold through cysteine.

22. S. Horowitz and M. Purdon, *J. Biomed. Mater. Res.* **29**, 477–484 (1995).

23. R. Friedman et al., *J. Bone Jt. Surg., Am. Vol.* **75-A**, 1086–1109 (1993).

24. L. Jones and D. Hungerford, *Clin. Orthop.* **225**, 192–206 (1987).

25. R. Austin and P. Stoney, *Injury* **13**(5), 414–418 (1982).

26. H.D. Huddleston, *J. Arthroplasty* **3**(4), 285–297 (1988).

27. J. Maguire, *Rheum. Dis. Clin. North Am.* **14**(3), 519–535 (1988).

28. J. Galante et al., *J. Orthop. Res.* **9**(5), 760–765 (1991).

29. A. Newens and R. Volz, *Anesthesiology* **36**(3), 298–300 (1972).

30. S. Bengston, K. Knutson, and L. Lidgren, *Clin. Orthop.* **245**, 173–178 (1989).

31. T. Kallos, J. Enis, F. Gollan, and J. Davis, *J. Bone Jt. Surg., Am. Vol.* **56-A**(7), 1363–1367 (1974).

32. K. Schulte, J. Callaghan, S. Kelley, and R. Johnston, *J. Bone Jt. Surg., Am. Vol.* **75-A**(7), 961–975 (1993).

33. D. Collins, S. Heim, C. Nelson, and P.I. Smith, *Clin. Orthop. Relat. Res.* **267**, 128–135 (1989).

34. K. Vince, J. Insall, and M. Kelly, *J. Bone Jt. Surg., Br. Vol.* **71**(5), 793–797 (1989).

35. G. Scuderi, J. Insall, R. Windsor, and M. Moran, *J. Bone Jt.J. Surg., Br. Vol.* **71B**(5), 798–803 (1989).

36. H. Cameron, *Clin. Orthop.* **208**, 81–83 (1986).

37. R. Pilliar, *J. Biomed. Mater. Res.* **21**(A1 Suppl.), 1–33 (1987).

38. M. Spector, *J. Arthroplasty* **2**, 163–177 (1987).

39. R. Haddad, S. Cook, and K. Thomas, *J. Bone Jt. Surg., Am. Vol.* **69-A**, 1459–1466 (1987).

40. P. Ducheyne et al., *Acta Orthop. Belg.* **40**(5–6), 799–805 (1974).

41. K. Soballe et al., *J. Orthop. Res.* **10**(2), 285–299 (1992).

42. C. Tisdel et al., *J. Bone Jt. Surg., Am. Vol.* **76-A**(2), 159–171 (1994).

43. A. Hoffman, *Artif. Organs* **16**(1), 43–49 (1992).

44. R. Hynes, *Cell (Cambridge, Mass.)* **48**, 549–554 (1987).

45. J. Bassuk et al., *Eur. J. Biochem.* **218**(1), 117–127 (1993).

46. P. Cardarelli et al., *J. Biol. Chem.* **267**(32), 23159–23164 (1992).

47. S. Cheng et al., *J. Med. Chem.* **37**(1), 1–8 (1994).

48. D. Cheresh and R. Mecham, eds., *Integrins: Molecular and Biological Responses to the Extracellular Matrix*, Academic Press, San Diego, Calif., 1994.

49. J. Clover, R. Dodds, and M. Gowen, *J. Cell Sci.* **103**, 267–271 (1992).

50. E. Danen, D. Ruiter, and G. Van-Muijen, *Biochem. Soc. Trans.* **23**(3), 403S (1995).

51. M. Ginsberg et al., *J. Biol. Chem.* **260**(7), 3931–3936 (1985).

52. J. Graf et al., *Cell* **48**(6), 989–996 (1987).

53. W. Grzesik and P. Robey, *J. Bone Miner. Res.* **9**(4), 487–496 (1994).

54. W. Grzesik, Y. Grzesik, and B. Ivanov, *17th Annu. Meet. Am. Soc. Bone Miner. Res.*, September 9–13, 1995, p. M268.

55. Y. Hirano et al., *J. Biomed. Mater. Res.* **25**, 1523–1534 (1991).

56. J. Hubbell, S. Massia, and P. Drumheller, *Ann. N.Y. Acad Sci* **665**, 253–258 (1992).

57. D. Hughes, D. Salter, S. Dedhar, and R. Simpson, *J. Bone Miner. Res.* **8**(5), 527–533 (1993).

58. K. Hultenby, F. Reinholt, and D. Heinegard, *Eur. J. Cell Biol.* **62**, 86–93 (1993).

59. Y. Iwamoto et al., *J. Cell. Physiol.* **134**(2), 287–291 (1988).

60. T. Lane, M. Iruela-Arispe, and E. Sage, *J. Biol. Chem.* **267**(23), 16736–16745 (1992).

61. T. Lane, M. Iruela-Arispe, R. Johnson, and E. Sage, *J. Cell Biol.* **125**(4), 929–943 (1994).

62. F. Maquart et al., *J. Clin. Invest.* **92**(5), 2368–2376 (1993).

63. S. Massia and J. Hubbell, *Anal. Biochem.* **187**, 292–301 (1990).

64. S. Massia and J. Hubbell, *Ann. N.Y. Acad. Sci.* **589**, 261–270 (1990).

65. A. Oldberg, A. Franzen, and D. Heingard, *J. Biol. Chem.* **263**, 19430–19432 (1988).

66. V. Pesakova, J. Novotna, and M. Adam, *Biomaterials* **16**(12), 911–915 (1995).

67. M. Pfaff et al., *J. Biol. Chem.* **269**(32), 20233–20238 (1994).

68. D. Puleo and R. Bizios, *Bone* **12**, 271–276 (1991).

69. E. Ruoslahti and M. Pierschbacher, *Science* **238**, 491–497 (1987).

70. T. Saito, S. Albelda, and C. Brighton, *J. Orthop. Res.* **12**(3), 384–394 (1994).

71. S. Van Dijk et al., *J. Bone Miner. Res.* **8**(12), 1499–1506 (1993).

72. B. Vogel et al., *J. Cell Biol.* **121**(2), 461–468 (1993).

73. J. Qian and R. Bhatnagar, *J. Biomed. Mater. Res.* **31**(4), 545–554 (1996).

74. S. Akiyama, K. Olden, and K. Yamada, *Cancer Metastasis Rev.* **14**(3), 173–189 (1995).

75. K. Gehlsen, W. Argraves, M. Pierschbacher, and E. Ruoslahti, *J. Cell. Biol.* **106**(3), 925–930 (1988).

76. I. Hart and N. Hogg, *Cell Adhesion and Cancer*, Cold Spring Harbor Lab. Press, Plainview, N.Y., 1995.

77. M. Humphries, K. Olden, and K. Yamada, *Science* **233**, 467–470 (1986).

78. M. Ginsberg, J. Loftus, and E. Plow, *Thromb. Haemostasis* **59**, 1–6 (1988).

79. W. Craig et al., *Biopolymers (Pept. Sci.)* **37**, 157–175 (1995).

80. M. Chorev, P. Dresner, Y. Eshel, and M. Rosenblatt, *Biopolymers* **37**(6), 367–375 (1995).

81. R. Dresner-Pollak and M. Rosenblatt,, *J. Cell. Biochem.* **56**(3), 323–330 (1994).

82. Y. Danilov and R. Juliano, *Exp. Cell Res.* **182**(1), 186–196 (1989).

83. M. Takatsuka, *ASAIO J.* **38**(3), M275–M278 (1992).

84. H. Lin et al., *J. Biomed. Mater. Res.* **28**, 329–342 (1994).

85. G. Sephel et al., *Biochem. Biophys. Res. Commun.* **162**(2), 821–829 (1989).

86. S. Aota, M. Nomizu, and K. Yamada, *J. Biol. Chem.* **269**(40), 24756–24761 (1994).

87. M. Pierschbacher et al., *Ciba Found Symp.* **136**, 131–141 (1988).

88. R. Howlett et al., *Biomaterials* **15**(3), 213–222 (1994).

89. B. Callen, R. Sodhi, R. Shelton, and J. Davies, *J. Biomed. Mater. Res.* **27**, 851–859 (1993).

90. J. Davies, *The Bone-Biomaterial Interface*, University of Toronto Press, Toronto, Ontario, Canada, 1991.

91. K. Healy et al., *Biomaterials* **17**(2), 195–208 (1996).

92. T. Matsuda and J. Davies, *Biomaterials* **8**, 275–284 (1987).

93. S. Peel, R. Sodhi, T. Duc, and J. Davies, *Mater. Res. Soc. Symp. Proc.* **252**, 71–77 (1992).

94. D. Puleo and R. Bizios, *J. Biomed. Res.* **26**, 291–301 (1992).

95. G. Schneider and K. Burridge, *Exp. Cell Res.* **214**, 264–269 (1994).

96. S. Cheng, S. Zhang, R. Civitelli, and L. Avioli, *17th Annu. Meet. Am. Soc. Bone Miner. Res.*, 1995, T223.

97. S. Dedhar, *J. Cell. Physiol.* **138**(2), 291–299 (1989).

98. R. Pytela et al., *Methods Enzymol.* **144**, 475–489 (1987).

99. B. Brandley and R. Schnaar, *Anal. Biochem.* **172**, 270–278 (1988).

100. S. Massia and J. Hubbell, *J. Biomed. Mater. Res.* **25**, 223–242 (1991).

101. J. Hubbell, S. Massia, N. Desai, and P. Drumheller, *Bio/Technology* **9**, 568–572 (1991).

102. S. Massia and J. Hubbell, *J. Cell Biol.* **114**(5), 1089–1100 (1991).

103. S. Massia, S. Rao, and J. Hubbell, *J. Biol. Chem.* **268**(11), 8053–8059 (1993).

104. Y. Ito, M. Sisido, and Y. Imanishi, *J. Biomed. Mater. Res.* **20**, 1157–1177 (1986).

105. H. Lin et al., *J. Biomater. Sci., Polym. Ed.* **3**(3), 217–227 (1992).

106. H. Lin et al., *J. Biomater. Sci., Polym. Ed.* **4**(3), 183–198 (1993).

107. H. Lin et al., *Biomaterials* **13**(13), 905–914 (1992).

108. M. Yanagi et al., *ASAIO J.* **40**(3), M412–M418 (1994).

109. W. Breuers, D. Klee, H. Hocker, and C. Mittermayer, *J. Mater. Sci. Mater. Med.* **2**, 106–109 (1991).

110. N. Desai and J. Hubbell, *Biomaterials* **12**, 144–153 (1991).

111. K. Tweden et al., *J. Heart Valve Dis.* **4**(Suppl. 1), S90–S97 (1995).

112. J. Beer, K. Springer, and B. Coller, *Blood* **79**(1), 117–128 (1992).

113. G. Plant, S. Woerly, and A. Harvey, *Exp. Neurol.* **143**, 287–299 (1997).

114. M. Moghaddam and T. Matsuda, *J. Polym. Sci., Part A: Polym. Chem.* **31**, 1589–1597 (1993).

115. S. Woerly et al., *Brain Res. Bull.* **30**, 423–432 (1993).

116. S. Woerly, Morassutti-DJ, *Cell Transplant.* **2**, 229–239 (1993).

117. T. Matsuda, A. Kondo, K. Makino, and T. Akutsu, *Trans. Am. Soc. Artif. Intern. Organs* **35**, 677–679 (1989).

118. T. Sugawara and T. Matsuda, *J. Biomed. Mater. Res.* **29**, 1047–1052 (1995).

119. T. Vargo et al., *J. Biomed. Mater. Res.* **29**, 767–778 (1995).

120. J. Ranieri et al., *J. Biomed. Mater. Res.* **29**, 779–785 (1995).

121. R. Valentini et al., *Trans. Soc. Biomater., 23rd Ann. Meet.*, April 30–May 4, 1997, Vol. 20, p. 55.

122. R. Valentini, L. Zou, and H. Kim, *Trans. Soc. Biomater., 21st Ann. Meet.*, March 18–22, 1995, Vol. 18, p. 65.

123. M. Sherling et al., *Artif. Organs* **21**(6), 497 (1997).

124. C. Bain and G. Whitesides, *Science* **240**, 62–63 (1988).

125. C. Duschl, M. Liley, and H. Vogel, *Angew. Chem., Int. Ed. Engl.* **33**(12), 1274–1276 (1994).

126. C. Duschl, M. Liley, G. Corradin, and H. Vogel, *Biophys. J.* **67**, 1229–1237 (1994).

127. G. Whitesides and P. Laibinis, *Langmuir* **6**(1), 86–96 (1990).

128. C. Bain and G. Whitesides, *J. Am. Chem. Soc.* **111**, 7164–7175 (1989).

129. G. Moodie et al., *Trans. Soc. Biomater., 24th Annu. Meet.*, April 22–26, 1998, Vol. 21, p. 116.

TRANSDERMAL DRUG DELIVERY, ELECTRICAL

Janet Tamada
Cygnus, Inc.
Redwood City, California

KEY WORDS

Electrical

Electroosmosis

Electroporation

Enhancer

Iontophoresis

Skin

Stratum corneum

Transdermal

OUTLINE

INTRODUCTION

Electrically assisted transdermal delivery uses electric fields to enhance transport of active agents across the skin. Iontophoresis and electroporation are the two major methods of electrically assisted transdermal delivery. These methods avoid the gastrointestinal degradation and hepatic first-pass metabolism found in oral administration. Both local delivery (e.g., lidocaine for topical anesthesia) and systemic drug administration (e.g., fentanyl for pain relief) are possible. Both methods can enhance drug flux up to several orders of magnitude above that allowed by passive diffusion (as in conventional skin patches), depending on the nature of the solute. Whereas the effective delivery range for passive diffusion across the skin is constrained to small, hydrophobic agents, electrically enhanced delivery can be used for larger, hydrophilic molecules, which is particular advantageous for peptide and oligonucleotide drug administration. Additionally, these methods can be programmed to varied levels for nonconstant delivery patterns, such as for pain management. However, there are practical constraints. The efficiency of transdermal delivery is low, so applications are limited to potent compounds. Irritation, metabolism, and interaction of the agent with the skin can also limit application. The literature on electrically enhanced delivery is extensive, particularly for iontophoresis, and the reader is directed to more complete reviews (1–8).

The skin functions as a physical, chemical, and microbial barrier to transport and is divided into the subcutaneous tissue, the dermis, and the epidermis. The outermost layer of the epidermis is the stratum corneum, which is generally the primary barrier to transport across the skin. In a classic description, the stratum corneum is described as being composed of dense, protein-rich, keratin "bricks" and a more fluid, lipid filled "mortar" (9), which is a multilamellar structure of lipid bilayers that forms a circuitous pathway around the keratinocytes. Additionally, structures such as hair follicles, sebaceous glands, and sweat ducts, collectively known as skin appendages, play a major role in electrically enhanced transport. The skin poses another barrier in that it can metabolize compounds, and the extent of drug loss prior to absorption by the blood stream will adversely affect its effective transport (10). Comprehensive reviews of skin physiology, particularly relating to transdermal delivery, are available (11,12).

IONTOPHORESIS

Iontophoresis involves application of a low-level electrical current across the skin. Iontophoresis uses two electrodes, the anode and the cathode, each of which is in contact with a reservoir containing an electrically conductive medium, which is, in turn, in contact with the skin (Fig. 1). The agent to be delivered is contained in one the reservoirs in an aqueous solution. An electrical potential is applied across the electrodes, causing current to flow across the skin and facilitating delivery of the therapeutic agent. The first well-documented experiments that reported using iontophoresis for delivery of an active agent were performed in 1900 by LeDuc, who demonstrated the delivery of positively charged strychnine sulfate into rabbits, causing convulsions when placed in the anode but no effect when placed in the cathode. Negatively charged cyanide caused poisoning when delivered from the cathode but no effect when delivered from the anode (13).

Transport Pathway

The transport pathway of molecules through skin under the influence of an electric field may be through the skin appendages, across the keratinocytes, or through the multilamellar lipid bilayers. For passive transdermal diffusion, it has been established that diffusion through the lipid layers is the dominant transport mechanism. However, for iontophoresis, substantial evidence indicates that most ion transport occurs through the pathways of lowest electrical resistance, which consist of hair follicles, sweat ducts, and skin imperfections (4). It has been shown in a number of studies that the route of ion transport is elevated in localized areas (14). Evidence includes methylene blue iontophoresis showing a pattern of blue dots on the skin (15), a vibrating-probe study showing locally high areas of current flow (16), and iontophoretic transport of $Fe(CN)_6^4$ coupled with scanning electrochemical microscopy (17) showing that areas of ion transport were associated with hair follicles. However, results also indicate that hair follicles alone do not account for the totality of transdermal flux (18), and some additional route may be present. Confocal microscopy of two dyes with different physicochemical properties indicated that the transport pathways can vary with the properties of the permeant (19). Evidence of transport through the lipid bilayer route has been found in studies of mercuric chloride iontophoresis through porcine skin. Transmission electron microscopy showed evidence of staining by the transported compound within the lipid bilayers (20).

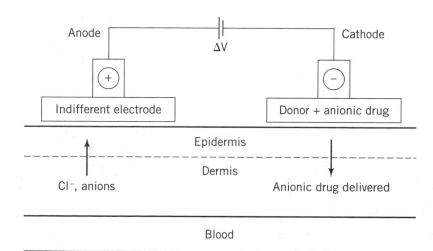

Figure 1. Schematic of iontophoretic drug delivery system. Example shows delivery of an anionic agent from the cathodal reservoir. The agent goes through the nonvascularized epidermis and into the dermis, where it can be transported into the blood through the capillary loops. The counter electrode is sometimes known as the indifferent electrode.

Description and Mechanisms of Transport

Mechanisms of Transport. Drug transport under the influence of iontophoretic current has three main contributions: electrophoretic, passive, and electroosmotic. The electrophoretic transport is caused by the electrical potential gradient applied to the charged species. Anionic (negatively charged) species are driven away from the cathode and towards the anode; cationic (positively) charged species are driven away from the anode and towards the cathode.

The electrophoretic transport for charged species is giving by the following equation:

$$J_{i,\text{electrophoretic}} = D_i C_i \frac{z_i F}{RT} \frac{dE}{dx}$$

where J_i is the flux of the ith species, D_i is its diffusion coefficient, C_i is its concentration, and z_i is its charge. F is Faraday's constant, R is the gas constant, T is absolute temperature, and E is the electric field.

Passive diffusion results from the concentration driving force. The passive diffusion contribution is described by the classic Fick's Law description:

$$J_{i,\text{positive}} = D_i \left(\frac{dC_i}{dx_i} \right)$$

The Nernst–Planck equation is the sum of the electrophoretic and passive diffusive contributions.

Electroosmotic transport is a convective flow of solvent induced by the application of a voltage gradient across a charged, porous medium (14,21). The transport pathways in the stratum corneum generally have a net negative charge. When an electric field is applied across the skin, cations, mostly sodium in the case of a physiological system, are preferentially passed through the skin due to the net negative charge. Volume flow toward the cathode is created by momentum transfer from the cations to the surrounding fluid (22,23). The magnitude of the flow is small, on the order of μL/cm^2/h, but for large or neutral molecules, it can have a substantial impact on skin flux (24,25). The electroosmotic effect can decrease the transport from the cathode compared with passive diffusion, because the molecule is moving against the direction of electroosmotic flow, impeding its progress (26).

Electroosmotic transport has the following form:

$$J_{i,\text{electroosmotic}} = C_i v$$

where v is the electroosmotic flow rate. In-depth mathematical descriptions and derivations are available (27–29).

Transport Number. An important concept in iontophoretic delivery is the transport, or transference, number. The transport number is a measure of how efficiently the agent of interest is transported relative to the other ions present in the system. It is an indicator of the permselectivity properties of the skin (30). A detailed description of the concept is give by Phipps and Gyory (31). The flux is characterized by

$$J_i = \frac{t_i I_i}{z_i F}$$

where t_i is the ion transport number and I_t is the total current density applied. F is Faraday's constant, and z_i is the charge on the ith ion. For example, for skin at physiological pH the transport numbers of sodium and chloride are approximately 0.66 and 0.33, respectively, indicating that for a given current, more sodium will flow across the skin than chloride and that the skin has a higher permselectivity for sodium than chloride. Therefore, the flux of the molecule of interest is controlled by its mobility *relative* to the other ions that undergo transport. Thus, increasing passive permeability of the skin does not necessarily lead to increased iontophoretic transport of the target molecule. If the mobility of permeants through the skin increases due to an increase in skin permeability, sodium and chloride are also more easily transported, and the applied voltage necessary to generate a current decreases, which may counteract any enhanced mobility of the target permeant.

Factors Controlling Delivery Rate

Experimental Methods. Skin flux of the drug of interest is commonly tested in vitro in diffusion cells with a layer of skin between the two reservoirs. Various configurations of diffusion cells are available (32–35). Common skin sources are cadaver skin; hairless mouse, rat, and guinea pig skin; pig skin; and shed snake skin (36). Animal models, such as hairless rat, mouse, and guinea pig and pigs, are used for in vivo studies, but studies on human subjects are limited to relatively few compounds. In vivo and in vitro results have been shown to correlate well (37,38), although the correlation may vary with the particular compound and drug of interest.

A novel model that is intermediate between a live animal and cadaver or animal skin is the isolated perfused porcine skin flap, developed by Riviere et al. This model uses excised tissue from the belly of the pig, which can be perfused to maintain tissue viability over the course of a 1-day experiment (39–41).

Drug Physicochemical Properties. Generally, smaller and more highly charged molecules will be delivered more effectively by iontophoresis than larger, neutral molecules (42–45). The isoelectric point of the skin is between 4 and 5, so molecules that are charged between the pI of the skin and physiological pH are most suitable (46). Under most conditions, the skin has a net negative charge, so cationic compounds are transported more readily than similar anionic compounds. Hydrophilic compounds transport more readily than similar hydrophobic compounds (47). There is no particular molecular weight cutoff for iontophoretic delivery; however, 1,000 to 3,000 Da is probably the highest molecular weight that could be effectively delivered with present technology. Analysis of a variety of compounds of various molecular weights have been reported (48,49), including an elegant study of various molecular weights of poly(ethylene glycol), an uncharged polymer (50).

Certain compounds can change the electroosmotic transport properties of the skin as they are delivered

(23,51,52). This was discovered from the observation that drug flux for certain peptides did not increase as expected with increasing peptide donor concentration. An investigation of the transport of mannitol, an uncharged compound commonly used to investigate electroosmosis, with the concurrent delivery of the peptides leuprolide and Nafarelin showed a decrease in electroosmotic flow in the presence of the peptide. The mechanism is proposed to be peptide binding to the transport pathway in the skin, with the positive charge of the peptide decreasing the permselectivity of the skin toward sodium and decreasing electroosmotic flow. Electroosmotic flow was increased slightly by using an anionic compound, poly-l-lysine, but the effect was less dramatic than the converse decrease for the cationic peptides (53).

The rational design of drug compounds to enhance their iontophoretic mobility, thereby increasing therapeutic efficacy, is an emerging development (54). Systematic modifications of insulin analogs, generated by recombinant DNA technology, have been studied. The delivery of monomeric insulin with two additional negative charges, created by substitute of aspartate and glutamate for uncharged residues, was 100 times more than regular, hexameric human insulin (55).

Current Application Protocol. The current levels used are low, typically in the mA to sub-mA range, with a typical maximum current density of 0.5 mA/cm^2 of skin. The practical current density maximum is primarily limited by the skin irritation that results from the current flow, although sensation associated with the current can be limiting for large application areas. Normally, current is applied across the skin in a constant, direct-current mode. Numerous studies have established the linearity of drug flux with current density for the vast majority of compounds (30,32,44,56,57).

Neutral molecules also show a linear flux relationship to current density because the electroosmotic flow is proportional to sodium transport, which is proportional to current density. The amount of drug delivered is proportional to the amount of delivery time, although there can be an onset period before flux stabilization occurs. However, as iontophoresis duration progresses, accumulation of ions in the reservoir, depletion in drug donor concentration, pH changes, or interaction of the drug with skin can cause a decrease in flux over long-duration experiments (58).

The application of the iontophoretic current has been shown to affect the subsequent passive diffusion of molecules, suggesting that the intrinsic permeability of the skin is increased by the applied current (24,25,27,59–62). Studies of electrical resistance indicate there are changes in the skin following iontophoresis (63,64), but the exact mechanism is unknown. There are no apparent changes in skin permselectivity, as evidenced by the linear relationship of drug flux to current and duration of application.

Constant-voltage, rather than constant-current, iontophoresis has also been used (65). There has also been work using pulsed, rather than constant-current, iontophoresis (5,66) showing enhanced transport from high-frequency pulsing. Interpretation of the effectiveness of these techniques relative to conventional iontophoresis can be complex. Constant-voltage iontophoresis is complicated by the decrease in skin resistance that occurs after application of current (63). From Ohm's Law, as the resistance decreases, current increases, which causes an increase drug transport. However, there is no evidence that the inherent efficiency of transport has been improved. The concept of rapid pulsing developed from the observed decrease in electrical skin impedance as pulse frequency increases. However, it is resistance, not impedance, that is related to ion transport across the skin. Several controlled studies of pulsing showed little or no effect of pulse frequency on ion transport (2,67,68).

Characteristics of the Reservoir Medium. The composition of the reservoir formulation can profoundly affect the delivery rate of the therapeutic agent (69). The concentration of the drug in the donor reservoir is one important parameter. Generally, the drug flux is linear with increasing concentration (47,70), although aggregation, interaction with the skin, and other factors can lead to nonlinear concentration effects (23). Maximum drug concentration is dictated by solubility, although self-aggregation, cost, and other factors affect optimal drug donor concentration.

The pH of the medium affects the drug charge, which, depending on the pK_a, affects its mobility. As stated earlier, charged, especially positively charged, drugs are transported more easily through the skin. A pH gradient between the donor formulation and physiological pH can cause the drug to get "stuck" in the middle of the skin. As the drug moves through different pH environments, it reverses charge and will be driven back in the direction from which it came (41,71). In addition to affecting the charge on the drug, the pH of the medium changes the relative charge on the skin, thus changing its permselectivity (72). As pH of the reservoir is decreased to less than 4.0–5.0, the skin undergoes a transition from being a net negatively charged membrane to a positively charged membrane, and it will become increasingly favorable to anion permeation. Conversely, as pH increases above 4.0–5.0, the skin becomes negatively charged, and cation and electro-osmotic delivery will be favored. The range of physiologically acceptable pH is usually considered to be pH 4.0–9.0.

Another important characteristic of the donor reservoir is the ionic strength and presence of competing ions in the formulation (70,73). Because the total amount of current delivered is constant, a high ionic strength donor and competing ions compete with the drug for the charge transfer and decrease the drug flux. Therefore, it is generally good practice to keep extraneous ions at an absolute minimum. However, the donor must be sufficiently buffered to prevent any side reactions from electrode reactions and to keep the drug in the appropriately ionized state.

Skin Pretreatment. Skin pretreatments have been used with varying effects. Some have reported successful synergistic enhancement over iontophoresis and passive enhancement alone for using oleic acid for AZT (74), ethanol for insulin (55,75,76), and depilatory lotion for insulin (77), whereas others report no enhancement effect (78) or varied enhancement (79). Vasomodulating agents can also alter drug flux. Co-iontophoresis of vasoconstrictors decrease flux, whereas co-iontophoresis of vasodilators increase delivery (80). The application of proteolytic enzyme inhibitors to prevent the metabolism of peptides in the skin, thereby increasing the absorption efficiency, has been reported (81,82).

Toxicology

The application of the iontophoretic current can cause skin irritation and possibly affect the skin barrier function (83,84). Erythema (redness) and edema (swelling) can result to various degrees depending on formulation, duration, current density, and polarity. Generally, the irritation decreases within hours, although it may take a few days for complete resolution. Additionally, the active agent itself may cause irritation or sensitization of the skin. Studies of prostaglandin E2 (PGE2) release, by sampling using reverse iontophoresis, shows a difference in PGE2 release for several different active agents. PEG2 was correlated with erythema/edema scores (85). The effect of the pK_a of the transported species, among salicylic acid, salicylamide, m-nitrobenzoic acid, and m-anisic acid (pK_a range from 3.0 to 8.1) showed a sharp increase in irritation as the pK_a of the drug decreased to less than 4 (86). Irritation resulting from lidocaine and luteinizing hormone–releasing hormone (LH-RH) iontophoresis has been examined for gross changes (erythema and edema) and histologically, and the alteration caused by the iontophoresis resolved and had minimal toxicological significance (87,88). Studies using techniques such as measurement of transepidermal water loss, laser Doppler flowmetry, skin capacitance, and skin temperature postiontophoresis showed moderate response and no change in skin permeability or integrity (89,90).

Electrode Design

Electrode design is an important part of an iontophoretic device (33). A number of different types of electrodes have been used in iontophoresis, both for research and commercial applications, including platinum, stainless steel, and carbon. A widely used electrode system is the Ag/AgCl system (91) because it maintains the pH of the iontophoretic medium and has no negative toxicological implications. For Ag/AgCl electrodes, the following reactions occur stoichiometrically:

$$\text{Reaction on the anode: Ag + Cl}^- \rightarrow \text{AgCl + e}^-$$

$$\text{Reaction on the cathode: AgCl + e}^- \rightarrow \text{Ag + Cl}^-$$

These reactions maintain the pH of the reservoir at a constant level. Platinum and other metal electrodes can have an undesirable hydrolysis reaction, particularly at the cathode:

$$\text{Reaction on the cathode: H}_2\text{O + e}^- \rightarrow \text{OH}^- + 1/2\text{H}_2$$

The resultant high pH is not compatible with living skin tissue. Furthermore, the hydroxide ions formed from the reaction are driven into the skin by the negative charge on the cathode, which can cause a small, but relatively deep, localized skin injury. However, it is possible to circumvent the pH changes caused by water hydrolysis by buffering the medium sufficiently to prevent large pH swings (92).

Another aspect of electrode design is prevention of accumulation of unwanted ions as iontophoresis current accumulates. For example, if the drug is anionic and is being delivered from the cathode, for the Ag/AgCl system, the concentration of chloride ions in the medium will increase over time and will eventually compete with the drug for the available current flow. This would cause a steady decrease in drug transport over the duration of the iontophoresis application period.

Applications of Iontophoresis

Several local and subcutaneous conditions have been treated by iontophoresis. Lidocaine iontophoresis for localized analgesia is a common commercial application (93,94). The Iontocaine® (Iomed, Salt Lake City) is a U.S. FDA–approved combination drug–device system. Topical epinephrine (93), dexamethasone, hydrocortisone (95), and prednisolone has been reported. Antiinflammatory drugs (e.g., diclofenac and ketoprofen) have been given to relieve pain, and steroids and retinoids have been used to treat scarring (46). Other local applications include delivery of antivirals and corticosteroids for herpes infections (96). Irritation reduction by administration of antiflammin 1 peptide has been demonstrated (97). Iomed (Salt Lake City), Iontophor-PM (Life-Tech, Houston, TX), and other companies also produce commercial power supplies with multipurpose electrode reservoirs and electrodes for iontophoresis, which are marketed primarily for localized applications.

Systemic administration of drugs is also possible. Fentanyl is in clinical trials for pain relief (46). Apomorphine, for treatment of idiopathic Parkinson's disease, has been tested in human subjects (37,98). Peptide drugs have been a major target of iontophoresis, and various reviews are available (1,2,4,5,41,99–101). Peptides that have been tested include thyotropin release hormone (56), various series of amino acid derivatives and tripeptides (45,60,62), LH-RH and analogs (23,38,57), vasopressin (5,71,73,75), and calcitonin (102,103). Transdermal delivery of insulin has been reported in vitro and in animal models (41,54,55,77,104–110).

There are applications of iontophoresis in addition to transdermal delivery of a therapeutic agent, and in fact some of these have been the most commercially successful applications (111). Hyperhydrosis, excessive sweating, has been successfully treated with application of iontophoretic current and no additional therapeutic agent (112–116). The Drionic device (General Medical Products, Los Angeles) is a commercial example. Iontophoresis has been applied to the eye to deliver compounds intraocularly (117–121), to the teeth to reduce hypersensitivity (96,122,123), across the nail (124), and to the ear (125). One of the first commercial uses of iontophoresis was for a cystic fibrosis diagnostic test (126): Iontophoresis is used to deliver pilocarpine to the skin to induce sweating, and the sweat is collected and tested for chloride content, which is used as a diagnostic marker for cystic fibrosis (127,128). This device is available from Wescor, Inc. (Logan, Utah). A newer application of iontophoresis is to extract substances from the body for diagnostic purposes (129–131). Proof of concept of this application for a noninvasive glucose-monitoring system for diabetics has been established. The electroosmotically extracted glucose flux was found to be proportional to the concentration of glucose in the blood (132).

ELECTROPORATION

Basic Principles

Electroporation involves the application of a short, high-voltage pulse across a lipid membrane, which creates transient pores in the lipid bilayers, a phenomenon sometimes known as reversible electrical breakdown (REB) (133). Electroporation has been used for a number of years in cell biology and biophysics, primarily as a method to introduce DNA into isolated cells (134–136). The idea of applying electroporation to whole tissues to increase permeability for drug delivery is a relatively recent development (137). Electropermeabilization of tissue has been used to deliver chemotherapy agents to tumors in vivo, increasing the efficacy of uptake of the agent into the tumors and thus improving effectiveness of the chemotherapy (138–143). Electroporation has also been used to deliver DNA into intact tissue in vivo (144,145). Pioneering work by Prausnitz et al. on transdermal electroporation demonstrated enhanced delivery of molecules through the skin after application of short, high-voltage pulses (146). Electroporation of mammalian skin was shown to increase flux by up to four orders of magnitude over passive delivery for three polar molecules with molecular weights up to slightly more than 1,000 Da. Studies on hairless rats showed similar increases in flux in vivo. After the pulsing was stopped, transdermal flux decreased by more than 99% within 1 or 2 h, indicating significant reversibility of the permeability increase. The transient nature of the permeability change is consistent with the proposal that there is reversible electric breakdown in the skin lipid layers.

There is strong evidence in the literature that in isolated cells, electroporation causes the molecules in the lipid bilayer of the cell membrane to reorient themselves to form a transient hydrophilic pore. After the pulse application is stopped, the pores can reseal over a period of milliseconds to hours, depending on the duration and magnitude of the applied pulse. This allows large molecules, such as DNA, to get into the cell but allows for resealing so that the cell retains viability. The lipid bilayer structure of the skin suggests that it could also be effectively electroporated. However, the skin lipid layers are multilamellar and are composed of different types of lipids than unilamellar cell membranes, so the conditions for skin and cell electroporation may differ. The required transdermal potential to create sufficient transbilayer potentials in the multiple lipid bilayers of the skin for electroporation is in the tens to hundreds of volts. The pulse duration can be a

square or an exponentially decaying capacitive discharge, with time constants in the micro- to millisecond range.

Comparison of Tissue Electroporation and Iontophoresis

Although electroporation and iontophoresis both involve application of an electric current across the skin, the mechanism of transport enhancement is generally accepted to be different. Iontophoresis enhances transport through the electric field–gradient driving force. Electroporation enhances the permeability of the skin by altering skin structure. Any driving force—iontophoretic, passive, electroosmotic—can be applied postelectroporation to effect flux enhancement compared with nonelectroporated skin. At this time, the mechanism for electroporation of skin is not as well understood as for cell membranes. Actual visualization of the pores is difficult, owing to their small size and fluctuating nature, so lipid reorientation to form hydrophilic pores must be inferred.

There is mounting evidence that electroporation creates dramatic alterations of the skin structure, as shown from studies of skin permeability changes, skin electrical impedance, microscopic imaging, and mathematical modeling (147). Studies of calcein flux showed that there is a sharp increase in skin flux at a threshold of about 60 V across the skin, followed by linear transport increases and then a plateau. The flux rapidly decreases when pulsing is stopped. The sudden increase in permeability once a voltage threshold has been attained and the reversibility of the permeability increase suggest that the mechanism of enhanced transport in skin lipids may be similar to that of electroporation in individual cells. Studies of the electrical properties of the skin demonstrated that changes in the skin barrier properties from pore formation did occur during high-voltage pulsing and did not occur during low-voltage iontophoresis (148,149). Confocal microscopy, a technique that images fluorescent molecules within the skin, has shown localized transport regions associated with electroporation that are not present under iontophoretic conditions (150,151). These regions may be associated with altered skin structure resulting from electroporation. Modeling of theoretical flux under low- and high-field strengths has led to the hypothesis that electroporation causes a unique form of transport enhancement (152).

Examinations of the transport number to compare efficiency of transport between electroporated and nonelectroporated skin have been reported. The flux of calcein, a highly charged model compound, was compared under a series of high-voltage pulses versus low-voltage iontophoresis. Enhancement of transport efficiency for both small and large ions was demonstrated (153). Electroporation has been used in conjunction with iontophoresis, and studies of the effect of electroporation on iontophoretic transport number were performed. Transdermal skin flux under iontophoresis of LH-RH, vasopressin, and neurotensin were three to eight times greater after the application of a single electroporative pulse than the same iontophoretic current without the pulse. This suggests some modification of the skin transport properties due to the electroporative pulse (154).

Conversely, Higuchi et al. have hypothesized that traditional low-voltage iontophoresis induces pore formation and that large-voltage pulses are not necessary (26,155,156). It is well documented that regular iontophoresis has been shown to increase passive skin permeability and change the electrical properties of the skin (61). However, it is uncertain whether this is actual electroporation of the lipid bilayers of the skin or some other phenomenon. In a combined theory, it has been proposed that application of voltages in the 1- to 5-V range, levels found in typical iontophoresis, causes electroporation through breakdown of the epithelial cells lining the walls of the skin appendages (sweat ducts and/or hair follicles). Further increases in voltage to tens of volts can cause the stratum corneum lipid lamellae to form pores, but the authors propose that such a pathway is not sufficient to provide a continuous pathway for effective transport. They suggest that a combination of passage through the keratinocytes and lipid bilayers is the transport pathway in high-voltage, pulsed electroporation (157).

Applications of Skin Electroporation

Practical application of electroporation is less advanced than for iontophoresis. A number of researchers have completed initial studies of potential applications of electroporation. Faster response has been suggested as an advantage of electroporation over iontophoresis and passive transdermal delivery, which could be an advantage for pain management applications (158). Vanbever et al. have studied the kinetics of transport of fentanyl, an analgesic therapeutic agent, both in vitro (159) and in vivo (160). Effective analgesia was achieved in hairless rats with rapid onset. Vanbever studied transport of metoprolol (161). Wang et al. have examined topical delivery of cyclosporin A for the treatment of psoriasis (162,163). Jadoul and Preat investigated electroporative and iontophoretic flux of domperidone (164). Delivery of various peptides are discussed by Potts et al. (165). Prausnitz et al. studied transdermal delivery of heparin, an anticoagulant. The anticoagulant activity of the delivered heparin was one-eighth of the donor heparin, indicating preferential transport of the small (less active) heparin molecules (166). The transport of DNA antisense oligonucleotides of 15 mer in length were demonstrated. Zewert et al. have proposed transdermal transport of anticancer nucleotides for treatment of melanomas (167).

Weaver et al. examined a method to increase the lifetime of the pathways created by electroporative pulses (168). It was hypothesized that long, highly charged molecules can act as separators, holding open the pathways in the lipid layers. Molecules such as heparin, dextran sulfate, neutral dextran, and polylysine were shown to enhance electroporation-assisted delivery of mannitol as a model compound. Postpulse skin permeability was higher and skin resistance was lower in the treated skin compared to control. The same molecules did not enhance passive or iontophoretic transport (169). Hofmann (170) and Zhang (171) have proposed enhancing the effect of electroporation of the skin by cocontacting the therapeutic agent with micron-sized particles, followed by the application of pressure. This method was studied for 2- to 20-μm Lupron Depot microspheres and the lacZ reporter gene. Addition-

ally, the use of electroporation in conjunction with encapsulation of the agent into vesicles has been proposed (170). Electroporation has also been studied in conjunction with ultrasound to synergistically enhance the effects of both methods (172).

Physiological Effects

Sensation caused by the pulsed current would be expected to be an issue in practical application of the technology. There has not been any significant testing on human subjects under the conditions for transdermal delivery. Studies of transcutaneous electrical neural stimulation (TENS), a technique of applying electrical pulses across the skin to reduce pain, show significant sensation associated with the method (173,174). The applied charge in TENS units are typically less than 25 μC, produced by 30 to 60 V of 200-μs duration or 500 V of 15-μs duration. This is substantially less than those used in in vitro skin electroporation studies (100 to 300 V for millisecond to tens of millisecond duration). The electroporative pulses also cause muscle contraction, which may not be acceptable for some applications. However, there are engineering designs to mitigate the sensation and muscle contracts caused by the pulses. Theoretical work has been done in designing systems to take the electrodes and tissue physiology into account. Closely spaced electrodes could effectively localize the electric field to the stratum corneum, where there are no nerve endings. Such localization would reduce or eliminate sensation, muscle contraction, and damage to underlying viable epidermal tissue

Because the use of electroporation across the skin is a new development, the physiological effects of skin electroporation have not yet been studied extensively. Riviere et al. (88) studied changes in the skin toxicology following electroporation. Vanbever et al. compared the irritation caused by iontophoresis and electroporation (175). In these studies, there was no additional irritation associated with electroporation compared to iontophoresis. On the other hand, tissue injury above that created by thermal burns that occur in accidents involving high-voltage power lines has been related to tissue electroporation causing damage to cell membranes in the injured area (176,177). However, the voltages and currents are at a much higher level than that used in skin electroporation, and the relevance to skin electroporation may be limited. Tissue electropermeabilization has been use in preliminary studies on human subjects to enhance tumor cell permeability for the treatment of squamous cell carcinoma (178). Subjects reported some sensation and muscle contraction associated with the electrical pulses but completed the treatment. The demonstration of human use of tissue electroporation suggests that transdermal electroporation is feasible in human subjects. Ultimately, more work on living skin tissue is needed to assess the viability of electroporation for practical drug delivery.

BIBLIOGRAPHY

1. B.G. Amsden and M.F.A. Goosen, *AIChE J.* **41**, 1972–1997 (1995).

2. M. Pikal, *Drug Target. Delivery* **4**, 83–109 (1995).

3. J.E. Riviere and M.C. Heit, *Pharm. Res.* **14**, 687–697 (1997).

4. C. Cullander and R.H. Guy, *Adv. Drug Delivery Rev.* **8**, 291–329 (1992).

5. Y.W. Chien et al., *J. Controlled Release* **13**, 263–278 (1990).

6. P.G. Green, M. Flanagan, B. Shroot, and R.H. Guy, in K.A. Walters and J. Hadgraft, eds., *Pharmaceutical Skin Penetration Enhancement*, Dekker, New York, 1993, vol. 59, pp. 311–333.

7. R.H. Guy, *Pharm. Res.* **13**, 1765–1769 (1996).

8. P. Singh and H.I. Maibach, *Crit. Rev. Ther. Drug Carrier Syst.* **11**, 161–213 (1994).

9. A.S. Michaels, S.K. Chandrasekaran, and J.E. Shaw, *AIChE J.* **21**, 985–996 (1975).

10. I. Steinstrasser and H.P. Merkle, *Pharm. Acta Helv.* **70**, 3–24 (1995).

11. N.A. Monteiro-Riviere, in D.W. Hobson, ed., *Dermal and Ocular Toxicology Fundamentals and Methods*, CRC Press, Boca Raton, Fla., 1991, pp. 3–18.

12. N.A. Monteiro-Riviere, in F.N. Marzulli and H.I. Maibach, eds., *Dermatotoxicology*, Taylor & Francis, Washington, D.C., 1996, pp. 3–18.

13. S. LeDuc, *Ann. D'Electrobiol.* **3**, 545–560 (1900).

14. R.R. Burnette and B. Ongpipattanakul, *J. Pharm. Sci.* **77**, 132–137 (1988).

15. H.A. Abramson and M.H. Gorin, *J. Phys. Chem.* **44**, 1094–1102 (1940).

16. C. Cullander and R.H. Guy, *J. Invest. Dermatol.* **97**, 55–64 (1991).

17. R.D. Lee, H.S. White, and E.R. Scott, *J. Pharm. Sci.* **85**, 1186–1190 (1996).

18. E.R. Scott, A.I. Laplaza, H.S. White, and J.B. Phipps, *Pharm. Res.* **10**, 1699 (1993).

19. N.G. Turner and R.H. Guy, *J. Pharm. Sci.* **86**, 1385–1389 (1997).

20. N. Monteiro-Riviere, A.O. Inman, and J.E. Riviere, *Pharm. Res.* **11**, 251–256 (1994).

21. B.D. Bath, R.D. Lee, H.S. White, and E. Scott, R., *Anal. Chem.* **70**, 1047–1058 (1998).

22. M.J. Pikal, *Adv. Drug. Delivery Rev.* **9**, 201–237 (1992).

23. M.B. Delgado-Charro and R.H. Guy, *Pharm. Res.* **11**, 929–935 (1994).

24. M.J. Pikal and S. Shah, *Pharm. Res.* **7**, 213–221 (1990).

25. M. Pikal and S. Shah, *Pharm. Res.* **7**, 222–229 (1990).

26. S.M. Sims, W.I. Higuchi, and V. Srinivasan, *Int. J. Pharm.* **69**, 109–121 (1991).

27. G.B. Kasting, *Adv. Drug Delivery Rev.* **9**, 177–199 (1992).

28. R.R. Burnette, in J. Hadgraft and R.H. Guy, eds., *Transdermal Drug Delivery: Developmental Issues and Research Initiatives*, Dekker, New York, 1989, vol. 35, pp. 274–291.

29. M.J. Pikal, *Pharm. Res.* **7**, 118–126 (1990).

30. R.R. Burnette and B. Ongpipattanakul, *J. Pharm. Sci.* **76**, 765–773 (1987).

31. J.B. Phipps and J.R. Gyory, *Adv. Drug Delivery Rev.* **9**, 137–176 (1992).

32. N.H. Bellantone, S. Rim, M.L. Francoeur, and B. Rasadi, *Int. J. Pharm.* **30**, 63–72 (1986).

33. J.B. Phipps, R.V. Padmanabhan, and G.A. Lattin, *J. Pharm. Sci.* **78**, 365–369 (1989).

34. P. Glikfeld, C. Cullander, R.S. Hinz, and R.H. Guy, *Pharm. Res.* **5**, 443–446 (1988).

35. R. Van Der Geest, M. Danhof, and H. E. Bodde, *J. Controlled Release* **51**, 85–91 (1998).

36. R.L. Bronaugh, in R.L. Bronaugh and H.I. Maibach, eds., *Percutaneous Absorption: Mechanisms-Methodology, Drug Delivery* Dekker, New York, 1989, Chapter 16.

37. R. Van Der Geest et al., *Pharm. Res.* **14**, 1804–1810 (1997).

38. M.C. Heit et al., *J. Pharm. Sci.* **82**, 240–243 (1993).

39. J.E. Riviere et al., *Fundam. Appl. Toxicol.* **7**, 444–453 (1986).

40. J.E. Riviere and N.A. Monteiro-Riviere, *CRC Crit. Rev. Toxicol.* **21** (1991).

41. B.H. Sage, Jr., R. Bock, J.D. DeNuzzio, and R.A. Hoke, *Drug Target. Delivery* **4**, 111–134 (1995).

42. M.S. Roberts, P.M. Lai, S.E. Cross, and N.H. Yoshida, *Drugs Pharm. Sci.* **83**, 291–349 (1997).

43. C.R. Behl et al., *J. Pharm. Sci.* **78**, 355–360 (1989).

44. J.B. Phipps, R.V. Padmanabhan, and G.A. Lattin, *Solid State Ionics* **28–30**, 1778–1783 (1988).

45. P.G. Green et al., *Pharm. Res.* **8**, 1113–1119 (1991).

46. V. Merino, Y. Kalia, and R.H. Guy, *Trends Biotechnol.* **15**, 288–290 (1997).

47. S. Del Terzo, C.R. Behl, and R.A. Nash, *Pharm. Res.* **6**, 85–90 (1989).

48. N.H. Yoshida and M.S. Roberts, *J. Controlled Release* **25**, 177–195 (1993).

49. N. Turner et al., *Pharm. Res.* **14**, 1322–1331 (1997).

50. S.B. Ruddy and B.W. Hadzija, *Drug Des. Discovery* **8**, 207–224 (1992).

51. A.J. Hoogstraate, V. Srinivasan, S.M. Sims, and W.I. Higuchi, *J. Controlled Release* **31**, 41–47 (1994).

52. J. Hirvonen and R.H. Guy, *Pharm. Res.* **14**, 1258–1263 (1997).

53. J. Hirvonen and R.H. Guy, *J. Controlled Release* **50**, 283–289 (1998).

54. J. Brange, *Diabetologia* **40**, S48–S53 (1997).

55. L. Langkjaer, J. Brange, G.M. Grodsky, and R.H. Guy, *J. Controlled Release* **51**, 47–56 (1998).

56. R.R. Burnette and D. Marrero, *J. Pharm. Sci.* **75**, 738–743 (1986).

57. L.L. Miller, C.J. Kolaskie, G.A. Smith, and J. Riviere, *J. Pharm. Sci.* **79**, 490–493 (1990).

58. P.C. Panus et al., *Pharm. Sci.* **2**, 467–469 (1996).

59. V. Srinivasan, W.I. Higuchi, and M.-H. Su, *J. Controlled Release* **10**, 157–165 (1989).

60. P.G. Green et al., *J. Controlled Release* **20**, 209–217 (1992).

61. P.G. Green, in K.R. Brain, V.J. James, and K.A. Walters, eds., *Prediction of Percutaneous Penetration*, Vol. 36, STS Publishing, Cardiff, U.K., 1993.

62. P.G. Green et al., *Pharm. Res.* **8**, 1121–1127 (1991).

63. R.R. Burnette and T.M. Bagniefski, *J. Pharm. Sci.* **77**, 492–497 (1988).

64. Y.N. Kalia, L.B. Nonato, and R.H. Guy, *Pharm. Res.* **13**, 957–960 (1996).

65. V. Srinivasan et al., *J. Pharm. Sci.* **78**, 370–375 (1989).

66. K. Okabe, H. Yamaguchi, and Y. Kawai, *J. Controlled Release* **4**, 79–85 (1986).

67. T. Bagniefski and R.R. Burnette, *J. Controlled Release* **11**, 113–122 (1990).

68. M.J. Pikal and S. Shah, *Pharm. Res.* **8**, 365–369 (1991).

69. S.K. Gupta et al., *J. Controlled Release* **30**, 253–261 (1994).

70. P. Lelawongs, J.-C. Liu, O. Siddiqui, and Y.W. Chien, *Int. J. Pharm.* **56**, 13–22 (1989).

71. B.H. Sage, R.A. Hoke, A.C. McFarland, and K. Kowalczyk, in K.R. Brain, V.J. James, and K.A. Walters, eds., *Prediction of Percutaneous Penetration*, Vol. 36, STS Publishing, Cardiff, U.K., 1993.

72. P. Santi and R.H. Guy, *J. Controlled Release* **38**, 159–165 (1996).

73. W.H.M. Craane-van Hinsberg, et al., *Pharm. Res.* **11**, 1296–1300 (1994).

74. S.Y. Oh, S.Y. Jeong, T.G. Park, and J.H. Lee, *J. Controlled Release* **51**, 161–168 (1998).

75. V. Srinivasan, M.-H. Su, W.I. Higuchi, and C.R. Behl, *J. Pharm. Sci.* **79**, 588–591 (1990).

76. K. Bhatia and J. Singh, *J. Pharm. Sci.* **87**, 462–469 (1998).

77. C.A. Zakzewski, J. Wasilewski, P. Cawley, and W. Ford, *J. Controlled Release* **50**, 267–272 (1998).

78. L. Wearley and Y.W. Chien, *Pharm. Res.* **7**, 34 (1990).

79. C.L. Gay, P.G. Green, R.H. Guy, and M.L. Francoeur, *J. Controlled Release* **22**, 57–68 (1992).

80. J.E. Riviere, B. Sage, and P.L. Williams, *J. Pharm. Sci.* **80**, 615–620 (1991).

81. K. Morimoto, Y. Kwakura, E. Nakatani, and M. Miyazaki, *Int. J. Pharm.* **81**, 119–125 (1992).

82. K. Morimoto et al., *J. Pharm. Pharmacol.* **44**, 216–218 (1992).

83. P.W. Ledger, *Adv. Drug Delivery Rev.* **9**, 289–307 (1992).

84. N.G. Turner, Y.N. Kalia, and R.H. Guy, *Pharm. Res.* **14**, 1252–1257 (1997).

85. N.K. Mize et al., *Exp. Dermatol.* **6**, 298–302 (1997).

86. B. Berner et al., *Pharm. Res.* **5**, 660–663 (1988).

87. N.A. Monteiro-Riviere, *Fundam. Appl. Toxicol.* **15**, 174–185 (1990).

88. J.E. Riviere et al., *J. Controlled Release* **36**, 229–233 (1995).

89. R. Van Der Geest et al., *J. Controlled Release* **41**, 205–213 (1996).

90. E. Camel et al., *Fundam. Appl. Toxicol.* **32**, 168–178 (1996).

91. C. Cullander, G. Rao, and R.H. Guy, in K.R. Brain, V.J. James, and K.A. Walters, eds., *Prediction of Percutaneous Penetration*, Vol. 36, STS Publishing, Cardiff, U.K., 1993.

92. J.E. Sanderson, S. de Riel, and R. Dixon, *J. Pharm. Sci.* **78**, 361–364 (1989).

93. J.M. Maloney, *Arch. Dermatol.* **128**, 331–333 (1992).

94. T. Petelenz et al., *J. Clin. Pharmacol. Ther. Toxicol.* **22**, 152–155 (1984).

95. W. Murray, L.S. LKavine, and E. Seifter, *J. Am. Phys. Ther. Assoc.* **43**, 579 (1963).

96. L.P. Gangarosa, Sr. and J.M. Hill, *Int. J. Pharm.* **123**, 159–171 (1995).

97. N.K. Mize et al., *Exp. Dermatol.* **6**, 181–185 (1997).

98. R. Van Der Geest, M. Danhof, and H. E. Bodde, *Pharm. Res.* **14**, 1798–1803 (1997).

99. S. Singh and J. Singh, *Med. Res. Rev.* **13**, 569–621 (1993).

100. W. Hinsberg, H.M. Craane-Van, J.C. Verhoef, and H.E. Bodde, *Drug Target. Delivery* **3**, 199–220 (1994).

101. J.-C. Liu and Y. Sun, *Drugs Pharm. Sci.* **62**, 247–272 (1994).

102. P. Santi et al., *Farmaco* **52**, 445–448 (1997).

103. S. Thysman, C. Hanchard, and V. Preat, *J. Pharm. Pharmacol.* **46**, 725 (1994).

104. Y.W. Chien et al., *Ann. N. Y. Acad. Sci.* **507**, 32–51 (1988).

105. Y.W. Chien et al., *J. Pharm. Sci.* **78**, 376–383 (1989).

106. B. Kari, *Diabetes* **35**, 217–221 (1986).

107. O. Siddiqui, Y. Sun, J.-C. Liu, and Y.W. Chien, *J. Pharm. Sci.* **76**, 341–345 (1987).

108. R.L. Stephen, T.J. Petelenz, and S.C. Jacobsen, *Biomed. Biochim. Acta* **43**, 553–558 (1984).

109. J.-C. Liu et al., *Int. J. Pharm.* **44**, 197–204 (1988).

110. Y. Tomohira, Y. Machida, H. Onishi, and T. Nagai, *Int. J. Pharm.* **155**, 231–239 (1997).

111. A. Banga and K., Y.W. Chien, *J. Controlled Release* **7**, 1–24 (1988).

112. E. Holzle and N. Alberti, *Dermatologica* **175**, 126–135 (1987).

113. K. Sato et al., *J. Appl. Physiol.* **78**, 2258–2264 (1993).

114. J.B. Sloan and K. Soltani, *J. Am. Acad. Dermatol.* **15**, 671–684 (1986).

115. R.L. Dobson, *Arch. Dermatol.* **123**, 883–884 (1987).

116. L.P. Stolman, *Arch. Dermatol.* **123**, 893–896 (1987).

117. M.O. Yoshizumi, A. Dessouki, D.A. Lee, and G. Lee, *J. Ocul. Pharmacol. Ther.* **13**, 529–536 (1997).

118. D. Sarraf and D.A. Lee, *J. Ocul. Pharmacol.* **10**, 1 (1994).

119. D.M. Maurice, *Ophthalmology* **93**, 128–132 (1986).

120. M. Barza, C. Peckman, and J. Baum, *Ophthalmology* **93**, 133–139 (1986).

121. J.M. Hill, Y. Shimomura, B.S. Kwon, and L.P. Gangarosa, *Invest. Ophthalmol. Visual Sci.* **26**, 1299–1303 (1985).

122. W.D. Lutkins, G.W. Greco, and W.T. McFall, Jr., *J. Am. Dent. Assoc.* **111**, 761–765 (1985).

123. K.M. Brough, D.M. Anderson, J. Love, and P.R. Overman, *J. Am. Dent. Assoc.* **111**, 761–765 (1985).

124. M.P. James, R.M. Graham, and J. English, *Clin. Exp. Dermatol.* **11**, 54–61 (1986).

125. R.T. Ramsden, W.P.R. Bigson, and D.A. Moffat, *J. Laryngol. Otolaryngol.* **91**, 779–785 (1977).

126. L.E. Gibson and R.E. Cooke, *Pediatrics* **23**, 545–549 (1959).

127. W.H. Yeung et al., *Clin. Pediatr.* **23**, 603–607 (1984).

128. C.R. Denning, N.N. Huang, and L.R. Cuasay, *Pediatrics* **66**, 752–757 (1980).

129. G. Rao, P. Glikfeld, and R. Guy, *Pharm. Res.* **10**, 1751–1755 (1993).

130. G. Rao et al., *Pharm. Res.* **12**, 1869–1873 (1995).

131. P. Glikfeld, R.S. Hinz, and R.H. Guy, *Pharm. Res.* **6**, 988–990 (1989).

132. J.A. Tamada, N.J.V. Bohannon, and R.O. Potts, *Nat. Med.* **1**, 1198–1201 (1995).

133. J.C. Weaver, *J. Cell. Biochem.* **51**, 426–435 (1993).

134. E. Neumann, A.E. Sowers, and C.A. Jordan, eds., *Electroporation and Electrofusion in Cell Biology*, Plenum, New York, 1989.

135. D.C. Chang, B.M. Chassy, J.A. Saunders, and A.E. Sowers, *Guide to Electroporation and Electrofusion*, Academic Press, New York, 1992.

136. R. Chakrabarti, D.E. Wyle, and S.M. Schuster, *J. Biol. Chem.* **264**, 15494–15500 (1989).

137. K.T. Powell, A.W. Morgenthaler, and J.C. Weaver, *Biophys. J.* **56**, 1163–1171 (1989).

138. L.M. Mir, S. Orlowski, J. Belehradek, Jr., and C. Paoletti, *Eur. J. Cancer* **27**, 63–72 (1991).

139. L. Mir, S. Orlowski, B. Poddevin, and J. Belehradek, Jr., *Eur. Cytokine Network* **3**, 331–334 (1992).

140. J. Belehradek et al., *Eur. J. Cancer* **27**, 73–76 (1991).

141. M. Okino et al., *Jpn. J. Cancer Res.* **83**, 1095–1102 (1992).

142. M. Okino and K. Esato, *Jpn. J. Surg.* **20**, 197–204 (1990).

143. M. Okino and H. Mohri, *Jpn. J. Cancer Res.* **78**, 1319–1321 (1987).

144. A. Titomirov, S. Sukharev, and E. Kistanova, *Biochim. Biophys. Acta* **1088**, 131–134 (1991).

145. R. Heller et al., *FEBS Lett.* **389**, 225–228 (1996).

146. M.R. Prausnitz, V.G. Bose, R. Langer, and J.C. Weaver, *Proc. Natl. Acad. Sci. U.S.A.* **90**, 10504–10508 (1993).

147. M.R. Prausnitz, *J. Controlled Release* **40**, 321–326 (1996).

148. U.L. Pliquett, R. Langer, and J.C. Weaver, *Biochim. Biophys. Acta* **1239**, 111–121 (1995).

149. U. Pliquett and J. Weaver, *J. Controlled Release* **38**, 1–10 (1996).

150. U. Pliquett et al., *Biophys. Chem.* **58**, 185–204 (1996).

151. M.R. Prausnitz *et al., J. Pharm. Sci.* **85**, 1363–1370 (1996).

152. D.A. Edwards, M.R. Prausnitz, R. Langer, and J.C. Weaver, *J. Controlled Release* **34**, 211–221 (1995).

153. M.R. Prausnitz et al., *J. Controlled Release* **38**, 205–217 (1996).

154. D.B. Bommannan, J. Tamada, L. Leung, and R.O. Potts, *Pharm. Res.* **11**, 1809–1814 (1994).

155. S.K. Li, A.-H. Ghanem, K.D. Peck, and W.I. Higuchi, *J. Pharm. Sci.* **87**, 40–48 (1998).

156. H. Inada, A.H. Ghanem, and W.I. Higuchi, *Pharm. Res.* **11**, 687–697 (1994).

157. Y.A. Chizmadzhev, V.G. Zarnitsin, J.C. Weaver, and R.O. Potts, *Biophys. J.* **68**, 749–765 (1995).

158. M.R. Prausnitz, U. Pliquett, R. Langer, and J.C. Weaver, *Pharm. Res.* **11**, 1834–1837 (1994).

159. R. Vanbever, G. Langers, S. Montmayeur, and V. Preat, *J. Controlled Release* **50**, 225–235 (1998).

160. R. Vanbever, E. Le Boulenge, and V. Preat, *Pharm. Res.* **13**, 559–565 (1996).

161. R. Vanbever, N. Lecouturior, and V. Preat, *Pharm. Res.* **11**, 1657–1662 (1994).

162. S. Wang, M. Kara, and T.R. Krishnan, *J. Controlled Release* **50**, 61–70 (1998).

163. S. Wang, M. Kara, and T.R. Krishnan, *Drug Dev. Ind. Pharm.* **23**, 657–663 (1997).

164. A. Jadoul and V. Preat, *Int. J. Pharm.* **154**, 229–234 (1997).

165. R.O. Potts et al., *Pharm. Biotechnol.* **10**, 213–238 (1997).

166. M.R. Prausnitz et al., *Bio/Technology* **13**, 1205–1209 (1995).

167. T.E. Zewert, U.F. Pliquett, R. Langer, and J.C. Weaver, *Biochem. Biophys. Res. Commun.* **212**, 286–292 (1995).

168. J.C. Weaver, R. Vanbever, T.E. Vaughan, and M.R. Prausnitz, *Biochem. Biophys. Res. Commun.* **234**, 637–640 (1997).

169. R. Vanbever, M.R. Prausnitz, and V. Preat, *Pharm. Res.* **14**, 638–644 (1997).

170. G.A. Hofmann, W.V. Rustrum, and K.S. Suder, *Bioelectrochem. Bioenerg.* **38**, 209–222 (1995).

171. L. Zhang et al., *Bioelectrochem. Bioenerg.* **42**, 283–292 (1997).

172. J. Kost et al., *Pharm. Res.* **13**, 633–638 (1996).

173. J.P. Reilly, *Electrical Stimulation and Electropathology*, Cambridge University Press, New York, 1992.

174. J.A. Balogun, *J. Sports Med. Phys. Fitness* **31**, 521–526 (1991).

175. R. Vanbever et al., *Skin Pharmacol. Appl. Skin Physiol.* **11**, 23–24 (1998).

176. R.C. Lee et al., *Proc. Natl. Acad. Sci. U.S.A.* **89**, 4524–4528 (1992).

177. R.C. Lee and M.S. Kolodney, *Plast. Reconstr. Surg.* **80**, 672–679 (1989).

178. L.M. Mir et al., *C.R. Sciences Acad. Sci.* **313**, 613–618 (1991).

See also Transdermal drug delivery, passive.

TRANSDERMAL DRUG DELIVERY, PASSIVE

Robert Gale
James Hunt
Mary E. Prevo
ALZA Corporation
Palo Alto, California

KEY WORDS

Absorption

In vitro

In vivo

Nonclinical toxicology

Permeation enhancement

Predictive models

Skin permeation

Transdermal

OUTLINE

INTRODUCTION

The use of the skin as a route of drug delivery has a long history; throughout the ages, many types of plasters and poultices have been used to treat various local and systemic complaints. It is only within the last 30 years that increased understanding of the skin and its barrier properties has allowed the development of more reliable and efficacious means of safely delivering therapeutic agents through the skin.

The skin functions as the largest organ in the body and is comprised of several layers that protect the underlying tissues. Absorption of chemicals by the skin may have substantive local and systemic consequences, and a number of factors influence the rate and extent of chemical transport through human skin. A variety of qualitative and quantitative methods are used to determine percutaneous absorption of drugs, and the results of both in vitro and in vivo studies may be used to predict absorption in humans. It has been demonstrated that there are intraindividual and interindividual differences in percutaneous absorption; understanding these differences is key in the design of a reliable transdermal system. The use of predictive models is extremely important in preclinical testing of new transdermal formulations and drug delivery systems. These studies include assessment of transdermal drug permeability and the potential for drug toxicity; skin irritation, immunological responses, and systemic toxicity are also important testing parameters.

The simplest of today's transdermal or topical drug delivery systems incorporate a vehicle such as a liquid, gel, or cream for direct application to skin. Hydrocortisone lotions and acne treatments are prime examples of topical formulations. More recently, transdermal therapeutic systems have been introduced, offering a more sophisticated and more reliable means of administering drug through the skin. Greater understanding of the pharmacokinetics of percutaneously administered drugs has led to the development of rate-controlled systems with optimized delivery profiles, and the use of permeation enhancers has expanded the number of drugs that can be administered transdermally.

In the United States, transdermal systems are now used for analgesics (fentanyl), hormone replacement therapies (estradiol and testosterone), and for the treatment of angina (nitroglycerin), hypertension (clonidine), and motion sickness (scopolamine). Transdermal nicotine replacement therapy for smoking cessation is also available, and a number of other drugs are being studied for possible inclusion in transdermal systems. As compared with other means of drug administration, transdermal systems have been associated with improved bioavailability, sustained therapeutic effect, diminished side effects, and convenient, noninvasive use that allows easy termination of therapy.

In this article, a review of skin biology and permeability is provided, and a discussion of the predictive models and toxicology testing employed in the development of transdermal products is presented. An overview of marketed transdermal systems technology is also presented with an emphasis on product characteristics and the clinical performance measures of safety, efficacy, reliability, and acceptability of drug treatment.

STRUCTURE, COMPOSITION, AND FUNCTION OF SKIN

The skin and other tissues protect internal organs from heat, humidity, pollution, radiation, and other potential insults. Human skin is comprised of the unvascularized epidermis and the highly vascularized dermis just below it (Fig. 1). The external layer of the epidermis is called the stratum corneum, which in Latin means "horny layer." This layer of skin is considerably less permeable than the dermis itself and protects the more permeable skin layers beneath it. The human stratum corneum varies from 10 to 50 μm in thickness and is a heterogeneous structure of dead, flattened, interdigitated keratinocytes that are each 0.5–1.0 μm thick. The constituents of these cells are protein, water, and lipids, the latter are concentrated largely in the extracellular phase and serve to cement the structure together into a coherent membrane (1). The range of stratum corneum thickness varies depending upon anatomic location. On the palms of the hands and soles of the feet, the stratum corneum is adapted for friction and weight bearing, respectively, and is considerably thicker than at other locations. Below the stratum corneum, the living epidermis ranges from 50 to 100 μm and proliferates rapidly by cellular differentiation. Cells migrate from the basal layer toward the skin surface at a rate of one new cell layer per day and undergo keratinization as they approach the external skin surface; the stratum corneum is completely replaced every 15 to 30 days. The epidermis itself is capable of most biotransformation reactions that are seen in the liver; the specific enzyme activity of the skin sometimes surpasses that of the hepatic enzymes. Phase I reactions include oxidation, reduction, and hydrolytic reactions, and Phase II reactions are conjugation reactions such as methylation, glucuronidation, and sulfatation.

The dermis is relatively thick compared with the stratum corneum and epidermis, comprising approximately 2,000 μm and containing a matrix of connective tissue that is penetrated by nerves, blood vessels, and lymphatics. Localized structural features of the skin include the hair follicles, sweat glands, and sebaceous glands, which may serve as permeation pathways to the underlying vascular bed.

PERMEABILITY OF HUMAN SKIN

Although the skin serves as a barrier and was once thought to be virtually impermeable, it is now recognized as a permeable organ capable of local absorption that may have substantive systemic consequences. Many factors influence the rate and extent of drug transport through human skin.

Mechanism of Permeation

It has been clearly demonstrated that the mechanism of permeation through skin is a partition-diffusion process

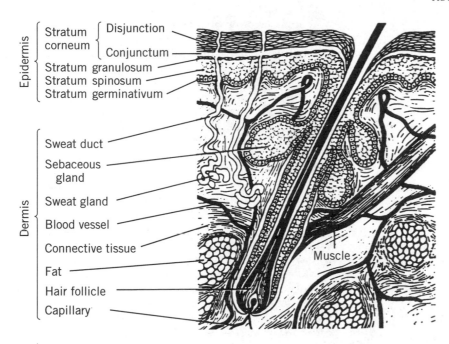

Epidermis
- Stratum corneum
  - Disjunction
  - Conjunctum
- Stratum granulosum
- Stratum spinosum
- Stratum germinativum

Dermis
- Sweat duct
- Sebaceous gland
- Sweat gland
- Blood vessel
- Connective tissue
- Fat
- Hair follicle
- Capillary

Muscle

Figure 1. Structure of normal skin. *Source:* From *Casarett and Doull's Toxicology: The Basic Science of Poisons* 3rd C.D. Klaassen, M.O. Amdur, and J. Doull, ed., Macmillan, New York, 1986, p. 414.

rather than an active process (2–5) and, therefore, follows the diffusion principles described by Fick (6). In skin that is intact, the major barrier to drug penetration is the stratum corneum with its bilayer arrays of lipids. These well-organized and repetitive arrangements of lipids form "seals" such that material exchange between the skin surface and the layers beneath it is inefficient. There are various micro routes of drug permeation that have been suggested (Fig. 2) (7).

Techniques for Measuring Skin Permeation

There are a number of methods, both qualitative and quantitative, that may be used to determine the extent and rate of percutaneous absorption of drugs. Results of in vitro and in vivo study may be used to predict absorption in humans (Fig. 3) (8).

In vivo methods. In vivo permeation may be measured by determining what remains of a known amount of a sub-

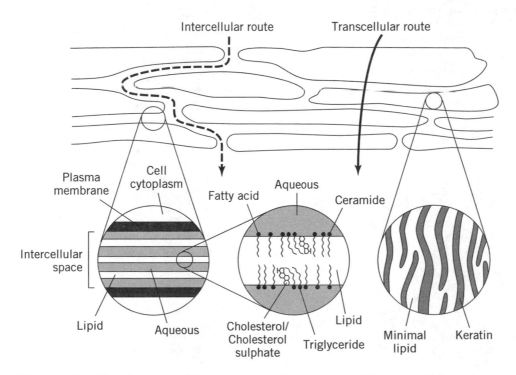

Intercellular route   Transcellular route

Plasma membrane   Cell cytoplasm   Fatty acid   Aqueous   Ceramide

Intercellular space

Lipid   Aqueous   Cholesterol/Cholesterol sulphate   Triglyceride   Lipid   Minimal lipid   Keratin

Figure 2. Possible microroutes of drug permeation through human skin—intercellular or transcellular pathways. *Source:* After Ref. 1.

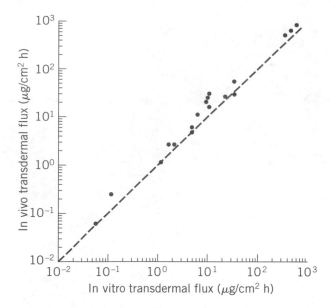

Figure 3. Correlation between in vivo and in vitro transdermal drug flux. Each data point represents a different drug. Dashed line indicates perfect correlation between in vivo and in vitro transdermal drug flux. *Source:* Ref. 8.

stance after it is applied to skin for a given time period. This "residual drug" method of determination is based on the assumption that the difference between the dose initially applied and the residual represents the amount of drug that permeated the skin and has been or will be absorbed by the underlying capillaries. In fact, the drug may have been absorbed in the epidermis or stratum corneum and metabolized in those structures. The "pharmacokinetic method" is an alternative and relies on measured serum or plasma concentrations and the predetermined clearance rate of the compound for calculation of the steady-state permeation rate. Variability in skin permeation between individuals or at different skin sites (Fig. 4) may confound these results.

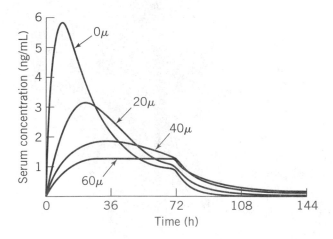

Figure 4. Effect of skin thickness on serum fentanyl concentrations (TTS (fentanyl)-100, 72h).

A number of other methods of determining skin permeation in vivo are also available. Topical application of a radiolabeled compound allows measurement of the amount of radioactivity in excreta, and the final amount of radioactivity is expressed as the percentage of the applied dose that was absorbed. Determination of percutaneous absorption by this method does not account for skin metabolism. Absolute bioavailability of a topically applied compound may be determined by measuring the compound by specific assay in blood or urine after topical and intravenous administration, but this is often difficult because drug plasma concentrations are frequently low after topical administration (9). Estimation of percutaneous absorption may also be determined by substituting a biological assay for a chemical assay and estimating (10); however, this method is only appropriate to use in studying compounds that elicit an easily measurable response.

Skin stripping may be used to determine the concentration of chemical in the stratum corneum after short-term topical exposure. The compound is applied to skin for a period of 30 minutes, and then the stratum corneum is removed by successive application and "stripping" of cellophane tape from the skin. Tape strippings are assayed for chemical content, and linear extrapolation predicts the percutaneous absorption of the chemical for longer application periods (11,12). This method eliminates the use of radiolabeled compounds and the need to measure absorption via excreta. More recently, a number of other methods for in vivo determination of percutaneous absorption have been reported, including infrared spectroscopy (13–15), microdialysis (16), and a laser-photoacoustic method for percutaneous absorptiometry (17).

In vitro methods. In vitro methods of determining the skin permeability of various substances may be more convenient; correlation of in vitro and in vivo flux of a variety of compounds has been described previously (8). In one method, skin specimens may be mounted as a membrane in a diffusion chamber with two compartments. The compound to be tested is placed in contact with the stratum corneum side of the skin at a relatively high concentration or level of activity, and an appropriate receptor vehicle is placed in the other compartment in contact with the dermal side of the skin. The diffusion chambers allow evaluation of mass-transport phenomena through the skin (18). Excised human or animal skin may be used, and the skin can be intact or separated from the epidermis (9). Apparent correlation of any of these data do, however, need to be verified with in vivo pharmacokinetic data. Another in vitro model that employs a partition coefficient of a drug or chemical in vehicle with powdered human stratum corneum has been used to determine the proportion of chemical bound to the skin particles (9).

Regional Differences in Permeation

Research has demonstrated the existence of both intraindividual and interindividual differences in percutaneous absorption. The extent of these differences varies considerably and is affected by the physiochemical nature of the penetrant (19). In evaluations of permeation rates that have tested skin from the same and different donors, regional intraspecimen variability has been shown to be less than regional interspecimen variability (20). Explanations for these regional differences have been ascribed to a variety of factors, including differences in blood flow, the thickness and lipid content of the stratum corneum, and the number of sweat ducts and hair follicles at the skin site. Percutaneous absorption may also be influenced by other conditions such as temperature, friction, and hydration of the skin (19).

Dermal absorption studies of polycyclic aromatic hydrocarbons demonstrate low but variable regional differences in absorption. Skin at the shoulder is two times more permeable than skin on the forearm; the skin of the ankle and at the palm of the hand is two times less permeable than that on the forearm (19). In vivo permeation of caffeine, benzoic acid, and acetylsalicylic acid have also been demonstrated to be site dependent (12), as has the permeability of scopolamine (Fig. 5) (21). In the latter study, the postauricular epidermis was shown to be about twice as permeable as specimens from the trunk and was even more permeable than epidermis from the forearm and thigh. Scrotal skin has been shown to be considerably more permeable than skin at other anatomic locations; this phenomenon is thought to be the result of its superficial vascularity (22).

Study of in vitro permeation of fentanyl and sufentanil at different skin sites yielded results that contrasted with those of in vivo studies (23). The permeability coefficients obtained on skin from a single cadaver at the upper arm, thigh, abdomen, chest, and sole of the foot were all quite similar. Fentanyl, however, was less permeable at the sole of the foot than at other sites. Both drugs are quite permeable due to high lipophilicity (favoring partitioning in the stratum corneum), and thus their in vitro permeation rates through cadaver skin may not be influenced greatly by skin site. Differences in age and gender did not appear to affect the permeation of these drugs.

Skin permeability frequently differs among patients, leading investigators to study the effects of age, gender, and race on percutaneous absorption using a variety of chemical agents. Advancing age appears to compromise

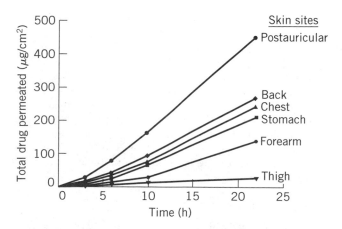

Figure 5. Variation in cumulative scopolamine flux as a function of skin site.

skin, causing the epidermis to atrophy, the dermoepidermal junction to flatten, and the dermis to thin. The majority of published literature indicates that irritant and allergic inflammatory reactions are weaker in older subjects. There is a lack of consensus, however, as to whether there are measurable differences in percutaneous absorption between young and old subjects (24). Gender differences in percutaneous absorption have been postulated, but in general, no significant gender-related differences in barrier integrity or barrier recovery have been found (25). Study of skin structure indicates that the thickness and lipid content of stratum corneum of men and women is similar (26).

The question of whether or not there are racial differences in percutaneous absorption is difficult to answer with complete certainty. Wester and colleagues (27) and Lotte and colleagues (28) studied the percutaneous absorption of benzoic acid, caffeine, and acetylsalicylic acid and found no significant differences in absorption between Asians, Blacks, and Caucasians (Fig. 6). However, a study of nitroglycerin absorption indicates Black subjects had lower systemic drug concentrations than Asians or Caucasians (29). Black skin also showed increased resistance to tape stripping as compared with Caucasian skin and has been thought to resist chemical irritation better than lighter skin. This general assumption, however, may be based primarily on differences in the appearance of erythema, which is far more difficult to detect in Black skin than in light-colored skin (9).

Transepidermal Water Loss and Water Content of the Stratum Corneum

The measurement of transepidermal water loss (TEWL) and the water content of the stratum corneum provide important information about skin function and integrity. The skin loses water as vapor, which evaporates from the skin surface. Occlusion of the surface prevents water loss and increases the water content of the stratum corneum. Healthy skin is characterized by direct proportionality of TEWL and hydration of the skin. Damage to the skin raises TEWL as compared with that of intact skin (30).

In its fully hydrated state, the permeability of the stratum corneum to water can be substantially higher than during its normal state. Occlusion of human skin with vinylidiene polymer film indicated skin was fully saturated with water within 24 hours and reverted to preocclusion values within 18 hours of film removal (31). The increasing permeability of skin under occlusion is attributed to an increasing fluidity of the stratum corneum that is induced by moisture.

Immature, Diseased, or Damaged Skin

Changes in the integrity of skin affect TEWL. The immature skin of infants with a gestational age of less than 36 weeks has significantly greater TEWL than that of a full-term infant (32). In infants over 37 weeks of gestational age, however, TEWL is lower than in adults, suggesting a more efficient stratum corneum. As the skin ages, TEWL and hydration decrease, maintaining their directly proportional relationship. In people over 60 years of age, a number of factors may contribute to decreased TEWL, includ-

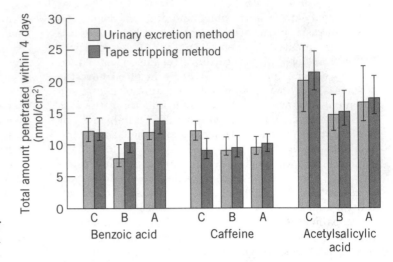

Figure 6. Influence of race on percutaneous absorption of benzoic acid, caffeine, and acetylsalicylic acid in Caucasian (C), Black (B), and Asian (A) subjects. *Source:* After Ref. 28.

ing increases in the size of corneocytes and in the thickness of stratum corneum, the latter is likely related to impaired desquamation of corneocytes (30).

In skin that is damaged or diseased, there is an inverse correlation between TEWL and the stratum corneum water content; the lower the skin hydration, the higher the TEWL (Fig. 7). Alteration of the skin barrier and/or the keratinization of cells are thought to be potential causes of defective stratum corneum water-holding capacity (30). Hyperproliferative diseases, such as psoriasis and exfoliative dermatitis, may lead to significant increases in TEWL due to weakening of the permeation barrier (33). Although this damaged skin is frequently thickened, increased percutaneous absorption is characteristic in patients with inflamed eczematous skin (34,35). Essential fatty acid deficiency or ultraviolet radiation damage may also induce epidermal hyperproliferation and increase TEWL and percutaneous absorption (36–38). TEWL may also be increased by tape stripping or abrading the skin surface; permeability is increased in these settings (36).

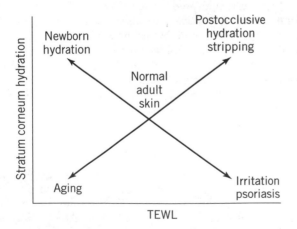

Figure 7. Relationship between TEWL and skin surface hydration. The quantification of hydration and transepidermal water loss may allow the differentiation between physiologic dry skin and pathologic dry skin. In the latter, damage to the water barrier is present. *Source:* After Ref. 30.

PERMEABILITY MODELS FOR STRATUM CORNEUM

The use of a model to predict skin permeability is important in determining the local and systemic characteristics of transdermal drug administration and in providing an understanding of the skin's barrier properties. Several types of models have proven useful in predicting skin permeability to penetrants.

Effects of Stratum Corneum Lipids on Diffusivity

The lipid components of skin appear to play a significant role in the permeability of the stratum corneum. Delipidizing the tissue with a solvent such as a chloroform–methanol mixture removes lipid components without discernible mechanical or morphological alteration of the membrane. The water permeability of the delipidized, hydrated stratum corneum is three to four times greater than that of the normal tissue, and its permeability to larger molecules may be as much as six times greater than that of normal tissue (5).

The importance of lipids as a primary permeability barrier is evidenced by the "brick and mortar" model in which lipids are envisioned as a mortar that holds keratinized stratum corneum cells together (39). Clinical evidence—such as abnormally high TEWL seen in patients with essential fatty acid deficiencies or abnormalities of keratinocytes related to lipid impairment in the stratum corneum—supports the idea that an intact lipid phase is crucial to the integrity of the stratum corneum (1). Permeability of a substance is determined by its solubility and diffusivity in the aqueous protein and lipid phases of the stratum corneum (40). Bearing these principles in mind, low rates of permeability are associated with substances that possess low aqueous or lipid solubility, whereas highly water- or lipid-soluble compounds exhibit relatively high permeation rates (41).

Predictive Models

Several predictive models for skin permeation have been developed. A two-compartment model employs a mineral oil–water partition coefficient and accounts for the water solubility of penetrant molecules to generate a predicted maximum permeation rate through human epidermis in vitro (39). A stratum corneum diffusion model based on ion–dipole and lipid–lipid interactions resulted in drug flux equations that predicted a linear dependence of flux on the dipole moment of penetrant and on the solubility of penetrant models in a cosolvent system (Fig. 8) (42). The model assumes two separate diffusion pathways for polar and lipid-soluble compounds as follows: (*1*) the skin permeation rate of polar compounds decreases in a linear fashion with interactions between the penetrant dipole and ionized amino acids in the stratum corneum; and (*2*) the nonpolar penetrants interact with the van der Waals and other dispersion forces in tissue. Another skin permeation model, in which the stratum corneum is treated as a homogeneous, passive lipid membrane, indicates the maximum percutaneous absorption rate is a function of molecular weight and melting point. Molecular weight is assumed to affect diffusivity, whereas melting point is assumed to predict the solubility of the penetrant in the stratum corneum lipids (43).

In contrast to the phenomenological approaches used in the predictive models already described, Lien and Gao (44) pioneered a model based on a classic quantitative structure activity relationship. These authors considered as predominant permeability factors the octanol–water partition coefficient, hydrogen bonding characteristics, and the molecular weight of drug molecules. The former two properties are estimated from the structures of drugs. A good log-linear relationship between skin permeability and these three molecular properties was obtained for selected drugs (Fig. 9). Depending on the vehicles used, the opti-

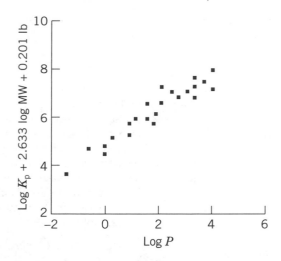

Figure 9. Log K_p after correcting for differences in log MW and H_6 vs log P (Equation 8, $n = 23$, $r = 0/965$, $s = 0.361$). *Source:* After Ref. 44.

mum octanol–water partition coefficient of drug for a maximum skin permeability changes. However, the hydrogen-bonding has a negative effect on the skin permeability. As in the phenomenological models, the molecular weight always has a negative effect on the permeability.

ANIMAL MODELS FOR PERCUTANEOUS ABSORPTION

The use of animal models is less than ideal in predicting the percutaneous absorption of chemicals in man. However, many compounds are potentially toxic and must be tested first in vitro or in vivo in animals to determine relative safety for experimentation in humans. In general, primates and miniature pigs are thought to be relatively good models for human percutaneous absorption, whereas the smaller laboratory animals (rabbit, rat, mouse) are poor animal models (9). The Rhesus monkey and the marmoset have demonstrated particular usefulness as models for human skin permeability (9,45).

The skin permeability of certain compounds as tested in the guinea pig and hairless mouse were also comparable to that of human skin (36). Hairless animal skin has the advantage of not requiring any shaving prior to testing. Although it has been hypothesized that the hair follicle represents a cutaneous absorption pathway, the skin of hairless guinea pigs has been shown to be much more permeable to some compounds than the skin of haired guinea pigs (46).

Lipids extracted from skin have utility in the preparation of skin models and for study of the effects of various compounds on stratum corneum lipids (47). Simple in vitro skin models have been prepared by air-drying liposomal suspensions containing epidermal ceramides, cholesterol, free fatty acids, and cholesterol sulfate on hydrophilic filter disks (48). Water permeabilities through these filter-supported lipid lamellae were measured using a diffusion cell; the ultrastructure was characterized by scanning and thin-section electron microscopy. Water flux data and the

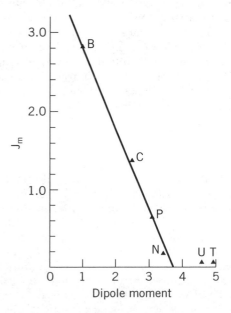

Figure 8. Regression of dipole versus absorption rate. J_m maximum percutaneous absorption rate (%/h); B. benzoic acid dipole moment; C, caffeine dipole moment; N, nicotinamide dipole moment; P, *p*-aminobenzoic acid dipole moment; U, urea dipole moment; T, thiourea dipole moment. *Source:* After Ref. 42. Reproduced with permission of the copyright owner, the American Pharmaceutical Association.

ultrastructure of the model were shown to be similar to that of the native human stratum corneum.

TOXICOLOGY

The assessment of the potential for drug toxicity is an important consideration in the evaluation of any transdermal drug candidate. Toxic consequences of percutaneous administration may include skin irritation, immunological responses, and systemic toxicity. Many factors influence absorption of and skin response to a compound; the dose, concentration, occlusion, vehicle, mode and site of application, frequency of use, skin physiology, and the nature of the compound are all important variables.

Skin Metabolism

The metabolic activity of the skin can alter the delivery profile and pharmacologic effects of substances that undergo percutaneous absorption. A topically applied drug can be transformed into either active or inactive metabolites that are capable of different levels of toxicity than the parent compound (27). For example, epidermal keratinocytes have the potential to metabolize propranolol via a pathway that includes formation of an aldehyde intermediate (49). Changes in the pharmacologic or toxicologic profile that result from skin metabolism may have local as well as systemic effects.

In Vivo Testing

Irritation. Reliable testing for skin irritation should provide a means for differentiating substances that produce different degrees of skin irritation. In this context, irritation is the local inflammatory response of normal living skin to direct injury by single, repeated, or prolonged contact with a chemical agent. Macroscopic manifestations of such irritation are erythema and edema. Acute and subchronic irritation testing is used to place compounds into general groups according to their irritant properties. The most standardized toxicological procedures are based on the methods described by Draize, Woodard, and Calvery (50). The primary irritation of the skin is measured by the skin patch technique on intact and intentionally abraded skin of albino rabbits. In contrast, the subchronic skin irritation test measures the cumulative irritation on intact skin that has been exposed to the chemical agent for an extended amount of time. The Draize rabbit skin irritancy test is valuable for its ability to distinguish between chemical agents that are moderate to severe irritants. This method of testing, however, does not allow accurate distinctions between mild and moderate irritants.

Sensitization. Toxicological study also includes evaluation of hypersensitivity. The guinea pig and, more recently, the hairless guinea pig strain, have been widely accepted as the animals of choice for studying this phenomenon because of their genetically based proclivities to sensitization (51). These animals may be used as predictive models to study mechanisms involved in contact sensitization to therapeutic agents. Compounds intended for cutaneous application that are capable of producing sensitization are readily identified by predictive testing (51). The hairless guinea pig has all the humoral and cellular components necessary for sensitization and is responsive to known sensitizers (52,53). A parallel does exist in the sense that the strong and weak sensitizers in man are, respectively, the strong and weak sensitizers of the guinea pig (54–56).

Contact sensitivity is characterized by cellular mediated (thymocyte) allergic reactions of the skin that may be induced by a single contact or may require repeated contacts with the sensitizer, with or without potentiation (57). Potentiation may be provided by physical or chemical irritants such as sodium lauryl sulfate (used in the Kligman Maximization Test) (58) or by immunopotentiators such as Freund's complete adjuvant. The ensuing sensitization response develops slowly on challenge and may require from 8 to 35 hours to appear; it generally persists for 24 hours or more.

Freund's complete adjuvant test is an appropriate method for screening single chemical substances for their immunogenic properties. It is a semiquantitative method for measuring the minimal concentration needed to elicit a response in sensitized animals. The test can establish the allergenicity of a chemical substance, but it cannot establish the actual risk of contact sensitization under conditions of use (51).

In Vitro Testing

Irritation. Organ and cell cultures can help predict whether or not application of some agents results in damage to keratinocytes or to other types of cells. Endpoints used to assess cytotoxicity include cell growth, which may be determined by protein analysis and cell counts. In addition, characteristics such as enzyme release, release of radioactive markers, exclusion of dyes, metabolism, and plating efficiency are all measurable endpoints of cell function. Because these endpoints involve active cellular processes, false-negative results are infrequent. In contrast, tests that interfere with passive structures such as the cell membrane may yield false negatives because testing agents that kill by fixation preserve structural components of the membrane (59). Other types of assays measure sublethal and lethal endpoints.

In vitro testing includes direct and indirect test methods. The latter involve testing individual components or combinations of chemicals as extracts. The types of characteristics not measured by in vitro assays are those that are time dependent or reversible; likewise, complex in vivo interactions are not measured by in vitro assays. The atypical pharmacokinetic profile seen with some compounds may produce changes in vitro that are normally not seen in vivo. It has been reported that the high in vitro toxicity associated with some agents is not representative of local irritation in vivo. When choosing a testing strategy, investigators are wise to select a battery of in vitro assays that assess both active and passive cellular processes.

The use of standard in vitro testing may link the study of toxicity and its mechanism (60). In vitro testing that employs standardized methods can determine a maximum tolerated concentration and the concentration that reduces a study parameter by 50% of the control value. The neutral red uptake assay, for example, is a test in which the drug effects on the membrane or its ability to alter lysosomes then influences binding of the cationic dye to anionic sites in the lysosome matrix (61). In another similar assay, the metabolic reduction of 3-(4,5-dimethylthiozol-2-yl)-2,5-diphenyltetrazolium bromide (MTT) by cells results in formation of a blue formazon dye (62). Modification of this MTT assay has allowed its use for screening of compounds for their in vitro cytotoxicity in human keratinocytes (63). Inhibitory concentration values, such as the IC_{50}, represent the molar concentration of the drug compound required to kill 50% of fibroblast cells and are also used in screening of compounds for in vitro toxicity (64).

Sensitization. Evaluating the potential for sensitization may include assay of the lymphokines released by antigens from sensitized lymphocytes and lymphocyte proliferation assays (60). Another assay is the murine lymph node assay that studies lymphocyte proliferation and provides both objective and quantitative results. A modification of this procedure involves occluded application of the compound on the shaved abdomen of the animal for 24 hours. Another application is repeated on day 5 and on day 6; the animals are sacrificed, and the brachial and inguinal lymph nodes are removed. Measurement of the spontaneous proliferation capacity of cells seeded in the microtiter well is measured by incorporation of [³H]thymidine. A percent stimulation index is calculated by dividing test-cell incorporation by control-cell incorporation. Results may be correlated with those obtained from in vivo guinea pig sensitization assays. The murine node lymph assay provides a relatively simple, rapid, and inexpensive way to identify agents that exhibit moderate to strong sensitizing potential.

Other Preclinical Testing Requirements

In addition to the determination of irritation and sensitization potential, drugs that are to be used in pharmaceutical products must undergo standardized preclinical testing as part of the requirements for marketing approval. The U.S. FDA considers transdermal drugs as if they were new drugs. Transdermal products that include approved drugs are likely to be approved more readily, however. It is widely accepted that transdermal systems generally produce plasma levels of drug that are considerably lower than those resulting from other administration methods; systemic safety may be less of a concern in such cases.

TRANSDERMAL DRUG DELIVERY

Since the introduction of the first transdermal therapeutic system, the field of transdermal drug delivery has advanced rapidly through greater understanding of the mechanisms, variables, and measurement of percutaneous absorption. Greater understanding of the pharmacokinetics of percutaneously administered drugs has led to the development of systems with optimized delivery profiles. Use of permeation enhancers has increased the number of drugs available for transdermal therapy. The potential ad-

vantages of rate-controlled transdermal therapy include the following:

- Improved bioavailability for many drugs
- Reliable blood levels of drug
- Sustained therapeutic effect, allowing use of drugs with short half-lives
- Diminished side effects
- Daily, multiday, or weekly dosing to improve patient compliance
- Simple, noninvasive administration, particularly important for patients who are unable to take medication orally
- Reduced overall treatment costs in many instances

These advantages of transdermal therapy may yield enhanced safety, efficacy, reliability, and acceptability of drug treatment.

Permeation Enhancement

Chemical Enhancers. The skin's physical structure provides a barrier that may limit the permeation of some agents. Skin permeation enhancers broaden the range of drugs that can be delivered transdermally by increasing the penetration of permeants through enhanced diffusion of the stratum corneum and/or by increasing the solubility of the penetrant. Protein denaturation may disrupt the barrier as may fluidization and randomization of intercellular lipids or intercellular delamination and expansion (65).

Ideally, a permeation enhancer functions only to reduce the barrier resistance of the stratum corneum and does not damage any viable cells. The necessary attributes of an enhancer have been reviewed by Barry (7); the ideal enhancer is:

- Pharmacologically inert
- Nontoxic
- Nonirritating
- Nonallergenic
- Rapid-acting with a duration of activity that is predictable and suited to its use
- Chemically compatible and easily formulated into a variety of systems
- Inexpensive
- Odorless
- Tasteless
- Colorless

The enhancer should not extract endogenous material out of the skin but should spread well on skin and have a suitable skin feel. If the substance is a liquid and is to be used at high volume fractions, it should be a suitable solvent for drugs (7).

There are numerous chemical permeation enhancers now being used to facilitate transdermal drug administration. Solvents are frequently used and include alcohol, dimethyl sulfoxide, dimethylformamide, dimethylacetamide, propylene glycol, pyrrolidones, and water. Other enhancers include Azone® and its derivatives, surfactants, fatty acids, terpenes and their derivatives, alkyl sulfoxides, phosphine oxides, sugar esters, urea and its long chain analogues, N,N-diethyl-m-toluamide, calcium thioglycolate, and anticholinergic agents (7).

Ethanol has been used very successfully as a permeation enhancer in a variety of commercial transdermal systems (66), including those that deliver estradiol and fentanyl. Pure ethanol-enhanced permeation of solutes across the skin in vitro is thought to be a result of the extraction of skin lipids by ethanol, but apparent diffusivity has not been significantly altered in in vivo studies (67). For example, the flux of estradiol across viable human skin was shown to be increased in vivo only with saturated solutions of estradiol, indicating the increased solubility of estradiol in ethanol and an increased concentration gradient of estradiol across the skin. Knowledge of the apparent partitioning of the solute into the stratum corneum and the solute concentration in the vehicle allow prediction of the flux of estradiol across human skin in vivo.

More recently, use of composite lipidic agent-carriers such as liposomes and niosomes has been tried. These agents have been less successful than conventional enhancers because of their inability to pass through the narrow intracellular passages in the outer skin layers. A more deformable supramolecular aggregate known as the transfersome has been described and is thought to use the transepidermal gradient as a means of permeation enhancement. Successful use of transfersomes to achieve transcutaneous peptide and protein delivery in animals and in humans has been reported (Fig. 10) (47).

Epidermal enzymes have also been identified as potentially valuable permeation enhancers in transdermal drug delivery (68). It has been demonstrated that epidermal enzymes play an important role in the differentiation of keratinocytes, and that epidermal phospholipids undergo enzymatic conversion to nonpolar species and contribute to the barrier function of the stratum corneum. In vitro study of the role of these enzymes on the permeation of benzoic acid, mannitol, and testosterone in an excised human skin model reveal that enzymes may have remarkable effects on the permeation of topically applied compounds. Of the enzymes studies (phospholipase C, triacylglycerol hydrolase, acid phosphatase, phospholipase A_2), phopholipase C was the most effective in facilitating the transport of all solutes. The effects of these topical enzymes appear to be mediated through their influence on skin lipids.

Pharmacokinetics

The successful delivery of drugs through skin and into the systemic circulation may require four to five biological half-lives of a compound to transpire before steady-state blood levels are reached (41). Thus, the plasma half-life of a drug is a major consideration when selecting a drug for transdermal administration. Drugs with shorter half-lives are ideal, whereas agents with longer half-lives may interfere with the ability to achieve and maintain close control over drug levels in plasma. However, modifications in transdermal system design may allow the use of drugs with a less than ideal pharmacokinetic profile. Examples of two transdermal drugs, nicotine and fentanyl, are presented to illustrate differences in pharmacokinetic properties and, thus, system requirements.

Nicotine is an example of an agent that is highly soluble, readily penetrates the skin, and possesses a relatively short half-life. It is administered transdermally to aid in smoking cessation. Following intravenous (IV) administration of nicotine, the volume of distribution is approximately 2–3 L/kg and its half-life ranges from 1 to 2 hours. In one nicotine transdermal system (Nicoderm® CQ, SmithKline Beecham Consumer Healthcare, Pittsburgh, PA), approximately 68% of the nicotine released from the system enters the systemic circulation (69). Plasma nicotine concentrations rise rapidly when the system is applied, plateau within 2–4 hours, and slowly decline until the system is removed (Fig. 11) (69,70). Plasma nicotine concentrations achieved are proportional to system size (dose); linear kinetics are observed (70). Nicotine kinetics are similar for all sites of application on the upper body and upper outer arm, and no gender-related differences in nicotine kinetics have been observed. Removal of the nicotine transdermal system results in an exponential decline in plasma nicotine levels with an apparent mean half-life of 3–4 hours. The half-life of transdermally administered nicotine is longer than that seen with IV administration because of continued absorption from the skin depot (70).

Fentanyl is an opioid analgesic that has a longer IV half-life (3–12 hours) than nicotine and penetrates the skin slowly, requiring a permeation enhancer (ethanol) for adequate delivery (71,72). The drug's average volume of distribution is 6 L/kg, and the variability in reported ranges of distribution volumes is large (73). Transdermal absorption of fentanyl is generally characterized by a zero-order process. In the fentanyl transdermal system, a permeation

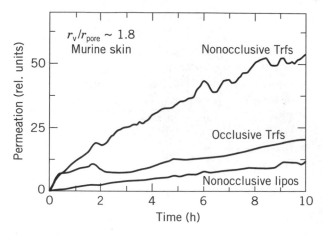

Figure 10. The penetration of standard liposomes (dotted curve) and of the highly deformable transfersomes (full curve) through the murine skin after an occlusive or nonocclusive application. Only an open suspension of transfersomes results in significant transfer of the fluorescently labeled lipids incorporated into the lipid vesicles through the intact murine skin. The small signals observed in the other cases are largely due to the permeation of the free label. *Source:* From Ref. 47.

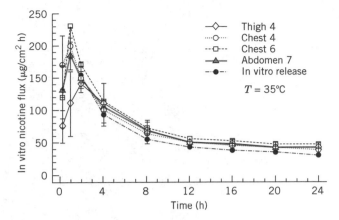

Figure 11. Mean (SD) in vitro nicotine flux for the Nicoderm®
system.

enhancer increases the rate of drug flux through skin, resulting in effective blood concentrations for a prolonged period. Transdermal fentanyl is 92% bioavailable and, thus,
does not appear to be metabolized by skin nor significantly
degraded by the skin's bacterial flora (71). Following application of Duragesic® [fentanyl transdermal system] CII
(ALZA Corporation, Palo Alto, CA, and Janssen Pharma-
ceutica, Titusville, NJ), the skin absorbs fentanyl and dis-
sipates it into the systemic circulation (71,72). Absorption
continues throughout the 72-hour dosing interval (Fig. 12).
Low enhancer flux minimizes the skin drug depot (74). Serum fentanyl concentrations increase gradually following
initial application of the system, generally leveling off between 12 and 24 hours and remaining relatively constant
for the remainder of the 72-hour dosing period. Peak serum
levels of fentanyl generally occur between 24 and 72 hours
after initial application. Serum fentanyl concentrations
are proportional to the delivery rate, and after several sequential 72-hour applications, patients reach and maintain a steady-state serum concentration that is determined
by individual variation in skin permeability and body
clearance of fentanyl (71,72).

MARKETED TRANSDERMAL SYSTEMS

There are a number of transdermal systems now available.
Generally speaking, however, system design can be classified based on the type of rate control employed (skin-
controlled vs. system-controlled drug delivery) and by the
presence or absence of permeation enhancers in the delivery system. Skin-controlled drug delivery devices rely on
the skin's barrier properties to control the rate of drug input to the body. These devices may include a matrix or
multilaminate design to act as a carrier that maintains
drug in contact with the surface of the skin. Drug diffuses
through the skin at a rate dictated by the concentration of
drug on the skin and by the permeability of the skin to the
drug. Because rate control relies completely on the skin's
diffusive properties, variations in skin permeability (e.g.,
at different sites) may have variable effects on the delivery
rate of systems without built-in control mechanisms (75).

System-controlled drug delivery requires a rate-
controlling element such as a polymeric membrane (Fig.
13). The membrane allows measured release of drug
throughout the wearing period and provides more protection from potential drug overdose than skin-controlled delivery. Drug delivery with a system that incorporates a
rate-controlling membrane produces less variability in
drug input, yielding a more predictable and reproducible
pharmacokinetic profile (75).

The need for permeation enhancers is determined by
the nature of the drug intended for use in the transdermal
delivery system. Highly skin-permeable drugs agents,
such as nicotine, do not require a permeation enhancer.
The transcutaneous flux of most hormones, however, is
low, requiring the use of a permeation enhancer such as
ethanol or triethanloamine. These solvents permeate the
skin but without rate control or occlusion, their effectiveness is brief and limited. The use of certain types of permeation enhancers has been associated with skin irritation.

Types of Transdermal Systems

Worldwide, a variety of transdermal systems are available.
In the United States, transdermal systems are used for
delivery of analgesics (fentanyl), hormone replacement
therapies (estradiol and testosterone) and medications for
angina (nitroglycerin), hypertension (clonidine), and motion sickness (scopolamine) (Table 1). Transdermal systems that deliver nicotine for use in smoking cessation are
also available. In Japan and in parts of Europe, systems
that incorporate antiinflammatory drugs (flurbiprofen and

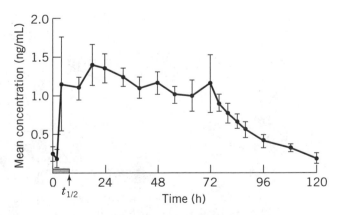

Figure 12. Fentanyl concentrations from TTS (fentanyl)-75 (72 h
application).

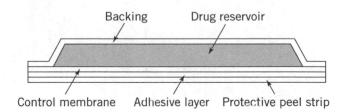

Figure 13. System-controlled drug delivery system.

Table 1. Advantages of Rate-Controlled Transdermal Drugs: Three Examples

Drug	Use	Dosing frequency via transdermal delivery	Dosing frequency via other means	Improved selectivity of action with transdermal delivery	Other advantages of transdermal delivery
Scopolamine	Motion sickness	Once every 3 days	4–6 times per day	CNS effects diminished or absent	May be used in the presence of nausea/vomiting
Nitroglycerin	Prophylaxis of angina	Once daily	2–3 times per day		Prevents massive drug degradation in the liver
Clonidine	Treatment of hypertension	Once daily	2–3 times per day	Dry mouth, drowsiness, sexual dysfunction lessened or absent	

ketaprofen) and monoamine oxidase inhibitors such as selegiline have also been introduced. In this section, a review of a selected group of systems is provided with an emphasis on product characteristics and the clinical performance measures of safety, efficacy, reliability, and acceptability of drug treatment.

Fentanyl. The successful management of chronic pain frequently requires long-term administration of opioids such as fentanyl. Fentanyl is an opioid analgesic that has been used parenterally to treat chronic pain for more than 20 years and has been available in a transdermal delivery system (Fig. 14) (Duragesic® [fentanyl transdermal system] CII, ALZA Corporation, Palo Alto, CA, and Janssen Pharmaceutical, Titusville, NJ) since 1990. For patients who require continuous opioid analgesia for pain that cannot be managed by lesser means, the development of a transdermal system that delivers fentanyl over 72 hours confers a number of advantages over traditional IV administration, including prolonged dosing that does not require an indwelling catheter and maintenance of drug presence that may prevent breakthrough pain. The system com-

prises a peel-off protective liner and four functional layers: a backing of polyester film, a drug reservoir containing fentanyl base and alcohol, an ethylene–vinyl acetate copolymer membrane that controls the rate of drug delivery to the skin, and a fentanyl-containing adhesive layer. The impermeable outer layer prevents loss of drug from the system and entry of water into the drug reservoir. The inclusion of alcohol in the reservoir enhances drug flux through the rate-limiting membrane and increases the skin's permeability to fentanyl (Fig. 15); the amount of alcohol released during the 72-hour application period is small (<0.1 mL/10 cm^2). The adhesive layer, which contains a bolus of drug, allows initial administration of fentanyl with system application. The system is available in four strengths that deliver fentanyl at rates of 25, 50, 75, or 100 μg per hour. The amount of fentanyl released from each system is proportional to its surface area (2.5 μg/h/cm^2).

The analgesic activity of transdermal fentanyl has been demonstrated in a number of clinical trials (72,76–78). System functionality and a pharmacokinetic model have also been studied, and these results indicate the serum fentanyl profile for the transdermal system is a net result of system performance and drug absorption and elimination (79).

Estradiol. A variety of transdermal systems are available for use in hormone replacement therapy. Estraderm® (Ciba-Geneva Pharmaceuticals, Summit, NJ) is available in 0.05 mg and 0.1 mg dosage forms and incorporates a

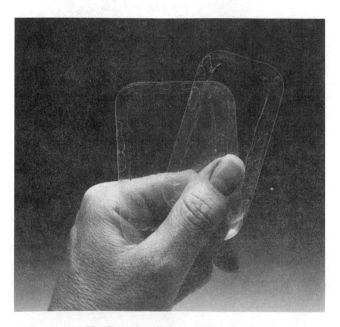

Figure 14. The Duragesic® (fentanyl transdermal system).

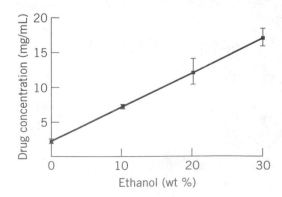

Figure 15. Fentanyl Concentration in Human Epidermis (room temperature).

rate-controlling membrane that allows controlled release of estradiol from a drug reservoir. Climara® estradiol transdermal system (Berlex Laboratories, Wayne, NJ), uses an acrylate adhesive matrix that contains estradiol in a 0.05 mg or 0.1 mg strength. The Vivelle® estradiol transdermal system (Ciba-Geneva Pharmaceuticals, Summit, NJ) is available in the following strengths: 0.0375 mg, 0.05 mg, 0.075 mg, and 0.1 mg of estradiol. The system contains estradiol in a multipolymeric adhesive and releases the hormone continuously upon application to the skin. FemPatch® (Parke-Davis, Morris Plains, NJ) is a self-adhesive matrix system that delivers estradiol at a rate of 0.025 mg/day for 7 days and contains a silicone-based contact adhesive. Alora® (Proctor and Gamble Pharmaceuticals, Cincinnati, OH) is another self-adhesive matrix system that incorporates an acrylate contact adhesive and delivers estradiol at rates of 0.05, 0.075, and 0.1 mg/day for 3–4 days.

Transdermal administration of estradiol has proven to be a very successful means of hormone replacement therapy, alleviating the vasomotor and other estrogen deficiency symptoms among postmenopausal women. These symptoms include hot flushes and other discomforts such as vaginal atrophy, vaginitis, and atrophic changes of the lower urinary tract. Hormone replacement therapy is also given to prevent osteoporosis. The transdermal route is associated with fewer adverse effects than oral regimens and allows serum estrogen levels of remain quite steady over the 3–4-day application period; daily peaks and troughs are minimized (Table 2). The direct absorption of estradiol into the circulation allows peripheral metabolization to estrone and achieves a premenopausal pattern of estrogen as well as premenopausal levels of the hormone (80).

Testosterone. Currently, two transdermal products are available for testosterone replacement therapy: a scrotal system (Testoderm® Testosterone Transdermal System, ALZA Pharmaceuticals, Palo Alto, CA) and a nonscrotal system (Androderm® Testosterone Transdermal System, SmithKline Beecham Pharmaceuticals, Philadelphia, PA) that may be applied to the torso or appendages. The efficacy of both products in establishing optimal levels of testosterone in hypogonadal males was demonstrated in clinical trials (22). Transdermal administration has several benefits over other routes of testosterone administration. It minimizes the nonphysiologic peaks and troughs associated with intramuscular (IM) or oral dosing, and avoids the inconvenience of frequent injections. Unlike absorption via the oral route, transdermal absorption is not affected by food intake or hepatic first-pass metabolism, which may increase dosage requirements, produce unusual metabo-

lites, or possibly result in liver toxicity (81–84). Testosterone transdermal systems have demonstrated an ability to approximate the natural endogenous pattern of serum testosterone levels in normal males and have been shown to produce positive effects on fatigue, mood, and sexual function, as well as significant increases in sexual activity (85–88).

The Testoderm® testosterone transdermal system is designed for scrotal application to take advantage of the unique superficial vascularity and highly permeable nature of the scrotal skin. Application of the Testoderm® system at this site allows a high transfer rate of the hormone without the use of a permeation enhancer, adhesives, or preservatives. The scrotal system is designed to release controlled amounts of testosterone continuously upon application to dry-shaved scrotal skin. A single scrotal system delivers either 4 mg or 6 mg of testosterone over a 24-hour period in a pattern that approximates normal circadian rhythms of testosterone secretion. Data suggest testosterone delivery is negligible when the scrotal system is applied to nonscrotal skin (unpublished data, ALZA Corporation, 1991).

The Androderm® testosterone transdermal system is designed to deliver testosterone through intact nonscrotal skin—for example, on the back, abdomen, thighs, and upper arms. The system contains a drug reservoir gel that is surrounded by a peripheral adhesive area and relies on the barrier properties of the skin to control permeation. Testosterone flux is facilitated by permeation enhancers in the system that assist the transport of drug across the skin. Originally, two Androderm® systems (each 2.5 mg) were applied nightly to deliver approximately 5 mg of testosterone over a 24-hour period. Recently, however, a 5 mg Androderm® system has been developed to allow nightly application of a single system. Both the 2.5 and 5 mg systems produce hormone levels that mimic the daily pattern of testosterone release in healthy men.

In one study comparing the two marketed testosterone transdermal systems (89), the scrotal system was shown to be better tolerated. In those using the permeation-enhanced Androderm® system, allergic contact dermatitis and spontaneous flaring of prior application sites occurred in 7 (12%) subjects using Androderm® systems on day 12. In contrast, use of the Testoderm® testosterone transdermal system resulted in no confirmed cases of allergy ($P < 0.001$). For Testoderm® and Androderm® systems, respectively, moderately intense irritation was noted in 5% and 32% of subjects ($P < 0.001$) and in 1% and 7% of application sites ($P < 0.001$). The Testoderm® system produced no confirmed contact allergy and less topical irritation than the Androderm® system, and patients with contact allergy to Androderm® used the Testoderm® system without a reaction, suggesting testosterone was not the allergen.

Nitroglycerin. Nitroglycerin has been used in the treatment of angina pectoris for more than a century. Nitroglycerin ointment preceded the development of nitroglycerin patch systems and is still available (Nitro-Bid® Ointment 2%, Hoechst Marion Roussel, Kansas City, MO). Plasma concentrations of nitroglycerin with ointment treatment, however, are subject to a rapid rise following

Table 2. Benefits of Transdermal Estradiol

Use of natural hormone
Effective treatment of hot flushes
Therapeutic hormone levels with low daily dose
Restoration of premenopausal ratio of estradiol to estrone
Avoidance of dose-related hepatic effects
Rapid initiation and termination of therapy

application and a sharp decline after approximately 8 hours (90). There have been a number of nitroglycerin systems that have come to market, including Deponit® (Schwarz-Pharma, Milwaukee, WI) Nitrodisc® (Roberts Pharmaceutical Corp., Eatontown, NJ), Nitro-Dur® (Key Pharmaceuticals, Inc., Kenilworth, NJ), Minitran® (3M Pharmaceuticals, Northridge, CA) and Transderm-Nitro® (Ciba-Geneva). The rate of delivery of the drug from the inner surface of the patches is controlled either by dispersing it in a solid-nitroglycerin-impregnated polymer (Nitrodisc®), incorporating it in a gel-like matrix (Nitro-Dur®) or adhesive matrix (Deponit®, Minitran®), or by placing a permeability-modulating membrane between the drug and the skin (Transderm-Nitro®).

Studies have demonstrated clinical efficacy, indicating effectiveness over 24 hours or longer and decreased frequency, severity, and duration of anginal attacks and S-T segment depression during treadmill tests (91). A number of studies have also investigated patient preference, including factors such adhesion, incidence of local skin reactions, and cosmetic properties. In a comparison of Transderm-Nitro® and Nitro-Dur® systems, the former was associated with superior adhesive properties and a lower incidence of local reactions such that the patient preference was nearly 10 to 1 in favor of Transderm-Nitro® (92). In another comparison of the two systems, a preference for Transderm-Nitro® was also cited based on adhesion, a lower rate of local reactions, and better cosmetic properties (93). Comparison of Transderm-Nitro®, Nitrodisc®, and Nitro-Dur® revealed that patient preferences varied considerably and that use of Transderm-Nitro® was associated with significantly fewer intolerable skin reactions than Nitro-Dur® and caused less discomfort upon removal as compared with Nitrodisc® (94). Results of a later study by Chinoy and colleagues (95) indicate the Tranderm-Nitro® system showed better adhesion than Deponit® ($P < 0.0001$) and improved tolerability at the site of application ($P < 0.0588$).

Clonidine. Clonidine is a potent, central-acting hypotensive agent. The drug is widely used and normally administered orally two to three times daily. A transdermal therapeutic system with a rate-controlling membrane (Catapres®-TTS, Boehringer Ingelheim Pharmaceuticals, Inc., Ridgefield, CT) administers this drug over 7 days after a single application (Fig. 16). Following system application to intact skin, clonidine in the adhesive layer saturates the skin site below the system; clonidine from the drug reservoir then begins to diffuse through the rate-controlling membrane and through the skin for absorption by the capillaries beneath the skin. Therapeutic clonidine levels are achieved 2–3 days after application of the first system; application of a new system at weekly intervals maintains therapeutic drug levels. To ensure constant release over 7 days, the total drug content of the system is maintained at or above saturation. The mean plasma concentration of clonidine is proportional to the surface area of the system, demonstrating the linearity between the system size (dose) applied and associated plasma levels. A comparison of oral clonidine (three times daily) with once-weekly transdermal administration revealed that the for-

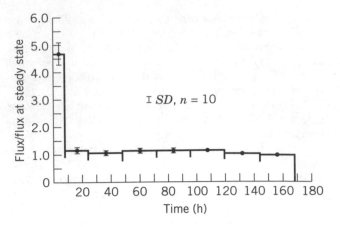

Figure 16. Mean in vitro drug release rate from Catapres-TTS® (Water receptor, $T = 32°C$).

mer resulted in a seesaw pattern of drug concentration in plasma. Virtually steady plasma concentrations of clonidine are produced by transdermal dosing over 7 days (8). In a clinical trial of patients suffering from mild hypertension, 48 of the 69 subjects achieved long-term control of blood pressure with Catapres®-TTS. Side effects associated with orally administered clonidine, such as drowsiness and dry mouth were reduced by rate-controlled transdermal administration (41).

Scopolamine. The first controlled-release transdermal dosage form was Transderm-Scop® (Ciba Self-Medication, Inc., Woodbridge, NJ). One application of the system, which incorporates a rate-controlling membrane, delivers 0.5 mg scopolamine over 3 days to prevent motion sickness. Transdermal administration allows reduction in the total dose required and is a clear improvement over the usual intramuscular injections that require four to six daily doses. A loading dose is released from the transdermal system in the first two hours of application, and then drug release declines rapidly to a constant rate designed to maintain steady-state levels. It has been demonstrated that when scopolamine is administered transdermally or intravenously at similar constant rates over 24 to 72 hours, the rates of urinary excretion of the drug are also similar (96). These results suggest blood levels via the two different administration methods are also similar. Rate-controlled transdermal delivery under steady-state conditions can be compared with continuous, controlled, IV infusion.

Clinical results with the Transderm-Scop® system indicate considerable success in the treatment of motion sickness. In one controlled trial, the system prevented motion sickness in 75% of the susceptible subjects and yielded a low incidence of side effects (Fig. 17) (97). Although the drug has a narrow therapeutic index, study of the general use of Transderm-Scop® indicates that the efficacy of the transdermal dosage form has been excellent and that the incidence of side effects of a parasympatholytic nature have been low (98). Clearly, the clinical performance of this dosage form is related to the rate-controlled delivery of the

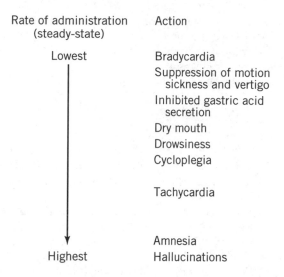

Figure 17. Zero-order pharmacology of scopolamine.

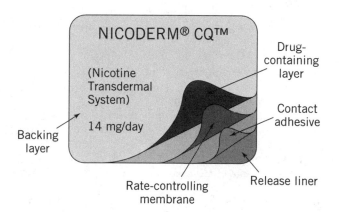

Figure 18. NicoDerm® CQ® nicotine transdermal system.

Table 3. Nicotine Transdermal Systems: Comparative Functionality

Parameter	Nicoderm®	Habitrol®	Prostep®
Dose (mg/day)	21	21	22
C_{max} (ng/mL)	23	17	16
C_{avg} (ng/mL)	17	13	11
C_{min} (ng/mL)	11	9	5
T_{max} (hours)	4	6	9

system, which regulates systemic drug input in the therapeutic range.

Nicotine. The addictive properties of nicotine are well known, and its potential for abuse is well established (99). Withdrawal from nicotine causes physical complaints that are abated by smoking, and thus, smoking behavior is reinforced by the disappearance of these symptoms. The administration of nicotine to nicotine-dependent individuals is the most successful pharmacologic approach to smoking cessation (75), significantly decreasing the severity of nicotine withdrawal symptoms (100,101).

There are a number of nicotine transdermal systems now available worldwide, including Habitrol® (Ciba Self-Medication, Woodbridge NJ), Nicoderm® CQ (SmithKline Beecham Consumer Healthcare, Pittsburgh PA), Nicotrol® (McNeil Consumer Products Company, Fort Washington, PA), and Prostep® (Lederle Laboratories, Wayne, NJ). These systems have several features in common: they are self-adhesive, multilayered, and possess a removable protective liner. The patches vary in their methods of nicotine storage, mode of drug release, and degree of rate control. Habitrol® and Nicotrol® have a drug reservoir that equilibrates within the system after manufacture; neither possess any rate control features. Prostep® contains a nonadhesive drug gel, and the system is not self-adhesive,

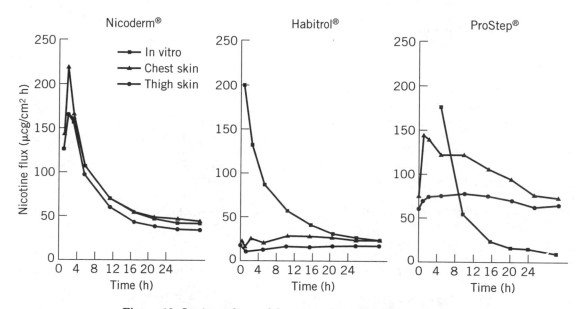

Figure 19. In vitro release of three transdermal nicotine products.

requiring a peripheral adhesive to adhere the product to the skin.

Habitrol®, Nicotrol®, and Prostep® are examples of products that depend on the rate-controlling properties of the skin to modulate nicotine input. In contrast, Nicoderm® (Fig. 18) possesses a membrane that controls the rate of drug input through the skin. This system provides several advantages over its non-rate-controlled counterparts, including rapid onset of therapeutic levels of nicotine in plasma, more consistent drug input among application sites (Fig. 19), greater control over absorption and drug-blood levels (Table 3), and improved protection from abuse and drug overdose (75,102,103).

Treatment with nicotine transdermal systems should be used as part of a comprehensive behavioral smoking-cessation program and has been shown to result in significantly higher "quit rates" than placebos (104).

SUMMARY

Transdermal therapy has advanced rapidly amid greater understanding of the skin's permeability characteristics. Techniques for measuring permeation of chemical agents and the development of appropriate predictive models have been extremely important in the design of safe and effective transdermal systems. A number of pharmacotherapeutic and pharmacoeconomic benefits have been realized with transdermal therapy, and research and development programs will undoubtedly reveal additional merits of this important technology.

BIBLIOGRAPHY

1. P.M. Elias, *J. Invest. Dermatol.* **80**(6), 44S–49S (1983).
2. R.J. Scheuplein, *J. Invest. Dermatol.* **45**, 334–346 (1965).
3. R.J. Scheuplein, *J. Invest. Dermatol.* **48**, 79–88 (1967).
4. R.J. Scheuplein, *J. Invest. Dermatol.* **60**, 263–269 (1973).
5. R.J. Scheuplein and I.H. Blank, *Physiol. Rev.* **51**(4), 702–747 (1971).
6. A. Fick, *Annln. Phys.* **170**, 59 (1855).
7. B.W. Barry, *Molec. Aspects. Med.* **12**, 195–241 (1991).
8. J.E. Shaw, M.E. Prevo, and A. Amkraut, *Arch. Dermatol.* **123**, 1548–1556 (1987).
9. R.C. Wester and H.I. Maibach, *Clin. Pharmacokinet.* **23**, 253–266 (1992).
10. A.W. McKenzie and R.B. Stoughton, *Arch. Dermatol.* **86**, 608–610 (1962).
11. A. Rougier et al., *J. Invest. Dermatol.* **81**, 275–278 (1983).
12. A. Rougier et al., *Arch. Dermatol. Res.* **278**, 465–470 (1986).
13. V.H. Mak, R.O. Potts, and R.H. Guy, *Pharm. Res.* **7**, 835–841 (1990).
14. B. Sennhenn et al., *Skin Pharmacol.* **6**, 152–160 (1993).
15. N. Higo et al., *Pharm. Res.* **10**, 1500–1506 (1993).
16. C. Anderson, T. Anderson, and M. Molander, *Acta. Derm. Venereol.* **71**, 389–393 (1991).
17. R. Takamoto, R. Namba, M. Matsuoda, and T. Sawada, *Anal. Chem.* **64**, 2661–2663 (1992).
18. S.K. Chandrasekaran, P.K. Campbell, and A.S. Michaels, *Am. Inst. Chem. Eng. J.* **23**, 810–816 (1977).
19. J.G. VanRooij, J.H. De Roos, M.M. Bodelier-Bade, and F.J. Jongeneelen, *J. Toxicol. Environ. Health* **38**, 355–368 (1993).
20. S. Southwell, B. Barry, and R. Woodford, *Int. J. Pharmacol.* **18**, 299–309 (1984).
21. J.E. Shaw and S.K. Chandrasekaran, in ed., *Drug Absorption, Proceedings of the International Conference on Drug Absorption.* ADIS Press, Edinburgh, Scotland, 1979, pp. 186–193.
22. *Physicians' Desk Reference*, 51st ed., Medical Economics Data Production Company, Montvale, New York, 1997.
23. S.D. Roy and G.L. Flynn, *Pharm. Res.* **7**, 842–847 (1990).
24. J.D. Harvell and H.I. Maibach, *J. Am. Acad. Dermatol.* **31**, 1015–1021 (1994).
25. J.T. Reed, R. Ghadially, and P.M. Elias, *Arch. Dermatol.* **131**, 1134–1138 (1995).
26. D. Weigand, C. Haygood, and G. Gaylord, *J. Invest. Dermatol.* **62**, 563–568 (1974).
27. R.C. Wester, A. Rougier, C. Lotte, and H. Maibach, *Pharm. Res.* **7**, S211 (1990).
28. C. Lotte, R.C. Wester, A. Rougier, and H.I. Maibach, *Arch. Dermatol. Res.* **284**, 456–459 (1993).
29. R.L. Williams et al., *Pharm. Res.* **8**, 744–749 (1991).
30. E. Berardesca, and H.I. Maibach, *Dermatosen* **38**, 50–53 (1990).
31. R. Aly, *Sem. Dermatol.* **1**, 137–142 (1982).
32. V.A. Harpin and N. Rutter, *J. Pediat.* **102**, 419–425 (1983).
33. W. Schalla, B. Lambrey, E. Lamand, and H. Schaefer, *Pharmacol. Skin* **1**, 190–200 (1987).
34. K. Arndt and R. Clark, in T.B. Fitzpatrick et al., eds., *Dermatology in General Medicine*, McGraw-Hill, New York, 1979, pp. 1753–1758.
35. I. Gigli and R. Baer, in T.B. Fitzpatrick et al., eds., *Dermatology in General Medicine*, McGraw-Hill, New York, 1979, pp. 520–528.
36. R. Bronaugh and R. Stewart, *J. Pharm. Sci.* **74**, 1062–1066 (1985).
37. A. Solomon and N. Lowe, *Arch. Dermatol.* **114**, 1029–1034 (1978).
38. H. Shaefer et al., *Pharmacol. Skin* **1**, 50–56 (1987).
39. A.S. Michaels, P.S.L. Wong, R. Prather, and R.M. Gale, *Am. Inst. Chem. Eng. J.* **21**, 1073–1080 (1975).
40. R.J. Scheuplein, in W. Montagna, E.J. Van Scott, and R.B. Stoughton, eds., *Advances in Biology of Skin*, vol. 12, Appleton-Century-Crofts, New York, 1972, pp. 135–148.
41. J.E. Shaw, M.E. Prevo, R.M. Gale, and S.I. Yum, in L.A. Goldsmith, ed., *Physiology, Biochemistry, and Molecular Biology of the Skin*, 2nd ed., Oxford University Press, New York, 1991, pp. 1447–1479.
42. H.Y. Ando, R.L. Schultz, R.L. Schaare, and E.T. Sugita, *J. Pharm. Sci.* **73**, 461–467 (1984).
43. G.B. Kasting, R.L. Smith, and E.R. Cooper, *Pharmacol. Skin* **1**, 138–153 (1987).
44. E.J. Lien and H. Gao, *Pharm. Res.* **12**(4), 583–587 (1995).
45. R.C. Scott, M.A. Corrigan, F. Smith, H. Mason, *J. Invest. Dermatol.* **96**, 921–925 (1991).
46. G. Hisoire and D. Bucks, *J. Pharm. Sci.* **86**(3), 398–400 (1997).
47. G. Cevc, *Critical Reviews in Therapeutic Drug Carrier Systems* **13**, 257–388 (1996).
48. W. Abraham and D.T. Downing, *J. Invest. Dermatol.* **93**, 809–813 (1989).

49. M. Cormier, P.W. Ledger, J.P. Marty, and A. Amkraut, *J. Invest. Dermatol.* **97**, 447–453 (1991).

50. J.H. Draize, G. Woodard, and H.O. Calvery, *J. Pharmacol. Exp. Ther.* **82**, 377–390 (1944).

51. G. Klecak, in F.N. Marzulli and H.I. Maibach, eds., *Dermatotoxicology*, 2nd ed. Hemisphere Publishing Corp., Washington, D.C., 1983, pp. 200–203.

52. D.F. Woodard et al., in H.I. Maibach and N.J. Lowe, eds., *Models in Dermatology*, Karger, New York, 1989, pp. 71–78.

53. A.E. Chester et al., *J. Toxicol.* **7**, 273–281 (1988).

54. H.C. Maguire, in H.I. Maibach, ed., *Animal Models in Dermatology*, Churchill-Livingstone, New York, 1975, pp. 67–75.

55. J.F. Griffith, *Toxicol. Appl. Pharmacol.* **3**, 90–102 (1969).

56. E.V. Buehler, *Arch. Dermatol.* **91**, 171–175 (1965).

57. E.V. Buehler, in K.E. Anderson and H.I. Maibach, eds., *Contact Allergy Predictive Tests in Guinea Pigs*, Karger, New York, 1985, pp. 39–44.

58. A.M. Kligman, *J. Invest. Dermatol.* **47**, 369–374 (1966).

59. B. Ekwall, *Ann. N.Y. Acad. Sci.* **407**, 64–77 (1983).

60. W.E. Parish, *Food Chem. Toxicol.* **24**, 481–494 (1986).

61. E. Borenfreund and J.A. Puerner, *J. Tissue Cult.* **9**, 7–9 (1984).

62. L. Green, J.L. Reade, and C.F. Ware, *J. Immunol. Methods* **70**, 257–268 (1984).

63. D.A. Swisher, J. Johnson, and P.W. Ledger, *J. Invest. Dermatol.* **88**, 520–524 (1987).

64. N.K. Mize, J.A. Johnson, C. Hansch, and M. Cormier, *Curr. Prob. Dermatol.* **23**, 224–229 (1995).

65. R.J. Scheuplein and L. Ross, *J. Soc. Cosmet. Chem.* **21**, 853–873 (1970).

66. S.I. Yum, E. Lee, and F. Theeuwes, in D.S. Hsieh, ed., *Drug Permeation Enhancement: Theory and Applications*, Marcel Dekker, New York, 1994, pp. 143–170.

67. L.K. Pershing, L.D. Lambert, and K. Knutson, *Pharm. Res.* **7**, 170–174 (1990).

68. S. Patil, P. Singh, C. Szolar-Platzer, and H. Maibach, *Am. Chem. Soc. Am. Pharm. Assoc.* **85**(3), 249–252 (1996).

69. J. Gorsline, *Health Values*, **17**, 20–24 (1993).

70. S.K. Gupta et al., *J. Clin. Pharmacol.* **33**, 169–174 (1993).

71. J.R. Varvel et al., *Anesthesiology* **70**, 928–934 (1989).

72. R.K. Portenoy et al., *Anesthesiology* **78**(1), 36–43 (1993).

73. K.A. Calis, D.R. Kohler, and D.M. Corso, *Clin. Pharm.* **11**, 22–36 (1992).

74. M.A. Southam, *Anti-Cancer Drugs* **6**(suppl 3), 29–34 (1995).

75. J.A. Hunt and D.J. Enscore, *Pharm. Res.* **10**, S-252 (1993).

76. R.A. Caplan et al., *JAMA, J. Am. Med. Assoc.* **261**, 1036–1039 (1989).

77. C. McLeskey and J. McRae, *Anesth. Analg.* **70**, S264 (1990).

78. D.J. Rowbotham et al., *Br. J. Anaesth.* **63**, 56–59 (1989).

79. S.K. Gupta, M. Southam, R. Gale, and S.S. Hwang, *J. Pain Symptom Manag.* **7**, S17–26 (1992).

80. Transdermal HRT Investigators Group, *Int. J. Fertil.* **38**, 5–11 (1993).

81. R.D. McClure, R. Oses, and M.L. Ernest, *Urology* **37**(3), 224–228 (1991).

82. J.C. Findlay, V. Place, and P.J. Snyder, *J. Clin. Endocrinol. Metab.* **64**(2), 266–268 (1987).

83. S. Bhasin, *J. Clin. Endocrinol. Metab.* **74**(6), 1221–1225 (1992).

84. H.M. Behre, F. Oberpenning, and E. Nieschlag, in E. Nieschlag and H.M. Behre, eds., *Testosterone: Action, Deficiency, Substitution.* Springer-Verlag, Berlin, Germany, 1990, pp. 115–135.

85. S.G. Korenman, S. Viosca, and D. Garza, *Am. J. Med.* **83**, 471–478 (1987).

86. R. Ahmed, A.E. Boucher, and A Manni, *J. Clin. Endocrinol. Metab.* **66**, 546–556 (1988).

87. A.W. Meikle et al., in S. Bhasin, ed., *Pharmacology, Biology, and Clinical Applications of Androgens*, Wiley Liss, New York, 1996, pp. 449–457.

88. A.W. Meikle, N.A. Mazer, J.F. Moellme, J.D. Stringham, K.G. Tolmar, S.W. Stencels, and W.D. Odel, *J. Clin Endocrinol. Metab.* **76**, 623–628 (1992).

89. W. Jordan, *Am. J. Contact. Derm.* **8**(2), 103–113 (1997).

90. A. McCallister, H. Mosberg, J.A. Settlage, and J.A. Steiner, *Br. J. Clin. Pharmacol.* **21**, 365–369 (1986).

91. *The Medical Letter on Drugs and Therapeutics* **26**, 59–60 (1984).

92. D. Chinoy, P. Breaux, and F. Ibrahim, *Clin. Ther.* **8**, 30–34 (1985).

93. K. Gatlin, *Curr. Ther. Res.* **38**, 733–737 (1985).

94. B.J. Schrader et al., *Pharmacother.* **6**, 83–86 (1986).

95. D. Chinoy et al., *Clin. Ther.* **11**(5), 678–684 (1989).

96. J.E. Shaw and J. Urquhart, *Trends Pharmacol. Sci.* **1**, 208–211 (1980).

97. N.M. Price et al., *Clin. Pharmacol. Ther.* **29**, 414–419 (1981).

98. J.E. Shaw, M.P. Cramer, and R.M. Gale, in A.F. Kyodenieus and B. Berner, eds., *Transdermal Delivery of Drugs*, vol. 1, CRC Press, Boca Raton, FL, 1987, pp. 101–116.

99. J.E. Henningfield and R.M. Keenan, *J. Consult. Clin. Psychol.* **61**, 743–750 (1993).

100. Transdermal Nicotine Study Group, *JAMA, J. Am. Med. Assoc.* **266**, 3133–3138 (1991).

101. D.M. Daughton et al., *Arch. Intern. Med.* **151**, 749–752 (1991).

102. S.K. Gupta, C.N. Rolf, and J. Gorsline, *J. Pharm. Res.* **8**, S-299 (1991).

103. J. Gorsline, S.K. Gupta, D. Dye, and C. Rolf, *J. Clin. Pharmacol.* **33**, 161–168 (1993).

104. *Physicians' Desk Reference for Non-Prescription Drugs*, 18th ed., Medical Economics Data Production Company, Montvale, New York, 1997, pp. 795–802.

See also TRANSDERMAL DRUG DELIVERY, ELECTRICAL.

V

VACCINE DELIVERY

GERARDO P. CARINO
Brown University
Providence, Rhode Island

KEY WORDS

OUTLINE

Immunization against infectious diseases is arguably the most effective intervention to improve public health. There are over 50 vaccine formulations currently available in the United States (1), but a great worldwide need for effective vaccines remains as this represents only a small minority of all infectious diseases. Also, there is still need for improvement among the existing vaccines. These needs are particularly evident in the developing world, where infectious diseases continue to be one of the leading causes of morbidity and mortality despite widescale vaccination pro-

grams (2). In addition, the emergence of a number of drug-resistant organisms, such as multidrug-resistant *Mycobacterium tuberculosis*, and pathogens for which a totally effective treatment has yet to be developed, most notably HIV, have also highlighted the need for improved preventative measures.

A number of authors have described the ideal vaccine and the various properties that it would have to possess. Most importantly, an ideal vaccine would have the ability to elicit the appropriate immune response for the pathogen under consideration. Many bacterial and viral infections can be successfully stopped by serum antibodies that confer immunity while intracellular microbes, like *M. tuberculosis*, require a cell-mediated response. Some pathogens, such as HIV, might be best controlled by a combination of both types of immunity. Ideally, the immune response would be long term, preferably for life. It should under no circumstances cause the disease that it is supposed to prevent and possess minimal side effects. To make the widespread use of the vaccine economically feasible, the vaccine should be easily administered in a single dose, preferably close to birth to initiate protection when people are most vulnerable, and production conditions should be well defined and reproducible. Finally, the vaccine itself must be stable enough to maintain immunogenicity before administration without the use of an expensive cold chain (3). None of the existing vaccines meet all of the requirements for being ideal. However, the use of controlled-release technology may allow for the development of vaccines that better approach all these criteria, which are summarized in Table 1.

This article concentrates on describing some of the work being conducted toward the development of controlled-release vaccines. After a brief description of some of the relevant concepts in immunology and current vaccines, descriptions of some of the existing research follow. The types of vaccines considered have been broken down into two types, either liposome- or polymer microsphere–based, as these have received the most attention. Special emphasis will be placed on mucosal immunology and the development of oral controlled-release formulations. This article is not meant to be exhaustive in its coverage of the work conducted so far but should serve as a good starting point in describing some of the key concepts and developments in controlled-release vaccine technology, with emphasis on liposome- and thermoplastic polymer–based systems.

Table 1. Properties of the Ideal Vaccine

Biologic considerations	Economic considerations
Confers lifelong immunity	Administered in a single dose
Never causes disease	Reproducible production conditions
Minimal side effects	Stable without a cold chain
Administered perinatally	Medically trained individuals not required for administration

Source: Modified from Ref. 3.

VACCINE IMMUNOLOGY

The immune response to natural infection is generally characterized by an initial antibody response to the pathogen followed by a prolonged memory response with continued exposure. Upon first exposure to an antigen, the immune system responds by an increase in serum antibody levels (within 2–4 weeks), followed by a relatively rapid drop-off of antibody levels. However, this initial exposure to the antigen enhances the body's ability to respond because of the proliferation of those lymphocytes specific for that particular antigen. The immune system becomes primed, and any further exposures to the same antigen are usually larger, more rapid, and longer lasting than the first (4). To take advantage of these natural immune responses, vaccines need to be presented once in an initial dose and then in booster shots to achieve long-lasting immunity. It is this natural limitation that presents one of the most difficult challenges in the development of an effective, widespread vaccination program. In fact, the World Health Organization (WHO) estimates that only 70% of people in developing countries receiving the initial dose of a vaccine return for the booster, leading to an extraordinary waste of limited resources and an undervaccinated population. Considering this, controlled-release technology has great promise in improving these numbers with the development of vaccines that would combine an initial immunization and boosters in a single shot or dose, thus hurdling this obstacle presented by the body's immune system.

Types of Vaccines

By definition, a *vaccine* is a material that induces an immunologically mediated resistance to a disease but not necessarily infection. It is important to understand this distinction when developing new vaccines as colonization by a pathologic organism would be acceptable if disease could still be controlled. The different types of vaccines include live or inactivated organisms as well as subunits or DNA. All of these forms of vaccines can potentially be delivered by controlled release.

Live Vaccines. Edward Jenner's smallpox vaccine of 1798 was based on the coxpox virus (bovine vaccinia virus), which was unable to produce clinical disease in humans but homologous enough to the human vaccinia virus to produce immunity. With this type of vaccine, a closely related organism of lesser virulence is administered, and the resulting immune response is sufficient to stop the virulent organism. This was certainly fortuitous in the case of smallpox, but even in cases where a naturally occurring attenuated organism does not exist, one can be produced in vitro by culturing under adverse conditions. This results in the selection of certain mutants that have adapted to grow well under these conditions but poorly in the human host. The BCG (for tuberculosis), oral polio (OPV), yellow fever, measles, and pertussis vaccines are all based on attenuated organisms produced in the laboratory. The immune response is usually good, producing both humoral and cell-mediated responses. Lifelong immunity is often achieved with a single dose. However, although much success has been achieved with attenuated organisms, they

do possess major problems. These include the potential reversion of the vaccine to virulence especially in the immunodeficient, a huge group considering the world's aging population, the spread of HIV infection and the prevalence of diabetes mellitus and cancer. In fact, OPV, which has long been the preferred vaccine for the prevention of polio in the United States, is currently being replaced by the inactivated polio vaccine (IPV) for this reason because the chance of obtaining polio from the vaccine is actually becoming more likely than obtaining it from the general population! In addition to this, live vaccines need to be stored frozen, which is often prohibitively expensive.

Live recombinant vaccines have also been explored. Bacterial or viral vectors are genetically engineered to express an immunogenic protein of another organism. After administration, this recombinant would replicate and express the foreign antigen to induce an immune response to that protein. These systems are currently still only in the experimental phase.

Killed Vaccines. Entire viruses or bacteria can be killed and delivered as vaccines. These vaccines are not infectious, assuming that all the pathogens are actually killed in the fabrication process, and are therefore generally safe. Of course, they must be carefully monitored to ensure that all the infective organisms are indeed inactivated. This type of vaccine has the advantage of possessing all the necessary antigens, but immunogenicity is often reduced, leading to the need for repeated boosters. The inactivated polio vaccine is an example of this type and, as mentioned earlier, is regaining popularity.

Subunit Vaccines. In cases where protective immunity is known to be directed against one or two proteins of an organism, often surface proteins, purified antigens can be used as an effective, well-defined vaccine. For diseases that are caused by toxins produced by the infectious agent (such as diphtheria, tetanus, and cholera), the subunit can be inactivated toxoids of the bacteria. The subunits can also be surface polysaccharides (as used for the *Hemophilus influenzae* vaccine) or specific viral proteins (as in the hepatitis B vaccine.) There is great potential in this type of vaccine because the development of recombinant DNA technology can allow for the synthesis of desired antigenic epitopes in large and well-defined quantities. However, the greatest problem in the development of this type of vaccine lies in identifying the epitopes that possess sufficient antigenicity to produce long-term immunity. DNA vaccines, vaccines in which cells of the recipient are transfected to produce an immunogenic protein (often a subunit), have been proposed and are being worked on by many investigators.

Mucosal Immunology

Much of the early work on vaccine development has concentrated on the induction of antibody-based humoral immunity toward specific pathogens. This type of immunity is conferred within the bloodstream and is most effective against organisms that have a significant presence or portion of its life cycle within the bloodstream. However, a great deal of the recent work has focused on the development of new vaccines that induce mucosal immunity. Mucosally delivered, most often by the oral route, controlled-release vaccines have been shown to be effective in inducing this type of immunity. An immune response focused at the mucosal surfaces may be sufficient to prevent the colonization of these surfaces and therefore help prevent the spread of the pathogen even before it enters the bloodstream. This mucosal immune response is characterized by a secretory immunoglobulin A (sIgA) response towards the antigen at mucosal surfaces (gastrointestinal, respiratory, rectal, vaginal, etc.). There is evidence that all these sites are linked so that vaccination at any mucosal surface, such as the gut wall after oral dosing, will induce secretory IgA responses at not only that specific mucosal site but also at the other mucosal sites (McGhee, 1993 #3). This property of the mucosal immune system, although somewhat oversimplified as stated, has great implications for the development of effective mucosal vaccines. More than 70% of the body's antibody-producing lymphocytes are part of this mucosal immune system and are located in the intestinal tract (5). Considering its size and pervasiveness and the fact that all vaccines currently available (except the oral polio virus) are given systemically and do not elicit a meaningful mucosal immune response, it is safe to say that mucosal immunology has yet to be exploited to its full potential. The greatest promise of controlled-release vaccine development lies in its potential of harnessing this powerful natural barrier to infection.

The mucosal immune system has evolved into a complex system to deal with the many foreign antigens presented at the mucosal surfaces. There are two areas of antigen processing where mucosal immune responses can be induced: the gut-associated lymphoreticular tissue (GALT) and the nasal-associated lymphoreticular tissue (NALT), both of which possess similar cell architecture. The GALT is made up of the Peyer's patches (collections of lymphoid tissue located in the small intestines, mostly in the terminal ileum), isolated lymphoid follicles of the appendix, and the mesenteric lymph nodes. The GALT is covered by a special epithelium, the follicle-associated epithelium (FAE), which is lined by M cells, which sample intestinal antigens and particulates and deliver them to the underlying lymphoid tissue (6). Here, antigen-presenting cells present the antigens to Th2 and B lymphocytes, which can then travel systemically to the mucosal effector sites. These effector sites include, but are not limited to, the lamina propria of gastrointestinal (GI), respiratory, and genitourinary tracts. At these sites, B cells are then stimulated to secrete IgA.

Most work on mucosal controlled-release vaccines has been focused on trying to immunize the GALT by delivering the antigen in either liposomes or thermoplastic microspheres directly to the M cells of the Peyer's patch following oral administration. Therefore, understanding the interactions between luminal particulates and the cells lining the FAE is critical to the design of vaccines meant to illicit a mucosal immune response. Some of the work at quantifying the uptake of liposomes and microspheres by the GALT is reviewed in this section and followed by a description of some of the controlled-release vaccines described in the literature.

PARTICLE UPTAKE BY INTESTINAL M CELLS

As early as 1961, it was known that the intestine is an imperfect barrier to small particulates. Polystyrene beads of 220-Å diameter were shown to cross gastrointestinal epithelial cells and appeared in the liver following oral administration to rats (7). Other work, 17 years later, showed that commercially available 2-μm polyvinyltoluene particles chronically fed to mice would accumulate in the Peyer's patches, intestinal villi, and mesenteric lymph nodes (8). However, the connection of this phenomenon to the potential development of oral vaccine delivery systems was yet to be made. A large body of work now exists in which investigators attempt to document the uptake of orally fed particulates, specifically by M cells lining the Peyer's patches, to establish the feasibility of an oral controlled-release vaccine. Such particles with an affinity for uptake by the Peyer's patch could be used to encapsulate an antigen and elicit a mucosal immune response.

Microscopy has been the most common method used to follow the uptake of microspheres or other particulates by the GI epithelium. In particular, light microscopy has been used extensively. Rabbits have been used frequently as the animal model in this type of research as they possess a relatively large number of Peyer's patches in their GI tracts when compared to other mammals. In one specific study, light microscopy was used to show the translocation of fluorescent, polystyrene microparticles through the intestinal wall of rabbits. The temporal movement of these 600- to 700-nm beads across the epithelial surface of the FAE was followed after intraluminal instillation. Translocation occurred within 10 min, approximately the same amount of time that soluble tracers needed to cross the epithelium. The authors estimated that 5% of the intraluminal dose entered the FAE. These results implied that translocation of thermoplastic microparticles did indeed quickly occur into the Peyer's patch and could potentially be utilized for vaccine delivery (9).

In another study, chronically fed polystyrene microspheres of different sizes (50 nm to 3 μm) were also shown to appear in rat Peyer's patches, villi, liver, spleen, and mesenteric lymph nodes. No spheres were seen in the heart, kidney, or lungs. Radiolabelling of the spheres with ^{125}I allowed quantification of spheres in tissues and demonstrated that, in general, smaller spheres had greater uptake than larger particles (Table 2). However, a few interesting observations, were made. In particular, the largest spheres examined (3 μm) appeared to show greater uptake

Table 2. Total Uptake of Various Sized Polystyrene Beads following Oral Administration

Polystyrene microsphere size	uptake (%)
50 nm	33.7 ± 3.7
100 nm	25.9 ± 3.2
300 nm	9.5 ± 1.25
500 nm	13.7 ± 1.2
1 μm	4.6 ± 0.7
3 μm	≈12

Source: Data from Ref. 10.

than the 1-μm spheres, but they were not observed in the bloodstream or in the liver as the smaller spheres were. This was explained by the authors as being due to a large number of 3-μm spheres that were adsorbed and immobile within the submucosal layer of the Peyer's patch and therefore not allowed into the circulation. The smaller spheres were quickly translocated into the serosal layer and appeared in the circulation (11). Histological work by the same group indicated that most of the uptake of these spheres did occur through the Peyer's patch and that particles in the liver were mainly in the Kupffer cells (macrophages) or endothelial cells lining the sinusoids, not the hepatocytes themselves.

Other methods of microsphere identification and/or quantification have also been used, including confocal microscopy (12), electron microscopy (13–15), extraction of the polymer from tissue followed by quantification by gel permeation chromatography (11), and flow cytometry (16). All of these studies came to similar conclusions: Polymer microparticulates of <10 μm in diameter indeed can enter the GALT, often within 1 h of oral administration, and have promise as antigen carriers for controlled-release vaccine applications.

Although particle uptake has been demonstrated using hard, nonbiodegradable microspheres, it is clear that biodegradable polymers would be more useful for the development of a controlled release system. Such a polymer, poly (D, L-lactic-co-glycolic acid) (PLGA), in the form of 1- to 10-μm microspheres, has also been shown to be transported into rabbit Peyer's patches following intraluminal instillation. This system has advantages over the other mentioned in that the PLGA is biodegradable and has already been studied and used extensively as the carrier in a number of controlled-release devices. Electron microscopy shows that microspheres of this copolymer are taken up by M cells and translocated toward the underlying lymphatic tissue within 1 h (17). This rapid uptake of PLGA microspheres and its biodegradative properties has led to extensive work with this polymer in vaccine applications. Many of these are discussed later in this section. Other degradable polymers, most notably polyanhydrides, have also been shown to exhibit uptake properties. Light and transmission electron microscopy studies with poly-(fumaric-co-sebacic) anhydride fabricated into microspheres of 0.5–5 μm in diameter show translocation across the epithelium of the GI tract. The spheres were seen as early as 1 h postfeeding and were observed in the Peyer's patch at 3, 6, 12, and 24 h following oral administration (18).

LIPOSOME UPTAKE

In addition to thermoplastic microspheres, studies have also been conducted to determine the extent of uptake of orally administered liposomes. Significant uptake after intraluminal administration of a fluorescent marker, 6-carboxyfluorescein, was seen only when enclosed in negatively charged liposomes greater than 374 nm and made up of at least 25 mol % phosphatidylserine. The uptake was seen predominantly by the ileal Peyer's patches in rats as compared to those in the more proximal small intestine. The authors suggested that these findings indicate that these liposomes could therefore be used to specifically target the Peyer's patch (19). To address the issue of the stability of these liposomes in the harsh conditions of the GI tract, the same investigators demonstrated that liposomes made of distearoylphasphatidylcholine or dipalmatidyldiphosphaidylcholine, phosphatidylserine, and cholesterol were stable in simulated gastric, bile, and pancreatic fluids. These findings lend greater support to the belief that such liposomes could successfully deliver antigens to the Peyer's patch and indeed were seen to enter the Peyer's patch after oral administration (20). Further support to this hypothesis was provided by a study in which gold-labeled liposomes intraluminally administered to isolated intestinal loops of rats were seen within endocytic vesicles in M cells of the Peyer's patch with transmission electron microscopy (TEM) (21). Many other investigators, both before and after these findings, have used antigen-loaded liposomes to elicit immune responses. These will be addressed later in this section.

LIPOSOME-BASED VACCINES

As mentioned earlier, the greatest problem with subunit vaccines is their decreased immunogenicity. A large number of materials, known as adjuvants, can potentiate immune responses to weak antigens. These include Freund's incomplete antigen, a water-in-oil emulsion containing the antigen, Freund's complete adjuvant (FCA), the same water-in-oil emulsion including killed tubercule bacilli, aluminum hydroxide (alum), and others. However, alum is the only material approved for human use as the others are quite toxic; FCA causes undesirable granulomas at the site if injected. Alum has been shown to be inadequate in many situations because of variations in its adjuvant effect with different antigens and formulations. Despite their differences in structure, most adjuvants are believed to derive their ability to increase immune responses by forming emulsions or depots with the antigen and by slowly releasing it over a period of time. Controlled-release systems behave similarly and, in fact, it has been known for many years that liposomes act as immunological adjuvants.

Liposomes loaded with proteins or other antigens have been shown to slow the release of these antigens and act as immunological adjuvants. In the seminal work on liposome-based antigen presentation, mice immunized with diphtheria toxoid (DT) loaded in multilayered, negatively charged liposomes made of egg lecithin, cholesterol, and phosphatidic acid showed greater primary and secondary immune responses than mice administered free DT (22). These results were observed with all three different routes of administration tested, intravenous, subcutaneous, and intramuscular. Unlike the other types of adjuvants, the liposomes caused no granulomas or other undesired immune reactions at the site of injection.

This work was followed by many others exploring the possibility of taking advantage of this adjuvant property and the apparent safety of liposomes to produce liposome-based vaccines. There are certainly a great number of variations possible when designing liposome-based vaccines. Vesicle size, lipid composition, antigen loading (including how much and where the antigen is loaded), lamellarity, and surface composition of the liposomes can all be modified to try to optimize the adjuvant effect on the desired antigen. However, a wide variety of liposomal formulations have shown increased immunogenicity, suggesting that specific liposomal properties such as size, composition, lamellarity, and charge may be less important to the systems adjuvanticity than the simple act of the antigen's release being slowed by its interaction with the lipids (23). Liposome technology has been applied to many different types of antigens—bacterial, protozoal, viral, protein, and others. In fact, there have been over 100 (and counting) international patents issued for variations on this type of technology (24). It would be impossible to describe all of the systems that have been explored, so only a few representative ones are discussed here. Table 3 shows just a few of the recent papers based on liposome-encapsulated vaccines and demonstrates the wide variety of antigens that have been attempted, including a description of some of these liposome-based vaccines.

Model Vaccines Delivered in Liposomes

Bovine Serum Albumin. In a search for easier routes of vaccine delivery, the intranasal route has received a large share of interest, especially when dealing with infectious

agents that gain entry through the respiratory tract. In these cases, a local sIgA response on the nasopharyngeal mucosa would be extremely beneficial. This route of delivery targets the nasal-associated lymphoreticular tissue and thus may also induce a disseminated mucosal immune responses. Work with a model protein antigen, bovine serum albumin (BSA), showed that serum IgG and salivary IgA were significantly elevated after nasal administration of BSA-loaded liposomes (26). Antigen localization, whether within aqueous spaces in the liposomes or attached to the outer surfaces, did not seem to influence the systemic IgG response. However, salivary sIgA responses were noted to be significantly higher with antigen linked to the outer surface of the liposomes, hinting that the immune processing of the two types of liposomes may be different.

T-Independent Antigens. As is discussed in the following section on *Streptococcus mutans* vaccines, conjugated polysaccharide and protein antigens can be delivered by liposomes to elicit a long-term immune response to polysaccharide antigens. This conjugation of polysaccharide and protein antigens is a common immunological method used to induce T cell–dependent response (normal for protein antigens) to antigens that normally induce T cell–independent responses (polysaccharides). However, it has been shown that the conjugation of polysaccharide and protein

Table 3. Examples of Liposome-Based Vaccines

Antigen	Comments
Ascaris suum crude antigen	Slightly increased protection from nematode infection, especially when combined with levamisole (25)
BSA as a model antigen	Increased IgG and sIgA after nasal administration of liposomes in mice (26)
Conalbumin as model antigen	In vivo to in vitro comparing encapsulated antigen to surface-linked antigen (27)
Diptheria, tetanus, IIAV, HBV, and influenza	Shows good immunogenicity and tolerance in humans; may lead to development of new combined vaccines (28).
Ferritin as a model antigen	Increased IgA responses to rectally administered vaccine, especially when combined with cholera toxoid and LPS (29)
Hepatitis A virus, formalin-inactivated	Protective antibody levels in clinical trials; currently marketed in Europe (30)
HIV-1, subunit from gp120	Antigen in "protein cochleates" induces humoral and cellular immunity after both oral and intramuscular administration (31).
HIV-1, subunit from gp120	Increased antibody and cytotoxic T cell lymphocyte responses in vaccinated mice (32)
Influenza virus, HA and NA	Phase 1 clinical trials showing slightly more adverse reactions than those receiving standard HA vaccine (33)
Influenza virus, HA3/NA2	Increased primary and secondary immune responses to HA3/NA2 in hamsters (34)
Influenza virus, LPS and HA2	Liposomes induce a T cell–dependent response to loaded LPS in mice (35).
Measles virus inactivated	Increased serum IgG and sIgA in respiratory tract in mice after intranasl administration (36)
Plasmodium falciparum circumsporozoite protein (Malaria)	The protein loaded into liposomes, but not unencapsulated protein, resulted in cytolytic T cell–lymphocytes and an antibody response. This reactant serum inhibited sporozoite invasion of hepatoma cells in vitro. [White, 1993 #259]
Streptoccocus mutans glucosyltransferase	Increased salivary IgA in humans after oral dosing; serum IgG not greatly increased (37)
Streptoccocus mutans, purified antigens	Oral liposomes induce salivary IgA and result in increased protection from dental caries (38).
Streptoccocus sobrinus ribosomal antigen	Orally immunized rats showed greater salivary IgA and were more protected from dental caries (39).
Vibrio cholerae cell-free lysate	Liposome vaccines were effective orally and parenterally. Polyester-loaded antigens were only effective parenterally (40).

is not actually necessary when delivering the antigens in a liposome formulation. Liposomes have been shown to provide T cell–dependent help to T cell–independent antigens by simply loading both polysaccharide and protein in the same liposome. DNP-aminocaproyl phosphatidyl-ethanolamine (DNP-CapPE), a well-characterized T cell–independent antigen and influenza hemagluttinin A2 (HA2), a well-known T cell–dependent antigen, were loaded into phosphatidylcholine liposomes by the dehydration–rehydration technique. These liposomes elicited a memory response made up of all the IgG subclasses to DNP-CapPE after injection in mice. When liposomes containing just DNP-CapPE were used, an IgM response was observed. These results are very interesting in that one of the tenets of immunology, T cell–independent antigens can only elicit a T cell–dependent response when conjugated to a T cell–dependent antigen, can be circumvented by the delivery of both antigens, unconjugated to one another, in liposomes (41).

This work also illustrates another important concept: In addition to the desired antigen, other potentially helpful compounds or adjuvants can be encapsulated in or conjugated to the liposome formulation. For example, cholera toxin (CT) or the cholera toxin B (CTB) subunit, known mucosal adjuvants, can be incorporated to the liposome vaccine to produce a greater response after oral vaccination. The adjuvant effect of the CT and CTB may be due to its targeting of intestinal ganglioside on the epithelial cell surface or increasing cell permeability of the antigen. The coupling of biologically active CT or CTB to small unilamellar liposomes by a thioether bond retains their immunogenicity (42). The authors suggest that these formulations may be helpful in specifically targeting the liposomes to the Gm1 ganglioside receptors on the Peyer's patch M cells, resulting in greater uptake after oral delivery of the vaccine. These last two studies illustrate an important point about controlled-release formulations that deserves emphasis: In addition to the specific antigen, other desired agents (such as adjuvants, targeting molecules, or even other antigens) can be coadministered in the controlled-release system and potentially improve the response.

Effect of Antigen Association. Liposomal antigens have been shown to influence different immune responses depending on how the antigen is associated to the liposome and whether it is encapsulated within the aqueous portion inside the liposome or surface linked within the lipid bilayer (27). Encapsulation was performed by using a dehydration–rehydration technique, and surface linkage was accomplished by covalently attaching lipid to protein by using a heterobifunctional reagent. Mice intraperitoneally immunized with encapsulated antigen showed only a short-lived antibody response, while those immunized with surface-linked microspheres showed a longer-lasting effect. However, as stated earlier, a multitude of different liposome formulations have proven effective in the induction of long-lasting immune responses implying that generalizations about optimal liposome formulations for different antigens may not be possible to make. Further study is needed into how different liposome structure, size, lamellarity, and other properties lead to the activation of different immune pathways. The examples of just a few of the current vaccines under development for specific diseases shown in Table 3 demonstrate the diversity of liposomal formulations that can be used.

Specific Liposome Vaccines under Development

Dental Caries. The bacterium *Streptococcus mutans* has been identified as the major causative agent of human dental caries. The bacteria colonize the mouth, adhere to teeth, and, with sugar as a food source, produce acids that cause cavities. Increased salivary IgA responses to antigens from this bacteria are expected to control this colonization and potentially offer protection from dental cavities. As a result, a number of studies have attempted to present streptococcal antigens in a liposome vaccine. Purified surface polysaccharide and proteins (43), ribosomal proteins (38), and bacterial glucosyltransferase (37,38,44) have all been explored as potential antigens.

The adherence of *S. mutans* to teeth was found to be dependent on a complex mechanism that involves many of the bacteria's cell wall components, including certain polysaccharides, proteins, and lipoteichoic acids. Secretory IgA responses to any or all of these components would be expected to inhibit bacterial attachment. In general, polysaccharides are thymus-independent (TI) antigens that can induce short-term IgM responses but can not induce immunological memory. This problem can be overcome by conjugating the polysaccharide to a protein, a thymus-dependent (TD) antigen. This conjugate can then be used to elicit a long-term immunological response, as is done in the current *H. influenzae* vaccine. Such a protein–polysaccharide conjugate was associated with liposomes to produce both serum and salivary immune responses following oral administration (43). Briefly, conjugates were formed from polysaccharide and protein obtained from bacterial cell cultures and loaded into liposomes that were then administered orally to rats. Salivary IgA to the polysaccharide were evident in rats fed the conjugate liposome vaccine but not in rats fed vaccines containing only polysaccharide or protein. Salivary IgA responses to the more immunogenic protein occurred with both unconjugated and conjugated antigens. As demonstrated by some of the work with model antigens described earlier, this experiment demonstrated that although it is not able to produce an immune response to unconjugated polysaccharide, a liposome formulation could deliver a thymus-independent antigen when conjugated to a protein and produce an extended response.

It is well known that certain surface antigens of *S. mutans* can induce antibodies cross-reactive to the patient's own heart. The perceived danger of this cross-reactivity led to work on developing a vaccine based on a ribosomal preparation. These ribosomal vaccines have been shown to react to many strains of *S. mutans*, inhibiting adherence, acid production, and growth. Encapsulation of the ribosomal antigen into dipalmitoyl phosphatidylcholine, cholesterol, and dicetylphosphate was accomplished by a modified dehydration–rehydration procedure. All rats vaccinated with these liposomes elicited salivary IgA responses, but so did all rats fed just the ribosomal antigen.

No or low levels of salivary IgG, serum IgA, and IgG were seen in all cases. In bacterial challenge experiments, fewer adherent bacteria were found in rats given the liposome vaccine than in unvaccinated animals. In addition, there were significantly fewer carious lesions in liposome-vaccinated rats than in those that received only free ribosomes or no vaccine (39).

The final antigen to be discussed here that has been studied for the induction of sIgA to *S. mutans* after incorporation in a liposomal vaccine is the bacterial glucosyltransferase. This protein has been loaded into well-characterized dipalmitoyl phosphatidylcholine, cholesterol, and dicetylphosphate (16:7:1) unilamellar liposomes of uniform size (~100 nm) and loading. Administration of these liposomes to rats showed a 25–38% reduction in *S. mutans* colonization and a 30–40% reduction in caries (38). Human studies using similar liposomes that were dehydrated and loaded into gelatin capsules also showed increased levels of salivary IgA lasting for 56 days and minimal plasma immune responses. This was the first evidence that a dehydrated liposome preparation could rehydrate after oral dosing and still successfully elicit an immune response in humans (37,44).

Hemophilus influenza. The currently available *H. influenza* type B vaccine consists of a purified surface lipopolysaccharide (LPS) from the bacteria surface conjugated with a protein carrier, which allows the polysaccharide to achieve a T cell response. The necessity for a "carrier" protein has also been shown to be required when LPS is loaded into liposomes for vaccine applications. Incorporation of LPS and HA2 peptide from the influenza virus in liposomes resulted in anti-LPS-specific IgG responses following subcutaneous immunization (35). This response was characterized by IgG1, IgG2, and IgG3 subclasses, indicating that the normally T cell–independent antigen had been given a T cell–dependent quality, allowing for immune recognition by both T cell–helper and T cell–cytotoxic lymphocytes. Liposomes loaded with only LPS maintained their T cell–independent status and elicited only low levels of IgG3 responses.

Hepatitis A. A commercially available and very effective liposome-based hepatitis A vaccine is currently licensed and available in Europe. This vaccine is based on a specific type of liposome dubbed an immunostimulating reconstituted influenza virosome (IRIV); these are described as spherical, unilamellar vesicles of approximately 150 nm in size. The IRIVs are made of 70% egg yolk phosphatidylcholine, 20% phosphatidylethanolamine, and 10% envelope phospholipids from the H1N1 influenza virus. In addition, biologically active neuraminidase (NA) and hemagluttin (HA) glycoproteins from the influenza virus are located in the lipid bilayer of the virosome, forming short surface projections of 10–15 nm in size. These surface glycoproteins are meant to contribute to the effect of encapsulation within the virosome. HA is a major antigen of the influenza virus and thus a major constituent of its vaccine, and it is responsible for the fusion of the influenza virus with cell membranes. The presence of HA on the surface of the virosome is expected to lead to greater uptake and immune processing of the antigen by macrophages (30).

A number of variations have been made on the successful IRIV hepatitis A vaccine. As stated earlier, one of the properties of an ideal vaccine is the ability to confer immunity after a single dose, yet this vaccine is given as part of a recommended vaccination schedule of three doses of 0, 1, and 6 or 0, 1, and 12 months apart. In a human trial, three vaccine formulations were compared to determine the efficacy of a single-dose vaccine. One group received intramuscular injections of purified inactivated hepatitis A vaccine (HAV) in IRIVs, one received (HAV) absorbed to alum, and the other received soluble HAV. Although 100% of all the subjects showed responses to each of the formulations at 6 months, the mean antibody levels for the virosome vaccines were greater than the alum-associated and soluble vaccines at 14 days, 28, days and 6 months. However, owing to individual variability among the immune responses, the differences among antibody titers were only significant at 14 days (45). Work continued with this system until a safe and effective IRIV-based hepatitis A vaccine was produced (46). The IRIV system has also been used in an attempt to create a combination vaccine containing five commonly used inactivated vaccines that are usually delivered as alum-associated products: hepatitis A and B, diphtheria toxoid, tetanus toxoid, and two different strains of influenza. For diphtheria, tetanus, and influenza, the combined vaccine showed greater immune responses than single vaccines at almost all times tested (28, 90 and 180 days). The immune response at 28 days for the hepatitis A vaccine in the combined vaccine was statistically less than the response to a single vaccine; however, this difference disappeared at the other two time points. This work showed that a number of different antigenic could successfully be incorporated into the same IRIVs and that showed promise as combined vaccines (28).

Human Immunodeficiency Virus. Most of the examples considered thus far have concentrated on vaccination strategies designed to elicit a predominantly humoral immune response. However, both humoral immunity and cellular immunity are required for the effective prevention of a number of diseases, most notably AIDS. The human immunodeficiency virus (HIV) is blood borne, and thus potentially stoppable by serum antibodies, and takes up residence in T lymphocytes, thus requiring the presence of cell-mediated immunity. In addition, because HIV infects across mucosal membranes, a mucosal immune response is thought to also be beneficial. A vaccine that results in cellular, humoral, and mucosal immune responses to HIV has the potential to protect HIV-negative individuals and help stop the spread of the current pandemic of HIV infection.

A lipid-based HIV vaccine has been developed that successfully induces each of the three branches of the immune response. It possesses original structures called protein cochleates that are stable protein and phospholipid bilayers rolled up into a "jellyroll" shape. This rolled-up lipid structure is stabilized by the presence of calcium ions that cross-link successive layers. In a low-calcium environment or in the presence of chelating agents, the calcium is removed, and the cochleates unroll and form unilamellar liposomes with the antigenic proteins incorporated in the lipid bilayers (31). When the envelope protein gp160 from HIV-1 is incorporated into protein cochleates and administered intramuscularly to mice, a strong anti-gp160 antibody response at 8 weeks was measured as well as a strong response (60–70% specific kill at 17 weeks) was observed (47). Following two oral administrations, this type of liposome has proven to induce both high sIgA and systemic antibodies. In addition to HIV, protein cochleate vaccines for influenza and parainfluenza viruses have been studied in experimental animals (47).

Influenza Virus. The vaccine for influenza changes from one year to the next. Based on epidemiological studies around the world, the strain of influenza virus most expected to spread the following year is identified, and the appropriate HA and NA proteins are incorporated into that year's vaccine. As a result, a great deal of work goes into the production of the influenza vaccine each year. In addition, a number of liposome-based strategies have been explored to improve on this current method. In one example, influenza (A/PR/8 strain) envelopes and influenza (A/Sichuan/87 [H3N2] strain) surface antigens were encapulsulated in phospholipid/cholesterol liposomes using a dehydration–rehydration technique. The liposomes produced had encapusulation efficiencies of approximately 40%, which is very good for liposome fabrication. These liposomes were administered to mice intramuscularly in a primary dose and booster dose after 4 weeks, which resulted in increased antibody responses to both HA and NA. This was compared with no response toward unencapsulated HA and NA, which are normally not very immunogenic. The authors concluded that such a system could be used to improve the efficacy of the influenza vaccine and could quite possibly be used for combination vaccines (34). Another liposome-based influenza vaccine has gone through phase I clinical trials in human volunteers showing that it was safe and did indeed produce greater anti-HA antibodies than the standard vaccine. The liposomes were made from B30-MDP, cholesterol, and octyl glucoside. As this was a phase I study, it concentrated on safety of the vaccine and not efficacy. Unfortunately, it was found to have slightly greater side effects than the standard vaccine (reddening at the injection site and deviations from the norm on blood and urine tests). Clearly, more work on this vaccine needs to be done (33).

Measles Virus. The current measles vaccine generally consists of a live, attenuated organism given parenterally, most often intramuscularly. Although these vaccines have been shown to be very effective, they do not induce a secretory IgA response, which may be of great importance in protecting from airborne virus particles. In addition, as discussed earlier, there are other advantages in developing inactivated whole virus or subunit vaccines. In work to this end, an inactivated whole virus vaccine mixed with phosphatidylcholine, dicetyl phosphate, and cholesterol (4:1:5) liposomes showed a significant increase in serum IgG and sIgA in the lungs and nasal cavity. Free inactivated virus was unable to induce an sIgA response. In addition, intra-

muscularly administered virus-containing liposomes elicited an IgG response but not an sIgA response. This is important as it shows that the route of administration is crucial in obtaining the desired immune response and that nasally administered liposomes can indeed present antigens to the nasopharyngeal lymphoid tissue (48).

POLYMER-BASED DEVICES

A great deal of work has also been conducted with polymer-based, controlled-release vaccine formulations. In the earliest application of this technology, an antigen released from a polymeric device made of nonbiodegradable ethylene-vinyl acetate copolymer (EVAc) enhanced antibody formation for more than 6 months in mice (49). In this work, a 1-mm EVAc pellet loaded with model antigens (albumin, gamma globulin, and ribonuclease) was implanted subcutaneously in mice; the immune response was comparable to antigen emulsified in FCA. The three different proteins used resulted in different antibody responses, which was considered to be due to the fact that larger proteins resulted in slower release, thus resulting in a greater adjuvant effect and immune response. These results were very encouraging and began a new field of inquiry into this type of antigen-loaded polymers.

Adjuvant Effect of Degradation Products

In addition to the adjuvant effect gained by the slow release of an antigen, a number of individuals have theorized that beyond the intrinsic adjuvant effects of controlled-release systems, other biodegradable systems can be engineered that possess added adjuvancy in the form of degradation products. A biodegradable polymer based on poly(CTTH-iminocarbonate) degrades into N-benzyloxycarbonyl-L-tyrosyl-L-tyrosine hexyl ester (CTTH), which is as potent an immunological adjuvant as FCA. It was hypothesized that an antigen delivered in a matrix of such a material would benefit by the adjuvant effects of the degradation products. BSA loaded into this polymer and delivered subcutaneously in mice did elicit a much greater immune response than BSA loaded into a comparable control polymer made of EVAc (50). This provides evidence for the idea that there is indeed difference between the adjuvancy of different polymers and that the effect can not solely be attributed to the slow release of antigen from these devices. Although this is a very interesting concept and one that should certainly be considered when selecting specific polymers for use in a vaccine formulation, not much more specific research along these lines has been published since this work.

Model Vaccines

Many of the early experiments conducted on controlled-release vaccines concentrated on illicting immune responses to model antigens loaded into thermoplastic matrices. The purpose of these studies was not to develop a specific protective immunity to a pathogen but to prove that antigens could successfully be included in a controlled-release device and retain immunogenicity. The most popular of these model controlled-release vaccines incorporate ovalbumin (51–56) or BSA (49,57) as an antigen. Table 4 offers a brief description of some of these model controlled release vaccines.

Many of the important general characteristics of controlled-release vaccine systems were elucidated in these studies. However, only a few of these are discussed further, and the remainder of this section concentrates mainly on vaccines potentially effective for specific pathogens. Most work on controlled-release vaccines from biodegradable microspheres has been based on poly(lactide-co-glycolide) (PLGA), which is approved by the U.S. FDA for specific applications and is widely used in biodegradable sutures. The literature contains many examples of controlled-release formulations based on this system.

By far, the most common polymer used for the development of controlled release vaccines has been PLGA. Ovalbumin (OVA), a poorly immunogenic model antigen, when loaded into PLGA, is able to elicit a strong immune response after intraperitoneal or subcutaneous administration (61). Microspheres were prepared by solvent evaporation from an oil-in-water emulsion and had an average size of 5.3 μm and protein content of 1%. After 10 weeks, mice immunized by a single ip injection of encapsulated OVA showed significantly higher serum IgG levels than animals given an equivalent dose of OVA emulsified with FCA. However, after 12 weeks, the antibody levels were not significantly different. After sc booster doses, the secondary responses to OVA in microparticles remained higher than responses to unencapsulated OVA. Further experimentation yielded information on how the size of the microparticles effected immune response. Microspheres of 1.5 μm were significantly more immunogenic than 72.6-μm microspheres (54).

Positive results have also been obtained with model oral vaccines. Orally fed ovalbumin-loaded polyacrylamide microspheres of 2.55 μm in diameter were shown to induce a increase of IgA response when compared to a soluble control group (62). The rats were primed intraperitoneally 14

days before receiving oral doses of microspheres for 4 consecutive days. The primary and memory sIgA response in saliva were measured at 14 and 65 days postimmunization, respectively. Primary responses lower in encapsulated formulations, but memory responses were higher.

It is important to keep in mind, before discussing any specific formulations, that a major goal of controlled-release vaccines is to provide the initial immunization and booster doses in a single shot. Patients would no longer need to return for three or four doses to gain immunity, and medical personnel costs would be greatly reduced. Therefore, determinants of the release rates from various formulations are vital to the development of "single-shot" vaccines. Most of the examples in the literature address this issue and are careful to include good descriptions of the release characteristics of their specific formulation. These examples of microsphere-based vaccines are numerous, many more than can be fully presented here. A description of some, categorized by disease, follows.

Specific Vaccine Formulations

Again, most of the work on polymer-based vaccines, whether delivered parenterally to elicit systemic IgG immune responses or orally to elicit mucosal IgA responses, has been centered on PLGA microspheres. Table 5 summarizes some of the literature on polymer-based vaccines, including information about the specific antigen delivered, polymer used, route of delivery, and size of formulation. The section following Table 5 describes a few of these examples further.

Diphtheria. Diptheria is a localized infection of either mucous membranes (most often the oropharynx) or skin caused by *Corynebacterium diptheriae*. The infection causes pathology by means of DT produced by the bacteria. DT is currently included in the diphtheria–tetanus–pertussis (DTP) vaccine, commonly included in vaccination schedules worldwide, and is effective at preventing diph-

Table 4. Examples of Polymer-Based Vaccines Using Model Antigens

Model antigen	Comments
Bovine serum albumin	10- to 100-μm spheres made of PLGA showed greater adjuvanticity than both Alum and FCA when administered subcutaneously (57).
Bovine serum albumin	Poly(methyl methacrylate) and polystyrene particles between 62 and 306 nm possess adjuvant effect after intramuscular administration (58).
Bovine serum albumin, gamma globulin, and ribonuclease	First study to show that an antigen in a subcutaneously implanted polymer pellet (EVAc) elicited long-term antibody responses (49).
Human serum albumin	Intraperitoneal administration of polyacryl starch particles elicited both humoral and cellular response (59).
Ovalbumin	Antigen absorbed onto poly(butyl-2-cyanoacrylate) particles demonstrated increased oral immunogenicity in rats (53).
Ovalbumin	Intraperitoneal administration in poly(lactic acid) microspheres showed greater primary and secondary responses (60).
Ovalbumin	Oral administration in an acid-resistant acrylic polymer results in IgA and IgG responses (55).
Ovalbumin	Particle size study for subcutaneously administered PLGA microspheres showed better response with 3.5-μm spheres than 1.2-μm spheres (51).
Ovalbumin	Subcutaneously administered PLGA microspheres demonstrated antibody response. 1.5-μm spheres were more effective than 72.6-μm spheres (54).

Table 5. Examples of Polymer-Based Controlled Release Vaccines showing Antigen and Polymer Used, Microsphere Size and Route of Vaccine Delivery

Antigen	Polymer	Particle size	Route Delivery	Refs.
Bordatella pertussis fimbriae	PLGA	0.8–5.3 μm	ip	63
Bordatella pertussis hemagluttinin	PLGA	1 μm	in	64
Diphtheria toxoid	PLGA	30–100 μm	im	65
Escherichia coli, CFA/I	PLGA	10–200 μm	ig	66
Escherichia coli, CFA/II	PLGA	Not stated	po	67
Hepatitis B surface antigen	PGA	1–10 μm and 20–60 μm	ip	68
Human imunodeficiency virus, gp120	PLGA	Not stated	sc	69
Influenza virus, formalinized	PLGA	2.2–10.8 μm	sc and po	70
Malarial antigen	PLA and PLGA	1–10 μm and 10–100 μm	sc	71
Mycobacteria tuberculosis, 38-kDA antigen	PLGA	0.67 μm mean	ip	72
Simian immunodeficiency virus, formalinized	PLGA	Not stated	im, po, and it	73
Staphylococcal enterotoxin B	PLGA	1–10 μm	sc	74
Staphylococcal enterotoxin B	PLGA	1–10 μm	po	75
Staphylococcal enterotoxin B	PS, PMMA, PLA and PLGA	1–10 μm	po	76
Tetanus toxoid	PLA and PLGA	10–60 μm	sc	77
Tetanus toxoid	PLA and PLGA	1–10 μm and 10–100 μm	sc	71
Venezuelan equine encephalitis, formalinized	PLGA	<10 μm	sc	78
Vibrio cholerae cell-free lysate	PLGA	1–10 μm	po and ii	40

Note: PLA = polylactic acid, PLGA = poly(lactide-*co*-glycolide), PS = polystyrene, PMMA = poly(methyl methacrylate), ii = intraileal, im = intramuscular, in = intranasal, sc = subcutaneous, ip = intraperitoneal, it = intrathecal, po = oral.

theria. However, in an attempt to improve the delivery of this toxoid, it has been encapsulated in PLGA microspheres by the in-water encapsulation technique (65). In vitro drug release studies of this formulation show that 90% percent of the drug was released in 60 days. When mice were subcutaneously immunized once with these microspheres, antibody titers over 3 months were comparable to mice receiving the conventional three-injection schedule. It appears that the toxoid retained its antigenicity upon encapsulation, and its slow release from the microspheres allows for a boosting effect. This controlled release of the diphtheria toxoid certainly appears to show promise for the development of a single-dose vaccine, and further work needs to be conducted to determine the longevity of the immune response and whether the other vaccines traditionally given with diphtheria toxoid can also be incorporated.

Enterotoxigenic Escherichia coli. Vaccination of rabbits with entererotoxigenic *E. coli* colonization factor antigen (CFA/I), a surface fimbrial adhesion that is important for successful adhesion of the bacteria to the intestinal wall, induces intestinal mucosal responses and protects from colonization and disease (66). CFA/I fimbriae were purified and encapsulated into a 50:50 PLGA copolymer at 0.1% w/w. In vitro release of the encapsulated antigen began within 2 h and occurred for up to 72 h. Rabbits were intragastrically immunized with either encapsulated or soluble antigen, resulting in greater systemic immune responses in those fed encapsulated antigen. One of the animals also showed sIgA antibodies in its feces. In clinical trials, 10 human volunteers vaccinated with a prototype vaccine based on this work tolerated it well, and 5 developed IgA responses. When challenged by live enterotoxigenic bacteria, the vaccine showed a 30% efficacy, hardly over-

whelmingly protective but still very promising. Work continues on variations of this vaccine, which is now in phase II clinical trials (67).

Hepatitis B. Recombinant Hepatitis B surface antigen (HBSA) has been shown to be effective as a hepatitis B vaccine. This vaccine has recently been added to the standard vaccinations administered to children and people at risk in the United States. However, to achieve a long-lasting immune response, one needs a minimum of three intramuscular injections. In order to improve this system, HBSA has also been encapsulated in polymer microspheres for sustained release. In one very interesting study, five different formulations of HBSA encapsulated in polyglycolic acid (PGA) microspheres were studied. Solvent evaporation and solvent extraction methods were used to produce microspheres of either 1–10 or 20–60 μm in size. In addition, formulations containing the known adjuvants MDP (*N*-acetyl-muramyl-L-alanyl-D-isoglutamin) and Alum were also fabricated and studied. The in vivo studies called for groups of guinea pigs to receive the equivalent of 20 μg of antigen or a negative control of blank microspheres intraperitoneally. Blood samples were obtained periodically, and a booster was given at 16 weeks. The smallest spheres, 1–10 μm, showed the best early response at 2 and 4 weeks; however, this decreased at 6 weeks when the 20- to 60-μm spheres showed the highest antibody response. A combination of these two formulations showed the longest immune response (16 weeks) and is possibly the more favorable formulation. Although the vaccine including Alum did not show any improved response, the greatest response by far was seen with the microspheres that were loaded with both MDP and HBSA. This demonstrates that known immunological adjuvants can indeed be coincorporated into microsphere formulations with the antigen and still contribute to an increased immune response (68). With further work, such a system may be able to reduce the number of injections needed for immunity and therefore allow for a more effective vaccination program against hepatitis B.

Human and Simian Immunodeficiency Virus. A large number of possible vaccines for AIDS are currently under investigation. Many of them are focused at stopping the colonization of mucosal surfaces by the causative virus, HIV. PLGA microspheres loaded with formalin-treated simian immunodeficiency virus (SIV), the simian virus analogous to HIV, have been shown to induce effective protection from vaginal challenge of virus in female macaques (73). A number of immunization routes (oral, im, intrathecal) were used in a variety of schedules. Animals immunized orally showed IgM, IgG, and IgA responses after all doses, but none showed protection from intravaginal viral challenge. When intramuscular priming in the thighs was combined with oral boosting, systemic IgG levels were maintained, and transient increases in vaginal sIgA levels were seen. Five of six macaques immunized this way and vaginally challenged by SIV did not become infected. Although it is unclear whether the vaginal antibodies were the result of successful oral vaccination or intramuscular vaccination close to this site, these results have promise for the development of an HIV vaccine that protects at the vaginal mucosa level. This is incredibly important to help control the spread of HIV infection, as the male–female spread of the virus is currently its fastest-growing means of transmission.

Other PLGA-based vaccines for HIV are also under development. One is directed toward a peptide taken from the principal neutralizing determinant of HIV-1. The vaccine has been extremely well characterized, with good assessments of particle size and distribution, microsphere surface structure, antigen loading and efficiency, in vitro release rates, and measures of stability during storage. After oral administration and combined oral and subcutaneous administration to guinea pigs, the microspheres were shown to elicit high levels of serum IgG toward HIV. Future work will seek to combine this immunogen with approximately 15 other HIV peptides in an attempt to cover much of the worldwide variability of HIV and use the controlled-release vaccine in clinical trials (79).

Another single-shot HIV-1 vaccine based on PLGA microspheres is also in development (69). The HIV-1 subunit antigen, MN rgp120, is encapsulated by a double-emulsion technique. Release from the microspheres was studied to determine whether a release profile mimicking repeated administration could be engineered. An initial release of MN rpg120 occurred over a period of 2 days. This was followed by a lag phase; the microspheres began to release protein in a continuous manner over 4 weeks as part of the second burst. This second burst occurred due to the bulk erosion of the polymer matrix. The second burst has been successfully controlled by different formulations to occur at 1, 2, 3, or 4 months. Guinea pigs given a single injection of a microsphere formulation with a second burst that occurred at 6 weeks postinjection showed much greater immune responses than control animals immunized with MN

rgp 120 and Alum. This work is promising in that it suggests that a common feature of controlled-release formulations, the burst effect, may actually be beneficial in the design of self-boosting, single-dose vaccines.

Influenza Virus. Biodegradable microspheres can also be used to encapsulate and orally deliver whole, inactivated pathogens. A good example of this exists with the influenza virus. Formalin-treated influenza virus was encapsulated in 2- to 10-μm PLGA microspheres. After systemic immunization, encapsulated vaccine induced antibody levels comparable to the virus in solution. When oral formulations were used as boosters for animals initially vaccinated systemically, mucosal antibodies were higher than and systemic antibodies were comparable with levels in animals vaccinated and boosted solely systemically. Again, this type of protection is important for pathogens such as influenza that generally infect through mucosal surfaces, specifically the nasal mucosa in this case. Animals challenged by active virus after this vaccination produced antibodies and were virtually completely protected (70).

Pertussis. Pertussis, or whooping cough, is a disease of the respiratory tract that, although under good control in the United States and other countries with widespread use of the combined DTP vaccine, is a major cause of worldwide morbidity and mortality. The existing vaccine has been based on a killed, whole-cell vaccine of the causative bacteria, *Bordatella pertussis*. However, because of some serious adverse effects to this killed vaccine, a new acellular pertussis vaccine has been developed and incorporated in the new combined vaccine, the DTaP (diphtheria–tetanus–acellular pertussis). One of the antigens included in this acellular vaccine, filamentous haemagglutinin (FHA), has been incorporated in biodegradable PLGA microspheres for delivery as a controlled-release vaccine. FHA, like CFA/I in *E. coli*, is important in the attachment of the bacteria to the mucosal surfaces of the host. Intranasal administration of FHA-loaded PLGA spheres showed both strong systemic IgG and pulmonary sIga, similar to that obtained with soluble FHA. Protection from intranasal challenge was very good, with improved clearance of bacteria from the respiratory tract in those animals vaccinated intranasally compared to those vaccinated intraperitoneally (64).

Staphylococcal Enterotoxin B. Staphylococcal enterotoxin B (SEB) is a toxin produced by *Staphylococcus aureus*, which causes food poisoning. SEB was encapsulated in 1- to 10-μm PLGA microspheres made from an emulsion-based solvent extraction technique and delivered both orally and subcutaneously. In the earlier oral study, the PLGA microspheres (<10 μm) were observed to be taken up by the Peyer's patch with "good" uptake and could therefore be useful in this application (76). Those that were >5 μm remained fixed in the lymphoid tissue for an extended period of time, but the smaller spheres were able to cross through, entering the mesenteric lymph nodes, systemic circulation, and eventually the spleen. The oral vaccination with these spheres resulted in disseminated sIgA immune responses at various sites including saliva, gut, and bronchioles. Soluble enterotoxoid delivered orally showed no immune response (75). When injected subcutaneously, these microspheres induced an antibody response 500 times that of soluble SEB and approximately equal to that induced by the same amount of antigen administered with FCA. Another important finding included in this work was that vaccine-loaded microspheres >10 μm did not possess nearly as great a response as those 1- to 10-μm. This finding was explained by the fact that those spheres greater than 10 μm could not enter draining lymph nodes and thus were less effective. Also, a mixture of blank microspheres and soluble toxin showed just the same response as the soluble antigen, thus indicating that the vaccine needs to be incorporated into a slow-release polymer device and not just presented together with it to obtain an adjuvant effect (74).

Tetanus. A different type of single-shot system has been studied to deliver tetanus toxoid. Instead of a single, extended release, pulsed-release formulations have been suggested based on different-sized PLGA microspheres (80). In such a system, the vaccine is a mixture of different-sized vaccine-loaded PLGA microspheres with various release times. Specifically, 2-μm spheres were engineered to release their contents over 1–14 days, followed by larger spheres that released at 1–2 months and 9–12 months for boosting purposes. This straightforward approach may prove to be more useful, as the pulsed formulation may be more effective in delivering a booster dose, which is necessary for a long-term humoral response. However, it is complicated by the fact that the vaccine is actually a combination of two (or more) different controlled-release formulations and would therefore involve more steps in manufacture.

Tuberculosis. An effective vaccine for tuberculosis still does not exist. The efficacy of the BCG vaccine used in Europe is questionable, considered somewhere between zero and total depending on which population study is considered. In addition to this, vaccination with the BCG vaccine causes people to that positive for purified protein derivative permanently, thus obscuring people who have been exposed to the mycobacteria. As a result, the vaccine has not gained worldwide acceptance, and the United States, in particular, has opted against its use in favor of being able to identify exposed individuals. PPD-positive individuals can then be entered into aggressive antibiotic therapy for 6 months. This option is obviously not ideal. And now, with the emergence of multidrug-resistant *M. tuberculosis* in various areas around the world and the strong association between HIV infection and tuberculosis, the need for an effective vaccine has never been greater.

A 38-kDa antigen from *M. tuberculosis* has been encapsulated in PLGA microspheres and tested for immunogenicity in vivo. When compared to antigen delivered subcutaneously and intraperitoneally with incomplete Freund's adjuvant (IFA) delivered similarly, the PLGA vaccine showed both increased systemic IgG and improved T cell responses (important for intracellular organisms such as *M. tuberculosis*). In another measure of improved cellular immune responses, in vitro antigen-induced gamma interferon (IFN-γ) levels in T cells from microsphere-administered animals were 10 times greater than those given the IFA vaccine. Unfortunately, challenge experiments comparing PLGA vaccine, IFA vaccine, the BCG vaccine, and a control of blank microspheres did not show any differences in the health of the animals (72). Still, these results, specifically the induction of cellular immune responses by microsphere formulations, is promising for the development of vaccines for intracellular organisms.

COMPARISON BETWEEN LIPOSOMES AND MICROSPHERES

This article has described quite a few examples of controlled-release vaccines based on either liposomes or thermoplastic microspheres; other systems are also being explored and may prove to be effective in the future. These include vaccines based on hydrogels (81,82) and starches (59,83), but they are not discussed further here. It is unclear which type of system is the most promising. Very few studies have been conducted comparing liposomes and microspheres with one another. One direct comparison between PLGA-encapsulated and liposome-encapsulated antigens from *Vibrio cholerae* has shown that a liposome-based vaccine induced the greater immune response (40). Antigenic proteins from lysed *V. cholerae* were collected and loaded into PLGA microspheres and liposomes. PLGA microspheres were made by a modified water-in-oil solvent extraction method. Multilamellar liposomes were made using the process known as dehydration–rehydration vesicles. Rabbits were immunized by multiple regimens, and systemic IgG and intestinal sIgA were measured. Immune protection was assessed by measuring the fluid volume in ileal loops. The greatest protection was offered by intra-ileally administered liposomes followed by intravenous boosters. Orally administered microspheres followed by oral boosters showed a 33% immunity to challenge. Although in this one case liposomes appeared to work better, it is unclear if any generalizations can be made. Of course, different investigators will have different opinions. Liposomes seem to be closer to widespread use (as stated earlier, there is already a liposome-based vaccine licensed in Europe), but this is probably just because liposome technology is a bit more established. As time passes, it is likely that a microsphere-based system will also be proven effective and used in humans. Both methods do have great promise and may have their own advantages and disadvantages depending on the specific antigen under consideration.

FUTURE DIRECTIONS

As mentioned, a large number of investigators are working on controlled-release vaccines, and only some of the current literature has been presented here. Many of the vaccines have made it to clinical trials and, as mentioned earlier, a liposome-based hepatitis vaccine is already licensed in Europe. Future work needs to concentrate on more fully understanding the interactions among polymer, antigen, and biological organism so that formulations best suited to induce the type of immune response desired can be engineered. For example, the uptake of particulates by the GALT needs to be better understood, and materials other than PLGA, that may exhibit greater uptake by this tissue and greater potential to elicit immune responses need to be identified. Substantial advances in vaccine technology are likely to come using controlled-release technology, with the most exciting potentially being the development of oral vaccines that induce mucosal immunity.

As this article is being written, new directions and applications for controlled-release vaccines are being considered. With the development of better nonviral vectors for gene therapy, controlled-release DNA vaccines are likely sometime in the future. Very recent studies have shown that thermoplastics can indeed be used to deliver plasmid DNA both subcutaneously (84) and orally (18), resulting in transfection and protein production. Plasmid DNA encoding the insect protein luciferase has been successfully encapsulated in PLGA microspheres and delivered to mice orally successfully, eliciting both systemic and mucosal antibody responses to the luciferase (85). This is an extremely exciting development that opens up a new avenue of research toward the development of controlled-release vaccines.

BIBLIOGRAPHY

1. G.T. Keusch and K.J. Bart, *Harrison's Principles of Internal Medicine*, vol. 14, McGraw-Hill, New York, 1998, pp. 758–771.

2. P.P.H. Lambert, *Rev. Med. Suisse Romande* **113**, 193–198 (1993).

3. D.E. Helland and A.W. Hey, *Scand. J. Infect. Dis.* **76**, 32–38 (1990).

4. A.K. Abbas, A.H. Lichtman, and J.S. Pober, *Cellular and Molecular Immunology*, Saunders, Philadelphia, 1991.

5. W.S. Shalaby, *Clin. Immunol. Immunopathol.* **74**, 127–134 (1995).

6. D.F. Keren, *Semin. Immunol.* **4**, 217–226 (1992).

7. E. Sanders and C.T. Ashworth, *Exp. Cell Res.* **22**, 137–145 (1961).

8. M.E. LeFevre, J.W. Vanderhoff, J.A. Laissue, and D.D. Joel, *Experientia* **34**, 120–122 (1978).

9. J. Pappo and T.H. Ermak, *Clin. Exp. Immunol.* **76**, 144–148 (1989).

10. P. Jani, G.W. Halbert, J. Langridge, and A.T. Florence, *J. Pharm. Pharmacol.* **41**, 809–812 (1989).

11. P. Jani, G.W. Halbert, J. Langridge, and A.T. Florence, *J. Pharm. Pharmacol.* **42**, 821–826 (1990).

12. C. Porta et al., *Exp. Physiol.* **77**, 929–932 (1992).

13. M.A. Jepson et al., *Cell Tissue Res.* **271**, 399–405 (1993).

14. T. Landsverk, *Immunol. Cell Biol.* **66**, 261–268 (1988).

15. W. Sass, H.P. Dreyer, and J. Seifert, *Am. J. Gastroenterol.* **85**, 255–260 (1990).

16. J.P. Ebel, *Pharm. Res.* **7**, 848–851 (1990).

17. T.H. Ermak et al., *Cell Tissue Res.* **279**, 433–436 (1995).

18. E. Mathlowitz et al., *Nature (London)* **386**, 410–414 (1997).

19. H. Tomizawa et al., *Pharm. Res.* **10**, 549–552 (1992).

20. Y. Aramaki et al., *Pharm. Res.* **10**, 1228–1231 (1993).

21. N.K. Childers, F.R. Denys, N.F. McGee, and S.M. Michalek, *Reg. Immunol.* **3**, 8–16 (1990).

22. A.C. Allison and G. Gregoriadis, *Nature (London)* **252**, 252 (1973).

23. G. Gregoriadis, I. Gursel, M. Gursel, and B. McCormack, *J. Controlled Release* **41**, 49–56 (1996).

24. R. Glück, *Vaccine Design: The Subunit and Adjuvant Approach*, Plenum, New York, 1994, pp. 325–345.

25. S. Lukes, *Vet. Parasitol.* **43**, 105–113 (1992).

26. Y. Aramaki et al., *Vaccine* **12**, 1241–1245 (1994).

27. E. Shahum and H. Thérien, *Vaccine* **12**, 1125–1131 (1994).

28. B. Mengiardi, R. Berger, M. Just, and R. Gluck, *Vaccine* **13**, 1306–1315 (1995).

29. F. Zhou, J.P. Kraehenbuhl, and M.R. Neutra, *Vaccine* **13**, 637–644 (1995).

30. R. Glück, *Vaccine* **10**, 915–919 (1992).

31. S. Gould-Fogerite et al., *AIDS Res. Hum. Retroviruses* **10**, S99–S103 (1994).

32. W.I. White et al., *Vaccine* **13**, 1111–1122 (1995).

33. M. Kaji et al., *Vaccine* **10**, 663–667 (1992).

34. G. Gregoriadis, L. Tan, E.T.S. Ben-Ahmeida, and R. Jennings, *Vaccine* **10**, 747–753 (1992).

35. P.J.F. Pietrobon, N. Garcon, C.H. Lee, and H.R. Six, *Immunomethods* **4**, 236–243 (1994).

36. A. de Haan, J. Tomee, J. Huchshorn, and J. Wilschut, *Vaccine* **13**, 1320–1324 (1995).

37. N.K. Childers, S.S. Zhang, and S.M. Michalek, *Advances in Mucosal Immunology*, Plenum New York, 1995, pp. 1481–1484.

38. S.M. Michalek et al., *Genetically Engineered Vaccines*, Plenum, New York, 1992.

39. R.L. Gregory et al., *Infect. Immun.* **54**, 780–786 (1986).

40. U. Chandrasekhar, S. Sinha, H.R. Bhagat, V.B. Sinha, and B.S. Srivastava, *Vaccine* **12**, 1384–1387 (1994).

41. N.M. Garcon and H.R. Six, *J. Immunol.* **146**, 3697–3702 (1991).

42. E. Harokopakis et al., *J. Immunol. Methods* **185**, 31–42 (1995).

43. D. Wachsmann et al., *Infect. Immun.* **52**, 408–413 (1986).

44. N.K. Childers, S.S. Zhang, and S.M. Michalek, *Oral Microbiol. Immunol.* **11**, 146–153 (1994).

45. M. Just et al., *Vaccine* **10**, 737–739 (1992).

46. Y. Poovorawan et al., *Vaccine* **13**, 891–893 (1995).

47. R.J. Mannino, *Vaccine Design: The Subunit and Adjuvant Approach*, Plenum, New York, 1995, pp. 363–387.

48. A. de Haan et al., *Vaccine* **13**, 155–162 (1995).

49. I. Preis and R.S. Langer, *J. Immunol. Methods* **28**, 193–197 (1979).

50. J. Kohn et al., *J. Immunol. Methods* **95**, 31–38 (1986).

51. T. Uchida, S. Goto, and T.P. Foster, *J. Pharm. Pharmacol.* **47**, 556–560 (1994).

52. D.T. O'Hagan et al., *Advances in Mucosal Immunology*, Plenum, New York, 1995, pp. 1463–1467.

53. D.T. O'Hagan, K.J. Palin, and S.S. Davis, *Vaccine* **7**, 213–216 (1989).

54. D.T. O'Hagan, H. Jeffery, and S.S. Davis, *Vaccine* **11**, 965–969 (1993).

55. S.L. Jain, K.S. Barone, M.P. Flanagan, and J.G. Michael, *Vaccine* **14**, 42–48 (1996).

56. R. Kakaoka, Y. Tabata, and Y. Ikada, *J. Controlled Release* **37**, 215–224 (1995).

57. H. Sah, R. Toddywala, and Y.W. Chien, *J. Controlled Release* **37**, 137–144 (1995).

58. J. Kreuter et al., *Vaccine* **4**, 125–129 (1986).

59. L. Degling and P. Stjarnkvist, *Vaccine* **13**, 629–636 (1995).

60. R. Nakaoka, Y. Tabata, and Y. Ikada, *J. Controlled Release* **37**, 215–224 (1995).

61. D.T. O'Hagan et al., *Immunology* **73**, 239–242 (1991).

62. D.T. O'Hagan et al., *Vaccine* **7**, 421–424 (1989).

63. D.H. Jones et al., *Infect. Immun.* **64**, 489–494 (1996).

64. E.S. Cahill et al., *Vaccine* **13**, 455–462 (1995).

65. M. Singh, A. Singh, and G.P. Talwar, *Pharm. Res.* **8**, 958–961 (1991).

66. R. Edelman et al., *Vaccine* **11**, 155–158 (1993).

67. C.O. Tacket et al., *Vaccine* **12**, 1270–1274 (1994).

68. R.V. Nellore, P.G. Pande, D. Yound, and H.R. Bhagat, *J. Parenter. Sci. Technol.* **46**, 176–180 (1992).

69. J.L. Cleland et al., *AIDS Res. Hum. Retroviruses* **10**, S21–S26 (1994).

70. Z. Moldoveanu et al., *J. Infect. Dis.* **167**, 84–90 (1993).

71. C. Thomasin et al., *J. Controlled Release* **41**, 131–145 (1996).

72. H.M. Vordermeier et al., *Vaccine* **13**, 1576–1582 (1995).

73. P.A. Marx et al., *Science* **260**, 1323–1327 (1993).

74. J.H. Eldridge et al., *Infect. Immun.* **59**, 2978–2986 (1991).

75. J.H. Eldridge et al., *Adv. Exp. Med. Biol.* **25**, 192–202 (1989).

76. J.H. Eldridge et al., *J. Controlled Release* **11**, 205–214 (1990).

77. M.A. Alonso et al., *Pharm. Res.* **10**, 945–953 (1993).

78. T.E. Greenway et al., *Vaccine* **13**, 1411–1420 (1995).

79. D.T. O'Hagan et al., *J. Controlled Release* **37**, 75–84 (1995).

80. M.T. Aguado and P.H. Lambert, *Immunobiology* **184**, 113–125 (1992).

81. T.L. Bowersock et al., *Am. J. Vet. Res.* **55**, 502–509 (1994).

82. G.B. Pier et al., *Infect. Immun.* **62**, 3972–3979 (1994).

83. D.T. O'Hagan, D. Rafferty, S. Wharton, and L. Illum, *Vaccine* **11**, 660–664 (1993).

84. Y.S. Jong et al., *J. Controlled Release* **147**, 123–134 (1997).

85. D.H. Jones et al., *Vaccine* **15**, 814–817 (1997).

VETERINARY APPLICATIONS

MICHAEL J. RATHBONE
InterAg
Hamilton, New Zealand

LEONORE WITCHEY-LAKSHMANAN
Schering-Plough Research Institute
Kenilworth, New Jersey

KADRIYE CIFTCI
Temple University
Philadelphia, Pennsylvania

KEY WORDS

Anithelmintics

Companion animal

Ectoparasites

Endoparasites

Estrous control

Growth enhancement

Intramammary

Intravaginal

Long-acting injectables and implants

Postruminal

Proteins and peptides

Ruminal

Steroids

Veterinary drug delivery

Veterinary gene therapy

Veterinary medicine

Veterinary vaccines

OUTLINE

Introduction

Factors Influencing Controlled Drug Delivery in Animals

Comparison of Human and Animal Controlled Drug Delivery

    Reasons for Producing Controlled Drug Delivery Systems

    Dosing Interval

    Drug Candidates

    Pharmacokinetics

    Physiology and Anatomy

    Delivery System Design

    Site of Absorption

    Means of Administration

    Storage Conditions

    Regulatory Considerations

    In Vivo/In Vitro Correlations

Veterinary Controlled-Release Drug Delivery and Delivery Systems

    Intraruminal Drug Delivery

    Postruminal drug delivery

    Intramammary Drug Delivery

    Steroid Hormone-Containing Growth Promotants

    Vaginal Drug Delivery

    Long-Acting Injectable Products Used in Food-Producing Animals

    Topical Dosage Forms for Food-Producing Animals

    Controlled-Release Technologies in Companion Animals

    Ophthalmic Drug Delivery

    Protein and Peptide Delivery

Recent Initiatives

    Vaccine Delivery

    Gene Therapy

    Trends and Future Directions of Vaccines and Gene Therapy

Concluding Remarks

Bibliography

INTRODUCTION

Veterinary medicine offers many challenges to the scientist developing controlled-release products (1). These challenges arise from the diverse nature of the field, which covers a multitude of animal species that differ in size, habits, social behavior, and so on; farm management practices in which farmers may not have any direct contact with their flock or herd for many weeks or even months; and anatomical and physiological constraints that are peculiar to an individual animal species. These factors present the formulation scientist with a unique opportunity to develop innovative solutions to challenging and demanding delivery problems (1).

The purpose of this article is to provide a comparison between human and veterinary controlled-release drug delivery, to highlight some of the factors that influence the development of controlled-release products for animals, to describe relevant issues pertaining to the design and development of controlled-release products for various routes/clinical conditions, and to describe the various conceptual and commercially available controlled-release drug delivery systems that are available for those routes or conditions.

Because the largest body of veterinary and controlled-release literature focuses on food-producing and companion animals, these two areas are also the focus of this article. However, it should be realized that there are other areas of minor market interest such as the fur industry, wildlife management, and zoological medicine that also present unique and interesting opportunities for controlled drug delivery. For example, consider the challenges within the area of wildlife management. Not only would it be desirable to have the formulation fulfill all the normal physical and chemical stability criteria associated with a controlled-release product, but there may also be the need for it to be designed to allow delivery through the barrel of a dart gun!

FACTORS INFLUENCING CONTROLLED DRUG DELIVERY IN ANIMALS

Controlled drug delivery to animals can be conveniently divided into two broad categories—those delivery systems developed for food-producing animals and those developed for companion animals. Food-producing animals consist primarily of cattle, sheep, swine, and poultry, together with fish and any other animal from which meat or other products such as eggs or milk are obtained. Companion animals are those that are considered pets, primarily dogs and cats, but animals such as horses, birds, lizards, rabbits, and so on can also be considered companion animals. Rabbits, birds, and lizards are sometimes classified as "exotic" animals. Because the latter species represent only a small proportion of the companion animal market, drug delivery systems that have been developed for the more mainstream species (e.g., dogs and cats) or indeed, for children, are often adapted for use in the exotic species because the markets are not usually large enough to warrant development of such specialized products.

In the food animal pharmaceutical business, many issues make the development of a controlled drug delivery system particularly challenging. For example, the profit margins associated with the raising and selling of farmed animals are rather slim. As a result, it is not atypical for only a few cents per dose to make a large difference to the farmer's overall profit. Therefore, the formulation scientist must produce a product under considerable cost constraints. In addition, the product manufacturers must also accept that their profit margins will be slim. However, this low profit margin can actually be used to the controlled release formulator's advantage because every visit of the veterinarian is associated with the cost of his or her time and expertise to the farmer as well as the cost of rounding up individual animals for treatment. Thus, the more frequently a product needs to be administered (e.g., once a day versus once a season), the more the cost of the treatment increases for the animal handler. Therefore, it behooves the formulation personnel to develop a controlled release product to reduce the number of times an administration procedure is required during the treatment period. Innovative adjustments in a once-a-day administration to make it a one-time-only administration can vastly improve the marketability of the product. Moreover, the development of a more complex controlled-release delivery system that delivers the active agent over an entire season has the potential to open huge areas of the market, allowing the handling of the animals only once, when they are turned to pasture.

In contrast, the companion animal market is somewhat different in that the potential cost and profit margins associated with a product developed for a companion animal can be much higher compared to one developed for the food animal market. First, the companion animal owner does not own, and therefore does not have to treat, several hundred animals in his or her herd or flock. Rather, the outlay is directed toward a single animal. Second, the price of the delivery system is not determined by the profitability of the animal but by the arbitrary value of the animal to the owner. Theoretically, therefore, the companion animal market will support the development of more complex and expensive dosage forms.

When one analyzes markets in the United States for both food and companion animals, one can divide the markets into three areas: pharmaceuticals, biologicals and feed additives. The breakdown of each of these U.S. markets is listed in Table 1, in which both the companion animal and food animal markets are combined. It is interesting to note that in contrast to human health, where one single drug formulation can accrue over $1 billion sales to a company, the entire animal health market in the United States has been estimated to be less than $3 billion total.

The highest yields (in market dollars) within the veterinary field are in the areas of antibiotics and endoparasiticides, each grossing over $500 million total in 1997. Biologicals offer the next largest portion, at nearly $500 million. This latter category includes items such as vaccine dosage forms of all kinds for all species. Insecticides and parasiticides account for the next largest category, while hormones and vitamin nutritionals account for

Table 1. Summary of Market Areas in the Animal Health Industry

Therapeutic area	1997 U.S. sales (millions of $)
Antibacterials	551.9
Biologicals	483.2
Hormones	266.6
Insecticides and parasiticides	414.1
Internal parasiticides	540.2
Vitamins and nutritionals	134.7
Other (analgesics, anesthetics, lab diagnostics, antiseptics, grooming aids)	415.3
Total	2,806

the remaining largest portions of the market. The remainder of the market still represents a large portion in total; however, these are the sum of several individual therapeutic areas, each of which represents only a fraction of total U.S. animal health sales.

In relation to the global economy, U.S. sales represent almost one-third of the entire world animal health industry. Table 2 shows that the next largest animal health products consumer is Russia, but it accounts for less than 10% of the entire world market. Japan follows closely behind Russia, with China and France each accounting for about 5–6% of the entire world market. The total contribution of all the other countries represents at most 5% of the global market. It should be noted, however, that with the establishment of the European Union, the numbers in Table 2 will inevitably change owing to the unification of the animal health market within this region. In addition, given the large Chinese population coupled with the small fraction of the world market, many have suggested that the most untapped potential for veterinary pharmaceuticals lies within China.

From Tables 1 and 2 it can be calculated that the total worldwide market is estimated to be approximately $9–10 billion. This offers many global opportunities worldwide, and therefore it is no wonder that several animal health companies have consolidated in the last several years to

Table 2. Market Share of Specific Countries in the World Animal Health Market

Country	Worldwide sales (%)
U.S.A.	28.7
Russia	8.8
Japan	7.6
China	5.4
France	5.4
Brazil	4.6
Germany	4.6
U.K.	2.9
Spain	2.8
Italy	2.5
Central Europe	2.2
South Korea	2.0
Others	22.5

improve their efficiency in the light of the broad-reaching competitiveness of the industry.

COMPARISON OF HUMAN AND ANIMAL CONTROLLED DRUG DELIVERY

Reasons for Producing Controlled Drug Delivery Systems

In humans one reason for developing a drug into a controlled-release drug delivery system is to reduce the dose frequency to improve patient compliance (2–4). An additional reason is to improve the efficiency of therapy and thereby improve the health of the patient (2,3). In the veterinary field, the reason for developing a drug into a long-acting controlled-release drug delivery system is to minimize animal handling to reduce the stress to animals from repeated administration and to reduce the cost in terms of money and time spent by the end-user on drug administration.

Dosing Interval

The dosing interval of human and veterinary products differs widely. In humans it is common that an improvement in compliance and efficacy is obtained if the number of required doses is reduced twofold, resulting in (approximately) an 8- to 12-h duration of action of the drug (5). In a few cases the aim to decrease the number of required doses multifold to provide a very extended duration of drug action in the order of months also exists, as in Norplant (6). This contrasts markedly to the animal case, where an increase in drug action by only several hours would rarely be useful. In animals, in most cases, the duration of drug action though the development of a controlled-release product must be extended by at least several days, and in the vast majority of cases, in the order of months to cover an entire season (e.g., a flea or tick season for companion animals or a growing season for food-producing animals).

Drug Candidates

In humans, typical drug types that are incorporated into controlled-release products have short biological half-lives (2,7,8), which is the reason why a twofold increase in drug delivery can result in improvements over single-dose therapy. In contrast, drugs used in the veterinary field may possess half-lives that may be very short or very long. It is the need to deliver that drug over an entire season (for weeks or months) and not the short duration of biological activity of the drug, that dictates the need to incorporate it into a controlled-release formulation.

Pharmacokinetics

The pharmacokinetics of a given drug in humans differs between infants, children, and adults and may change as a function of disease status. The same applies to animals. In addition, in the veterinary field, the pharmacokinetics of a given drug differs markedly between different species. The pharmacokinetics of a given drug in a given animal is an important consideration when developing an animal health product and presents challenges when developing the same drug product for different animal species. Commonly, more than one formulation of delivery device must be prepared based on species as well as the age of the animal.

Physiology and Anatomy

The physiological and anatomical characteristics of the human species differ only slightly between the young and adult of the species. However, the physiological characteristics of the different routes for drug delivery differ substantially between various animal species. The differences that exist in skin between animal species (e.g., thickness, composition, number of hair follicles, etc.) can influence the design of transdermal preparations where, for example, different mechanisms for absorption can be exploited. For instance, follicular penetration routes may be exploited in sheep but not in pigs. The differences in anatomy between species can also influence the design of a delivery system as is observed in ruminant versus monogastric animals. Because of the peculiarities of the ruminant gastrointestinal tract, delivery systems can be designed to be retained for months in a manner impossible to mimic in monogastrics.

Delivery System Design

There are vast differences between human and animal controlled drug delivery with respect to the scope and latitude associated with the geometry of the delivery system. For example, with human controlled-release drug delivery systems, dose size can be product limiting (8). For example, the physical size of a solid oral dosage form can limit its development because its size influences the ease of swallowing (8). A similar scenario applies to the development of implants for human use. The pain associated with too large a volume of an injection or too large an implant can prohibit the development of a controlled-release injection or implant in humans. In contrast, although there are constraints on the physical size of a delivery system, whether oral, implant or injection, in general in animals (particularly farmed animals), the overall size of a delivery system can be much larger such that dose size is not the limiting factor in the design of the delivery system. It should be noted, however, that because the animal is generally much larger than its human counterpart, it will require larger doses to be administered to produce the desired therapeutic effect. It should also be realized that this is not the case for all animals because the size of different species varies—for example, compare cattle with cats. The geometry of the delivery system for humans is in general defined by history and revolves around product shapes that humans are used to seeing, such as round flat tablets. In contrast, in animals the geometry of the delivery system is generally dictated by the administration devices that are available for that route for drug delivery, such as balling guns, intravaginal applicators, implanters, and so on.

Site of Absorption

In humans oral products would be expected to traverse the length of the gastrointestinal tract and release drug along its entire length. Subcutaneous or intramuscular injections or implants would be expected to release from the injection site. With veterinary products orally administered products to ruminant animals are often retained at a specific site within the gastrointestinal tract (the rumer) (9) for several months, as opposed to continuing along the length of the gastrointestinal tract. Injections are more preferably placed subcutaneously in animals. Intramuscular administration is less favored because it can decrease meat quality in food-producing animals.

Means of Administration

Administration is an interesting aspect in the development of a controlled-release product for animals. In the case of humans, self-administration is feasible, and orally administered products usually are easily swallowed with a glassful of water. Topical products are specifically designed to be easily placed on the skin. Factors such as size, shape, ease of administration, and safety to the person administering the product over a series of time intervals are built into the product. Injections or implants are often administered by a second person; however, a patient can be trained to self-administer an injection, or products may be designed to facilitate this process (e.g., insulin pens). In contrast, with a veterinary product, the means of administration must be carefully considered and be part of the product development process. The issues of safety, ease of use, and so on just outlined must still be thought through for animal products but in addition, so should a series of other additional considerations. These include

- How will the delivery system be administered?
- What will the handler safety be for one person administering to several hundred animals over several time intervals (e.g., feedlot cattle for every shipment that comes in)?
- Is the administration device easy to use, or has it the potential to cause repeated stress syndromes?
- Will it be easy to train nontechnical people in its use?
- Can standard equipment be used to administer the product?
- How does the required administration method of the product fit into to current animal-handling practices?
- Can the device withstand "downstream" operations (such as rendering) without harming the equipment used in those operations?
- Can the package it is presented in withstand the various field conditions it will be subjected to (e.g., plastic versus glass)?
- Can the administration device withstand several hundred administrations, severe weather conditions, rough handling, and large animals (i.e., what is the administration device's life expectancy?).

Storage Conditions

The required storage conditions for the product can also be contrasted between human and veterinary medicine. Human products can be refrigerated relatively easily if necessary and indeed some human products, for example, insulin and other biologicals, carry this provision on the label. However, this is not the case for veterinary pharmaceuticals. A veterinarian or other end-user would not typically have access to a refrigerator. Indeed, once the product has left the ideal storage conditions of the supply warehouse or surgery, most veterinary products are stored in the back of a car or in a non-temperature-controlled environment on the farm. Veterinary products are therefore required to be developed to withstand higher temperatures. This impacts heavily on the product's stability requirements, which must be addressed and overcome by the formulator during the development stages of the controlled-release product.

Regulatory Considerations

For human products, regulatory requirements include toxicity, safety, dosing intervals, therapeutic effect, stability, approved excipients, and the like. Veterinary products not only include all of the above but also require tissue residue and handler safety issues to be addressed, particularly for food-producing animals. This typically involves a full tissue-residue analysis to be performed, first with radiolabeled drug to determine the sites of deposition and then with nonradiolabled drug to prove it in the final formulation. From these data, a "tissue withdrawal" time is determined to inform the farmer of when the animal is fit for slaughter. Obviously, the shorter the withdrawal time is for the product, the more desirable the overall product profile.

In Vivo/In Vitro Correlations

In vivo/in vitro correlations for the purpose of product development, quality control, and so on are much more challenging for a product required to release over several months versus a few hours or a day. In animals, therefore, proof of control of the release to prevent dose dumping can be more challenging when the dose is for several months as opposed to a single day. Rarely do in vitro correlations exist to predict exact performance. The final determination is in the actual use.

VETERINARY CONTROLLED-RELEASE DRUG DELIVERY AND DELIVERY SYSTEMS

Intraruminal Drug Delivery

Intraruminal drug delivery systems are designed to be administered to, and retained in, the rumen of ruminant animals (e.g., cattle, sheep) and to deliver drugs over extended periods (months).

The anatomical and physiological characteristics of the stomach of ruminant animals are relatively complex. The stomach is large and composed of four compartments: the rumen, reticulum, omasum, and abomasum. The rumen is the largest compartment and may contain 80–200 L of ruminal fluid of pH 5–7 (9). The temperature of the rumen is in the range of 38–42°C and has a total internal gas pressure in the range of 1–1.1 atm arising from the conversion of foodstuffs into absorbable nutrients through mi-

crobial fermentation (9). This process is accompanied by the evolution of up to 600 L/day of gas. The composition and density of ruminal materials varies with the location (9). At the bottom of the rumen, the material is relatively well digested and mixed with copious amounts of fluid and is, therefore, of relatively high density. The upper layers of the rumen contain the newly ingested materials, which are much drier and of relatively low density (9).

A characteristic of the ruminant animal is that it spends much of its life grazing open pasture and is not extensively handled by the farmer. Consequently, the administration of pharmaceuticals is challenging, time-consuming, and costly because of the need to initially herd the animals into a convenient location to permit drug administration. The need to reduce handling of such animals on a regular basis for drug administration provides one of the biggest opportunities for the application of controlled-release technology to animal health and production.

Cardinal has recently outlined several key design features that are required of a controlled-release intraruminal drug delivery system (9). These include the inherent needs to (1) design the delivery system around a balling gun to allow for oral administration, (2) design the delivery system with a shape compatible with passage down the esophagus, (3) design the device with some mechanism that allows for long-term retention in the rumen of the animal (i.e., prevents regurgitation), and (4) incorporate some form of controlled-release technology that allows for the long-term delivery of the drug (up to 180 days) (8).

Several balling guns are commercially available (10). Regurgitation of the delivery system by the animal is prevented by either geometric design or density of the product. The literature suggests that a density of 1.8 or greater is required to prevent regurgitation of delivery systems from the rumen of cattle (11). When the density is less than 1.6, a significant number are not retained in cattle. The concept behind retention of the device in the rumen through geometry relies on creating a device that can be administered in a small enough size to allow for administration but will change its size or shape following administration to a form that is much greater in size than the esophagus.

Many controlled-release drug delivery systems have been developed for intraruminal administration over the last few decades (Table 3). For extensive reviews on intraruminal drug delivery, the reader is referred to Refs. 9, 36, 59, and 60.

Postruminal drug delivery

The process that allows the ruminant to utilize cellulose and nonprotein nitrogen is called rumen fermentation (61). Although this biological process is beneficial to the animal, it presents challenges to the drug delivery formulator because it also destroys or modifies bioactive materials (nutrients and drugs) that have been administered orally to prevent or treat disease (61). Thus, although ruminants could potentially benefit from the administration of bioactive materials (such as supplemental amino acids or saturated fatty acids), the administration of such materials orally through simple addition to feed is not practical. If the formulator wishes to persist with the administration of such bioactive materials orally, they must develop delivery systems that are stable in the rumen (i.e., that protect the drug from the harmful environment of the rumen) and that release their contents postruminally. Ideally, nutrients, drugs, and other active compounds incorporated into postruminal delivery systems should be fully protected from fermentation in the rumen and then be completely released and available for absorption or for performing their intended postruminal function (61). Many factors need to be considered when developing and designing a postruminal drug delivery system, including the typical retention times of particles and solids in the rumen and abomasum, pH of the rumen and abomasal fluid, the ruminant digestive process, the dynamics of ruminal motility, and the effects of rumination on particle degradation.

Several methods have been developed for protecting nutrients, drugs, and other active compounds from the environment of the rumen and are shown in Table 4 (61).

Intramammary Drug Delivery

The intramammary route for drug delivery is primarily used for the treatment of mastitis in cows and can be classified according to two main areas: lactating and dry (non-lactating). A once-only administration is beneficial to both these areas because it reduces handling of the animal. Each of these areas offers specific challenges to the delivery of an active agent. For example, the requirements for drug delivery to lactating cattle requires that the active ingredient be removed from the mammary gland or milk as soon as possible after the treatment period has elapsed so that there is no issue with regard to the presence of drug in the milk. In contrast, intramammary delivery in dry cows would allow for the formulation to be developed such that the drug persisted for a longer period of time after the treatment period had elapsed. Dry cow applications, therefore, lend themselves more readily to controlled drug delivery applications because the prolonged exposure of the infected site to drug improves the efficacy of treatment, and the concerns for drug residues in milk are not an issue.

A list of the various formulation types which have been explored for the intramammary route is shown in Table 5. Early developed formulations for intramammary drug delivery were aqueous based. Such formulations suffered from the disadvantage that they were short acting; however, they did distribute well over the infected areas (66). To overcome the problem of the short action, aqueous-based formulations have been developed that are coformulated with a water-soluble polymer such as poly(ethylene glycol). Oil-based formulations have also been investigated that allow for prolonged release of the active ingredient in the udder (66–71); however, they suffer from the disadvantage that they often irritate the udder mucosa (67) and distribute less homogeneously throughout the udder than aqueous preparations (66). Ointment-based products have also been studied and appear to offer an improvement over oil-based products. A further formulation type that has been investigated is the encapsulated drug product (68,69,72). Such formulations appear less irritating and more uniformly distributed around the udder. In addition, in some cases they also release drug over a prolonged period of time.

In recent years, with the rise of biotechnology, researchers have been investigating the use of vaccines and recombinant therapies to treat mastitis (73–78). These vaccines should offer the longest-term protection because they allow the animal to develop an immunity to the organisms that are causing the mastitis in the first place. However, because several types of organisms have been implicated in the cause of mastitis, the best vaccine would have to offer protection against a large spectrum of organisms and to date, no such vaccine exists.

Steroid Hormone-Containing Growth Promotants

Steroid hormone-containing implants improve the average growth of the animal. They contain either singularly or in combination estrogenic, androgenic, or progestegenic drugs (Table 6) (79). Growth response depends on the level and type of hormone incorporated into the delivery system, and commercially available controlled-release products differ in their hormone content, delivery matrix, and release pattern. Implants contain drugs incorporated into either lactose, cholesterol, polyethylene, or silicone rubber delivery matrix. Lactose-based implants are shorter acting (approximately 40 days) compared to cholesterol-based implants (approximately 80 days). Silicone rubber matrices provide the longest duration of release for estrogens (approximately 200–400 days). The amount of drug released from these delivery systems is greatest initially and slowly decreases with time, and release kinetics are typically described by either a first-order kinetics or a square-root-of-time mechanism (80). The most comprehensively described steroid hormone-containing implant is the Compudose delivery system (36,81,82). Compudose is a silastic implant composed of a drug-free silastic cylinder coated with a layer of silastic containing 20% dispersion estradiol. It has a surface area of 4.84 cm^2 and has been shown to release drug by a square-root-of-time mechanism.

Development of a steroid hormone-containing controlled-release implant requires that the implantation procedure is given consideration. Implants should not cause tissue irritation, and the administration site must be chosen such that it does not allow the delivery system to enter the food chain. Historically, the ear has been chosen as the site for administration because it represents an inedible portion of the carcass and is discarded on slaughter, accessible to the administrator, and well perfused with blood; as well, administration is relatively pain free and, therefore, provides minimal distress to the animal. The disadvantage of using this site is the need for restraint of the animal. Steroid hormone-containing controlled-release implants are not manufactured sterile, and therefore there is the need for an aseptic administration procedure. Implantation of commercially available implants into the subcutaneous tissue of the ear requires the use of a specially designed implanter.

The route of administration dictates the maximum size of the implant, which is an important consideration because modifying the surface area of the implant is an effective way of modifying release rate. The literature suggests that the optimum release profile for a steroid

Table 3. Intraruminal Drug Delivery Systems

Product name/ inventor	Description of delivery system	Drug	Retention mechanism	Animal and approximate release time	Mechanism of release
Paratect bolus	Hollow stainless steel cylinder about 4 in. in length and 1 in. in diameter that is filled with a drug reservoir comprising a paste of the drug/poly(ethylene glycol) 400. Each end of the cylinder is capped with rate-controlling membranes prepared from a microporous sintered polyethylene disk whose pores are filled with cellulose triacetate (12–15).	Morantel tartrate	Density	Cattle (90 days)	Diffusion through the water-filled channels of the two porous membranes at each end of the cylinder
Paratect Flex (16,17)	A central sheet of drug loaded a 50:50 mixture of ethyl vinyl-acetate coated on both sides with a layer of ethyl-vinyl acetate that renders each surface of the drug reservoir impermeable to drug to form a trilaminate structure. A series of holes is then punched in the device that transverse the complete trilaminate. The trilaminate sheet is then rolled into a cylinder and maintained as a roll with a water-soluble tape.	Morantel tartrate	Geometry trilaminate sheet that unrolls following administration to increase its dimensions	Cattle (90 days)	Moratal tartrate is a water-soluble salt and cannot permeate EVA. Drug is released from both the outer edges of the trilaminate and from the inner surface of each hole that was punched through the matrix. The kinetics of drug release from the outer edges follows the typical $t^{1/2}$ kinetics. The release from each hole is a function of increasing surface area at the receding drug boundary and increase in the diffusional pathlength over time within the depleted zone, which results in a net overall decrease in the release rate with time and thus a release rate that is relatively constant with time. The release rate is a function of the number and the diameter of the perforations and the rate of release from dispersed matrix devices.
Spanbolet II	Rectangular-shaped delivery systems approximately 3.5 in. by 0.5 in. by 0.5 in. in size. Manufactured by compressing drug, carnauba wax, barium sulphate, poly(ethylene glycol) and iron powder (18)	Oxytetracyclines	Density	Cattle (50 days)	Slow erosion of device within rumen

Laby	The device is composed of a hollow cylinder capped at both ends. One end is closed and serves to help constrain a spring that acts against a piston that in turn acts against an erodible composition containing drug or nutrient. The erodible composition comes in contact with the exterior environment via a portal in the second endcap. Attached to the cylinder are polymeric wings that are constrained to the side of the cylinder during administration by a water-soluble tape. This basic design has been subject of extensive work that has appeared in the patent literature, which describes improvements in device-retention mechanisms, core composition, piston/spring design, and delivery of multiple drugs with a single device (19–27).	This device design has been commercialized for the delivery of various compounds (e.g., albendazole and monensin) for sheep and cattle.	Geometry (expanding polyethylene wings that fold against the device on insertion but open within the rumen)	Sheep and cattle (100 or ~35 days)	The drug/nutrient-release rate is controlled via erosion of the tablet formulations incorporated into the device via the portal in the second endcap.
Beecham I	A matrix device in the form of a large sheet that can be rolled up to form a cylinder and constrained by a water-soluble tape; the size of the sheet is such that its unrolled dimensions are greater than that of the diameter of the esophagus. The device utilized a trilaminate sheet in which the inner lamina was composed of a core matrix of drug dispersed in an ethylene-vinyl acetate copolymer. This inner lamina was coated with a layer that was either impervious to fluid (and drug) or prepared with a filler such as starch or lactose to control the overall drug permeability properties in the coating (28).		Geometry; water-soluble tape dissolves and trilaminate unrolls.	Cattle (90 days)	Controlled release is achieved via two rate-limiting barriers containing a highly water-soluble compound that rapidly dissolves, leaving water-filled pores through which the drug leaches out.
Beecham II	A similar device configuration to the one above was also described by Griffin and Brewer but was composed of two lamina: One lamina was impermeable to drug, whereas the second lamina was an erodible dispersed matrix of drug plus ethylene-vinyl acetate (29).		Geometry; water soluble-tape dissolves and the laminate unrolls.	Cattle (90 days)	The drug-release rate was controlled via erosion of the erodible lamina.
Time capsule	A core containing zinc oxide and binding and releasing agents covered over all but one open end by a waxy coat (30)	Zinc oxide (± selenium and cobalt)	Density	Cattle (4 weeks) and sheep (6 weeks)	

Table 3. Intraruminal Drug Delivery Systems (*continued*)

Product name/inventor	Description of delivery system	Drug	Retention mechanism	Animal and approximate release time	Mechanism of release
Pulsatile bolus (Hollaway device)	Cylindrical device loaded with a steel ball in its rounded base for retention; the inside of the cylinder is filled with a series of drug-containing compartments, each separated by layers of degradable cellulosic partitions (31).	Monensin	Density	Cattle	A dose of drug is delivered (pulsed) from each drug-loaded compartment following exposure after dissolution/erosion of each of the cellulosic partitions. The dosage regimen can be controlled via the composition of each drug compartment and by the thickness and composition of the dividing layers.
IVOMEC SR Bolus	The device has recently been described by cardinal (9): The product is composed of a membrane cup that is extruded from cellulose acetate and various plasticizers. This cup is filled with an osmotic tablet that swells following the imbibement of water through the membrane cup. Placed above the tablet are a partition layer, a drug-containing layer, and a densifier. Both the partition layer and the drug layer are prepared from paraffin waxes and Cab-O-Sil. Drug is suspended at a concentration of 22% in the drug layer. The softening point of the partition layer is somewhat higher than the drug layer so that the partition layer will basically serve as a piston to help direct the flow of the drug-containing layer through the exit port channel located centrally in the densifier. The drug layer begins to soften in the range of 31–35°C. Under these conditions the drug is maintained as a suspension during storage and delivery without settling. At temperatures greater than about 35°C, the material has the requisite fluidity to flow through the exit channel and exit port screen. The densifier is made of sintered iron fillings designed such that it has a crush strength similar to that of bone (32,33). This is to ensure that the densifier will not harm the equipment utilized in rendering plants following slaughter of the animal. The central port in the densifier is covered with a capscreen made from plastic and designed such that the drug suspension is forced through a series of small openings in the capscreen (34).	Ivermectin	Density	Cattle (110 days)	Imbibement of water through the semipermeable membrane followed by expansion of the hydrogel that constantly forces a drug-containing vehicle through an exit port

Osmotic pressure–based ruminal bolus	Thombre et al. (35) describe a delivery device similar in overall design to that of the Paratect bolus but utilizing a novel osmotic technology suitable for the long-term delivery of drugs in which the drug is delivered as a solution in oil. This system utilized both the cylinder and membranes of the Paratect bolus as described above; however, the membranes and core formulations were suitably modified to convert the overall mechanism of drug delivery from diffusion control to an osmotic-based mechanism. In this system the core formulation was composed of an oil such as octanol, isopropyl myristate, or soybean oil and a swellable polymer such as PEG 600 or poly-vinyl alcohols dispersed as pellets within the oil. The drug was dissolved within the oil phase. One microporous polyethylene membrane was impregnated with cellulose triacetate and wetted with PEG 400. The other microporous membrane was either unimpregnated or treated with various other options to permit the membrane to be permeable to oil.	An ionophore with potential as a growth promotant	Density	Cattle	Osmotic-based release mechanism
Rumensin ABC	Consists of a plastic capsule about 16 cm long (utilizes Laby device technology) (36,37)	Monensin sodium	Geometry; following administration, two plastic wings unfold.	Cattle (100 days)	
Autoworm/Multidose 130	The delivery system is made up of a steel endweight connected to a magnesium alloy spindle. Around the spindle are placed five drug-loaded lifesaver-shaped tablets that are encased in PVC caps and separated by sealing washers (36,37).	Oxfendazole	Density	Multidose 130 delivers five doses of oxfendazole to grazing cattle over approximately 130 days. The first dose is delivered at about 21 days following administration.	Pulsed delivery at 23 days intervals as the drug-loaded lifesavers become exposed, following corrosion of the metal at a relatively constant rate
Marston erodible system	Erodible bolus containing cobalt oxide and other diluents (38)	Cobalt	Density		Erosion due to dissolution or abrasion due to the solution or mechanical action of the rumen

Table 3. Intraruminal Drug Delivery Systems (*continued*)

Product name/inventor	Description of delivery system	Drug	Retention mechanism	Animal and approximate release time	Mechanism of release
Pierce et al. erodible bolus	An erodible bolus comprising 2% active in combination with 5% monostearin, 10% carnauba wax, and 83% barium sulfate (39)	S-methoprene		Cattle	Erosion
Wood et al.	A combination of glycerol monostearate, carnauba wax, and barium sulfate (40)	Potent antiparasitacides		Cattle (120–180 days)	The devices can be configured to deliver drug at rates that range from about 0.001 to about 0.075 mg/kg/day.
Hemingway et al.	An erodible device composed of a core matrix of compressed particles containing the drug or nutrient, which is then coated with a rigid polymeric coat (41)	Minerals and vitamins	Density		The coating is insoluble in rumen fluids and is brittle and progressively fractures off following erosion of the core matrix. The duration of activity of this device is a function of the composition of the core matrix.
Baker	The delivery system is a relatively rapidly acting bolus composed of a core layer and an outer layer. Each layer is composed of the therapeutic agent, a water-swellable polymer, and inert materials so blended as to create a rapidly acting outer layer and a slower-dissolving core matrix (42).	Antibacterials			Dissolution
Soluble glass bolus	Glass-based delivery systems formed by melting the glass and nutrient components at high temperatures (up to 700°C) and drawing the melt into the desired shape (43–49)	Trace nutrients, copper, cobalt, and selenium	Density	Sheep (365 days)	Drug is released by diffusion of drug and/or dissolution of the glass.
Lilly	Comprises a stainless steel cylinder that is coated with a mixture of drug dispersed in a copolymer of lactic acid and glycolic acid (50–52)	Density	Monensin	Cattle (90 days)	Erosion of the drug-loaded polymer

Name	Description	Drug		Animal/Release	Mechanism
Monensin RDD	The core matrix is a mixture of 40% drug and a biodegradable copolymer prepared from lactic and glycolic acids (80:20 w/w). The core matrix is adhered to the inner surface of a metal cylinder by hot-melt adhesives and then placed inside a plastic case that has openings in the end large enough to allow drug release but of sufficient dimensions to prevent solid foreign material from the rumen contents from entering the device and physically abrading the core (53–55).	Monensin	Density	Cattle (150 days)	Controlled hydrolysis and degradation of the low-molecular-weight copolymer
Bagnall and Gyuril device	The device is composed of a series of cylindrical drug reservoirs. The drug formulation is maintained within the cylindrical reservoir by a plug (56).	Oxfendazole	Density	Cattle (three pulses at 30-day intervals)	Expulsion of the plug through the generation of a gaseous internal pressure within the cylindrical reservoir; the timing of release is regulated by an electrical circuit and a chemical squib that generates the necessary pressure. The squib is activated via a current that is controlled by an electrical circuit that regulates the timing for the application of current. The whole system is activated by placement within the rumen fluids that acts to close the circuit.
Kwan and Steber	A system that is composed of several doses of drug held together using an adhesive; each dose is composed of a bilaminated core that contains a layer containing drug and a layer that is comprised of sufficient weight to retain the delivery system in the rumen. Each dose is coated with a hydrophobic polymer that controls the time that the drug is exposed to ruminal fluid. A delivery system is described that contains three doses, each coated with a different biodegradable polymer (57,58)		Density	Multiple pulses	Degradation of polymer matrix; the polymer coatings surrounding each dose degrade at different rates and control the time of release of drug.

Table 4. Methods for Protecting Nutrients, Drugs, and Other Active Compounds from the Environment of the Rumen

Approach	Method	Advantages	Disadvantages
Heat treatment	Heat treatment of proteins reduces their solubility and degradation in the rumen (62).	Low cost	Heat treatment promotes reaction of amino acids with carbohydrates and reduces their bioavailability. Predictability and control of rumen protection is poor. Postruminal release of the active material is generally inversely related to the degree of rumen protection.
Chemical treatment	Chemical treatment reduces protein solubility and increases the amount of protein escaping rumen fermentation. A variety of chemical agents have been evaluated including formaldehyde, other aldehydes, acetic acid, and tannins among others (63,64).	Generally low cost	Use of formaldehyde raised significant safety concerns and has been abandoned in some countries. Chemical treatment is unsuitable for amino acids and other nutrients or drugs. Rumen protection and postruminal availability are quite variable.
Low-solubility peptides, amino acid derivatives or analogs, and calcium salts; for example, peptides of lysine and/or lysine with other amino acids have been investigated.	Analogs tested include N-stearyl-methionine, N-hydroxymethyl-methionine (HMM-Ca), α-hydroxy-γ-methyl-mercapto butyrate calcium, and methionine hydroxy calcium (HMB-Ca) (65).		Poor bioavailability postruminally (e.g., lysine peptides); Limited protection from rumen degradation for methionine analogs (65)
Lipid-based formulations (embedding in a fatty matrix) (61)	To formulate a lipid-based product, active compounds are either embedded in a lipid matrix or are formulated in small spheres and coated with lipid. The low solubility of the formulation in the rumen allows a large part of these materials administered orally to reach the small intestine and be absorbed. For this reason, they are formulated as calcium salts or in lipids that have poor solubility in the rumen. Lipid-protected products rely on their inherent resistance to enzymes in the rumen to maintain the integrity of the protective coating and their digestion by enzymes postpostruminally to release the active component.	Embedding in a lipid matrix or the process of applying a lipid coating has the advantage of using low-cost food-grade materials compared with formulated polymeric coatings.	Lipid matrix systems exhibit low payloads. Postruminal release of the active material for absorption is usually low and generally inversely related to the degree of rumen protection. Amino acids and small peptides are readily water soluble and do not remain inside the lipid matrix and become released into the rumen.
Ruminally inert, pH-sensitive polymers (reverse-enteric coating system) (61)	The bioactive material is coated with a coating system composed of a basic polymer such as poly(2-vinylpyridine-co-styrene, 8020), a pigment material such as talc or aluminum, and a hydrophobic substance such as stearic acid at a typical ratio of 31.5:63.5:5.0 by weight.	Process can be applied to a variety of nutrients, drug, or other active compounds	The coating efficiency was shown to be highly dependent on the solubility of active ingredients, pellet size, and smoothness of pellet surfaces. Because the polymeric coating is soluble in acid, the coating should not be in direct contact with acidic feed components such as silage. The coated particles should not be added along with other feed ingredients into a feed-pelleting machine because the coating cannot survive in a high-shear and abrasive pelleting process. Only a few polymers are suitable as the coating material.

Table 5. Delivery Systems for Intramammary Applications

Types of delivery formulations	Reference
Water- and ointment-based systems	66–69
Oil-based systems	66,68–71
Encapsulated systems	68,72
Polymeric aqueous systems	68,69,72
Vaccines and recombinant therapies	73–78

hormone-containing controlled-release implant is unknown (80). The literature is unclear as to whether an initial burst followed by a declining release rate, a constant release rate, or an increasing release rate is desirable (80).

The need to remove the implant is not a consideration because the delivery system will remain in the animal for its life span and be discarded at slaughter with the inedible portion of the carcass.

Vaginal Drug Delivery

The use of controlled-release drug delivery systems in estrous control has a history dating back to the early 1960s when polyurethane sponges were first investigated as a means to deliver synthetic progestagens to sheep (83). Both the intravaginal and subcutaneous route for drug delivery are used to administer controlled-release drug delivery systems for estrous control (Table 7). Compounds used to control the estrous cycle include progesterone, methyl acetoxy progesterone, fluorogestone acetate, and estradiol. Other drugs for example, melatonin, antibiotics, oxytocin, prostaglandins, GnRH, and a variety of other synthetic progestagens, have been shown to be systemically absorbed from the vagina of farmed animals. To date, polymers utilized for systemically delivering drugs via the vaginal cavity of animals in commercially available products have been limited to polyurethane and silicone (85).

Several factors that affect the design and development of an intravaginal veterinary drug delivery system have recently been identified and discussed by Rathbone et al. (87). These include applicator design, end-user acceptance, dimensions and geometry of delivery system, retention rate, retention mechanism, dimensions of the device, release rate, ease of use, animal comfort, irritation (mucopurrelant discharge production), polymer used to manufacture delivery system, drug properties, presence or absence of additives, ease of removal, damage to vaginal mucosa and cervix, applicator design, removal mechanism, and manufacturing process (87). A further valuable overview of this area has been published by Chien (88).

Long-Acting Injectable Products Used in Food-Producing Animals

Many of the various long-acting injectable drug delivery systems discussed elsewhere in this encyclopedia have also been explored in veterinary medicine. For example, biodegradable polymers, liposomes, and other microencapsulated materials have been investigated for use in animals; however, to date none have been commercialized (89–92). Carter et al. (93) provide an excellent overview of long-acting injectables in veterinary medicine. Implants containing steroids for growth promotion and those formulated for estrous control have already been presented, and injectables used in companion animals are discussed in a following section. Therefore, the focus of this section are the other applications for long-acting injectables for food-producing animals, such as antibiotics and antiparasiticides.

The use of the more technologically advanced systems, such as polylactide–glycolide polymers, has not been widely applied in the markets of veterinary injectables be-

Table 6. Controlled-Release Steroid Hormone-Containing Implants

Product	Estrogen	Androgen	Progesterone	Time to hormone concentration at which production is no longer enhanced (days)
Ralgro®	36 mg resorcyclic acid lactone (zeranol)			70
Ralgro Magnum	72 mg zeranol			Unpublished
Calfoid	10 mg estradiol 17β		100 mg	Unpublished
Synovex-C	10 mg estradiol 17β		100 mg	120
Synovex-S	20 mg estradiol 17β		200 mg	120
Synovex-H	20 mg estradiol 17β	200 mg testosterone		120
Synovex-Plus	28 mg estradiol benzoate	200 mg trenbolone acetate		Unpublished
Implus-S	20 mg estradiol 17β		200 mg	Unpublished
Implus-H	20 mg estradiol 17β	200 mg testosterone		Unpublished
Torevex-S	20 mg estradiol 17β		200 mg	
Finaplix-S		140 mg trenbolone acetate		105
Finaplix-H		200 mg trenbolone acetate		105
Revalor-G	8 mg estradiol 17β	40 mg trenbolone acetate		Unpublished
Revalor-H	14 mg estradiol 17β	140 mg trenbolone acetate		120 (estimated)
Revalor-S	24 mg estradiol 17β	120 mg trenbolone acetate		120
Compudose 200	24 mg estradiol 17β			200
Compudose 400	45 mg estradiol 17β			400

Source: Ref. 79.

Table 7. Controlled-Release Intravaginal Inserts and Subcutaneous Drug Delivery Systems Used for the Control of the Estrous Cycle in Cattle

Delivery system	Description of delivery system	Principle animal for which delivery system designed	Drug	Route
PRID	Comprises micronized progesterone (1.55 g) uniformly suspended throughout silicone rubber that is cured onto a stainless steel spiral coiled to produce a spiral-shaped cylinder approximately 4 cm in diameter and with a length of 12 cm; the delivery system has a hard gelatin capsule attached to its inner surface and a string to aid removal.	Cattle	Progesterone	Intravaginal
CIDR-B	Consists of a preformed T-shaped nylon spine over which is molded a silicone rubber skin containing 1.9 g of micronised progesterone; one end of the device has two flattened wings that are hinged to the body of the device. The wings retain the device in the vagina by gently exerting pressure against the walls of the anterior vagina. At the bottom end of the device is attached a plastic tail to aid removal.	Cattle	Progesterone	Intravaginal
Sponge	Cylindrical-shaped polyurethane sponges impregnated with varying amounts of synthetic progestagens	Sheep and goats	Fluorogestone acetate; methyl acetoxy progesterone	Intravaginal
Rajamehendran rubber tubing	The device contained progesterone and estradiol 17β and was manufactured by cutting silicone rubber tubing into 20-cm lengths, sealing one end with silicone medical adhesive, and then pouring in diethyl ether containing 1 g of progesterone. After the diethyl ether had evaporated, the open end of the tubing was sealed with more adhesive. Approximately 1 mL of adhesive containing 10 mg estradiol 17β was then coated around the end of each tube. Two of these tubes were then centrally tied together, and lengths of string were secured to each of the free ends to be pulled together and knotted to form the umbrella-shaped intravaginal device. Following insertion, the string was allowed to protrude from the vulva to enable removal of the device at the end of treatment.	Cattle	Progesterone/estradiol	Intravaginal
IBD	The Intelligent Breeding Device is a technologically advanced, controlled-release drug delivery system in which estradiol, prostaglandin, and progesterone are released at different rates and at specific times (estradiol, 1 h after insertion; prostaglandin, 6 days later; and progesterone, continuously for 10 days).	Cattle	Progesterone/estradiol/ prostaglandin	Intravaginal

Name	Description	Animal	Drug	Route
SYNCRO-MATE-B	A small ear implant containing 6 mg norgestomet (= 5% load) in the polymer Hydron, which measures approximately 3 mm × 18 mm and weighs approximately 0.125 g. The implants come encased within a protective plastic sheath and are supplied in individually sealed foil packaging.	Cattle	Norgestomet	Subcutaneous (ear)
SYNCRO-MATE-C	An ear implant that utilized the Microsealed Drug Delivery® (MDD) technology. The ear implant was formed by dispersing crystalline norgestomet in microreservoirs of aqueous PEG 400 throughout a matrix of polymerized silicone. The resulting solid composition was then cut into tiny cylindrical forms for implantation in the ear of cattle.	Cattle	Norgestomet	Subcutaneous (ear)
Ear implant (Crestar)	An ear implant containing 3 mg norgestomet homogeneously dispersed throughout a silicone matrix	Cattle	Norgestomet	Subcutaneous (ear)
CIDR-S	CIDR-S was rabbit eared in shape, containing 9% w/w micronized progesterone homogeneously distributed throughout silicone cured over a nylon spine. The device had a string attached to its lower end to aid removal.	Sheep	Progesterone	Intravaginal
CIDR-G	The CIDR-G is a T-shaped intravaginal device comprising of a preformed nylon spine than has a filament of flexible nylon preformed onto it to aid its removal. The device is coated with silicone impregnated with 9% w/w USP-grade micronized progesterone	Sheep	Progesterone	Intravaginal
Sil-Estrus	Comprised a solid silicone rod containing 375 mg of progesterone (10% w/w initial load), which measured 0.9 cm in diameter and 5.0 cm in length	Sheep	Progesterone	Subcutaneous (in the wool-free area under the foreleg along the brisket)
C-shaped plasthyd device	Comprised of a C-shaped delivery system manufactured from the polymer Plasthyd	Sheep	Progesterone	Intravaginal
Lutamate Plus	Poly(D,L-lactide) microspheres	Horse	Progesterone/estradiol	Intramuscular
Ovuplant	A cylindrical implant 2.3 mm in diameter and 3.6 mm in length containing 2.1 mg of Deslorelin (as Deslorelin acetate) in an inert matrix	Horse	Deslorelin	Subcutaneous

Source: Refs. 84–86.

cause the development of such products for a veterinary market is not economically favorable. As a result, the development of a controlled-release injectable in veterinary medicine has been based on three approaches: reliance on the pharmacokinetics of the particular drug compound, the use of a nonaqueous vehicle, or the manipulation of drug and/or vehicle composition to create a suspension.

For example, Ivomec® injection (Merial) is a solution of 1% w/w ivermectin in propylene glycol and glycerol formal that is given subcutaneously at ~200 µg/kg in cattle and 300 µg/kg in pigs. This injection is given once a month for the treatment of endoparasites. The main reason the injection is so long lasting is that the half-life of ivermectin in cattle is long and the potency of the compound is high, allowing even trace levels of the drug in the blood to be effective (94). The half-life of the drug, combined with its formulation into a nonaqueous vehicle (which allows for the creation of a depot at the site of injection), prolongs the action of the drug for over a month. Similar results are also seen with the doramectin and moxidectin products because they are of the same drug classification and exhibit similar half-life profiles.

In the area of antibiotics, florfenicol and oxytetracycline have been developed as long-acting injectables, Nulfor® injection (florfenicol) was developed by Schering-Plough to replace a chloramphenicol product needed to be administered at frequent intervals to combat bovine respiratory disease, or shipping fever. The dose of florfenicol is approximately 20 mg/kg; however, its solubility is low in most solvents. Therefore, to improve the drug's solubility, the formulators devised a complex nonaqueous cosolvent system that allowed for sufficient drug to be administered to allow administration once every two days. The solvents added to the formulation included propylene glycol, poly(ethylene glycol) and n-methyl pyrrolidone (95). This system allows for dosing at 48-h intervals.

Similarly, oxytetracycline was also developed to combat shipping fever. The development of the Liquamycin® LA by Pfizer has been well documented in the literature (96). In this case, tetracyclines were well known to also be insoluble as well as irritating, upon injection. To alleviate this problem, the formulators identified 2-pyrrolidone as a solubilizer and developed methods of chelating the oxytetracycline with magnesium ion to reduce the irritation upon injection. The theory was to prepare a solution of drug that was close to saturation so that upon injection, the drug would slowly deposit a fine precipitate, creating in effect a drug suspension depot at the injection site. This depot formulation would reduce the irritation and necrosis that had been previously observed. The resulting formulation succeeded in reducing the irritation and provided release of drug over 2 to 3 days.

Topical Dosage Forms for Food-Producing Animals

Various classes of long-acting topical formulations have been used in food-producing animals (Table 8). Historically, the application of topicals for food-producing animals has been primarily for ectoparasite control. The short-term formulations were applied by hand as dusts, ointments, sprays, and/or liquids. Dips have also been used in which

Table 8. Classes of Long-Acting Topical Formulations for Food Animals

Class of formulation	References
Oil-based liquids; spot-ons	97
Wax bars/cables/dust bags	97
Ear tags, e.g., PVC matrices	98
Ear tags, reservoir type	99,100
Microencapsulation formulations	101

a vat is prepared containing the active ingredient, and the cattle is trotted down into the vat and run up a ramp on the other side. Each of these formulation types, however, would only provide treatment for a few days at the most, because they would inevitably be rubbed off by the animals or washed off by the rain. Therefore, it became necessary to develop methods for prolonging the delivery of active agents over longer periods of time so that the animals would not have to be handled frequently (97).

The earliest controlled-release dosage forms for topical delivery were oil-based, which promoted the adhesion of the drug to the skin. Another early approach was to create a system in which the animals repeatedly dosed themselves. This was the principle behind the oil cables, wax bars, and dust bags that were impregnated with the active agents and left hanging near the locations in which the animals resided (97). The cattle would rub against the cable, bar, or bag and then rub itself or others, administering the active agent. The disadvantage of these systems was that the level of dosing could not be controlled and relied heavily on the behavior of the animal.

Eventually, people recognized the utility of placing the active ingredients into polymer matrices such as poly(vinyl chloride) (98). In these cases, the drug substances were blended into a monolithic structure and molded into a tag that was, for example, fixed on the ear. The tag then released the active agent over a prolonged period of time, such as several months. The active ingredient was transferred over the body of the animal by the natural rubbing motion of the animal on itself, as well as onto other animals. This dosage form is the most common in use today for the controlled release of topical ectoparasiticides.

In spite of its broad use, the monolithic tag concept does have disadvantages. For example, the tag delivers the largest portion of the active agent in the first part of the efficacious life span of the product. This is because the high concentrations of active agent provides a large driving force for delivery. In the latter half of the product life, the amount of drug substance delivered is greatly reduced because of the lower amount of active agent remaining in the matrix. Moreover, drug utilization is poor, and only a fraction of the active agent that is loaded into the matrix is actually released. Because of these limitations of the monolithic tag, a second generation of tag devices was developed in which the release profile was more zero-order, or more uniform, over the life of the product. This resulted in products that utilized a greater percentage of the total active agent loading (99–101). Such devices are based on reservoir technology rather than matrix technology. The tag is comprised of a depot of the active agent imbedded into a drug reservoir within the tag, which is covered by a membrane whose properties control the release of the active ingredient. Because the active agent exists as a solid in the depot, the rate of release is governed by the vapor pressure of the active, its solubility in the membrane, and its diffusivity through the membrane. These types of tags can also release drug substance to the animal for several months (99).

Microencapsulation has also been explored for the prolonged delivery of topical ectoparsiticides. For example, Despins et al. (101) developed a microencapsulated formulation containing permethrin and compared it with an emulsifiable product. The authors found that the microencapsulation product prolonged its efficacy but only by a short period of time. The release of the active ingredient to the skin appeared to be limited by the residence time of the formulation on the skin.

In addition to those formulations just described, there exist pour-on or spot-on applications, such as IVOMEC pour-on. These dosage forms are low-volume products that are applied (poured) directly over the back of the animal. In the case of IVOMEC pour-on, the prolonged pharmacokinetics of the active ingredient, ivermectin, is the main reason for the long-acting efficacy. Ivermectin is efficacious in very low quantities, and at a dose of 5 mg/10 kg body weight, enough of the active agent is absorbed to be efficacious for up to 28 days (102). A similar duration length is observed for other avermectin-type pour-on products containing ingredients such as duramectin and moxidectin.

Controlled-Release Technologies in Companion Animals

The therapeutic applications for companion animal health are as diverse as those already discussed for the food animal species. Those areas that will be discussed in this section include parasite control technologies; chemotherapeutic parenteral systems such as antibiotics, insulin, and estrous control; and finally ophthalmics. Products available for dogs and cats will be primarily reviewed, with the understanding that similar technologies could be employed for the other species, and in fact the exact same products are typically used and adapted for use in more exotic species.

Parasite Control.   One of the largest markets in companion animal drug delivery is in endo- and ectoparasite control and elimination. In ectoparasite control, the most popular compounds are included in the Interceptor (Norvartis) and Heartgard (Merial) products. These are milbemycin based and ivermectin based, respectively. The main reason for the long-acting nature of these orally administered dosage forms is the high potency of the compounds combined with their long biological half-lives. This allows for small dosages to be formulated into tablets that are easily given to companion animals, in particular dogs, at monthly intervals.

The most traditional mode of ectoparasite control is the ubiquitous flea collar. First developed in the late 1960s from vinyl resins containing dichlorvos, these collars have progressed to a variety of polymers containing an equally broad spectrum of active agents. The main basis of the technology of these collars is the incorporation of an active ingredient blended into the plastic matrix. The basic incompatibility between the plastic and the liquid and/or solid active agent forces the active to migrate to the surface of the collar, allowing it to be available to the fur of the animal, thereby eliminating the parasites.

Other technologies have also been explored for the release of ectoparasiticides. Reservoir systems in which the active agent is incorporated into a depot that is surrounded by a rate-controlling membrane have been explored, as have mechanical approaches (such as pumps) that release the active agent slowly over a long period of time. A history of ectoparasiticide collars has recently been published that discusses the development of the technologies used in this area from the vinyl collars to the recent technologies of today (L.C. Witchey-Lakshmanan, unpublished data).

The two most dramatic improvements in ectoparasite control have been in the development of spot-on products and orally active compounds, which provide protection for as long as 1 month per administration. Spot-on products can be applied with only a few milliliters of liquid along the back of the animal or at the base of the neck, and the duration of action of the active ingredient is sufficient to allow for control over approximately 30 days. Examples of these products include Frontline® TopSpot by Merial, Advantage® by Bayer, and Ex-Spot® by Schering-Plough (103). The staying power of these medications depends on the unique properties of the active agents and excipients with which they are compounded. For example, the active ingredient in Frontline is purported to remain unaffected by rain or washing because it sequesters into the sebaceous oils of the animal and releases slowly from there.

Program® and Sentinal® from Novartis also provide month-long protection; however, the initial presentations were in oral tablet form and are not effective against adult fleas. In this case, the long half-life of the drug substance allows for the long-acting control of the ectoparasites, similar to the mode discussed for the endoparasite products. More recently, Novartis has released an injection suspension in a prefilled syringe for which they claim 6-month efficacy against fleas. This is currently available for cats but is contraindicated for dogs due to injection site irritation.

Parenteral Chemotherapeutic Systems *Antibiotics and Cancer Therapies.*   In companion animal medicine, it can be advantageous to formulate the therapeutic ingredient into a sustained-release injectable dosage form that would allow administration of the active ingredient by the veterinarian at the clinic and would obviate the need for the pet owner to have to administer tablets. The administration of tablets can be quite challenging for the owner of a companion animal, especially for those who own cats, because the animal will often spit the tablet or liquid out of its mouth if the flavor is not to its liking. Indeed, once an adverse taste or feel of an oral preparation has been established to the feline patient, the owner will most likely find the animal under the furniture or behind a cabinet at the next dosing time. Therefore, a long-acting injection can improve the convenience to the owner, improve "patient compliance," and reduce the stress of the administrator.

As with long-acting injectable products used in food-producing animals, most of the long-acting injectable formulations discussed in other parts of this encyclopedia, such as implants, PLGA microspheres, liposomes, and so on, have also been investigated in companion animals. In contrast to human medicine, the use of advanced drug delivery approaches in animals is still primarily used only experimentally. For example, antimicrobial-laden poly-(methyl methacrylate) beads have been used in human medicine since the 1970s for the treatment of internal infection. These beads are typically on a wire "string" and surgically implanted into the location of interest. Once the infection is eliminated, these beads are then surgically removed. A similar application can be found in experimental companion animal medicine for the treatment of osteomyelitis and other internal infections (104). Naturally, one would wish to avoid the second surgery for the removal of the polymer beads once they are spent. This would lead one to the development of a biodegradable system that would deliver the active agent and then be absorbed by the body. Examples of such work can be seen by Garvin et al. (105) and Gupta et al. (106). Here, polylactide–glycolide-type polymers were prepared as microspheres or compressed rods and administered to dogs. Although these studies were developed for eventual use in humans, these still demonstrate the feasibility of such drug delivery approaches in the canine itself.

Liposomes have also been used for a variety of infections and cancers in animals (107–110). Gentamicin can be encapsulated for injectable delivery (107), as can other chemotherapeutic agents (108). Kruth (109) has presented an interesting article on the delivery of various biologically active agents for treatment of infections and cancers in companion animals. Included in this review is the use of liposomes in small-animal practice. Collagen implants loaded with chemotherapeutic products have also been used in companion animals for intratumoral treatment of skin cancers in veterinary patients (110).

Insulin. The types of insulin used for the treatment of diabetes in dogs and cats are often those also used in humans. For example, diabetes can be treated in humans by using porcine or beef insulin. This is acceptable because human insulin is similar to bovine and nearly identical to porcine insulin, differing only by one amino acid. Similarly, dog insulin is identical to porcine insulin and cat insulin is nearly identical to bovine insulin, which also only differs by one amino acid group (111). Now that recombinate human insulin is available, companion animals can be treated with that as well.

The insulins currently available on the market for use in animals include short-, intermediate-, and long-acting insulins. Short-acting insulin is designed to be released for the immediate treatment of high glucose levels in the animal. Intermediate, or lente, insulin is typically given to the animal twice per day, with feedings scheduled according to the injection times. Long-acting, or ultralente, insulin can be used for once-a-day delivery. In addition, there are several combinations of insulin that have been specifically formulated to provide certain release profiles and are available on the market. Greco et al. (111) present an excellent table of the types of insulin that are available commercially for companion animal use.

For the most part, the pharmacokinetics of these three types of insulin is determined by the crystal size of the insulin itself. For example, lente insulin is composed of 30% prompt zinc–insulin crystals and 70% extended insulin zinc. The small zinc–insulin crystals allow for a slower release than what would be observed over a regular insulin preparation but still allows for fairly complete dissolution into the bloodstream. In contrast, ultralente insulin is compose of large zinc crystals that dissolve more slowly.

As in humans, research continues in the exploration of implanting islet cells into animals to produce insulin under more naturally modulated circumstances. In brief, the islets are generally encapsulated into a hydrophilic polymer that allows the glucose to migrate into the cells and allows the insulin to migrate out. In addition, implantable reservoirs containing insulin have been formulated in hydrogel-type materials to provide a similar effect. Various types of glucose-sensitive moieties are placed onto the polymer, which will cause the polymeric material to expand in the presence of glucose. The expansion in the polymer network allows for the unhindered diffusion of the insulin out of the reservoir. Once the glucose level decreases, the moieties respond by causing the contraction of the polymeric material, thereby trapping the remaining insulin within the reservoir and impeding its diffusion out of the hydrogel. Both of these approaches are in the experimental stage. Further reading on this topic can be found in Refs. 112–115.

Estrous Control. Estrous control in companion animals is important for many reasons, from controlling the numbers of the canine and feline population to synchronizing the estrous in a manner predictable for breeders. To this end, several products are available, but most of them are not long acting. Some research has explored the use of a medroxyprogesterone acetate product for canine population control. This product, known as Perlutex Leo® in Norway, has become popular in replacing surgery and has reduced the number of dogs in various locations (116). However, the use of the product has also been associated with the formation of uterine lesions and canine mammary tumors (116,117).

The potential use of testosterone implants has been examined in a few studies for the purpose of inhibition of estrous in dogs (118,119). For example, Vincent et al. (119) have examined the plasma concentrations of testosterone in castrated dogs following the administration of implants composed of poly(dimethylsiloxane) capsules that were filled with various amounts of testosterone.

Bone Growth Therapies. In the last 10 years the presence and activity of bone morphogenic proteins (BMP) have become known. These are biological factors whose function is to differentiate mesenchymal cells into chondroblasts and osteoblasts, inducing the formation of bone. Interestingly, these factors can be included into implants that can be placed into fractures to promote healing in instances that would not normally heal properly on their own.

A review of the development of delivery devices containing BMPr has been published (120). This review primarily discusses the patents issued that discover the BMPs as well as those regarding the delivery devices and methods. A review of BMP technology as it relates to veterinary medicine has also been published (121). Kirker-Head discusses the function of BMPs, the delivery devices, and other potential applications from bone graft replacement to soft tissue joining with bone.

Ophthalmic Drug Delivery

Historically, ophthalmic dosage forms have been ointments or drops that are cleared from the eye quite quickly, requiring that the medicine be delivered several times in a day. When the challenges of dosing ophthalmic drops to a 50- to 500-kg animal by holding it still enough to apply the medication and repeating this activity several times a day are considered, one can easily see the need for a long-acting ophthalmic dosage form.

A thorough review of ocular delivery in veterinary medicine has been presented recently by Baeyens et al. (122). They include a discussion of ocular diseases and the agents used to treat them, an excellent list of the available products currently on the market, and a disclosure of the technologies being explored to prolong the release of the active agents.

The typical excipient added to prolong the release of an ophthalmic product is a hydrophilic polymer, such as a cellulosic, which increases the viscosity of the ophthalmic solution and increases the duration of the solution in the conjunctival sac. Another method that has been used is to add gums such as gellan or carrageenan that cross-link in the presence of the calcium ions in the tear fluid. This cross-linking also increases the viscosity and thereby the residence time of the product in the eye. A final mechanism found in aqueous gels is to use poloxamers, which can be formulated as liquids at room temperature but will gel at body temperature.

Inserts and implants have also been developed for ophthalmic drug delivery. Soluble inserts are most desirable because they do not have to be removed. However, some of these inserts have been shown to be irritating to the eye (122). Gurtler et al. (123) discuss the development of a veterinary insert that releases gentamicin for the treatment of ocular infections. This device is prepared with a combination of ethylcellulose and carbomer (poly[acrylic acid]) and can provide efficacious drug levels for as long as 72 h. A silicone implant has also been used experimentally for the treatment of glaucoma in dogs (124). However, these implants required surgical removal once the therapy was complete.

Protein and Peptide Delivery

Somatotropins. Somatotropins (growth hormones) are protein hormones produced by the anterior pituitary that stimulate growth in virtually all vertebrate species (125) as a result of direct receptor stimulation and stimulation of insulinlike growth factor I (IGF-I), a related anabolic protein hormone (126).

The gastrointestinal tract is a hostile environment for somatotropins. Administration by this route results in extensive degradation. In addition, because of the size and physicochemical properties of somatotropins, they are poorly absorbed via this route. The administration route of choice is parenterally. However, somatotropins are relatively large water-soluble molecules with a molecular weight of approximately 21,000 comprising 191 amino acid residues and contain two disulphide linkages. In addition, these molecules have a tendency to form aggregates within both the delivery system and in the biological environment that are biologically inactive or poorly absorbed. As a result of these features, somatotropins present challenges to the formulation scientists developing controlled-release parenteral drug delivery systems. Several important factors must be considered when formulating somatotropins into controlled-release parenteral drug delivery systems. Such factors include the following (125,127–130):

Properties of the Somatotropin.
- Stability of the protein drug during drying, formulation, manufacturing, and postadministration must be ensured. Somatotropin degradation can occur through aggregation, deamination or oxidation.
- The inherent bioactivity of the somatotropin will dictate, amongst other things, its selection and dose size.
- Physiochemical properties of the protein such as isoelectric point, molecular weight, amino acid composition, aqueous solubility at different pHs, and salt concentrations and organic solubilities are also important.

Properties of the Formulation
- Shelf-life stability should be as long as possible. One method to prolong the chemical shelf-life of a somatotropin product is to manufacture and store the formulation in the dry state, for example, as a pellet or implant. Alternatively, oily preparations can be formulated. To increase the physical stability of liquid preparations, viscosity-inducing agents can be added to the formulation.
- Commercially feasible delivery systems must be small to be easily administered. Given the high level of active-agent loads in the delivery system required to achieve therapeutic levels over extended periods of time, the size of the delivery systems may becoming the rate-limiting factor in their success.
- A zero-order release profile seems preferable, but most drug delivery systems currently available release somatotropins through a pseudo-first-order process. Pulsed delivery offers an alternative and mimics the natural method by which somatotropins appear in the blood.
- The duration of delivery of somatotropins to farmed animals is at least 1–2 weeks and up to 6 weeks. Such extended times offer stability and efficacy challenges, given the other factors discussed in this section.
- Administration must be able to be integrated into different management practices. The administration

procedure must also be relatively free from discomfort for the animal, and the delivery systems must not cause local irritation or a reaction while in the animal. For parenteral applications, solutions are easier to administer compared with implants, which may require specially designed implanters with large-bore needles.

- The bioactivity of the somatotropin needs to be considered and maintained throughout the shelf-life of the delivery system.
- The formulation needs to be such that aggregation of the somatotropin is avoided or minimized throughout the shelf-life of the sustained-release system.
- Interaction between the somatotropin and formulation should be considered and avoided to maximize shelf-life stability.
- The price of the controlled-release delivery system must be cost effective to realize commercial potential.
- The delivery system must be designed to efficiently utilize the incorporated dose.
- The delivery system must be reasonably aesthetic to appeal to the end-user. It must also be easily administered, offer improvements in control of therapy, adapt to farm management practices, be safe to the end-user and to the environment, and offer increased return on investment.

Considerations during Manufacture

- The bioactivity of the somatotropin needs to be considered and maintained during manufacture.
- Interaction between the somatotropin and formulation ingredients during the manufacture process should be identified and avoided.
- Issues such as method of drying the protein, storage conditions before and during processing, formulation processing conditions (e.g., light, time, heat, shear, etc.) and sterilization must be taken into consideration.

Considerations after Administration

- After administration, the formulation will absorb water from the surrounding environment and hydrate. This will result in the somatotropin existing at high concentrations in an aqueous environment and being exposed to elevated temperatures (37–39°C) for the duration of release. Thus, the aqueous stability of the somatotropin must be considered and known in the development of a controlled-release delivery system. Indeed, the in vivo stability of the somatotropins is the primary limitation for extending the duration of release, and formulators must investigate a variety of methods to improve to aqueous stability of somatotropins when their delivery system is exposed to condition typical of the in vivo environment.
- Because the animal enters the food chain, the level of somatotropin in the tissues must be evaluated so that none is left at the time of slaughter.
- The bioactivity of the somatotropin needs to be considered and maintained after implantation in the animal.

- The formulation needs to be designed such that aggregation of the somatotropin is avoided or minimized within the biological milieu.
- Interaction between the protein drug and formulation in the in vivo environment should be considered and investigated.

Table 9 documents various somatotropin drug delivery systems.

Other Peptides and Proteins. Many of the same controlled-release delivery systems that have been developed for somatotropins have been evaluated for the delivery of other proteins and peptides to animals. A prerequisite to the transfer of technologies between proteins is an inherent knowledge of the physicochemical properties of each individual protein or peptide prior to successful transposition of the technology. A delivery system and manufacturing process appropriate for the formulation of one protein or peptide may not be appropriate for a second. Table 10 documents delivery systems investigated for various protein and peptide compounds.

RECENT INITIATIVES

Vaccine Delivery

The market share for veterinary vaccines represents approximately 1% of the total world pharmaceutical market. With the increasing cost of research and development, production, licensing, and marketing of all medicinal products—including immunological veterinary products, their development, and clinical application—must be carefully considered. This section summarizes recent developments in the area of immunological veterinary products and discusses their potential applications. In addition, the specific application of molecular biology for the diagnosis, therapy, and basic investigation of diseases in animals is discussed.

The purpose of a vaccine is to protect a human or an animal against future exposure to an organism or pathogen that could potentially cause disease. Immunological veterinary products such as veterinary vaccines contribute greatly to the health of animals and reduced economic losses resulting from diseases, increase productivity, and ensure high-quality food for the customer.

There are two important issues that must be considered when formulating a veterinary vaccine: (1) the ability of the vaccine to protect against disease, that is, the need to identify what kind of immune response best controls the exposure to a particular pathogen and (2) the potential tissue damage that the vaccine may cause at the injection site. It is important to select the best vaccine for a particular pathogen or disease; the failure of the vaccine to protect against the particular disease for which it is administered results in animals that become ill later and therefore require additional treatment and costs. The dosage form, dose, route, and frequency of administration of a vaccine all play important roles in ensuring that an effective immune response is stimulated (186,187). The traditional means of evoking an immune response to an nu-

tigens to achieve adequate and lasting immunity is to administer it at timed intervals (initial and booster shot[s]) (Table 11).

Conventional vaccine formulations possess inherent disadvantages, and as a result, researchers have recently been focusing on the development of more suitable vaccine formulations. One approach has been the delivery of an antigen from an oil-based vehicle such as Freund's adjuvant (188). Such an approach has resulted in the reduction of the number of doses needed; however, because of the toxicity of the oil-based adjuvants, the search for a safer and more potent adjuvant continues. This search has resulted in the formulation of antigens into delivery systems that administer the antigen in particulate form rather than as soluble molecules. This approach facilitates recognition by the phagocytic systems and results in presentation of the antigen to the lymphocyte (189). Several particulate systems have been studied as vaccine delivery systems. These include emulsions, liposomes, nanoparticles, and microparticles. Each of these approaches are discussed in more detail in the following sections. The advantages of such vaccine delivery systems is that they can provide the ability to deliver antigens in a continuous manner or result in more control over the production of antibodies (190).

Emulsions. The manufacturing procedure of vaccine emulsions is relatively simple: The antigens are dissolved in a water phase and then emulsified in the oil in the presence of an appropriate emulsifier. The physicochemical characteristics of the final emulsion play an important determinant in the efficacy and handling of the vaccine. The controlled-release characteristics of an emulsion and dependent on certain properties of the emulsion, such as the viscosity of the oil phase, the oil–water phase ratio, and the emulsion droplet size. For example, a high oil content can cause unnecessary injection site irritation, and too large a droplet size can result in a physically unstable product, thereby reducing its shelf-life. Some problems may be observed with the oil/water emulsion type, but these can be overcome with multiple emulsion formulations (water/oil/water).

Foot and mouth disease (FMD) is as a highly contagious disease of domesticated and wild animals. FMD outbreaks can have devastating effects on the agricultural economies of developed, particularly FMD-free, countries, owing to the direct cost of control and indirect cost of trade embargoes. Oil-based FMD vaccines have been used in the field for many years, particularly in cattle in South America (191). Two novel oil-based FMD vaccines (FMDVs) were investigated by Salt et al., who examined their protective ability in pigs (191). In this study, the FMDV was formulated with new-generation, ready-to-formulate, mineral oil–based adjuvants. Basically, type C1 Oberbayyern FMDV antigen concentrate was emulsified using ISA 206 (Seppic, Paris) or ISA 25 as a water/oil/water or oil/water emulsion. Both formulations were shown to protect pigs against FMD virus within 4 days of vaccination. However, reimmunization was shown to be necessary after 21–28 days because of the continued risk of challenge.

Similar emulsion formulations were developed to protect a wild population of elephants against a natural outbreak of diseases caused by encephalomyocarditis virus (EMC)(192). The economic concerns associated with a wild population of elephants contracting EMC is that if the EMC virus spreads to swine, it may result in high piglet mortality due to myocarditis and respiratory failure (192). The experimental vaccine developed by Hunter et al. was tested in elephants, mice, and pigs. Their results showed that elephants vaccinated with the EMC vaccine formulation developed high antibody titers, whereas controls developed fatal or subclinical myocarditis. Similar results were also observed in mice and pigs. The vaccinated animals showed persistent antibody responses after a single vaccination and a lack of reaction to the adjuvant used (192). Their results suggested that the vaccine may be useful in wildlife species in zoos.

Perhaps nowhere in veterinary medicine has the practical application of vaccinations been more visible and rewarding than in the development of vaccines and diagnostics to assist in the control and eradication of pseudorabies (PR). Pensaert et al. (193) developed an emulsion vaccine formulation for PR in pigs (Aujeszky's disease). In this study, Aujeszky's disease vaccines and their ability to induce an immune response, which suppresses virus excretion optimally upon infection, were compared. All the pigs were vaccinated with glycoprotein deletion vaccines suspended in phosphate-buffered saline (PBS). Two additional groups were vaccinated with a gI-deleted vaccine virus suspended in an oil/water emulsion–excreted vaccine 2–6 days after injection. A 100- to 1,000-fold reduction in excreted virus titers was observed in vaccinated pigs compared with unvaccinated ones. Some vaccines suppressed virus excretion better than others, but no correlation could be made between the type of deletion and the degree of reduction in virus excretion. Similar results were obtained with two applications of inactivated vaccines. The lowest number of excreting pigs, the lowest duration of excretion, and the lowest titers were obtained in groups vaccinated with the attenuated vaccine suspended in emulsion (194).

Gliding bacterial adjuvant (GBA) has been characterized as a potent immune modulator, stimulating the growth of murine B lymphocytes in mice, inducing murine natural killer-cell activity, and promoting the release of several murine cytokines. Zeidner et al. tested gliding GBA emulsion formulations for their ability to activate feline peripheral T cells to secrete cytokines and to potentiate specific antibody responses in cats against a well-characterized T cell–dependent antigen and a recombinant immunogen derived from *Dirofilaria immitis* (194). The results of the trial showed that GBA also appeared to be a potent stimulator of feline T cell proliferation and induced both IFN and IL-2 production in cats. GBA has relatively low local and systemic toxicity and exhibits potent activity, both in PBS or within an oil vehicle. These characteristics make GBA an attractive new adjuvant for use in feline vaccines (194).

Liposomes. A variety of lipids have been used to create bilayer liposomal structures. Phospholipids were among the first chemicals used to form bilayer structures to mimic

Table 9. Parenterally Administered Somatotropin Controlled-Release Drug Delivery Systems

Delivery system type	Formulation of delivery system	Drug	Factors affecting release and stability	Disadvantages
Nonaqueous gels	Biocompatible vegetable oil (e.g., sesame oil, peanut oil) containing a dispersion of the somatotropin and incorporating thickening agents (e.g., aluminium monostearate, white beeswax, yellow beeswax). Appropriate amounts of thickening agent need to be added to achieve a compromise between physical stability and ease of injectability (126). Examples of nonaqueous gels for the delivery of somatotropins can be found in references (131–134)	N-terminated bovine somatotropin zinc salt (135) Bovine somatotropin (136)	Absence of water within the formulation results in a relatively long-term shelf-life. Viscosity of formulation can be modified to increase duration of release; can be achieved by selecting an oil from the range of hydrophobicity of oils or addition of excipients (e.g., esters of glycerol) or thickening agents. Improvement of the shelf stability, drug loading, injectability, and injection site; chemical and physical stability of the somatotropins, once injected into the animals, can also be achieved by alteration of the viscosity of the formulation.	Injectable nonaqueous gels form variable-shaped depots, which may affect the release profile from animal to animal (125) Release profiles are not zero order.
Microparticles (microspheres or microcapsules)	Microsphere matrix prepared from lactide/glycolide copolymers (D,L-lactide 50:50) using an anatomization process in liquid nitrogen containing about 10% drug load (137) Microsphere matrix prepared from glyceryl tristearate or glyceryl distearate using a spray prilling technique; microspheres containing 24.5% were suspended in soybean oil/Miglyol®812 and administered subcutaneously (138). Microspheres of polyglycholic acid (139).	Human growth hormone Bovine somatotropin Porcine somatotropin	Fat-based formulations provided better physical stability and shelf-life for glyceryl tristearate or glyceryl distearate microspheres when reconstituted in an oil vehicle (140). Aggregation of somatotropin reported to occur within the polymer	Animal growth-rate studies suggest that the release profiles from such formulations are not zero order.
Liposome	Egg phosphatidylcholine, ethanolamine, and α-tocopheryl hemisuccinate and Tris salt vescicles (141) Hydrogenated soy phosphatidylcholine–cholesterol hemisuccinate liposomes (142)	Bovine somatotropin Bovine somatotropin	Coformulation of liposomes with other delivery systems may provide opportunities to exploit liposomes as delivery systems for somatotropins, e.g., Refs. 143–145.	Low product loadings, difficulty and cost of manufacture, and stability issues are associated with the use of liposomes as delivery systems for somatotropins.
Emulsion (multiple water-in-oil-in-water type)	Appropriately buffered aqueous phases (e.g., carbonate-buffer) and oil phases (e.g., mineral oil) and stabilizing agents (e.g., sorbitan surfactants) (146,147)	Bovine somatotropin	Somatotropin was incorporated into the primary aqueous phase. Multiple emulsion was achieved using polyoxyethylene sorbitan surfactants.	
Aqueous solutions gelled with polymers	Aqueous injections using carbohydrate polymers such as dextrins, heteropolysaccharides, and various gums (148)	Bovine somatotropin		Injectable nonaqueous gels form, variable-shaped depots that may affect the release profile from animal to animal.

Aqueous conjugates (suspended complex)	HGH- and BST-prepared conjugates with bovine serum albumin using glutaraldehyde or with immunoglobulin using carboimide (149)	Bovine somatotropin	The conjugated molecule exhibited increased solubility over BST alone in solutions of pH less than 5 (149)
Hydrogels	Somatotropins suspended in silicone oil and placed into hydroxyethyl methacrylate–methyl methacrylate copolymer and hydroxyethyl methacrylate homopolymer cross-linked with ethyene glycol dimethacrylate cylindrical reservoirs that acted as a rate-limiting membrane have been described (150)	Ovine, equine, and bovine somatotropins	
	Small spheres of somatotropin–chitosin (60:40) coated with a hydrogel comprising poly(vinyl alcohol) have also been described (151)	Porcine somatotropin	
	In a matrix system, biodegradable thermoplastic hydrogels consisting of ABA or AB block polymers, where the block A is a glycolide and block B is polyethylene oxide or in the case of an ABA block polymer, a glycolide and trimethylene carbonate (152)	Bovine somatotropin	
	Delivery systems comprising polymers of D,L-lactide–glycolide containing poly(ethylene glycol) (153)	Bovine somatotropin	
Implants	A variety of methods are described in the patent literature, which describe the formulation and manufacture of both uncoated (154–158) and coated implants (by either a spray technique (e.g., ethyl cellulose/poly(ethylene glycol), poly(vinyl alcohol), poly(ethylacrylate methylmethacrylates) (159–162) or dip coating (e.g., molten blend of beeswax, carnauba wax, and Mazol®) (163). Controlled release from implants have also been achieved by placing the implant inside silicone tubes which had their ends covered by microporous polyethylene disks each having a 70-μm pore. The release of somatotropin from silicone tube-covered implants was designed to occur from the ends of the tubes (164).	Porcine somatotropin Bovine somatotropin Silicone tube-covered implants were prepared containing 40 mg of porcine somatotropin alone or 40 mg porcine somatotropin with sucrose.	Implants contain somatotropins at much higher concentrations than injection formulations. This may impact on the stability of the somatotropin following administration. Implant administration requires a relatively large bore needle. Implantation requires the design of a more complex administration system than a hypodermic syringe. Implants generally require a more complex manufacturing process, particularly if an aseptic implant is required. Factors affecting release from coated implants include thickness of coating, ratio of drug to excipients, type of excipients, degree of polymer cross-linking, surface area of the rate-limiting membrane, coating material, presence/absence of coating, and solubility of the somatotropin.
Osmotic devices	Several osmotic devices have been described in the patent literature. The constant delivery of drug from the devices relies on the incorporation of expandable excipients surrounded by a semipermeable wall into specially designed dispensers (165–169).	Porcine somatotropin	Cost of final product, final product size, administration difficulties, and delivery system recovery issues after slaughter limit the application of this technology to the administration of somatotropins.

Table 10. Delivery Systems for Various Protein and Peptide Compounds

Peptide or protein	Use	Formulation of delivery systems
Somatotropins	Increased milk yield Accelerated growth Increased feed conversion efficiencies Increase in lean-to-fat ratio Reduced fat deposition Increased ovulation	See Table 9.
Somatotropin releasing hormone (growth hormone–releasing hormone)	Increased milk production Accelerated growth Increased feed conversion efficiencies Increase in lean-to-fat ratio Reduced fat deposition Increased ovulation	Silicone rubber matrix (170) Collagen implant (171,172) Cholesterol acetate implants (173) 50:50 poly(D,L-lactide-co-glycolide pellets (174)
Luteinizing hormone–releasing hormone	Control of fertility Stimulation of spermatogenesis and ovulation	Compressed implants containing lactose and calcium phosphate and coated with Eudragit NE30 D (175–177); compressed core excipient ratios, percentage active present, and coating thickness affected rlease rate.
Luteinizing hormone–releasing hormone agonists (e.g., nafarelin acetate, leuprolide acetate)	Estrus suppression	Microspheres of various ratios of poly(D,L-lactide-co-glycolide (178–182) Silicone rubber implant (183) Crosslinked poly(orthoester) (184,185)

Table 11. Examples of Conventional Veterinary Vaccines on the Market

Vaccine	Animal	Disease
PHF-VAX-3	Horse	Tetanus, fever,
EWTF	Horse	Influenza, tetanus
MHB[a]	Pigs	Pneumonia
Prime Pac_R PRRS	Pigs	Respiratory viruses
Scourmune[R] CRT	Pigs	*Escherichia coli*
AR-Pac[R]	Pigs	Atropic rhinitis
Pliguard[R] *E. coli*-1	Calves	*E. coli*
Eclipse[R]3	Feline	Panleukopenia
Fevaxyn FeLV	Cats	Leukemia
Galaxy[R]D	Dogs	Distemper vaccine

cell membranes (195). Liposomes can induce both a humoral and cell-induced immunity, which is clearly an advantage when formulating a vaccine (196). In addition, liposomes can serve as carriers of antigens and adjuvants, as depots for the controlled release of antigens, and as targeting agents for the delivery of novel antigens and adjuvants to antigen-presenting cells (APCs). Although, liposomes have limited applications in veterinary medicine, the literature contains several encouraging experimental results that demonstrate their potential application in this field.

Nakanishi et al. showed that the pulsed administration of APCs with various antigens to mice resulted in the introduction of potent antigen-specific immune responses (197). These authors investigated the relationship between the liposome surface charge and the adjuvant action of liposomes in inducing immune responses to soluble antigen. Results revealed that the positive charge on the surface of the liposomes was important for enhancing their immunoadjuvancy in the induction of antigen-specific immune responses (197).

Enteric diseases remain one of the great causes of motility and morbidity in both human and veterinary species. However, mucosal surfaces are also the target of significant diseases. Although immunization strategies have been available for many years and have achieved significant success in the reduction of disease incidence and mortality when applied to diseases affecting organs, there has been a remarkable lack of success in vaccination to control mucosal disease (198). It has therefore become apparent that novel strategies are required to achieve effective defenses at such sites.

All mucosal surfaces, but particularly the intestine, represent a physiological dilemma whereby selective absorption of essential nutrients must occur with concomitant exclusion of pathogen (198). The oral route of immunization is a trustworthy way to induce mucosal IgA antibody responses. However, this immunization route has the problem of antigen degradation by gastric acidity and proteolytic enzymes in the intestinal lumen. The poor immunogenicity of ganglioside antigen such as ganglioside-GM1 is well documented (199). Therefore, the stability of ganglioside liposomes to acidic solution, bile, and pancreatic solution has been examined in the literature (200). Liposomes that contained the antigen ganglioside-GM1 demonstrated that their stability to acidic solution, bile, and pancreatin solution would permit them to effectively serve as an oral vaccine delivery vehicle for inducing mucosal immune response (200).

Saponin (201) and muramyldipeptide (MDP) (202) was used as an adjuvant to deliver ovalbumin (OVA) intraperitoneally (ip) in rats based on their availability, ease of preparation and previously demonstrated adjuvanticity in systemic immunization applications. The subsequent anti-OVA–containing cell response in the intestine was assessed in the study. The adjuvants were formulated in either vegetable oil emulsion or liposome vehicles, these formulations being biodegradable alternatives to the mineral oil component used in Freund's adjuvants. Results showed that both saponin and MDP exhibited adjuvant activity for IgA responses to OVA when administered ip. Although data showed that both MDP and saponin given in an emulsion provided an alternative to Freund's adjuvant for ip stimulation of IgA responses, the success of liposomes as a systemic antigen delivery system suggested their potential as an alternative vehicle for ip use. Although these alternatives have been developed for veterinary applications in which they have proved to be both effective and practical, they also show promise for the development of improved delivery systems for human mucosal vaccines (203).

Nanoparticles and Microspheres. Microspheres are defined as small particles typically no greater in size than 1 μm. Nanospheres are defined as colloidal particles with a diameter less than 1 μm. In contrast to liposomes, microspheres or nanospheres are prepared from polymers that can be manipulated according to the release requirements of the formulation. Preparation of these particles is discussed elsewhere in this encyclopedia.

The advantages of delivering vaccines in microparticles is that they may reduce the number of vaccinations required to give a prolonged protective response and/or that release of the vaccine can be controlled by a number of different mechanisms. Antigen is released from microparticles either by diffusion through pores or by erosion of the matrix. Among the acceptable polymers available to prepare microparticles, poly(lactic acid) and poly(lactide-*co*-glycolide) (PLGA) have been chosen the most often. These polymers are biodegradable, biocompatible, and FDA approved for use in therapeutic products (204). Veterinary applications of microparticulate vaccines are limited, but investigations in this area are increasing rapidly. For example, a two-bait delivery systems for oral immunization of dogs against rabies was tested in small-scale field trials in Tunisia (205). The bait consisted of a freeze-dried core unit containing a biomarker covered with a paraffin matrix. The baits were placed on transect lines, which offered the possibility to vaccinate certain categories of dogs that were not accessible via a dog owner–mediated approach. Unfortunately, the method offered less safety than other systems, was less specific, was not readily accepted by the human population, and was costly.

Immunization against luteinizing hormone–releasing hormone (LH-RH) may offer an interesting experimental tool and also a veterinary vaccine capable of increasing meat production by immunological castration. Production of antibodies against LH-RH has been reported in sheep, cattle, rats, rabbits, and primates (206). However, because this decapeptide is only a weak antigen, immunization has traditionally required repeated injections of the synthetic hormone conjugated to a carrier and emulsified in Freund's complete adjuvant. However, Carelli et al. investigated a more superior method of immunization by using the synthetic adjuvant MDP conjugated with polylysine (207). Results revealed that those synthetic haptens and the synthetic adjuvant MDP could be usefully coupled to the polymeric carrier. Moreover, LH-RH mixed with MDP or conjugated with MDP–lysine and injected in an aqueous medium produced a greater binding activity than that observed with Freund's adjuvant alone (207).

Yersinia pestis is the causative agent of pneumonic and bubonic plague. *Y. pestis* vaccine offers protection against bubonic plague; however, vaccinated animals acquired pneumonic plague (207). Therefore, the ability of the vaccine to confer protection against pneumonic plague is questionable. In addition, undesirable side effects are common immunity induced by the vaccine is short lived, and further doses (one given every 6 months) are required to maintain the same level of protection (208). Subunit vaccines using protective components from *Y. pertis* may avoid adverse effects but require adjuvants or appropriately formulated delivery systems to boost immunity (209). To achieve this, one approach is to encapsulate antigenic material within polymeric carriers such as PLGA. For example, F1 antigen from *Y. pestis* was encapsulated in PLGA microparticles, which induced high serum titers when injected ip in mice (209). In addition, mucosal IgA was also detected. The 1-μm-diameter PLGA microparticles gave effective protection against challenge with *Y. pestis* after only one dose, which may be due to the microspheres having depot-release properties; therefore, less antigen and fewer doses were necessary for protection (209).

It is known that small particles are able to cross the mucosal barrier and penetrate into the blood circulation when administered nasally. Animal experiments using microspheres induced significantly higher levels of serum antibodies to the antigen than when the free antigen was administered to the nasal mucosa. In a similar study, F1 and V subunits of *Y. pestis* were encapsulated in PLGA and administered intranasally to mice. Results revealed that encapsulated subunits induced significantly elevated serum antibody titers to F1 and V relative to free antigen, and served to protect 66% of the vaccinated animals from inhalation challenge (210).

Nonparenteral immunization, such as simple mucosal application of antigenic proteins (for example, in the gastrointestinal or respiratory tracts), is usually ineffective in terms of vaccination (211). This is a result of enzymatic or chemical destruction combined with poor absorption into subepithelial compartments. To overcome these problems, some form of an antigen delivery system needs to be formulated, for example, biodegradable microspheres that protect the antigen from enzyme degradation in the lumen. Several investigations suggest the applicability of such an approach. Atarki et al. (212) investigated the possibility of using an inert oral delivery system to stimulate mucosal antiphosphorylcholine immunity. Phosphorylcholine was noted to be a hapten present on different pathogenic bacteria such as *Streptococcus pnemoniae*, *Salmonella typhimurium*, *Proteus morganii*, and *Neisseria menengiditis* and on parasites such as *Ascaris suum* and *Trichinella spiralis*, which invade or colonize via the mucosa at different anatomical sites. Oral administration of biodegradable microspheres loaded with phosphorylcholine induced a specific IgA response in intestinal, pulmonary, and vaginal secretions as well as a strong specific immune response in female Balb/c mice (211).

Genetically Engineered Vaccines. Modern vaccine technology has now provided us, through genetic engineering, the ability to use genetic material as a vector to protect animals and human against a variety of diseases (213). These vaccines, especially those constructed of genetically engineered proteins, are expensive. However, currently available (nongenetically engineered) vaccines are not cheap. In addition, many of them provide only temporary immunity, and the weaker the vaccine, the greater the dose necessary to stimulate an immune response and the greater the risk of overactivating the immune response, resulting in shock and death. Genetically engineered vaccines have the potential to overcome these latter problems; however, when the first genetically engineered hepatitis-B vaccine was developed, it cost $150 for three injections. The vaccine was safe and effective. Nevertheless, few farmers or pet owners would be willing to pay so costly a price for a vaccine. The issue surrounding the cost of genetically engineered vaccines is the current stumbling block in their acceptance and use in veterinary medicine.

The new generation of vaccines include subunit, synthetic peptide, and live recombinant vaccines, which contain only the most critical proteins involved in inducing protection, or live attenuated vaccines, in which specific genes involved in virulence have been deleted, with a low probability of back mutation and reservation to virulence. However, genetically engineered vectors offer the advantage of being able to carry multiple antigens from a variety of pathogens and therefore provide the opportunity for immunizing animals with delivery systems that would be adaptable to various species. Hence, the induction of various types of immune responses, depending on the agent and the animal being immunized, might be possible.

The first recombinant DNA-derived modified live vaccine was licensed for manufacture and sale in 1986. Gene-deleted PR vaccines (PRV) OMNIVAC-PRV and OMNIMARK-PRV were a major breakthrough for PR control and eradication (214). PR is caused by a herpes virus that induces acute or fetal infections of baby pigs and a variety of clinical symptoms in older animals. Cattle, sheep, dogs, cats, rodents, and raccoons are also susceptible to fetal PRV infections. The annual cost to the U.S. producer of a PR outbreak has been estimated at $30–72 million. Unfortunately, vaccination does not prevent latent infection by field strains. Neither modified live virus (MLV) or inactivated conventional PRV vaccines have prevented infection. To maximize safety, a purified clone of a Bucharest (BUK) vaccine strain of PRV was chosen as the starting material for the genetic engineering of OMNIVAC-PRV and OMNIMARK-PRV. Although total eradication of PRV may be unrealistic, previous studies have shown that a saturation vaccination program using OMNIVAC-PRV with culling is effective without having to resort to depopulation.

The forms of antigen and its formulation have a significant influence on vaccine efficacy and on the duration of immunity. This is particularly important if the immunity is cell mediated or mucosal. With viral infections, the major targets for immunity are often surface glycoproteins that are found in mucosa. Hence, the surface glycoproteins are important for the attachment and entry of the virus to host cells; consequently, a virus vaccine in one species might be used in another. Babik et al. tested this hypothesis using purified glycoprotein B and C of the herpes virus to use as an experimental vaccine in cattle (215). In all cases, the purified protein induced neutralizing antibodies, and more importantly, calves were protected from infection.

The other type of live recombinant vaccine uses the most studied poxvirus, vaccinia virus (VV), as a vector, by incorporating immunogenic genes of disease agents into the VV genome (216). Vaccinia was used for almost 200 years as a vaccine for smallpox. A large variety of genes have been expressed in vaccinia virus recombinants, including enzymes, clotting factors, hormones, and importantly, genes that encode for protective immunogens. These latter genes have been derived from other viruses, bacteria, and parasitic organisms. This can be exploited to produce a recombinant vaccine directed toward multiple pathogens pertinent to a specific population. One of the potential advantages of the poxvirus vector is its large volume, which has a large capacity available for the insertion of multiple foreign genes. In addition, unlike many live vaccines, the lyophilized form of VV is heat stable. This is a major advantage in carrying out successful vaccination programs in developing tropical countries. When the VV vector is introduced into an animal, the virus replicates in the host cell, and the foreign genes are expressed together with those of VV. For example, rinderpest is an acute, febrile, and highly contagious viral disease of ruminants with a rapid course and a mortality rate exceeding 90% (216). It is characterized by inflammation, hemorrhaging, necrosis, and erosion of the gastrointestinal tract, accompanied by bloody diarrhea, wasting, and death. Cattle vaccinated with a VV vaccine were shown to be completely protected from rinderpest and exhibited no detectable illness or clinical disease (216,217).

Panicali et al. constructed recombinant VVs containing the cloned hemagglutinin gene from the influenza virus (217). Immunization of rabbits with recombinant poxviruses resulted in the production of antibodies reactive with authentic influenza HA. The production of antibodies directed against influenza HA suggested that the HA gene expressed in vaccinia is immunogenic. These data indicate the potential of genetically engineered poxvirus for use in generic live vaccine vehicles that have veterinary or human application (217).

Marek's disease (MD) is a malignant T-lymphomatosis of chickens and is caused by Marek's disease virus type 1 (MDV1) (218). MD is the first cancer that was made preventable by vaccination and has been largely controlled by use of live attenuated or naturally avirulent vaccines since the early 1970s. To examine the protective efficacy of the recombinant MD vaccine, specific pathogen-free chickens were vaccinated with rMDV1. Almost all birds were protected from MDV challenge via intramuscular, ocular, intranasal, and intratracheal routes at 4 weeks after vaccination. In addition, the rMDV1 provided 100% protection against virulent MDV1 challenge in chickens. Antibody responses against MDV1 antigen were observed up to as long as 11 weeks after immunization (218).

In the case of bovine respiratory disease, management systems vary around the world, with economic losses often occurring following weaning, movement, and confinement of animals. Respiratory pathogens in cattle such as bovine respiratory syncytial virus (BRSV) and bovine herpes virus are challenging targets for DNA vaccine development (219). These viruses are important pathogens in cattle for which various live and inactivated vaccines are currently used in the field (220). Schrijver et al. compared the protection afforded by three different DNA application methods against BRSV infection in cattle (220). Intradermal (id) administration with a needleless injector reduced BRSV excretion significantly better after BRSV challenge than when administered iv or id with a needle. Serum antibody levels against G protein were high and showed less variation in calves vaccinated with needleless injectors compared with those in id- and im-vaccinated calves. Parenteral DNA application was shown to be capable of inducing the priming of the immune response at the respiratory mucosa (220).

DNA plasmid vaccines can stimulate very specific and powerful long-term immune responses against virtually any pathogen. These vaccines can be delivered by either direct injection or by gene gun. Delivery of genes via a gene gun involves coating gold particles with the plasmid of interest (221). Direct injection of DNA into all species requires larger quantities of plasmid to induce an immune response than if administered by a gene gun. The reason for this may be degradation of the plasmids before they are taken up by the cells in vivo and transported to the nucleus. Lodmell et al. demonstrated that direct intracellular epidermal delivery of plasmid DNA–coated gold particles via a handheld helium-powered gene gun would elicit protective immune responses against a rabies virus (222). The gun system permitted a more simple and rapid delivery of DNA compared with the more typical needle injection, and more importantly, the force of the particle bombardment propulsion was thought to propel the DNA-coated beads through the plasma membrane of the cells. In another study using an AccellR gene gun, particle-mediated immunization with DNA encoding the glycoprotein gene of the standard strain of rabies virus was shown to elicit highly protective levels of rabies virus–neutralizing antibody in mice. At 315 days postprimary immunization, 100% of the mice survived intraplantar rabies virus challenge (223).

It has also been shown that plasmid DNA-encoding canine parvovirus (CPV) induced immunity may protect dogs against challenge with virulent virus (224). Nucleic acid (NA)–vaccinated dogs showed an increase of serum IgG titer starting 1 week postinjection, which peaked at 2 weeks and remained detectable for at least 14 weeks. All NA-accinated dogs were protected against infection after virulent CPV challenge regardless of dose, whereas the control dog was fully susceptible. This study demonstrated for the first time that NA can protect dogs against an infectious disease (224).

In addition to inducing immune responses to infectious diseases, DNA immunization has also the potential for the control of ectoparasites (225,226). Recently, investigators have used concealed antigens as vaccines. Concealed antigens are antigens that do not normally induce immune responses during ectoparasite infestations because they are rarely exposed to the immune system (225). However, if the host contains antibodies to these antigens in the blood, these antibodies interact with the concealed antigen in the gastrointestinal tract and in combination with complement may result in lysis or disruption of gastrointestinal tract cell function and death of the ectoparasite. These concealed antigens are glycoproteins; therefore, administration of genes encoding these glycoproteins in plasmid should induce very high levels of immune responses to the appropriate epitope (226). Although there is limited literature indicating that DNA immunization works with concealed ectoparasite antigens, some reported studies have been promising (226). For example, immunization of rabbits against the midgastrointestinal tract antigen of mosquitoes demonstrated a lower survival rate of mosquitoes in those fed on immunized rabbit versus those fed on normal (nonimmunized) rabbits (225).

Gene Therapy

The identification of underlying genetic disorders has recently made gene therapy an attractive treatment option for a wide variety of disorders in both humans and animals. Gene therapy offers new opportunities to treat these disorders both by restoring gene functions that have been lost through mutation and/or by introducing genes that can inhibit the replication of infectious agents. Genes used in such therapies are viewed as medicines, and their development as a therapeutic agent faces similar issues to those encountered during the development of other drugs and proteins such as bioavailability, toxicity, activity, and cost/risk/benefit (227). The ideal gene therapy vector should be easy to formulate, nonimmunogenic, and nontoxic and should have a low cost/risk ratio; it has to reach to target cells and then should be transported to the nucleus where gene expression takes place, and it must be expressed in predictable controlled fashion.

The development of gene delivery systems has included both nonviral and viral vector systems. Viral vectors can arise from viruses that are extensively modified to provide immune responses with increased cloning capacity to permit the incorporation of genes and complex regulatory elements. Other viral vectors emerge through the modification of existing, relatively inefficient, nonviral delivery systems. Therapeutic applications of gene therapy in animals are currently limited, except for the genetically engineered vaccines that have been previously discussed in this section. However, the number of applications of nucleic acid probes or recombinant DNA products for clinical or diagnostic use in veterinary medicine is increasing rapidly (228,229).

Hormones, growth-stimulating factors, enzymes, cytokines, and immunomodulating proteins have all been cloned from the human genome for use in veterinary medicine.

Only a small number of genes from species of veterinary importance have been cloned so far. Two immunomodulating cytokines have been cloned for the cat α-interferon and tumor necrosis factor. Human interferon can also be administered either orally or subcutaneously to cats for the treatment of feline leukemia virus infection. Recombinant interferon acts as immunomodulator and antiviral agent (230).

Hemaropeietic growth factor is a regulatory molecule essential for controlling blood cell differentiation and in vitro proliferation and survival. Potentially, this agent may be useful in prevention and treatment of chemotherapy- or radiation-induced cytopenia and treatment of suppression of bacterial infections associated with clinical feline panleukopenia virus infection of kittens (231).

Hemophilia is a bleeding disorder caused by a deficiency in the clotting factor VIII. A canine model was used to determine if an adenoviral vector expressing a human factor VIII cDNA could be used to correct the hemophilia A phenotype. Results showed that the disease in dogs could be treated effectively using the human factor VIII. However, further advances in vector design are needed to enable sustained expression. Correction of the coagulation defect in a large-animal model is a crucial step to verifying the feasibility of gene therapy for this disease (232).

The polymerase chain reaction (PCR) is particularly important for identification and diagnosis of parasites as well as for many other applications in veterinary medicine. The key to the development of a nucleic acid probe is to identify nucleotide sequences that are unique to the particular organism of interest. The application of molecular biology in veterinary parasitology requires the classification of parasites, the diagnosis of infection, the development of the antiparasitic vaccine, the development of antiparasitic drugs, and the selection of a host with genetic resistance (233). This reaction can be used to screen a cDNA or genomic DNA library for classification and diagnosis and many other purposes. PCR primers and a probe derived from a gene encoding an intraerythrocytic piroplasm surface protein of *Theileria sergenti* has used. *Babesia bovis* has been diagnosed in chronically infected cattle by using PCR for a merozoite surface protein. High sensitivity was achieved with a limit of detection of parasitemia (233,234).

Molecular biology is also being applied to the improvement of chemotherapy against veterinary parasites. The use of antisense nucleotides for therapy generally relies on the synthesis of an antisense oligonucleotide and the delivery to the target, which is the parasite's nucleic acid. Therefore, an antisense oligonucleotide has to be synthesized and delivered into the parasite's cells, where it must not be degraded too rapidly and must hybridize with the parasite's nucleic acid to prevent the protein expression, which is essential for the survival of the parasite. Adequate delivery systems remain a problem in the practical application of antisense therapeutics to parasites.

Trends and Future Directions of Vaccines and Gene Therapy

This section has considered some of the recent progress in the development of new vaccines and genetically engineered products for improving animal health and their veterinary application using by molecular biology and biotechnology techniques. Vaccines have played, and will continue to play, a critical role in presenting, controlling, and eliminating diseases in animals and humans. Although applications of genetically engineered products are presently limited, the use of recombinant products is increasing. We are confident that in the future we will have unlimited potential for the production of safer and more effective vaccines, therapeutic proteins, and recombinant products and more sensitive diagnostic reagents.

CONCLUDING REMARKS

The veterinary area offers unique opportunities to the formulation scientist that arise from the diverse nature of the field, the desire of the end-user to fit drug therapy around farm management practices, and the anatomical and physiological peculiarities of an individual animal species. Many technologies have been developed to overcome the challenges associated with the delivery of drugs to animals, and numerous examples of innovative controlled-release drug delivery systems exist in the literature.

BIBLIOGRAPHY

1. M.J. Rathbone, *Adv. Drug Delivery Rev.* **28**, 301–302 (1997).
2. P.G. Welling and M.R. Dobrinska, in J.R. Robinson and V.H.L. Lee, eds., *Controlled Drug Delivery: Fundamentals and Applications*, 2nd ed., Dekker, New York, 1978, pp. 253–291.
3. W.-Y. Kuu, R.W. Wood, and T.J. Roseman, in A. Kydonieus, ed., *Treatise on Controlled Drug Delivery: Fundamentals, Optimization, Applications*, Dekker, New York, 1992, pp. 37–154.
4. T.J. Roseman and N.F. Cardarelli, in A. Kydonieus, ed., *Controlled Release Technologies: Methods, Theory, and Applications*, CRC Press, Boca Raton, Fl., 1980, pp. 37–154.
5. V.H.K. Li, J.R. Robinson, and V.H.L. Lee, in J.R. Robinson and V.H.L. Lee, eds., *Controlled Drug Delivery: Fundamentals and Applications*, Dekker, New York, 1978, pp. 3–94.
6. Y.W. Chien, in Y.W. Chien, ed., *Novel Drug Delivery Systems*, 2nd ed., Dekker, New York, 1991, pp. 381–528.
7. B.M. Silber, M. Bialer, and A. Yacobi, in J.R. Robinson and V.H.L. Lee, eds., *Controlled Drug Delivery: Fundamentals and Applications*, 2nd ed., Dekker, New York, 1978, pp. 213–251.
8. P.K. Gupta and J.R. Robinson, in A. Kydonieus, ed., *Treatise on Controlled Drug Delivery: Fundamentals, Optimization, Applications*, Dekker, New York, 1992, pp. 255–313.
9. J.R. Cardinal, *Adv. Drug Delivery Rev.*, 303–322 (1997).
10. D.W. Cook, in G.E. Hardee and J.D. Baggott, eds., *Development and Formulation of Dosage Forms*, 2nd ed., Dekker, New York, 1998, pp. 305–356.
11. J.L. Riner, R.L. Byford, L.G. Stratton, and J.A. Hair, *Am. J. Vet. Res.* **43**, 2023–2030 (1982).
12. R.M. Jones, *Vet. Parasitol.* **12**, 223–232 (1983).
13. U.S. Pat. 4,220,153 (1980), D.S. Dresback.
14. H. Prosl et al., *Vet. Parasitol.* **12**, 251–260 (1983).
15. F.H.M. Borgsteed, *Vet. Parasitol.* **12**, 251–260 (1983).
16. W.A. Boettner et al., *J. Controlled Release* **8**, 23–30 (1984).
17. U.S. Pat. 4,601,893 (1986), J.R. Cardinal.
18. R.L. Byford, J.L. Riner, and J.A. Hair, *Bovine Pract.* **15**, 91–94 (1981).
19. U.S. Pat. 3,844,285 (1974), R.H. Laby.
20. U.S. Pat. 4,416,659 (1983), B.E. Simpson and N.A. Gervais.
21. U.S. Pat. 4,671,789 (1985), R.H. Laby.
22. U.S. Pat. 4,687,480 (1987), R.H. Laby and M.A. Lance.
23. U.S. Pat. 4,883,484 (1989), M.T. Shepard and S.R. Edwards.

24. U.S. Pat. 5,162,116 (1991), M.T. Shepard.

25. U.S. Pat. 5,198,222 (1993), M.O. Scully and D. Woodling.

26. U.S. Pat. 5,277,912 (1994), L.B. Lowe and T. McArthur.

27. U.S. Pat. 5,562,915 (1996), L.B. Lowe and C.J. McArthur.

28. U.S. Pat. 4,228,149 (1980), M.D. Brewer and G.J.L. Griffin.

29. U.S. Pat. 4,308,250 (1981), G.J.L. Griffin and M.D. Brewer.

30. U.S. Pat. 5,720,972 (1998), R. Munday.

31. E.P. 0,062,391 (1982), J.W. Hollaway.

32. P.K. Wilkinson and J.B. Eckenhoff, *Proc. Int. Symp. Controlled Release Bioact. Mater.* (1987).

33. U.S. Pat. 5,206,024 (1993), R.B. Eckenhoff.

34. U.S. Pat. 5,122,128 (1992), J.R. Cardinal, P.K. Wilkerson, and J.L. Zingerman.

35. A.G. Thombre, J.R. Cardinal, and L.A. Fournier, *J. Controlled Release* **18**, 221–234 (1992).

36. J.R. Cardinal and L.C. Witchey-Lakshmanan, in A. Kydonieus, ed., *Treatise on Controlled Drug Delivery*, Dekker, New York, 1992, pp. 465–489.

37. R. Duncan and L.W. Seymour, *Controlled Release Technologies*, Elsevier, Oxford, U.K., 1989.

38. U.S. Pat. 3,056,724 (1962), H.R. Marston.

39. R.C. Pierce, T.P. Bowman, J. McDaniel, and R. Winslow, *Proc. Int. Symp. Controlled Release Bioact. Mater.* **15**, 294–295 (1988).

40. U.S. Pat. 5,322,692 (1994), I.B. Wood, R.B. Toothill, and J.C. Dietz.

41. U.S. Pat. 4,732,764 (1988), R.G. Hemingway, N.S. Ritchie, and J.J. Parkins.

42. U.S. Pat. 5,190,760 (1992), R.C. Baker.

43. U.S. Pat. 4,350,675 (1982), C.F. Drake.

44. U.S. Pat. 4,482,541 (1984), S.B. Telfer, G. Zervas, and P. Knott.

45. B.F. Alger, *Proc. Int. Symp. Controlled Release Bioact. Mater.* **14**, 89–90 (1987).

46. U.S. Pat. 4,662,879 (1987), C.F. Drake and M. Tripp.

47. U.S. Pat. 4,793,997 (1988), C.F. Drake and A.J. Arch.

48. U.S. Pat. 4,851,225 (1989), C.F. Drake and J.O. Alfred.

49. W.M. Allen et al., *Vet. Rec.* **115**, 55–57 (1984).

50. E.P. 0,025,697 (1983), J.W. Kleber and B.E. Simpson.

51. E.P. 0,026,599 (1984), R.S. Nevin.

52. E.P. 0,062,391 (1982), B.E. Simpson.

53. J.M. Conrad and D.S.J. Skinner, *J. Controlled Release* **9**, 133–147 (1988).

54. J.M. Parrott, J.M. Conrad, R.P. Basson, and L.C. Pendlum, *J. Anim. Sci.* **68**, 2614–2621 (1990).

55. U.S. Pat. 4,649,042 (1985), R.C. Davis et al.

56. U.S. Pat. 4,564,363 (1983), B.G. Bagnall and R.J. Gyurik.

57. U.S. Pat. 5,110,598 (1992), L. Kwan and W. Steber.

58. U.S. Pat. 5,178,874 (1993), L. Kwan and W. Steber.

59. J.R. Cardinal, *J. Controlled Release* **2**, 393–403 (1985).

60. P.R. Klink, T.H. Ferguson, and J.A. Magruder, in G.E. Hardee and J.D. Baggott, eds., *Development and Formulation of Dosage Forms*, 2nd ed., Dekker, New York, 1998, pp. 145–229.

61. S.H.W. Wu and A. Papas, *Adv. Drug. Delivery Rev.* **28**, 323–334 (1997).

62. W.C. Bergen and F.N. Owens, *Anim. Health Nutr.* **40**, 32–35 (1985).

63. U.S. Pat. 3,988,480 (1976), S.R. Ames and C.D. Robeson.

64. W. Chalupa, in Y. Ruckebusch and P. Thivend, eds., *Digestive Physiology and Metabolism in Ruminants*, Avi Pub. Co., Westport, Conn., 1980, pp. 325–347.

65. A. Papas, G.A.B. Hall, E.E. Hatfield, and F.N. Owens, *J. Nutr.* **104**, 653–659 (1974).

66. I. Schipper, *Am. Vet. Med.* **50**, 111–113 (1955).

67. W.G. Huber, C.E. Lofgrin, W. Reynolds, and H.G. Luther, *Vet. Med.* **55**, 35–38 (1960).

68. G. Ziv, in D.C. Monkhouse, ed., *Animal Health Products, Design and Evaluation*, American Pharmaceutical Association, Washington, D.C., 1978, pp. 32–66.

69. S. Vangelov, *Vet. Med. Nauki* **18**, 84–90 (1981).

70. J.K. Pearson and C.L. Wright, *Vet. Rec.* **84**, 294–298 (1959).

71. W.D. Schultze and H.D. Mercer, *Am. J. Vet. Res.* **37**, 1281–1284 (1976).

72. U.S. Pat. 3,639,560 (1972), D.M. Moran, B. Regis, and J. Croucher.

73. J.M. Finch, A. Winter, A.W. Walton, and J.A. Leigh, *Vaccine* **15**, 1138–1143 (1997).

74. J.S. Hogan et al., *J. Dairy Sci.* **78**, 285–290 (1995).

75. G.M. Pighetti and L.M. Sordilio, *J. Dairy Sci.* **78**, 528–537 (1995).

76. D.E. Shuster and M.E. Kehrli, *Am. J. Vet. Res.* **50**, 313–320 (1995).

77. P.G. Reddy et al., *Cytokine* **4**, 227–231 (1997).

78. M.J. Daley and E.R. Oldham, *Vet. Immunol. Immunopathol.* **31**, 301–312 (1992).

79. F.D. Lehman and J.R. Rains, *Compendium*, August, S174–S177, S206 (1996).

80. R.L. Preston, *Adv. Drug Delivery Rev.*, in press.

81. I.H. Ferguson, G.F. Needham, R.R. Pfeiffer, and J.F. Wagner, *Proc. Int. Symp. Controlled Release Bioact. Mater.* **14**, 51–52 (1987).

82. U.S. Pat. 4,191,741 (1980). J.L. Hudson and J.F. Wagner.

83. T.J. Robinson, *The Control of the Ovarian Cycle in the Sheep*, Sydney University Press, Australia, 1967.

84. M.J. Rathbone, K.L. Macmillan, C.R. Bunt, and S. Burggraaf, *Adv. Drug Delivery Rev.*, in press.

85. M.J. Rathbone et al., *J. Controlled Release*, in press.

86. M.J. Rathbone et al., *Crit. Rev. Ther. Drug Carrier Syst.* (in press).

87. M.J. Rathbone et al., *Adv. Drug Delivery Rev.*, in press.

88. Y.W. Chien, in Y.W. Chien, ed., *Novel Drug Delivery Systems; Fundamentals, Developmental Concepts, Biomedical Assessments*, Dekker, New York, 1982, pp. 413–463.

89. Q.A. McKellar, *Vet. Parasitol.* **54**, 249–258 (1994).

90. Y.S. Yang and K.F. Fung, *Acta Vet. Scand.* **87**, 406–407 (1991).

91. M. Onuma et al., *Zentralbl. Veterinaermed, Reihe B* **36**, 139–147 (1989).

92. S. Trostle, D. Hendrickson, W. Stone, and A. Klohen, *J. Am. Vet. Med. Assoc.* **208**, 404–407 (1996).

93. D. Carter, M. Luttinger, and D. Gardner, *J. Controlled Release* **8**, 15–22 (1988).

94. *Veterinary Pharmaceuticals and Biologicals*, 8th ed., 1993, pp. 730–731.

95. U.S. Pat. 5,082,863 (1992), H.M. Apelian, D. Coffee-Beach, and A. Hug.

96. A. Aguiar, W.A. Armstrong, and S.J. Desai, *J. Controlled Release* **6**, 375–385 (1987).

97. R.O. Drummond, *Vet. Parasitol.* **18**, 111–119 (1985).

98. W.O. Haufe, *Can. J. Anim. Sci.* **62**, 567–573 (1982).

99. S.M. Herbig and K. Smith, *J. Controlled Release* **8**, 63–72 (1988).

100. E.P. 0,152,190 (1985), C.A. Speckman.

101. J.L. Despins, J.S. Hunter, R.B. Davey, and J.E. George, *J. Agric. Univ. P. R.* **79**, 93–98 (1995).

102. *Veterinary Pharmaceuticals and Biologicals*, 8th ed., 1993, p. 732.

103. J. Cunningham, R. Everett, P. Tanner, and P. Jeannin, *Proc. North Am. Vet. Conf.*, January, 1997.

104. K. Tobias, R. Schneider, and T. Besser, *J. Am. Vet. Med. Assoc.* **208**, 841–845 (1996).

105. K. Garvin et al., *J. Bone Joint Surg.* **76**, 1500–1506 (1994).

106. P.H. Gupta, H. Johnson, and C. Allexon, *J. Controlled Release* **26**, 229–238 (1993).

107. T. Hernandez-Caselles, A. Vera Crespo, F.J. Villalain, and J. Gomez-Fernandez, *Am. J. Vet. Res.* **50**, 1486–1488 (1989).

108. E. MacEwen et al., *J. Natl. Cancer Inst.* **81**, 935–938 (1989).

109. S. Kruth, *Vet. Clin. North Am.: Small Anim. Pract.* **28**, 269–295 (1998).

110. E. Orenbuer, E. Luck, D. Brown, and B. Kitchell, *Clin. Dermatol.* **9**, 561–568 (1991).

111. D. Greco, J. Broussard, and M. Peterson, *Vet. Clin. North Am.: Small Anim. Pract.* **25**, 677–689 (1995).

112. D. Church, *J. Small Anim. Pract.* **22**, 301–310 (1981).

113. E. Bertoy, R. Nelson, and E. Feldman, *J. Am. Vet. Med. Assoc.* **206**, 1729–1731 (1995).

114. S. Moise and T. Reimers, *J. Am. Vet. Med. Assoc.* **182**, 158–164 (1983).

115. P. Graham, A. Nash, and Q. McKellar, *J. Small Anim. Pract.* **38**, 434–438 (1997).

116. A. von Berky and W. Townsend, *Aust. Vet. J.* **70**, 249–250 (1993).

117. M. Stovring, L. Moe, and E. Glattre, *Acta Pathol. Microbiol. Immunol. Scand.* **105**, 590–596 (1997).

118. J. Simmons and C. Hammer, *Am. J. Vet. Res.* **34**, 1409–1419 (1973).

119. D. Vincent et al., *Am. J. Vet. Res.* **40**, 705–709 (1979).

120. L. Appel and L. Witchey-Lakshmanan, *Crit. Rev. Patol.* **10**, 30 (1994).

121. C. Kirker-Head, *Vet. Surg.* **24**, 408–419 (1995).

122. V. Baeyens et al., *Adv. Drug Delivery Rev.* **28**, 335–361 (1997).

123. F. Gurtler, V. Kaltsatos, B. Boisrame, and R. Gurny, *J. Controlled Release* **33**, 31–236 (1995).

124. T. Glover, M. Nasisse, and M. Davidson, *Am. J. Vet. Res.* **56**, 936–940 (1995).

125. S.M. Cady and W.D. Steber, in L.M. Sanders and P. Hendren, eds., *Protein Delivery: Physical Systems*, Plenum, New York, 1997, pp. 289–317.

126. I.C. Hart and I.D. Johnson, in P.J. Buttery, D.B. Lindsay, and N.B. Haynes, eds., *Control and Manipulation of Animal Growth*, Butterworth, London, 1986, pp. 135–159.

127. T.H. Ferguson, in K. Park, ed., *Controlled Drug Delivery*, American Chemical Society, Washington, D.C., 1997, pp. 289–308.

128. J.L. Cleland and R. Langer, *ACS Symp. Ser.* **567** (1994).

129. M.J. Hageman, J.M. Bauer, P.L. Possert, and R.T. Darrington, *J. Agric. Food Chem.* **40**, 348–355 1992.

130. T. Chen, *Drug Dev. Ind. Pharm.* **18**, 1311–1354 (1992).

131. U.S. Pat. 5,013,713 (1991), J.W. Mitchell.

132. U.S. Pat. 4,988,140 (1990), T.H. Ferguson, R.G. Harrison, and D.L. Moore.

133. U.S. Pat. 4,977,659 (1988), A.L. Thakkar, R.G. Harrison, and D.L. Moore.

134. Aust. Pat. 9,170,937 (1991), N.J. Kim, B.G. Rhee, and H.S.

135. U.S. Pat. 5,013,713 (1991), J.W. Mitchel.

136. U.S. Pat. 4,977,140 (1990) T.H. Ferguson, R.G. Harrison, and D.L. Moore.

137. WO 94/12158 (1994), H. Auer, M.A. Khan, and H. Bernstein.

138. U.S. Pat. 4,837,381 (1989), W.D. Steber, R. Fishbein, and S.M. Cady.

139. J.W. Wyse, Y. Takahashi, and P.P. DeLuca, *Proc. Int. Symp. Controlled Release Bioact. Mater.* **16**, 334–335 (1989).

140. U.S. Pat. 5,213,810 (1993), W. Steber.

141. U.S. Pat. 4,861,580 (1989), A.S. Janoff et al.

142. WO 89/05151 (1989), A.L. Weiner, L.F. Estis, and A.S. Janoff.

143. T.M. Feeser and M.A. Wheatley, *Proc. Int. Symp. Controlled Release Bioact. Mater.* **20**, 32–33 (1993).

144. T.M. Feeser and M.A. Wheatley, *Proc. Int. Symp. Controlled Release Bioact. Mater.* **21**, 196–197 (1994).

145. G. Gregoriadis and B. McCormack, *Proc. Int. Symp. Controlled Release Bioact. Mater.* **21**, 89–90 (1994).

146. U.S. Pat. 4,857,506 (1989), P. Tyle.

147. P. Tyle and S.M. Cady, *Proc. Int. Symp. Controlled Release Bioact. Mater.* **17**, 49–50 (1990).

148. U.S. Pat. 5,266,333 (1993), S.M. Cady et al.

149. U.S. Pat. 5,045,312 (1991), R. Aston, R. Bomford, and A.T. Holder.

150. U.S. Pat. 4,959,217 (1990), L.M. Sanders and A. Domb.

151. C. Younsik et al., *Proc. Int. Symp. Controlled Release Bioact. Mater.* **18**, 595–596 (1991).

152. U.S. Pat. 4,882,168 (1989), D.J. Casey and L. Rosati.

153. E.P. 809,482 (1983), J.R. Churchill and F.G. Hutchinson.

154. U.S. Pat. 5,198,422 (1993), M.T. Clark et al.

155. U.S. Pat. 5,015,627 (1991), T.O. Lindsay and M.T. Clarke.

156. U.S. Pat. 4,863,736 (1989), M.J. Azain, K.E. Eigenberg, T.R. Kasser, and M.J. Sabacky.

157. U.S. Pat. 5,328,697 (1994), S.N. Raman and M.W. Gray.

158. WO 91/05548 (1991), K.N. Sivaramakrishnan.

159. U.S. Pat. 5,015,627 (1991), T.O. Lindsay and M.T. Clarke.

160. E.P. 462,959A1 (1991), E.J. Castillo, K.E. Eigenberg, K.R. Patel, and M.J. Sabacky.

161. U.S. Pat. 5,213,810 (1993), W. Steber.

162. WO 92/07556 (1992), C.G. Pitt, Y. Cha, E.M. Donaldson, and E. McLean.

163. WO 90/11070 (1990), K.N. Sivaramakrishnan and L.F. Miller.

164. U.S. Pat. 4,917,685 (1990), R. Viswanathan and R.B. DePrince.

165. U.S. Pat. 5,023,088 (1991), P.S.L. Wong et al.

166. U.S. Pat. 5,110,597 (1992), P.S.L. Wong et al.

167. U.S. Pat. 4,959,218 (1990), J.B. Eckenhoff et al.

168. U.S. Pat. 5,110,596 (1992), J.A. Magruder et al.

169. U.S. Pat. 5,238,687 (1993), J.A. Magruder, J.R. Perry, and J.B. Eckenhoff.

170. E.P. 219,076 (1987), K. Fujioka, S. Sato, N. Tamura, and Y. Takada.

171. Aust. Pat. 8,655,983 (1986), K. Fujioka, S. Sato, and Y. Takada.

172. E.P. 326,151 (1989), K. Fujioka et al.

173. U.S. Pat. 5,039,660 (1991), R.J. Leonard and S.M. Harman.

174. B. Mariette et al., *J. Controlled Release* **24**, 237–246 (1995).

175. WO 90/11070 (1990), A.H. Williams et al.

176. R.C. Oppenheim et al., *Proc. Int. Symp. Controlled Release Bioact. Mater.* **15**, 54–55 (1988).

177. W.J. Theil and K.C. Tsui, *Proc. Int. Symp. Controlled Release Bioact. Mater.* **18**, 207–208 (1991).

178. L.M. Sanders, G.I. McRea, J.S. Kent, and B.H. Vickery, *Proc. Int. Symp. Controlled Release Bioact. Mater.* **10**, 91–96 (1983).

179. L.M. Sanders et al., *J. Pharm. Sci.* **73**, 1294–1297 (1984).

180. R. Burns and J. Sanders, *Proc. Int. Symp. Controlled Release Bioact. Mater.* **15**, 452–453 (1988).

181. H. Okada, *Proc. Int. Symp. Controlled Release Bioact. Mater.* **16**, 12–13 (1989).

182. J.R. Lawter, N.S. Brizzolara, M.G. Lanzilotti, and G.O. Morton, *Proc. Int. Symp. Controlled Release Bioact. Mater.* **14**, 99–100 (1987).

183. R. Burns, G. McRea, and L. Sanders, *Proc. Int. Symp. Controlled Release Bioact. Mater.* **15**, 64–65 (1988).

184. J. Heller, L.M. Sanders, P. Mishky, and S.Y. Ng, *Proc. Int. Symp. Controlled Release Bioact. Mater.* **13**, 69–70 (1986).

185. J. Heller et al., *J. Controlled Release* **6**, 217–224 (1987).

186. T.W.F. Pay and P.J. Hingley, *Vaccine* **5**, 60–65 (1987).

187. J.G. Hu, A. Ide, T. Yokoyoma, and T. Kitagava, *Chem. Pharm. Bull.* **37**, 3042–45 (1989).

188. S.J. Brett, L. Dunlop, F.Y. Liew, and J. Tile, *Immunology* **80**, 306–310 (1993).

189. C. Andre, J.F. Heremans, J.P. Vearmen, and C.L. Combiaso, *J. Exp. Med.* **142**, 1509–1519 (1975).

190. E.C. Anderson, R.C. Masters, and G.N. Mowat, *Res. Vet. Sci.* **12**, 342 (1971).

191. J.S. Salt, P.V. Barnett, P. Dani, and L. Williams, *Vaccine* **16**, 746–754 (1998).

192. P. Hunter et al., *Vaccine* **16**, 55–61 (1998).

193. M.B. Pensaert, K. Desmet, and K. Dewaele, *Vet. Microbiol.* **22**, 107–117 (1990).

194. N.S. Zeidner et al., *Vaccine* **14**, 1294 (1995).

195. H. Mizugichi et al., *Br. J. Cancer* **73**, 472–476 (1996).

196. C. Alving, *J. Immunol. Methods* **140**, 1–13 (1991).

197. T. Nakanishi et al., *Biochem. Biophys. Res. Commun.* **240**, 793–797 (1997).

198. D. Rowley, *Aust. J. Exp. Biol. Med. Sci.* **55**, 1–10 (1977).

199. A. Makita and N. Tanuguchi, *Glycosphingolipids*, Elsevier, Amesterdam, 1985, p. 1.

200. M. Han, S. Watarai, K. Kobayashi, and T. Yasuda, *J. Vet. Med. Sci.* **59**, 1109–1114 (1997).

201. A.A. MacColm, R. Bomford, and L. Dalton, *Parasite Immunol.* **4**, 455–461 (1982).

202. H. Kiyano, J.R. McGhee, J.F. Kearny, and S.M. Mealek, *Scand. J. Immunol.* **15**, 329–332 (1982).

203. M.L. Dunkley and A.J. Husband, *Immunology* **61**, 475 (1986).

204. J.H. Eldridge, J.K. Staas, J.A. Meulborek, and T.R. Tice, *Infect. Immunol.* **59**, 2978–2983 (1991).

205. H.C. Matter et al., *Vaccine* **16**, 657–665 (1998).

206. I.S. Robertson, J.C. Wilson, and H.M. Fraser, *Vet. Rec.* **105**, 556–557 (1979).

207. C. Carelli, F. Audibert, J. Gaillard, and L. Chédid, *Proc. Natl. Acad. Sci. U.S.A.* **79**, 5392–5395 (1982).

208. P. Bartelloni, J.D. Marshal, and D.C. Cavanaugh, *Mil. Med.* **138**, 720–722 (1973).

209. K.M. Reddin et al., *Vaccine* **16**, 761–767 (1998).

210. J.E. Eyles et al., *Vaccine* **16**, 698–707 (1998).

211. D.T. O'Hagan, *Novel Delivery System for Oral Vaccines*, CRC Press, Boca Raton, Fla., 1994, pp. 1–268.

212. K.A. Atarki et al., *Vaccine* **16**, 685–691 (1998).

213. J.J. Donnely, J.B. Ulmer, and M.A. Liu, *J. Immunol. Methods* **176**, 145–152 (1994).

214. S. Kit, *Vaccine* **8**, 420–425 (1990).

215. L.A. Babiuk et al., *DNA Vaccines*, N. Y. Acad. Sci., New York, 1995, pp. 50–56.

216. T. Yilma, *Dev. Biol. Stand.* **82**, 201–209 (1994).

217. D. Panicali, W.S. Davis, L. Weinberg, and E. Paoletti, *Proc. Natl. Acad. Sci. U.S.A.* **80**, 5364–5368 (1983).

218. M. Sakaguchi et al., *Vaccine* **16**, 472–479 (1998).

219. R.S. Schrijver, J.P.M. Langedijik, and G.M. Keil, *Vaccine* **15**, 1908–1916 (1997).

220. R.S. Schrijver, J. Langedijik, G. Keil, and F.A.M. Rijsewijk, *Vaccine* **16**, 130–134 (1998).

221. J.B. Ulmer, J.J. Donnely, and S.E. Parker, *Science* **259**, 1745–1749 (1993).

222. D.L. Lodmell, N.B. Ray, and L.C. Ewalt, *Vaccine* **16**, 115–118 (1998).

223. E. Fynan et al., *Proc. Natl. Acad. Sci. U.S.A.* **90**, 11478–11482 (1995).

224. W. Jiang et al., *Vaccine* **16**, 601–607 (1998).

225. G. Nogge, *J. Insect Physiol.* **24**, 299–304 (1978).

226. C.H. Eisemann and K.C. Ginnigton, *Int. J. Parasitol.* **24**, 15–26 (1994).

227. F.D. Ledley, *Hum. Gene Ther.* **6**, 1129–1144 (1995).

228. D. Gillespie, *Vet. Microbiol.* **24**, 217–233 (1990).

229. E.W. Collission et al., *Vet. Microbiol.* **24**, 261–271 (1990).

230. P. Jameson and M. Essex, *Antiviral Res.* **3**, 115–118 (1983).

231. M.L. Martinez and R.C. Weiss, *Vet. Clin. North Am.: Small Anim. Prac.* **23**, 213–226 (1993).

232. S. Connelly et al., *Blood* **88**, 3846–3852 (1996).

233. R. Prichard, *Vet. Prasitol.* **71**, 155–175 (1997).

234. W.C. Brown et al., *Infect. Immun.* **61**, 236–244 (1993).

INDEX